WILEY SERIES IN PROBABILITY
AND MATHEMATICAL STATISTICS

ESTABLISHED BY WALTER A. SHEWHART AND SAMUEL S. WILKS
Editors
Vic Barnett, Ralph A. Bradley, J. Stuart Hunter,
David G. Kendall, Rupert G. Miller, Jr., Adrian F. M. Smith,
Stephen M. Stigler, Geoffrey S. Watson

Probability and Mathematical Statistics

(*continued on back*)

(*continued from front*)

Modern
Mathematical
Statistics

Modern Mathematical Statistics

EDWARD J. DUDEWICZ

Department of Mathematics
Syracuse University
Syracuse, New York

SATYA N. MISHRA

Department of Mathematics and Statistics
University of South Alabama
Mobile, Alabama

JOHN WILEY & SONS
New York • Chichester • Brisbane • Toronto • Singapore

Library of Congress Cataloging in Publication Data:
Dudewicz, Edward J.
Modern mathematical statistics.

(Wiley series in probability and mathematical
statistics. Probability and mathematical statistics, ISSN 0271-6232.)
Includes indexes.
1. Mathematical statistics.   I. Mishra, Satya
Narain.   II. Title.

QA276.D814   1988   519.5   87-14279

Printed in Singapore

10 9 8 7 6 5 4 3 2 1

To my wife, for her constant support—EJD
In the memory of my parents—SNM

Preface

The term "statistics" used to mean simply a collection of numbers. Today "statistics" is a broad term, whose meaning has breadth the framers of the word could barely conceive when they planted the seed that has now grown into a mighty and ever-expanding oak. The original collection of numbers is now called **data**, and **statistics** is now defined as "the science of decision making." In this book we aim to cover this field from the modern point of view, taking advantage of the knowledge acquired over the past decades, which now integrates the subject into a unified whole (and eliminates historical aberrations that were the result of partial knowledge at earlier stages of development).

This text is intended for use in calculus-based courses in probability and/or mathematical statistics. Chapters 1 through 6 are devoted to introduction of the basic concepts of probability theory that are required prerequisites for any course in mathematical statistics. The topics are covered in sufficient depth and detail to make the coverage self-contained for a course in probability, and exceptional care has been taken to choose examples that further the theoretical development as well as give a flavor of the applications. In addition to classical probability theory, such modern topics as order statistics (Section 5.6) and limiting distributions (Section 6.3) are discussed, along with many applied examples from a great variety of fields.

Once the groundwork in probability (Chapters 1 through 6) has been laid, the core mathematical statistics topics of estimation, testing, and confidence intervals are covered in Chapters 7 through 10. In addition to numerous examples in all chapters, the text includes exercises at the end of each section (as a source of homework problems specifically on that material), as well as a comprehensive set of problems at the end of each chapter. Following the core topics in Chapters 7 through 10, such modern topics as ranking and selection procedures (Chapter 11), decision theory (Chapter 12), nonparametric statistics (Chapter 13), regression and ANOVA (Chapter 14), and robust statistical procedures (Chapter 15) are covered. Computer-assisted data analysis is discussed at several points (e.g., in Chapter 14 on regression and analysis of variance), since it is very important in our view for students of modern probability and mathematical statistics to have a comprehensive view that includes a glimpse of the importance of statistical computation to the field. Our discussions include FORTRAN programs and BMDP routines, but emphasize SAS routines due to the wide popularity of that package of statistical routines. Some discussion of the coming contribution of expert systems is also given.

The prerequisites needed will vary according to such local characteristics as depth of coverage desired, length of course, and ability and motivation of the students; as a usual minimum we recommend a working knowledge of calculus including multiple integration, infinite series, and partial differentiation. Such topics are generally covered in a first-year calculus course. (**No prerequisites in probability and statistics are required.**) If an additional idea from Mathematics is needed, we give an explanation sufficient for our use of it at the point where it is needed. Anticipating the broad range of student preparations now encountered in the first course in Mathematical Statistics/Probability in the departments (of statistics/mathematics/mathematical-sciences/mathematics-and-statistics/operations-research/computer science/management science/etc.) that offer this course, we have maintained the junior/senior level of presentation. Starred sections, examples, and Honors Problems can (and usually should) be skipped over easily at that level, but these and the comprehensive modern coverage and extensive examples also mean the text will be found appropriate by some departments for their graduate course as well. In addition, the book will be a valuable reference for researchers and practitioners in many fields because of its encyclopedic coverage.

Although this book is derived in part from *Introduction to Statistics and Probability* by E. J. Dudewicz, the idea for the present book arose from the second author while he was taking a course in first-year mathematical statistics using the aforementioned book with the first author at Ohio State University. The second author's proposal was to develop a book that would integrate modern and classical statistical results, with the full complement of examples and problems needed for a variety of student needs that arise where e.g. some students are desirous of understanding the theory in order to use it properly in their fields (whether engineering, computer science, operations research, social sciences, forestry, or another specific field), while others wish a theoretical grounding and preparation for advanced work.

This book has the ambitious coverage needed to allow course content to vary from year to year (both for variety and to suit the needs of diverse student groups); to allow the material to be either skimmed or delved into more deeply as seems appropriate; to allow the exceptionally advanced students to delve into subjects in detail so they can go to the literature and do introductory research; to allow researchers in statistics and allied fields to use the text as a reference; and, to provide an introduction to such modern areas as robust statistics and bootstrap procedures.

This book has been class-tested at the University of South Alabama (in a two-quarter sequence in Probability and Statistical Theory), and at Case Western Reserve University (in a year sequence at the undergraduate/graduate level in Mathematical Statistics). Results at these two different institutions were very positive.

A book at this level should, in the view of many, include more material than most courses will cover, for several reasons. First, if time permits one to cover material that had not originally been planned, then instructor and students will not need to try to find a source for it at the last minute. Second, students will have a resource book that they can add to their library for future use and reference. Third, after meeting the requirements of the syllabus, instructors will have available material allowing them to teach their "favorite topic." With this material, an instructor can easily design a quarter/semester or two-quarter/semester or three-quarter/semester sequence. Dependence on the text is usually linear through Chapters 1 through 8, and thereafter can branch as indicated in the following diagram:

$$11$$
$$\nearrow \searrow$$
$$1 \to 2 \to 3 \to 4 \to 5 \to 6 \to 7 \to 8 \to 9 \to 10 \to \{12, 13, 14, 15\}$$

where { } indicates that one can proceed to any of the chapters in the brace after Chapter 10.

Those who wish to cover Chapters 1 through 6 in a first semester, 7 through 15 in a second semester, or 1 through 15 in a year course, may (depending on local conditions such as number of hours of the course, goals, preparation of students, and the like) desire to omit some topics. Certain topics and sections are "starred" in the text; they are (in many cases) slightly more advanced, or more specialized, and may be omitted (at a first reading) without loss of continuity. Since it may help instructors to have a collected list of such instances, we provide that at this point:

Multivariate parts of Sections 3.4, 3.5, 3.6
Theorem 4.1.4 (decomposition of a d.f. into d, ac, and sc parts)
Example 4.2.18 (Cantor-type distributions)
Multivariate parts of Sections 4.4, 4.5, 4.6
Methods for generation of uniform r.v.'s in Section 4.7
Multivariate moments in Section 5.3
Characteristic functions in Section 5.5, and Theorems 5.5.13 and 5.5.14
Theorem 6.1.10 (Jensen's Inequality)
Theorem 6.3.9 (Multivariate Lindberg–Levy CLT) and Theorem 6.3.10 (Lindeberg's
    Condition CLT), Theorem 6.3.18
Theorem 8.1.25 and Example 8.1.29
Chapter 15

Suggested curricula options follow. These will meet the needs of courses at many colleges and universities and bear in mind typical course organization at many institutions.

Option 1: 3 or 4 semester/quarter hour course in Probability

Chapter	Coverage
1	Full (Reading Assignment)
2	Full

Chapter	Coverage
3	Full
4	A brief introduction (do not spend to much time on Section 4.1). Then cover 4.2, 4.3, some time to cover 4.4, and 4.5. Two lectures on 4.6 and briefly cover 4.7 and 4.8.
5	All except characteristic functions
6	All (very important)

Option 2: 3 or 4 semester/quarter hour course on Statistics, Mathematical Statistics, or Probability and Statistics

Chapter	Coverage
1	Full (Reading Assignment)
2	2.1, 2.2, briefly cover 2.3 and 2.4
3	3.1, 3.2, 3.3, 3.6
4	4.2, 4.3, 4.6, briefly 4.7 and 4.8
5	5.1, 5.2, 5.3, briefly 5.5
6	6.1 (Chebyshev's Inequality only), briefly 6.2 and 6.3
7	7.1, 7.2, 7.3, briefly 7.4
8	Skip
9	9.1, 9.2, 9.3, 9.5–9.8, 9.12, 9.13
10	All
14	If time permits

Option 3: Two 4-quarter hour course sequence on Probability and Statistical Theory

Chapters	Coverage
1–6	As in Option 1, then
7	All
8	Skim the ideas in 3 lectures
9	All (except 9.9 and 9.10)
10	All
14	All

Option 4: 3 semester hours for 2 semesters (or, 4-quarter hours for 3 quarters) course

Chapters	Coverage
1–10	All

Then choose topics of your choice from $\{11, 12, 13, 14, 15\}$.

Thanks are due to our teachers, colleagues, publishers, editors, reviewers, students, assistants, and typists for their contributions from which this book has benefited. Particular thanks go to Professors Moshe Shaked (University of Arizona), Donald Fridshal (California State University at Chico and Worcester Polytechnic Institute), J. Gehrmann (California State University at Sacramento), and to Robert W. Pirtle (Statistics Editor, John Wiley & Sons). Finally, thanks are due to our families, and the second author takes this opportunity to thank his wife Sushila and children Prashant and Shruti for forgiving him the time stolen from their lives and spent on writing this book.

Syracuse University
Syracuse, New York

Edward J. Dudewicz

University of South Alabama
Mobile, Alabama

Satya N. Mishra

August 1987

Contents

NUMBERING SYSTEM

The numbering system is designed to enable quick location of theorems, examples, and so on, which are referred to in the text. Theorems, Lemmas, Definitions, and so on, are numbered sequentially along with equations and expressions within each Section (e.g.: Definition 1.2.1 is in Chapter 1, Section 2; it is followed by expression (1.2.2); and so on). [This is simpler to use than the common system wherein Theorems, Lemmas, Definitions, and so on are numbered sequentially in a *separate* system from the equations and expressions; such a system can have a Definition 1.2.1 as well as an expression (1.2.1), often separated by several pages.]

Figures in the text have a separate numbering system (necessitated by the fact that their placement in the text must often differ from their placement in the manuscript that preceded it); for example Figure 1.2-2 is the second figure in Section 2 of Chapter 1. Tables, except for those appearing at the back of the book, are numbered similarly in a separate system. Footnotes are numbered sequentially $(1, 2, \ldots)$ within each chapter.

MATHEMATICAL NOTATIONS*

$\{x: \mathscr{A}(x)\}$	the set of all x such that $\mathscr{A}(x)$ holds; for example, $\{x: x \text{ is an integer}\} = \{\ldots, -3, -2, -1, 0, 1, 2, 3, \ldots\}$
$\in$	is a member of (belongs to)
$\notin$	is not a member of (does not belong to)
$\Rightarrow$	implies
$\nRightarrow$	does not imply
$\ni$	such that
iff	if and only if
$\Leftrightarrow$	if and only if
$\geq$	greater than or equal to
$>$	greater than
$\leq$	less than or equal to
$<$	less than
$\gg$	much larger than
$\equiv$	identically equal to
$\varnothing$	the empty set

*Common notations (such as $\neq$ for not equal, ∞ for infinity, Π for a product, and Σ for a summation) are not listed. Specialized notations (such as ! for a factorial) are given in the Glossary of Symbols.

GREEK ALPHABET

A	α	alpha	N	ν	nu
B	β	beta	Ξ	ξ	xi
Γ	γ	gamma	O	o	omicron
Δ	δ	delta	Π	π	pi
E	ε	epsilon	P	ρ	rho
Z	ζ	zeta	Σ	σ	sigma
H	η	eta	T	τ	tau
Θ, Θ	θ	theta	Υ	υ	upsilon
I	ι	iota	Φ	ϕ, φ	phi
K	κ	kappa	X	χ	chi
Λ	λ	lambda	Ψ	ψ	psi
M	μ	mu	Ω	ω	omega

CHAPTER 1

Naive Set Theory

In this chapter we introduce the basic notions and notations needed for dealing with **sets** (collections of objects of various kinds, such as numbers or pairs of numbers, called **points**). Although you may have dealt with these concepts since grade school, it is important that this chapter be utilized (at least by independent study) to assure a sound base for the applications in probability that follow in Chapter 2. **Most courses will not spend too much time on this chapter.**

"Set" is an undefined notion (like "point" or "line" in high-school geometry); it is assumed that at least one exists, and attention is restricted to a **universe** or **universal set** Ω. All operations are with respect to Ω in order to avoid paradoxical situations. For further details, see the Problems at the end of this chapter or Feferman (1964). ("Naive" set theory is to be contrasted with "axiomatic" set theory, which is an advanced treatment arranged to obviate the possibility of paradoxes.)

How sets arise in probability and statistics is illustrated by examples and discussed in Section 1.4. At this point, the examples are simple and convenient probability-related illustrations of set concepts and operations. Realistic probabilistic problems using these concepts, such as the post office operations problem discussed following Definition 2.2.20 and Problem 2.8H, are deferred since their proper discussion entails probabilistic concepts introduced in Chapter 2.

On reaching Section 1.4 (with the resulting universe Ω given in Example 1.4.1), you should return to Sections 1.1 through 1.3 and draw illustrations of the definitions and theorems with the universe Ω of ordered pairs.

1.1. BASIC DEFINITIONS

Let A and B be sets.[1] We now define four set operations and illustrate their meanings with diagrams called **Venn diagrams**. These diagrams are slightly unreliable, as are arguments by diagram in geometry (e.g., the "typical" cases

---

[1] We generally denote *points* by lowercase Greek letters, *sets* by capital italic letters, collections of sets by capital script letters, and the *universe* by capital omega.

drawn often do not show any relations of inclusion or disjointness; a specific instance is given in Example 1.2.9).

Definition 1.1.1.[2]   **Union** (or **join**,[3] or **sum**[3]) of sets A and B (see Figure 1.1-1):

$$A \cup B \equiv A + B \equiv \{\omega: \omega \in A \text{ or } \omega \in B\}. \tag{1.1.2}$$

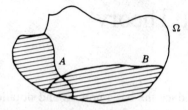

Figure 1.1-1. The shaded region is $A \cup B$.

Definition 1.1.3.   **Intersection** (or **meet**,[3] or **product**[3]) of sets A and B (see Figure 1.1-2):

$$A \cap B \equiv AB \equiv A \cdot B \equiv \{\omega: \omega \in A \text{ and } \omega \in B\}. \tag{1.1.4}$$

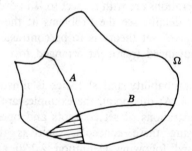

Figure 1.1-2. The shaded region is AB.

Definition 1.1.5.   **Complement** of a set A (see Figure 1.1-3):

$$A^c \equiv \overline{A} \equiv A' \equiv \{\omega: \omega \in \Omega \text{ and } \omega \notin A\}. \tag{1.1.6}$$

Note that we have two notations for set unions ($A \cup B$ and $A + B$), three for set intersections ($A \cap B$, AB, and $A \cdot B$), and three for set complements (A^c, $\overline{A}$, and A'). Each notation is widely used in the fields of statistics and probability, and each seems more convenient in certain contexts. We try to use the first or

---

[2] In this text "or" is used in the usual mathematical sense; that is, "$\omega \in A$ or $\omega \in B$" means "either $\omega \in A$, or $\omega \in B$, *or both.*" As used in equation (1.1.2), $\equiv$ defines the symbols $A \cup B$ and $A + B$; they are by definition shorthand for $\{\omega: \omega \in A \text{ or } \omega \in B\}$.

[3] Although this terminology (and some of the notation that follows) is not now in widespread use, it is important to be exposed to it in order to be able to read other (and older) books and writings.

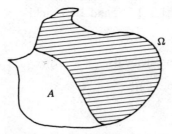

Figure 1.1-3. The shaded region is $\bar{A}$.

second notations given most of the time. However, as all these notations are in widespread use, it is important to become familiar with them. Since various ones are easier to use in various situations, we have not settled on one to use exclusively in this text.

Definition 1.1.7. Difference of sets A and B (see Figure 1.1-4):

$$A - B \equiv A \cap B^c. \qquad (1.1.8)$$

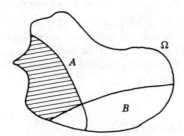

Figure 1.1-4. The shaded region is $A - B$.

Example 1.1.9. As an illustration, suppose that Ω is the set of all positive integers, that A is the set of even positive integers, that B is the set of odd positive integers, and that C is the set of positive integers which are powers of 2. Then

$$\begin{cases} A = \{2, 4, 6, 8, 10, 12, \ldots\}, \\ B = \{1, 3, 5, 7, 9, 11, \ldots\}, \\ C = \{1, 2, 4, 8, 16, \ldots\}, \end{cases} \qquad (1.1.10)$$

are each subsets of $\Omega = \{1, 2, 3, 4, 5, 6, 7, 8, 9, 10, 11, 12, \ldots\}$: Simple calculations from Definitions 1.1.1, 1.1.3, 1.1.5, and 1.1.7 yield

$$
\begin{cases}
A \cup B = \Omega, \\
A \cap B \quad \text{contains no elements,} \\
A \cap C = \{2,4,8,16,\dots\}, \\
B \cap C = \{1\}, \\
\overline{A} = B, \\
\overline{B} = A, \\
\overline{C} = \{3,5,6,7,9,10,11,12,13,14,15,17,\dots\} = \Omega - C, \text{ and} \\
A - C = \{6,10,12,14,18,\dots\}.
\end{cases}
\tag{1.1.11}
$$

PROBLEMS FOR SECTION 1.1

1.1.1 Draw a Venn diagram similar to Figure 1.1-1 or Figure 1.1-4, and on it shade the area corresponding to the set described by: **(a)** $\overline{AB}$; **(b)** $\overline{A}\overline{B}$; **(c)** $\overline{A} + \overline{B}$; **(d)** $\overline{A} - \overline{B}$. Use a different diagram for each part of this problem.

1.1.2 Let $\Omega = \{1,2,3,4,5,6,7,8,9,10\}$, $A = \{1,2,3,4,5\}$, and $B = \{3,4,5,6,7,8\}$. For each of the sets in Problem 1.1.1, find which numbers are members of that set.

1.1.3 Let $\Omega = \{(x,y): x \geq 0, \ y \geq 0\}$, $A = \{(x,y): x \geq 0, 0 \leq y \leq 10\}$, $B = \{(x,y): 0 \leq x \leq 10, \ y \geq 0\}$. On a set of coordinate axes, shade the area corresponding to each of the sets in Problem 1.1.1. Write each of the resulting sets in the simplest possible form of the type used to describe A and B in this problem. Use a different diagram for each shaded area.

1.2. ADDITIONAL DEFINITIONS

Definition 1.2.1. **Identity** of sets A and B:

$$A = B \text{ iff (for each } \omega \in \Omega)\,\omega \in A \text{ iff } \omega \in B. \tag{1.2.2}$$

Definition 1.2.3. A is a **subset** of B, written $A \subseteq B$, if $\omega \in A \Rightarrow \omega \in B$.

Definition 1.2.4. A is a **proper subset** of B, written $A \subsetneqq B$, if $A \subseteq B$ and $A \neq B$ [where, of course, "$A \neq B$" means "not $A = B$"; i.e., the right side of equivalence (1.2.2) is false].

[*Note*: $A \subseteq B$ will sometimes be shortened to $A \subset B$; some authors, however, use the latter notation for $A \subsetneqq B$.]

Definition 1.2.5. The **empty set** (or **null set**), usually written $\varnothing$ or 0, is the unique set such that for all $\omega \in \Omega$, $\omega \notin \varnothing$. (In other words, the empty set is the set containing no points at all. Such a set, $A \cap B$, was encountered in Example 1.1.9.)

Definition 1.2.6. $A \supseteq B$, $A \supset B$, and $A \supsetneq B$ mean, respectively, $B \subseteq A$, $B \subset A$, and $B \subsetneq A$.

Definition 1.2.7. Sets A and B are said to be **mutually exclusive** (or **disjoint**) if $A \cap B = \varnothing$.

Definition 1.2.8. Three (or more) sets A, B, C are said to be **pairwise disjoint** (or **mutually exclusive**) if every two of them are disjoint (as in Definition 1.2.7).

Example 1.2.9. At the beginning of Section 1.1 we noted that Venn diagrams are not considered sufficient proof of a theorem of set theory since their "typical" cases may be misleading. Figure 1.2-1 could, for example, be used as a proof of the statement "$A \cup B$ is *not* a subset of B" if Venn diagrams were considered to be sufficient proof. As we see in Figure 1.2-2, the statement can be false. We therefore employ Venn diagrams solely as convenient aids to our intuition, recognizing that proofs of theorems about sets cannot rely solely on Venn diagrams.

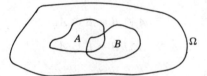

Figure 1.2-1. Is $A \cup B$ a subset of B?

Figure 1.2-2. $A \cup B$ may be a subset of B.

PROBLEMS FOR SECTION 1.2

1.2.1 For the sets A and B of Example 1.1.9, determine whether A and B are disjoint. Similarly for sets B and C. Similarly for sets A and C. Are sets A, B, C pairwise disjoint?

1.2.2 For sets A and B of Example 1.1.9, determine for each of the following whether or not it is a true statement. **(a)** $A = B$. **(b)** $A \subseteq B$. **(c)** $B \subseteq A$. **(d)** $A \neq B$. **(e)** A and B are mutually exclusive.

1.2.3 As in Problem 1.2.2, but for the sets A and B of Problem 1.1.2.

1.2.4 As in Problem 1.2.2, but for the sets A and B of Problem 1.1.3.

1.3. SIMPLE LAWS AND SOME EXTENSIONS

In the following theorem, we state some simple laws dealing with operations (such as union and intersection) on sets and prove one in order to show how a formal proof (as contrasted with an intuitive Venn diagram proof) proceeds. It is known that the set of statements 1 through 9 is **complete** in the sense that any equation formed using $\varnothing$, Ω, $\cap$, $\cup$, and $\subset$ and any number of variables $A, B, C, \ldots$ which is true for every set Ω and subsets $A, B, C, \ldots$ of Ω can be deduced from statements 1 through 9.

Theorem 1.3.1. Let Ω be a set and let A, B, C be subsets of Ω. Then

1. **Idempotency laws**

$$A \cap A = A,$$

$$A \cup A = A.$$

2. **Commutative laws**

$$A \cap B = B \cap A,$$

$$A \cup B = B \cup A.$$

3. **Associative laws**

$$A \cap (B \cap C) = (A \cap B) \cap C,$$

$$A \cup (B \cup C) = (A \cup B) \cup C.$$

4. **Distributive laws**

$$A \cap (B \cup C) = (A \cap B) \cup (A \cap C),$$

$$A \cup (B \cap C) = (A \cup B) \cap (A \cup C).$$

5. $A \cap \varnothing = \varnothing$, and $A \cup \varnothing = A$.

6. Ω and $\varnothing$ act as **identity elements** for $\cap$ and $\cup$:

$$A \cap \Omega = A,$$

$$A \cup \varnothing = A.$$

7.
$$A \cap A^c = \varnothing,$$

$$A \cup A^c = \Omega.$$

8. De Morgan's laws

$$(A \cap B)^c = A^c \cup B^c,$$

$$\overline{(A \cup B)}^c = A^c \cap B^c.$$

9. $$(A^c)^c = A.$$

10. $$B \subseteq A \text{ iff } A \cap B = B.$$

11. $$B \subseteq A \text{ iff } A \cup B = A.$$

Proof of the commutative law $A \cap B = B \cap A$. We will prove that $A \cap B \subseteq B \cap A$. Since the proof that $B \cap A \subseteq A \cap B$ is similar, it then follows from Definitions 1.2.1 and 1.2.3 that $A \cap B = B \cap A$. Proof that $A \cap B \subseteq B \cap A$:

$$\omega \in A \cap B \Rightarrow \omega \in A \text{ and } \omega \in B$$

$$\Rightarrow \omega \in B \text{ and } \omega \in A$$

$$\Rightarrow \omega \in B \cap A. \qquad \blacksquare$$

Extended intersections and unions. Let $\mathcal{M}$ be any nonempty collection of subsets of Ω. Define

$$\bigcap_{A \in \mathcal{M}} A = \{\omega: \omega \in A \text{ for every } A \in \mathcal{M}\}, \qquad (1.3.2)$$

$$\bigcup_{A \in \mathcal{M}} A = \{\omega: \omega \in A \text{ for some } A \in \mathcal{M}\}. \qquad (1.3.3)$$

[Thus, (1.3.2) is the collection of those points ω that are in every set $A \in \mathcal{M}$, while (1.3.3) is the collection of those points ω that are in at least one set $A \in \mathcal{M}$. This notation allows us to talk with ease of intersections and unions of infinitely many sets.]

Many of the laws of Theorem 1.3.1 can be generalized to arbitrary unions and intersections. For example, De Morgan's laws become

$$\left(\bigcap_{A \in \mathcal{M}} A\right)^c = \bigcup_{A \in \mathcal{M}} A^c, \qquad (1.3.4)$$

$$\left(\bigcup_{A \in \mathcal{M}} A\right)^c = \bigcap_{A \in \mathcal{M}} A^c. \qquad (1.3.5)$$

Example 1.3.6. Let Ω be a set and let A, B, C be subsets of Ω. Prove that

$$A \cap (B \cup C) \subseteq (A \cap B) \cup (A \cap C).$$

We will in fact prove the two sets are equal, as follows:

$$\omega \in A \cap (B \cup C) \Leftrightarrow \omega \in A \text{ and } \omega \in B \cup C$$

$$\Leftrightarrow (\omega \in A) \text{ and } (\omega \in B \text{ or } \omega \in C)$$

$$\Leftrightarrow (\omega \in A \text{ and } \omega \in B) \text{ or } (\omega \in A \text{ and } \omega \in C)$$

$$\Leftrightarrow (\omega \in A \cap B) \text{ or } (\omega \in A \cap C)$$

$$\Leftrightarrow \omega \in (A \cap B) \cup (A \cap C).$$

Example 1.3.7. For the Ω, A, B specified in Example 1.1.9,

$$\begin{cases} A \cap B = \varnothing, \\ A \cup B = \Omega, \\ \overline{A} = B, \\ \overline{B} = A. \end{cases} \tag{1.3.8}$$

Hence,

$$\begin{cases} (A \cap B)^c = \Omega = A \cup B = A^c \cup B^c, \\ (A \cup B)^c = \varnothing = A \cap B = A^c \cap B^c, \end{cases} \tag{1.3.9}$$

which verifies some special cases of De Morgan's laws (statement 8 of Theorem 1.3.1).

PROBLEMS FOR SECTION 1.3

1.3.1 For the Ω, A, B, and C specified in Example 1.1.9, directly verify the validity of the following parts of Theorem 1.3.1: (1) Idempotency laws; (2) Commutative laws; (3) Associative laws; (4) Distributive laws; (5); (6) Identity elements; (7); (8) De Morgan's laws; (9); (10); (11).

1.3.2 Directly verify De Morgan's laws for the Ω, A, and B specified in Problem 1.1.2.

1.3.3 Directly verify De Morgan's laws for the Ω, A, and B specified in Problem 1.1.3.

1.4.   SETS IN PROBABILITY AND STATISTICS

In probability and statistics we usually study phenomena that are **random** (as opposed to phenomena that are **deterministic**); that is, we wish to consider some **experiment's results** and the experiment does not always produce the same results. We then become involved with the collection of **all possible outcomes** of the experiment, and this functions as our universal set Ω. Subsets $A, B, C, \ldots$ of Ω will then represent possible occurrences, and we will be interested in the "chances" (or probability) of their occurrence; in calculating those "chances," it will often be desirable (and sometimes necessary) to use the manipulations of set theory covered in the preceding sections. Example 1.4.1 details some sets of interest when a pair of dice is rolled. (This example is simply a convenient illustration of the concepts involved; more realistic examples will be covered in due course, as in Problem 1.8.)

Example 1.4.1. Suppose that two six-sided dice are rolled. If each has its sides marked with one through six dots in the usual manner, one way of looking at the experiment is as resulting in a pair of integers (i, j) with $1 \leq i, j \leq 6$, where i is the number that "shows" on die 1 and j is the number that "shows" on die 2 (see Figure 1.4-1). We may then take our universal set Ω as

$$
\Omega = \begin{cases}
(1,1),(2,1),(3,1),(4,1),(5,1),(6,1), \\
(1,2),(2,2),(3,2),(4,2),(5,2),(6,2), \\
(1,3),(2,3),(3,3),(4,3),(5,3),(6,3), \\
(1,4),(2,4),(3,4),(4,4),(5,4),(6,4), \\
(1,5),(2,5),(3,5),(4,5),(5,5),(6,5), \\
(1,6),(2,6),(3,6),(4,6),(5,6),(6,6)
\end{cases}.
$$

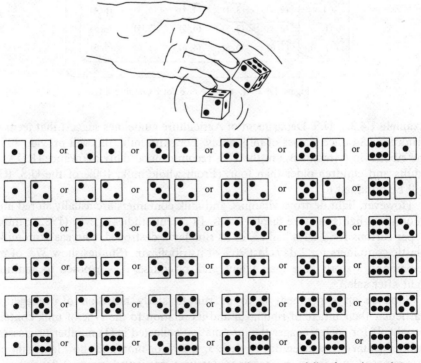

Figure 1.4-1. Results of dice-rolling experiment (with only tops of dice shown in results).

The "sum is 7" when and only when the result of the experiment is a point in

$$A = \{(1,6),(2,5),(3,4),(4,3),(5,2),(6,1)\},$$

which is a subset of Ω. "Neither die shows a 1" when and only when the result of the experiment is a point in

$$B = \left\{ \begin{array}{l} (2,2),(3,2),(4,2),(5,2),(6,2), \\ (2,3),(3,3),(4,3),(5,3),(6,3), \\ (2,4),(3,4),(4,4),(5,4),(6,4), \\ (2,5),(3,5),(4,5),(5,5),(6,5), \\ (2,6),(3,6),(4,6),(5,6),(6,6) \end{array} \right\}.$$

The "sum is 7, and neither die shows a 1" when and only when the result of the experiment is a point in $A \cap B = \{(2,5),(3,4),(4,3),(5,2)\}$. (See Figure 1.4-2.)

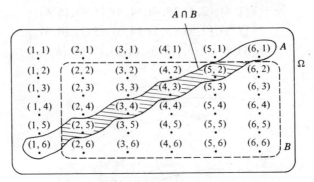

Figure 1.4-2. Ω, A, B, $A \cap B$ for Example 1.4.1.

Example 1.4.2. U.S. Department of Agriculture guidelines suggest that teenagers drink four 8-ounce glasses of milk a day. For skim milk, this will provide 80% of the riboflavin (vitamin B_2) in the U.S. recommended daily allowance (RDA) for adults and children older than four. (From whole milk, 100% of the U.S. RDA will be obtained.)

However, light destroys vitamins, and milk containers are usually stored under fluorescent lights in store display cases. In recent studies (Levey (1982)), milk in paper cartons for 2 days had 2% of its riboflavin destroyed, whereas skim milk in plastic containers for 2 days lost 20% of its riboflavin. (Studies show 37% of milk remains in a store more than 1 day, and, of course, it is exposed to additional light after sale.)

Suppose an experiment is to be run to study nutrition of teenagers, in particular their intake of riboflavin and its relation to the type of milk container bought. If for each teenager the information collected is (1) number of glasses of milk consumed in a given day (0, 1, 2, 3, 4, or 5-or-more), (2) how long that milk was exposed to light in its containers (assume this is 0, 1, or ≥ 2 days), and (3) type of milk container used (plastic or paper), then for each teenager studied the sample space Ω will have 36 possible points (i, j, k), where i denotes the number of glasses of milk consumed, j denotes days of light exposure, and k denotes type of container (0 for plastic, 1 for paper). This is shown in Figure 1.4-3, on which are marked the sets A (4 or 5-or-more glasses a day) and B (paper cartons).

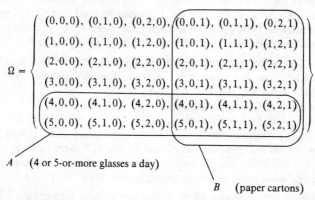

Figure 1.4-3. Sample space Ω and events A, B for nutrition study of Example 1.4.2.

PROBLEMS FOR SECTION 1.4

1.4.1 In Example 1.4.1, another possible choice of the set of all possible outcomes is $\Omega_1 = \{ S_2, S_3, S_4, S_5, S_6, S_7, S_8, S_9, S_{10}, S_{11}, S_{12} \}$, where S_i denotes that "the sum of the numbers showing on die 1 and die 2 is i." Is A of Example 1.4.1 ("sum is 7") a subset of Ω_1 (and if so, list its members)? Is B of Example 1.4.1 ("neither die shows a 1") a subset of Ω_1 (and if so, list its members)?

1.4.2 Specify a universal set Ω for all possible outcomes of the experiment of tossing four coins. Be sure that the outcome set "at least two heads, and no tails before the first head" is a subset of the Ω you choose. (As we saw in Problem 1.4.1, in general there are many ways to specify the possible outcomes of an experiment, some containing more detail than others. Here, we wish to have enough detail retained to study outcome sets such as the one specified.)

1.4.3 Specify a universal set Ω for all possible outcomes of the experiment of interviewing families and determining the sexes of their children. Choose the universal set as small as possible, but such that "the family has i boys and j girls" is a subset of the Ω you choose ($i, j = 0, 1, 2, \ldots$).

1.4.4 List the universal set Ω of Problem 1.4.3 that you would use when it is known that no family has more than 25 children. On that list, mark (as done in Figure 1.4-2, for example) the sets

A: the family has more boys than girls

and

B: the family has enough children to field a baseball team.

[*Note*: A baseball team has nine players.]

PROBLEMS FOR CHAPTER 1[4]

1.1 Sets A, B, C, D are defined by $A = \{w_1, w_2, w_3\}$, $B = \{w_3, w_4, w_5\}$, $C = \{w_6\}$, $D = \{w_1, w_2, w_4, w_5\}$. Find $A \cup B$, $A \cap B$, $S(A, B)$ (see Problem 1.6 for the definition of this set), $A \cap B \cap C \cap D$, and $(B \cap C)^c$.

1.2 Suppose that the Librarian of Congress compiles, for inclusion in the Library of Congress, a bibliography of those bibliographies in the Library of Congress that do not list themselves. Should this bibliography list itself? How does this show that "not every property determines a set?" (Be explicit; e.g., what property?)

1.3 B. Russell discovered that unrestricted formation of sets can lead to a contradiction that, in consequence, has come to be known as **Russell's paradox**. Namely, form the set $A = \{B : B \text{ is a set, and } B \notin B\}$. Show that
(a) $A \in A \Rightarrow A \notin A$ (a contradiction).
(b) $A \notin A \Rightarrow A \in A$ (a contradiction).
How was such a contradiction avoided in the formulation of set theory in Chapter 1? (Prove that it was avoided.) [In "axiomatic set theory," there exists a systematization in which one explicitly lists all assumptions needed for a development consistently extending our conception of sets to the realm of infinite sets.]

1.4 **The Barber of Seville** shaves all men who don't shave themselves. Who shaves the Barber of Seville?

1.5 (**Poretsky's law**) Let X and T be given sets. Prove that $X = \varnothing$ iff

$$T = (X \cap T^c) \cup (X^c \cap T).$$

1.6 Let A and B be given sets. Define a new set $S(A, B) = (A - B) \cup (B - A)$, called the **symmetric difference** of A and B. Prove that

$$S(A_1 \cup A_2, B_1 \cup B_2) \subseteq S(A_1, B_1) \cup S(A_2, B_2).$$

[*Note*: The result of Problem 1.5 says $X = \varnothing$ iff $T = S(T, X)$. Thus, introduction of the concept of the symmetric difference of two sets allows for a simplified notation.]

1.7 (*Suggested by P. Zuckerman*) In the definitions of extended intersections and unions, (1.3.2) and (1.3.3), we required $\mathscr{M} \neq \varnothing$. If we make the same definitions but allow $\mathscr{M} = \varnothing$, what sets will $\bigcap_{A \in \mathscr{M}} A$ and $\bigcup_{A \in \mathscr{M}} A$ be identical to when in fact $\mathscr{M} = \varnothing$? Check to see that your answer satisfies De Morgan's laws, (1.3.4) and (1.3.5). (A reference is Halmos, (1950), pp. 13–14.)

1.8 Suppose that one part of an experiment is to consist of observing the random phenomena (such as time of birth) that arise in a human birth. We may regard these phenomena in many different ways, depending on our experiment's purpose. (For example, we could regard the random phenomena as simply "year of birth," or more complexly as "year of birth, month of birth, day of birth, hour of birth, place of birth, weight at birth, sex at birth.")
(a) If the purpose of the experiment is to answer the question "Do more births occur from 1 A.M. to 6 A.M. than from 6 A.M. to 1 A.M.?" what minimal information

---

[4] Problems 1.2 through 1.4 relate to the paradoxes of set theory mentioned in the introduction to this chapter. For details see Nakano (1969), p. 764, and Takeuti and Zaring (1971), pp. 9–13.

should the statement of results contain? In that case, what is the universal set Ω? How many points does Ω contain?

(b) If the purpose of the experiment is as stated in (a), it may still be desirable to have a more detailed statement of results. Why? Give an example.

1.9 Suppose that three six-sided dice are rolled. If each has its sides marked with one through six dots in the usual manner, what universal set Ω would you, in analogy with Example 1.4.1, choose to represent the outcomes of the experiment? For what subset of Ω is the sum equal to 10? 11?

HONORS PROBLEMS FOR CHAPTER 1

1.1H Let $\Omega = \{1, 2, 3, 4, 5, \ldots\}$ be the set of all positive integers. Let $\mathscr{F}$ be the set whose members are Ω; $\varnothing$; all subsets of Ω that contain only a finite number of positive integers; and all subsets of Ω whose complements contain only a finite number of positive integers. Prove that $A \in \mathscr{F} \Rightarrow \bar{A} \in \mathscr{F}$, and that $A, B \in \mathscr{F} \Rightarrow A \cup B \in \mathscr{F}$. Prove that if $A_n \in \mathscr{F}$ ($n = 1, 2, \ldots$), it is not necessarily the case that

$$\bigcup_{n=1}^{\infty} A_n \in \mathscr{F}.$$

[*Hint*: Consider the set $C = \{1, 3, 5, 7, \ldots\}$ of odd positive integers.] (In terms of the terminology of Problem 2.2, $\mathscr{F}$ is an algebra of sets, but is not a σ-algebra of sets.)

1.2H Let $A_1, \ldots, A_n$ be sets each of which contains a finite number of elements. Let

$$\Omega = A_1 \cup A_2 \cup \cdots \cup A_n.$$

Suppose that for some fixed integer k ($1 \leq k \leq n$),

$$A_{\lambda_1} \cup \cdots \cup A_{\lambda_k} = \Omega$$

for every specification $(\lambda_1, \ldots, \lambda_k)$ of k of the integers $(1, 2, 3, \ldots, k, k + 1, \ldots, n)$, *but* that for $j = 1, 2, \ldots, k - 1$,

$$A_{\lambda_1} \cup \cdots \cup A_{\lambda_j} \subsetneqq \Omega$$

for every specification $(\lambda_1, \ldots, \lambda_j)$ of j of the integers $(1, 2, 3, \ldots, k, k + 1, \ldots, n)$. *Find* formulas (involving k and n) for **(a)** the smallest possible number of elements in Ω; **(b)** the number of elements in each of $A_1, \ldots, A_n$ when Ω contains the smallest possible number of elements; and **(c)** the number of elements in $A_{\lambda_1} \cap \cdots \cap A_{\lambda_j}$ when Ω contains the smallest possible number of elements. Illustrate your answers for the case $n = 5$, $k = 4$. [*Hint*: See the problem by H. Lass and P. Gottlieb that is solved in Bloom (1972).]

CHAPTER 2

Probability

In Section 1.4 we have already discussed informally and briefly the idea of **the "chance" of obtaining a certain type of outcome from an experiment** that deals with random phenomena (i.e., the "chance" of obtaining an outcome that belongs to some $A \subseteq \Omega$). In this chapter we introduce the idea of **"probability," which formalizes our intuitive notion of "chance,"** and define a "probability function." We then illustrate basic definitions and rules for computing probabilities with a number of examples. (For simplicity, almost all of these examples deal with finite, discrete sample spaces and equally likely outcomes; more complex situations are covered in Chapter 3.)

2.1. AXIOMS OF PROBABILITY; ELEMENTARY PROPERTIES

Let Ω be a set (called the **sample space**). The points $\omega \in \Omega$ are called **elementary events**. Ω corresponds to the collection of distinct outcomes that may result when we perform some particular experiment of interest. Each $A \subseteq \Omega$ is called an **event**. (For instance, in Example 1.4.1 Ω consisted of 36 possible outcomes resulting from a roll of dice, and any subset of Ω was an event.) We now wish to formalize the notion of the "chance" of obtaining an outcome lying in a specified subset A of Ω into a definition of probability; we will wish to talk of the probability of each event $A \subseteq \Omega$ and will hence need a *function* that assigns a unique number (called **probability**) to each such A. (For instance, in Example 1.4.1 the probability of a sum equal to 7 resulting from a roll of the dice is the probability of the set A of outcomes defined in that example.) After giving the formal definition, we will relate it to the "classical definition of probability" and to the frequency interpretation of probability. The latter [see equation (2.1.6) and the text that follows] provides the intuitive basis for Definition 2.1.1.

Definition 2.1.1. $P(\cdot)$ is a **probability function**[1] if to each event $A \subseteq \Omega$ it assigns a number $P(A)$ such that

$$P(A) \geq 0, \tag{2.1.2}$$

$$P(\Omega) = 1, \tag{2.1.3}$$

and
   (Countable additivity) If $A_1, A_2, \ldots$ are events with $A_i \cap A_j = \varnothing$ $(i \neq j)$, then

$$P\left(\bigcup_{n=1}^{\infty} A_n \right) = \sum_{n=1}^{\infty} P(A_n). \tag{2.1.4}$$

Example 2.1.5. Let Ω be the set of possible outcomes when a six-sided die with the sides marked with one through six dots is rolled, that is,

$$\Omega = \{1, 2, 3, 4, 5, 6\}$$

where outcome "i" means "i dots show on the die that is rolled." For each subset A of Ω, assign the number

$$f(A) = \frac{\text{Number of points in } A}{6}.$$

Then $f(\cdot)$ is a probability function, as we will now verify.
   First, if A is a subset of Ω, then (Number of points in A) is either 0 or 1 or 2 or 3 or 4 or 5 or 6, hence (Number of points in A) ≥ 0, hence (Number of points in A)/6 ≥ 0, hence $f(A) \geq 0$, as was to be shown and property (2.1.2) holds. **Second,** $f(\Omega) =$ (Number of points in Ω)/6 $= 6/6 = 1$, since $A = \Omega$ is a subset of Ω, hence property (2.1.3) holds. **Finally,** the set that is the union of all the sets A_n contains some of the points of Ω and no other points (since no A_n contains any points other than points that are in Ω); call this union the set A. Now $f(A) =$ (Number of points in A)/6. Now each point of Ω that is in A has $\frac{1}{6}$ counted for it on the left side of equation (2.1.4). Such a point must be in at least one of the A_n's (or it would not be in A), so at least $\frac{1}{6}$ is counted for such a point on the right side of equation (2.1.4). However, no more than $\frac{1}{6}$ can be counted for such a point on the right side, because then it would need to be in at least two of the A_n's, say A_i and A_j (with $i \neq j$); this is impossible since the A_n's have been assumed to be pairwise disjoint. Since no other points except the points of A can be in any of the A_n's (since A is the union of the A_n's), it follows that the right side of equation (2.1.4) equals the sum of $\frac{1}{6}$, summed once for every point in A; that is, it equals (Number of points in A)/6, as was to be shown.

---

[1] This is sometimes also called a **probability measure**.

The probability function we have displayed in Example 2.1.5 is one that has been found to be appropriate in many classical simple games of chance (such as rolling dice, tossing coins, and dealing cards). It is formalized in the so-called **classical definition of probability**, which is actually a rule for assigning a function $P(\cdot)$ to certain types of Ω's. It says: **If an experiment can lead to n mutually exclusive and equally likely outcomes, and if $n(A)$ of these outcomes have an attribute A, then**

$$P(A) = \text{The probability of } A = \frac{n(A)}{n}. \qquad (2.1.6)$$

This definition applies in many simple games of chance (cards, dice, balls in cells) but not usually in more complex situations. In Section 2.2 we study precisely those cases where this assignment of $P(\cdot)$ is appropriate.

In order to make the connection between probability as embodied in Definition 2.1.1 and the real world, we now ask **"How is a probability function $P(\cdot)$ obtained in practice?"** To answer this question, we need to specify *what $P(A)$ is trying to represent, which is "the proportion of the experiments of this type on which, in the long run, we will find on examination that A has occurred."* Thus if $P(A) = .85$ and we make 100 experiments of this type, we expect to find that $(.85)(100)$ of the experiments had A occur (though actually the exact number will vary).

If we make n unrelated trials of an experiment and an event A occurs some number $n(A)$ times, based on those trials our best estimate of $P(A)$ would seem to be $n(A)/n$, the **relative frequency** in those trials we observed.

Example 2.1.7. A pair of dice is rolled 1000 times, and the event $A =$ "The sum of the faces showing is 7" occurs 251 times. Our best estimate of the relative frequency with which A will occur with this pair of dice is

$$\frac{n(A)}{n} = \frac{251}{1000} = .251.$$

In **frequency probability** we define

$$R(A) = \frac{n(A)}{n}$$

for all events A [sometimes, if we want explicitly to display the fact that this depends on how many trials we have, we write it as $R_n(A)$] and think of this as an approximation to the "true" probability function that underlies the experiment in the sense that when n grows large $R_n(A)$ will become close to $P(A)$:

$$P(A) = \lim_{n \to \infty} R(A) = \lim_{n \to \infty} \frac{n(A)}{n}. \qquad (2.1.8)$$

Suppose we do not have an infinite number of trials (in fact, we never do), and based on n trials we define a probability function by $P(A) = R_n(A)$ for all A: **Is this a probability function?** First, for any A, $n(A)$ is the number of the n trials on which A has occurred, hence $n(A) \geq 0$, hence $P(A) = R_n(A) = n(A)/n \geq 0$, so that property (2.1.2) holds. Second, $P(\Omega) = n(\Omega)/n = n/n = 1$ since Ω occurs on each of the trials, so property (2.1.3) holds. Finally, if $A_1, A_2, \ldots$ are pairwise disjoint events, let A denote their union. Then

$$\sum_{n=1}^{\infty} P(A_n)$$

$$= \sum_{n=1}^{\infty} R(A_n)$$

$$= \frac{(\text{Number of times } A_1 \text{ occurs})}{n} + \frac{(\text{Number of times } A_2 \text{ occurs})}{n} + \cdots$$

$$= \frac{(\text{Number of times } A_1 \text{ occurs}) + (\text{Number of times } A_2 \text{ occurs}) + \cdots}{n}$$

$$= \frac{(\text{Number of times } A \text{ occurs})}{n} = R(A) = P(A),$$

so that equation (2.1.4) holds and we have shown that **relative frequency yields a probability function.** [*Note*: The number of times A occurs is the sum of the number of times that $A_1, A_2, \ldots$ occur, since the A_n's are pairwise disjoint (and hence at most one of them can occur on any one trial).]

We can reason to many **other properties of frequency probability.** For example, $n(A)$ is the number of the n trials on which A occurs; therefore it must be between 0 and n. Therefore $R(A) = n(A)/n$ must be between $0/n = 0$ and $n/n = 1$:

$$0 \leq R(A) \leq 1. \tag{2.1.9}$$

Also, on any trial either A or not-A (i.e., A^c) occurs, hence $n(A) + n(A^c) = n$ or $n(A)/n + n(A^c)/n = n/n = 1$, or $R(A) + R(A^c) = 1$, or in other words we can find the relative frequency of A^c from that of A:

$$R(A^c) = 1 - R(A). \tag{2.1.10}$$

As a final property of frequency probability, let A and B be any two events. Then $n(A + B) = n(A) + n(B) - n(AB)$, since the number of times the union of A and B occurs, $n(A + B)$, is the sum of the number of times A occurs and the number of times B occurs less the number of times A and B both occur [since the number of trials on which both occur is counted in both $n(A)$ and $n(B)$, and we subtract $n(AB)$ to reduce the count to one time]. Therefore,

$n(A + B)/n = n(A)/n + n(B)/n - n(AB)/n$, or

$$R(A + B) = R(A) + R(B) - R(AB), \qquad (2.1.11)$$

which allows us to compute $R(A + B)$ from the relative frequencies of A, B, and their intersection.

Although *we can thus reason to many other properties* of frequency probability besides (2.1.2), (2.1.3), (2.1.4), (2.1.9), (2.1.10), and (2.1.11), and this yields intuitive insight, we do not do so beyond these few properties (which themselves contain much of this insight). This is because we wish to reduce down to the minimal assumptions and derive all other properties from them. It is known that the assumptions of a probability function are this minimal set, and thus **we will derive all properties of probability from properties (2.1.2), (2.1.3), and (2.1.4).** Another reason is that the development using frequency probability is somewhat intuitive; this is a plus for understanding, but it is a minus for a rigorous development in which one derives properties from precisely stated axioms. Therefore, we will now prove that probability functions, which we have, to this point, only assumed satisfy the three axioms (2.1.2), (2.1.3), and (2.1.4), possess properties corresponding to equations (2.1.9), (2.1.10), and (2.1.11)[2] and other properties of relative frequencies; hence, they furnish a reasonable abstraction of our notion of "chance."

In this rigorous development, we first need to show that two properties which are obvious in the frequency probability interpretation, namely that the empty set has probability zero and that equation (2.1.4) continues to hold if one has only a finite number of sets A_n, follow from Definition 2.1.1.

Theorem 2.1.12. $P(\varnothing) = 0$.

Proof: Let $A_n = \varnothing$ $(n = 1, 2, \ldots)$. Then $\displaystyle\bigcup_{n=1}^{\infty} A_n = \varnothing$ and, by countable additivity (since $A_i A_j = \varnothing$),

$$P(\varnothing) = P\left(\bigcup_{n=1}^{\infty} A_n \right) = \sum_{n=1}^{\infty} P(A_n) = \sum_{n=1}^{\infty} P(\varnothing).$$

Since $P(\cdot)$ is a real-valued function, $P(\varnothing) = 0$. ∎

Theorem 2.1.13. Finite Additivity. Let $A_1, \ldots, A_n$ be disjoint events. Then

$$P(A_1 \cup \cdots \cup A_n) = P(A_1) + \cdots + P(A_n).$$

---

[2] The proof of the property corresponding to equation (2.1.11) is deferred to Corollary 2.3.17, where it follows easily from a more general result about probability functions.

Proof: Let $A_{n+1} = A_{n+2} = \cdots = \varnothing$. Then

$$P(A_1 \cup \cdots \cup A_n) = P\left(\bigcup_{n=1}^{\infty} A_n\right) = \sum_{k=1}^{\infty} P(A_k)$$

$$= \sum_{k=1}^{n} P(A_k) + 0 = P(A_1) + \cdots + P(A_n). \qquad \blacksquare$$

Now we are in a position to establish Theorem 2.1.14 and its Corollary 2.1.15, which together allow us to establish property (2.1.9) for general probability functions.

Theorem 2.1.14. If A and B are events and $A \subseteq B$, then $P(A) \le P(B)$.

Proof: Since $B = A \cup \bar{A}B$ and $A \cap \bar{A}B = \varnothing$, then by Theorem 2.1.13, $P(B) = P(A) + P(\bar{A}B)$. This is $\ge P(A)$ since $P(\bar{A}B) \ge 0$. $\qquad \blacksquare$

Corollary 2.1.15. For every A, $P(A) \le 1$.

Proof: $A \subseteq \Omega$, so $P(A) \le P(\Omega) = 1$. $\qquad \blacksquare$

In Theorem 2.1.16 we show an important general property of probability (Boole's inequality), and then establish (in Theorem 2.1.17) the equivalent of property (2.1.11) for general probability functions.

Theorem 2.1.16. Boole's Inequality. If $A_1, A_2, \ldots$ are events, then

$$P\left(\bigcup_{n=1}^{\infty} A_n\right) \le \sum_{n=1}^{\infty} P(A_n).$$

Proof: Let $B_1 = A_1$ and (for $n \ge 2$) $B_n = \bar{A}_1 \cdots \bar{A}_{n-1} A_n$. Then $B_i \cap B_j = \varnothing$ $(i \ne j)$ and $\bigcup_{n=1}^{\infty} B_n = \bigcup_{n=1}^{\infty} A_n$, so

$$P\left(\bigcup_{n=1}^{\infty} A_n\right) = P\left(\bigcup_{n=1}^{\infty} B_n\right) = \sum_{n=1}^{\infty} P(B_n).$$

But $B_n \subseteq A_n$ $(n \ge 1)$, so $P(B_n) \le P(A_n)$ and the theorem follows. $\qquad \blacksquare$

Theorem 2.1.17. $P(A^c) = 1 - P(A)$.

Proof: Since $A \cap \bar{A} = \varnothing$,

$$1 = P(\Omega) = P(A \cup \bar{A}) = P(A) + P(\bar{A}). \qquad \blacksquare$$

In the remainder of this section we examine several important examples. Then Section 2.2 studies the special case of classical probability, whereas Sections 2.3

20   PROBABILITY

and 2.4 return to the general case. Section 2.3 studies use of prior information (and additional probability properties), and Section 2.4 studies the notion of independence (one event not influencing another).

Example 2.1.18. A sample space, the set of possible outcomes of a certain experiment or observation, may (in certain cases) be chosen in several ways. We must choose the one that is appropriate for our aims. If a fair coin is tossed 100 times, we have many possible sample spaces. Let us consider two simple ones. First, the set of 100-tuples with T or H in each position (the possible results on each toss):

$$\Omega_1 = \{(x_1, x_2, \ldots, x_{100}): x_i = T \text{ or } H, i = 1, 2, \ldots, 100\}. \quad (2.1.19)$$

Second, the set of 2-tuples where the first entry is the number of tails and the second entry is the number of heads:

$$\Omega_2 = \{(x_1, 100 - x_1): x_1 = 0, 1, \ldots, 100\}. \quad (2.1.20)$$

An event is a subset of the points in the sample space. Thus, "The 5th and 99th tosses result in H" would be an event in Ω_1, but not in Ω_2.

Example 2.1.21. Care in specifying the sample space is essential. Suppose our experiment consists of drawing two medical patients' names at random with replacement from a roster that contains 10 names. Let the names be numbered serially (1 through 10), let i be the number of the patient drawn on the first draw, and let j be the number of the patient drawn on the second draw. Then one possible sample space is

$$\Omega_1 = \{(i, j): 1 \leq i \leq 10, 1 \leq j \leq 10\}, \quad (2.1.22)$$

which contains 100 points, each a pair of numbers. Here we are dealing with what is called **sampling with replacement**, since after the first draw the first name is placed back on the roster before the second draw is made.

If, on the other hand, the first name is not replaced before the second choice is made, we have what is called **sampling without replacement**. Then a pair such as (3, 3), that is, patient number 3 chosen both times, is not possible, so Ω_1 contains outcomes that are not possible for our experiment. All possible outcomes are contained in the new sample space

$$\Omega_2 = \{(i, j): 1 \leq i \leq 10, 1 \leq j \leq 10, i \neq j\}, \quad (2.1.23)$$

which contains 90 points. All possible outcomes are also represented in the sample space

$$\Omega_3 = \{\{a, b\}: 1 \leq a \leq 10, 1 \leq b \leq 10, a \neq b\}, \quad (2.1.24)$$

which contains 45 points, each of which specifies *which* two patients were chosen, but *not the order* in which they were chosen. Which of the sample spaces Ω_2 and Ω_3 is appropriate for this experiment of sampling without replacement depends on the level of detail we need in order to answer the questions of interest to us:

Ω_2 is appropriate if which patient was chosen first has some importance, whereas Ω_3 is sufficient if we only need to know which two patients were chosen (but not which was first and which was second).

[*Note*: Ω_3 contains 45 points, not 90 points, since points in Ω_3 are *sets* that each contain the names of two patients. Thus $\{3, 5\}$ and $\{5, 3\}$ are two ways of writing the same point in Ω_3, the point consisting of patients 3 and 5. Another way of writing the 45-point sample space would be as ordered pairs with the smaller patient number first:

$$\Omega_4 = \{(a, b): 1 \le a < b \le 10\}.]$$

Example 2.1.25. After defining a probability function $P(\cdot)$ in Definition 2.1.1, we discussed two ways of obtaining such a function: the **classical definition of probability** (which is typically useful only in very simple situations), and **frequency probability** (which is widely useful). Another method is **subjective (or personal) probability**. In this method, a person assigns probabilities in accord with his or her subjective assessment (taking into account all his or her knowledge and experience) and then is interested in seeing the implications for more complicated events than the simple events to which the basic probabilities are assigned (implications that are not obvious). Thus, this allows a *manager* (or other *business decision-maker*) to act rationally in accord with his or her beliefs. Of course, the assigned probabilities are also formulated taking into account all the prejudices of the decision-maker, and so are in this sense nonobjective; hence, this method is felt by many to be *inappropriate in scientific studies*.

Suppose a stockbroker states that his or her personal assessment is that the probability that the Dow-Jones average will be below 2000 at the end of the next year is .10. Similarly, the stockbroker gives an assessment for each of the following ranges as: between 2000 and 2100 with probability .25, between 2100 and 2200 with probability .25, between 2200 and 2300 with probability .25, between 2300 and 2400 with probability .10, between 2400 and 2500 with probability .04, and more than 2500 with probability .01. If the stockbroker takes a certain action, he or she will become a millionaire if the Dow-Jones average is at least 2200 at year's end. In the broker's personal assessment (personal belief) system as quantified by personal probabilities, what is the probability of becoming a millionaire if the action is taken? Here,

P (Becomes a millionaire if takes action)

= P (Dow-Jones average at least 2200 at year's end)

= P (Dow-Jones between 2200 and 2300)

    + P (Dow-Jones between 2300 and 2400)

    + P (Dow-Jones between 2400 and 2500)

    + P (Dow-Jones more than 2500)

= .25 + .10 + .04 + .01

= .40.

Thus, to be consistent with the stated personal beliefs about the likelihood (probability) of the various Dow-Jones year-end ranges, the stockbroker should act as if the action will result in millionaire status with a probability of .40 (and, most likely, pauperhood with a probability of .60 if the Dow-Jones average is below 2200 at year's end).

PROBLEMS FOR SECTION 2.1

2.1.1 A single die with six sides marked with one through six dots is rolled once. Consider the sample space $\Omega = \{1, 2, 3, 4, 5, 6\}$, and for each $A \subseteq \Omega$ define the function $P_1(A) = $ (Number of points in A)/6. (a) Find $P_1(A)$ for all $A \subseteq \Omega$. (b) Verify that $P_1(\cdot)$ is a probability function (i.e., satisfies Definition 2.1.1).

2.1.2 Consider the sample space of Problem 2.1.1, and for each $A \subseteq \Omega$ define the function $P_2(A)$ by $P(\varnothing) = 0$, on singleton sets by (for some r, $0 \leq r \leq 6$)

$$P_2(\{1\}) = \frac{r}{6},$$

$$P_2(\{2\}) = (6 - r)/6,$$

$$P_2(\{3\}) = P_2(\{4\}) = P_2(\{5\}) = P_2(\{6\}) = 0,$$

and on other sets using finite additivity. (a) Find $P(A)$ for all $A \subseteq \Omega$. (b) Verify that $P_2(\cdot)$ is a probability function. [*Note*: It follows from Problems 2.1.1 and 2.1.2 that infinitely many probability functions can be defined on the same sample space.]

2.1.3 Define the function $P_3(A)$ on $A \subseteq \Omega = [0, 1]$ by

$$P_3(A) = \int_A dx$$

for any A for which this integral is defined. Note that $P_3(\{r\}) = 0$ for any singleton set $\{r\}$ if $0 \leq r \leq 1$, and that $P_3(J) = $ (Length of the interval J) if J is a subinterval of $[0, 1]$. Show that $P_3(\cdot)$ is a probability function.

2.1.4 Consider the sample space $\Omega = \{1, 2, 3, 4, 5, 6\}$, which could be used to represent the outcome of one roll of a six-sided die. Define $P_4(\varnothing) = 0$, $P_4(\{x\}) = x/21$ for $x \in \Omega$, and $P_4(A)$ for all other $A \subseteq \Omega$ by finite additivity. Show that $P_4(\cdot)$ is a probability function.

2.1.5 Let $f(x) = k/x^3$ for $1 \leq x < \infty$, and for any A for which the integral is defined set

$$P_5(A) = \int_A f(x)\, dx$$

for all $A \subseteq \Omega$. Show that $P_5(\cdot)$ is a probability function if and only if $k = 2$.

2.2. FINITE DISCRETE SAMPLE SPACE AND COMBINATORICS

A sample space Ω is called **discrete** if it contains only finitely many points or infinitely many points that can be arranged in a simple sequence $\omega_1, \omega_2, \ldots$; in the second case Ω is called **denumerably infinite**. In either case, the probability of the event $A_i = \{\omega_i\}$, which should be denoted $P(\{\omega_i\})$, is written more simply as $P(\omega_i)$. With a *finite discrete sample space*, if the points are **equally probable** [i.e., $P(\omega_1) = P(\omega_2)$ for every $\omega_1, \omega_2 \in \Omega$], then we can find $P(A)$ by finding the number $n(A)$ of points where A occurs, since then

$$P(A) = \frac{n(A)}{n}, \tag{2.2.1}$$

where n is the total number of points in Ω. In such a case, we find a need for **combinatorics** or **combinatorial analysis** (permutations, combinations, and so on) to find n and $n(A)$. The following theorem states a basic counting principle.

Theorem 2.2.2. Multiplets. Given n_1 elements $a_1, \ldots, a_{n_1}$; and n_2 elements $b_1, \ldots, b_{n_2}$; and $\ldots$; and n_r elements $x_1, \ldots, x_{n_r}$, it is possible to form precisely $n_1 \cdot n_2 \cdot \ldots \cdot n_r$ distinct ordered r-tuplets $(a_{j_1}, b_{j_2}, \ldots, x_{j_r})$ containing one element of each kind.

Proof: This is easy for $r = 2$ (matrix of pairs) and in general follows by induction on r (a 3-tuple is a 2-tuple and a 1-tuple, and so on). More specifically, in the case $r = 2$, consider forming a matrix with n_1 rows and n_2 columns, with the entry in the matrix at row i and column j being the ordered pair (i, j). Now each pair (i, j) with i between 1 and n_1, and j between 1 and n_2, appears exactly once in the matrix. Since a matrix with n_1 rows and n_2 columns has $n_1 n_2$ elements, it follows that there are $n_1 n_2$ ordered 2-tuples.

In the case $r = 3$, by the result already shown for $r = 2$ we know that there are $n_1 n_2$ 2-tuples based on the n_1 elements $a_1, a_2, \ldots, a_{n_1}$ and the n_2 elements $b_1, b_2, \ldots, b_{n_2}$. If we form a matrix with $n_1 n_2$ rows and n_3 columns, whose entry at row i and column j is $((a, b)_i, c_j)$, where $(a, b)_i$ is the ith of the (a, b) pairs (we put the $n_1 n_2$ such pairs into some arbitrary order so we can speak of an "ith" pair), then such a matrix has $n_1 n_2 n_3$ elements. Since each matrix entry can be considered a 3-tuple by removing one set of parentheses, there are $n_1 n_2 n_3$ 3-tuples.

The case of general r follows by the process called **mathematical induction.**[*] ∎

Example 2.2.3. A "word" is an ordered tuple of letters. In the English language, how many four-letter words are possible? Since a four-letter word is a 4-tuple, with the first letter chosen from $n_1 = 26$ letters, the second letter chosen from $n_2 = 26$ letters, the third letter chosen from $n_3 = 26$ letters, and the fourth letter chosen from $n_4 = 26$ letters, by the Multiplets Theorem there are $(26)(26)(26)(26)$ $= 456,976$ possible four-letter words. (As a matter of interest, it has been estimated that in the unabridged English dictionary there are approximately 8000 four-letter words. Thus, even if one counts the words that do not appear in the

---

[*]Those not familiar with this process may skip this last part of the proof without loss of continuity in the remainder of the text.

dictionary, only some 2% of the possible four-letter words are actually words of the language.)

We will now introduce the concepts of sampling from a finite population, since probability problems with a finite discrete sample space with equally likely outcomes have a simple interpretation in this context. Suppose we have a **population** (set) of n distinct elements (points) $a_1, \ldots, a_n$. An ordered arrangement $a_{j_1}, a_{j_2}, \ldots, a_{j_r}$ of r symbols is called an **ordered sample of size r**. If elements are selected from the population one by one, two simple (plus more complex) selection procedures are available. Under **simple random sampling (SRS) with replacement**, each selection is made from the entire population (so the same element may be drawn more than once) and each item is equally as likely to be drawn as any other item at any stage. Under **SRS without replacement**, an element once chosen is removed from the population (so there cannot be repetitions, and we must have $r \leq n$) and each item remaining is equally as likely to be drawn as any other item remaining at any stage. In Theorem 2.2.7 (which follows easily from the Multiplets Theorem 2.2.2) we note the number of possible samples under these two sampling procedures. (A "sample" is a "possible outcome" of the sampling experiment; how many such possible outcomes are there?) The notation of Definitions 2.2.4 and 2.2.5 will make the task of writing down the formulas involved easier.

Definition 2.2.4. $(n)_0 \equiv 1$. If n, r are positive integers,

$$(n)_r = \begin{cases} n(n-1) \cdots (n-r+1), & \text{if } r \leq n, \\ 0, & \text{if } r > n. \end{cases}$$

Definition 2.2.5 n-factorial. $0! \equiv 1$. If n is a positive integer,

$$n! = n(n-1) \cdot \cdots \cdot 2 \cdot 1.$$

(See Table 2 in the Statistical Tables of this book for some values.)

Example 2.2.6. If $n = 5$ and $r = 3$, then $n - r + 1 = 5 - 3 + 1 = 3$ and

$$(n)_r = (5)_3 = (5)(4)(3) = 60.$$

Also,

$$n! = 5! = (5)(4)(3)(2)(1) = 120.$$

Theorem 2.2.7. For a population of n elements and a prescribed sample size r, there exist

$$n^r \text{ samples under SRS with replacement,}$$

$$(n)_r \text{ samples under SRS without replacement.}$$

Proof: A sample under SRS with replacement consists of an ordered specification of r elements, namely the 1st chosen, the 2nd chosen, $\ldots$, the rth chosen. On each of these choices, n elements are available to be chosen, hence by the Multiplets Theorem with $n_1 = n_2 = \cdots = n_r = n$ there are $n_1 n_2 \cdots n_r = nn \cdots n = n^r$ possible samples.

A sample under SRS without replacement is also an ordered specification of r elements. On the 1st choice, there are n elements available. On the 2nd choice, there are only $n - 1$ elements available (since the sampling is without replacement, and 1 element has already been removed). On the 3rd choice, there are only $n - 2$ elements available since the sampling is without replacement, and two elements have already been removed. Similarly, down to the rth choice, where there are only $n - (r - 1)$ elements available since the sampling is without replacement and $r - 1$ elements have already been removed. Hence we use the Multiplets Theorem with $n_1 = n$, $n_2 = n - 1$, $n_3 = n - 2, \ldots, n_r = n - (r - 1)$ and find there are $n_1 n_2 \cdots n_r = n(n - 1)(n - 2) \cdots (n - r + 1) = (n)_r$ possible samples under SRS without replacement.   ∎

Corollary 2.2.8.   The number of different orderings of n elements is $n!$. (These are called the **permutations** of the n elements.)

Proof: This is the number of samples under SRS without replacement when $r = n$, namely $(n)_n$, and $(n)_n = n!$.   ∎

Example 2.2.9.   In a certain small lottery, 100 tickets have been sold. The first-prize winner will receive \$10, the second-prize winner \$5, and the third-prize winner \$1. Winners are selected by drawing from a large bowl containing the 100 lottery tickets. The selection is made without replacement. Each ticket has been sold to a different person. How many outcomes of (1st-prize winner, 2nd-prize winner, 3rd-prize winner) are possible?

Here we have SRS without replacement with $n = 100$ and $r = 3$, hence the number of possible outcomes is $(n)_r = (100)_3 = (100)(99)(98) = 970{,}200$. (If tickets were replaced, so the same person could possibly win more than once, there would be $n^r = 100^3 = 1{,}000{,}000$ possible outcomes.)

Example 2.2.10.   There are five entrants in a contest where all finish and ties are not possible. How many different outcomes of (1st to finish, 2nd to finish, 3rd to finish, 4th to finish, 5th to finish) are possible?

These are the number of different orderings of $n = 5$ elements, namely $n! = 5! = (5)(4)(3)(2)(1) = 120$.

We will also often be interested in unordered sets of elements from a given population. An unordered collection $\{a_{j_1}, a_{j_2}, \ldots, a_{j_r}\}$ of r distinct symbols is called an **unordered sample of size** r, or a **subpopulation of size** r. The number of subpopulations is specified in Theorem 2.2.15; it will be useful to first introduce a special notation (binomial coefficients).

Definition 2.2.11.   Binomial Coefficients. If n and r are nonnegative integers,

$$\binom{n}{r} \equiv {}^n C_r \equiv \frac{(n)_r}{r!}.$$

(Thus, $\binom{n}{0} \equiv 1$.) (See Table 3 for some values.)

Example 2.2.12. If $n = 6$ and $r = 2$, then

$$\binom{n}{r} = \binom{6}{2} = \frac{(6)_2}{2!} = \frac{(6)(5)}{(2)(1)} = 15.$$

Corollary 2.2.13. $\binom{n}{r} = \binom{n}{n-r}$.

Proof: The left side is

$$
\begin{aligned}
{}^nC_r &= \frac{(n)_r}{r!} = \frac{n(n-1)(n-2)\cdots(n-r+1)}{r!} \\
&= \frac{n(n-1)(n-2)\cdots(n-r+1)}{r!}\frac{(n-r)!}{(n-r)!} \\
&= \frac{n!}{r!(n-r)!}
\end{aligned}
$$

while the right side is

$$
\begin{aligned}
{}^nC_{n-r} &= \frac{(n)_{n-r}}{(n-r)!} = \frac{n(n-1)(n-2)\cdots(n-(n-r)+1)}{(n-r)!} \\
&= \frac{n(n-1)(n-2)\cdots(r+1)}{(n-r)!}\frac{r!}{r!} = \frac{n!}{r!(n-r)!}.
\end{aligned}
$$

We see, thus, that the two sides are equal, as was to be shown. ∎

Example 2.2.14. If $n = 10$ and $r = 2$, then

$$\binom{n}{r} = \binom{10}{2} = \frac{(10)_2}{2!} = \frac{(10)(9)}{(2)(1)} = 45,$$

and

$$
\begin{aligned}
\binom{n}{n-r} &= \binom{10}{10-2} = \binom{10}{8} = \frac{(10)_8}{8!} = \frac{(10)(9)(8)(7)(6)(5)(4)(3)}{(8)(7)(6)(5)(4)(3)(2)(1)} \\
&= \frac{(10)(9)}{2} = 45,
\end{aligned}
$$

which illustrates the equality established in general in Corollary 2.2.13.

Theorem 2.2.15. A population of n elements possesses $\binom{n}{r}$ different subpopulations of size $r(\le n)$.

Proof: $(n)_r$ = Number of ordered samples (of size r) under SRS without replacement;

$\quad\quad\quad = r! \cdot$ (number of distinct subpopulations of size r),

since each distinct subpopulation of size r yields $r!$ ordered samples (by

Corollary 2.2.8). Solving for the factor (Number of distinct subpopulations of size r) yields the result of this theorem.   ∎

Example 2.2.16.   A box contains 25 one-sided five-inch floppy computer diskettes, of which five are defective. The manufacturer inspects the boxes before shipment, as follows. Five diskettes are chosen at random (without replacement) from the box and tested; each that does not meet specifications is called a "**defective**". If the number of defectives found in the five tested is at most two, then the box is accepted, otherwise it is rejected. What is the probability that the box with five defective diskettes will be shipped?

Here

$$P \text{ (The box is shipped)} = P \text{ (At most 2 defectives in the 5 tested)}$$

$$= P \text{ (0 defectives, or 1 defective, or 2 defectives)}$$

$$= P \text{ (0 defectives)} + P \text{ (1 defective)} + P \text{ (2 defectives)}$$

where we used the finite additivity of Theorem 2.1.13 on the disjoint events A_1 (0 defectives), A_2 (1 defective), A_3 (2 defectives). Since the diskettes tested are chosen at random, all samples of 5 from the box of 25 are equally likely, so by equation (2.2.1)

$$P \text{ (}i \text{ defectives)} = \frac{\text{Number of ways to draw a sample of 5 containing } i \text{ defectives}}{\text{Number of ways to draw a sample of 5}}$$

$$= \frac{(\text{No. ways to draw } i \text{ from 5}) \times (\text{No. ways to draw } 5 - i \text{ from 20})}{(\text{Number of ways to draw 5 from 25})}$$

$$= \frac{\binom{5}{i}\binom{20}{5-i}}{\binom{25}{5}}.$$

Thus,

$$P \text{ (The box is shipped)} = \frac{\binom{5}{0}\binom{20}{5}}{\binom{25}{5}} + \frac{\binom{5}{1}\binom{20}{4}}{\binom{25}{5}} + \frac{\binom{5}{2}\binom{20}{3}}{\binom{25}{5}}$$

$$= \frac{15504 + 24225 + 11400}{53130} = .96234.$$

Example 2.2.17.   Consider the box of Example 2.2.16, which contains 25 diskettes, of which 5 are defective. What is the probability we obtain 3 defectives when we sample 3 diskettes from the box?

If we sample with replacement, then there are $n = 25$ items of which $r = 3$ are sampled, and the number of possible samples is $n^r = 25^3$. The number of possible samples that have all 3 defective is 5^3 (since we must then choose 1 of the 5 defectives on each draw), so that

$$P \text{ (All 3 are defective, with replacement)} = \frac{5^3}{25^3} = .008.$$

Note that this can be written as $(5/25)(5/25)(5/25)$, where $5/25 = .2$ is the probability that a single diskette drawn at random is defective. Since the sampling is with replacement, what happens on draw 1 does not affect what happens on draws 2 or 3, a setting where we say the results of **the draws are independent**. This is formalized in Section 2.4, where Definition 2.4.6 states that, for example, $P(ABC) = P(A)P(B)P(C)$ if A, B, C are independent events. Here we have seen this for the events $A = $"1st draw yields a defective", $B = $"2nd draw yields a defective", and $C = $"3rd draw yields a defective"; when sampling with replacement.

If we sample without replacement, then there are $(n)_r = (25)_3 = 13,800$ possible samples. The number of samples that have all 3 defective is $(5)_3 = 60$, so that

$$P \text{ (All 3 are defective, without replacement)} = \frac{(5)_3}{(25)_3} = \frac{60}{13800} = .0043,$$

where we see the event is less likely than under sampling with replacement (since the defectives become much less likely on successive draws when they are depleted). Here, **the draws are dependent**, and

$$P \text{ (Defective on the 1st draw)} = \frac{5}{25} = .2;$$

P (Defective on the 2nd draw, given that there was a defective on
  the first draw and sampling is random without replacement)

$$= \frac{4}{24} = .1667$$

since with one draw having been made there are only 24 diskettes left, and with that draw having been a defective, there are only 4 defectives left; and,

P (Defective on the 3rd draw, given that there were defectives
  drawn on the first and second draws and sampling is
  random without replacement)

$$= \frac{3}{23} = .1304$$

since with two draws having been made, there are only 23 diskettes left, and with those draws having been both defectives, there are only 3 defectives left. Now note that $(.2)(.1667)(.1304) = .0043$. This property is formalized in the **Multiplica-**

tion Rule of Theorem 2.3.6, which states that $P(ABC) = P(A)P(B$ given $A)P(C$ given A and B have occurred) for any dependent events A, B, and C. Here we have seen this for the events $A =$ "1st draw yields a defective"; $B =$ "2nd draw yields a defective"; and $C = $ 3rd draw yields a defective", when sampling without replacement.

Theorem 2.2.15 may be considered appropriate, for example, for selecting a committee of r people from a legislature of n people. Theorem 2.2.18 answers the question of how many ways we can form k disjoint committees having $r_1, \ldots, r_k$ members, respectively.

Theorem 2.2.18. Multinomial Coefficients. Let $r_1, \ldots, r_k$ be integers such that $r_1 + \cdots + r_k = n$ $(r_i \geq 0)$. The number of ways in which a population of n elements can be partitioned into k subpopulations of which

the 1st contains r_1 elements,

the 2nd contains r_2 elements,
$$\vdots$$
the kth contains r_k elements

is

$$\frac{n!}{r_1!r_2! \cdots r_k!} = \binom{n}{r_1}\binom{n - r_1}{r_2}\binom{n - r_1 - r_2}{r_3} \cdots \binom{n - r_1 - \cdots - r_{k-2}}{r_{k-1}}.$$

Proof: To effect the desired partition, we first select r_1 elements out of the given n in $\binom{n}{r_1}$ ways, then select r_2 of the $n - r_1$ remaining elements in $\binom{n - r_1}{r_2}$ ways, and so on. After forming the $(k - 1)$st group, there remain $n - r_1 - \cdots - r_{k-1} = r_k$ elements, and these form the last group. The expression $n!/(r_1!r_2! \cdots r_k!)$ follows on writing the binomial coefficients in terms of factorials and canceling equal terms. The product of binomial coefficients arose via use of the multiplets theorem (Theorem 2.2.2). (The present theorem may also be proven by induction.) ∎

Example 2.2.19. A condominium management committee has 11 members and wishes to divide into three committees with everyone serving on at least one committee, and no one serving on more than one committee. The committees are "Facilities," which is to have three members; "Services," which is to have five members; and "Entertainment," which is to have three members. How many ways can the 11 be split into these committees?

Here we use Theorem 2.2.18 with $k = 3$ subcommittees, of sizes $r_1 = 3$, $r_2 = 5$, and $r_3 = 3$, chosen from the $r_1 + r_2 + r_3 = 11 = n$ members. Therefore the number of possibilities is

$$\frac{11!}{3!5!3!} = \frac{(11)(10)(9)(8)(7)(6)(5!)}{(3)(2)(6)(5!)} = (11)(10)(3)(4)(7) = 9240.$$

Many problems occur naturally (or are conveniently stated) in the form of **ball and cell models**. We will now explore some relationships between these models of tossing balls into cells and sampling.

Definition 2.2.20. If r balls are placed at random successively into n cells and each cell can hold $1, 2, \ldots, i$ balls, we will say we have **model** $(BC)_i$ $(1 \le i \le \infty)$. **At random** means that, when any ball is to be tossed, all cells remaining eligible to receive it are equally likely to receive it.

Thus, under model $(BC)_1$ each cell can hold only one ball, under model $(BC)_\infty$ each cell can hold unlimited balls, and in general under model $(BC)_m$ each cell can hold up to m balls.

Corollary 2.2.21.[3] $(BC)_1$ is equivalent[4] to SRS sampling r times from a population of n objects, without replacement. $(BC)_\infty$ is equivalent[4] to SRS sampling r times from a population of n objects, with replacement.

Due to the correspondence to random samples noted in Corollary 2.2.21, examples of $(BC)_1$ and of $(BC)_\infty$ models are easily given. For example, often when cargo is being unloaded from a ship and the total cargo weight is to be determined, only some of the cargo is weighed and observations of its weight are used to estimate the weight of the whole cargo. In such an instance, we have a $(BC)_1$ model where n (the number of cells) is the number of cargo units and r (the number of balls) is the number of cargo units actually weighed.[5] Sampling with replacement here would yield a $(BC)_\infty$ model, but this is seldom used except in special circumstances since there is usually no gain from examining (e.g., weighing) the same unit more than once.

Examples of $(BC)_m$ models can also be given. For example, a **post office** with n post office boxes with a capacity of m letters each might be considered, as a first approximation, to be a $(BC)_m$ situation. In such a situation, how many boxes could we expect to overflow each day? We are not in a position to study this question yet. The question could arise in a post office attempt to select box size m. (See Problems 2.8H and 5.5H.)

Example 2.2.22. Suppose r balls are to be tossed at random into n cells. If $r = 4$ and $n = 7$ and the balls are basketballs, and the "cells" are basketball boxes, then often **model (BC)₁** would be appropriate; that is, often **each box could hold only one basketball.** (Of course some boxes will be empty when we are done, since we have only 4 basketballs and there are 7 boxes.) *The number of ways to*

[3] This is a "corollary" to our discussion.

[4] The equivalences arise from the fact that (considering the "cells" to be members of the populations) the cells that are "balled" may be considered as the members of the sample. We then have, for example, order or not depending on whether the balls carry numbers or not.

[5] An example involving $n = 1267$ bales of tobacco, of which some number r are to be weighed, is discussed by Deming (1966), p. 108. In that example, r is set so as to obtain a desired accuracy of the estimate of the total cargo weight, resulting in $r = 93$. Note that weighing such a sample will, in general, be much less costly than weighing the whole cargo.

distribute the balls is equal to the number of ways to select 4 items from 7 **without** replacement, which is (by Theorem 2.2.7) $(7)_4 = 840$. For example, one of these possible ways is $(5, 3, 7, 2)$, which states that basketball number 1 goes into the 5th box, basketball number 2 goes into the 3rd box, basketball number 3 goes into the 7th box, and basketball number 4 goes into the 2nd box; of course, then boxes 1, 4, and 6 are empty.

If the boxes used were large bins that could hold any number (more precisely, at least the total number of basketballs we have, which is seven) of basketballs, **model (BC)$_\infty$** would be appropriate; that is, **each box could hold all the basketballs.** (Of course, up to 6 of the boxes will be empty since we have 4 basketballs and 7 boxes, each of which could hold all the balls.) *The number of ways to distribute the balls* is equal to the number of ways to select 4 items from 7 **with** replacement (since a box may hold any number of the balls), which is (by Theorem 2.2.7) $7^4 = 2401$. For example, one of these possible ways is $(5, 3, 3, 7)$, which states that basketball number 1 goes into the 5th box, basketball number 2 goes into the 3rd box, basketball number 3 goes into the 3rd box, and basketball number 4 goes into the 7th box; of course, then boxes 1, 2, 4, and 6 are empty.

Note that in each case just presented, the specification tells *to which box each of the balls is assigned.* For this reason, the specification is called an **assignment vector**, and the number of specifications is called **the number of assignment vectors.** We know this number under both $(BC)_1$ and $(BC)_\infty$ and can make a table of it:

	Number of assignment vectors
Model $(BC)_1$	$(n)_r$
Model $(BC)_\infty$	n^r

We now wish to distinguish two ways of specifying the outcomes of tossing r balls into n cells. The first way (**assignment vectors**) specifies which cell each ball entered. The second way (**occupancy vectors**) specifies how many balls entered each cell. For example, if 2 balls are tossed into 3 cells we have (under $(BC)_\infty$):

Possible Assignment Vectors (Ω_A)	Possible Occupancy Vectors (Ω_0)
$(1, 1)$	$(2, 0, 0)$
$(2, 2)$	$(0, 2, 0)$
$(3, 3)$	$(0, 0, 2)$
$(1, 2)$ or $(2, 1)$	$(1, 1, 0)$
$(1, 3)$ or $(3, 1)$	$(1, 0, 1)$
$(2, 3)$ or $(3, 2)$	$(0, 1, 1)$

Thus, there are 9 possible assignment vectors, but only 6 possible occupancy vectors; hence, in calculating probabilities it will matter which items ($\omega \in \Omega_A$ or $\omega \in \Omega_0$) we consider to be equally likely outcomes. If $\omega \in \Omega_A$ are equally likely,

P [Both balls land in the same cell] $= \frac{3}{9} = \frac{1}{3}$; if $\omega \in \Omega_0$ are equally likely, we obtain P [Both balls land in the same cell] $= \frac{3}{6} = \frac{1}{2}$. [Under $(BC)_1$ yet another result is found: P [Both balls land in the same cell] $= 0$.] As noted in detail in Feller (1968), pp. 38–42, in physics three possibilities are studied:

	Ω_A	Ω_0
$(BC)_\infty$	**Maxwell-Boltzmann** statistical mechanics	**Bose-Einstein** statistical mechanics
$(BC)_1$		**Fermi-Dirac** statistical mechanics

For each of Maxwell-Boltzmann, Bose-Einstein, and Fermi-Dirac "statistical mechanics" (i.e., for these three ways of describing the distribution of r balls at random into n cells), it is believed that there are particles in physics which are equally likely to be found in any one of the outcomes. For example, if a system contains r indistinguishable particles and the "phase space" is divided into n parts (often with n large, so no part will hold more than one particle), the number of assignment vectors will be n^r. **Maxwell-Boltzmann statistical mechanics** *treats all these n^r possibilities as equally likely to occur.* In **Bose-Einstein statistical mechanics**, and in **Fermi-Dirac statistical mechanics**, on the other hand, *it is the possible arrangements as specified by the occupancy vector that are treated as being equally likely.* The Bose-Einstein model is often used for photons, nuclei, and some atoms (those with an even number of elementary particles), whereas the Fermi-Dirac model is often used for electrons, neutrons, and protons. [*Note:* **No particles are believed to have equally likely assignment vectors under (BC)$_1$:** whereas this model is SRS without replacement in probability and statistics (and is the most common situation in practice), it is apparently not of use in physics.]

We will now formally define assignment vectors and occupancy vectors, and then count how many there are under the two models for number of balls in each cell.

Definition 2.2.23. $\Omega_A = \{(x_1, \dots, x_r): x_i \text{ is the number of the cell ball } i \text{ goes into}\}$ is called the set of **assignment vectors**. $\Omega_0 = \{(r_1, \dots, r_n): r_j \text{ is the number of balls in cell } j\}$ is called the set of **occupancy vectors**. Let $\#(\Omega)$ denote the number of points in Ω.

Theorem 2.2.24.

(i) Under $(BC)_1$, $\#(\Omega_A) = (n)_r$.
   Under $(BC)_\infty$, $\#(\Omega_A) = n^r$.

(ii) Under $(BC)_1$, $\#(\Omega_0) = \binom{n}{r}$.
   Under $(BC)_\infty$, $\#(\Omega_0) = \binom{n+r-1}{r}$.

Proof: (i) These results follow from the correspondences with SRS sampling and Theorem 2.2.7.

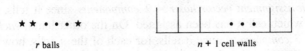

r balls   n + 1 cell walls

Figure 2.2-1.

(ii) Under $(BC)_1$, $\Omega_0 = \{(r_1, \ldots, r_n): r_j \text{ is } 0 \text{ or } 1 \text{ and } r_1 + \cdots + r_n = r\}$. Thus, $\#(\Omega_0)$ is the number of ways of choosing r places out of n for 1's.

Under $(BC)_\infty$, $\Omega_0 = \{(r_1, \ldots, r_n): r_j \text{ is the number of balls in cell } j, r_1 + \cdots + r_n = r, r_j \geq 0\}$. If we consider that we have r balls (represented by stars) and n cells, thus $n + 1$ cell walls (represented by bars) (Figure 2.2-1), then we must put one cell wall on the outside on each end in any distribution of balls into cells (distribution of stars and bars in a line); the $n - 1$ walls and r balls can be mixed up in any way, the number of such ways being the number of ways of choosing, out of $n + r - 1$ places, r for balls. ∎

It may be helpful to put the results of Theorem 2.2.24 in tabular form:

	Number of assignment vectors	Number of occupancy vectors
Model $(BC)_1$	$(n)_r$	$\binom{n}{r}$
Model $(BC)_\infty$	n^r	$\binom{n + r - 1}{r}$

For example, if $r = 2$ balls are tossed into $n = 3$ cells the numbers are

	Number of assignment vectors	Number of occupancy vectors
Model $(BC)_1$	6	3
Model $(BC)_\infty$	9	6

The elements that comprise those counted in the bottom row in this $r = 2$, $n = 3$ case were listed in detail in the discussion following Example 2.2.22. We now give a similar table listing in detail all the elements counted in each cell above:

	Assignment vectors	Occupancy vectors
Model $(BC)_1$	$(1,2), (1,3), (2,1), (2,3),$ $(3,1), (3,2)$	$(1,1,0), (1,0,1), (0,1,1)$
Model $(BC)_\infty$	$(1,2), (1,3), (2,1), (2,3),$ $(3,1), (3,2), (1,1), (2,2),$ $(3,3)$	$(1,1,0), (1,0,1), (0,1,1),$ $(2,0,0), (0,2,0), (0,0,2)$

Note that *each assignment vector has r = 2 components* since it tells, for each of the r balls, to which cell it has been assigned. On the other hand, *each occupancy vector has n = 3 components* since it tells, for each of the n cells, how many balls have been assigned to it. For example, assignment vector $(3, 2)$ means ball number 1 is assigned to cell number 3, and ball number 2 is assigned to cell number 2. And, occupancy vector $(1, 0, 1)$ means cell number 1 has 1 ball in it, cell number 2 is empty, and cell number 3 has 1 ball in it.

Note that **in most probability problems** (outside of physics) **it is the assignment vectors that are considered equally likely**; sometimes the occupancy vectors are counted as part of a problem, but they are rarely considered equally likely.

Example 2.2.25. $r = 6$ balls are distributed at random into $n = 7$ cells of unlimited capacity. What is the probability that the occupancy numbers are $2, 2, 1, 1, 0, 0, 0$ in some order?

Here the number of assignment vectors such that the occupancy numbers are $2, 2, 1, 1, 0, 0, 0$ *in that order* is the number of ways of ordering six items, of which two are "1," two are "2," one is "3," and one is "4." That number of ways is

$$\frac{6!}{2!2!1!1!} = \frac{6!}{2!2!} = 180.$$

The number of *different* occupancy vectors with two doubly occupied cells, two singly occupied cells, and three unoccupied cells is the number of ways of dividing 7 objects into three groups of sizes 2, 2, 3. That number of ways is

$$\frac{7!}{2!2!3!} = 210.$$

There are 7^6 equally likely assignment vectors (since there are 7 choices for each of the six balls, or 7^6 assignment vectors). Therefore, the probability desired is

$$\frac{(180)(210)}{7^6} = \frac{5400}{7^5} = .3213.$$

A similar problem, with different number r of balls, is considered in Example 2.2.26.

Example 2.2.26. $r = 7$ balls are distributed at random into $n = 7$ cells of unlimited capacity. [Thus, model $(BC)_\infty$ holds and each of the n^r possible assignment vectors has probability n^{-r}.] What is the probability that the occupancy numbers are $2, 2, 1, 1, 1, 0, 0$ in some order?

The assignment vectors are $\Omega_A = \{(x_1, \ldots, x_7): x_i$ is the number of the cell ball i goes into$\}$. How many assignment vectors lead to occupancy numbers $2, 2, 1, 1, 1, 0, 0$ *in that order*? (This order implies two "1's," two "2's," one "3", one "4", one "5," zero "6's," zero "7's" in some order.) The number of such assignment vectors is

$$\frac{7!}{2!2!1!1!1!0!0!} = \frac{7!}{2!2!}$$

by Theorem 2.2.18. How many *different* occupancy vectors are there with 2 doubly occupied, 3 singly occupied, and 2 unoccupied cells? (This eliminates the order on the occupancy vector.) This is the number of ways of subdividing 7 objects into 3 groups, of 2, 3, 2:

$$\frac{7!}{2!3!2!}.$$

Since there are 7^7 assignment vectors, the probability of occupancy numbers 2, 2, 1, 1, 1, 0, 0 in some order is

$$\frac{\frac{7!}{2!3!2!} \times \frac{7!}{2!2!}}{7^7} = \frac{45 \times 5!}{7^5}.$$

This number can be calculated with little trouble (e.g., on a desk calculator). For cases where we need $n!$ and n is large, **Stirling's formula** yields a useful approximate evaluation:

$$n! \sim \sqrt{2\pi n}\left(\frac{n}{e}\right)^n. \tag{2.2.27}$$

Here the " $\sim$ " means that

$$\lim_{n \to \infty} \frac{n!}{\sqrt{2\pi n}\left(\frac{n}{e}\right)^n} = 1. \tag{2.2.28}$$

Example 2.2.29. Assume that a year has 365 days and that all birthdays are equally likely. What is the probability that, in a group of 60 people (whose birthdays are assumed unrelated), *some* 5 people will have the same birthday and all the other people will have different birthdays, none of which falls on the birthday of the 5?

Here, $r = 60$ balls are distributed at random into $n = 365$ cells of unlimited capacity. [Thus, model $(BC)_\infty$ holds and each of the n^r possible assignment vectors has probability n^{-r}.] We desire

$$P \left(\text{Occupancy numbers are } \overbrace{5,}^{1} \overbrace{1,1,\ldots,1}^{55}, \overbrace{0,\ldots,0}^{309} \text{ in some order}\right).$$

Here $\Omega_A = \{(x_1, \ldots, x_{60}): x_i$ is the number of the cell ball i goes into$\}$. Now

$$
\begin{bmatrix} \text{No. of assignment} \\ \text{vectors leading to} \\ \text{occupancy nos.} \\ 5, 1, \ldots, 1, 0, \ldots, 0 \\ \textit{in that order} \end{bmatrix}
=
\begin{bmatrix} \text{No. of assignment} \\ \text{vectors with} \\ 5 \text{ "1's"} \\ 1 \text{ "2"} \\ \vdots \\ 1 \text{ "56"} \\ 0 \text{ "57's"} \\ \vdots \\ 0 \text{ "365's"} \\ \text{in some order} \end{bmatrix}
= \frac{60!}{5!1! \cdots 1!0! \cdots 0!},
$$

and

$$
\begin{bmatrix} \text{No. of occupancy} \\ \text{vectors with} \\ 1 \text{ cell with 5 occupants} \\ 55 \text{ cells with 1 occupant} \\ 309 \text{ cells with 0 occupants} \end{bmatrix}
=
\begin{bmatrix} \text{No. of ways to} \\ \text{subdivide 365} \\ \text{objects into} \\ 3 \text{ groups of} \\ 1, 55, 309 \end{bmatrix}
= \frac{365!}{1!55!309!}.
$$

Thus, the desired probability is

$$
\frac{\dfrac{60!}{5!1!1! \cdots 1!0! \cdots 0!}}{365^{60}} \times \frac{\dfrac{365!}{1!55!309!}}{} = \frac{\binom{60}{5}(365)_{56}}{365^{60}}.
$$

In this last form, the result can be reasoned to as follows. Select 5 people to have the same birthday. This can be done in $\binom{60}{5}$ ways. For each of these ways, there are $(365) \cdots (310) = (365)_{56}$ different choices of 56 birthdays that are distinct, whereas with no restrictions there are 365^{60}.

Example 2.2.30. Seven people enter an elevator together on the first floor of an 11-floor building. Assume that the "egress pattern" to floors $2, 3, \ldots, 11$ is the same (i.e., passengers leave independently and in random manner, with each floor equally likely to be selected). What is the probability of event A: All get off at different floors?

Again we use assignment vectors, with $\Omega_A = \{(x_1, \ldots, x_7): $ passenger i gets off at floor $x_i, 2 \le x_i \le 11\}$. $\#(\Omega_A) = 10^7$, $\#(A) = (10)_7$, so

$$
P(A) = \frac{\#(A)}{\#(\Omega_A)} = \frac{10!}{10^7(10-7)!} = \frac{189}{3125} \approx .065.
$$

Example 2.2.31. Alcohol Tasting. As reported in a UPI story (e.g., see *The Times-Union*, Rochester, New York, October 26, 1971, p. 9A), the Internal Revenue Service's argument that neutral grain alcohol tastes the same to everybody (and that special claims for various brands could, hence, not be permitted) suffered a blow when the quality control director of Joseph E. Seagram & Sons correctly identified the distilleries from which 14 such alcohol samples had come, by tasting and smelling the samples. What is the probability that a person with no such organoleptic abilities would obtain the same result? (Ignore the possibility of trickery.)

Suppose we are told that one sample came from each of 14 distilleries. There are 14! ways to assign distilleries to samples, and we have a probability of 1/14! of selecting the correct one by guessing. Our chances of getting at least one distillery correctly paired with a sample by random guessing are studied in Example 2.3.17.

PROBLEMS FOR SECTION 2.2

2.2.1 Let m, n, and r be nonnegative integers. Show that binomial coefficients have the properties

(a) $\binom{n}{r} = \binom{n-1}{r} + \binom{n-1}{r-1}$ for $n \geq r$;

(b) $\sum_{r=0}^{k} \binom{m}{r}\binom{n}{k-r} = \binom{m+n}{k}$;

(c) $\sum_{r=0}^{n} \binom{n}{r} = 2^n$;

(d) $\sum_{r=0}^{n} r\binom{n}{r} = n2^{n-1}$;

(e) $\sum_{r=0}^{n} (-1)^r \binom{n}{r} = 0$ if $n \geq 1$.

2.2.2 A fair coin is tossed independently five times. Find the probability that exactly three of the tosses yield heads.

2.2.3 A and B are mutually exclusive events with $P(A) = .25$ and $P(B) = .50$. Find: (a) $P(\overline{A})$; (b) $P(A \cup B)$; (c) $P(\overline{A} \cup \overline{B})$; (d) $P(\overline{A} \cap \overline{B})$.

2.2.4 A and B are events with $P(A) = .40$, $P(B) = .75$, and $P(AB) = .25$. Find: (a) $P(A \cup B)$; (b) $P(A \cap \overline{B})$; (c) $P(\overline{A} \cap B)$; (d) $P(\overline{A} \cap \overline{B})$.

2.2.5 A **standard deck of cards** (a "standard" deck consists of **52 cards**, of which 13 are in each of **4 suits**: 13 are **spades**, 13 are **hearts**, 13 are **diamonds**, and the remaining 13 are **clubs**; each suit has one each of cards marked ace, K, Q, J, 10, 9, 8, 7, 6, 5, 4, 3, 2) is shuffled and dealt to the four players A, B, C, D so that each has a 13-card hand. Compute the probability of each of the following events.
(a) E_1: "A gets all spades, B gets all hearts, C gets all diamonds, D gets all clubs."
(b) E_2: "Each player gets cards of only one suit."
(c) E_3: "Player A gets all spades."
(d) E_4: "Player D gets all aces."

2.2.6 Player A deals 5 cards to player B from a standard (see Problem 2.2.5) deck of cards. Compute the probabilities of the following events.
(a) A deals a royal flush to B (i.e., A deals B one each of ace, K, Q, J, 10, all of the same suit).

(b) B has "four of a kind" (i.e., four cards with the same marking, such as K, with the fifth card being of a different marking).

(c) B has "three of a kind" (i.e., three cards with the same marking, such as Q, with the other two cards being different from the marking common to the three cards that have the same marking).

2.2.7 Suppose a college has five dormitories of the same size, and incoming students are assigned at random to dormitories. If 17 high-school friends are assigned at random, what is the probability we find 5 assigned to dorm 1, 2 to dorm 2, 7 to dorm 3, 1 to dorm 4, and 2 to dorm 5?

2.2.8 In Problem 2.2.7, what is the probability that the numbers in each of the five dormitories are 5, 2, 7, 1, 2 in *some* order?

2.2.9 From a list of m positive integers and n negative integers, four integers are chosen at random (without replacement). Find the probability that
(a) The product of the four integers is a positive number.
(b) The product of the four integers is a negative number.

2.2.10 n friends share a season ticket that entitles one person to attend (one person per game) each of a series of basketball games. If before each game the friends draw a name at random from a box containing their n names to see who will attend the game, what is the probability that exactly t of them ($t < n$) will not get to see any game at all?

2.3. CONDITIONAL PROBABILITY; BAYES' RULE; ADDITIONAL PROPERTIES

Often we have **partial information** about a certain phenomenon and wish to know **how this affects the probabilities** of outcomes of interest to us (e.g., what is the probability of rain tomorrow given rain today). For this reason, we will introduce conditional probability and rules for dealing with it. We then study additional properties of probability and give some examples.

To introduce conditional probability, let us *first reason to the definition using frequency probability* as in equation (2.1.8) and then give the formal definition. Recall that if we have n unrelated trials of an experiment and look after each trial to see if an event A of interest has occurred or not, we will find that A has occurred on some number $n(A)$ of the n trials; then the relative frequency of A in those n trials is $n(A)/n$, which is denoted as $R(A)$. Now suppose *we are interested in the relative frequency of A on those trials where B occurred* (e.g., this might be of interest if A is the event "has lung cancer," B is the event "smokes," and we study n persons). Now B occurred on some number $n(B)$ of the trials, and the number of those on which A occurs equals the number of all n trials on which A and B *both* occur. Thus,

$$\left(\begin{array}{l} \text{Relative frequency of } A \text{ on those} \\ \text{trials where } B \text{ occurred} \end{array} \right) = \frac{n(AB)}{n(B)}.$$

We call this the **conditional relative frequency of A given B**, and denote it by **R(A|B)**. Now we can see that

$$R(A|B) = \frac{n(AB)}{n(B)} = \frac{n(AB)/n}{n(B)/n} = \frac{R(AB)}{R(B)}. \tag{2.3.1}$$

As n grows large, the relative frequencies in equation (2.3.1) approach the corresponding probabilities. We therefore are led to think of defining the conditional probability of A given B as the ratio of the probability of AB and the probability of B, in order to answer the question "How likely is A to occur when we know B has occurred?" Formally, we give

Definition 2.3.2. A and B are events in a sample space Ω, and if $P(B) > 0$, then the **conditional probability of A given B** (say $P(A|B)$) is defined by

$$P(A|B) \equiv \frac{P(AB)}{P(B)}.$$

Example 2.3.3.   Two fair six-sided dice are rolled. Let A be the event "Sum is 7" and B the event "First die shows a 6." Find the probability of A. In some cases, we might see the outcome on the first die (but not that on the second) and ask "What is the conditional probability A occurs given we know B has occurred?"; so, find $P(A|B)$ also.

Here there are 36 equally likely outcomes of the experiment, as listed in Figure 1.4-2. $P(A) = 6/36 = 1/6 = .1667$, since for 6 of the 36 outcomes the sum is 7. Next, $P(A|B) = P(AB)/P(B)$ by Definition 2.3.2, and we have $P(B) = 6/36$, $P(AB) = 1/36$, hence $P(A|B) = (1/36)/(6/36) = 1/6 = .1667$. Thus, the chances of A are the same when we have no information about B, as when we know B has occurred.

Example 2.3.4.   Two fair dice are rolled. Let A be the event "Sum is 7" and C the event that "At least one of the dice shows a 1." Find the conditional probability of A given we know C has occurred (which might occur if, after the dice are rolled but before the result is announced, a tall person in the crowd around the craps game tells us "I see one of the dice, and it shows a 1").

Here $P(A|C) = P(AC)/P(C)$, $P(AC) = 2/36$, and $P(C) = 11/36$, hence $P(A|C) = (2/36)/(11/36) = 2/11 = .1818$. Note that this is greater than $P(A) = .1667$, so that with this information A is more likely to occur.

In many problems involving conditional and unconditional probability, the possible values of some variable (of possible interest) **stratify** the sample space into mutually exclusive and exhaustive subsets whose probabilities are either given or are easy to compute. Theorems 2.3.5, 2.3.7, and 2.3.9 consider how we can use such stratification. For example, suppose that in a certain species a family chosen at random has exactly j children with probability p_j ($j = 0, 1, 2, \ldots$) where $0 \le p_0 \le 1$, $0 \le p_1 \le 1, \ldots$ and $p_0 + p_1 + p_2 + \cdots = 1$. Also, suppose that for any given number i of children, the 2^i possible sex distributions each have the same probability $1/2^i$. Let C_m denote the event "a family chosen at random has m children," for which $P(C_m) = p_m$ ($m = 0, 1, 2, \ldots$). Let D be the event "a family chosen at random has either all boys or all girls," and let E be the event "a family chosen at random has at least one child but no girls." Then $P(D)$ (the probability of an unmixed family) and $P(C_1|E)$ (the probability of an only child given at least one child and no girls) are of interest, and their calculation requires use of Theorems 2.3.7 and 2.3.9, respectively. The calculation is left as an exercise (see Problem 2.12H); however, other examples are given following the proof of Theorem 2.3.9.

Theorem 2.3.5. If B is an event and $P(B) > 0$, then $P(\cdot|B)$ is a probability function; that is,

(i) $P(A|B) \ge 0$, for all events A;

(ii) $P(\Omega|B) = 1$;

(iii) $P\left(\bigcup_{n=1}^{\infty} A_n \middle| B\right) = \sum_{n=1}^{\infty} P(A_n|B)$, if $A_i \cap A_j = \emptyset$ ($i \ne j$).

Proof: Use Definition 2.3.2 and the properties of probability. ∎

Theorem 2.3.6. Multiplication Rule. For each $n + 1$ events $A_0, A_1, \ldots, A_n$ for which $P(A_0 A_1 \cdots A_n) > 0$, we have

$$P(A_0 A_1 \cdots A_n) = P(A_0)P(A_1|A_0)P(A_2|A_0 A_1) \cdots P(A_n|A_0 A_1 \cdots A_{n-1}).$$

Proof: Since

$$A_0 A_1 \cdots A_{n-1} \subseteq A_0 A_1 \cdots A_{n-2} \subseteq \cdots \subseteq A_0,$$

we have

$$0 < P(A_0 A_1 \cdots A_{n-1}) \le \cdots \le P(A_0),$$

so all conditional probabilities involved are defined. [Recall (see Definition 2.3.2) that $P(A|B)$ is defined only when $P(B) > 0$.] It is easy to show the result for $n = 1$, and the general result follows by mathematical induction. ∎

Theorem 2.3.7.   Theorem of Total Probabilities. If

$$P\left(\bigcup_{n=1}^{\infty} B_n\right) = 1,$$

$$B_i \cap B_j = \varnothing \quad (i \neq j),$$

$$P(B_n) > 0 \quad \text{for each } n,$$

then (for any event A)

$$P(A) = \sum_{n=1}^{\infty} P(A|B_n)P(B_n).$$

Proof: If we denote $A \cap \left(\bigcup_{n=1}^{\infty} B_n\right)$ by X and $A \cap \left(\bigcup_{n=1}^{\infty} B_n\right)^c$ by Y, then $X \cap Y = \varnothing$, $X \cup Y = A$, and therefore $P(A) = P(X) + P(Y)$. Thus,

$$P(A) = P\left(A \cap \bigcup_{n=1}^{\infty} B_n\right) + P\left(A \cap \left(\bigcup_{n=1}^{\infty} B_n\right)^c\right)$$

$$= P\left(A \cap \bigcup_{n=1}^{\infty} B_n\right) + 0, \text{ since } P\left(\bigcup_{n=1}^{\infty} B_n\right) = 1 \text{ implies } P\left(\overline{\bigcup_{n=1}^{\infty} B_n}\right) = 0$$

and hence $P(Y) = 0$

$$= P\left(\bigcup_{n=1}^{\infty} AB_n\right) = \sum_{n=1}^{\infty} P(AB_n) = \sum_{n=1}^{\infty} P(A|B_n)P(B_n).$$ ∎

Corollary 2.3.8. Theorem 2.3.7 holds if ∞ is replaced by some finite number N.

Theorem 2.3.9.   Bayes' Rule. If

$$P\left(\bigcup_{n=1}^{\infty} B_n\right) = 1,$$

$$B_i \cap B_j = \varnothing \quad (i \neq j),$$

$$P(B_n) > 0 \quad \text{for each } n,$$

and A is an event with $P(A) > 0$, then for each k,

$$P(B_k|A) = \frac{P(A|B_k)P(B_k)}{\displaystyle\sum_{n=1}^{\infty} P(A|B_n)P(B_n)}.$$

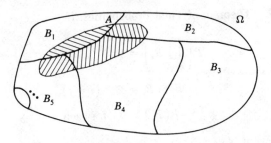

Figure 2.3-1.

Proof: By the definition of conditional probability and the Theorem of Total Probabilities (2.3.7),

$$P(B_i|A) = \frac{P(AB_k)}{P(A)} = \frac{P(A|B_k)P(B_k)}{\sum\limits_{n=1}^{\infty} P(A|B_n)P(B_n)}. \qquad \blacksquare$$

The hypotheses of the Theorem of Total Probabilities and of Bayes' Rule can be visualized as follows. Ω is essentially decomposed into disjoint sets $B_1, B_2, \ldots$. Then (Theorem of Total Probabilities) we can find $P(A)$ by adding up the probabilities of those parts of A that lie in $B_1, B_2, \ldots$. A diagram may help (Figure 2.3-1). [The final result is stated somewhat differently, since $P(AB_n) = P(A|B_n)P(B_n)$.] In Bayes' Rule we look at an inverse problem: "Given that an outcome has occurred which is in A, what is the probability that it is in B_k?" (At this point, examine Example 2.3.18 briefly to see some practical implications.)

Example 2.3.10. In a certain country, all legislative committee members are either Communists or Republicans. There are 3 committees. Committee 1 has 5 Communists, committee 2 has 2 Communists and 4 Republicans, and committee 3 consists of 3 Communists and 4 Republicans. A committee is selected at random, and a person is then selected at random from that committee. **(a)** Find the probability that the person selected is a Communist. **(b)** Given that the selected person is a Communist, what is the probability that he/she came from committee 2? committee 3? committee 1?

(a) Let A denote the event that the selected person is a Communist, and B_n denote the event that initially committee n is selected ($n = 1, 2, 3$). Then by Theorem 2.3.7,

$$P(A) = \sum_{n=1}^{3} P(A|B_n)P(B_n) = 1 \cdot \frac{1}{3} + \frac{2}{6} \cdot \frac{1}{3} + \frac{3}{7} \cdot \frac{1}{3} = \frac{37}{63}.$$

(b) Here, using Bayes' Rule (Theorem 2.3.9), we have

$$P(B_2|A) = \frac{P(B_2 \text{ and } A)}{P(A)} = \frac{P(A|B_2)P(B_2)}{P(A)} = \frac{\frac{2}{6} \cdot \frac{1}{3}}{\frac{37}{63}} = \frac{7}{37},$$

$$P(B_3|A) = \frac{P(A|B_3)P(B_3)}{P(A)} = \frac{\frac{3}{7} \cdot \frac{1}{3}}{\frac{37}{63}} = \frac{9}{37},$$

$$P(B_1|A) = \frac{P(A|B_1)P(B_1)}{P(A)} = \frac{1 \cdot \frac{1}{3}}{\frac{37}{63}} = \frac{21}{37}.$$

Example 2.3.11. A factory has 4 machines that produce the same item. Machines 1 and 2 each produce 20% of the total output, while machines 3 and 4 are larger and each produce 30% of the total output. It is known that 6% of machine 1's output is defective, while machine 2 produces 5% defective items, and machines 3 and 4 each produce 8% defective items. An item is chosen at random from the output of the factory. **(a)** What is the probability that this item is defective? **(b)** Given that the item selected in part (a) is defective, what is the probability that it was produced by machine 2?

(a) Let A be the event that the item chosen is defective, and B_n be the event that the item chosen was produced by machine n ($n = 1, 2, 3, 4$). Then by the Theorem of Total Probabilities (2.3.7),

$$P(A) = \sum_{n=1}^{4} P(A|B_n)P(B_n)$$

$$= .06 \times .20 + .05 \times .20 + .08 \times .30 + .08 \times .30 = .07.$$

(b) Here, using Bayes' Rule, we find that

$$P(B_2|A) = \frac{P(A|B_2)P(B_2)}{P(A)} = \frac{.05 \times .20}{.07} = \frac{1}{7}.$$

Example 2.3.12. An urn contains a white chips and b blue chips. A chip is chosen at random from the urn, discarded, and replaced by one of the opposite color; a second chip is then drawn. What is the probability that the second chip drawn is blue? What is the probability that the second chip is white?

Let W_i denote the event that the ith draw results in selection of a white chip, and B_i denote the event that the ith draw results in selection of a blue chip

($i = 1, 2$). Then the desired probabilities are $P(B_2)$ and $P(W_2)$. By the Theorem of Total Probabilities (Theorem 2.3.7),

$$P(B_2) = P(B_2|W_1)P(W_1) + P(B_2|B_1)P(B_1)$$

$$= \frac{b+1}{a+b} \cdot \frac{a}{a+b} + \frac{b-1}{a+b} \cdot \frac{b}{a+b} = \frac{(b-1)b + (b+1)a}{(a+b)^2}.$$

Now, since $W_2 = \overline{B}_2$, it follows (see Theorem 2.1.17) that

$$P(W_2) = 1 - P(B_2) = 1 - \frac{(b-1)b + (b+1)a}{(a+b)^2} = \frac{(a-1)a + (a+1)b}{(a+b)^2}.$$

As an example, suppose that a certain city consists of 1000 law-abiding citizens ($a = 1000$) and 200 miscreants ($b = 200$). This city is in a totalitarian country, and a random screening process is used to seek out the criminals. If a criminal is found in the first stage, he/she is turned into a law-abiding citizen by a certain "treatment"; while if a law-abiding citizen is selected in the first stage, then he/she becomes angry at society and a miscreant in the second stage. Then the probability of a citizen being a miscreant before the police treatment is $P(B_1) = 200/1200 = .1667$, while the probability of a citizen being a miscreant after the police screening (the first stage selection) is

$$P(B_2) = \frac{(199)(200) + (201)(1000)}{(1200)^2} = .1672.$$

Thus the treatment (similar to a roadblock through which both the bad and the innocent must pass) increases the bad by $100\,(.1672 - .1667)/.1667 = 0.3\%$.

Example 2.3.13. A bin contains 100 items, of which 10% are bad. A second bin contains 100 items, of which 90% are good. Since such a large proportion of the second bin is good, by selecting an item at random from the second bin and adding it to the first bin do we increase the probability that an item chosen from the first bin will be good?

We can model this situation as follows. We have $n = 2$ urns, each of which contains a white balls and b blue balls (in our example, $a = 90$ and $b = 10$). A ball chosen at random from urn 1 has probability $a/(a + b)$ of being white. If an item is chosen at random from urn 2 and added to urn 1, what then is the probability of an item selected from urn 1 being white? Letting W_i and B_i respectively denote the events that draw i yields a white or blue ball, we have

$$P(W_2) = P(W_2|W_1)P(W_1) + P(W_2|B_1)P(B_1)$$

$$= \frac{a+1}{a+b+1} \cdot \frac{a}{a+b} + \frac{a}{a+b+1} \cdot \frac{b}{a+b}$$

$$= \frac{a^2 + a + ab}{(a+b+1)(a+b)} = \frac{(a+1+b)a}{(a+b+1)(a+b)} = \frac{a}{a+b}.$$

Thus, this process cannot improve the chances of obtaining a good item.

2.3. CONDITIONAL PROBABILITY; BAYES' RULE; ADDITIONAL PROPERTIES   45

Example 2.3.14.   If a certain country has n states, and the proportion of the voters who are Democrats is the same in each state (p, where p is between 0 and 1), must it be the case that proportion p of the voters in the country overall are Democrats?

Let A_i be the event that a voter comes from state i $(i = 1, \ldots, n)$, and B be the event that a voter is a Democrat. We know that $P(B|A_i) = p$ for all i $(i = 1, \ldots, n)$. Using the Theorem of Total Probabilities, it then follows that

$$P(B) = \sum_{i=1}^{n} P(B|A_i)P(A_i) = \sum_{i=1}^{n} pP(A_i) = p\sum_{i=1}^{n} P(A_i) = p \cdot 1 = p,$$

so the conjectured property holds—$100p\%$ of the country also is Democratic.

We already know how to find $P(A_1 \cup \cdots \cup A_n)$ if $A_1, \ldots, A_n$ are disjoint events (Theorem 2.1.13). If $A_1, \ldots, A_n$ are not disjoint, however, in general we have only the bound of Boole's Inequality 2.1.16. We now wish to remedy this lack (Theorem 2.3.15) and to give examples of the use of our new result (Examples 2.3.17 and 2.3.19).

Theorem 2.3.15.   Let $A_1, \ldots, A_n$ be events. Then

$$P(A_1 \cup A_2 \cup \cdots \cup A_n) = \sum_{i=1}^{n} P(A_i) - \sum_{i<j} P(A_i \cap A_j)$$

$$+ \sum_{i<j<k} P(A_i \cap A_j \cap A_k) - \cdots$$

$$+ (-1)^{n+1} P(A_1 \cap \cdots \cap A_n).$$

Proof (Ω finite or denumerable):   Suppose a point ω is in $A_1 \cup \cdots \cup A_n$. Then its probability is counted once on the left side. How many times is its probability counted on the right side? Suppose, without loss of generality, that ω is in exactly l of $A_1, \ldots, A_n$ $(1 \le l \le n)$. Without loss of generality, we may assume ω is in $A_1, \ldots, A_l$. Then

$$\begin{pmatrix} \text{Number of times } \omega\text{'s probability is} \\ \text{counted on the right side} \end{pmatrix} = l - \binom{l}{2} + \binom{l}{3} - \cdots + (-1)^{l+1}\binom{l}{l}.$$

But, by the binomial theorem, $(a + b)^n = \sum_{k=0}^{n} \binom{n}{k} a^k b^{n-k}$. Thus

$$0 = (1 - 1)^l = \sum_{k=0}^{l} \binom{l}{k}(-1)^k = 1 - \binom{l}{1} + \binom{l}{2} - \cdots + (-1)^l\binom{l}{l}$$

$$= 1 - \left\{ l - \binom{l}{2} + \binom{l}{3} - \cdots + (-1)^{l+1}\binom{l}{l} \right\},$$

so ω has its probability counted exactly once on the right side also. On the other

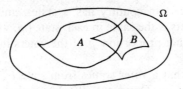

Figure 2.3-2.

hand, if ω is not in $A_1 \cup \cdots \cup A_n$, its probability is counted zero times on each side (why?), so the proof is complete. [*Note*: This proof only covers the case of a finite or denumerable sample space Ω. Other cases are covered in the Honors Problems.] ■

Corollary 2.3.16. Let A, B be events. Then

$$P(A \cup B) = P(A) + P(B) - P(AB).$$

Proof: This is the result of Theorem 2.3.15 with $n = 2$. A Venn diagram may be intuitively helpful. See Figure 2.3-2. ■

An **alternative proof** can be given as follows. First $A = (AB) \cup (A\overline{B})$ and $A \cup B = B \cup (A\overline{B})$ are each disjoint unions [i.e., $(AB) \cap (A\overline{B}) = \varnothing$ and $B \cap (A\overline{B}) = \varnothing$]. Hence,

$$P(A) = P(AB) + P(A\overline{B}),$$

$$P(A \cup B) = P(B) + P(A\overline{B}),$$

and

$$P(A) - P(A \cup B) = P(AB) - P(B),$$

or

$$P(A \cup B) = P(A) + P(B) - P(AB). \qquad ■$$

Example 2.3.17. Probleme des Rencontres. Suppose that N $(N \geq 1)$ **cards** (numbered $1, 2, \ldots, N$) **are placed at random onto N numbered places** on a table (the places being numbered $1, 2, \ldots, N$), each place receiving one card. We say a match or rencontre occurs at the ith place if the card numbered i is placed there. **What is the probability of at least one match?**

Let A_i be the event "rencontre at the ith place" $(i = 1, \ldots, N)$. Then $P(A_1 \cup \cdots \cup A_N)$ is what we wish to find. Since our Ω consists of $N!$ orderings of N objects and each has probability $1/N!$, and since event $A_1 A_2 \cdots A_j$ occurs *iff* the cards numbered $1, 2, \ldots j$ fall on the places numbered $1, 2, \ldots, j$, respectively ($1 \leq j \leq N$), we find

$$P(A_1) = \frac{(N-1)!}{N!},$$

$$P(A_1 A_2) = \frac{(N-2)!}{N!},$$

$$\vdots$$

$$P(A_1 A_2 \cdots A_N) = \frac{1}{N!}.$$

However, the probability of the event $A_{i_1} \cdots A_{i_j}$ (where $i_1, \ldots, i_j$ are j distinct members of the set $\{1, \ldots, N\}$) is the same as the probability of the event $A_1 \cdots A_j$ ($1 \leq j \leq N$). Thus, by Theorem 2.3.15,

$$P(A_1 \cup \cdots \cup A_N) = N\frac{(N-1)!}{N!} - \binom{N}{2}\frac{(N-2)!}{N!} + \binom{N}{3}\frac{(N-3)!}{N!} - \cdots$$

$$= N\frac{(N-1)!}{N!} - \frac{N!}{2!(N-2)!}\frac{(N-2)!}{N!} + \frac{N!}{3!(N-3)!}\frac{(N-3)!}{N!} - \cdots$$

$$= 1 - \frac{1}{2!} + \frac{1}{3!} - \frac{1}{4!} + \cdots + (-1)^{N+1}\frac{1}{N!}.$$

Since (for any real number x) $e^x = 1 + x + \frac{x^2}{2!} + \frac{x^3}{3!} + \cdots$, for N very large

$$P(A_1 \cup \cdots \cup A_N) = 1 - \left(1 - 1 + \frac{1}{2!} - \frac{1}{3!} + \cdots + (-1)^N\frac{1}{N!}\right) \approx 1 - e^{-1}.$$

Example 2.3.18.   How Not to Run a Presidential Poll. For the 1936 election, the *Literary Digest* picked names at random out of telephone books in some cities and sent these people sample ballots, attempting to predict the election results, Roosevelt versus Landon, by the returns. Now, even if 100% returned the ballots, even if all told how they really felt, even if all would vote, even if none would change their minds by election day, still this method could be (and was!) in trouble: They estimated a conditional probability in that part of the American population which had telephones, and (assuming their estimate in this sector was close to the true value) showed that that part was not typical of the total population in this regard (Roosevelt versus Landon) in 1936. [For a discussion of many such interesting examples of applications of statistics, see Wallis and Roberts (1962).]

Example 2.3.19. The Late Commuter. Ten pairs of shoes (20 individual shoes) are in a closet. If four shoes are selected at random, what is the probability of obtaining at least one pair?

Let A_i be the event "pair i is included in the sample" $(i = 1, \ldots, 10)$. Then

$$P(A_i) = \frac{\binom{2}{2}\binom{18}{2}}{\binom{20}{4}}, \qquad P(A_1 A_2) = \frac{1}{\binom{20}{4}},$$

$$P(A_1 A_2 A_3) = P(A_1 A_2 A_3 A_4) = \cdots = P(A_1 A_2 A_3 A_4 \cdots A_{10}) = 0,$$

so by Theorem 2.3.15,

$$P(A_1 \cup \cdots \cup A_{10}) = 10 \frac{\binom{2}{2}\binom{18}{2}}{\binom{20}{4}} - \binom{10}{2}\frac{1}{\binom{20}{4}} + 0 = \frac{99}{323} \approx \frac{1}{3}.$$

For your interest, we state a further result along the lines of Theorem 2.3.15.

Theorem 2.3.20. Let $A_1, \ldots, A_N$ be events. Then

P (Exactly m of $A_1, \ldots, A_N$ occur)

$$= \sum_{i_1 < \cdots < i_m} P(A_{i_1} \cdots A_{i_m}) - \binom{m+1}{m} \sum_{i_1 < \cdots < i_{m+1}} P(A_{i_1} \cdots A_{i_{m+1}})$$

$$+ \binom{m+2}{m} \sum_{i_1 < \cdots < i_{m+2}} P(A_{i_1} \cdots A_{i_{m+2}}) - \cdots \pm \binom{N}{m} P(A_1 \cdots A_N).$$

Lest we lost sight of our purposes, it may be helpful to recall, at this point, **how we got involved with counting problems (combinatorics)** at equation (2.2.1): If Ω is finite and discrete, for example $\Omega = \{a_1, \ldots, a_n\}$, and if $P(a_i) = P(a_j)$ for all i, j $(1 \le i, j \le n)$, then for any $A \subseteq \Omega$

$$P(A) = \frac{n(A)}{n}.$$

Example 2.3.21. In Problem 1.6 we defined the symmetric difference of two sets A and B as

$$S(A, B) = (A - B) \cup (B - A) = (A\bar{B}) \cup (\bar{A}B).$$

If A and B are events (subsets of some sample space Ω), then prove that

$$P(S(A, B)) = P(A) + P(B) - 2P(AB). \tag{2.3.22}$$

First, since $(A\bar{B}) \cap (\bar{A}B) = \varnothing$, it follows that

$$P(S(A, B)) = P(A\bar{B}) + P(\bar{A}B). \tag{2.3.23}$$

Now $A = (AB) \cup (A\bar{B})$ and $B = (AB) \cup (\bar{A}B)$ are also disjoint unions; hence, $P(A) = P(AB) + P(A\bar{B})$ and $P(B) = P(AB) + P(\bar{A}B)$, or $P(A\bar{B}) = P(A) - P(AB)$ and $P(\bar{A}B) = P(B) - P(AB)$. Using these last two relations in equation (2.3.23) proves equation (2.3.22).

[*Note*: **The results of this section** (conditional probability, multiplication rule, Theorem of Total Probabilities, Bayes' Rule, 2.3.15, 2.3.16, 2.3.20), **are entirely general** (although some of the examples illustrating them involve such special cases as finite or denumerable Ω's and equally likely outcomes).]

PROBLEMS FOR SECTION 2.3

2.3.1 Suppose that birth months are chosen independently and at random from the set of 12 possible months. What is the probability that in a group of 10 people exactly 3 people will have the same birth month, which will be different from the birth month of the other 7 people (all of whom will have different birth months)?

2.3.2 Suppose that birthdays are chosen independently and at random from the set of 365 possible birthdays.
(a) What is the probability that in a group of n people at least two people will have the same birthday?
(b) Compute the probability in part (a) for $n = 5(5)50(10)100, 365, 366$, and present the results in tabular form.

2.3.3 Assume birth months are chosen as in Problem 2.3.1.
(a) What is the probability that in a group of n people at least two people will have the same birth month?
(b) Compute the probability in part (a) for $n = 5(1)12, 13$ and present the results in tabular form.

2.3.4 A fair six-sided die is rolled twice. What is the conditional probability that both faces will show even numbers, given that the sum of the faces is 8?

2.3.5 Let A, B, C be events with $P(A) > 0$, $P(B) > 0$, $P(C) > 0$, and $P(BC) > 0$. Show that
(a) $P(AB|C) = P(A|BC)P(B|C)$.
(b) $P(A|B)P(B) = P(B|A)P(A)$.

2.3.6 A box contains three coins. One coin is two-headed, a second is a fair coin, and the third coin is a biased coin with probability p of tails. A coin is chosen at random from the box, and the chosen coin is then flipped.
(a) What is the probability that the flip results in heads?
(b) Suppose the flip yields tails. Find the conditional probability that the coin chosen was the biased coin.

2.3.7 A fair coin is independently tossed n times. Find the probability of obtaining a head on the nth toss, given that there were $n - 1$ tails consecutively on the first $n - 1$ tosses.

2.3.8 Car rental agencies are widespread. There are three car rental agencies (A, B, and C) in a certain town. Suppose that agency A has probability .1, agency B has probability .08, and agency C has probability .125 of renting a customer an

"unsafe" car (i.e., a car that would fail mandated safety tests for brakes, lights, horn, and the like). An agency is chosen at random and a car rented from it is found to be unsafe. What is the conditional probability that
(a) The car came from agency A.
(b) The car came from agency B.
(c) The car came from agency C.

2.3.9 The game of "craps" is played as follows. A player rolls a pair of fair six-sided dice. If the sum is 7 or 11, he wins. If the sum is 2, 3, or 12 he loses (and is said to "crap out"). With any other sum, he continues to roll until he either rolls that same number again (then he wins), or he rolls a 7 (in which case he loses). What is the probability of winning at craps?

2.3.10 A fair six-sided die is rolled once. If the number on the face is an even number, then a fair coin is tossed; otherwise, a fair roulette wheel is spun. A "win" in this game occurs if the player obtains either a head on the toss of the coin or an even number on the spin of the roulette wheel (which has positions $0, 1, 2, 3, \ldots, 36, 00$; of these, only $2, 4, 6, \ldots, 36$ are considered "even"). Find the probability of winning this game.

2.3.11 As in Problem 2.3.10, except that when the fair six-sided die is rolled once, if the number on the face is 1 or 3 the coin is tossed; otherwise the roulette wheel is spun. Find the probability of winning.

2.4. INDEPENDENT EVENTS

In this section we briefly discuss the **notion of independent events**, formulating precisely what it means for one event to have no influence on another and indicating how this precise formulation fits our intuitive idea of "independence."

To introduce independence, let us **first reason to the definition using frequency probability** as in equation (2.1.8), and then give the formal definition. If we have events A and B and n unrelated trials, then we can find both $R(A)$ and $R(A|B)$. If A and B are unrelated, then intuitively it should be the case that

$$R(A|B) = R(A), \qquad (2.4.1)$$

that is, the frequency with which A occurs when we know B has occurred ought to be the same as when we do not know about B. Now equation (2.4.1) can be rewritten as

$$R(A|B) = \frac{n(AB)}{n(B)} = \frac{n(A)}{n} = R(A),$$

or

$$n(AB) = \frac{n(A) \cdot n(B)}{n},$$

or

$$\frac{n(AB)}{n} = \frac{n(A)}{n} \cdot \frac{n(B)}{n},$$

which states

$$R(AB) = R(A)R(B). \tag{2.4.2}$$

We are therefore led to think of defining **independence** of events A and B as meaning that the probability of the event AB equals the product of the probability of A and the probability of B, as in the following definition.

Definition 2.4.3. Two events A and B are said to be **independent** if $P(AB) = P(A)P(B)$.

Intuitively, it ought not to matter if we talk of independence for A and B, or for A and the complement of B (B^c), and Property 2.4.4 states this is in fact the case.

Property 2.4.4. If A and B are independent events, then A and B^c are independent.

Another question that one may think of is, "Why not use equation (2.4.1) rather than equation (2.4.2) to lead us to a definition of independence?" In fact, a definition based on equation (2.4.1) might be more intuitive to many people, but as we know from Definition 2.3.2, $P(A|B)$ is only defined when $P(B) > 0$. Since we would like to be able to talk of events being independent even when their probabilities might (in some cases) be zero, we (and virtually all works in the field of probability and statistics) give the basic definition of independence as in Definition 2.4.3. Then, we note that the more intuitive statement is one which is true as long as $P(B) > 0$.

Property 2.4.5. If A and B are independent events, and if $P(B) > 0$, then $P(A|B) = P(A)$.

Proof: Since A and B are independent events, $P(AB) = P(A)P(B)$, and [since $P(B) > 0$ so that $P(A|B)$ is defined by Definition 2.3.2] $P(A|B) = P(AB)/P(B)$. Therefore $P(A|B) = P(A)P(B)/P(B) = P(A)$, as was to be shown. ∎

Property 2.4.4 is also easy to show, but we leave that as an exercise. As noted above, Property 2.4.5 seems to some, including these authors, to be a better expression of the intuitive idea of independence: Events A and B are independent if knowing that B has occurred tells us nothing about the chances of A occurring. (The only reason we have not taken this as our *definition* is to avoid the requirement $P(B) > 0$ in our definition.) If independence is viewed through the conditional probability viewpoint of Property 2.4.5, then the concepts of positive, negative, and no information (to be considered in Example 2.4.10) clarify the content of the "independence" concept immediately. Before considering this, we note that (since **often more than two events will be of interest** to us) definitions and properties corresponding to Definition 2.4.3 and Properties 2.4.4 and 2.4.5 are needed for arbitrary numbers of events. We will now state these.

Definition 2.4.6. Let $\mathscr{B} = \{ B_\lambda \colon \lambda \in \Lambda \}$ be a set of events. These events are said to be **independent** if for every positive integer n and each n distinct elements $\lambda_1, \ldots, \lambda_n$ in the indexing set Λ we have

$$P(B_{\lambda_1} \cdots B_{\lambda_n}) = \prod_{j=1}^{n} P(B_{\lambda_j}).$$

Property 2.4.7. If $\mathscr{C}$ is a collection of independent events, if $A_1, \ldots, A_n$, $B_1, \ldots, B_m$ are $m + n$ distinct events in $\mathscr{C}$, and if $P(B_1 \cdots B_m) > 0$, then

$$P(A_1 \cdots A_n | B_1 \cdots B_m) = P(A_1 \cdots A_n).$$

Property 2.4.8. If $\mathscr{C}$ is a class of independent events, and if each event in some subset of $\mathscr{C}$ is replaced by its complement, then the new class of events is also a class of independent events.

Example 2.4.9. Consider the set of events $\{ B_1, B_2, B_3, B_4 \}$. What properties need to be shown to establish that these events are independent?

By Definition 2.4.6, for any finite subset of the events in the set, we must show that the probability of the intersection equals the product of the probabilities of the individual events. Thus, we must show that all the following hold:

$$P(B_1B_2) = P(B_1)P(B_2), \ P(B_1B_3) = P(B_1)P(B_3), \ P(B_1B_4) = P(B_1)P(B_4),$$

$$P(B_2B_3) = P(B_2)P(B_3), \ P(B_2B_4) = P(B_2)P(B_4), \ P(B_3B_4) = P(B_3)P(B_4),$$

$$P(B_1B_2B_3) = P(B_1)P(B_2)P(B_3), \ P(B_1B_2B_4) = P(B_1)P(B_2)P(B_4),$$

$$P(B_1B_3B_4) = P(B_1)P(B_3)P(B_4), \ P(B_2B_3B_4) = P(B_2)P(B_3)P(B_4),$$

$$P(B_1B_2B_3B_4) = P(B_1)P(B_2)P(B_3)P(B_4).$$

As we will see in Problem 2.4.1, having some of these hold is not sufficient to show that all of them hold: We must check all of them to demonstrate independence.

Recall (Definition 1.2.7) that events A and B are said to be **mutually exclusive** if $AB = \varnothing$. This is often confused with the concept of independence, and we should be careful to see that we understand the difference. (Essentially, mutually exclusive events and independent events are mutually exclusive. See Problem 2.26 for a precise statement of this result.)

Example 2.4.10. Negative Information. Suppose $P(B) > 0$ and $P(A) > 0$. We sometimes say that event B carries **negative information** about event A if $P(A|B) < P(A)$. [**Positive information** may be defined as the case when $P(A|B) > P(A)$. No information, or $P(A|B) = P(A)$, corresponds to independence.] Then $P(A|B) < P(A)$ implies $P(B|A) < P(B)$, for

$$P(B|A) = \frac{P(AB)}{P(A)} = \frac{P(A|B)P(B)}{P(A)}$$

$$< \frac{P(A)P(B)}{P(A)} = P(B).$$

Example 2.4.11. If $A_1, \ldots, A_n$ are independent events with probabilities $p_1, \ldots, p_n$ of occurring, respectively, what is the probability that all the events occur? That at least one of the events occurs?

The probability that all the events occur is

$$P(A_1 \cdots A_n) = P(A_1) \cdots P(A_n) = p_1 \cdots p_n = \prod_{i=1}^{n} p_i,$$

and the probability at least one of the events occurs is

$$P\left(\bigcup_{i=1}^{n} A_i\right) = 1 - P\left(\overline{\bigcup_{i=1}^{n} A_i}\right) = 1 - P(\overline{A}_1 \cap \cdots \cap \overline{A}_n)$$

$$= 1 - P(\overline{A}_1) \cdots P(\overline{A}_n)$$

$$= 1 - (1 - p_1) \cdots (1 - p_n) = 1 - \prod_{i=1}^{n} (1 - p_i).$$

Example 2.4.12. A certain **water-supply system** consists of a source, five pumping stations, and a destination. If each pumping station has probability p ($0 \le p \le 1$) of being operable at a specified time t_0, if the stations are operable or failed independently of one another, and if the stations are connected as in Figure 2.4-1, find the probability $R(p)$ that water is available to the destination at time t_0. [$R(p)$ is sometimes called the **reliability** of the system.]

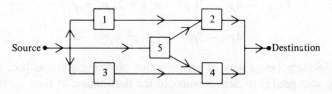

Figure 2.4-1. A water-supply system.

Let A_i denote the event that pumping station i is operable at time t_0 $(1 \le i \le 5)$. Then $P(A_1) = P(A_2) = \cdots = P(A_5) = p$. Let B denote the event that water is available to the destination at time t_0. Then $P(B) = R(p)$. Now

$$P(B) = P(BA_5) + P(B\bar{A}_5)$$

$$= P(B|A_5)P(A_5) + P(B|\bar{A}_5)P(\bar{A}_5)$$

$$= pP(B|A_5) + (1-p)P(B|\bar{A}_5).$$

But (using Property 2.4.7 in the third equality)

$$P(B|\bar{A}_5) = P((A_1 A_2) \cup (A_3 A_4)|\bar{A}_5)$$

$$= P(A_1 A_2|\bar{A}_5) + P(A_3 A_4|\bar{A}_5) - P(A_1 A_2 A_3 A_4|\bar{A}_5)$$

$$= p^2 + p^2 - p^4 = 2p^2 - p^4,$$

and

$$P(B|A_5) = P(A_2 \cup A_4|A_5)$$

$$= P(A_2|A_5) + P(A_4|A_5) - P(A_2 A_4|A_5)$$

$$= p + p - p^2 = 2p - p^2.$$

Hence,

$$P(B) = p(2p - p^2) + (1-p)(2p^2 - p^4)$$

$$= 4p^2 - 3p^3 - p^4 + p^5.$$

Alternatively, we may express B as

$$B = (A_1 A_2) \cup (A_3 A_4) \cup (A_5 A_2) \cup (A_5 A_4)$$

and use Theorem 2.3.15:

$$P(B) = 4p^2 - 3(p^4 - p^3) + 2(p^4 + p^5) - p^5$$

$$= 4p^2 - 3p^3 - p^4 + p^5.$$

Can you devise a better way of utilizing five pumping stations [i.e., a way such that, if the *sole* goal is to deliver water to the destination at time t_0, the new way yields a larger $R(p)$]? [*Hint*: Pipe water through each station directly to the destination.] Can you do better if water must (because of the distances involved) pass through at least two pumping stations and must (because of the pipe strengths involved) pass through at most two pumping stations (i.e., if water must pass through exactly two pumping stations)?

Example 2.4.13. Simpson's Paradox. Two companies manufacture a certain type of sophisticated electronic equipment for the government; to avoid lawsuits, let us call them company C and company $\bar{C}$. In the past, company C has had 5% good output, whereas company $\bar{C}$ has had 50% good output (i.e., 95% of C's output and 50% of $\bar{C}$'s output is not of acceptable quality). The government has just ordered 21,100 of these electronic devices, 10,100 from company $\bar{C}$ and 11,000 from company C. (Company C often does receive part of the order, for political reasons, or because company $\bar{C}$ does not have a capacity large enough to allow it to take the whole order, and so on.)

Since the electronic devices are critically needed for an important government program, before production of the 21,100 devices starts, government scientists develop a new manufacturing method that they believe will almost double the percentage of good devices received. Companies C and $\bar{C}$ are given this information, but (because of limited lead-time) its use is largely optional: they must each use the new method for at least 100 of their devices, but use of the new method beyond that point is left to their discretion.

When the devices are received and tested some time later, analysis of the 21,100 items shows a breakdown as in Table 2.4-1, which horrifies the government: 46% of items produced by the usual method were good, but only 11% of items produced by the new method were good. This shocks the responsible government officials, who begin to berate (and worse!) their scientists and companies C and $\bar{C}$ for the "lousy new method" and for producing so many of the items with the clearly inferior new method, respectively. Yet the scientists and the companies insist that the new method *has* almost doubled the percentage of good items. *Can they possibly be right?*

The answer is (amazingly) *yes*, as we see in Table 2.4-2. The new method has nearly doubled the percent good in each case (10% versus 5% for company C and 95% versus 50% for company $\bar{C}$). The totals put into the experimental (new)

TABLE 2.4-1
Analysis of Total Production

		Production Method	
		Standard	New
Results	Bad	5950	9005
	Good	5050 (46%)	1095 (11%)

TABLE 2.4-2
Production Analysis by Company

		Company			
		C		$\overline{C}$	
		Production Method		Production Method	
		Standard	New	Standard	New
Results	Bad	950	9000	5000	5
	Good	50 (5%)	1000 (10%)	5000 (50%)	95 (95%)

method by each company are also quite reasonable: company $\overline{C}$ (which knew its implementation of the standard method was already quite good) put the minimum allowed (100), whereas company C (which knew its implementation of the standard method was inferior) put 10,000 of its 11,000 through the new method.

The fact that results like those displayed here can occur is, when stated in terms of probabilities, called **Simpson's paradox: It is possible to have** $P(A|B) <$ $P(A|\overline{B})$ **even though both**

$$P(A|BC) \geq P(A|\overline{B}C),$$
$$P(A|B\overline{C}) \geq P(A|\overline{B}\,\overline{C}). \tag{2.4.14}$$

Simpson's paradox, just discussed for the case of two populations, applies equally well to cases with several populations; it is discussed further in Problems 2.32, 2.33, and 2.34. It was first discussed by E. H. Simpson (1951); more recent references are Blyth (1972) and Wagner (1982). *The crux of why it can occur is as follows.* Suppose that in *population 1* (the standard production method), the rate of occurrence of good results is r_1 in one segment of the population (company C), and r_2 in the rest of that population (company $\overline{C}$). The overall good rate for that population (the standard production method) is $r = w_1 r_1 + w_2 r_2$ (where $w_2 = 1 - w_1$). In our example, $r_1 = .05$ with $w_1 = 1000/11000$, and $r_2 = .50$ with $w_2 = 1 - w_1$, hence

$$r = \frac{1000}{11000}(.05) + \frac{10000}{11000}(.50) = \frac{5050}{11000} = .46.$$

In population 2 (the new production method), the comparable figures are $R_1 = .10$, $W_1 = 10000/10100$, and $R_2 = .95$, $W_2 = 1 - W_1$, so that

$$R = W_1 R_1 + W_2 R_2 = \frac{10000}{10100}(.10) + \frac{100}{10100}(.95) = \frac{1095}{10100} = .11.$$

Although $.05 = r_1 < R_1 = .10$ (the standard method is inferior to the new method in company C) and $.50 = r_2 < R_2 = .95$ (the standard method is inferior to the new method in company $\overline{C}$), yet

$$.46 = r = w_1 r_1 + w_2 r_2 > W_1 R_1 + W_2 R_2 = R = .11.$$

This can occur since $w_1 \neq W_1$ (the proportion of production devoted to each method differs in the companies).

Example 2.4.15. Independence / Nonindependence for Sampling With / Without Replacement. Suppose that a box of chocolates contains 12 solid chocolates and 12 crème-filled chocolates. The candies are drawn at random from the box one at a time. Find the probability that a solid chocolate is drawn for the fourth time on the 7th draw if **(a)** sampling is done with replacement (the candies are examined, but not eaten); **(b)** the sampling is done without replacement (as is usual in such situations).

(a) When sampling is with replacement, the results of the individual random draws are independent (draw i does not affect the results of draw j) and hence

$$P(\text{4th solid occurs on draw 7})$$

$$= P(\text{Exactly 3 solids in first 6 draws, and solid on draw 7})$$

$$= P(\text{3 solids and 3 crème in first 6 draws}) \, P(\text{Solid on draw 7})$$

$$= \binom{6}{3}\left(\frac{1}{2}\right)^6\left(\frac{1}{2}\right)^1 = \frac{20}{128} = \frac{5}{32} = .15625.$$

(b) When sampling is without replacement, the draws are not independent (hence conditional probability is used to obtain the values of the terms that make up the probability of interest):

$$P(\text{4th solid occurs on draw 7})$$

$$= P(\text{Exactly 3 solids in first 6 draws, and solid on draw 7})$$

$$= \binom{6}{3}\frac{12}{24} \cdot \frac{11}{23} \cdot \frac{10}{22} \cdot \frac{12}{21} \cdot \frac{11}{20} \cdot \frac{10}{19} \cdot \frac{9}{18} = \frac{18150}{100947} = .1798.$$

(Here note that which draws in the first six are the solids affects only the order of the numerator terms, not the overall value; the binomial coefficient gives the number of possible orders, which reduces to 20 possibilities for the ordering of the 3 solids and 3 crèmes on the first 6 draws. On the seventh draw, there are $12 - 3 = 9$ solids left, and a total of $24 - 6 = 18$ candies in the box, for a 9/18 probability of a solid on the 7th draw given that exactly 3 of the previous draws yielded solids.)

58   PROBABILITY

PROBLEMS FOR SECTION 2.4

2.4.1 **Pairwise independence does not imply independence.** A number is chosen at random from the set $\{1, 2, 3, 4\}$. Define the events

$$A = \{1, 3\},\ B = \{1, 2\},\ C = \{1, 4\}.$$

Show that $P(A) = 1/2 = P(B) = P(C)$, and $P(AB) = P(AC) = P(BC) = 1/4$. Deduce that A and B are independent events. Also, that A and C are independent events. And, that B and C are independent events. We then say A, B, C are **pairwise independent events** (since each two are independent events). However, A, B, C are *not* independent events since

$$P(ABC) = 1/4 \neq 1/8 = P(A)P(B)P(C).$$

Find an example where the events A, B, C have different probabilities and are pairwise independent (but not independent).

2.4.2 Suppose the events A, B, C are independent. Show that
(a) A and $B \cup C$ are independent events.
(b) A and $S(B, C)$ are independent events [where $S(B, C)$ is the symmetric difference of B and C—see Problem 1.6].
(c) $P(B|A \cap C) = P(B|A \cup C) = P(B)$.

2.4.3 (a) Show that if event A is independent of itself, then either $P(A) = 0$ or $P(A) = 1$.
(b) Show that $\varnothing$ and A are always independent events for any event A.
(c) Show that Ω and A are independent events.

2.4.4 A fair coin is tossed three times independently. Determine whether the events

$$A: \text{"At least 2 heads occur"}$$

and

$$B: \text{"A head occurs on toss 1"}$$

are independent.

2.4.5 A card is chosen at random from a standard deck (see Problem 2.2.5) of 52 cards. Show that
(a) The events "spade" and "red" are not independent.
(b) The events "spade" and "king" are independent.

2.4.6 Given that each of the events A and B has positive probability, prove that $P(A) = P(B)$ iff $P(A|B) = P(B|A)$.

2.4.7 Given that $P(A) = .4$, $P(A \cup B) = .9$, find $P(B)$ if
(a) A and B are mutually exclusive events.
(b) A and B are independent events.
(c) $P(A|B) = .4$.

2.4.8 A nursery claims that 95% of its seeds germinate. Assume this is true, in the sense that each seed has probability .95 of germinating. Find the probability that if we plant 10 seeds, then at least 8 will germinate.

2.4.9 Five fair six-sided dice are rolled simultaneously. Find the probability that
(a) Exactly i of a kind faces result; that is, i faces are the same (and the others are all different from this one, and at most i of them are the same) ($1 \le i \le 5$).
(b) At least i of a kind faces result ($2 \le i \le 5$).

2.4.10 Bonferroni's Inequality. Suppose that $P(A) = \alpha$ and $P(B) = \beta$. Show that

$$P(AB) \ge \alpha + \beta - 1.$$

PROBLEMS FOR CHAPTER 2

2.1 A pair of dice is rolled once. Construct a sample space for this experiment and list its elements in full detail. [*Hint*: Number the sides of each die 1, 2, 3, 4, 5, 6 and consider 2-tuples.] On your diagram, circle and mark the following events:

A: faces are equal.

B: sum of faces is ≥ 10.

C: faces sum to 7.

2.2 An **algebra** (or **field**) **of sets** is a collection $\mathscr{B}$ of subsets of a given set Ω such that

(a) $\Omega \in \mathscr{B}$,

(b) $A \in \mathscr{B} \Rightarrow \overline{A} \in \mathscr{B}$,

(c) $A, B \in \mathscr{B} \Rightarrow A \cup B \in \mathscr{B}$.

An algebra of sets $\mathscr{B}$ is called a **σ-algebra** (or **Borel field**) if also

$$A_n \in \mathscr{B} \ (n = 1, 2, \ldots) \Rightarrow \bigcup_{n=1}^{\infty} A_n \in \mathscr{B}.$$

Prove that (for a given set Ω) the collection $\mathscr{B}_0$ of all subsets of Ω is a σ-algebra.

2.3 Given that $P(\overline{A}) = .3$, $P(B) = .4$, and $P(A\overline{B}) = .5$, find
(a) $P(A)$,
(b) $P(AB)$,
(c) $P(A \cup B)$.

2.4 A certain city council consists of 4 Democrats and 6 Republicans. What is the probability that a Councillor drawn at random will be a Democrat?

2.5 If two space vehicles (e.g., one from the U.S.A. and one from the U.S.S.R.) attempt to land on Mars, what is the probability that exactly one suceeds? (Correct formulation of a model is part of this problem.)

2.6 If the three buttons on a push-button combination lock are pushed in random order, what is the probability that they will be in the correct order to unlock the lock? (Assume that each button is pushed exactly once, and that some one permutation unlocks the device.)

2.7 As in Problem 2.6, but a 24-button lock.

2.8 As in Problem 2.6, but an n-button lock ($n \ge 1$).

2.9 As in Problem 2.6, but a 24-button lock that opens no matter which button is used first as long as the the successive pushes follow according to one basic sequence (e.g., if 312 is basic, then 123 and 231 also work on a comparable 3-button lock).

2.10 (a) Prove Theorem 2.2.2 (the multiplets theorem).
(b) Prove Theorem 2.2.18 (multinomial coefficients) by induction.

2.11 How many 3-digit numbers can be formed with the integers 1, 2, 3, 4, 5 if duplication of the integers is not allowed? If duplication is allowed?

2.12 A kindergarten teacher has 10 chocolate bars, 5 bags of popcorn, and 5 ice cream bars to distribute to her class of 20 pupils. (Each pupil is to receive 1 item.) The chocolate bars are all alike; so are the bags of popcorn and the ice cream bars.
(a) In how many different ways can the teacher distribute these items?
(b) If the items are distributed at random, what is the probability that a given pair of boys in the class receive the same item?

2.13 If n persons, including Art and Bob, are randomly arranged in a straight line, what is the probability that there are exactly r persons in the line between Art and Bob?

2.14 Given that $P(A) = .7$ and $P(A \cup B) = .8$, find $P(B)$
(a) If A and B are mutually exclusive.
(b) If A and B are independent.
(c) If $P(A|B) = .6$.

2.15 Given that $P(\overline{A}) = .3$, $P(B) = .4$, and $P(A\overline{B}) = .5$, find $P(B|A \cup \overline{B})$.

2.16 Calculate (as a decimal) the probability in Example 2.2.29. [*Hint*: This can be done either by using tables and/or a desk calculator, *or* by using a digital computer.]

2.17 Twelve dice are cast. What is the probability that each of the six faces will appear at least once? [*Hint*: If we regard this experiment as one of tossing 12 balls at random into 6 cells, each of which has unlimited capacity, then we are seeking $1 - P$ $(A_1 \cup \cdots \cup A_6)$ where A_i is the event "cell i is empty" $(i = 1, \ldots, 6)$.]

2.18 Let $\mathscr{B} = \{B_\lambda : \lambda \in \Lambda\}$ be a set of events. These events are said to be **pairwise independent** if for every 2 distinct elements λ_1, λ_2 in the indexing set Λ, we have

$$P\left[B_{\lambda_1}B_{\lambda_2}\right] = P\left[B_{\lambda_1}\right]P\left[B_{\lambda_2}\right].$$

Does pairwise independence imply independence? (Prove your assertion.) [*Hint*: Let $\Omega = \{\omega_1, \omega_2, \omega_3, \omega_4\}$ with $P(\omega_i) = \frac{1}{4}$ $(i = 1, 2, 3, 4)$ and choose

$$A = \{\omega_1, \omega_2\}, \ B = \{\omega_1, \omega_3\}, \ C = \{\omega_1, \omega_4\}.]$$

2.19 Let k be a positive integer. Let $X_1, X_2, \ldots, X_k$ be a sample of size k, drawn at random with replacement, from the population of digits $0, 1, 2, 3, \ldots, 9$. (Each digit has probability $p = \frac{1}{10}$ of being drawn at each drawing, and drawings are unrelated.)
Let A be the event "neither 0 nor 1 appears in the sample," and let B be the event "1 does not appear but 2 does." Find
(a) $P(A)$.
(b) $P(B)$.
(c) $P(AB)$.
(d) $P(A \cup B)$.

2.20 A pair of fair dice is rolled as long as necessary for a score of 7 to turn up. Assuming that 7 does not appear on the first throw, what is the probability that more than two throws will be necessary?

2.21 (a) If three distinguishable balls are placed at random into two numbered cells, find the probability that all cells are occupied.

(b) If $n + 1$ distinguishable balls are placed at random into n numbered cells, find the probability that all cells are occupied. (n is a positive integer.)

2.22 An urn contains 7 red balls and 3 black balls. One ball is drawn at random and replaced by a ball of the opposite color; then a second ball is drawn at random. Given that the second ball is red, what is the conditional probability that the first ball was also red?

2.23 Balls are randomly drawn one at a time from an urn in which there are initially 5 red and 10 black balls. After each draw, the ball is replaced and one additional ball of the same color is added.

(a) Given that the first n balls drawn are black, calculate the probability α_n that the $(n + 1)$st is black, and find $\lim_{n \to \infty} \alpha_n$.

(b) Given that the 2nd through $(n + 1)$st balls are black, calculate the probability β_n that the first ball drawn was black, and find $\lim_{n \to \infty} \beta_n$.

2.24 Let A, B, C be events (subsets of some sample space Ω). Assume $P(C) > 0$ and $P(BC) > 0$. Prove or disprove each of the following:

(a) $P(AB|C) = P(A|BC)P(B|C)$.

(b) $P(AB|C) = P(A|C)P(B|C)$ if A, B are independent.

If you disprove an equation, give two or more conditions under which it is true.

2.25 Imagine a population of $N + 1$ urns. Urn number k contains $\{k$ red, $N - k$ white$\}$ balls $(k = 0, 1, \ldots, N)$. An urn is chosen at random and n random drawings are made from it, the ball drawn being replaced each time. Define

Event A: All n balls turn out to be red,

Event B: The $(n + 1)$st draw yields a red ball.

(a) Find $P(A|$Urn k is chosen$)$ $(k = 0, 1, \ldots, N)$.

(b) Find $P(A)$.

(c) Find $P(AB)$.

(d) Find $P(B|A)$.

(e) Find an approximation to $P(B|A)$, using the fact that if N is large,

$$\frac{1}{N} \sum_{k=1}^{N} \left(\frac{k}{N} \right)^n \sim \int_0^1 x^n \, dx = \frac{1}{n + 1}.$$

2.26 Let A and B be events. Assume $P(A) > 0$ and $P(B) > 0$. Prove: If A, B are mutually exclusive, then A, B are not independent; if A, B are independent, then A, B are not mutually exclusive. Thus, "mutually exclusive events and independent events are mutually exclusive."

2.27 Let A_n, B_n $(n \geq 1)$ be events (subsets of some sample space Ω). Prove that if $\lim_{n \to \infty} P(B_n) = 1$, then $\lim_{n \to \infty} \{P(A_n|B_n) - P(A_n)\} = 0$. (You must prove that the latter limit exists.) Hence, show that if $\lim_{n \to \infty} P(A_n|B_n)$ or $\lim_{n \to \infty} P(A_n)$ exists, both exist and

$$\lim_{n \to \infty} P(A_n|B_n) = \lim_{n \to \infty} P(A_n).$$

2.28 Show that negative information (see Example 2.4.10) is not transitive; that is, $P(A|B) < P(A)$ and $P(B|C) < P(B)$ do not imply $P(A|C) < P(A)$. [*Hint*: Let $\Omega = \{\omega_1, \omega_2, \omega_3, \omega_4\}$ with $P(\omega_i) = \frac{1}{4}$ ($i = 1, 2, 3, 4$) and choose

$$A = \{\omega_1, \omega_2\}, \qquad B = \{\omega_3, \omega_4\}, \qquad C = \{\omega_1\}.]$$

Find another example that also shows that negative information is not transitive, but in which all probabilities of interest are positive.

2.29 The confidential-data computing facility of a corporation contains 15 locked computer consoles. Each console is openable by a different key. Suppose that someone has obtained the 15 keys, but they are coded and the person does not know the code; also, if a key is inserted into a wrong console lock, it is frozen in place electronically (it cannot be removed, and the console cannot be operated).

   If the person (e.g., an executive whose assistants are unavailable) goes down the line inserting keys into consoles at random, what is the probability that he unlocks at least one console?

2.30 Suppose we have a **network** of cities and roads. Each **segment** of road (i.e., each piece of road on which one can go from one city to another without encountering a third city) has probability p of being open, independently of the other segments. The probability $R(p)$ that one can now go from city A to city B depends on the network. For the network

(which has one segment) $R(p) = p$. For the network

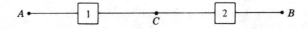

(which has two segments) $R(p) = p^2$. Not all two-segment networks have the same $R(p)$, for example, for the network

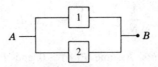

we find $R(p) = 2p - p^2$. Find $R(p)$ for the network

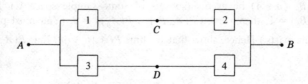

2.31 A **system** is made up of n parts. At any time t each part is either functional (1) or nonfunctional (0). We may regard the basic sample space Ω as consisting of all 2^n possible assignments of 1, 0 to each part. The sample space Ω is partitioned into two sets $\Omega = F \cup W$ (with $F \cap W = \varnothing$); if an $\omega \in F$ occurs at time t, the system will not work (has failed); whereas if an $\omega \in W$ occurs at time t, the system will work (has not failed).

Suppose that each part has probability p of being functional at time t, and that parts fail or operate independently of one another. $P(W)$ is a function of p, say $R(p)$, and is called the **reliability of the system**.

(a) A **series system** fails iff at least one of its parts fails. This situation may be diagrammed as

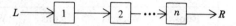

and the system works iff there is a *path* (connected sequence of functional parts) from L to R. Find $R(p)$ for such a system.

(b) A **parallel system** fails iff all its parts fail. The situation may be diagrammed as

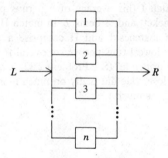

and the system works iff there is a path from L to R. Find $R(p)$ for such a system.

2.32 Use the example of Simpson's paradox involving manufacture of electronic devices (see Example 2.4.13) to show that it may be the case that B gives positive information about A, both when C obtains and when C does not obtain, but that B gives negative information about A.[6] [*Hint*: Identify A with good output, B with the new method, and $C, \overline{C}$ with companies.] Also show that the **sure-thing principle** ("If you would definitely prefer g to f, either knowing that the event C obtained, or knowing that the event C did not obtain, then you definitely prefer g to f.") is false. [*Hint*: Identify g, f with standard and new methods.]

2.33 Suppose that Democrat D and Republican R are running for the U.S. Presidency. Is it possible that a poll taken before the election could show that, in each of the 50

---

[6] See Example 2.4.10 for the concepts of positive and negative information, which were apparently first introduced and studied by Chung (1942). The authors are grateful to Professor Colin R. Blyth for this reference.

states, nearly twice the percentage of people under 30 prefer D to R as do people over 30, but that overall (i.e., for the 50 states combined) a higher percentage of people over 30 prefer D to R than do people under 30? If so, give a numerical example demonstrating your contention. How could a pollster prevent such paradoxical situations from arising in his polls?

2.34 In **cricket**[7] one's bowling average is (number of runs) divided by (number of wickets taken). If bowlers A and B compete in matches I and II with runs and wickets taken as follows

	Match			
	I		*II*	
	Runs	Wickets	Runs	Wickets
A	185	31	99	9
B	186	31	38	2

then A beats B in match I (his average of $5\frac{30}{31}$ runs per wicket is less than B's average of 6 runs per wicket) and A beats B in match II (11 runs per wicket versus 19 runs per wicket). If matches I and II comprise a tournament, who wins the tournament (i.e., has the lowest runs-per-wicket overall)? Why is this so? How is this related to the sure-thing principle? (See Problem 2.32.) Could such a result happen in golf? Did A deserve to lose? (He did badly on much more play in match II and did B, who played only $\approx \frac{1}{3}$ as much.)

HONORS PROBLEMS FOR CHAPTER 2

2.1H Our proof of Theorem 2.3.15 was valid only for a finite or denumerable sample space Ω. Prove the result in general. [*Hint*: Most books that consider the general case only prove the result for $n = 2$ or $n = 3$ (e.g., Tucker, (1962), p. 12). Such proofs may furnish you with a hint for the general case (e.g., use induction).]

2.2H Prove Theorem 2.3.20, first for the denumerable case, then in the general case.

2.3H Given that events A and B are independent and that $P(A - B) = p_1$, $P(B - A)$ $= p_2$ $(0 \le p_1, p_2 \le p_1 + p_2 \le 1)$, find $r = P(AB)$.
   What restrictions must be placed on p_1, p_2 besides those stated?

2.4H A **probability space** is a triplet $(\Omega, \mathscr{B}, P)$ where
   (a) Ω is a set called the **sample space** whose points ω are called **elementary events**;
   (b) $\mathscr{B}$ is a σ-algebra of subsets of Ω;

---

[7]This example was brought to the authors' attention by M. C. Mitchelmore and is contained (in a slightly different form) in Mitchelmore and Raynor (1969), Example 7, p. 192.

(c) $P(\cdot)$ is a function called a **probability function** which assigns to each event $A \in \mathscr{B}$ a real number $P(A)$ such that
  (i) $P(A) \geq 0$ for every $A \in \mathscr{B}$,
  (ii) $P(\Omega) = 1$,
  (iii) (**Countable additivity**) I. $A_1, A_2, \ldots \in \mathscr{B}$ and

$$A_i \cap A_j = \varnothing \; (i \neq j), \quad \text{then } P\left(\bigcup_{n=1}^{\infty} A_n\right) = \sum_{n=1}^{\infty} P(A_n).$$

1. It is sometimes implied that $\mathscr{B}_0$ = collection of all subsets of Ω is always our choice, in which case we could dispense with $\mathscr{B}$ and just talk of (Ω, P). Show that this is not so. [*Hint*: Exhibit a well-known $(\Omega, \mathscr{B}, P)$ such that it is a probability space but $(\Omega, \mathscr{B}_0, P)$ is not. (Why not?)]

2. **Complete additivity** means that if $A_\lambda \in \mathscr{B}$ for all $\lambda \in \Lambda$ (here Λ is some index set) and if $A_{\lambda_1} \cap A_{\lambda_2} = \varnothing$ for all $\lambda_1 \neq \lambda_2$, λ_1 and $\lambda_2 \in \Lambda$, then

$$P\left(\bigcup_{\lambda \in \Lambda} A_\lambda\right) = \sum_{\lambda \in \Lambda} P(A_\lambda).$$

Give an example of the sort of contradiction that can arise if we attempt to substitute complete additivity for countable additivity in our definition of a probability space.

2.5H Research the history of the "probleme des rencontres" (matching problem) of Example 2.3.17, and write a well-documented paper on it.

Try to use the field of information theory to explain the fluctuations (with N) of P (At least one match), which goes up when N becomes odd and goes down when N becomes even (fluctuating about $1 - e^{-1}$).

Number of cards N	P (At least one Match)
1	1.00000
2	.50000
3	.66667
4	.62500
5	.63333
6	.63196
⋮	
∞	.63212

Suppose that the matching problem is modified as follows: N ($N \geq 1$) cards (numbered $1, 2, \ldots, N$) are shuffled thoroughly. Then N successive draws are made at random from the deck, with replacement. We say a match occurs at the ith draw if the card numbered i is drawn on that draw. Find the probability of at least one match, and show that it $\rightarrow 1 - e^{-1}$ as $N \rightarrow \infty$.

2.6H Magazines, newspapers, and other printed media have been known to print a collection of N pictures of individuals, followed by a list (in scrambled order) of N identifying characteristics (e.g., names), one of which belongs to each individual.
(a) Suppose a movie magazine prints $N = 4$ baby pictures of movie stars, along with the 4 stars' names in scrambled order. Find, by direct enumeration, the

probability that a person matching names with pictures purely at random would get at least 2 correct matchings.

(b) Suppose a newspaper, not to be outdone, prints $N = 52$ pictures, along with 52 names in scrambled order. We wish to find the probability that a person matching names with pictures purely at random would get at least 2 correct matchings.

There are $\binom{N}{2}$ distinct pairs of pictures. Mimicing the use of Theorem 2.3.15 in Example 2.3.17, let B_i be the event that pair i of pictures is correctly matched with names $\left(i = 1, 2, \ldots, \binom{N}{2}\right)$. Then $P(B_1 \cup B_2 \cup \cdots \cup B_{\binom{N}{2}})$ is what we wish to find. Why will this method of Theorem 2.3.15 not work here? [If you think it *will* work, do the calculation for $N = 4$ and compare with the answer found in part **(a)** by direct enumeration.] Finally, use Theorem 2.3.20 to solve this problem.

2.7H $r(\geq 1)$ balls are placed at random into n cells, which consist of the following types:

$$n_1 \text{ which can hold 1 ball}$$

$$n_2 \text{ which can hold 2 balls}$$

$$\vdots$$

$$n_{l-1} \text{ which can hold } l - 1 \text{ balls}$$

$$n_l \text{ which can hold } l \text{ balls}$$

$$\vdots$$

$$n_\infty \text{ which can hold unlimited balls,}$$

where $n_1, n_2, \ldots, n_\infty$ are nonnegative integers that sum to n. The set of assignment vectors is then

$$\Omega = \left\{ (x_1, \ldots, x_r) : x_i \text{ is the cell ball } i \text{ falls into } (1 \leq i \leq r) \right\}.$$

If we denote the

$$n_1 \text{ cells by } c_1, \ldots, c_{n_1},$$

$$n_2 \text{ cells by } c_{n_1+1}, \ldots, c_{n_1+n_2},$$

$$\vdots$$

$$n_\infty \text{ cells by } c_{1+n_1+n_2+\cdots}, \ldots, c_{n_\infty+n_1+n_2+\cdots},$$

then we note that the cell types impose restrictions on the x_i in $(x_1, \ldots, x_r)$; for example, at most one may be c_1. (In the "usual" problems either $n_\infty = n$ or $n_1 = n$.) Let

$$\#_r(\Omega) = \text{The number of distinct assignment vectors.}$$

(a) Prove that $\dfrac{n!}{(n-r)!} \leq \#_r(\Omega) \leq n^r$.

(b) Suppose that from a population of n elements we draw a random sample of size r with replacement, but that n_i elements are so fragile that after being drawn i times they cannot be returned again ($i = 1, 2, \ldots, \infty$). How many samples are possible?

(c) Find $\#_1(\Omega)$, $\#_2(\Omega)$, $\#_3(\Omega)$. Find $\#_r(\Omega)(r \geq 1)$. [*Note:* Tossing a ball into a cell reduces, for the next toss, the number of cells of that type and increases the number of cells of another type (unless the cell is of n_1 or n_∞ type).]

(d) Find a recursion relation between $\#_r(\Omega)$ and $\#_{r+1}(\Omega)$, or between $\#_1(\Omega), \ldots, \#_r(\Omega)$ and $\#_{r+1}(\Omega)$. Then solve it.

2.8H Following the definition of ball and cell model $(BC)_i$ (Definition 2.2.20), we noted an example dealing with post office boxes: a post office has n post office boxes, each with a capacity of m letters. Let X represent the number of boxes that overflow when N letters are distributed to the boxes at random.

If overflow letters must be handled by inserting special notices into boxes, then the post office could well wish to choose m so that X is suitably small; for example, so that $P(X \geq 1)$ is very small [$P(X \geq 1)$ is the probability that one or more boxes overflow]. The problem can be approached in the following way: Consider a $(BC)_\infty$ model; then X is the number of cells that receive $\geq m$ balls when N balls are tossed into n cells. Find $P(X \geq 1)$, which is a function of n, m, N. For $n = 100$ and $N = 200$ compute $P(X \geq 1)$ for $m = 1, 2, 3, \ldots, 100$.

2.9H Consideration of P(All cells are occupied) when $n + 1$ balls are distributed at random into n cells (each of which has unlimited capacity) by two methods leads (show this) to two expressions, which must therefore be equal (see Problem 2.21):

$$P[\text{All cells are occupied}] = \sum_{k=0}^{n} \binom{n}{k}(-1)^k \frac{(n-k)^{n+1}}{n^{n+1}} = \frac{(n+1)!}{2n^n}.$$

Thus, it follows that

$$\sum_{k=0}^{n} \binom{n}{k}(-1)^k (n-k)^{n+1} = \frac{n}{2} \cdot (n+1)!. \qquad (*)$$

Calculate each side of $(*)$ for $n = 1, 2, 3, 4$ in order to check its veracity in those cases. Then prove $(*)$ in general.

2.10H (This problem is analogous to Example 2.2.29, but is more realistic.) Assume that there are 366 possible birthdays, the first 365 of which are equally likely, but the last of which is only one-fourth as likely as each of the others. What is the probability that, in a group of 60 people (whose birthdays are assumed unrelated), *some* 5 people will have the same birthday and all the other people will have different birthdays (none of which falls on the birthday of the 5)?

Calculate this probability as a decimal and compare it with the answer of Problem 2.16.

2.11H Suppose that a machine is built that takes a deck of 52 cards and shuffles them. If it always uses the same shuffle (e.g., one simple shuffle would be to put the top card on the bottom of the deck), what is the largest number of shuffles that can possibly occur before the deck returns to its original order? For which shuffle can this occur? (We conceive of *exactly* the same operation being repeatedly applied to the deck. The deck then passes through a well-defined succession of orders, eventually returning to the original order. It cannot pass through all 52! possible orders. How many can it pass through at most? What rule achieves this?) [*References*: Feller (1968), pp. 406–407, 422–423; and the problem by T. Hughes that is solved in Heuer (1972).]

2.12H Immediately preceding Theorem 2.3.5, we stated a problem of sex composition of families that (for its solution) requires use of Theorems 2.3.7 and 2.3.9, namely, find $P(D)$ (the probability of an unmixed family) and $P(C_1|E)$ (the probability of an only child given at least one child and no girls).

(a) Find $P(D)$ and $P(C_1|E)$ as explicit formulas.

(b) For human families in the United States (or some other specific country) find $p_0, p_1, p_2, \ldots$ (the family size distribution) from statistical abstracts of the country for recent years. Then evaluate $P(D)$ and $P(C_1|E)$ as explicit numbers.

CHAPTER 3

Random Variables:
Discrete Case

The outcome of an experiment (e.g., the outcome of playing a game of chance) is completely described by a sample space Ω with probability function $P(\cdot)$ on its events, and by observing an $\omega \in \Omega$ selected according to $P(\cdot)$ one can answer questions concerning the experiment. However, usually we need only observe some *function* of ω (for historical reasons such functions are called **random variables**) in order to answer the questions of interest.[1] [For example, we may toss a pair of dice and, instead of observing the pair (Number on first die, Number on second die), simply report the resulting sum; this sum is a *function* of (Number on first die, Number on second die), i.e., the sum of the two numbers, and is often sufficient to answer the questions of practical import.] By the *discrete* case, we refer to random variables arising from discrete sample spaces Ω (and certain others to be specified in Definition 3.1.6).

3.1. DISCRETE PROBABILITY FUNCTIONS AND DISTRIBUTION FUNCTIONS

For the reasons just specified (which will become clearer as we progress to Chapter 6ff), we now introduce random variables (Definition 3.1.1) and their distribution functions (Definition 3.1.2) in the general case, and note some of their properties (Theorems 3.1.3, 3.1.4, and 3.1.5) in the general case; we *then* proceed to the discrete case.

Definition 3.1.1. A **random variable** X is a real-valued function with domain Ω [i.e., for each $\omega \in \Omega$, $X(\omega) \in \mathcal{R} = \{ y: -\infty < y < +\infty \}$]. An **n-dimensional random variable** (or n-dimensional random vector, or vector random variable),

---

[1]Indeed, often we only can observe some function of ω (e.g., whether a patient who is administered a new treatment is cured in a specified time period or not) and not the basic ω (which may belong to an Ω much too complex to even attempt to specify). For example, refer back to Problem 1.8.

69

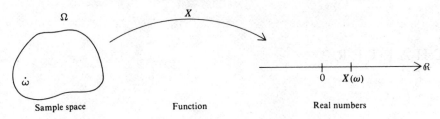

Figure 3.1-1.

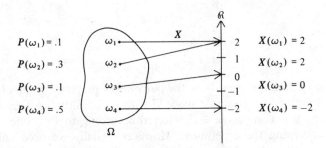

Figure 3.1-2.

$X = (X_1, \ldots, X_n)$, is a function with domain Ω and range in Euclidean n-space $\mathscr{R}^n$ [i.e., for each $\omega \in \Omega$, $X(\omega) \in \mathscr{R}^n = \{(y_1, \ldots, y_n): -\infty < y_i < +\infty \; (1 \le i \le n)\}$].

We may picture the situation as in Figure 3.1-1.

We can associate probabilities with values of X (or $\mathbf{X}$) because probabilities are already associated with points $\omega \in \Omega$ by the probability function $P(\omega)$. For example, suppose we have the situation as shown in Figure 3.1-2. Then $P[X = 2] = P(\{\omega: \omega \in \Omega, X(\omega) = 2\}) = P(\{\omega_1, \omega_2\}) = .4$, $P[X = 0] = .1$, $P[X = -2] = .5$. Our discussion will now be for a one-dimensional random variable X.

Definition 3.1.2. If X is a random variable, its **distribution function** (or **cumulative distribution function**, or **d.f.**, or **c.d.f.**) is defined by

$$F_X(x) = P[X \le x], \qquad \text{for all } x \in (-\infty, +\infty).$$

Theorem 3.1.3. If X is a random variable (**r.v.**), then its d.f. $F_X(x)$ has the following properties:

  (i) $F_X(x)$ is nondecreasing [i.e., $F_X(x) \le F_X(y)$ if $x \le y$].

  (ii) $F_X(-\infty) \equiv \lim_{x \to -\infty} F_X(x) = 0$, $F_X(+\infty) \equiv \lim_{x \to +\infty} F_X(x) = 1$.

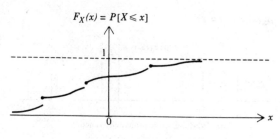

$$F_X(x) = P[X \leqslant x]$$

Figure 3.1-3.

(iii) $F_X(x)$ is continuous from the right [i.e., $\lim_{h \downarrow 0} F_X(x + h) = F_X(x)$ for all x].

We will not formally prove Theorem 3.1.3. A heuristic proof follows easily from the fact that $F_X(x) = P[X \leq x]$. You should graph the d.f. of some very simple r.v. X. A typical $F_X(x)$ with the properties **(i), (ii), (iii)** of Theorem 3.1.3 is shown in Figure 3.1-3.

Theorem 3.1.4. $F_X(x)$ has at most a countable number of discontinuities, and they are all jumps. [For a discussion of discontinuities other than jumps, see Rudin (1964), pp. 81–82.]

Theorem 3.1.5. If $F(x)$ is a function defined over $(-\infty, +\infty)$ that satisfies (i), (ii), (iii) of Theorem 3.1.3, then there exists a sample space Ω with a probability function $P(\cdot)$, and a r.v. X defined over Ω, such that $F_X(x) = F(x)$ for all x.

Theorem 3.1.5, whose proof we will omit, says that a real-valued function is a d.f. iff it satisfies (i), (ii), (iii) of Theorem 3.1.3. Note that, *up to this point, our results have been completely general* (in particular, not restricted to the discrete case). We now consider the discrete case. (The discrete case excludes such examples as picking a number at random from all numbers between 0 and 1. These are covered in Chapter 4.)

Definition 3.1.6. X is called a (one-dimensional) **discrete random variable** if it is a random variable that assumes only a finite or denumerable number of values.

Definition 3.1.7. The **probability function** of a discrete r.v. X that assumes values $x_1, x_2, \ldots$ is $p(x_1), p(x_2), \ldots$, where $p(x_i) = P[X = x_i]$ $(i = 1, 2, \ldots)$.

[Of course $P[X = y] = 0$ unless $y \in \{x_1, x_2, \ldots\}$, since $x_1, x_2, \ldots$ are all the possible values of X. The "probability function" of Definition 2.1.1 should not be confused with the present "probability function" (sometimes called a "point probability function"), which (as we will see in the proof of Theorem 3.1.8) can

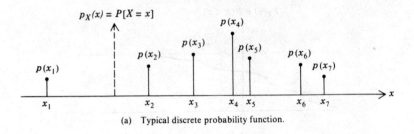

(a)   Typical discrete probability function.

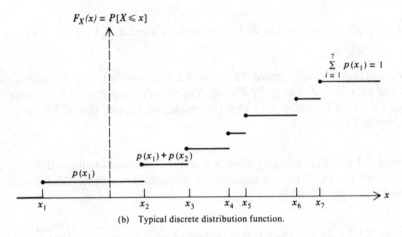

(b)   Typical discrete distribution function.

Figure 3.1-4.

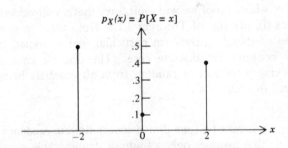

Figure 3.1-5. A particular discrete probability function.

be regarded as a special case of the one in Definition 2.1.1. In general, the context will make it clear which one is under consideration.]

For example, a typical discrete probability function and distribution function are shown in Figure 3.1-4. In the particular case $P(\omega_1) = .1$, $P(\omega_2) = .3$, $P(\omega_3) = .1$, $P(\omega_4) = .5$ with $X(\omega_1) = 2$, $X(\omega_2) = 2$, $X(\omega_3) = 0$, $X(\omega_4) = -2$, we obtain the discrete probability function and distribution function shown in Figures 3.1-5 and 3.1-6.

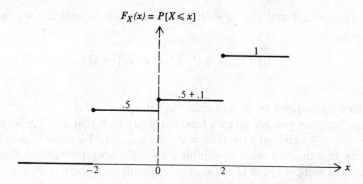

Figure 3.1-6. A particular discrete distribution function.

The following theorem says that all functions $p(x)$ with two very simple properties [(3.1.9) and (3.1.10)] are probability functions, and that all probability functions have those two properties. Thus, those two properties *characterize* probability functions. (Theorem 3.1.5 stated a similar result for general distribution functions.)

Theorem 3.1.8.   A function $p(x)$ is a probability function iff[2]

$$p(x) \geq 0, \qquad \text{for all } x \tag{3.1.9}$$

$$\sum_{i=1}^{\infty} p(x_i) = 1, \qquad \text{and } p(x) = 0 \quad \text{if } x \notin \{x_1, x_2, \dots\}. \tag{3.1.10}$$

Proof: First, suppose that $p(\cdot)$ is a probability function. Then there is some r.v. X such that $P[X = y] = p(y)$ for all values of y. (See Definition 3.1.7.) But $P[X = y]$ is the probability of $\{\omega: X(\omega) = y\} \subseteq \Omega$, and hence is ≥ 0, proving property (3.1.9). Now $P[X = y] = 0$ unless y is one of (a finite or denumerable number of values) $x_1, x_2, \dots$. Hence,

$$\sum_{x} p(x) = \sum_{i=1}^{\infty} p(x_i) = \sum_{i=1}^{\infty} P[X = x_i]$$

$$= \sum_{i=1}^{\infty} P(\{\omega: \omega \in \Omega, X(\omega) = x_i\}) \tag{3.1.11}$$

$$= P\left(\bigcup_{i=1}^{\infty} \{\omega: \omega \in \Omega, X(\omega) = x_i\}\right) = P(\Omega) = 1$$

and properties (3.1.10) hold. [In equation (3.1.11) we used the facts that $\{\omega$:

---

[2]If only a finite number of distinct x's have $p(x) > 0$, we could replace ∞ by the number n of x's with $p(x) > 0$. Instead, we adjoin x's with probability $p(x) = 0$ to $x_1, \dots, x_n$. *The point* is that at most a countable number of distinct x's may have $p(x) > 0$, and we wish to make this point in a simple notation.

$\omega \in \Omega$, $X(\omega) = x_i\}$ and $\{\omega: \omega \in \Omega, X(\omega) = x_j\}$ are disjoint if $i \neq j$, and that

$$\bigcup_{i=1}^{\infty} \{\omega: \omega \in \Omega, X(\omega) = x_i\} = \Omega$$

since each ω is mapped by X into either x_1, or x_2, or $\dots$.]

Second, suppose you are given a function $p(y)$ such that $p(y) \geq 0$, $p(x_1) + p(x_2) + \cdots = 1$, and $p(y) = 0$ if $y \notin \{x_1, x_2, \dots\}$. To show that $p(\cdot)$ is a probability function we need to exhibit a r.v. X whose probability function is $p(\cdot)$. Define a sample space $\Omega = \{\omega_1, \omega_2, \dots\}$ with probabilities $P(\omega_1) = p(x_1)$, $P(\omega_2) = p(x_2), \dots$. (You should check to see that Definition 2.1.1 is satisfied by this definition.) Define a r.v. X by $X(\omega_1) = x_1$, $X(\omega_2) = x_2, \dots$. Then (check this) $p(\cdot)$ *is* the probability function of X, which completes our proof. ∎

Example 3.1.12. Find all numbers k for which the following function

$$g(x) = \begin{cases} (x+1)k, & \text{for } x = 1, 2, 3, 14 \\ 0, & \text{otherwise} \end{cases}$$

is a probability function. Then find the corresponding d.f.

From Theorem 3.1.8, we need to find those k such that

$$g(x) \geq 0 \text{ for all } x \qquad\qquad (3.1.13)$$

and

$$\sum_x g(x) = 1. \qquad\qquad (3.1.14)$$

Now property (3.1.13) requires that $k(x+1) \geq 0$ for $x = 1, 2, 3, 14$. Since each of these x's is positive, $k \geq 0$ meets (3.1.13). The second condition, (3.1.14), requires that

$$\sum_x g(x) = (1+1)k + (2+1)k + (3+1)k + (14+1)k = 1,$$

that is, $24k = 1$, hence $k = 1/24$. Thus, the only $g(x)$ of the form given that is a probability function is the one with $k = 1/24$, namely

$$g(x) = \begin{cases} (x+1)/24, & \text{for } x = 1, 2, 3, 14 \\ 0, & \text{otherwise.} \end{cases}$$

In computing the d.f., for example,

$$F(x) = \begin{cases} \dfrac{5}{24}, & \text{if } x = 2 \\[2mm] \dfrac{5}{24}, & \text{if } 2 < x < 3 \\[2mm] \dfrac{5}{24} + \dfrac{4}{24}, & \text{if } x = 3. \end{cases}$$

Here $F(2) = F(x)$ for any point x such that $2 < x < 3$, since between 2 and 3 (strictly between, that is) there is no point with positive probability, hence no probability is added to the original cumulated sum in that interval. However, as soon as x becomes 3 the d.f. $F(\cdot)$ takes a jump of size $4/24$ (the probability mass at $x = 3$). This process continues until we have added the probability at all points of positive probability, hence the d.f. is

$$F(x) = \begin{cases} 0, & \text{if } x < 1 \\[2mm] \dfrac{2}{24}, & \text{if } x = 1 \\[2mm] \dfrac{2}{24}, & \text{if } 1 < x < 2 \\[2mm] \dfrac{2}{24} + \dfrac{3}{24}, & \text{if } x = 2 \\[2mm] \dfrac{5}{24}, & \text{if } 2 < x < 3 \\[2mm] \dfrac{5}{24} + \dfrac{4}{24}, & \text{if } x = 3 \\[2mm] \dfrac{9}{24}, & \text{if } 3 < x < 14 \\[2mm] \dfrac{24}{24}, & \text{if } x = 14 \\[2mm] 1, & \text{if } 14 < x, \end{cases}$$

that is,

$$F(x) = \begin{cases} 0, & \text{if } x < 1 \\[2mm] \dfrac{2}{24}, & \text{if } 1 \le x < 2 \\[2mm] \dfrac{5}{24}, & \text{if } 2 \le x < 3 \\[2mm] \dfrac{9}{24}, & \text{if } 3 \le x < 14 \\[2mm] 1, & \text{if } 14 \le x, \end{cases}$$

which has the following graph:

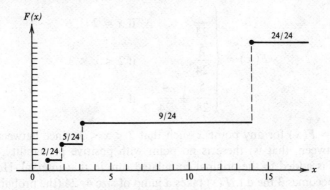

Example 3.1.15. **Finding a probability function from the distribution function** is straightforward. If $F_X(x)$ is the distribution function of a discrete r.v. X, one then finds the points at which the distribution function $F_X(x)$ jumps, and the jump sizes. The probability function has probability masses exactly at those jump points, with the probability masses being equal in magnitude to the respective jump sizes.

As an example, suppose X is a discrete r.v. with distribution function

$$F_X(x) = \begin{cases} 0, & \text{for } x < -2 \\ 1/6, & \text{for } -2 \leq x < 1 \\ 1/2, & \text{for } 1 \leq x < 5 \\ 3/4, & \text{for } 5 \leq x < 9 \\ 1, & \text{for } x \geq 9. \end{cases}$$

Then clearly $F_X(x)$ has jumps at $x = -2, 1, 5, 9$ (those are the jump points); hence the probability function of X has positive probability mass only at $x = -2, 1, 5, 9$. The respective masses are the sizes of the jumps, and can be determined from the formula

$$p_X(x) = F_X(x) - F_X(x^-), \tag{3.1.16}$$

where $F_X(x^-)$ **denotes the limit of** $F_X(y)$ **as** $y \uparrow x$ **with** $y < x$. Thus, in our example we find

$$p_X(-2) = F_X(-2) - F_X(-2^-) = \frac{1}{6} - 0 = \frac{1}{6},$$

$$p_X(1) = F_X(1) - F_X(1^-) = \frac{1}{2} - \frac{1}{6} = \frac{1}{3},$$

$$p_X(5) = F_X(5) - F_X(5^-) = \frac{3}{4} - \frac{1}{2} = \frac{1}{4},$$

$$p_X(9) = F_X(9) - F_X(9^-) = 1 - \frac{3}{4} = \frac{1}{4};$$

of course $p_X(a) = 0$ for any other point $a \notin \{-2, 1, 5, 9\}$, since $F_X(x) = F_X(x^-)$ for $x \notin \{-2, 1, 5, 9\}$.

The following example discusses a nonstandard probability function of a discrete r.v. that arose in practice.

Example 3.1.17. The number X of microorganisms occurring on a surface is important in the design of procedures for cleansing surgical instruments, space vehicles, and so on. One study in this area indicated that such organisms occur in "clumps," and that one basic distribution of interest would be that which allows some probability of one microorganism occurring in a clump and equal probability of having $2, 3, \ldots$, or k occur; namely,

$$P[X = x] = p_X(x) = \begin{cases} 0, & \text{if } x = 1 \\ (1 - \theta)/(k - 1), & \text{if } x = 2, \ldots, k \\ 0, & \text{otherwise,} \end{cases}$$

for some θ with $0 \le \theta \le 1$.[3] This example will be studied later (see Example 7.2.23) with regard to such questions as "How can I estimate θ?" (Usually in practice θ is unknown.)

For example, if singletons occur 75% of the time and clumps of up to 6 microorganisms may occur, then $\theta = .75$, $k = 6$, and

$$P[X = 1] = .75,$$

$$P[X = 2] = P[X = 3] = P[X = 4] = P[X = 5] = P[X = 6] = .05.$$

Example 3.1.18. Suppose a pair of fair dice is rolled once. A sample space for this experiment is given in Example 1.4.1. Define r.v.'s X_1 as the number of points that show on the first die, X_2 as the number of points that show on the second die, and $Y = X_1 + X_2$. Find the probability function of Y.

Recall from Example 1.4.1 that

$$\Omega = \{(i, j): i, j = 1, 2, 3, 4, 5, 6\}.$$

For each $\omega = (i, j) \in \Omega$,

$$Y(\omega) = Y((i, j)) = i + j,$$

hence the possible values of Y are $2, 3, 4, 5, 6, 7, 8, 9, 10, 11, 12$ and their probabilities are calculated using

$$P(Y = k) = P(\{\omega: \omega \in \Omega, Y(\omega) = k\}).$$

---

[3]"Verification of a sampling distribution for microbiological assays" by Bruce A. Nelson of the Martin Marietta Corporation, Denver, Colorado, presented at the Ninth Annual Symposium on Biomathematics and Computer Science in the Life Sciences, Houston, Texas, March 22–24, 1971. (An abstract was contained in an abstracts booklet issued by the University of Texas' Graduate School of Biomedical Sciences at Houston.)

For example,

$$P(Y = 8) = P(\{\omega: \omega \in \Omega, Y(\omega) = 8\})$$
$$= P(\{(2,6), (6,2), (3,5), (5,3), (4,4)\})$$
$$= P((2,6)) + P((6,2)) + P((3,5)) + P((5,3)) + P((4,4))$$
$$= \frac{5}{36}$$

since all 36 points in the sample space are equally likely. The complete probability function of Y is

k	2	3	4	5	6	7	8	9	10	11	12
$p_Y(k) = P(Y = k)$	$\frac{1}{36}$	$\frac{2}{36}$	$\frac{3}{36}$	$\frac{4}{36}$	$\frac{5}{36}$	$\frac{6}{36}$	$\frac{5}{36}$	$\frac{4}{36}$	$\frac{3}{36}$	$\frac{2}{36}$	$\frac{1}{36}$

with $p_Y(y) = 0$ otherwise.

Example 3.1.19. In Example 3.1.18, let $Z = \max(X_1, X_2)$. What is the probability function of Z?

Here, for each $\omega = (i, j) \in \Omega$,

$$Z(\omega) = \max(i, j),$$

the possible values of Z are 1, 2, 3, 4, 5, 6, and

$$P(Z = k) = P(\{\omega: \omega = (i, j) \in \Omega, \max(i, j) = k\})$$
$$= P(\{(i, j): \max(i, j) = k, 1 \le i, j \le 6\}).$$

Since all 36 points in the sample space are equally likely, finding $P(Z = k)$ reduces to a problem of counting, and we find

$$P(Z = 1) = P(\{\omega: \omega = (i, j) \in \Omega, \max(i, j) = 1\}) = P((1,1)) = \frac{1}{36},$$

$$P(Z = 2) = P(\{(1,2), (2,1), (2,2)\}) = \frac{3}{36},$$

$$P(Z = 3) = \frac{5}{36},$$

$$P(Z = 4) = \frac{7}{36},$$

$$P(Z = 5) = \frac{9}{36},$$

$$P(Z = 6) = \frac{11}{36}.$$

PROBLEMS FOR SECTION 3.1

3.1.1 Thirteen cards are dealt from a standard (see Problem 2.2.5) deck of cards. Let X be the number of spades dealt. Find the probability function of X, and the distribution function of X.

3.1.2 Verify that

$$F(x) = \begin{cases} .00, & \text{if} & x < -2.0 \\ .25, & \text{if} -2.0 \le x < 2.6 \\ .36, & \text{if} 2.6 \le x < 3.8 \\ .48, & \text{if} 3.8 \le x < 8.0 \\ .70, & \text{if} 8.0 \le x < 11.0 \\ 1.00, & \text{if} & x > 11.0 \end{cases}$$

is a distribution function of some r.v. X, and find the associated probability function of X. Compute $P(2 < X \le 4)$, $P(X < 4.6)$, $P(X \le 5.2)$, $P(X \ge 3.8)$, $P(X > 6)$, $P(-3 \le X < 8)$, and $P(X > 11)$. [*Hint*: Use Theorem 3.1.5 and Example 3.1.15.]

3.1.3 Verify that

$$F(x) = \begin{cases} .00, & \text{if} & x < 0 \\ .25, & \text{if } 0 \le x < 1 \\ .50, & \text{if } 1 \le x < 2 \\ .75, & \text{if } 2 \le x < 3 \\ 1.00, & \text{if} & x \ge 3 \end{cases}$$

is a distribution function of some r.v. X. Compute $P(X < 3)$, $P(X \le 2.6)$, $P(X \ge 1.2)$, $P(X > 1)$, $P(2 \le X < 3)$, and $P(-1 < X \le 2)$. Find the associated probability function of X.

3.1.4 Let $p(x) = c/(1 + x^2)$ for $x = -2, 0, 1, 5$ and zero for all other values of x. What value(s) of c are such that $p(x)$ is a probability function? Find and graph the corresponding distribution function.

3.1.5 A fair six-sided die is rolled independently three times. Define

$$X_i = \begin{cases} 1, & \text{if the } i\text{th roll yields an odd number of dots} \\ 0, & \text{otherwise.} \end{cases}$$

Find the probability function of each of X_1, X_2, and X_3. Further, let Y be the r.v. denoting the number of times odd dots appear in the three rolls; that is, $Y = X_1 + X_2 + X_3$. Find the probability function of Y, the distribution function of Y, and graph both of these.

3.1.6 In the game of craps (see Problem 2.3.9), two six-sided dice are rolled. Suppose you enter the game by paying $1. If 2, 3, or 12 shows you lose; if 7 or 11 shows you win $3; and otherwise you continue to roll the dice. Let X be the r.v. defined as

$$X = \begin{cases} 0, & \text{if you lose} \\ 1, & \text{if you win} \\ 2, & \text{if you continue to roll the dice.} \end{cases}$$

Find the probability function and distribution function of X.

3.1.7 A professor has five similar looking keys in his pocket, and only one of them will open his office door. He takes keys from his pocket at random (without replacement) until he finds one that opens the door. Let X be the number of keys he needs to try in order to open the door. Find the probability function of X, and the distribution function of X.

3.1.8 In a certain city, 60% of the people possess a gun. Of the people who possess a gun, 30% favor a new gun control law. If five people are chosen from this city at random, let X denote the number of people in the sample who both have a gun and also favor the new law. Find the probability function and the d.f. of X.

3.2. SPECIAL DISCRETE DISTRIBUTIONS

In this section we will define several very **important "discrete distributions"** (i.e., distribution functions and/or probability functions of discrete r.v.'s) and show by examples how they arise. Recall that a r.v. X has a discrete distribution if (with $p_i \geq 0$, $\sum_{i=1}^{\infty} p_i = 1$)

$$P[X = x] = p_X(x) = \begin{cases} p_i, & \text{if } x = x_i \ (i = 1, 2, \dots) \\ 0, & \text{otherwise.} \end{cases}$$

Definition 3.2.1. A r.v. X has the **Bernoulli** distribution if (for some p, $0 \leq p \leq 1$)

$$P[X = x] = p_X(x) = \begin{cases} p^x(1 - p)^{1-x}, & x = 0, 1 \\ 0, & \text{otherwise.} \end{cases}$$

[A table is not needed because of the simplicity of $p_X(x)$. Recall that $p^0 \equiv 1$.]

   To prove that this is a probability function, we need only show that $p(x_i) \geq 0$ $(i = 1, 2, \dots)$ and $\sum_{i=1}^{\infty} p(x_i) = 1$. For the Bernoulli distribution this is clear; note that a Bernoulli r.v. assumes but two values (0 and 1) with respective probabilities $1 - p$ and p, and that $1 - p + p = 1$. (In more complicated, nonBernoulli cases it will sometimes not be at all clear, and the proof will be difficult.) Note that the values 0 and 1 are usually associated with "failure" and "success" in some context (e.g., see Example 3.2.2).

Example 3.2.2. The green light at an intersection is on for 15 seconds at a time, the yellow for 5, and the red for 55. Assuming that traffic conditions induce random variations in arrival times at the light, so that "making the green light" is a chance event (called a "success") and we are equally likely to arrive at any time in the light cycle, *find* the distribution of X, the number of successes in one trial trip to the light.

   Let G denote green, Y yellow, R red; the complete cycle of lights is G, Y, R. The total cycle length is $T = 15 + 5 + 55 = 75$ seconds, and the probability that we arrive on that part of T that is G is $15/75 = .2$ (since we arrive at random within T and $15/75$ of T is G). So, $P[X = 0] = .8$, $P[X = 1] = .2$; thus, X is *Bernoulli* with $p = .2$. **(We can always interpret a Bernoulli r.v. Y as the number of successes in one trial of an experiment where the probability of success is p.)**

Definition 3.2.3. A r.v. X has the **binomial** distribution if (for some positive integer n, and some p with $0 \le p \le 1$)

$$P[X = x] = p_X(x) = \begin{cases} \binom{n}{x} p^x (1 - p)^{n-x}, & x = 0, 1, \ldots, n \\ 0, & \text{otherwise.} \end{cases}$$

[See Table 5 for a table of $p_X(x)$.]

Often, a binomial random variable (i.e., a random variable with a binomial distribution) arises from a sequence of Bernoulli trials with the properties that

(i) Trials are independent events.

(ii) Each trial results in exactly one of the same two mutually exclusive outcomes, usually called success (S) and failure (F).

(iii) The probability of outcome S is constant from trial to trial (and hence the probability of outcome F also remains constant from trial to trial).

Thus, on any trial $P(S) = p$ and $P(F) = 1 - p$ in this setting. If we define a random variable $X = 0$ when F occurs, and $X = 1$ when S occurs, then

$$p_X(x) = \begin{cases} p^x (1 - p)^{1-x}, & \text{if } x = 0, 1 \\ 0, & \text{otherwise,} \end{cases}$$

which is the probability function of a Bernoulli random variable (see Definition 3.2.1).

A binomial random variable can be considered as a sum of n Bernoulli random variables, that is, as the number of successes in n Bernoulli trials. In n Bernoulli trials, let X_i be the random variable

$$X_i = \begin{cases} 1, & \text{if the } i\text{th trial results in outcome S} \\ 0, & \text{if the } i\text{th trial results in outcome F,} \end{cases}$$

and define $X = X_1 + X_2 + \cdots + X_n$. Then X has possible values $0, 1, 2, \ldots, n$ and the binomial distribution with $n = $ (number of trials) and $p = $ (probability of S) as long as the trials are independent with constant probability of success. To see this, note that, for any $x \in \{0, 1, 2, \ldots, n\}$,

$$p_X(x) = P(x \text{ successes in } n \text{ trials}).$$

Now x successes can occur in n trials in $\binom{n}{x}$ "ways," the number of possible specifications of *which* x of the n trials the x S's occur at. One of these ways has

x successes followed by $n - x$ failures, and that way has probability

$$P(SS\ldots SFF\ldots F) = \overbrace{P(S)P(S)\ldots P(S)}^{x \text{ terms}}\ \overbrace{P(F)P(F)\ldots P(F)}^{n-x \text{ terms}}$$

$$= p \times p \times \cdots \times p(1 - p)(1 - p)\ldots(1 - p) \qquad (3.2.4)$$

$$= p^x(1 - p)^{n-x}$$

because of independence and constant probability of success as an outcome. However, any other "way" (ordering of x S's and $n - x$ F's) has the same probability since (because of independence and constant probability of success) its probability will be the product of x p's and $n - x$ $1 - p$'s, just in a different order than at equation (3.2.4). Thus

$$p_X(x) = \begin{cases} \binom{n}{x}p^x(1 - p)^{n-x}, & \text{if } x = 0, 1, 2, \ldots, n \\ 0, & \text{otherwise,} \end{cases}$$

which is the probability function of the binomial random variable in Definition 3.2.3.

Note that **if X has the binomial distribution with n (number of trials) and p (probability of success) [we denote this as $X \sim B(n, p)$] then $Y = n - X$ is also binomially distributed with n (number of trials) but probability of success $1 - p$.** In our new notation,

$$X \sim B(n, p) \Rightarrow n - X \sim B(n, 1 - p).$$

Example 3.2.5. The distribution of X, the number of successes in 25 unrelated trials at the light of Example 3.2.2 is (show this)

$$p[X = x] = \binom{25}{x}(.2)^x(.8)^{25-x}, \qquad x = 0, 1, \ldots, 25;$$

that is, X is *binomial* with $n = 25$, $p = .2$. [In general, if the occurrence of an event E is subject to chance, the number of occurrences of E in n independent trials is a discrete r.v. X with possible values $0, 1, \ldots, n$. If the probability of occurrence of E on a trial is constant at some value p $(0 \le p \le 1)$ from trial to trial, X is (show this) a binomial r.v.]

When sampling from finite populations, the binomial distribution arises only when the sampling is done with replacement (which keeps the probability of success constant from trial to trial), as in the following example.

Example 3.2.6. Chuck-a-Luck. A carnival game consists of rolling three fair dice. A player pays $1 to enter the game, wins $1 if on a roll of three dice exactly one 6 shows, $2 if two 6's show, and $3 if all three 6's show. (Otherwise, the player wins $0.) What is the probability function of the player's net winnings r.v.?

Let Y denote the net winnings. Then possible values of Y are 0–1, 1–1, 2–1, 3–1; that is, $-1, 0, 1, 2$. Let S denote the event a 6 shows on one roll of a single die, and note that the experiment is equivalent to sampling with replacement three times from an urn containing six balls numbered $1, 2, 3, 4, 5, 6$. If X denotes the total number of 6's rolled, then $X \sim B(3, p)$ where $p = P(S) = 1/6$, hence

$$p_X(x) = \begin{cases} \binom{3}{x} \left(\frac{1}{6}\right)^x \left(\frac{5}{6}\right)^{3-x}, & \text{if } x = 0, 1, 2, 3 \\ 0, & \text{otherwise.} \end{cases}$$

To obtain the probability function of Y, note that $Y = X - 1$. Thus,

$$p_Y(-1) = p_X(0) = \frac{125}{216}$$

$$p_Y(0) = p_X(1) = \frac{75}{216}$$

$$p_Y(1) = p_X(2) = \frac{15}{216}$$

$$p_Y(2) = p_X(3) = \frac{1}{216}.$$

Note that, *if sampling had been without replacement* from an urn containing each of $1, 2, 3, 4, 5, 6$ once, then we would have obtained

$$p_X(0) = \tfrac{1}{2}, \ p_X(1) = \tfrac{1}{2}, \ p_X(2) = p_X(3) = 0$$

since then either no 6 is drawn ($X = 0$) or the 6 is drawn, in which case it cannot be drawn again since sampling is without replacement ($X = 1$ therefore). In this setting, the winnings Y would have

$$p_Y(-1) = \tfrac{1}{2}, \ p_Y(0) = \tfrac{1}{2}.$$

Definition 3.2.7. A r.v. X has the **hypergeometric** distribution if (for some integers n, a, N with $1 \le n \le N$ and $0 \le a \le N$)

$$P[X = x] = p_X(x)$$

$$= \begin{cases} \dfrac{\binom{a}{x}\binom{N-a}{n-x}}{\binom{N}{n}}, & x = \max(0, n - (N - a)), \ldots, \min(n, a) \\ 0, & \text{otherwise.} \end{cases}$$

[See Table 6 for a table of $p_X(x)$. Note that the limits on x can also be written as

$$\max(0, n - (N - a)) \le x \le \min(n, a).]$$

As we noted after Definition 3.2.1, a direct proof that this is a probability function is difficult (see the Honors Problems). The next example gives an indirect, probabilistic proof.

Example 3.2.8. A population of N objects ($N \geq 1$) contains a of type A ($0 \leq a \leq N$). A random sample of size n ($1 \leq n \leq N$) is drawn under SRS without replacement. Let X be the number in the sample that are of type A. Then $X \geq 0$ and $X \geq n - (N - a)$ [since we cannot obtain a negative number of items of type A in our sample, and since $n - (N - a)$ is the difference between the sample size and the number of non-type A items, respectively]; thus, $X \geq \max(0, n - (N - a))$. Also $X \leq n$ (it cannot exceed the sample size) and $X \leq a$ (it cannot exceed the number of elements of type A); thus, $X \leq \min(n, a)$. Now there are $\binom{N}{n}$ possible unordered samples, of which $\binom{a}{x}\binom{N-a}{n-x}$ contain x elements of type A. (To obtain ordered samples, we multiply each of these by $n!$.) Thus, X is *hypergeometric* with n, a, N and therefore the probabilities of Definition 3.2.7 sum to 1.

Examples for the hypergeometric distribution. The hypergeometric model is used in a variety of fields, such as quality control (acceptance sampling) and ecology (wildlife sampling), as illustrated in the following two examples.

Example 3.2.9. Acceptance Sampling in Quality Control. Shipments of large quantities of an item arrive at a manufacturing plant. To find out the fraction of defective items, which is often a matter of concern, one could sample the entire shipment and test the items one by one. However, this process is usually economically infeasible. (Also, in some cases the testing must be destructive, i.e., result in the destruction of the item tested, as for example when a test of battery life in continuous use is conducted, and testing all items would yield none to use as the good would be destroyed with the defective.) Thus, usually the receiver takes a (small) random sample (without replacement) from the entire population of items in the shipment. The whole shipment (often called a **lot**) is accepted if in that sample there are not more than a predetermined number of defective items.

For example, suppose there are 200 items in the lot, and their manufacturer claims that no more than 10% are defective. Suppose once the shipment is received we take a random sample of size 10 from it without replacement and accept the lot if there are at most 2 defective items in the sample. What is the probability we accept the lot? Of course, this probability depends on the percentage of the lot that is defective, so let us denote by $A(p)$ the probability of accepting a lot which is $100p\%$ defectives.

If 0% are defective, then the probability of accepting the lot is 1.0000, since then there will be 0 defectives in the sample of 10. Thus,

$$A(.00) = P\left(\begin{array}{l} \text{0 or 1 or 2 defectives in a sample of 10} \\ \text{from a lot of which 0\% are defective} \end{array}\right) = 1.0000.$$

If 5% are defective in the entire lot, then it consists of 10 defectives and 190 good units. The number X of defectives in the sample of 10 then has a hypergeometric distribution and its probability function is

$$p_X(x) = \frac{\binom{10}{x}\binom{190}{10-x}}{\binom{200}{10}},$$

hence

$$A(.05) = P \text{ (Accepting a shipment that has 5\% defectives)}$$

$$= P(X \le 2) = p_X(0) + p_X(1) + p_X(2)$$

$$= \frac{\binom{10}{0}\binom{190}{10}}{\binom{200}{10}} + \frac{\binom{10}{1}\binom{190}{9}}{\binom{200}{10}} + \frac{\binom{10}{2}\binom{190}{8}}{\binom{200}{10}}$$

$$= .59145 + .32677 + .072715$$

$$= .990935.$$

If there are 10% defective, then there are 20 defective items and 180 nondefective items, hence

$$p_X(x) = \frac{\binom{20}{x}\binom{180}{10-x}}{\binom{200}{10}}$$

and

$$A(.10) = P \text{ (Accepting a shipment that has 10\% defectives)}$$

$$= p_X(0) + p_X(1) + p_X(2)$$

$$= \frac{\binom{20}{0}\binom{180}{10}}{\binom{200}{10}} + \frac{\binom{20}{1}\binom{180}{9}}{\binom{200}{10}} + \frac{\binom{20}{2}\binom{180}{8}}{\binom{200}{10}}$$

$$= .33977 + .39739 + .19754$$

$$= .9347.$$

Thus, the probability of accepting a 10% defective shipment is smaller than the probability of accepting a 5% defective shipment. In fact, a stronger result can be shown: The probability of accepting the shipment decreases as its percentage of defectives increases, and is between 1.0000 and .9347 if no more than 10% are defective.

Example 3.2.10. Wildlife Sampling. Often ecologists desire to estimate the total number (population size) of a certain kind of animal in a given area. If the population size remains constant throughout the sampling period, the **capture-recapture method** is often used. In this method, one samples a animals (where a is a fixed number) and releases them after "tagging." After sufficient time has elapsed for their thorough mixing with the untagged population, n animals are captured, the number of tagged animals in the n units is counted, and, based on this information, one estimates the unknown population size N.

Since in the population (after the tagging stage) there are a tagged animals and $N - a$ untagged, in the second sample of size n the number of tagged animals is a random variable X with the hypergeometric distribution

$$p_X(x) = \frac{\binom{a}{x}\binom{N-a}{n-x}}{\binom{N}{n}},$$

assuming of course that the probability of recapture is not dependent on whether the animal is tagged or untagged. (This is often true when the recapture is in the form of a "net" that captures all specimens in the given sampling area. It is often false in some degree when captured animals become "shy" of the apparatus used in the capture, and also when animals become easier to capture, such as when they become less wary of humans.)

We estimate N by that value of N which maximizes the probability $p_X(x_0)$ of observing what we did observe. But (check this), the N that maximizes $p_X(x_0)$ is

$$N = a\frac{n}{x_0},$$

where x_0 is the observed number of tagged units in the second sample. (Estimating an unknown quantity, such as N, to be that value that maximizes the probability of observing what we did observe, is called the **maximum likelihood method** of estimation of an unknown quantity; it is studied in detail in Chapter 7; see Example 7.2.24 for further discussion of this example.)

Definition 3.2.11. A r.v. X has the **Poisson** distribution if (for some $\mu > 0$, called a **parameter** of the distribution)

$$P[X = x] = p_X(x) = \begin{cases} e^{-\mu}\dfrac{\mu^x}{x!}, & x = 0, 1, 2, \ldots \\ 0, & \text{otherwise.} \end{cases}$$

[See Table 7 for a table of $p_X(x)$.]

Example 3.2.12. Suppose events occur randomly in time (and can therefore be represented as points along the time axis). Consider a time interval of length T

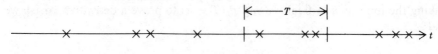

Figure 3.2-1.

anywhere on the time axis (Figure 3.2-1). We will find the probability of exactly n of these events occurring in the time interval T, say $P_n(T)$ (Assumption 3.2.13 justifies this notation) under the following assumptions.

Assumption 3.2.13.   Time homogeneity. $P_n(T)$ is independent of where T is on the time axis. [So we need not consider $P_n(t_1, t_2)$ with $t_2 - t_1 = T$.]

Assumption 3.2.14. As $T \to 0$, $[1 - P_0(T)]/T \to \lambda$ (for some $\lambda > 0$). This is equivalent to $1 - P_0(h) = \lambda h + o(h)$ where $\lim\limits_{h \to 0} \dfrac{o(h)}{h} = 0$. [Restriction on the probability of one or more events in a small time interval of length h.]

Assumption 3.2.15. $P_1(T) = \lambda T + o(T)$ and $P_2(T) + P_3(T) + \cdots = o(T)$. [Whatever the number of events during $(0, T)$, the probability that during $(T, T + h)$ an event occurs is $\lambda h + o(h)$, *and* the probability that more than one event occurs is $o(h)$.]

Now we will find **a system of differential equations for** $P_n(T)$. Suppose $n \geq 1$. Then[4]

$$\left\{ \begin{matrix} n \\ n-1 \\ \vdots \\ 0 \end{matrix} \right\} \qquad \left\{ \begin{matrix} 0 \\ 1 \\ \vdots \\ n \end{matrix} \right\}$$

$$\underset{\qquad\qquad T \qquad\qquad\qquad T+h}{\rule{8cm}{0.4pt}}$$

$$P_n(T + h) = P_n(T)[1 - \lambda h - o(h)] + P_{n-1}(T)[\lambda h + o(h)]$$

$$+ [P_{n-2}(T) + \cdots + P_0(T)](o(h))$$

or

$$\frac{P_n(T + h) - P_n(T)}{h} = -\lambda P_n(T) + \lambda P_{n-1}(T) + \frac{o(h)}{h}.$$

---

[4] To obtain n events in time $T + h$, we can obtain n in time T and 0 in time h; or obtain $n - 1$ in time T and 1 in time h; and so on.

Taking the limit as $h \to 0$ [also using $P_n(T - h)$ to prove a derivative exists], we find

$$P_n'(T) = -\lambda P_n(T) + \lambda P_{n-1}(T) \qquad (n \geq 1).$$

Suppose $n = 0$. Then $P_0(T + h) = P_0(T)[1 - \lambda h - o(h)]$, which leads to $P_0'(T) = -\lambda P_0(T)$.

Since $P_0(0) = 1$, from $P_0'(T) = -\lambda P_0(T)$ [which has as its solution $P_0(T) = ce^{-\lambda T}$], we find

$$P_0(T) = e^{-\lambda T}.$$

Since $P_1(0) = 0$, from $P_1'(T) = -\lambda P_1(T) + \lambda P_0(T)$, or $P_1'(T) + \lambda P_1(T) = \lambda e^{-\lambda T}$, we find the solution

$$P_1(T) = \frac{(\lambda T)e^{-\lambda T}}{1!}.$$

Proceeding,[5] we find

$$P_n(T) = \frac{e^{-\lambda T}(\lambda T)^n}{n!}.$$

[This derivation uses some ideas of differential equations that students are *not* expected to know. The important thing is to see how to obtain the differential equations; once obtained, reference to a book on the subject will allow solution. For example, see Martin and Reissner (1956), p. 44.] Thus X, the number of events in a specific interval of length T, is *Poisson* with $\mu = \lambda T$. (We will see later that λT is the "average" number of occurrences, so **we may interpret the parameter μ in the Poisson distribution as the "average" number of occurrences.**)

Example 3.2.16. Poisson Error Model. Suppose a certain high-speed printer makes errors at random on printer paper, making an average of 2 mistakes per page. Assuming that the Poisson distribution with $\mu = 2$ is appropriate to model the number of errors per page, what is the probability that of 10 pages produced by this printer at least 7 will have no errors? (Assume independence from page to page.)

---

[5] This method of derivation is stated as Complement 1A on p. 123 of Parzen (1962). Another derivation of $P_0(T) = e^{-\lambda T}$ is possible using the result that the only bounded functions such that $f(T_1 + T_2) = f(T_1)f(T_2)$ for all $T_1, T_2 > 0$ are (1) the function that is always zero and (2) $f(T) = e^{-\nu T}$ for $T > 0$ (for some $\nu > 0$); here since $P_0(T_1 + T_2) = P_0(T_1)P_0(T_2)$, we see immediately that $P_0(T) = e^{-\nu T}$ for some $\nu > 0$. Since $P_0(T) = 1 - \lambda T + o(T)$, it follows that $\nu = \lambda$.

Let X denote the number of errors per page, so that

$$p_X(x) = \frac{e^{-2}2^x}{x!}, \qquad x = 0, 1, 2, 3, \ldots .$$

The probability of any page being error-free is then

$$p_X(0) = \frac{e^{-2}2^0}{0!} = e^{-2} = .1353353.$$

Having no errors on a page is a "success," and there are 10 independent pages (trials), hence the number Y of pages without any errors is a binomial random variable with $n = 10$, $p = e^{-2}$:

$$p_Y(y) = \binom{10}{y}(e^{-2})^y(1 - e^{-2})^{10-y}, \qquad y = 0, 1, 2, \ldots, 10.$$

The probability of at least 7 error-free pages (out of 10 produced) is

$$P(Y \geq 7) = p_Y(7) + p_Y(8) + p_Y(9) + p_Y(10)$$

$$= (.64508 + .037862 + .0013169 + .000020612)10^{-4}$$

$$= .6842795 \times 10^{-4} \approx .00007,$$

indicating that this printer has a very low probability of satisfying this need.

Definition 3.2.17. A r.v. X has the **(discrete) uniform** distribution if (for some integer $n \geq 1$, and some n distinct numbers $x_1, \ldots, x_n$)

$$P[X = x] = p_X(x) = \begin{cases} \dfrac{1}{n}, & x = x_1, x_2, \ldots, x_n \\ 0, & \text{otherwise.} \end{cases}$$

[A table is not needed because of the simplicity of $p_X(x)$.]

Example 3.2.18. If Ω is a finite discrete sample space with equally likely points $\{\omega_1, \ldots, \omega_n\}$, then let $X(\omega_i) = x_i$ and [if $x_i \neq x_j$ $(i \neq j)$] X will be uniform on $x_1, \ldots, x_n$.

Example 3.2.19. Of five keys on a keychain, suppose exactly one will open a certain lock, but it is not known which key fits. Let X denote the number of keys tried in attempting to open the lock, assuming keys are tried at random without replacement. Find the probability function of X.

Here the possible values of X are 1, 2, 3, 4, 5 and

$$p_X(1) = P(X = 1) = P(\text{Correct key chosen on 1st try}) = \frac{1}{5}$$

$$p_X(2) = P(X = 2) = P\left(\begin{array}{l}\text{Incorrect key chosen for 1st try,}\\ \text{correct key chosen on 2nd try}\end{array}\right)$$

$$= \frac{4}{5} \cdot \frac{1}{4} = \frac{1}{5}$$

$$p_X(3) = P(X = 3) = \frac{4}{5} \cdot \frac{3}{4} \cdot \frac{1}{3} = \frac{1}{5}$$

$$p_X(4) = p_X(5) = \frac{1}{5},$$

or more simply we have found that the probability function of the number of keys tried has the discrete uniform probability function with $n = 5$, that is,

$$p_X(x) = 1/5 \quad \text{for } x = 1, 2, 3, 4, 5$$

[and of course $p_X(x) = 0$ for all other values of x].

Definition 3.2.20. A r.v. X has the **geometric** distribution if (for some p, $0 \le p \quad 1$)

$$P[X = x] = p_X(x) = \begin{cases} (1 - p)^{x-1}p, & x = 1, 2, 3, \ldots \\ 0, & \text{otherwise.} \end{cases}$$

[A table is not needed due to the simplicity of $p_X(x)$.]

Example 3.2.21. If an event E has constant probability p of occurring on any en trial, and if trials are independent, let X be the number of the trial on which E first occurs. Then X is *geometrically* distributed.

Example 3.2.22. Roulette. A **roulette wheel** usually has 38 "spots," of which 18 are black, 18 are red, and 2 are green. Let X be the number of spins necessary to get a green spot in independent spins of a "fair" wheel. **(a)** What is the probability that at least 4 spins are needed to get the first green? **(b)** What is the probability that an odd number of spins is needed to get the first green? Here

$$P(\text{Success}) = P(\text{Green on a given spin}) = \frac{2}{38} = \frac{1}{19} = p,$$

and the number X of trials needed to get the first green has the geometric distribution. Thus, for part **(a)** we find

$$P(X \geq 4) = 1 - P(X \leq 3)$$

$$= 1 - \sum_{x=1}^{3} (1 - p)^{x-1} p$$

$$= 1 - p\left((1 - p)^{0} + (1 - p)^{1} + (1 - p)^{2}\right)$$

$$= 1 - \frac{1}{19}\left(\left(\frac{18}{19}\right)^{0} + \left(\frac{18}{19}\right)^{1} + \left(\frac{18}{19}\right)^{2}\right)$$

$$= 1 - \frac{1}{19}\left(\frac{1027}{361}\right) = .8502697.$$

Thus, the chances of a green in the first three spins are slight (barely 15%). [*Note*: Part **(a)** can be worked in a simpler way also. Namely, the probability at least 4 spins are needed to obtain the first green is the probability that there is no green in the first 3 spins, which equals

$$[1 - P(\text{Green on a given spin})]^{3} = \left(\frac{18}{19}\right)^{3} = .8502697$$

(as we had already found).]

For part **(b)**,

$$P(\text{An odd number of spins is needed for 1st green})$$

$$= P(X \in \{1, 3, 5, 7, \ldots\})$$

$$= p_X(1) + p_X(3) + p_X(5) + \cdots$$

$$= p\left((1 - p)^{0} + (1 - p)^{2} + (1 - p)^{4} + (1 - p)^{6} + \cdots\right)$$

$$= p\frac{1}{1 - (1 - p)^{2}} = p\frac{1}{2p - p^{2}} = \frac{1}{2 - p} = \frac{1}{2 - \frac{1}{19}} = \frac{19}{37}.$$

In particular, note that it is more likely that an odd number of trials will be needed to produce the first green, than that an even number of trials will be needed to produce the first green.

Definition 3.2.23. A r.v. X has the **negative binomial** distribution if (for some integer $r \geq 1$, and some p with $0 \leq p \leq 1$)

$$P[X = x] = p_X(x) = \begin{cases} p^{r}\binom{x + r - 1}{r - 1}q^{x}, & x = 0, 1, 2, \ldots \\ 0, & \text{otherwise.} \end{cases}$$

(Here we have used the standard notation $q = 1 - p$.) (A table is not given; binomial coefficients are given in Table 3.)

Example 3.2.24. A given event occurs (success) with probability p (and therefore fails to occur with probability $q = 1 - p$), and independent trials are conducted. Let X be r fewer than the number of trials needed to produce r successes; so $X = x$ means we needed $x + r$ trials ($x = 0, 1, 2, \ldots$), and X is the number of failures encountered on the way to the first r successes. Then

$$P[X = x] = p\left(\begin{array}{c} x + r - 1 \\ r - 1 \end{array}\right) p^{r-1} q^x$$

since: The last trial must be a success (p), there are $\left(\begin{array}{c} x + r - 1 \\ r - 1 \end{array}\right)$ ways to order with $r - 1$ successes, and $p^{r-1} q^x$ is the probability of each such order. Thus, X is *negative binomial* with r. The *geometric* distribution is the case $r = 1$, with one added to X (i.e., in the geometric case we considered the number of trials needed to produce the first success, whereas **in the negative binomial case we consider the number of failures encountered on the way to the first r successes**).

Example 3.2.25. Baseball Hits. What is the probability that a "300 hitter" in the game of baseball (i.e., a person who has gotten a hit on the average in 300 of each 1000 trials, where each trial is called an "at-bat") will have his 3rd hit on his 5th time at bat in a given game (of course this may well be an extra-innings game, or else a high-scoring game, otherwise a single player might not have so many at-bats; the number of at-bats per game is at least 3, since there are at least 9 innings, each of which has 3 at-bats for each team).

If P(Making a hit on an at-bat) $= .300 = p$ is constant over trials and trials are independent, then the probability function of the number X of times at bat needed to get the third hit, minus 3, is negative binomial. Hence,

P(3rd hit is on 5th at-bat)

$= P(X + 3 = 5$ at-bats are needed to obtain $r = 3$ hits)

$= P(X = 2)$

$= p^3\left(\begin{array}{c} 4 \\ 2 \end{array}\right) q^2 = \left(\begin{array}{c} 4 \\ 2 \end{array}\right)(.3)^3(.7)^2 = .07938.$

[*Note*: This can also be reasoned to directly, as it is the probability of exactly 2 hits in the first 4 at-bats,

$$\left(\begin{array}{c} 4 \\ 2 \end{array}\right) p^2(1 - p)^2,$$

multiplied by the probability of a hit on the 5th at-bat (which is then the third hit).]

PROBLEMS FOR SECTION 3.2

3.2.1 A fair six-sided die is rolled until an even number of dots shows. Compute the probability that
(a) Five rolls are needed.
(b) Fewer than 3 rolls are needed.
(c) An even number of rolls is needed.

3.2.2 A certain college committee has 10 members, of whom 5 are seniors, 3 are juniors, 1 is a sophomore, and 1 is a freshman. A subcommittee of 4 is to be chosen. Let X be the r.v. denoting the number of seniors on the subcommittee and Y be the number of juniors on the subcommittee. Assuming subcommittee members are chosen at random, find the probability function of: (a) X; (b) Y.

3.2.3 If X has a Poisson distribution with parameter $\lambda > 0$, and $P(X = 1) = P(X = 2)$, find (a) $P(X < 3)$; (b) $P(2 \le X < 5)$; (c) $P(X \ge 6)$; (d) $P(1 \le X \le 4)$.

3.2.4 A breakfast cereal company claims its boxes contain 16 ounces of cereal. However, it is highly improbable for each of the boxes to have a content of *exactly* 16 ounces, so the company fills to "a little more" than 16 ounces to avoid possible legal problems. A consumer protection agency estimates that 10% of the boxes contain less than 16 ounces of cereal. Suppose they are correct. Then if we sample 20 boxes of cereal at random, compute the probability that
(a) At most 6 boxes will have less than 16 ounces.
(b) At least 3 boxes will have less than 16 ounces.
(c) At least 4, but no more than 8, boxes will contain less than 16 ounces of cereal.

3.2.5 It has been observed that a certain secretary makes 2 mistakes per page on the average when doing mathematical typing. Assume the number of mistakes made by the secretary is a Poisson r.v. with parameter $\lambda = 2$. If the secretary types 10 pages of a mathematical manuscript, what is the probability that
(a) Exactly 4 pages will have 2 mistakes.
(b) At least 3 pages will have 2 mistakes.
(c) At most 6 pages will have 2 mistakes.
(d) There are no mistakes in the typing.

3.2.6 At a certain intersection in a given city there are on the average 8 reported automobile accidents per year. Assuming that the Poisson model is appropriate, compute the probability that
(a) There will be 4 accidents in a given quarter.
(b) Four months will pass without any accidents.

3.2.7 Telephone calls come in at a reception desk very frequently, and it has been estimated that between the hours of 9:00 A.M. and 10:00 A.M. (the busiest hour in this office) on the average 5 calls are missed per day. Assuming that the number X of calls missed is a Poisson r.v. with parameter $\lambda = 5$, what is the probability that
(a) In a given week (Monday through Friday) no calls will be missed.
(b) Exactly 1 call will be missed on Monday and 3 calls will be missed on Thursday.
(c) Between 2 and 8 (both inclusive) calls will be missed on Friday.
(d) 1 call on Monday, 2 on Tuesday, 3 on Wednesday, 4 on Thursday, and 5 on Friday will be missed.

3.2.8 In an interview process seeking many workers for a new plant, job candidates are interviewed. Suppose each has the same chance of being selected for being hired, namely $p = .3$. Then

(a) Let X be the number of candidates interviewed before the first offer is made. Find the probability function and distribution function of X.

(b) What is the probability that the first offer will be made to the eighth candidate?

(c) What is the probability that the fourth offer will be made to the ninth candidate?

3.2.9 A certain basketball player has an 80% free-throw percentage. Assume independence from shot to shot. If in a game this player attempts 16 free throws, what is the probability that

(a) The player makes all the shots.

(b) The player makes exactly 13 shots.

(c) The tenth successful shot comes on the 14th try.

(d) The first successful shot comes on the 9th try.

(e) The player does not make any shots.

(f) The player makes at least 8 shots.

3.2.10 A company claims that its chocolate chip cookies have on the average 16 chocolate chips in each cookie. Assuming that a Poisson r.v. with $\lambda = 16$ is the appropriate probability model for the number of chips in a cookie, compute the following:

(a) If we sample 3 cookies at random, the probability that these will contain exactly 10, 12, and 15 chips.

(b) The probability that a cookie sampled at random will have fewer than 16 chips.

(c) The probability that a cookie will have at most 4 chips.

(d) The probability that a cookie will contain between 8 and 12 chips (both inclusive).

3.3. RELATIONS AMONG CERTAIN DISCRETE DISTRIBUTIONS

We will now show that certain of the distributions already discussed "tend to" (in senses yet to be specified) certain others as indicated in the diagram of Figure 3.3-1.

Bernoulli → Binomial. Suppose that $X_1, \ldots, X_n$ are r.v.'s with the common

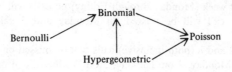

Figure 3.3-1.

Bernoulli distribution (for some p, $0 \le p \le 1$)

$$P[X_i = x] = p_{X_i}(x) = \begin{cases} p^x(1-p)^{1-x}, & x = 0,1 \\ 0, & \text{otherwise,} \end{cases}$$

and that they are based on independent events. Let $Y = X_1 + \cdots + X_n$. Then the distribution of Y is[6]

$$P[Y = y] = p_Y(y) = \begin{cases} \binom{n}{y}p^y(1-p)^{n-y}, & y = 0,1,\ldots,n \\ 0, & \text{otherwise;} \end{cases}$$

that is, Y is binomial with parameters n and p. (Intuitively, the number of successes in n trials is a sum, in which we count 1 for success and 0 for failure on each of the trials.)

Binomial $\rightarrow$ Poisson. Suppose that X is binomial with parameters n and p (i.e., for example, the number of successes in n trials taken independently with probability of success p, $0 \le p \le 1$, on each). Then X is approximately Poisson with $\lambda = np$. (The word "approximately" will be clarified in the derivation.)
 Fix $k = 0,1,2,\ldots$ and $\lambda > 0$. Then since

$$\lim_{n \to \infty} \left(1 + \frac{a}{n}\right)^n = e^a,$$

so that

$$\lim_{n \to \infty} \left(1 + \frac{-\lambda}{n}\right)^n = e^{-\lambda},$$

$$\lim_{n \to \infty} \binom{n}{k}\left(\frac{\lambda}{n}\right)^k\left(1 - \frac{\lambda}{n}\right)^{n-k}$$

$$= \lim_{n \to \infty} \frac{1}{k!}\lambda^k\left(1 - \frac{\lambda}{n}\right)^{n-k}\frac{n(n-1)\ldots(n-k+1)}{n^k} = e^{-\lambda}\frac{\lambda^k}{k!}.$$

Since this holds as a limit, it is true that for large n (and thus small p, so that $\lambda = np$ is moderate)

$$\binom{n}{k}p^k(1-p)^{n-k} \approx e^{-np}\frac{(np)^k}{k!}.$$

Hypergeometric $\rightarrow$ Binomial. A population of N objects contains a of type A. A random sample of size n is drawn without replacement. ($1 \le n \le N$, $0 \le a \le N$.) Let X be the number of type A in the sample, so that for $x = \max[0, n - (N$

---

[6]See Example 3.2.5.

$- a)], \dots, \min(n, a)$ we have (letting $p = a/N$, the proportion of items of type A in the original population)

$$P_X(x) = \frac{\binom{a}{x}\binom{N-a}{n-x}}{\binom{N}{n}} = \frac{a!}{x!(a-x)!}\frac{(N-a)!}{(n-x)!(N-a-n+x)!}\frac{n!(N-n)!}{N!}$$

$$= \binom{n}{x}a(a-1)\dots(a-x+1)$$

$$\cdot \frac{(N-a)(N-a-1)\dots(N-a-n+x+1)}{N(N-1)\dots(N-n+1)}$$

$$= \binom{n}{x}\frac{a^x}{N^n}(N-a)^{n-x}1\left(1-\frac{1}{a}\right)\cdots\left(1-\frac{x-1}{a}\right)$$

$$\cdot \frac{1\left(1-\frac{1}{N-a}\right)\cdots\left(1-\frac{n-x-1}{N-a}\right)}{1\left(1-\frac{1}{N}\right)\cdots\left(1-\frac{n-1}{N}\right)}$$

$$= \binom{n}{x}p^x(1-p)^{n-x}\left(1-\frac{1}{a}\right)\left(1-\frac{2}{a}\right)\cdots\left(1-\frac{x-1}{a}\right)$$

$$\cdot \frac{\left(1-\frac{1}{N-a}\right)\left(1-\frac{2}{N-a}\right)\cdots\left(1-\frac{n-x-1}{N-a}\right)}{\left(1-\frac{1}{N}\right)\left(1-\frac{2}{N}\right)\cdots\left(1-\frac{n-1}{N}\right)}.$$

Thus, it is clear that if

$$\frac{x}{a}, \qquad \frac{n-x}{N-a}, \qquad \frac{n}{N}$$

are small (say, $\leq .1$), then the probability that $X = x$ is approximately the same in sampling without replacement as it is in sampling with replacement. $\left(\frac{n}{N}, \frac{n-x}{N-a}, \frac{x}{a}\right.$ are, respectively, the proportion of the population that we sample, the proportion that the non-type A items in the sample are of the total non-type A items in the population, and the proportion that the type A items in the sample are of the total type A items in the population.)

Hypergeometric → Poisson. If $\frac{n}{N}, \frac{x}{a}, \frac{n-x}{N-a}$ are small and $\lambda = np = n\frac{a}{N}$ is moderate while n is large, then the above results imply

$$\text{Hypergeometric} \to \text{Binomial} \to \text{Poisson}.$$

This is easy to verify directly also.

Further results along these lines are noted in Feller (1968, vol. 1).

Example 3.3.1. Suppose that a certain small fixed volume of blood contains, on the average, 20 red blood cells for normal people. If a specimen of blood of this volume is taken from a normal person, what is the probability that it will contain fewer than 15 red cells? (By thus examining a blood specimen under a microscope, red blood cell deficiency can be determined.)

Suppose that N blood cells (red) are distributed at random in a volume of blood V, and that the small sample volume is D. Then, for $x = 0, \ldots, N$,

$$P[\text{Number in volume } D, \text{ say } X, = x] = \binom{N}{x}\left(\frac{D}{V}\right)^x\left(1 - \frac{D}{V}\right)^{N-x}$$

$$\approx e^{-\lambda}\frac{\lambda^x}{x!}$$

with $\lambda = Np = N\frac{D}{V} = 20$ (for "large" N). So,

$$P[X < 15] \approx \sum_{x=0}^{14} e^{-20}\frac{20^x}{x!} = .105.$$

Probabilities such as this can be found in many sources, for example, see Arkin and Colton (1963), pp. 129–139. See also Table 7. Note that in our example, since N and V are unknown, the exact binomial probability *cannot* be calculated.

PROBLEMS FOR SECTION 3.3

3.3.1 Let $X \sim B$ (1000, .001) (see note preceding Example 3.2.5 for this notation). Compute the probabilities **(a)** $P(X = 4)$; **(b)** $P(0 < X \le 5)$; **(c)** $P(X \ge 3)$; **(d)** $P(X \le 3)$.

3.3.2 A student takes 5 courses in a semester. For this student a "success" (S) in a course means obtaining a grade of A or B. Based on previous experience, the student estimates that $P(S) = .80$. Find the probability that
(a) The student will have exactly 4 successes this semester.
(b) The student will have at least 3 successes.
(c) The student has at most 4 successes.

3.3.3 In a population of 1000 light bulbs, it is known that there are 50 defective bulbs. 25 bulbs are chosen at random for testing. If at most 3 of the sampled bulbs are defective, we accept the lot. Use the binomial approximation to the hypergeometric to compute the probability of acceptance.

3.3.4 The probability that a certain computer will need service in a given week is .0025. Find the probability that this computer will need service
(a) Exactly once in the next 5 years.
(b) Exactly zero times in the next 5 years.
(c) At most twice in the next 5 years.
(d) Exactly once in 1 year.

3.3.5 In a large university, based on past experience, in any given semester 0.1% of the grades are erroneously reported. Suppose a student takes 40 courses as an undergraduate, and that the erroneous reports are spread at random over all grades reported (and are not, e.g., all due to one professor in a large course). Find the probability that
(a) None of this student's grades are erroneously reported.
(b) Exactly one of the student's grades is erroneously reported.

3.4. MULTIVARIATE DISTRIBUTIONS; INDEPENDENCE

In Sections 3.1 through 3.3 we studied r.v.'s X that could arise as follows. You go to a casino with \$100 and, following a predetermined strategy, bet on roulette until your strategy tells you to stop. Then a typical outcome $\omega \in \Omega$ would describe each outcome of each play, of which there could easily be hundreds. However, your only interest might be your winnings when outcomes specified by ω occurred [which is a function of ω, say $X_1(\omega)$]; this is a one-dimensional r.v.

In other instances, your interests might include not only $X_1(\omega)$ = winnings, but also $X_2(\omega)$ = number of plays completed before stopping. Our interest in this situation is in a r.v. $X(\omega) = (X_1(\omega), X_2(\omega))$ which for each outcome $\omega \in \Omega$ specifies two real numbers $X_1(\omega)$ and $X_2(\omega)$ (winnings and time to completion).[7] If we ask "What is the probability our winnings are at most \$1000 and we play at most 5000 plays," we desire $P[X_1 \leq 1000, X_2 \leq 5000]$; this is exactly the sort of information provided by a d.f. A d.f. for these situations is formally defined in Definition 3.4.1 (previously we only considered this concept for one r.v., in Definition 3.1.2).

Definition 3.4.1. If $X = (X_1, \ldots, X_n)$ is an n-dimensional r.v. ($n \geq 1$), its (joint) **distribution function** is defined by

$$F_X(x_1, \ldots, x_n) = P[X_1 \leq x_1, \ldots, X_n \leq x_n]$$

for $-\infty < x_i < +\infty$ ($i = 1, \ldots, n$). (This extends Definition 3.1.2 to the case of n-dimensional random variables.)

If we have an n-dimensional r.v. [such as (X_1, X_2, X_3) when $n = 3$], we are often interested in the distribution of a subset of the n variables [such as (X_1, X_3)]. This is called the **marginal distribution function** and can be easily obtained from the d.f. of the n-dimensional r.v., as in Lemma 3.4.3.

Definition 3.4.2. The joint distribution of any subset of the random variables $X_1, \ldots, X_n$ is called a **marginal distribution function** [of $F_{X_1, \ldots, X_n}(x_1, \ldots, x_n)$]. [For example, $F_{X_1, \ldots, X_{n-1}}(x_1, \ldots, x_{n-1})$ is a marginal d.f.]

---

[7]Some instructors may wish to carry this example through the section (perhaps generalizing it) to illustrate the various concepts. We have not done so in order not to obscure the development in a cloud of examples.

Lemma 3.4.3. If $X = (X_1, \ldots, X_n)$ is a vector r.v., then (for $n \geq 2$)

$$\lim_{x_n \to \infty} F_{X_1, \ldots, X_n}(x_1, \ldots, x_n) = F_{X_1, \ldots, X_{n-1}}(x_1, \ldots, x_{n-1}).$$

In Theorem 3.1.3 we saw some key properties of a one-dimensional d.f., and any function with those properties is a d.f. of some r.v. (that is the result of Theorem 3.1.5). Similar properties are true for n-dimensional d.f.'s [(i), (ii), and (iii) in Theorem 3.4.4, which follows]. However, those properties do *not* characterize n-dimensional d.f.'s: **There are (Problem 3.5H) n-dimensional functions satisfying (i), (ii), and (iii) of Theorem 3.4.4 that are *not* d.f.'s.** Therefore, in Theorem 3.4.4 we also show a property **(iv)**; in conjunction with the other 3 properties, **property (iv) guarantees that a function that has all these properties is a d.f. (Theorem 3.4.5).** Note that property **(iv)** states that the probability assigned to any n-dimensional rectangle (or *cell*) by the n-dimensional d.f. is ≥ 0.

Theorem 3.4.4* If $X = (X_1, \ldots, X_n)$ is an n-dimensional r.v., then

(i) $\lim_{\min x_i \to +\infty} F_X(x_1, \ldots, x_n) = 1.$

(ii) For each i ($1 \leq i \leq n$) $\lim_{x_i \to -\infty} F_X(x_1, \ldots, x_n) = 0.$

(iii) $F_X(x_1, \ldots, x_n)$ is continuous from above in each argument.

(iv) For each **cell (a, b]** $= \{ x = (x_1, \ldots, x_n): a_i < x_i \leq b_i, 1 \leq i \leq n \}$ in $\mathscr{R}^n$, letting $\Delta_{k,n}$ denote the set of $\binom{n}{k}$ n-tuples $(z_1, \ldots, z_n)$ where each z_i is a_i or b_i and such that exactly k of the z_i's are a_i's,

$$\sum_{k=0}^{n} (-1)^k \sum_{\delta \in \Delta_{k,n}} F_X(\delta) \geq 0.$$

We will, as in Section 3.1, not prove these or most other results.

[*Note:* $\Delta \equiv \bigcup_{k=0}^{n} \Delta_{k,n}$ is the set of the 2^n vertices of the cell **(a, b]** in $\mathscr{R}^n$. Also, examine the result of Theorem 3.4.4 in the cases $n = 1$ and $n = 2$ to see especially what **(iv)** means; it is the generalization of Theorem 3.1.3 needed for n-dimensions in order that Theorem 3.4.5 hold.]

Theorem 3.4.5. If a real-valued function F on $\mathscr{R}^n$ satisfies **(i)–(iv)** of Theorem 3.4.4, then there exists a sample space Ω with a probability function $P(\cdot)$, and r.v.'s $X_1, \ldots, X_n$ such that

$$F_{X_1, \ldots, X_n}(x_1, \ldots, x_n) = F(x_1, \ldots, x_n).$$

Up to this point, our results in this section *have been completely general* (in particular, not restricted to the discrete case) and also generalizations of results of Section 3.1 to n-dimensional r.v.'s. We will continue this, introducing *conditional d.f.'s* and *independent r.v.'s*; these will of course also have meaning for the

---

*May be omitted, if instructor desires, without loss of continuity.

one-dimensional case, but it seems most natural to introduce them at this point (rather than essentially twice).

Definition 3.4.6. The **conditional d.f.** of $X = (X_1, \ldots, X_n)$ given that $X \in G$, G some set in $\mathcal{R}^n$ (i.e., given that X lies in a specified subset G of n-space $\mathcal{R}^n$), is defined for $P(G) > 0$ as

$$F_{X|G}(x|G) = \frac{P[X_1 \le x_1, \ldots, X_n \le x_n; X \in G]}{P[X \in G]}.$$

[It may be verified that $F_{X|G}(x|G)$ is a d.f.]

Consider the case $X = (X_1, X_2)$, and let G be the set in $\mathcal{R}^2$ where $x_1'' < x_1 \le x_1'$ with $P(G) > 0$. Then $F_{X_1, X_2|G}(x_1, x_2|G) = P[X_1 \le x_1, X_2 \le x_2, X \in G] / P[X \in G]$, and

$$F_{X_1, X_2|G}(x_1', x_2|G) = \frac{P[X_1 \le x_1', X_2 \le x_2, x_1'' < X_1 \le x_1']}{P[x_1'' < X_1 \le x_1']}$$

$$= \frac{F_{X_1, X_2}(x_1', x_2) - F_{X_1, X_2}(x_1'', x_2)}{F_{X_1}(x_1') - F_{X_1}(x_1'')}.$$

Note that $F_{X_1, X_2|G}(x_1', x_2|G)$ is (show this) a d.f. as a function of x_2. If the limit exists as $x_1'' \to x_1'$, let

$$F_{X_2|X_1 = x_1'}(x_2|x_1') \equiv \lim_{x_1'' \to x_1'} F_{X_1, X_2|G}(x_1', x_2|G).$$

If $F_{X_2|X_1 = x_1'}(x_2|x_1')$ exists for every x_2, it can be shown that it is a d.f. as a function of x_2. It is called the **conditional d.f. of X_2 given $X_1 = x_1'$**.

Independence was a key concept for events. We now define the concept of **independence for r.v.'s**, relate it to independence of events, and give a key result (Lemma 3.4.9) used in determining independence. Then illustration of the concepts of this section thus far is made in Example 3.4.10.

Definition 3.4.7. Let $\{X_\lambda: \lambda \in \Lambda\}$ be a family of r.v.'s. They are said to be **independent** if for every integer $n \ge 1$ and every n distinct $\lambda_1, \ldots, \lambda_n \in \Lambda$,

$$F_{X_{\lambda_1}, \ldots, X_{\lambda_n}}(x_1, \ldots, x_n) = \prod_{j=1}^{n} F_{X_{\lambda_j}}(x_j) \qquad \text{all } x \in \mathcal{R}^n.$$

Suppose we have a sample space Ω and r.v.'s $X_1, X_2, \ldots, X_n$. Then $A_1, A_2, \ldots, A_n$ defined by

$$A_i = \{\omega: \omega \in \Omega, X_i(\omega) \le x_i\}$$

are events (i.e. is, subsets of Ω); for example A_2 is the event that $X_2 \le x_2$.

Previously (Section 2.4) we called $A_1, A_2, \ldots, A_n$ *independent* events iff

$$P(A_1 A_2 \cdots A_n) = P(A_1) P(A_2) \cdots P(A_n)$$

$$\vdots$$

$$P(A_1 A_2) = P(A_1) P(A_2).$$

This was a reasonable definition intuitively in terms of conditional probability and of positive and negative information. In Definition 3.4.7 we have defined independence of r.v.'s $X_1, \ldots, X_n$ as meaning that (for all $x_1, x_2, \ldots, x_n$) the events $A_1, A_2, \ldots, A_n$ are independent. (This is the case where $\Lambda = \{1, 2, \ldots, n\}$; our definition covered much more complex situations also; e.g., $\Lambda = \{1, 2, 3, \ldots\}$, which corresponds to a definition of independence of $X_1, X_2, X_3, \ldots$.) Note that **if r.v.'s are independent, their joint (multivariate) d.f. may be trivially obtained from their individual (univariate) d.f.'s.** However, often (for instance, in the example of X_1 = winnings, X_2 = number of plays, discussed at the beginning of this section) we have nonindependent r.v.'s.

Lemma 3.4.8. The r.v.'s $\{X_\lambda : \lambda \in \Lambda\}$ are independent iff those of every finite subset are independent.

Lemma 3.4.9. $X_1, \ldots, X_n$ are independent iff $F_{X_1, \ldots, X_n}(x_1, \ldots, x_n)$ $= \prod_{j=1}^{n} F_{X_j}(x_j)$, all $x \in \mathscr{R}^n$. (By our results on marginal d.f.'s, this follows directly; there is no need to check for subsets.)

Example 3.4.10. Statistical Analysis of Employment Discrimination Data. One example where multivariate r.v.'s are of common interest today is in the area of statistical analysis of employment discrimination data. Here one typically has available a set of data such as the following[8]:

	Percentage Promoted	
Pay Grade	Affected Class	Others
5	100(6)	84(80)
7	88(8)	87(195)
9	93(29)	88(335)
10	7(102)	8(695)
11	7(15)	11(185)
12	10(10)	7(165)
13	0(2)	9(81)
14	0(1)	7(41)

For a certain occupation within a certain company, this data specifies the pay grade and, within each pay grade, the percentage of employees who were

[8] This data is taken from Table 8 of Dawson, Hankey and Myers (1982).

promoted within the "affected class" (which might be a certain minority group, or a group such as women) and within "others." The question that such studies address is, "Does this data indicate discrimination against the affected class in promotions in this occupation in this company (or has such promotion been without regard to membership in the affected class)?"

To model this statistically, we need to deal with what is a random variable with three components, $X = (X_1, X_2, X_3)$, where X_1 is the pay grade of an employee in this occupation in this company and can have values $5, 7, 9, 10, 11, 12, 13, 14$; X_2 is an indicator of whether the employee is in the affected class or not and can have values $1, 0$; and X_3 is an indicator of whether the employee was promoted or not and can also have values $1, 0$. We will return to this example later in this chapter, and at that time will need to know not just the percentages, but also how many employees are in each "cell" of the table; those are given in parentheses. Thus, in pay grade 10 of this occupation ($X_1 = 10$) there were 102 members of the affected class and 695 members of other classes. Seven percent of the affected class in pay grade 10 had been promoted, that is $(102)(.07) = 7$ individuals out of the 102 had been promoted in the time period in question. Note that out of the 1950 employees, only 173 are in the affected class; this is not atypical in such studies.

If one selects an employee at random from the 1950 employees, then one can evaluate probabilities such as

$$P(X_1 = 10, X_2 = 1, X_3 = 1) = 7/1950 = .0036.$$

This is true since all employees are equally likely to be drawn, and of the total number of 1950 employees, there are 7 who are in pay grade 10 ($X_1 = 10$) who are in the affected class ($X_2 = 1$) and who were promoted ($X_3 = 1$). This is the basis for the **probability function of a discrete n = 3-dimensional r.v.** in Definition 3.4.12.

We can also evaluate the probability

$$P(X_1 = 10, X_3 = 1) = (7 + 56)/1950 = 63/1950 = .0323.$$

This is true since there are 63 employees in pay grade 10 ($X_1 = 10$) who were promoted ($X_3 = 1$): 7 in the affected class (7% of 102) and 56 in the others (8% of 695). This is the basis for the **marginal probability function** of X_1 and X_3 in Definition 3.4.14 below.

Conditional probabilities, such as the probability that an employee is in the other class ($X_2 = 0$) given that the employee is in pay grade 10 ($X_1 = 10$) and was promoted ($X_3 = 1$), can also be calculated:

$$P(X_2 = 0 | X_1 = 10, X_3 = 1) = \frac{P(X_1 = 10, X_2 = 0, X_3 = 1)}{P(X_1 = 10, X_3 = 1)}$$

$$= \frac{56/1950}{63/1950} = \frac{56}{63} = .89.$$

Here we have used the notion of conditional probability $P(A|B)$ to compute the desired probability as $P(AB)$ divided by $P(B)$. The numerator probability $P(AB)$ follows since 56 of the 1950 employees have the characteristics specified by $X_1 = 10$ (pay grade 10), $X_2 = 0$ (other class), and $X_3 = 1$ (were promoted); similarly for the denominator (where both those in the affected class and the other class are counted as X_2 is not specified, i.e., may have either value). This is the basis for the **conditional probability function** in Definition 3.4.16 below.

We now consider the discrete case. Definitions 3.4.11 and 3.4.12 are generalizations of Definitions 3.1.6 and 3.1.7, while the other concepts are first introduced now. (Here $i_1, \ldots, i_t$, e.g., are some $t \geq 1$ of the numbers $1, \ldots, n$. Similarly, for $i_{t+1}, \ldots, i_s$.)

Definition 3.4.11. $(X_1, \ldots, X_n)$ is called a **discrete n-dimensional r.v.** if it assumes as values only a finite or denumerable number of points $(x_1, \ldots, x_n)$ in $\mathscr{R}^n$.

Definition 3.4.12. The **probability function** of a discrete n-dimensional r.v. X that assumes values $x_1, x_2, \ldots$ is $p(x_1), p(x_2), \ldots$ where $p(x_i) = P[X = x_i]$ $(i = 1, 2, \ldots)$. [Of course $P[X = y] = 0$ unless $y \in \{x_1, x_2, \ldots\}$.]

Example 3.4.13. Suppose that (X_1, X_2) is a discrete r.v. such that the point $(1, 2)$ occurs with probability $1/8$, $(1, 3)$ occurs with probability $3/8$, $(2, 3)$ occurs with probability $1/4$, and $(3, 1)$ occurs with probability $1/4$. Then (X_1, X_2) assumes as values only one of the four points in the set of values $\{(1, 2), (1, 3), (2, 3), (3, 1)\}$, and is thus (by Definition 3.4.11) a discrete r.v. in two dimensions (since the points are 2-tuples). The probability function of (X_1, X_2) is

$$p((1, 2)) = 1/8, \ p((1, 3)) = 3/8, \ p((2, 3)) = 1/4, \ p((3, 1)) = 1/4$$

with $p((x_1, x_2)) = 0$ for all other pairs of numbers (x_1, x_2).

Just as we were interested in the d.f. of a subset of the variables in an n-dimensional r.v. at Definition 3.4.2, we are interested in the probability function of a subset of the variables in the discrete case.

Definition 3.4.14. The **marginal probability function** of $X_{i_1}, \ldots, X_{i_t}$ is the name given to [for $i_l \neq i_k (l \neq k)$]

$$P\left[X_{i_1} = x_{i_1}, \ldots, X_{i_t} = x_{i_t}\right] = \sum_{x_{i_{t+1}}, \ldots, x_{i_n}} P[X_1 = x_1, \ldots, X_n = x_n].$$

Example 3.4.15. In Example 3.4.13, we dealt with a two-dimensional r.v. (X_1, X_2) and found its probability function. The marginal probability functions are those of X_1, and of X_2. From Definition 3.4.14 (motivated by the Theorem of

Total Probabilities) we find these as

$$P(X_1 = 1) = p((1,2)) + p((1,3)) = 1/8 + 3/8 = 4/8 = 0.5,$$

$$P(X_1 = 2) = p((2,3)) = 1/4 = 0.25,$$

$$P(X_1 = 3) = p((3,1)) = 1/4 = 0.25,$$

$$P(X_1 = x_1) = 0 \text{ for all other } x_1;$$

and

$$P(X_2 = 1) = p((3,1)) = 1/4 = 0.25,$$

$$P(X_2 = 2) = p((1,2)) = 1/8 = 0.125,$$

$$P(X_2 = 3) = p((1,3)) + p((2,3)) = 3/8 + 2/8 = 5/8 = 0.625,$$

$$P(X_2 = x_2) = 0 \text{ for all other } x_2.$$

As we defined a conditional d.f. in and following Definition 3.4.6, we now define a conditional probability function in the discrete case. The interpretation and motivation is that, for example, in the case $n = 2$, this represents such items as $P(X_2 = x_2 | X_1 = x_1)$. Although in itself this probability is little new, as a function of x_2 it is a probability function, called the **conditional probability function** of X_2 given that $X_1 = x_1$.

Definition 3.4.16. The **conditional probability function** of $X_{i_1}, \ldots, X_{i_t}$ given $X_{i_{t+1}} = x_{i_{t+1}}, \ldots, X_{i_s} = x_{i_s}$ is, if $P[X_{i_{t+1}} = x_{i_{t+1}}, \ldots, X_{i_s} = x_{i_s}] > 0$ (for disjoint sets of variables)

$$P\left[X_{i_1} = x_{i_1}, \ldots, X_{i_t} = x_{i_t} | X_{i_{t+1}} = x_{i_{t+1}}, \ldots, X_{i_s} = x_{i_s}\right]$$

$$= \frac{P\left[X_{i_1} = x_{i_1}, \ldots, X_{i_t} = x_{i_t}, X_{i_{t+1}} = x_{i_{t+1}}, \ldots, X_{i_s} = x_{i_s}\right]}{P\left[X_{i_{t+1}} = x_{i_{t+1}}, \ldots, X_{i_s} = x_{i_s}\right]}.$$

Example 3.4.17. In Examples 3.4.13 and 3.4.15 we dealt with a two-dimensional r.v. (X_1, X_2) and its probability function and marginal probability functions. We will now find the conditional probability function of X_2 given $X_1 = 1$. Here,

$$P(X_2 = x_2 | X_1 = 1) = 0 \qquad \text{except for } x_2 = 2, 3.$$

Thus,

$$P(X_2 = 2 | X_1 = 1) = \frac{P(X_2 = 2, X_1 = 1)}{P(X_1 = 1)} = \frac{1/8}{1/2} = 1/4,$$

$$P(X_2 = 3 | X_1 = 1) = \frac{P(X_2 = 3, X_1 = 1)}{P(X_1 = 1)} = \frac{3/8}{1/2} = 3/4,$$

$$P(X_2 = x_2 | X_1 = 1) = 0 \qquad \text{if } x_2 \neq 2, 3.$$

Note that $\sum_{x_2} P(X_2 = x_2 | X_1 = 1) = 1/4 + 3/4 = 1$.

As we had a **simple criterion for independence** of the r.v.'s $X_1, X_2, \ldots, X_n$ in terms of their n-dimensional d.f. in Lemma 3.4.9, so we have a similar simple criterion in terms of the probability function in the discrete case.

Theorem 3.4.18. The discrete r.v.'s $X_1, \ldots, X_n$ are independent iff (for all $x_1, \ldots, x_n$)

$$p_{X_1, \ldots, X_n}(x_1, \ldots, x_n) = p_{X_1}(x_1) \ldots p_{X_n}(x_n).$$

Proof: First suppose that (for all $x_1, \ldots, x_n$)

$$p_{X_1, \ldots, X_n}(x_1, \ldots, x_n) = p_{X_1}(x_1) \ldots p_{X_n}(x_n).$$

Then for any $y_1, \ldots, y_n$ $(-\infty < y_1, \ldots, y_n < +\infty)$

$$F_{X_1, \ldots, X_n}(y_1, \ldots, y_n) = \sum_{x_1 \leq y_1} \cdots \sum_{x_n \leq y_n} p_{X_1, \ldots, X_n}(x_1, \ldots, x_n)$$

$$= \sum_{x_1 \leq y_1} \cdots \sum_{x_n \leq y_n} p_{X_1}(x_1) \ldots p_{X_n}(x_n)$$

$$= \left(\sum_{x_1 \leq y_1} p_{X_1}(x_1) \right) \cdots \left(\sum_{x_n \leq y_n} p_{X_n}(x_n) \right)$$

$$= F_{X_1}(y_1) \ldots F_{X_n}(y_n),$$

and (by Lemma 3.4.9) $X_1, \ldots, X_n$ are independent r.v.'s.

Second, suppose that $X_1, \ldots, X_n$ are independent discrete r.v.'s. Consider first the case $n = 2$. Then (for all x_1, x_2)

$$p_{X_1, X_2}(x_1, x_2)$$

$$= \lim_{\delta \downarrow 0} P[x_1 - \delta < X_1 \le x_1, x_2 - \delta < X_2 \le x_2]$$

$$= \lim_{\delta \downarrow 0} \{ P[X_1 \le x_1, X_2 \le x_2] - P[X_1 \le x_1 - \delta, X_2 \le x_2]$$

$$\qquad - P[X_1 \le x_1, X_2 \le x_2 - \delta] + P[X_1 \le x_1 - \delta, X_2 \le x_2 - \delta] \}$$

$$= \lim_{\delta \downarrow 0} \{ F_{X_1}(x_1) F_{X_2}(x_2) - F_{X_1}(x_1 - \delta) F_{X_2}(x_2)$$

$$\qquad - F_{X_1}(x_1) F_{X_2}(x_2 - \delta) + F_{X_1}(x_1 - \delta) F_{X_2}(x_2 - \delta) \}$$

$$= F_{X_1}(x_1) F_{X_2}(x_2) - P[X_1 < x_1] F_{X_2}(x_2) - F_{X_1}(x_1) P[X_2 < x_2]$$

$$\qquad + P[X_1 < x_1] P[X_2 < x_2]$$

$$= F_{X_2}(x_2) \big(F_{X_1}(x_1) - P[X_1 < x_1] \big)$$

$$\qquad - P[X_2 < x_2] \big(F_{X_1}(x_1) - P[X_1 < x_1] \big)$$

$$= F_{X_2}(x_2) p_{X_1}(x_1) - P[X_2 < x_2] p_{X_1}(x_1)$$

$$= p_{X_1}(x_1) \big(F_{X_2}(x_2) - P[X_2 < x_2] \big)$$

$$= p_{X_1}(x_1) p_{X_2}(x_2),$$

which proves the desired result. The general case follows easily by induction. ∎

Example 3.4.19. Continuing Example 3.4.17, we now ask whether X_1 and X_2 are independent r.v.'s. We know (by Theorem 3.4.18) that this will be true if and only if

$$p_{X_1, X_2}(x_1, x_2) = p_{X_1}(x_1) p_{X_2}(x_2) \qquad \text{for all } x_1, x_2.$$

Checking, we know that all the terms above are zero unless x_1 is one of 1, 2, 3 and x_2 is one of 1, 2, 3. Thus, the equality will be true for all (x_1, x_2) where either fails to be one of the numbers 1, 2, 3 (in which case both sides will be zero). So, we need only check $(3)(3) = 9$ more cases for equality; if all are equal, then X_1 and X_2 are independent r.v.'s, while if any one fails to be equal the r.v.'s are not independent. Starting the search, we find

$$p_{X_1, X_2}((1,1)) = 0$$

but

$$p_{X_1}(1) p_{X_2}(1) = (0.5)(0.25) = 0.125 \ne 0.$$

Hence equality does not hold for all (x_1, x_2), and X_1 and X_2 are not independent r.v.'s (and we need check no further; even if all the rest were equal, this one would mean independence could not be the case).

Example 3.4.20. Let X_1 and X_2 be two jointly discrete r.v.'s whose joint probability function is given by the following table:

$p_{X_1, X_2}(x_1, x_2)$		
x_2 \ x_1	-1	1
0	$\frac{1}{6}$	$\frac{1}{6}$
$.5$	$\frac{1}{3}$	$\frac{1}{3}$

Also, let Y_1 and Y_2 be two jointly discrete r.v.'s whose joint probability function is given by

$p_{Y_1, Y_2}(y_1, y_2)$		
y_2 \ y_1	-1	1
0	$\frac{1}{3}$	0
$.5$	$\frac{1}{6}$	$\frac{1}{2}$

Show that X_1 and Y_1 are identically distributed [i.e., $p_{X_1}(z) = p_{Y_1}(z)$ for all z], and that X_2 and Y_2 are identically distributed. Are the r.v.'s X_1 and X_2 independent? Are the r.v.'s Y_1 and Y_2 independent? Find the conditional probability function of Y_1 given $Y_2 = 0$. Find the conditional probability function of X_1 given $X_2 = 0$.

First (see Definition 3.4.14 of the marginal probability function),

$$p_{X_1}(-1) = p_{X_1, X_2}(-1, 0) + p_{X_1, X_2}(-1, .5) = \tfrac{1}{6} + \tfrac{1}{3} = \tfrac{1}{2},$$

$$p_{X_1}(1) = p_{X_1, X_2}(1, 0) + p_{X_1, X_2}(1, .5) = \tfrac{1}{6} + \tfrac{1}{3} = \tfrac{1}{2},$$

and

$$p_{Y_1}(-1) = p_{Y_1, Y_2}(-1, 0) + p_{Y_1, Y_2}(-1, .5) = \tfrac{1}{3} + \tfrac{1}{6} = \tfrac{1}{2},$$

$$p_{Y_1}(1) = p_{Y_1, Y_2}(1, 0) + p_{Y_1, Y_2}(1, .5) = 0 + \tfrac{1}{2} = \tfrac{1}{2},$$

so $p_{X_1}(z) = p_{Y_1}(z)$ for all z. Similarly, we find $p_{X_2}(0) = p_{Y_2}(0) = \tfrac{1}{3}$ and $p_{X_2}(.5) = p_{Y_2}(.5) = \tfrac{2}{3}$. Hence, X_2 and Y_2 (as well as X_1 and Y_1) are identically distributed.

X_1 and X_2 are independent (using the criterion of Theorem 3.4.18) since $p_{X_1, X_2}(x_1, x_2) = p_{X_1}(x_1) p_{X_2}(x_2)$ for all x_1, x_2. However, Y_1 and Y_2 are not independent since $p_{Y_1, Y_2}(y_1, y_2)$ does not equal $p_{Y_1}(y_1) p_{Y_2}(y_2)$ for all y_1, y_2; for example, $p_{Y_1, Y_2}(1, 0) = 0 \neq \tfrac{1}{2} \cdot \tfrac{1}{3} = p_{Y_1}(1) p_{Y_2}(0)$.

The conditional probability function of Y_1 given $Y_2 = 0$ (see Definition 3.4.16) is

$$P[Y_1 = -1 | Y_2 = 0] = \frac{P[Y_1 = -1, Y_2 = 0]}{P[Y_2 = 0]} = \frac{\frac{1}{3}}{\frac{1}{3}} = 1,$$

$$P[Y_1 = y | Y_2 = 0] = 0, \quad \text{if } y \neq -1.$$

The conditional probability function of X_1 given $X_2 = 0$ is

$$P[X_1 = -1 | X_2 = 0] = \frac{P[X_1 = -1, X_2 = 0]}{P[X_2 = 0]} = \frac{\frac{1}{6}}{\frac{2}{6}} = \frac{1}{2},$$

$$P[X_1 = 1 | X_2 = 0] = \frac{P[X_1 = 1, X_2 = 0]}{P[X_2 = 0]} = \frac{\frac{1}{6}}{\frac{2}{6}} = \frac{1}{2}.$$

This could be obtained directly since (by independence of X_1 and X_2) $P[X_1 = x_1 | X_2 = 0] = P[X_1 = x_1]$ for all x_1.

Example 3.4.21. Let (X_1, X_2, X_3) be a 3-dimensional r.v. with probability function

$$p_{X_1, X_2, X_3}(x_1, x_2, x_3) = \begin{cases} \dfrac{x_1 x_2 x_3}{72} & \text{if } x_1 = 1, 2; \, x_2 = 1, 2, 3; \, x_3 = 1, 3 \\ 0 & \text{otherwise.} \end{cases}$$

   (a) Find the marginal probability function of X_1; of X_2; of X_3.
   (b) Find the marginal probability function of (X_1, X_3).
   (c) Find the conditional probability function of $X_1 | X_2 = 2$, $X_3 = 1$ (i.e., of X_1 *given* that $X_2 = 2$ and $X_3 = 1$).
   (d) Find the conditional probability function of $X_1, X_3 | X_2 = 3$.
   (e) Are X_1 and X_3 independent?
   (f) Find $P(X_1 = X_2 = X_3)$.

Solutions to these problems follow from the definitions of the items needed to be calculated, which are motivated by such results as the Theorem of Total Probabilities (Theorem 2.3.7).
(a) By Definition 3.4.14, we desire to find $p_{X_1}(x_1) = P(X_1 = x_1)$. Since we know $p_{X_1, X_2, X_3}(x_1, x_2, x_3) = P(X_1 = x_1, X_2 = x_2, X_3 = x_3)$, it follows by the Theorem of Total Probabilities that (as was given in Definition 3.4.14)

$$p_{X_1}(x_1) = P(X_1 = x_1) = \sum_{x_2} \sum_{x_3} P(X_1 = x_1, X_2 = x_2, X_3 = x_3)$$

$$= \sum_{x_2} \sum_{x_3} p_{X_1, X_2, X_3}(x_1, x_2, x_3).$$

Now in the case that "matters" (i.e., when $x_1 = 1$ or 2... otherwise the probability being summed is zero), this equals

$$\sum_{x_3=1,3} \sum_{x_2=1}^{3} \frac{x_1 x_2 x_3}{72} = \frac{x_1}{72}\left(\sum_{x_3=1,3} \sum_{x_2=1}^{3} x_3 x_2\right) = \frac{x_1}{3},$$

hence

$$p_{X_1}(x_1) = \begin{cases} \dfrac{x_1}{3} & \text{if } x_1 = 1, 2 \\ 0 & \text{otherwise.} \end{cases}$$

Similarly,

$$p_{X_2}(x_2) = \begin{cases} \displaystyle\sum_{x_3=1,3} \sum_{x_1=1}^{2} \frac{x_1 x_2 x_3}{72}, & \text{if } x_2 = 1, 2, 3 \\ 0, & \text{otherwise} \end{cases}$$

$$= \begin{cases} \dfrac{x_2}{6}, & \text{if } x_2 = 1, 2, 3 \\ 0, & \text{otherwise,} \end{cases}$$

and

$$p_{X_3}(x_3) = \begin{cases} \dfrac{x_3}{4}, & \text{if } x_3 = 1, 3 \\ 0, & \text{otherwise.} \end{cases}$$

(b) In part (b) we desire to find the marginal probability function of (X_1, X_3), that is, $P(X_1 = x_1, X_3 = x_3)$, which is denoted $p_{X_1, X_3}(x_1, x_3)$. This follows as in part (a) from the Theorem of Total Probabilities as

$$p_{X_1, X_3}(x_1, x_3) = \begin{cases} \displaystyle\sum_{x_2=1}^{3} \frac{x_1 x_2 x_3}{72}, & \text{if } x_1 = 1, 2; \ x_3 = 1, 3 \\ 0, & \text{otherwise} \end{cases}$$

$$= \begin{cases} \dfrac{x_1 x_3}{12}, & \text{if } x_1 = 1, 2; \ x_3 = 1, 3 \\ 0, & \text{otherwise.} \end{cases}$$

(c) The conditional probability function is essentially a conditional probability, hence (now using a **new subscript notation for ease of reading the conditional probability function**)

$$p_{X_1|X_2=2, X_3=1}(1) = \frac{P(X_1 = 1, X_2 = 2, X_3 = 1)}{P(X_2 = 2, X_3 = 1)}$$

$$= \frac{1 \cdot 2 \cdot 1/72}{6/72} = \frac{1}{3}$$

where the numerator came from the probability function of (X_1, X_2, X_3), which was given in the problem statement, and the denominator is one of the values of the marginal probability function of (X_2, X_3), which is calculated as in part (b) [where we were dealing with the marginal probability function of (X_1, X_3)]. Now also

$$p_{X_1|X_2=2, X_3=1}(2) = \frac{P(X_1 = 2, X_2 = 2, X_3 = 1)}{P(X_2 = 2, X_3 = 1)}$$

$$= \frac{4/72}{6/72} = \frac{2}{3}.$$

At any x_1 other than 1 or 2, the numerator probability $P(X_1 = x_1, X_2 = 2, X_3 = 1) = 0$, so that combining these three parts we find the final answer

$$p_{X_1|X_2=2, X_3=1}(x_1) = \begin{cases} \frac{1}{3}, & \text{if } x_1 = 1 \\ \frac{2}{3}, & \text{if } x_1 = 2 \\ 0, & \text{otherwise.} \end{cases}$$

(d) Here note that the condition has probability $P(X_2 = 3) = 1/2$, hence

$$p_{X_1, X_3|X_2=3}(x_1, x_3) = \frac{P(X_1 = x_1, X_2 = 3, X_3 = x_3)}{P(X_2 = 3)}$$

$$= \frac{p_{X_1, X_2, X_3}(x_1, 3, x_3)}{1/2}$$

$$= \begin{cases} 2 \cdot \dfrac{x_1 3 x_3}{72}, & \text{if } x_1 = 1, 2; \ x_3 = 1, 3 \\ 0, & \text{otherwise} \end{cases}$$

$$= \begin{cases} \dfrac{x_1 x_3}{12}, & \text{if } x_1 = 1, 2; \ x_3 = 1, 3 \\ 0, & \text{otherwise.} \end{cases}$$

(e) From Theorem 3.4.18, we know that for discrete random variables (those that have probability functions), independence may be checked using the probability functions (we need not use the distribution functions, which are not usually given for discrete random variables and would need to be calculated for use as in Lemma 3.4.9): X_1 and X_3 are independent iff $p_{X_1, X_3}(x_1, x_3)$ equals the product $p_{X_1}(x_1) p_{X_3}(x_3)$ for all x_1 and all x_3. However, $p_{X_1}(x_1)$ and $p_{X_3}(x_3)$ were found in part (a). When we multiply them, we find the same function found in part (b) for $p_{X_1, X_3}(x_1, x_3)$, hence X_1 and X_3 *are* independent random variables.

(f) Here we calculate

$$P(X_1 = X_2 = X_3) = \sum_c P(X_1 = X_2 = X_3 = c) = \sum_c P(X_1 = c, X_2 = c, X_3 = c)$$

$$= \sum_c p_{X_1, X_2, X_3}(c, c, c) = \frac{1}{72}$$

since $c = 1$ is the only value that all three variables may take on simultaneously.

PROBLEMS FOR SECTION 3.4

3.4.1 Suppose that (X_1, X_2, X_3) has the three-dimensional distribution specified in Example 3.4.10, where X_1 is pay grade, X_2 indicates if the employee is a member of the affected class, and X_3 indicates whether the employee was promoted or not for a randomly chosen employee.
(a) Find the marginal probability function of X_1; of X_2; of X_3.
(b) Find the marginal probability function of (X_1, X_3).
(c) Find the conditional probability function of $X_3 | X_1 = 7, X_2 = 1$.
(d) Find the conditional probability function of $X_2, X_3 | X_1 = 7$.
(e) Are X_2 and X_3 independent?

3.4.2 Consider the following joint probability function of r.v.'s (X, Y):

	$p_{X,Y}(x, y)$			
y ╲ x	1	2	3	4
4	.08	.11	.09	.03
5	.04	.12	.21	.05
6	.09	.06	.08	.04

Find the probabilities: **(a)** $P(X + Y \le 8)$; **(b)** $P(X + Y > 7)$; **(c)** $P(XY \le 14)$; **(d)** $P(XY > 18)$; **(e)** $P(X = 3 | Y = 5)$; **(f)** $P(Y = 5 | X = 3)$.
Find **(g)** The marginal probability function of X; **(h)** The marginal probability function of Y; **(i)** The conditional probability function of X given $Y = 6$; **(j)** The conditional probability function of Y given $X = 3$.

3.4.3 A fair coin and an honest six-sided die are tossed and rolled simultaneously. Let X denote the number of heads on the face of the coin that shows, and let Y denote the number of dots on the face of the die that shows. Find
(a) The joint probability function of (X, Y).
(b) The marginal probability functions of X and of Y.
(c) Are X and Y independent r.v.'s? (Demonstrate your contention.)

3.4.4 Let $X \sim B(m, p)$ and $Y \sim B(n, p)$, with X and Y independent r.v.'s. Show that $X + Y \sim B(m + n, p)$.

3.4.5 Let (X, Y, Z) be a trivariate r.v. with equal probabilities at the six points $(0, 0, 1)$, $(0, 1, 0)$, $(1, 0, 0)$, $(0, 0, 0)$, $(1, 1, 1)$, $(2, 2, 2)$.
(a) Find the marginal probability function of each of X, Y, Z.
(b) Find the marginal probability function of (X, Y).

(c) Are X and Y independent r.v.'s?

(d) Find the conditional distribution of (X, Y) given $Z = 0$; $Z = 1$; $Z = 2$.

3.4.6 Let X and Y be two r.v.'s with only two possible values each, say $\{0, 1\}$. If $P(X = 1, Y = 1) = P(X = 1)P(Y = 1)$, then show that X and Y are independent r.v.'s. [*Hint*: First show that $P(X = 0, Y = 1) = P(X = 0)P(Y = 1)$. Then the other needed properties follow by a similar argument. Note that $P(X = 0, Y = 1) = P(Y = 1) - P(X = 1, Y = 1)$.]

3.4.7 If X and Y are independent r.v.'s, show that $f(X)$ and $g(Y)$ are also independent r.v.'s for any functions $f(\cdot)$ and $g(\cdot)$.

3.4.8 Let $X \sim B(m, p)$ and $Y \sim B(n, p)$, where X and Y are independent r.v.'s. Let $Z = X + Y$. Show that the conditional probability function of X given $Z = z$ is hypergeometric.

3.4.9 In Problem 3.2.2, find the joint probability function of (X, Y).

3.5. SPECIAL MULTIVARIATE DISCRETE DISTRIBUTIONS*

Definition 3.5.1. A r.v. $X = (X_1, \ldots, X_k)$ has the **multinomial distribution** if [for some integers $k \geq 2$, $n \geq 1$ and some $0 \leq p_i \leq 1$ $(i = 1, \ldots, k)$ with $p_1 + \cdots + p_k = 1$]

$$P[X_1 = x_1, \ldots, X_k = x_k] = \begin{cases} \dfrac{n!}{x_1! \cdots x_k!} p_1^{x_1 \cdots} p_k^{x_k}, & \begin{aligned} x_i &= 0, \ldots, n (1 \leq i \leq k) \\ x_1 + & \cdots + x_k = n \end{aligned} \\ 0, & \text{otherwise.} \end{cases}$$

Example 3.5.2. Suppose an experiment can result in exactly k possible outcomes, say $o_1, \ldots, o_k$, and that the probabilities of these outcomes are, respectively, $p_1, \ldots, p_k$ [where $0 \leq p_i \leq 1$ $(i = 1, \ldots, k)$ and $p_1 + \cdots + p_k = 1$]. Suppose the experiment is repeated n times independently, and let $X_i = $ number of outcomes of type o_i $(i = 1, \ldots, k)$. Then (show this) $(X_1, \ldots, X_k)$ has the *multinomial distribution* as given in Definition 3.5.1. Note that we could simply write $P[X_1 = x_1, \ldots, X_{k-1} = x_{k-1}]$ since $X_1, \ldots, X_{k-1}$ determine X_k since $X_1 + X_2 + \cdots + X_{k-1} + X_k = n$. (Similarly, any $k - 1$ of $X_1, \ldots, X_k$ determine the other X_i.)

Example 3.5.3. At a certain hour, people may be watching any of k (e.g., $k = 3$) television shows. If the probabilities are $p_1, \ldots, p_3$ that a person is watching shows 1, 2, 3 (respectively), and if n people are sampled independently as to show being watched, let $X_i = $ number watching show i $(i = 1, 2, 3)$. Then

$$P[X_1 = x_1, X_2 = x_2, X_3 = x_3] = \begin{cases} \dfrac{n!}{x_1! x_2! x_3!} p_1^{x_1} p_2^{x_2} p_3^{x_3}, & \begin{aligned} x_i &= 0, \ldots, n \\ x_1 + & x_2 + x_3 = n \end{aligned} \\ 0, & \text{otherwise.} \end{cases}$$

*May be omitted if instructor desires.

Example 3.5.4. Grade Distribution. In a certain course, students compete independently. There is a 5% chance of receiving a grade of A, 20% of B, 30% of C, 15% of D, and otherwise an F is received. Suppose that 30 students register for this course and complete it. What is the probability that there will be equal numbers of A's, B's, C's, D's, and F's assigned at the end of the course?

If we let $(X_1, X_2, X_3, X_4, X_5)$ be a 5-dimensional r.v. whose respective components are the numbers of A's, B's, C's, D's, F's assigned, then this r.v. has the multinomial distribution with $n = 30$ and $(p_1, p_2, p_3, p_4, p_5) = (.05, .20, .30, .15, .30)$, so that

$$p_{X_1, X_2, X_3, X_4, X_5}(x_1, x_2, x_3, x_4, x_5)$$

$$= \begin{cases} \dfrac{30!}{x_1! x_2! x_3! x_4! x_5!}(.05)^{x_1}(.20)^{x_2}(.30)^{x_3}(.15)^{x_4}(.30)^{x_5}, \\ \qquad \text{if } x_1 + x_2 + x_3 + x_4 + x_5 = 30 \text{ and each of } x_1, x_2, x_3, x_4, x_5 \\ \qquad\qquad\qquad\qquad \text{is one of the integers } 0, 1, 2, 3, 4, \ldots, 30 \\ 0, \qquad \text{otherwise.} \end{cases}$$

The desired probability is therefore

$$p_{X_1, X_2, X_3, X_4, X_5}(6, 6, 6, 6, 6)$$

$$= \frac{30!}{(6!)^5}(.05)^6(.20)^6(.30)^6(.15)^6(.30)^6 = .0000083,$$

indicating that this is a very unlikely event, in the sense of having a small probability. (Of course, in this example *all* events have small probabilities—the total probability mass of 1 is spread out over a large number of events, all with small probability.)

Example 3.5.5. Let X_1 and X_2 be two jointly discrete r.v.'s whose joint probability function is given by the following table in which $h = \frac{1}{60}$:

	$p_{X_1, X_2}(x_1, x_2)$			
x_2 \ x_1	0	1	2	$p_{X_2}(x_2)$
0	h	$4h$	$9h$	$14h$
1	$2h$	$6h$	$12h$	$20h$
2	$3h$	$8h$	$3h$	$14h$
3	$4h$	$2h$	$6h$	$12h$
$p_{X_1}(x_1)$	$10h$	$20h$	$30h$	

Are the r.v.'s X_1 and X_2 independent or dependent? What is $P[X_1 \geq X_2]$? What is $P[X_1 - X_2 = 1 \mid X_1 + X_2 = 3]$?

For independence of X_1 and X_2, we must have $p_{X_1, X_2}(x_1, x_2) = p_{X_1}(x_1)$ $\cdot p_{X_2}(x_2)$ for all x_1, x_2. But $p_{X_1, X_2}(0, 0) = h \neq 2\frac{1}{3}h = \frac{140}{60}h = (10h)(14h) = p_{X_1}(0) \cdot p_{X_2}(0)$. Next, $P[X_1 \geq X_2] = \sum_{x_1 \geq x_2} p_{X_1, X_2}(x_1, x_2) = 35h = \frac{7}{12}$. Finally,

$$P[X_1 - X_2 = 1 | X_1 + X_2 = 3] = \frac{P[X_1 - X_2 = 1, X_1 + X_2 = 3]}{P[X_1 + X_2 = 3]}$$

$$= \frac{P[X_1 = 2, X_2 = 1]}{P[X_1 + X_2 = 3]} = \frac{12h}{24h} = \frac{1}{2}.$$

PROBLEMS FOR SECTION 3.5

3.5.1 Suppose that $(X_1, X_2, X_3, X_4, X_5)$ has a multinomial distribution with $n = 30$ and some probabilities p_1, p_2, p_3, p_4, p_5. Show that (X_1, X_2, X_3, X_4) has a multinomial distribution with $n = 30$. What are the probabilities of this four-dimensional distribution?

3.5.2 Suppose that $(X_1, X_2, X_3, X_4, X_5)$ has the multinomial distribution given in Problem 3.5.1. Find the distribution of $x_1, x_2, x_3, x_4 | x_5 = 2$.

3.5.3 A college student senate has 16 members, 4 from each class (freshman, sophomore, junior, and senior). The senate is studying the problem of students talking in lecture who are dropped from the course for such talking. A subcommittee of 4 members is to be chosen at random. What is the probability that this subcommittee has
(a) All its members from the senior class?
(b) One member from each of the classes?
(c) Two members each from the senior and junior classes, and none from the freshman and sophomore classes?

3.6. DISTRIBUTIONS OF FUNCTIONS OF DISCRETE RANDOM VARIABLES*

Often we will observe a random variable, but real interest will center not about the distribution of the observed r.v. but about **the distribution of some function of the observed r.v.** (e.g., not sales but profit). We here state the (obvious) results for one- and n-dimensional r.v.'s.

Theorem 3.6.1. Let X be a discrete r.v. Define $Y = g(X)$ for some real-valued function $g(x)$. Then

$$F_Y(y) = P[Y \leq y] = P[g(X) \leq y] = \sum_{x: \, g(x) \leq y} p_X(x),$$

$$p_Y(y) = P[Y = y] = P[g(X) = y] = \sum_{x: \, g(x) = y} p_X(x).$$

*May be omitted if instructor desires.

Example 3.6.2. Let X be $B(n, p)$ and $Y = g(X) = 3X + 5$. Then the probability function of Y is

$$p_Y(y) = P(Y = y) = P(g(X) = y) = \sum_{x:\, g(x)=y} P(X = x)$$

$$= \sum_{\substack{x:\, 3x+5=y, \\ x=0,1,\ldots,n}} \binom{n}{x} p^x q^{n-x}.$$

For example,

$$p_Y(0) = \sum_{\substack{x:\, 3x+5=0, \\ x=0,1,\ldots,n}} \binom{n}{x} p^x q^{n-x} = \sum_{\substack{x:\, x=-5/3 \\ x=0,1,\ldots,n}} \binom{n}{x} p^x q^{n-x} = 0$$

since the set over which we are summing is empty (there are *no x's* such that both $x = -5/3$ *and x* is one of the numbers $0, 1, 2, \ldots, n$). Similarly,

$$p_Y(5) = \sum_{\substack{x:\, 3x+5=5, \\ x=0,1,\ldots,n}} \binom{n}{x} p^x q^{n-x} = \sum_{\substack{x:\, 3x=0, \\ x=0,1,\ldots,n}} \binom{n}{x} p^x q^{n-x}$$

$$= \sum_{x=0} \binom{n}{x} p^x q^{n-x} = \binom{n}{0} p^0 q^{n-0} = q^n.$$

In this simple example, since $Y = 3X + 5$ and the possible values of X are $0, 1, \ldots, n$, the possible values of y are $5, 8, 11, 14, \ldots, 3n + 5$ and (since exactly one x leads to each possible y) $P(Y = 3k + 5) = P(X = k)$ for $k = 0, 1, 2, \ldots, n$.

Example 3.6.3. Suppose that X is a r.v. with probability function

x	-3	-1	0	1	5
$p_X(x)$	.2	.2	.2	.3	.1

Then the possible values of $Y = X^2$ are $0, 1, 9, 25$ and the probability function of Y is

$$p_Y(0) = p_X(0) = .2$$
$$p_Y(1) = p_X(-1) + p_X(1) = .2 + .3 = .5$$
$$p_Y(9) = p_X(-3) = .2$$
$$p_Y(25) = p_X(5) = .1$$

with $p_Y(y) = 0$ for all other values y. In the form of a table, we have

y	0	1	9	25
$p_Y(y)$	.2	.5	.2	.1

Note that, as specified in Theorem 3.6.1, to find the $P(Y = y)$ we have summed the $P(X = x)$ over all x such that $g(x) = y$; that is, over all x such that $x^2 = y$.

Theorem 3.6.4. Let $X = (X_1, \ldots, X_n)$ be an n-dimensional discrete r.v. Define $Y = (Y_1, \ldots, Y_r) = (g_1(X), \ldots, g_r(X))$. Then

$$F_Y(y) = P[Y_1 \le y_1, \ldots, Y_r \le y_r] = P[g_1(X) \le y_1, \ldots, g_r(X) \le y_r]$$

$$= \sum_{\substack{x_1, \ldots, x_n \text{ such that} \\ g_1(x) \le y_1, \ldots, g_r(x) \le y_r}} p_{X_1, \ldots, X_n}(x_1, \ldots, x_n),$$

$$p_Y(y) = \sum_{\substack{x_1, \ldots, x_n \text{ such that} \\ g_1(x) = y_1, \ldots, g_r(x) = y_r}} p_{X_1, \ldots, X_n}(x_1, \ldots, x_n).$$

Example 3.6.5. For X_1 and X_2 as given in Example 3.4.20, find the distribution of $Y = |X_1 - X_2|$.

By Theorem 3.6.4, $p_Y(y) = P[Y = y] = P[|X_1 - X_2| = y]$ is the sum of $p_{X_1, X_2}(x_1, x_2)$ for all x_1, x_2 such that $|x_1 - x_2| = y$. We have

(x_1, x_2)	$p_{X_1, X_2}(x_1, x_2)$	$|x_1 - x_2|$
$(-1, 0)$	$\frac{1}{6}$	1
$(-1, .5)$	$\frac{1}{3}$	1.5
$(1, 0)$	$\frac{1}{6}$	1
$(1, .5)$	$\frac{1}{3}$	.5

Hence,

$$p_Y(y) = P[Y = y] = \begin{cases} \frac{1}{3}, & \text{if } y = 1.5 \\ \frac{2}{6} = \frac{1}{3}, & \text{if } y = 1 \\ \frac{1}{3}, & \text{if } y = .5. \end{cases}$$

Example 3.6.6. Suppose that (X, Y) is a two-dimensional discrete r.v. Then (Theorem 3.6.4)

$$P[X + Y = z] = \sum_{\substack{x, y \text{ such that} \\ x + y = z}} p_{X, Y}(x, y)$$

$$= \sum_x p_{X, Y}(x, z - x). \tag{3.6.7}$$

If, in addition, X and Y are independent [so that by Theorem 3.4.18, $p_{X, Y}(x, y) = p_X(x) p_Y(y)$],

$$P[X + Y = z] = \sum_x p_X(x) p_Y(z - x). \tag{3.6.8}$$

The probability distribution $p(z)$ defined in equation (3.6.8) is called the **convolution** of the probability distributions $p_X(\cdot)$ and $p_Y(\cdot)$. Hence, we have Theorem 3.6.9.

Theorem 3.6.9. If X and Y are independent discrete r.v.'s, then the distribution of $X + Y$ is the convolution of the distributions of X and of Y.

Example 3.6.10. (Due to W. J. Hall) Suppose that the distribution of $X + Y$ is the convolution of the distributions of X and of Y. Does it follow that X and Y are independent r.v.'s?

Suppose that X and Y have the joint probability function given by the following table (where θ is fixed, $|\theta| \leq \frac{1}{9}$):

y \ x	$p_{X,Y}(x,y)$			
	-1	0	1	$p_Y(y)$
-1	$\frac{1}{9}$	$\frac{1}{9} + \theta$	$\frac{1}{9} - \theta$	$\frac{1}{3}$
0	$\frac{1}{9} - \theta$	$\frac{1}{9}$	$\frac{1}{9} + \theta$	$\frac{1}{3}$
1	$\frac{1}{9} + \theta$	$\frac{1}{9} - \theta$	$\frac{1}{9}$	$\frac{1}{3}$
$p_X(x)$	$\frac{1}{3}$	$\frac{1}{3}$	$\frac{1}{3}$	

Then $P[X + Y = z] = \frac{1}{9}, \frac{2}{9}, \frac{3}{9}$ for $z = \pm 2, \pm 1, 0$ for all θ. Although this is the convolution of the distributions of X and of Y, X and Y are independent r.v.'s iff $\theta = 0$. Hence, the proposition that, under the stated conditions, X and Y are independent r.v.'s does not follow (i.e., the converse of Theorem 3.6.9 is false).

PROBLEMS FOR SECTION 3.6

3.6.1 Let $X \sim B(n, p)$. Find the probability function of each of the following functions of X: **(a)** $Y = 3X + 4$; **(b)** $Y = X - 3$; **(c)** $Y = X^2 + 2$; **(d)** $Y = \sqrt{X}$.

3.6.2 Let X be a Poisson r.v. with parameter λ. Find the probability function of each of the functions Y given in Problem 3.6.1.

3.6.3 Let X be a hypergeometric r.v. with $p_X(x)$ as in Definition 3.2.7. Find the probability functions of each of **(a)** $Y = 3X + 4$; **(b)** $Y = 3X - 2$.

3.6.4 Let X be a r.v. with distribution as given in Problem 3.1.2. Find the distribution function of **(a)** $Y = 3X + 4$; **(b)** $Y = X^2$.

3.6.5 Let X be a r.v. with the distribution function given in Problem 3.1.3. Find the distribution functions of
   (a) $Y = aX + b$, $a > 0$ and $b > 0$.
   (b) $Y = |X|$.
   (c) $Y = X^2 + 3$.

3.6.6 Let X_1, X_2, X_3 denote the respective numbers on the faces of three fair six-sided dice after one simultaneous roll. Find the probability function of $Y = (X_1 + X_2 + X_3)/3$.

PROBLEMS FOR CHAPTER 3

3.1 Let $\Omega = \{H, T\}$ with $P(H) = P(T) = \frac{1}{2}$. Define real-valued random variables X and Y by $X(H) = 1$, $X(T) = 0$, and $Y(H) = 0$, $Y(T) = 1$. Find and graph $F_X(x)$ and $F_Y(y)$.

3.2 Can two different random variables have the same d.f.? Prove your assertion.

3.3 Prove that (for $0 \le p \le 1$, n an integer ≥ 1)

$$p_X(x) = \begin{cases} \binom{n}{x} p^x (1-p)^{n-x}, & x = 0, 1, \ldots, n \\ 0, & \text{otherwise} \end{cases}$$

is a probability function (called the **binomial probability function**).

3.4 Prove that (for any fixed $\lambda > 0$)

$$p_X(x) = \begin{cases} e^{-\lambda} \dfrac{\lambda^x}{x!}, & x = 0, 1, 2, \ldots \\ 0, & \text{otherwise} \end{cases}$$

is a probability function (called the **Poisson probability function**).

3.5 Ten questions are directed at random to four students so that each question is equally likely to be directed to any student. What is the probability function for the number of questions directed to the first student? What is the d.f.?

3.6 A silver dollar is tossed repeatedly and independently until a head appears. What is the probability function for the number of tosses required?

3.7 Cards are drawn from an ordinary 52-card shuffled deck, without replacement, until a club appears. What is the probability function for the number of draws required?

3.8 A machine pits prunes with an average of 1% of its output being defective. What is the probability function of the number of defectives in a sample of 60 consecutive prunes if
(a) Each "pitted" prune has probability $1/100$ of being defective and is defective or good independently of the other prunes.
(b) The machine turns out cycle after cycle of prunes with 99 good followed by 1 bad, and the "time" we started to sample in a cycle was random.

3.9 The **World Series** is a best-of-7 group of American baseball games; that is, two teams play baseball games until one wins 4 games. (This must happen by game 7 in the series, as ties are not allowed—extra innings are played to end games that would otherwise end in a tie. The series can end in 4 games, if the same team wins the first 4 games of the series.)
Suppose that teams B and C are competing in the World Series, that the (at most) 7 games are independent, and that

$$P[\,B \text{ beats } C \text{ in any game}\,] = p$$

$(0 \le p \le 1)$. Let

$$X = \begin{cases} 1, & \text{if } B \text{ wins the series} \\ 0, & \text{if } C \text{ wins the series.} \end{cases}$$

Find $P[X = 1]$.

3.10 In Problem 3.9, $P[X = 1]$ is a function of p $(0 \le p \le 1)$. Plot a graph of $P[X = 1]$ against p, and include specifically the values of $P[X = 1]$ for $p = 0, .1, .2, .3, .4, .5, .6, .7, .8, .9, 1$.

3.11 Plot the probability function and d.f. of X (see Problem 3.10) for $p = .6$.

3.12 Suppose that teams B and C (Problem 3.9) played not 7 but $2n + 1$ games, for n some positive integer. In that case, what would $P[X = 1]$ be?

3.13 Suppose that a woman, in her lifetime, is equally likely to have 1, 2, or 3 female offspring, and suppose that these second-generation women are in turn each equally likely to have 1, 2, or 3 third-generation female offspring. What is the probability function of the number of third-generation women?

3.14 A telephone switchboard handles 600 calls, on the average, during an hour. The board can make a maximum of 20 connections per minute. Use the Poisson distribution to evaluate the probability that the board will be overtaxed during a given minute. What is the probability that 10 seconds elapse with no calls?

3.15 If X and Y are independent random variables, each having the Poisson distribution (with respective parameters λ_1 and λ_2), show that the conditional distribution of X, given $X + Y$, is binomial.

3.16 Let A and B be events such that $P(A) = \frac{1}{4}$, $P(B|A) = \frac{1}{2}$, and $P(A|B) = \frac{1}{4}$. Define random variables X and Y by

$$X = \begin{cases} 1, & \text{if } A \text{ occurs} \\ 0, & \text{if } A \text{ does not occur;} \end{cases}$$

$$Y = \begin{cases} 1, & \text{if } B \text{ occurs} \\ 0, & \text{if } B \text{ does not occur.} \end{cases}$$

Determine whether and why each of the following statements is true or false.
(a) X and Y are independent.
(b) $P[X^2 + Y^2 = 1] = \frac{1}{4}$.
(c) $P[XY = X^2Y^2] = 1$.
(d) X is uniformly distributed on the interval 0 to 1.
(e) X and Y are identically distributed.

3.17 The number X of calculators that a certain store sells in a week obeys the Poisson probability law with parameter $\lambda = 10$. The profit on each calculator sold is \$2. If at the beginning of the week 10 calculators are in stock, the profit Y from sale of calculators during the week is

$$Y = 2 \cdot \text{minimum} \,(X, 10).$$

Find the probability distribution of Y.

3.18 Prove that it is impossible for two independent identically distributed random variables X_1 and X_2, each taking values 1 to 6, to have the property that

$$P[X_1 + X_2 = k] = 1/11, \quad \text{for } k = 2, 3, \ldots, 12.$$

Is it possible to weight a pair of dice so that the probability of occurrence of every sum from 2 to 12 will be the same?

3.19 Let X, Y be independent discrete r.v.'s with Poisson distributions of parameters λ_1 and λ_2 respectively. Show that the distribution of $X + Y$ is Poisson. What is the parameter of the Poisson distribution of $X + Y$?

3.20 If X is a random variable with distribution function $F_X(x)$ $(-\infty < x < +\infty)$, and if $Y = aX + b$, where $a > 0$, express $P[Y \le z]$ using $F_X(\cdot)$.

3.21 **(a)** Let X be a binomial r.v. based on n trials each with probability p of success. Table 5 contains numerical values of $P[X = x]$ for various n, for $x = 0$, $1, \ldots, n$, and for $p = .05(.05).50$. How could we use this table to find $P[Y = y]$ if Y were a binomial r.v. based on n trials, each with probability of success $q = .75$?

   (b) Let X be a Poisson r.v. with parameter $\mu > 0$. If $P[X = y + 1] = P[X = y] > 0$, what value must μ have? Give an example of values of μ and y for which this equality $P[X = y + 1] = P[X = y]$ is exemplified in Table 7.

3.22 Suppose that S_n is a random variable whose probability distribution is binomial for some $p(0 \le p \le 1)$. If we observe $S_n = x_0$ (where x_0 is one of $0, 1, \ldots, n$), then the **maximum likelihood estimator (MLE)** of p based on S_n is that $\hat{p}(0 \le \hat{p} \le 1)$ which maximizes

$$P[S_n = x_0] = \binom{n}{x_0} p^{x_0}(1 - p)^{n - x_0}.$$

Find it.

The following material is used in Problems 3.23, 3.24, 3.25. It is sometimes the case that a sequence (say $Y_1, Y_2, \ldots$) of random variables cannot be observed, although we can observe functions of the values of $Y_1, Y_2, \ldots$ (say $X_1, X_2, \ldots$).

Let $Y_1, Y_2, \ldots$ be independent and identically distributed random variables. Let a be a fixed number $(-\infty < a < +\infty)$. For $i = 1, 2, \ldots$ define

$$X_i = \begin{cases} 1, & \text{if } Y_i \ge a \\ 0, & \text{if } Y_i < a. \end{cases}$$

Define $p = P[Y_1 \ge a]$, $q = 1 - p$, $S_n = X_1 + \cdots + X_n$. [*Note:* S_n is the number of $Y_1, \ldots, Y_n$ that exceed the threshold a.]

3.23 Let n be a fixed positive integer. Let $A_i(n)$ be the event "At least i of $Y_1, \ldots, Y_n$ are $\ge a$" $(i = 1, \ldots, n)$. Find (in terms of p, q, n)

   (a) $P\left[\bigcap_{i=1}^{n} A_i(n)\right]$,

   (b) $P\left[\bigcup_{i=1}^{n} A_i(n)\right]$,

   (c) $P\left[\bigcap_{i=1}^{j} A_i(n)\right]$,   where $1 \le j \le n$.

3.24 Let n be a fixed positive integer. Let $B_i(n)$ be the event "Exactly i of $Y_1, \ldots, Y_n$ are $\ge a$" $(i = 0, 1, \ldots, n)$. Find (in terms of p, q, n)

$$P[B_0(n) \cup B_1(n) \cup \cdots \cup B_n(n)].$$

3.25 (a) How many different values can the random vector $(X_1, \ldots, X_n)$ take on with positive probability? (Assume that $0 < p < 1$.)

(b) How many different values can $S_n = X_1 + \cdots + X_n$ take on with positive probability? (Assume that $0 < p < 1$.)

3.26 Show that if a random variable X is geometric,[9] that is, for some $p (0 \leq p < 1)$

$$P[X = x] = \begin{cases} (1 - p) p^x, & \text{for } x = 0, 1, \ldots \\ 0, & \text{otherwise}, \end{cases}$$

then it has the **lack of memory property**: for all positive integers j and k,

$$P[X \geq j + k | X \geq k] = P[X \geq j].$$

3.27 Suppose $X_1, X_2, \ldots, X_n$ are independent random variables and that $P[X_i = 0] = 1 - p$, $P[X_i = 1] = p$ for some p with $0 \leq p \leq 1$ for $i = 1, 2, \ldots, n$. Let X denote the number of $X_1, \ldots, X_n$ that are at least as large as X_1. Find $P[X = x]$ for all x. [*Hint*: First find $P[X = n]$.]

3.28 A fair coin is tossed 3 times independently. Define random variables X and Y by

$X =$ the number of heads occurring in the 3 tosses,

$Y =$ the number of tails occurring before the first head.

Tabulate (see Example 3.5.5) the joint probability function $p_{X,Y}(x, y) = P[X = x, Y = y]$. Determine whether or not X and Y are independent.

3.29 An unknown number N of rats live in a certain neighborhood. To design an effective rat control program, we need to have an estimate of N. Suppose the following experiment is performed. a of the N rats are caught, tagged, and released. After they have had time to mix thoroughly with the total population, we catch (at random without replacement) n of the rats. If x of the rats sampled have tags, what can we say about N? Specifically,

(a) What is the probability, say $p(N)$, that x of the rats sampled have tags?

(b) Regarding $p(N)$ as a function of N, for what value of N is $p(N)$ largest? [*Hint*: Find $p(N)/p(N-1)$. Now $p(N)$ increases if this ratio is > 1 and decreases if it is < 1.]

3.30 For a discrete random variable X the **conditional failure probability function** (or **discrete failure rate**) is defined as

$$q(x) = P[X = x | X \geq x]$$

for x such that $P[X \geq x] > 0$. If the r.v. X represents the life of some item, $q(x)$ can be interpreted as the conditional probability of death at x given that death has not occurred before x. Find and plot the discrete failure rate $q(x)$ if X has the geometric distribution (see Definition 3.2.20); the uniform distribution (see Definition 3.2.17).

[9]Note that this way of writing the geometric distribution looks at first to be different from that of Definition 3.2.20. However, both have the same probabilities, on shifted values of x (and hence are the same distribution). This form of the distribution is more convenient in this problem. [*Question*: Is the result true for the other form of the distribution, that is, for the distribution on $x = 1, 2, 3, \ldots$ instead of on $0, 1, 2, \ldots$?]

3.31 Let X be a discrete r.v. such that

$$\sum_{i=-\infty}^{\infty} p_i = 1,$$

where $p_i = P[X = i]$ (i.e., X assumes only integers as values). The distribution $\{p_i\}$ is said to be **unimodal** if there is at least one integer M such that

$$\begin{cases} p_i \geq p_{i-1}, & \text{whenever } i \leq M \\ p_{i+1} \leq p_i, & \text{whenever } i \geq M. \end{cases}$$

The distribution $\{p_i\}$ is said to be **log-concave** if

$$p_i^2 \geq p_{i+1}p_{i-1}, \qquad \text{for all } i.$$

Prove directly that the Poisson distribution is both unimodal and log-concave.[10] Prove directly that the binomial distribution is both unimodal and log-concave.

HONORS PROBLEMS FOR CHAPTER 3

3.1H In a rigorous theoretical development of probability theory, certain measurability restrictions are required on a "random variable" (and a "random n-vector"). What are they? Why are they needed?

3.2H Prove that the hypergeometric distribution for sampling without replacement n times at random from a population of N elements (a of which are of type A) is a probability distribution. Note that, if X = Number of type A in the sample, then

$$P[X = x] = p_X(x) = \begin{cases} \dfrac{\dbinom{a}{x}\dbinom{N-a}{n-x}}{\dbinom{N}{n}}, & x = \max(0, n-(N-a)), \ldots, \min(n, a) \\ 0, & \text{otherwise.} \end{cases}$$

3.3H Suppose given n items of type A and n items of type B ($n \geq 1$), as well as n cells (each with two positions, each position being capable of holding an item of type A or one of type B). Let the $2n$ items be distributed at random into the $2n$ cell positions, and define

$$X = \begin{pmatrix} \text{Number of cells containing one item} \\ \text{of type } A \text{ and one item of type } B \end{pmatrix}.$$

Find $p_X(x) = P[X = x]$, the probability function of X. [*Hint*: See Feller, Vol. I (3rd ed.), p. 55, No. 12, for a simpler problem in this set-up. See the journal article referenced there. Tossing the n of type A determines X, since the places to be occupied by the items of type B are then determined.]

---

[10]An indirect proof is also possible since Keilson and Gerber (1971) have proven that log-concavity implies unimodality.

3.4H   Give a complete derivation of the Poisson distribution as the solution to a problem of random events, along the lines indicated in Example 3.2.12. (In particular, show in detail the general solution of the differential equation

$$\frac{dy}{dx} + P(x)y = Q(x),$$

and indicate explicitly how you use it.) Give a second derivation along the lines of footnote 5: "Another derivation...."

3.5H   **Theorem 1:** If $X = (X_1, X_2)$ is a two-dimensional random variable, then

(i) $\lim\limits_{\min(x_1, x_2) \to +\infty} F_{X_1, X_2}(x_1, x_2) = 1;$

(ii) $\lim\limits_{x_i \to -\infty} F_{X_1, X_2}(x_1, x_2) = 0 \ (i = 1, 2);$

(iii) $F_{X_1, X_2}(x_1, x_2)$ is continuous from above in each argument;

(iv)   For all a, b, c, d (with $a < b, c < d$),

$$F_{X_1, X_2}(b, d) - F_{X_1, X_2}(a, d) - F_{X_1, X_2}(b, c) + F_{X_1, X_2}(a, c) \geq 0;$$

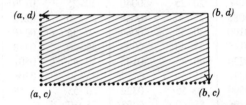

that is, $F_{X_1, X_2}(\cdot, \cdot)$ assigns positive mass to the indicated rectangle.

Theorem 2: If a real-valued function F on $\mathcal{R}^2$ satisfies (i) through (iv) of Theorem 1, then there is a probability space and r.v.'s X_1, X_2 such that $F_{X_1, X_2}(x_1, x_2) = F(x_1, x_2)$.

Show that if **(iv)** in Theorem 2 is replaced by **(iv')**: $F_{X_1, X_2}(x_1, x_2) \leq F_{X_1, X_2}(y_1, y_2)$ for $x_1 \leq y_1, x_2 \leq y_2$, then the result is false. [*Hint:* Find an $F(\cdot, \cdot)$ that satisfies (i) through (iv') but violates (iv).] Prove Theorem 1. Prove Theorem 2.

3.6H   Let X_1 and X_2 be two independent discrete random variables. Denote $P[X_1 = i] = p_i \geq 0 \ (1 \leq i \leq n)$, $P[X_2 = j] = q_j \geq 0 \ (1 \leq j \leq n)$, where $n \geq 2$ is a fixed positive integer, $\Sigma p_i = \Sigma q_j = 1$. Thus, each variable takes on only values in the set $\{1, 2, \ldots, n\}$. Prove that there do not exist $p_1, \ldots, p_n; \ q_1, \ldots, q_n$ such that $P[X_1 + X_2 = k] = 1/(2n - 1)$ for $k = 2, \ldots, 2n$. [*Note:* This is easily shown for $n = 2$. With the further restriction that $p_i = q_i \ (1 \leq i \leq n)$, the problem is well-known (Problem 3.18 covers the case $n = 6$) and we easily show that **it is not possible to weight a pair of n-sided dice so that the probability of occurrence of every sum from 2 to $2n$ will be the same.** We seek here to remove the requirement of identical weightings.]

3.7H   Prove or find a counterexample: If $F(x_1, \ldots, x_n)$ is the distribution function of an n-dimensional random variable, then its points of discontinuity are contained in an (at most countable) union of subsets of dimension $n - 1$. (The result for $n = 1$ is well-known—see Theorem 3.1.4.)

3.8H   Let X and Y be two discrete r.v.'s. Given $P[X = z]$, $P[Y = z]$, and $P[\max(X, Y) = z]$, find $P[\min(X, Y) = z]$. [*Reference:* Kazarinoff, Moser, and Wilansky (1969).] Generalize this in a meaningful way to n discrete r.v.'s $X_1, \ldots, X_n$.

3.9H   Investigate the discrete failure rate (see Problem 3.30) of the Poisson distribution.

3.10H   The following table (extracted from p. 150 of *Vital Statistics of the United States 1950, Volume I* by the National Office of Vital Statistics, Washington, D.C., 1954) gives the proportion of persons (in each of four groups) who would die in a specified age interval *if* these persons were to die in the same proportions as observed for their age and group in 1950 and were alive at the beginning of that interval. Thus, the tabulation essentially gives $P[X = x | X \geq x]$, the discrete failure rate (see Problem 3.30), for 19 values of x (age of death intervals).

White Male		White Female		Nonwhite Male		Nonwhite Female	
0–1	0.0302	0–1	0.0231	0–1	0.0492	0–1	0.0402
1–5	.0054	1–5	.0044	1–5	.0110	1–5	.0094
5–10	.0033	5–10	.0024	5–10	.0048	5–10	.0039
10–15	.0034	10–15	.0021	10–15	.0048	10–15	.0036
15–20	.0065	15–20	.0031	15–20	.0108	15–20	.0086
20–25	.0086	20–25	.0040	20–25	.0179	20–25	.0126
25–30	.0085	25–30	.0049	25–30	.0212	25–30	.0163
30–35	.0100	30–35	.0064	30–35	.0276	30–35	.0222
35–40	.0145	35–40	.0093	35–40	.0350	35–40	.0307
40–45	.0234	40–45	.0143	40–45	.0501	40–45	.0435
45–50	.0377	45–50	.0217	45–50	.0706	45–50	.0619
50–55	.0590	50–55	.0322	50–55	.1059	50–55	.0881
55–60	.0896	55–60	.0493	55–60	.1495	55–60	.1211
60–65	.1306	60–65	.0769	60–65	.1946	60–65	.1643
65–70	.1835	65–70	.1172	65–70	.2075	65–70	.1536
70–75	.2593	70–75	.1887	70–75	.2669	70–75	.2204
75–80	.3587	75–80	.2896	75–80	.3566	75–80	.2926
80–85	.4730	80–85	.4084	80–85	.3494	80–85	.2929
85 and over	1,0000	85 and over	1.0000	85 and over	1.0000	85 and over	1.0000

(a) Graph the discrete failure rate for all four groups. (Put all four curves on the same graph, and connect the 19 points by a smooth curve for each. Use semilog graph paper so that the whole curve can be fitted onto one graph.) Compare white and nonwhite males; white and nonwhite females; white males and females; and nonwhite males and females, each with regard to discrete failure rate (as estimated). What observations can you make about comparative failure rates that are true over a broad range of ages? What observations are true for only a narrow range of ages?

(b) For similar, more recent (1966) data that follows (extracted from p. 5–4 of *Vital Statistics of the United States 1966, Volume II—Mortality, Part A* by the Division of Vital Statistics of the National Center for Health Statistics, Washington, D.C., 1968) plot comparable failure rate curves. Compare these with each other, and with the 1950 curves. What progress has occurred? How are the comparisons changed (if at all)?

(c) Investigate the degree of confidence we can have in these comparisons (essentially the precision with which $P[X = x | X \geq x]$ has been estimated from the data for all x simultaneously).

White Male		White Female		Nonwhite Male		Nonwhite Female	
0–1	0.0234	0–1	0.0176	0–1	0.0422	0–1	0.0349
1–5	.0036	1–5	.0029	1–5	.0066	1–5	.0057
5–10	.0024	5–10	.0017	5–10	.0034	5–10	.0025
10–15	.0024	10–15	.0014	10–15	.0035	10–15	.0021
15–20	.0070	15–20	.0028	15–20	.0090	15–20	.0040
20–25	.0091	20–25	.0031	20–25	.0157	20–25	.0067
25–30	.0080	25–30	.0036	25–30	.0199	25–30	.0096
30–35	.0090	30–35	.0051	30–35	.0257	30–35	.0151
35–40	.0129	35–40	.0073	35–40	.0343	35–40	.0219
40–45	.0206	40–45	.0118	40–45	.0485	40–45	.0309
45–50	.0339	45–50	.0183	45–50	.0669	45–50	.0440
50–55	.0560	50–55	.0277	50–55	.0913	50–55	.0583
55–60	.0880	55–60	.0408	55–60	.1307	55–60	.0845
60–65	.1287	60–65	.0600	60–65	.1671	60–65	.1220
65–70	.1877	65–70	.0982	65–70	.2698	65–70	.1995
70–75	.2639	70–75	.1569	70–75	.3081	70–75	.2082
75–80	.3524	75–80	.2452	75–80	.3286	75–80	.2501
80–85	.4763	80–85	.3853	80–85	.3576	80–85	.3006
85 and over	1.0000	85 and over	1.0000	85 and over	1.0000	85 and over	1.0000

3.11H In Section 3.3 we proved that the binomial distribution "tends to" the Poisson in the sense that, if $n \to \infty$ and np $(= \lambda$, say) is held fixed, then

$$\binom{n}{k} p^k (1 - p)^{n-k} \to e^{-\lambda} \lambda^k / k!.$$

Let $h(0), h(1), h(2), \ldots$ be ≥ 0. Prove that

$$\lim_{n \to \infty} \sum_{k=0}^{\infty} h(k) \left| \binom{n}{k} p^k (1 - p)^{n-k} - e^{-\lambda} \frac{\lambda^k}{k!} \right| = 0$$

iff

$$\sum_{k=0}^{\infty} h(k) e^{-\lambda} \frac{\lambda^k}{k!} < \infty.$$

[*Reference*: Simons and Johnson (1971).]

CHAPTER 4

Random Variables: Continuous and Mixed Cases

In Chapter 3, we introduced the notions of random variables and n-dimensional random variables and discussed (for a general n-dimensional random variable)

1. Multivariate distribution functions,
2. Marginal distributions,
3. Conditional distributions, and
4. Independence.

For a **discrete** n-dimensional random variable we discussed

1. Probability functions,
2. Marginal probability functions,
3. Conditional probability functions,
4. Independence, and
5. Distributions of functions of r.v.'s.

In this chapter we discuss, for an **(absolutely) continuous** n-dimensional r.v.,

1. Multivariate density functions,
2. Marginal density functions,
3. Conditional density functions,
4. Independence, and
5. Distributions of functions of r.v.'s.

A simple example that illustrates how continuous r.v.'s may arise is given in Example 4.1.2. The coverage in Chapter 4 (for continuous distributions) closely parallels that of Chapter 3 (for discrete distributions). In the discrete case a distribution function may be expressed as a **sum** involving the **point probability function**; in the continuous case a distribution function may be expressed as an **integral** of what is called the **probability density function**. Other notions (such as

126

the marginal probability function and the marginal density function) also closely parallel each other, and the formulas involved are nearly identical.

4.1. CLASSIFICATION OF DISTRIBUTION FUNCTIONS

In Section 3.1 we defined the distribution function of any one-dimensional r.v. X as $F_X(x) = P[X \leq x]$ for all $x \in (-\infty, +\infty)$. Such a r.v. X was called *discrete* (see Definitions 3.1.6 and 3.1.7 for details) essentially iff (for all x)

$$F_X(x) = \sum_{\substack{x' \leq x \\ \text{with } p_X(x') > 0}} p_X(x').$$

Definition 4.1.1. X is called a (one-dimensional) **(absolutely) continuous random variable** if its d.f. $F_X(x)$ may be represented as

$$F_X(x) = \int_{-\infty}^{x} f_X(y)\, dy \qquad (-\infty < x < +\infty),$$

where $f_X(y)$ is a **probability density function (p.d.f.)**; that is by definition,

$$f_X(y) \geq 0 \quad \text{for all } y,$$

and

$$\int_{-\infty}^{\infty} f_X(y)\, dy = 1.$$

In this case $F_X(x)$ is called an **(absolutely) continuous d.f.**

Example 4.1.2. Suppose that we pick a number "at random" between 0 and 1, say X (a random variable). What is the d.f. of X, and is X absolutely continuous or discrete (or as is sometimes possible, neither)?

Since the number is picked at random between 0 and 1, it should have equal probability of being in the interval $(0, \frac{1}{2})$ and the interval $(\frac{1}{2}, 1)$, while its probability of being less than 0 is 0, and its probability of being greater than 1 is 0. Thus,

$$F_X(x) = 0, \qquad \text{if } x \leq 0,$$

$$F_X\left(\tfrac{1}{2}\right) = \tfrac{1}{2},$$

$$F_X(x) = 1, \qquad \text{if } x \geq 1.$$

However, since the point is chosen at random between 0 and 1, the probability that it lies in the interval $(0, x)$ should be the proportion that the length of the interval $(0, x)$ is of the interval $(0, 1)$; that is, $x/1 = x$ if $0 \leq x \leq 1$. Thus, $F_X(x) = x$ if $0 \leq x \leq 1$, and $F_X(x)$ is as given in Figure 4.1-1. Now let us define $f(x) = 1$ if $0 \leq x \leq 1$ and $f(x) = 0$ otherwise. Then $f(y) \geq 0$ for all y and

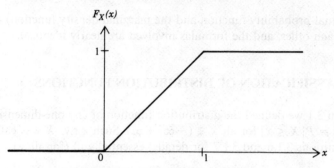

Figure 4.1-1. $F_X(x)$ for Example 4.1.2.

$\int_{-\infty}^{\infty} f(y)\, dy = 1$, so by Definition 4.1.1 $f(y)$ is a p.d.f. But, for all x,

$$F_X(x) = \int_{-\infty}^{x} f(y)\, dy,$$

so X is an (absolutely) continuous r.v. with p.d.f. $f(x)$.

Example 4.1.3. Is the function

$$G(x) = \begin{cases} \dfrac{e^x}{2}, & \text{if } x < 0 \\[2mm] 1 - \dfrac{e^{-x}}{2}, & \text{if } x \ge 0 \end{cases}$$

a distribution function? If so, and if it is a continuous d.f., find its p.d.f.

We will use Theorem 3.1.5 to check if $G(x)$ is a d.f. Recall that $G(x)$ is a d.f. iff three conditions are satisfied. *First* **(a)**, $G(x) \le G(y)$ if $x \le y$. This is clear when $0 \le x \le y$, and also if $x \le y < 0$. If $x < 0 \le y$, $G(x) = e^x/2$, $G(y) = 1 - e^{-y}/2$, and since $x < 0$, we have $G(x) < 1/2$, whereas since $0 \le y$, we have $1/2 \le G(y)$, whence $G(x) < G(y)$ in this case also. *Second* **(b)**,

$$G(-\infty) \equiv \lim_{x \to -\infty} G(x) = \lim_{x \to -\infty} e^x = 0$$

and

$$G(+\infty) \equiv \lim_{x \to \infty} G(x) = \lim_{x \to \infty} (1 - e^{-x}) = 1.$$

Finally **(c)**, since e^x is continuous and $1 - e^{-x}/2$ is continuous, $G(x)$ is continuous except *possibly* at $x = 0$. However,

$$\lim_{x \to 0^-} G(x) = \tfrac{1}{2} = G(0) = \lim_{x \to 0^+} G(x)$$

so that $G(x)$ is continuous, hence continuous from above. (Recall—see equation (3.1.16)—that in $G(0^-) = \lim_{x \to 0^-} G(x)$, x stays < 0.) Hence $G(x)$ *is* a d.f.

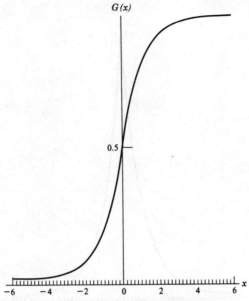

Figure 4.1-2. D.f. $G(x)$ of Example 4.1.3.

Since **any differentiable function is the integral of its derivative** (this is called the **Fundamental Theorem of Integral Calculus**, and holds as long as the derivative is continuous), and (see Definition 4.1.1) a continuous d.f. is the integral of its p.d.f., it follows that $G(x)$ is a continuous d.f. Thus, $G(x)$ equals the integral of its derivative, and its derivative is the p.d.f of Definition 4.1.1. Thus, differentiating $G(x)$ with respect to x, we find the p.d.f. is

$$g(x) = \frac{d}{dx}G(x) = \begin{cases} \dfrac{e^x}{2}, & \text{if } x < 0 \\ \dfrac{e^{-x}}{2}, & \text{if } x \geq 0 \end{cases}$$

$$= \frac{e^{-|x|}}{2}, \qquad -\infty < x < \infty.$$

This is called the **double-exponential (or Laplace) distribution,** and any r.v. with this distribution is called a double-exponential (or Laplace) r.v. The graphs of the d.f. $G(x)$ and the p.d.f. $g(x)$ are given in Figures 4.1-2 and 4.1-3.

Example 4.1.4. Is the function

$$g(x) = \begin{cases} 3(1-x)^2, & \text{if } 0 < x < 1 \\ 0, & \text{otherwise} \end{cases}$$

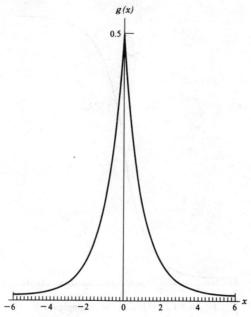

Figure 4.1-3. P.d.f. $g(x)$ of Example 4.1.3.

a probability density function? If so, find the corresponding distribution function.

To be a probability density function, $g(x)$ must (see Definition 4.1.1) satisfy the two properties

$$\textbf{(i)}\ \ g(x) \geq 0 \qquad \text{for all } x$$

and

$$\textbf{(ii)}\ \ \int_{-\infty}^{\infty} g(x)\, dx = 1.$$

For the given function $g(x)$, $g(x)$ is either 0 (in which case $g(x) \geq 0$) or $3(1 - x)^2$, which is ≥ 0 for all x [hence certainly for $0 < x < 1$ where $g(x)$ has this form], hence $g(x) \geq 0$ and **(i)** is satisfied. Also,

$$\int_{-\infty}^{\infty} g(x)\, dx = \int_{-\infty}^{0} 0\, dx + \int_{0}^{1} 3(1 - x)^2\, dx$$

$$+ \int_{1}^{\infty} 0\, dx$$

$$= 0 - (1 - x)^3 \Big|_{0}^{1} + 0 = 1,$$

so that **(ii)** is satisfied, hence $g(x)$ is a p.d.f.

The corresponding d.f. $G(x)$ is (see Definition 4.1.1) the integral of $g(x)$, that is,

$$G(x) = \int_{-\infty}^{x} g(y)\, dy = \begin{cases} 0, & \text{if } x < 0 \\ \int_{0}^{x} 3(1-y)^2\, dy = 1 - (1-x)^3, & \text{if } 0 \le x < 1 \\ 1, & \text{if } x \ge 1. \end{cases}$$

We now note two results on d.f.'s.

Theorem 4.1.5. If $F(x)$ is an absolutely continuous d.f., then [at all values of x where $f(x)$ is continuous]

$$F'(x) \equiv \frac{d}{dx} F(x) = f(x),$$

where $f(x)$ is the p.d.f. of $F(x)$.

Theorem 4.1.6.* Every d.f. $F(x)$ may be represented as

$$F(x) = c_1 F^d(x) + c_2 F^{ac}(x) + c_3 F^{sc}(x)$$

$(c_1, c_2, c_3 \ge 0,\ c_1 + c_2 + c_3 = 1)$ where $F^d(x)$ is a discrete d.f., $F^{ac}(x)$ is an (absolutely) continuous d.f., and $F^{sc}(x)$ is a **singularly continuous** d.f. [the latter being defined as a d.f. that is a continuous function of x but which has $F^{sc'}(x) = 0$ at almost all points x].

With regard to singularly continuous d.f.'s, the statement "in most practical cases $c_3 = 0$" has been made so often that it is a cliché. [Actually, Feller (1966) on p. 139 suggests that this cliché obscures the true nature of things: Singularly continuous d.f.'s are important, but their importance is hidden. An example of a singularly continuous d.f. will be given in Section 4.2.]

Example 4.1.7. Mixture-Type Distribution Functions. The function

$$F(x) = \begin{cases} 0, & \text{if } x < -2 \\ \frac{1}{3}, & \text{if } -2 \le x < 0 \\ \frac{1}{2}, & \text{if } 0 \le x < 5 \\ \dfrac{1}{2} + \dfrac{(x-5)^2}{2}, & \text{if } 5 \le x < 6 \\ 1, & \text{if } x \ge 6 \end{cases}$$

satisfies properties **(i)** through **(iii)** of Theorem 3.1.5 (check this), hence it is a distribution function. If X is a random variable with d.f. $F(x)$, then since $F(x)$ is

*May be omitted if instructor desires.

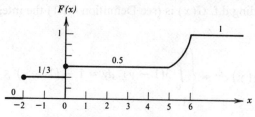

Figure 4.1-4. $F(x)$ for Example 4.1.7.

discontinuous at $x = -2$ and at $x = 0$, there are probability masses (of sizes $1/3$ and $1/6$, respectively) at those points; as we saw in Example 3.1.15, probability masses at points equal jump heights of the d.f., and here the jump heights are [see equation (3.1.16) for discussion of $F(2^-)$]

$$p_X(-2) = F(-2) - F(-2^-) = \tfrac{1}{3} - 0 = \tfrac{1}{3}$$

and

$$p_X(0) = F(0) - F(0^-) = \tfrac{1}{2} - \tfrac{1}{3} = \tfrac{1}{6}.$$

Since these are the only jumps (this is clear from plotting $F(x)$, as is done in Figure 4.1-4), and they do not sum to 1, $p_X(x)$ is not a probability function. Also note that although

$$\frac{d}{dx} F(x) = \begin{cases} x - 5, & \text{if } 5 \leq x < 6 \\ 0, & \text{otherwise (except at } x = -2, 0, 6, \text{ where it is undefined),} \end{cases}$$

neither $(d/dx)F(x)$ nor its completion to a function defined at all x (e.g., by defining the values at -2, 0, and 6 to be 0) is a p.d.f., since each integrates to $1/2$ instead of to 1 as required by Definition 4.1.1. [The Fundamental Theorem of Integral Calculus does not apply here; its conditions that $F(x)$ be differentiable at all points with a continuous derivative are not satisfied.] In fact, $F(x)$ is a distribution of mixture type, mixing discrete and continuous parts. It is easy to verify that

$$F(x) = c_1 F^d(x) + c_2 F^{ac}(x) + c_3 F^{sc}(x)$$

where

$$c_1 = \tfrac{1}{2}, \qquad F^d(x) = \begin{cases} 0, & \text{if } x < -2 \\ \tfrac{2}{3}, & \text{if } -2 \leq x < 0 \\ 1, & \text{if } x > 0, \end{cases}$$

$$c_2 = \tfrac{1}{2}, \qquad F^{ac}(x) = \begin{cases} 0, & \text{if } x < 5 \\ (x - 5)^2, & \text{if } 5 \leq x < 6 \\ 1, & \text{if } x \geq 6, \end{cases}$$

and (since $c_1 + c_2 + c_3 = 1$) $c_3 = 0$; that is, it is easy to verify directly that

$$F(x) = \tfrac{1}{2}F^d(x) + \tfrac{1}{2}F^{ac}(x)$$

with $F^d(x)$ and $F^{ac}(x)$ as specified above. Essentially, $F^d(x)$ is the d.f. of the discrete part of the r.v. X with d.f. $F(x)$, and takes account of the jumps of $F(x)$ at $x = 2$ and at $x = 0$; we have

$$c_1 = \text{(Sum of jump heights)} = \tfrac{1}{3} + \tfrac{1}{6} = \tfrac{1}{2}.$$

$F^{ac}(x)$ is the d.f. of the absolutely continuous part of the r.v. X, and takes account of the smoothly changing part of $F(x)$; we have

$$c_2 = \int_{-\infty}^{\infty} \frac{d}{dx} F(x)\, dx = \tfrac{1}{2}.$$

As noted after Theorem 4.1.6, **in almost all examples (except some very theoretical studies) $c_3 = 1 - c_1 - c_2 = 0$, as in this example.** (An exception, and the only one in this book, is Example 4.2.29, where $c_1 = $ (Sum of jump heights) $= 0$ since $F(x)$ there has no jumps (as it is continuous), and $c_2 = 0$ since $F(x)$ is essentially constant, hence has derivative 0, over "most" of the real line. Thus, there $c_3 = 1 - c_1 - c_2 = 1 - 0 - 0 = 1$.)

We will find the following special functions useful in defining and working with some of the most common and useful p.d.f.'s studied in Section 4.2.

Definition 4.1.8. **Beta Functions.** For $m > 0$, $n > 0$ (not necessarily integers)

$$\beta(m,n) \equiv \int_0^1 x^{m-1}(1 - x)^{n-1}\, dx$$

$$= 2\int_0^{\pi/2} (\sin\theta)^{2m-1}(\cos\theta)^{2n-1}\, d\theta.$$

[The transformation used was $x = \sin^2\theta$.]

Definition 4.1.9. **Gamma Functions.** For $n > 0$ (not necessarily an integer),

$$\Gamma(n) \equiv \int_0^{\infty} x^{n-1}e^{-x}\, dx = 2\int_0^{\infty} y^{2n-1}e^{-y^2}\, dy.$$

[The transformation used was $x = y^2$.]

Theorem 4.1.10. $\Gamma(1) = 1$. If n is a positive integer, then $\Gamma(n) = (n - 1)!$. $\Gamma(\tfrac{1}{2}) = \sqrt{\pi}$.

Proof:

$$\Gamma(1) = \int_0^\infty x^{1-1} e^{-x} \, dx = \int_0^\infty e^{-x} \, dx = -e^{-x}]_0^\infty = 1.$$

$$\Gamma(n) = \int_0^\infty x^{n-1} e^{-x} \, dx = -x^{n-1} e^{-x}]_0^\infty + \int_0^\infty e^{-x}(n-1)x^{n-2} \, dx$$

$$= (n-1)\Gamma(n-1).$$

Thus, we proved directly that $\Gamma(1) = 1$, and used integration by parts to show that for $n > 1$, $\Gamma(n) = (n-1)\Gamma(n-1)$. It follows by mathematical induction that $\Gamma(n) = (n-1)!$ when n is a positive integer. For a proof of $\Gamma(\frac{1}{2}) = \sqrt{\pi}$, see, for example, Wadsworth and Bryan (1960), pp. 3–4; this proof uses the material on Jacobians of transformations, which is discussed in our Theorem 4.6.16. ∎

Theorem 4.1.11.[1] $\beta(m, n) = \dfrac{\Gamma(m)\Gamma(n)}{\Gamma(m+n)}.$

Corollary 4.1.12. $\beta(m, n) = \beta(n, m).$

Example 4.1.13. Let X be an (absolutely) continuous random variable with density function given by

$$f_X(t) = \begin{cases} A(t^2 + 1), & \text{if } 0 \le t \le 1 \\ 0, & \text{otherwise.} \end{cases}$$

Determine the value of the constant A and sketch the graph of $f_X(t)$. Determine the distribution function $F(t)$ corresponding to the density function $f_X(t)$ and sketch its graph (see Figure 4.1-5).

$$1 = \int_{-\infty}^\infty f_X(t) \, dt = \int_0^1 A(t^2 + 1) \, dt = A\left[\frac{t^3}{3} + t\right]_0^1 = \tfrac{4}{3}A \Rightarrow A = \tfrac{3}{4}.$$

$$F(t) = \int_{-\infty}^t f_X(t) \, dt = \begin{cases} 1, & \text{if } t \ge 1 \\ \int_0^t A(t^2 + 1) \, dt = \dfrac{3}{4}\left(\dfrac{t^3}{3} + t\right), & \text{if } 0 < t < 1 \\ 0, & \text{if } t \le 0. \end{cases}$$

[1] The proof uses a transformation to polar coordinates and is omitted. [See, for example, Wadsworth and Bryan (1960), p. 5, for the details.]

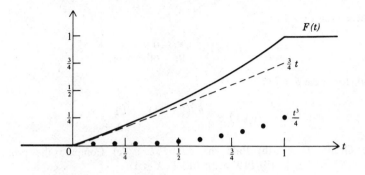

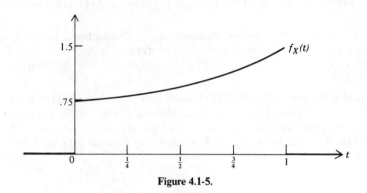

Figure 4.1-5.

PROBLEMS FOR SECTION 4.1

4.1.1 Let X be a random variable with p.d.f. $f_X(x) = x(1 - x)$ for $0 \le x \le 1$, and $= 0$ otherwise. **(a)** Find the d.f. $F_X(x)$ and graph it. **(b)** Find the following probabilities, using $F_X(x)$ only [and not $f_X(x)$]: **(i)** $P(X \le .75)$; **(ii)** $P(.25 < X < .6)$; **(iii)** $P(X \ge .80)$.

4.1.2 Consider the r.v. X with d.f.

$$F_X(x) = \begin{cases} 0, & \text{if } x < 0 \\ (4x - x^2)/8, & \text{if } 0 \le x < 2 \\ 1 + (x^2 - 4x)/8, & \text{if } 2 \le x < 4 \\ 1, & \text{if } x \ge 4. \end{cases}$$

(a) Find $f_X(x)$, the p.d.f. of X, and graph it. **(b)** Compute the probabilities **(i)** $P(X \le 1)$; **(ii)** $P(X \le 3.5)$; **(iii)** $P(1.2 < X \le 3.2)$; **(iv)** $P(X > 2.8)$.

4.1.3 Let X be an r.v. with p.d.f. $f_X(x) = \theta/x^{\theta+1}$ for $x \ge 1$, and $= 0$ otherwise, for some $\theta > 0$. Find the d.f. $F_X(x)$ and the probability $P(3 \le X < 7)$.

4.1.4 Let X (the mixture of two continuous r.v.'s) have p.d.f.

$$f_X(x) = c_1 f_{X_1}(x) + c_2 f_{X_2}(x)$$

where $c_1 = c_2 = 1$,

$$f_{X_1}(x) = \begin{cases} x, & \text{if } 0 \le x < 1 \\ 0, & \text{otherwise,} \end{cases}$$

and (for some $\theta > 0$)

$$f_{X_2}(x) = \begin{cases} \theta/(2x^{\theta+1}), & \text{if } 1 \le x \\ 0, & \text{otherwise.} \end{cases}$$

(a) Graph $f_X(x)$. (b) Find the d.f. $F_X(x)$. (c) Compute the probabilities (i) $P(.25 \le X \le 4)$; (ii) $P(X > 3)$; (iii) $P(X \le 1)$.

4.1.5 X is called a **Pareto r.v.** if the p.d.f. of X is $f_X(x) = \alpha/x^{\alpha+1}$ for $1 < x < \infty$, and $= 0$ otherwise. Find the d.f. of X. Graph $f_X(x)$ and $F_X(x)$ separately for $\alpha = 1, 2, 3, 4,$ and 5.

4.1.6 An r.v. X is said to have the standard **logistic distribution** if the p.d.f. of X is $f_X(x) = e^x/(1 + e^x)^2$ for $-\infty < x < +\infty$. (a) Graph $f_X(x)$. (b) Find the probabilities (i) $P(|X| \le 1)$; (ii) $P(|X| \le 2)$; (iii) $P(|X| \le 3)$. (c) Find the d.f. of X, $F_X(x)$.

4.1.7 Consider the unit semicircle ABC formed from a circle centered at the origin O. Let W be a random point on the circumference of the semicircle such that angle $WOC = X$. (a) Find the range of X. (b) Find the probabilities (i) $P(X < \pi/3)$; (ii) $P(\pi/3 \le X \le 3\pi/4)$; (iii) $P(X \ge 2\pi/3)$. (b) Find the p.d.f. of X and the d.f. of X.

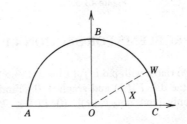

4.1.8 Let X be an r.v. with d.f. $F_X(x)$ and Y another r.v. with d.f. $F_Y(x)$. Prove or disprove (a) $F_X(x)F_Y(x)$ is a d.f. (b) $F_X(x) + F_Y(x)$ is a d.f. (c) $F_X(x) - F_Y(x)$ is a d.f. (d) $F_X(x)/F_Y(x)$ is a d.f. (e) $\max[F_X(x), F_Y(x)]$ is a d.f. (f) $\min[F_X(x), F_Y(x)]$ is a d.f.

4.1.9 Show that the function

$$F(x) = \begin{cases} 0, & \text{if } x < 0 \\ .25, & \text{if } 0 \le x < 1 \\ .40, & \text{if } 1 \le x < 2 \\ .50, & \text{if } 2 \le x < 3 \\ x - 2.5, & \text{if } 3 \le x < 3.5 \\ 1, & \text{if } x \ge 3.5 \end{cases}$$

is a d.f. [*Note*: This function is not differentiable at $x = 0, 1, 2, 3$; it is differentiable at all other x, but the area under the curve is not 1. Thus, it is a mixture distribution.] *Find* the discrete, absolutely continuous, and singular components F^d, F^{ac}, and F^{sc} of this d.f. as in Theorem 4.1.6. (Be sure to give c_1, c_2, and c_3.)

4.1.10 R.v. X is said to have a **median** m if (i) $P(X < m) \leq 1/2$ and (ii) $P(X \leq m) \geq 1/2$. If there is only one such point m, then we call it **the median** of X. *Find* a (or, the) median of the r.v.'s with the following p.d.f.'s: **(a)** $f_X(x) = (1/\theta)e^{-(x-\lambda)/\theta}$ for $x > \lambda$, and $= 0$ otherwise (where $\theta > 0$ and $-\infty < \lambda < +\infty$); **(b)** $f_X(x) = (1/\pi)/(1 + x^2)$ for $-\infty < x < +\infty$.

4.2. SPECIAL CONTINUOUS DISTRIBUTIONS

In this section we will define several very important continuous distributions.[2] Few examples will be given at this point, since these are more natural in Chapter 6 and the chapters on statistics (where continuous distributions are indispensable in the solution of practical problems).

Definition 4.2.1. A r.v. X has the **beta** distribution $B(x|\alpha, \lambda)$ if (for some α, $\lambda > -1$)

$$f_X(x) = \begin{cases} \dfrac{1}{\beta(\alpha + 1, \lambda + 1)} x^\alpha (1 - x)^\lambda, & 0 \leq x \leq 1 \\ 0, & \text{otherwise.} \end{cases}$$

It is easy to show that $f_X(x) \geq 0$ and (using Definition 4.1.8) $\int_{-\infty}^{\infty} f_X(x)\, dx = 1$ so that $f_X(x)$ is a p.d.f. by Definition 4.1.1. The fact that if $f(x)$ is a p.d.f., then $F(x) = \int_{-\infty}^{x} f(y)\, dy$ is a d.f. follows from Theorem 3.1.5. Of course (by Definition 4.1.1), $F(x)$ is then an absolutely continuous d.f. [See Table 8 for graphs and a table of x such that $F_X(x) = .05$.]

Definition 4.2.2. A r.v. X has the **uniform** distribution on $(0, 1)$ if

$$f_X(x) = \begin{cases} 1, & 0 \leq x \leq 1 \\ 0, & \text{otherwise.} \end{cases}$$

[Here $F_X(x)$ is easy to calculate, so a table is not needed.]

Example 4.2.3. The beta distribution $B(x|0, 0)$ is the uniform distribution on $(0, 1)$.

Remark 4.2.4. If $X \sim B(x|\alpha, \lambda)$ with $\lambda = 0$, then (check this, using Definition 4.2.1 and Theorems 4.1.10 and 4.1.11)

$$f_X(x) = \begin{cases} (\alpha + 1)x^\alpha, & \text{if } 0 \leq x \leq 1 \\ 0, & \text{otherwise.} \end{cases}$$

---

[2]At this point you should read the note that follows Definition 4.2.26. (It should also be reread after that definition.)

For every $\alpha > -1$, $f_X(x)$ is a probability density function. For positive integer values of α, $f_X(x)$ is a polynomial function. To find the value m such that $P(X \leq m) = 0.5$, that is, such that

$$\int_0^m f_X(x) \, dx = 0.5,$$

by integration we have

$$m^{\alpha+1} = 0.5$$

or

$$m = (0.5)^{1/(\alpha+1)}$$

For example, if $\alpha = 0$, then $m = 0.5$ and X is a uniform r.v. on $(0, 1)$.

Table 8 can be used to find that value of x such that $F_X(x) = .05$; for example, if $\alpha = 0$ and $\lambda = 0$, then $F_X(.05) = .05$. Similarly, if $\alpha = 4.5$ and $\lambda = 2.0$, then $F_X(.37203) = .05$. (Facts such as these are useful in statistical hypothesis testing, as we will see in Chapter 9.)

Definition 4.2.5.   A r.v. X has the **uniform** distribution on (b, c) (for $b < c$ fixed) if

$$f_X(x) = \begin{cases} \dfrac{1}{c - b}, & b \leq x \leq c \\ 0, & \text{otherwise.} \end{cases}$$

[Here $F_X(x)$ is easy to calculate, so a table is not needed.]

Example 4.2.6.   If Y is uniform on $(0, 1)$, then (for $b < c$ fixed) $X = (c - b)Y + b$ is uniform on (b, c).

Definition 4.2.7.   A r.v. X has the **gamma** distribution $G(x|\alpha, \beta, A)$ if (for some $\alpha > -1$, $\beta > 0$, $-\infty < A < +\infty$)

$$f_X(x) = \begin{cases} \dfrac{1}{\beta^{\alpha+1}\Gamma(\alpha + 1)}(x - A)^\alpha e^{-(x-A)/\beta}, & A \leq x < \infty \\ 0, & \text{otherwise.} \end{cases}$$

[See Table 9 for graphs and a table of $F_X(x)$.]

Example 4.2.8.   Let random variable X have the gamma distribution $G(x|4, 2, 3)$. Find the point a such that there is a 50% chance of obtaining a value of X smaller than or equal to a: $P(X \leq a) = 0.5$. (Note that such a value a is called a **median** of X, and also a median of the distribution of X.)

Here we seek a such that

$$\int_{-\infty}^{a} f_X(x)\, dx = \int_{3}^{a} \frac{1}{2^{4+1}\Gamma(4+1)} (x-3)^4 e^{-(x-3)/2}\, dx = 0.5.$$

In Table 9, from the row labeled $\alpha = 4$ and the column headed $\gamma = 0.5$, we read

$$\frac{a-3}{\beta} = 4.671,$$

hence (since $\beta = 2$)

$$a = 3 + (2)(4.671) = 12.342,$$

that is, the median of $G(x|4,2,3)$ is 12.342. Note that it has been necessary to use tables in this problem because there is no simple form for the gamma distribution function (whereas we do have a simple form for the gamma p.d.f.).

Example 4.2.9. If $X \sim G(x|4,3,2)$, find $P(X \geq 7)$.

We have $P(X \geq 7) = 1 - P(X < 7) = 1 - P(X \leq 7)$ since $X \geq 7$ and $X < 7$ are complementary events and since $P(X = 7) = 0$: to see this, write $P(a < X \leq 7)$ as an integral. Then $P(X = 7)$ is the limit as $a \uparrow 7$, that is, $P(X = 7) = 0$ (in fact, note that **for any r.v. which has a p.d.f., $P(X = x) = 0$ for all x**). Because $P(X \leq A) = 0$ and $A = 2$ here, we further find that

$$P(X \geq 7) = 1 - P(X \leq 7) = 1 - P(2 \leq X \leq 7).$$

Now

$$P(2 \leq X \leq 7) = \int_{2}^{7} \frac{1}{3^5 \Gamma(4+1)} (x-2)^4 e^{-(x-2)^3}\, dx.$$

From Table 9 (now with $\alpha = 4$) we find

$$P(2 \leq X \leq y) = .01 \text{ if } \frac{y-2}{3} = 1.279, \text{ that is, if } y = 5.837$$

$$P(2 \leq X \leq y) = .05 \text{ if } \frac{y-2}{3} = 1.970, \text{ that is, if } y = 7.910.$$

Thus,

$$.01 \leq P(2 \leq X \leq 7) \leq .05,$$

hence from the table we are able to state

$$.95 \leq P(X \geq 7) \leq .99,$$

but are not able to specify the exact value of $P(X \geq 7)$.

Definition 4.2.10. A r.v. X has the **exponential** distribution if (for some $\beta > 0$, $-\infty < A < +\infty$)

$$f_X(x) = \begin{cases} \dfrac{1}{\beta} e^{-(x-A)/\beta}, & A \leq x < \infty \\ 0, & \text{otherwise.} \end{cases}$$

Example 4.2.11. The exponential distribution is fairly easy to work with by direct integration, so tables are not needed as long as we know the values of β and A. For example, if $\beta = 4$ and $A = 3$, then the point that X will exceed 40% of the time can be determined as follows. We wish to find x such that

$$P(X > x) = 1 - P(X \leq x) = 0.4,$$

that is, such that $P(X \leq x) = 0.6$. Now (for $x \geq A$, as it must be else $F_X(x) = 0$)

$$F_X(x) = \int_A^x f_X(t)\, dt = \int_A^x \frac{1}{\beta} e^{-(t-A)/\beta}\, dt$$

$$= -e^{-(t-A)/\beta}\Big|_A^x = 1 - e^{-(x-A)/\beta},$$

hence

$$1 - e^{-(x-A)/\beta} = 0.6$$

$$e^{-(x-A)/\beta} = 0.4$$

$$-(x - A)/\beta = \ln(0.4)$$

$$x = A - \beta \ln(0.4).$$

With $\beta = 4$ and $A = 3$,

$$x = 3 - 4\ln(0.4) = 6.6652.$$

Example 4.2.12. The gamma distribution $G(x|0, \beta, A)$ is the exponential distribution.

Definition 4.2.13. A r.v. X has the **chi-square** distribution with n degrees of freedom, denoted by $\chi_n^2(0)$, if (for some integer $n > 0$)

$$f_X(x) = \begin{cases} \dfrac{1}{2^{n/2}\Gamma(n/2)} x^{(n/2)-1} e^{-x/2}, & 0 \leq x < \infty \\ 0, & \text{otherwise.} \end{cases}$$

The chi-square distribution is, of all statistical distributions, one of the most used in applications of statistics, hence it is very important to have a tabulation of its percentiles. Table 10 gives percentiles of $F_X(x)$ for selected percentages and degrees of freedom, and is preceded by a graph of $F_X(x)$.

Example 4.2.14. The gamma distribution $G(x|(n/2) - 1, 2, 0)$ (n an integer, $n > 0$) is the $\chi_n^2(0)$ distribution.

Example 4.2.15. Let X be $\chi_{10}^2(0)$. Find the 50th and 95th percentiles of X.
  We desire here to find a and b such that $P(X \leq a) = .5$, $P(X \leq b) = .95$. From Table 10 (for 10 degrees of freedom) with $\gamma = .5$ we find $a = 9.34182$; and, with $\gamma = .95$ we find $b = 18.3070$.

Definition 4.2.16. A r.v. X has the **noncentral chi-square** distribution with n degrees of freedom and noncentrality λ, say $\chi_n^2(\lambda)$, if (for some integer $n > 0$, $\lambda \geq 0$)

$$f_X(x) = \begin{cases} e^{-\lambda} \sum_{i=0}^{\infty} \dfrac{\lambda^i x^{(1/2)(n+2i)-1} e^{-x/2}}{i! 2^{(1/2)(n+2i)} \Gamma\left(\dfrac{n+2i}{2}\right)}, & 0 \leq x < \infty \\ 0, & \text{otherwise.} \end{cases}$$

Example 4.2.17. The noncentral chi-square distribution with n degrees of freedom and noncentrality $\lambda = 0$ *is* the chi-square distribution with n degrees of freedom (as our notation in Definitions 4.2.13 and 4.2.16 suggests).

Definition 4.2.18. A r.v. X has the **normal** distribution $N(\mu, \sigma^2)$ if (for some[3] $\sigma^2 > 0$ and $-\infty < \mu < +\infty$)

$$f_X(x) = \frac{1}{\sqrt{2\pi}\,\sigma} e^{-\frac{1}{2}\left(\frac{x-\mu}{\sigma}\right)^2}, \qquad -\infty < x < +\infty.$$

The $N(0, 1)$ distribution is called the **standard normal** distribution. [See Table 11 for graphs and a table of $F_X(x)$ that assumes $\mu = 0$ and $\sigma^2 = 1$.]

Example 4.2.19. To show that $f_X(x)$ in Definition 4.2.18 is a p.d.f., we need to show $f_X(x) \geq 0$ and $\int_{-\infty}^{\infty} f_X(x)\, dx = 1$. It is clear that $f_X(x) \geq 0$. To show the second property, we need to calculate

$$\int_{-\infty}^{\infty} \frac{1}{\sqrt{2\pi}\,\sigma} e^{-(x-\mu)^2/(2\sigma^2)}\, dx.$$

Letting $z = (x - \mu)/\sigma$, this is equal to

$$\int_{-\infty}^{\infty} \frac{1}{\sqrt{2\pi}} e^{-z^2/2}\, dz \equiv A \text{ (say)}.$$

---

[3]σ is used to denote the positive square root of σ^2.

Now

$$A^2 = \int_{-\infty}^{\infty} \int_{-\infty}^{\infty} \left(\frac{1}{\sqrt{2\pi}} \right)^2 e^{-(z^2 + y^2)/2} \, dz \, dy$$

and, transforming to polar coordinates via $z = r \cos \theta$, $y = r \sin \theta$, $r \, dr \, d\theta = dz \, dy$,

$$A^2 = \int_0^{\infty} \int_0^{2\pi} \left(\frac{1}{\sqrt{\pi}} \right)^2 re^{-r^2/2} \, d\theta \, dr = \int_0^{\infty} re^{-r^2/2} \, dr$$

$$= -e^{-r^2/2} \Big|_0^{\infty} = 1,$$

hence $A = 1$ as was to be shown and $f_X(x)$ is a p.d.f.

The normal distribution is the most used probability distribution model in statistics, and many other important models are byproducts of this basic distribution; for example, the chi-square, t, and F distributions (see, e.g., Example 4.2.22 below). In Chapter 6 we show that many important random variables used in statistics have a distribution that can be approximated by a normal distribution. In view of this importance, we need to be able to find probabilities for normal r.v.'s. In Example 4.2.21 we describe a technique for finding the percentile points of any normal r.v.

Theorem 4.2.20. If $X \sim N(\mu, \sigma^2)$, then $\dfrac{X - \mu}{\sigma} \sim N(0, 1)$. That is, if X is a normal r.v. with μ and σ^2, then by subtracting the value μ and dividing by σ, we can transform this random variable to a "standard" normal r.v., often denoted by Z.

Proof: By direct calculation,

$$F_{\frac{X-\mu}{\sigma}}(x) = P\left(\frac{X - \mu}{\sigma} \leq x \right) = P(X \leq \sigma x + \mu) = F_X(\sigma x + \mu)$$

$$= \int_{-\infty}^{\sigma x + \mu} \frac{1}{\sqrt{2\pi}\,\sigma} e^{-0.5(y - \mu)^2/\sigma^2} \, dy$$

and making the change of variable $z = (y - \mu)/\sigma$ we find

$$F_{\frac{X-\mu}{\sigma}}(x) = \int_{-\infty}^{x} \frac{1}{\sqrt{2\pi}} e^{-0.5z^2} \, dz,$$

which is the desired result.   ∎

Example 4.2.21. If $X \sim N(10, 25)$, find a such that $P(X \geq a) = .95$.

Here $\mu = 10$ and $\sigma^2 = 25$ (so $\sigma = 5$). Now, transforming X to a standard normal r.v. (called **standardizing** X) so that Table 11 [which is for a $N(0, 1)$ r.v.]

can be used, we find

$$P(X \geq a) = P\left(\frac{X - 10}{5} \geq \frac{a - 10}{5}\right) = P\left(Z \geq \frac{a - 10}{5}\right)$$

$$= 1 - P\left(Z \leq \frac{a - 10}{5}\right) = .95.$$

Hence from Table 11,

$$\frac{a - 10}{5} = -1.64, \qquad a = (-1.64)(5) + 10 = 1.8.$$

[*Note*: The graph of the p.d.f. $f_X(x)$ of a $N(\mu, \sigma^2)$ r.v. (see the graph accompanying Table 11) is symmetric about μ; that is, the value of $f_X(x)$ at $\mu + x$ equals the value at $\mu - x$ for all x:

$$f_X(\mu + x) = f_X(\mu - x), \qquad -\infty < x < \infty.$$

Distributions with this property are called **symmetric**. This relationship is often helpful in determination of probabilities; for example,

$$P(Z \leq -2) = P(Z \geq 2)$$

because Z, the standard normal random variable, is symmetric about 0. As another example,

$$P(Z > -1.84) = P(Z < 1.84) = .9671.]$$

Example 4.2.22. One byproduct of the normal distribution is the chi-square distribution. If Z is $N(0, 1)$, then Z^2 is **chi-square with 1 degree of freedom**. First, for $x < 0$

$$F_{Z^2}(x) = P(Z^2 \leq x) = 0$$

so

$$f_{Z^2}(x) = \frac{d}{dx}F_{Z^2}(x) = \frac{d}{dx}0 = 0, \qquad x < 0.$$

Now for $x \geq 0$,

$$F_{Z^2}(x) = P(Z^2 \leq x) = P(-\sqrt{x} \leq Z \leq \sqrt{x})$$

$$= F_Z(\sqrt{x}) - F_Z(-\sqrt{x})$$

$$= F_Z(\sqrt{x}) - (1 - F_Z(\sqrt{x})) \qquad \text{(by symmetry about 0)}$$

$$= 2F_Z(\sqrt{x}) - 1,$$

hence for $x \geq 0$

$$f_{Z^2}(x) = \frac{d}{dx} F_{Z^2}(x) = f_Z(\sqrt{x}) \frac{1}{\sqrt{x}}$$

$$= \frac{1}{\sqrt{2\pi}} x^{-1/2} e^{-x/2}$$

$$= \frac{1}{2^{1/2} \Gamma(1/2)} x^{0.5-1} e^{-x/2}.$$

From Definition 4.2.13 we recognize this as the p.d.f. of a chi-square random variable with 1 degree of freedom, as claimed.

If X is $N(\mu, \sigma^2)$, then we can calculate from Table 11 that

$$P\left(\frac{|X - \mu|}{\sigma} \leq 1 \right) = .6826,$$

$$P\left(\frac{|X - \mu|}{\sigma} \leq 2 \right) = .9544,$$

and

$$P\left(\frac{|X - \mu|}{\sigma} \leq 3 \right) = .9974.$$

Thus, for a standard normal distribution, although a standard normal r.v. can take on any value between $-\infty$ and $+\infty$ and the p.d.f. is strictly positive, the tail probabilities are negligibly small in the sense that "almost all" the probability is concentrated between -3 and $+3$.

Approximations to standard normal probabilities. Over the years, many approximations to the distribution function $F_Z(z)$ of a $N(0,1)$ r.v. Z have been considered, since there is no simple closed-form expression for $F_Z(z)$ in terms of polynomials, exponentials, or trigonometric functions of z. Although on modern computers algorithms are available to approximate $F_Z(z)$ to high accuracy, and thus approximations are not as important as formerly, they are still useful in obtaining fast approximations and in theoretical work. One such recent approximation is that of Shah (1985), which states that, for $0 \leq z \leq 2.2$,

$$F_Z(z) = \frac{z(4.4 - z)}{10} + \frac{1}{2} + \varepsilon,$$

where $|\varepsilon| \leq .005$. Thus, the first two terms may be used to approximate $F_Z(z)$ over this range with an error of at most .005. For example, this approximation yields

$$F_Z(2.0) \simeq .9800,$$

whereas from Table 11 we know the true value is $F_Z(2.0) = .9772$, for an error of the Shah approximation of $.9800 - .9772 = .0028$, less than the bound of $.005$ on error.

Definition 4.2.23. A r.v. X has the **F-distribution** $F(n_1, n_2)$ if (for some positive integers n_1, n_2)

$$
f_X(x) = \begin{cases} \dfrac{\Gamma\left(\dfrac{n_1 + n_2}{2}\right)\left(\dfrac{n_1}{n_2}\right)^{n_1/2}}{\Gamma\left(\dfrac{n_1}{2}\right)\Gamma\left(\dfrac{n_2}{2}\right)} \dfrac{x^{(1/2)(n_1 - 2)}}{\left(1 + \dfrac{n_1}{n_2}x\right)^{(1/2)(n_1 + n_2)}}, & 0 < x < \infty \\ 0, & \text{otherwise.} \end{cases}
$$

[See Table 12 for graphs and a table of $F_X(x)$.]

Definition 4.2.24. A r.v. X has the **noncentral F-distribution** $F(n_1, n_2, \lambda)$ with **noncentrality** λ if (for some positive integers n_1 and n_2, $\lambda \geq 0$)

$f_X(x) =$

$$
\begin{cases} e^{-\lambda} \displaystyle\sum_{i=0}^{\infty} \dfrac{\lambda^i x^{(1/2)(n_1 + 2i) - 1}}{i!\left(1 + \dfrac{n_1}{n_2}x\right)^{(1/2)(2i + n_1 + n_2)}} \dfrac{\Gamma\left(\dfrac{2i + n_1 + n_2}{2}\right)\left(\dfrac{n_1}{n_2}\right)^{(1/2)(2i + n_1)}}{\Gamma\left(\dfrac{n_2}{2}\right)\Gamma\left(\dfrac{2i + n_1}{2}\right)}, & x > 0 \\ 0, & \text{otherwise.} \end{cases}
$$

Example 4.2.25. $F(n_1, n_2, 0)$ is $F(n_1, n_2)$. Note that, in each case, n_1 and n_2 are called **degrees of freedom**. One should compare $F(n_1, n_2, \lambda)$ with $\chi_n^2(\lambda)$.

Definition 4.2.26. A r.v. X has **Student's t-distribution** with n degrees of freedom if (for some integer $n > 0$)

$$
f_X(x) = \frac{\Gamma\left(\dfrac{n+1}{2}\right)}{\sqrt{n\pi}\,\Gamma\left(\dfrac{n}{2}\right)} \frac{1}{\left(1 + \dfrac{x^2}{n}\right)^{(n+1)/2}}, \qquad -\infty < x < +\infty.
$$

[See Table 13 for graphs and a table of $F_X(x)$.]

[*Note*: At this point you are *not* expected to memorize these densities and are *not* expected to realize how or why they are reasonable or useful. (In many cases it is difficult even to show that they are p.d.f.'s!) This is simply the logical place to list them for use later in Chapter 6 and in the chapters on statistics. They should give you some idea of what an actual p.d.f. may look like.

Also note that various authors will define the parameters of a distribution differently; for example, α will be called $\alpha + 1$, and so on. (Also, the "starting point" A is often taken as 0 without a statement to that effect.)]

The F- and t-distributions, which are byproducts of chi-square and normal distributions, have important applications in statistical inference. For applications, selected percentage points are tabulated, though if one needs nontabulated t-, F-, chi-square, or normal probabilities, then computer programs such as those on pages 155–169 of Dudewicz and Ralley (1981) or in a statistical computer package such as the "Statistical Analysis System" (acronymed to "SAS") described in SAS Institute Inc. (1982) can be used. Examples 4.2.27 and 4.2.28 illustrate use of the F- and t-tables.

Example 4.2.27. If X is $F(n_1, n_2)$ with $n_1 = 10$ and $n_2 = 23$, find y such that

$$P(X \geq y) = .05.$$

Since y is also such that $P(X \leq y) = .95$, from Table 12 with $n_1 = 10$ and $n_2 = 23$ we find $y = 2.27$.

Example 4.2.28. If X has the t-distribution with $n = 16$ degrees of freedom, find y such that

$$P(X \leq y) = .75.$$

From Table 13, with $n = 16$ and $\gamma = .75$, we find $y = .690$.

Example 4.2.29.   Cantor-type Distributions[4]. A new casino has an automatic coin flipper containing a fair coin. If we deposit \$.75, the machine operates as follows. The machine flips the coin and if heads turns up it pays \$3/4; it then flips again and if heads turns up it pays \$3/16; it then flips again and if heads turns up it pays \$3/64; and so on. (Successive flips are assumed to be independent.) That is, on flip i ($i \geq 1$) it pays \$3/4^i for heads and \$0 otherwise, so that our total gross (that is, ignoring the \$.75 fee) winnings are

$$W = \sum_{i=1}^{\infty} \frac{3}{4^i} X_i, \qquad (4.2.30)$$

where $X_1, X_2, \ldots$ are independent r.v.'s and $P[X_i = 0] = P[X_i = 1] = .5$ ($i = 1, 2, \ldots$). *We now ask*: What is the d.f. of W? This will turn out to be *singularly continuous*.

Let us consider $F(x) = P[W \leq x]$. First let us note that

$$0 \leq W \leq \frac{3}{4} + \frac{3}{4^2} + \frac{3}{4^3} + \cdots = 1 \qquad (4.2.31)$$

---

[4] This example is not essential to an understanding of other material in this book.

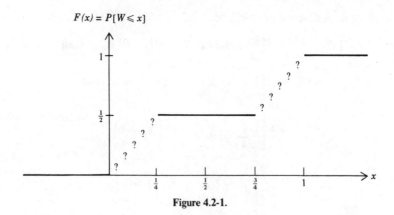

Figure 4.2-1.

[where we used the formula $1 + x + x^2 + \cdots = (1 - x)^{-1}$ for $0 < x < 1$], so that $F(x) = P[W \le x] = 0$ for $x < 0$ and $F(x) = P[W \le x] = 1$ for $x \ge 1$. Also $P[W \le 0] = P[W < 0] + P[W = 0] = 0 + P[W = 0] = 0$ since (for every integer $m > 0$)

$$P[W = 0] = P[X_1 = 0, X_2 = 0, X_3 = 0, \ldots]$$

$$\le P[X_1 = 0, X_2 = 0, \ldots, X_m = 0] \qquad (4.2.32)$$

$$= P[X_1 = 0]P[X_2 = 0] \cdots P[X_m = 0] = 1/2^m.$$

Now

$$X_1 = 1 \Rightarrow W \ge \tfrac{3}{4}$$

$$X_1 = 0 \Rightarrow W \le \frac{3}{4^2} + \frac{3}{4^3} + \cdots = \frac{1}{4}, \qquad (4.2.33)$$

so that $P[\tfrac{1}{4} \le W \le \tfrac{3}{4}] = 0$ and, for $\tfrac{1}{4} \le x \le \tfrac{3}{4}$, $F(x) = P[W \le \tfrac{1}{4}] = P[X_1 = 0]$ $= \tfrac{1}{2}$. [Any items like $P[W = y]$ that arise, e.g., $P[W = \tfrac{1}{4}]$, are handled as at inequality (4.2.32). For example, $P[W = .25] = P[X_1 = 0, X_2 = X_3 = \cdots = 1]$ $\le P[X_1 = 0, X_2 = \cdots = X_m = 1] = 1/2^m$ for every positive integer m, hence $P[W = .25] = 0$.] Thus, $F(x)$ has no jumps greater than $\tfrac{1}{2}$. [See Figure 4.2-1 for our information about $F(x)$ to this point.]

Now, the winnings on tosses $2, 3, \ldots$ are

$$3 \sum_{i=2}^{\infty} \frac{1}{4^i} X_i = \tfrac{1}{4} \cdot 3 \sum_{i=2}^{\infty} \frac{1}{4^{i-1}} X_i = \tfrac{1}{4} \cdot \left(3 \sum_{i=1}^{\infty} \frac{1}{4^i} X_{i+1} \right)$$

which has the same distribution as $\tfrac{1}{4} W$. Hence, $F(x)$ in $[0, \tfrac{1}{4}]$ can be related to

$F(x)$ in $[0, 1]$ as follows: For $0 < x < \frac{1}{4}$,

$$F(x) = P[W \le x] = P[W \le x \text{ and } X_1 = 0] + P[W \le x \text{ and } X_1 = 1]$$

$$= P\left[3 \sum_{i=2}^{\infty} \frac{1}{4^i} X_i \le x \text{ and } X_1 = 0\right] + 0$$

$$= P\left[3 \sum_{i=2}^{\infty} \frac{1}{4^i} X_i \le x\right] P[X_1 = 0]$$

$$= \frac{1}{2} P\left[\frac{1}{4} \cdot \left(3 \sum_{i=1}^{\infty} \frac{1}{4^i} X_{i+1}\right) \le x\right]$$ (4.2.34)

$$= \frac{1}{2} P\left[\left(3 \sum_{i=1}^{\infty} \frac{1}{4^i} X_{i+1}\right) \le 4x\right]$$

$$= \frac{1}{2} F(4x).$$

Thus, $F(x) = \frac{1}{4}$ for $\frac{1}{16} \le x \le \frac{3}{16}$. Similarly, $F(x)$ in $[\frac{3}{4}, 1]$ can be related to $F(x)$ in $[0, 1]$ as follows: For $\frac{3}{4} < x < 1$,

$$F(x) = P[W \le x] = P[W \le x \text{ and } X_1 = 0] + P[W \le x \text{ and } X_1 = 1]$$

$$= \frac{1}{2} + P\left[\frac{3}{4} + 3 \sum_{i=2}^{\infty} \frac{1}{4^i} X_i \le x \text{ and } X_1 = 1\right]$$

$$= \frac{1}{2} + P\left[3 \sum_{i=2}^{\infty} \frac{1}{4^i} X_i \le x - \frac{3}{4}\right] P[X_1 = 1]$$

$$= \frac{1}{2} + \frac{1}{2} P\left[\frac{1}{4} \cdot \left(3 \sum_{i=1}^{\infty} \frac{1}{4^i} X_{i+1}\right) \le x - \frac{3}{4}\right]$$ (4.2.35)

$$= \frac{1}{2} + \frac{1}{2} P\left[\left(3 \sum_{i=1}^{\infty} \frac{1}{4^i} X_{i+1}\right) \le 4\left(x - \frac{3}{4}\right)\right]$$

$$= \frac{1}{2} + \frac{1}{2} F\left(4\left(x - \frac{3}{4}\right)\right).$$

Thus, $F(x) = \frac{3}{4}$ for $\frac{13}{16} \le x \le \frac{15}{16}$. [See Figure 4.2-2 for our information about $F(x)$ to this point.]

We have now shown that in *each* of three intervals $F(x)$ is constant (at values $\frac{1}{4}, \frac{1}{2}, \frac{3}{4}$); these intervals have a total length $\frac{1}{8} + \frac{1}{2} + \frac{1}{8} = \frac{1}{2} + \frac{2}{8} = \frac{3}{4}$. It follows that, if $F(x)$ has a jump, that jump cannot be greater than $\frac{1}{4}$ (see Figure 4.2-2). In the remaining four intervals (each of which has length $\frac{1}{16}$) we can use the approach used at equation (4.2.34) to get the graph related to that of $F(x)$; hence the respective four intervals will contain subintervals of length $\frac{1}{32}$ in which $F(x)$ is constant at values $\frac{1}{8}, \frac{3}{8}, \frac{5}{8}$, and $\frac{7}{8}$.

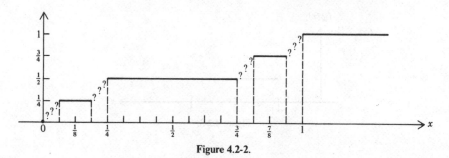

Figure 4.2-2.

Using mathematical induction, after m steps we will find $1 + 2 + 2^2 + 2^3 + \cdots + 2^{m-1}$ intervals with total length $2^{-1} + 2^{-2} + 2^{-3} + 2^{-4} + \cdots + 2^{-m} = 1 - 1/2^m$ in *each* of which $F(x)$ is constant. *It follows that*: $F(x)$ is a continuous nondecreasing function; $F(0) = 0$; $F(1) = 1$; and the subintervals of $[0, 1]$ where $F(x)$ is a constant have total length 1. Since the derivative of a constant is zero, $F'(x) = 0$ at almost all x, so $F(x)$ is *singularly continuous*.

[*Note*: $F(x)$ is constant at most of the interval $[0, 1]$, essentially because most values x with $0 \le x \le 1$ are not possible values of W. The possible values of W (e.g., $0, \frac{1}{4}, \frac{3}{4}, 1$) all have probability 0 as shown at (4.2.32); we have shown $F'(x) = 0$ except at such values.]

Example 4.2.36. A Life Distribution. Suppose that a certain company manufactures light bulbs that, while their life X is a random number of hours, have an exponential distribution for life with $\beta = 10$, $A = 0$. For what number of hours t is it the case that the probability is .9 that the bulb will burn out before t?

We wish to find t such that $P[X < t] = .9$. Since X has the exponential distribution with $\beta = 10$ and $A = 0$ (see Definition 4.2.10), we set

$$\int_0^t \frac{1}{10} e^{-x/10} \, dx = .9,$$

$$-e^{-x/10} \big|_0^t = 1 - e^{-t/10} = .9.$$

Hence, $e^{-t/10} = .1$ and $t = -10 \ln(.1) \approx 23$.

Example 4.2.37. Let W be a r.v. uniformly distributed over the interval $[1, 3]$. Determine the density function $f_W(x)$ of W and sketch its graph. If we define a random variable G by $G = 2W - 1$, determine the density function $f_G(x)$ of G and sketch its graph.

The height of $f_W(x)$ is constant on $[1, 3]$ and the integral of $f_W(x)$ from 1 to 3 is 1, so

$$f_W(x) = \begin{cases} \frac{1}{2}, & \text{if } 1 \le x \le 3 \\ 0, & \text{otherwise.} \end{cases}$$

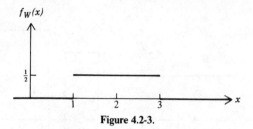

Figure 4.2-3.

(This could also be obtained directly from Definition 4.2.6.) Hence, the graph is as shown in Figure 4.2-3. The d.f. of W, say $F(t)$, is

$$F(t) = P[W \le t] = \begin{cases} 1, & \text{if } t > 3 \\ \dfrac{t-1}{2}, & \text{if } 1 \le t \le 3 \\ 0, & \text{if } t < 1. \end{cases}$$

We will now seek to directly find $F_G(x)$, the d.f. of G, and differentiate it to obtain $f_G(x)$ (see Theorem 4.1.5). Since $G = 2W - 1$,

$$F_G(x) = P[G \le x] = P[2W - 1 \le x]$$

$$= P\left[W \le \frac{x+1}{2}\right] = \begin{cases} 1, & \text{if } \dfrac{x+1}{2} > 3 \\ \dfrac{\dfrac{x+1}{2} - 1}{2}, & \text{if } 1 \le \dfrac{x+1}{2} \le 3 \\ 0, & \text{if } \dfrac{x+1}{2} < 1 \end{cases}$$

$$= \begin{cases} 1, & \text{if } x > 5 \\ \dfrac{x-1}{4}, & \text{if } 1 \le x \le 5 \\ 0, & \text{if } x < 1. \end{cases}$$

Differentiating, we find

$$f_G(x) = \begin{cases} \frac{1}{4}, & \text{if } 1 \le x \le 5 \\ 0, & \text{otherwise,} \end{cases}$$

which shows that G is uniform on $(1, 5)$. (This is a special case of Example 4.2.6; the proof in that case, which was omitted, is similar to the one we have just given.) The graph is as shown in Figure 4.2-4.

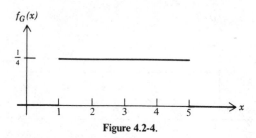

Figure 4.2-4.

Example 4.2.38. If a d.f. $F(x)$ has a p.d.f. $f(x)$, the ratio

$$q(x) = \frac{f(x)}{1 - F(x)} \qquad (4.2.39)$$

is defined for $F(x) < 1$ and is called the **failure rate** (or **hazard rate**, or **force of mortality**). If $F(x)$ is the d.f. of a r.v. Y that represents the life of some item, $q(x)\,dx$ can be interpreted as the conditional probability of death in $(x, x + dx)$ given that death has not occurred before x. We say $F(x)$ has an **increasing (decreasing) failure rate**—denoted **IFR (DFR)**—if $q(x)$ is increasing (decreasing). IFR intuitively represents "wear-out," while DFR represents "work-hardening."

For example, if an item has a random life length Y with d.f. $F(x)$, then the probability $Y \le 80$ given $Y > 70$ is

$$P[Y \le 80 | Y > 70] = \frac{P[70 < Y \le 80]}{P[Y > 70]}$$

$$= \frac{\int_{70}^{80} f(x)\,dx}{1 - F(70)} = \frac{F(80) - F(70)}{1 - F(70)}.$$

Find and plot the failure rate if Y has the exponential distribution (see Definition 4.2.10) with $A = 0$, $\beta = 1/\alpha$, namely,

$$f(t) = \begin{cases} \alpha e^{-\alpha t}, & t \ge 0 \\ 0, & t < 0. \end{cases} \qquad (4.2.40)$$

Also find and plot the failure rate if Y has the so-called **Weibull distribution** with $\alpha > 0$ and $\beta > 0$

$$f(t) = \begin{cases} \alpha \beta t^{\beta-1} e^{-\alpha t^{\beta}}, & t \ge 0 \\ 0, & t < 0. \end{cases} \qquad (4.2.41)$$

First, for the exponential distribution of equation (4.2.40) we find (for $x \ge 0$)

$$F(x) = \int_{0}^{x} \alpha e^{-\alpha t}\,dt = 1 - e^{-\alpha x} \Rightarrow 1 - F(x) = e^{-\alpha x},$$

$$q(x) = \frac{f(x)}{1 - F(x)} = \frac{\alpha e^{-\alpha x}}{e^{-\alpha x}} = \alpha.$$

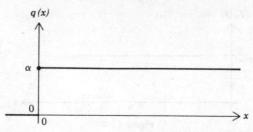

Figure 4.2-5. Failure rate of an exponential life.

In light of Problem 4.17 (the "lack of memory property," which we recommend reading at this point), this is not surprising. (See Figure 4.2-5.)

Second, for the Weibull distribution of equation (4.2.41) we find (for $x \geq 0$)

$$F(x) = \int_0^x \alpha\beta t^{\beta-1} e^{-\alpha t^\beta}\, dt = 1 - e^{-\alpha x^\beta} \Rightarrow 1 - F(x) = e^{-\alpha x^\beta},$$

$$q(x) = \frac{f(x)}{1 - F(x)} = \frac{\alpha\beta x^{\beta-1} e^{-\alpha x^\beta}}{e^{-\alpha x^\beta}} = \alpha\beta x^{\beta-1}.$$

Here we find constant failure rate if $\beta = 1$ [in which case $F(x)$ is just the exponential distribution previously discussed], while $\alpha\beta x^{\beta-1}$ is an increasing function of x for $\beta > 1$ and a decreasing function of x for $\beta < 1$. (See Figure 4.2-6.)

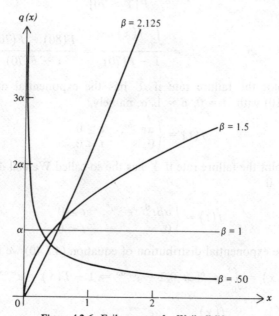

Figure 4.2-6. Failure rate of a Weibull life.

The Weibull distribution is important in applications for several reasons. First, by simply making an appropriate choice of β it can be used to model both increasing and decreasing failure rates. Second, it appropriately models cases where the failure rate $q(x)$ is proportional to powers of x. Third, if Y is exponential, then (as we will see in Example 4.6.5) $Y^{1/\beta}$ is Weibull.

PROBLEMS FOR SECTION 4.2

4.2.1 Connection between the Gamma Distribution and the Poisson r.v. If X has the gamma distribution $G(x|\nu + 1, 1, 0)$ and Y has a Poisson distribution with parameter μ, where ν is a positive integer, show that

$$P(X \geq \mu) = P(Y \leq \nu).$$

4.2.2 If X has the gamma distribution $G(x|\alpha, \beta, 0)$ with α a positive integer, and if Y is a Poisson r.v. with parameter μ, then show that

$$P(X \geq \beta\mu) = P(Y \leq \alpha - 1).$$

[*Hint:* Show that $X^* = X/\beta$ has the gamma distribution $G(x^*|\alpha, 1, 0)$ and then use the result of Problem 4.2.1.]

4.2.3 As shown in Example 4.2.22, if Z is $N(0,1)$, then Z^2 is chi-square with 1 degree of freedom. *Show* that if X has a t-distribution with n degrees of freedom, then X^2 has an F-distribution with $n_1 = 1$ and $n_2 = n$ degrees of freedom.

4.2.4 Show that:

(a) $\displaystyle\int_\alpha^\infty \frac{x}{\lambda} e^{-(x-\alpha)/\lambda}\,dx = \alpha + \lambda.$

(b) $\displaystyle\int_0^\infty \frac{x}{\Gamma(\alpha)\beta^\alpha} x^{\alpha-1} e^{-x/\beta}\,dx = \alpha\beta.$

(c) $\displaystyle\int_0^1 x \frac{\Gamma(\alpha+\beta)}{\Gamma(\alpha)\Gamma(\beta)} x^{\alpha-1}(1-x)^{\beta-1}\,dx = \frac{\alpha}{\alpha+\beta}.$

(d) $\displaystyle\int_{-\infty}^\infty x e^{-x^2/2}\,dx = 0.$

4.2.5 (*Continuing Problem 3.2.4.*) A cereal company claims its boxes contain 16 ounces of cereal. Let X be the weight of the cereal in any given box. Then X is often a continuous r.v., and hence has an absolutely continuous d.f., which implies that $P(X = 16) = 0$. So, the manufacturer fills to "a little more" to avoid possible legal problems.
Assuming X is normally distributed with $\mu = 16$ and $\sigma = .2$,
(a) What is the probability that a given box will have
    (i) More than 16 ounces of cereal?
    (ii) Less than 16 ounces of cereal?
    (iii) Less than 15.95 ounces of cereal?
    (iv) More than 16.1 ounces of cereal?
    (v) Between 15.95 and 16.1 ounces of cereal?

(b) If a consumer protection agency samples 20 boxes of cereal at random, what is the probability that

    (i) At least 3 boxes will have more than 16 ounces?

    (ii) Between 4 and 12 boxes will have anywhere between 15.95 and 16.1 ounces of cereal?

4.2.6 Suppose that in any year the proportion of soft drinks consumed that contain no caffeine, no artificial color, and no artificial sweeteners, in the United States follows a beta distribution with $\alpha = 2$, $\lambda = 3$. Compute the probability that **(a)** the proportion is less than .5; **(b)** the proportion is between .35 and .65; **(c)** the proportion is at least .60.

4.2.7 Suppose the percentage of gun owners in a certain state who favor a gun control law follows a beta distribution with $\alpha = 1$, $\lambda = 4$. **(a)** Find the median of this distribution. **(b)** What is the probability that the percentage is at least 60%? **(c)** What is the probability that the percentage is between 40 and 60%?

4.2.8 **Relationship between the Binomial and Beta Distributions.** If X is $B(n, p)$, then show that, for any $0 \le a \le n$,

$$\sum_{x=a}^{n} \binom{n}{x} p^x q^{n-x} = \frac{\Gamma(n+1)}{\Gamma(a)\Gamma(n-a+1)} \int_0^p x^{a-1}(1-x)^{n-a}\, dx.$$

Thus, $P(X \ge a) = P(Y \le p)$, where $Y \sim B(x \mid \alpha = a, \lambda = n - a + 1)$.

4.2.9 Let X_1, X_2, and X_3 be three independent uniform r.v.'s, with $f_{X_i}(x) = 1/(b-a)$ for $a < x < b$ $(a < b, i = 1, 2, 3)$.

    (a) Find the median of X_i.

    (b) Let $Y = \min(X_1, X_2, X_3)$, and $a < c_i < b$ $(i = 1, 2)$. Compute $P(Y > c_1)$ and $P(Y < c_2)$.

    (c) Let $U = \max(X_1, X_2, X_3)$ and $a < c_i < b$ $(i = 1, 2)$. Compute $P(U > c_1)$ and $P(U < c_2)$.

    (d) If $c_1 < c_2$, then compute $P(U < c_2, Y > c_1)$.

4.2.10 A point where a p.d.f. achieves a relative maximum is called a **mode** of the distribution. A p.d.f. that has only one maximum is called a **unimodal** density, a density with two, three,... maxima is respectively called **bimodal, trimodal,**... (and in general **multimodal**).

Find the mode(s) of the p.d.f.

(a) $f_X(x) = \dfrac{1}{\sqrt{2\pi}\,\sigma} e^{-(x-\mu)^2/(2\sigma^2)}$ for $-\infty < x < +\infty$;

(b) $f_X(x) = \dfrac{1}{\beta^\alpha \Gamma(\alpha)} e^{-x/\beta} x^{\alpha-1}$ for $0 < x < \infty$;

(c) $f_X(x) = \dfrac{\Gamma(\alpha + \lambda + 2)}{\Gamma(\alpha + 1)\Gamma(\lambda + 1)} x^\alpha (1-x)^\lambda$ for $0 < x < 1$.

4.2.11 An r.v. X is said to be **truncated** at $x = a$ if its p.d.f. or probability function is zero below or at a. If $f(x)$ is a p.d.f. and $F(x)$ is the corresponding d.f., define

$$f_a(x) = \frac{1}{1 - F(a)} f(x), \quad \text{if } x > a$$

(and 0 otherwise) and

$$F_a(x) = \begin{cases} \dfrac{F(x) - F(a)}{1 - F(a)}, & \text{if } x \geq a \\ 0, & \text{otherwise.} \end{cases}$$

(a) Verify that $f_a(\cdot)$ is a p.d.f.
(b) Verify that $F_a(\cdot)$ is a d.f.
(c) Let X be the r.v. arising from a $N(10,4)$ distribution truncated at 6. Find the probabilities (i) $P(X < 8)$; (ii) $P(X > 11)$; (iii) $P(7 < X < 12)$.

4.2.12 Let X be the r.v. arising from a $G(x|2,2,0)$ truncated (see Problem 4.2.11) at $x = 2$. Find (a) $P(X > 3)$; (b) $P(X \leq 10)$.

4.2.13 A random variable X_c is called **contaminated** if its p.d.f. is a convex combination of two or more p.d.f.'s, that is, if

$$f_{X_c}(x) = \sum_{i=1}^{k} a_i f_{X_i}(x) \text{ with } a_1 + a_2 + \cdots + a_k = 1.$$

(a) Verify that

$$f_X(x) = \frac{1}{2\sqrt{2\pi}} \left(e^{-(x-\mu)^2/2} + e^{-(x+\mu)^2/2} \right) \quad (-\infty < x < \infty)$$

is a p.d.f. In general show that $f_{X_c}(x)$ is a p.d.f.
(b) Show that $f_X(x)$ from part (a) is a bimodal p.d.f., with modes at $x = \pm\mu$.

4.3. RELATIONS AMONG CONTINUOUS DISTRIBUTIONS

It is most natural to postpone relations among the distributions of Section 4.2 until later, since they are derived using results of Section 4.6 on distributions of functions of continuous random variables and results on characteristic functions (Chapter 5). Certain of these results go by special names, for example, the Central Limit Theorem (Chapter 6). Some relations of the sort "the A distribution is a special case of the B distribution" were given in Section 4.2.

4.4. MULTIVARIATE CONTINUOUS DISTRIBUTIONS; INDEPENDENCE

In Section 3.4 we defined the distribution function of any n-dimensional r.v. $X = (X_1, \ldots, X_n)$ as $F_X(x_1, \ldots, x_n) = P[X_1 \leq x_1, \ldots, X_n \leq x_n]$ for $-\infty < x_i < +\infty$ $(i = 1, \ldots, n)$. Such a r.v. X was called *discrete* (see Definitions 3.4.11 and 3.4.12 for details) essentially iff (for all $x_1, \ldots, x_n$)

$$F_X(x_1, \ldots, x_n) = \sum_{\substack{x_1' \leq x_1, \ldots, x_n' \leq x_n \\ \text{with } p_X(x_1', \ldots, x_n') > 0}} p_X(x_1', \ldots, x_n').$$

We now develop the analogous results for the (absolutely) continuous case, that is, the case where there is an n-dimensional version of the p.d.f. of Definition 4.1.1.

Definition 4.4.1. X is called an (n-dimensional) **(absolutely) continuous random variable** if its d.f. $F_X(x_1, \ldots, x_n)$ may be represented as

$$F_X(x_1, \ldots, x_n) = \int_{-\infty}^{x_n} \int_{-\infty}^{x_{n-1}} \cdots \int_{-\infty}^{x_1} f_X(y_1, \ldots, y_n) \, dy_1 \ldots dy_{n-1} \, dy_n,$$

where $f_X(x_1, \ldots, x_n)$ is a **probability density function (p.d.f.)**; that is, by definition

$$\begin{cases} f_X(y_1, \ldots, y_n) \geq 0 & \text{for all } y_1, \ldots, y_n, \text{ and} \\ \int_{-\infty}^{\infty} \cdots \int_{-\infty}^{\infty} f_X(y_1, \ldots, y_n) \, dy_1 \ldots dy_n = 1. \end{cases}$$

In this case $F_X(x_1, \ldots, x_n)$ is called an **(absolutely) continuous d.f.**

Note that Theorems 4.1.5 and 4.1.6 generalize to n-dimensional random variables.

Definition 4.4.2. If $X = (X_1, \ldots, X_n)$ is an (absolutely) continuous n-dimensional r.v., the d.f. of any subset of $X_1, \ldots, X_n$ is (absolutely) continuous and its p.d.f. is called a **marginal density function**.

Example 4.4.3. If $X = (X_1, \ldots, X_n)$ is an (absolutely) continuous n-dimensional r.v., the d.f. of $(X_1, \ldots, X_{n-1})$ is (absolutely) continuous. We may calculate (by Lemma 3.4.3)

$$F_{X_1, \ldots, X_{n-1}}(x_1, \ldots, x_{n-1})$$

$$= F_{X_1, \ldots, X_{n-1}, X_n}(x_1, \ldots, x_{n-1}, +\infty)$$

$$= \int_{-\infty}^{\infty} \int_{-\infty}^{x_{n-1}} \cdots \int_{-\infty}^{x_1} f_{X_1, \ldots, X_n}(y_1, \ldots, y_n) \, dy_1 \ldots dy_{n-1} \, dy_n$$

$$= \int_{-\infty}^{x_{n-1}} \cdots \int_{-\infty}^{x_1} \left[\int_{-\infty}^{\infty} f_{X_1, \ldots, X_n}(y_1, \ldots, y_n) \, dy_n \right] dy_1 \ldots dy_{n-1}.$$

Hence,

$$f_{X_1, \ldots, X_{n-1}}(x_1, \ldots, x_{n-1}) = \int_{-\infty}^{\infty} f_{X_1, \ldots, X_n}(x_1, \ldots, x_{n-1}, y) \, dy,$$

the marginal p.d.f. of $(X_1, \ldots, X_{n-1})$.

If $X = (X_1, X_2)$ is an (absolutely) continuous r.v., then (under certain assumptions; see Definition 3.4.6 ff) the conditional d.f. of X_2 given $X_1 = x_1'$ is

$$\lim_{x_1'' \to x_1'} \frac{\int_{x_1''}^{x_1'} \int_{-\infty}^{x_2} f_{X_1, X_2}(x_1, x_2) \, dx_2 \, dx_1}{\int_{x_1''}^{x_1'} f_{X_1}(x_1) \, dx_1} = \frac{\int_{-\infty}^{x_2} f_{X_1, X_2}(x_1', x_2) \, dx_2}{f_{X_1}(x_1')}. \tag{4.4.4}$$

[This requires that $f_{X_1}(x_1)$ and $\int_{-\infty}^{x_2} f_{X_1, X_2}(x_1, x_2) \, dx_2$ are continuous functions of x_1 at x_1' and that $f_{X_1}(x_1') > 0$.] This suggests that we define the **conditional density of X_2 given $X_1 = x_1'$** to be

$$f_{X_2 | X_1 = x_1'}(x_2 | x_1') \equiv \frac{f_{X_1, X_2}(x_1', x_2)}{f_{X_1}(x_1')} \tag{4.4.5}$$

[or zero if $f_{X_1}(x_1') = 0$], since integrating on x_2 will then yield the conditional d.f. of X_2 given $X_1 = x_1'$. We will not formalize this definition, but will note that it extends to the case of n-dimensional r.v.'s; this will be made explicit by example in Example 4.4.7.

Theorem 4.4.6.   The (absolutely) continuous r.v.'s $X_1, \ldots, X_n$ are independent iff (for all $x_1, \ldots, x_n$)

$$f_{X_1, \ldots, X_n}(x_1, \ldots, x_n) = f_{X_1}(x_1) \cdots f_{X_n}(x_n).$$

The proof of this theorem uses differentiation to prove the "only if" and integration to prove the "if." (See Definition 3.4.7.)

Example 4.4.7.   Let the three-dimensional vector $X = (X_1, X_2, X_3)$ have p.d.f.

$$f_X(x_1, x_2, x_3) = \begin{cases} 6x_1 x_2^2 x_3, & \text{if } 0 \le x_1 \le 1, 0 \le x_2 \le 1, 0 \le x_3 \le \sqrt{2} \\ 0, & \text{otherwise.} \end{cases}$$

(a) Show that $f_X(x_1, x_2, x_3)$ is a p.d.f.
(b) Find the marginal p.d.f.'s of X_1, of X_2, of X_3, and of (X_1, X_3).
(c) Find the conditional p.d.f.'s $f_{X_1, X_2 | X_3 = x_3'}(x_1, x_2 | x_3')$ and $f_{X_3 | X_1 = x_1'}(x_3 | x_1')$.
(d) Are X_1, X_2, and X_3 independent r.v.'s?

(a) To show that $f_X(x_1, x_2, x_3)$ is a p.d.f., first note that $f_X(x_1, x_2, x_3) \ge 0$ for all (x_1, x_2, x_3). Next, since

$$\int_{-\infty}^{\infty} \int_{-\infty}^{\infty} \int_{-\infty}^{\infty} f_X(x_1, x_2, x_3) \, dx_1 \, dx_2 \, dx_3 = \int_0^{\sqrt{2}} \int_0^1 \int_0^1 6x_1 x_2^2 x_3 \, dx_1 \, dx_2 \, dx_3 = 1,$$

by definition (Definition 4.4.1) $f_X(x_1, x_2, x_3)$ is a p.d.f.

(b) Here

$$f_{X_1}(x_1) = \int_{-\infty}^{\infty} \int_{-\infty}^{\infty} f_{X_1, X_2, X_3}(x_1, x_2, x_3) \, dx_2 \, dx_3$$

$$= \begin{cases} \int_0^{\sqrt{2}} \int_0^1 6x_1 x_2^2 x_3 \, dx_2 \, dx_3 = 2x_1, & \text{if } 0 \leq x_1 \leq 1 \\ 0, & \text{otherwise.} \end{cases}$$

Similarly,

$$f_{X_2}(x_2) = \begin{cases} \int_0^{\sqrt{2}} \int_0^1 6x_1 x_2^2 x_3 \, dx_1 \, dx_3 = 3x_2^2, & \text{if } 0 \leq x_2 \leq 1 \\ 0, & \text{otherwise,} \end{cases}$$

$$f_{X_3}(x_3) = \begin{cases} \int_0^1 \int_0^1 6x_1 x_2^2 x_3 \, dx_1 \, dx_2 = x_3, & \text{if } 0 \leq x_3 \leq \sqrt{2} \\ 0, & \text{otherwise,} \end{cases}$$

and

$$f_{X_1, X_3}(x_1, x_3) = \begin{cases} \int_0^1 f_X(x_1, x^2, x_3) \, dx_2 = 2x_1 x_3, & \text{if } 0 \leq x_1 \leq 1, 0 \leq x_3 \leq \sqrt{2} \\ 0, & \text{otherwise.} \end{cases}$$

(c) From the discussion at and after equation (4.4.5), conditional p.d.f.'s behave like conditional probabilities [where $P(A|B) = P(AB)/P(B)$], hence

$$f_{X_1, X_2|X_3 = x_3'}(x_1, x_2 | x_3')$$

$$= \begin{cases} \dfrac{f_X(x_1, x_2, x_3')}{f_{X_3}(x_3')}, & \text{if } f_{X_3}(x_3') > 0 \\ 0, & \text{otherwise} \end{cases}$$

$$= \begin{cases} \dfrac{f_X(x_1, x_2, x_3')}{x_3'}, & \text{if } 0 \leq x_3' \leq \sqrt{2} \\ 0, & \text{otherwise} \end{cases}$$

$$= \begin{cases} \dfrac{6x_1 x_2^2 x_3'}{x_3'} = 6x_1 x_2^2 & \text{if } 0 \leq x_3' \leq \sqrt{2}, 0 \leq x_1 \leq 1, 0 \leq x_2 \leq 1 \\ 0, & \text{otherwise,} \end{cases}$$

and

$$f_{X_3|X_1=x_1'}(x_3|x_1') = \begin{cases} \dfrac{f_{X_1,X_3}(x_1',x_3)}{f_{X_1}(x_1')}, & \text{if } f_{X_1}(x_1') > 0 \\ 0, & \text{otherwise} \end{cases}$$

$$= \begin{cases} \dfrac{2x_1'x_3}{2x_1'} = x_3, & \text{if } 0 \le x_1' \le 1, 0 \le x_3 \le \sqrt{2} \\ 0, & \text{otherwise.} \end{cases}$$

(d) Using Theorem 4.4.6, we will check whether $f_X(x_1, x_2, x_3)$ equals the product $f_{X_1}(x_1)f_{X_2}(x_2)f_{X_3}(x_3)$ for all (x_1, x_2, x_3). From part (b), we find that

$$f_{X_1}(x_1)f_{X_2}(x_2)f_{X_3}(x_3)$$

$$= \begin{cases} (2x_1)(3x_2^2)(x_3) = 6x_1x_2^2x_3, & \text{if } 0 \le x_1 \le 1, 0 \le x_2 \le 1, 0 \le x_3 \le \sqrt{2} \\ 0, & \text{otherwise,} \end{cases}$$

which, for all (x_1, x_2, x_3), equals $f_{X_1,X_2,X_3}(x_1, x_2, x_3)$ as given in the statement of this problem, hence X_1, X_2, X_3 are independent random variables.

Example 4.4.8. Let (X_1, X_2) be the coordinates of a point chosen at random in a disk of radius $r > 0$. Then the p.d.f. of (X_1, X_2) is zero outside the disk (since points outside the disk are never chosen) and is constant on the disk [since points inside the disk are equally likely to be chosen, in the sense of having the same density function value $f_{X_1,X_2}(x_1, x_2)$]. That constant density value on the disk must be $1/(\pi r^2)$ so that the density will integrate to 1, hence we have

$$f_{X_1,X_2}(x_1, x_2) = \begin{cases} 1/(\pi r^2), & \text{if } x_1^2 + x_2^2 \le r^2 \\ 0 & \text{otherwise.} \end{cases}$$

Find the marginal p.d.f.'s of each of X_1 and X_2. Find the conditional density of X_2 given that $X_1 = x_1'$. Are X_1 and X_2 independent r.v.'s?
  Here we calculate

$$f_{X_1}(x_1) = \int_{-\infty}^{\infty} f_{X_1,X_2}(x_1, x_2)\, dx_2 = \int_{\{x_2:\, x_1^2+x_2^2 \le r^2\}} 1/(\pi r^2)\, dx_2$$

$$= \begin{cases} \displaystyle\int_{-\sqrt{r^2-x_1^2}}^{\sqrt{r^2-x_1^2}} \dfrac{1}{\pi r^2}\, dx_2, & \text{if } -r \le x_1 \le r \\ 0, & \text{otherwise} \end{cases}$$

$$= \begin{cases} \dfrac{2}{\pi r^2}\sqrt{r^2 - x_1^2}, & \text{if } -r \le x_1 \le r \\ 0, & \text{otherwise.} \end{cases}$$

Similarly,

$$f_{X_2}(x_2) = \begin{cases} \dfrac{2}{\pi r^2}\sqrt{r^2 - x_2^2}, & \text{if } -r \le x_2 \le r \\ 0, & \text{otherwise.} \end{cases}$$

Thus, we are now in a position to calculate

$$f_{X_2|X_1 = x_1'}(x_2|x_1') = \begin{cases} \dfrac{f_{X_1, X_2}(x_1', x_2)}{f_{X_1}(x_1')}, & \text{if } f_{X_1}(x_1') > 0 \\ 0, & \text{otherwise} \end{cases}$$

$$= \begin{cases} \dfrac{1}{2\sqrt{r^2 - x_1'^2}}, & \text{if } x_2^2 + x_1'^2 \le r^2 \\ 0, & \text{otherwise} \end{cases}$$

$$= \begin{cases} \dfrac{1}{2\sqrt{r^2 - x_1'^2}}, & \text{if } |x_2| \le \sqrt{r^2 - x_1'^2}, -r \le x_1' \le r \\ 0, & \text{otherwise.} \end{cases}$$

X_1 and X_2 are not independent since for any (x_1, x_2) on the disk

$$f_{X_1}(x_1)f_{X_2}(x_2)$$

$$= \begin{cases} \left(\dfrac{2}{\pi r^2}\right)^2 \sqrt{r^2 - x_1^2}\sqrt{r^2 - x_2^2}, & \text{if } -r \le x_1 \le r \text{ and } -r \le x_2 \le r \\ 0, & \text{otherwise} \end{cases}$$

does not equal $f_{X_1, X_2}(x_1, x_2)$.

A *simple argument for the nonindependence* of X_1 and X_2 can also be given, proceeding from the joint density of (X_1, X_2), which is positive only for (x_1, x_2) on the disk of radius r. It follows that X_1 can take on any value between $-r$ and r, and also that X_2 can take on any value between $-r$ and r. If X_1 and X_2 were independent, (X_1, X_2) would be able to take on any value in the square where $-r \le x_1 \le r$ and $-r \le x_2 \le r$. This is a contradiction (of the fact that the density is concentrated on the disk of radius r), hence X_1 and X_2 cannot be independent r.v.'s.

Example 4.4.9. Let X and Y have the joint p.d.f.

$$f(x, y) = \begin{cases} \dfrac{k}{x}, & \text{if } 0 < y < x, 0 < x < 2 \\ 0, & \text{otherwise.} \end{cases}$$

(a) Find the unique value of k for which $f(x, y)$ is a p.d.f. When k has the value found in part **(a)**: **(b)** Find $f_X(x)$ and $f_Y(y)$; **(c)** Find $f_{X|Y=y_1}(x|y_1)$; **(d)** Are X and Y independent r.v.'s?

(a) In order for $f(x, y)$ to be a p.d.f., it must be nonnegative and integrate to 1. Since x is positive, k must be positive [and for any positive value of k we have $f(x, y)$ nonnegative]. For the integral to be 1,

$$1 = \int_0^2 \int_0^x \frac{k}{x}\, dy\, dx = \int_0^2 \frac{k}{x} x\, dx = 2k,$$

hence $k = 1/2$ is the unique value such that $f(x, y)$ is a p.d.f.

(b) Here

$$f_X(x) = \int_{-\infty}^\infty f(x, y)\, dy = \begin{cases} \int_0^x \frac{1}{2x}\, dy = \frac{1}{2}, & \text{if } 0 < x < 2 \\ 0, & \text{otherwise} \end{cases}$$

and

$$f_Y(y) = \int_{-\infty}^\infty f(x, y)\, dx$$

$$= \begin{cases} \int_y^2 \frac{1}{2x}\, dx = \frac{1}{2}\ln(x)\Big|_0^2 = \frac{1}{2}[\ln(2) - \ln(y)], & \text{if } 0 < y < 2 \\ 0, & \text{otherwise.} \end{cases}$$

[As a check on the work, note that $f_Y(y)$ integrates to 1; verification is left as an exercise.]

(c) Now

$$f_{X|Y=y_1}(x|y_1) = \begin{cases} \dfrac{f(x, y_1)}{f_Y(y_1)}, & \text{if } f_Y(y_1) > 0 \\ 0, & \text{otherwise} \end{cases}$$

$$= \begin{cases} \dfrac{\dfrac{1}{2x}}{\dfrac{1}{2}[\ln(2) - \ln(y_1)]}, & \text{if } 0 < y_1 < x < 2 \\ 0, & \text{otherwise} \end{cases}$$

$$= \begin{cases} \dfrac{1}{x[\ln(2) - \ln(y_1)]}, & \text{if } 0 < y_1 < x < 2 \\ 0, & \text{otherwise.} \end{cases}$$

[Again, as a check on work note that

$$\int_{-\infty}^{\infty} f_{X|Y=y_1}(x|y_1)\,dx = \int_{y_1}^{2} \frac{1}{x[\ln(2) - \ln(y_1)]}\,dx = 1.\,\Bigg]$$

(d) Finally, X and Y are not independent since

$$f_X(x)f_Y(y) = \begin{cases} \frac{1}{4}[\ln(2) - \ln(y)], & \text{if } 0 < x < 2, 0 < y < 2 \\ 0, & \text{otherwise} \end{cases}$$

does not equal $f(x, y)$.

Note that since (for x such that $f_X(x) > 0$)

$$f_{Y|X=x}(y|x) = \frac{f_{X,Y}(x, y)}{f_X(x)},$$

if X and Y are independent we have

$$f_{Y|X=x}(y|x) = \frac{f_X(x)f_Y(y)}{f_X(x)} = f_Y(y)$$

(and similarly, still when X and Y are independent r.v.'s ,

$$f_{X|Y=y}(x|y) = f_X(x)).$$

PROBLEMS FOR SECTION 4.4

4.4.1 Let (X_1, X_2) be a point randomly chosen on the circle $x_1^2 + x_2^2 = r^2$ ($r > 0$), so that $f_{X_1, X_2}(x_1, x_2) = 1/(2\pi r)$ if $x_1^2 + x_2^2 = r^2$ (and $= 0$ otherwise). Find the marginal p.d.f.'s $f_{X_1}(x_1)$ and $f_{X_2}(x_2)$ and the conditional distribution of X_2 given $X_1 = x_1'$. Are X_1 and X_2 independent r.v.'s?

4.4.2 Let $f(x_1, x_2) = 24(1 - x_1)x_2$ if $0 < x_1 < 1$ and $0 < x_2 < 1$, $= 0$ otherwise.
(a) Show that $f(x_1, x_2)$ is a joint p.d.f. of some two-dimensional r.v., say (X_1, X_2).
(b) Find the marginal p.d.f.'s $f_{X_1}(x_1)$ and $f_{X_2}(x_2)$.
(c) Show that the joint p.d.f. can be written as the product of the two marginals.
(d) Are X_1 and X_2 independent r.v.'s?
(e) Find the probability $P(X_1 < 1/2 | X_2 > 1/3)$.

4.4.3 Let (X_1, X_2) be a two-dimensional r.v. with joint p.d.f. $f_{X_1, X_2}(x_1, x_2) = x_1 + x_2$ if $0 < x_1 < 1$ and $0 < x_2 < 1$ (and $= 0$ otherwise).
(a) Find the marginal p.d.f.'s of X_1 and X_2.
(b) Find the conditional p.d.f. of X_2 given $X_1 = x_1$.
(c) Are X_1 and X_2 independent r.v.'s?

4.4.4 Let $X_1 \sim B(x|\alpha = 0, \lambda)$, $X_2 \sim B(x|\alpha, \lambda = 0)$, with X_1 and X_2 independent r.v.'s.
(a) Find the joint p.d.f. of (X_1, X_2).
(b) Find the p.d.f. of $X_1 X_2$.

4.4.5 Let the joint p.d.f. of a two-dimensional r.v. be $f_{X_1, X_2}(x_1, x_2) = 6(1 - x_1 - x_2)$ if $0 < x_2 < 1 - x_1$ and $x_1 > 0$ (and $= 0$ otherwise).

(a) Find the conditional p.d.f. of X_2 given $X_1 = x_1$.

(b) Find the conditional p.d.f. of X_1 given $X_2 = x_2$.

4.4.6 Let $f_{X_1, X_2}(x_1, x_2) = 2e^{-(x_1 + x_2)}$ if $0 < x_1 < x_2$ and $x_2 > 0$ (and $= 0$ otherwise).

(a) Find $f_{X_1}(x_1)$ and $f_{X_2}(x_2)$.

(b) Find $f_{X_1|X_2}(x_1|x_2)$ and $f_{X_2|X_1}(x_2|x_1)$.

(c) Are X_1 and X_2 independent r.v.'s?

4.4.7 Let $f_{X_1, X_2}(x_1, x_2) = 1/(2x_1^2 x_2)$ if $1 < x_1 < \infty$ and $1/x_1 < x_2 < x_1$ (and $= 0$ otherwise).

(a) Find the marginal p.d.f.'s $f_{X_1}(x_1)$ and $f_{X_2}(x_2)$.

(b) Find the conditional p.d.f.'s $f_{X_1|X_2}(x_1|x_2)$ and $f_{X_2|X_1}(x_2|x_1)$.

(c) Are X_1 and X_2 independent r.v.'s?

4.4.8 Let the d.f. of a two-dimensional r.v. be

$$F_{X_1, X_2}(x_1, x_2) = 1 - (1 + x_1)^{-\alpha} - (1 + x_2)^{-\alpha} + (1 + x_1 + x_2)^{-\alpha}$$

for $x_1 > 0$ and $x_2 > 0$ (for some $\alpha > 0$), and $= 0$ otherwise.

(a) Find the marginal d.f.'s of X_1 and X_2.

(b) Find the joint p.d.f. of (X_1, X_2).

(c) Find the marginal p.d.f.'s of X_1 and X_2.

4.4.9 Suppose (X_1, X_2) has joint p.d.f.

$$f_{X_1, X_2}(x_1, x_2) = \tfrac{1}{4}\left(1 + x_1 x_2 \left(x_1^2 - x_2^2\right)\right)$$

for $|x_1| < 1$ and $|x_2| < 1$ (and $= 0$ otherwise).

(a) Find the marginal p.d.f.'s of X_1 and X_2.

(b) Are X_1 and X_2 independent r.v.'s?

4.5. SPECIAL MULTIVARIATE CONTINUOUS DISTRIBUTIONS[5]

In this section, we will introduce the single most important multivariate continuous distribution, the multivariate normal distribution $N(\mu, \Sigma)$. Its properties and uses will be developed in more detail in the chapters on statistics. We will proceed as follows: Recall the definition of the univariate normal distribution, define the bivariate normal distribution and develop some of its properties, and define the multivariate normal distribution (of which the two previous distributions are special cases).

Definition 4.5.1. A r.v. X has the **(univariate) normal** distribution $N(\mu, \sigma^2)$ if (for some[6] $\sigma^2 > 0$ and $-\infty < \mu < +\infty$)

$$f_X(x) = \frac{1}{\sqrt{2\pi}\,\sigma} e^{-\frac{1}{2}\left(\frac{x-\mu}{\sigma}\right)^2}, \qquad -\infty < x < +\infty.$$

---

[5] This section, from Definition 4.5.4 on, may be omitted if the instructor desires. Although much of the nonintuitive content of statistics lies in multivariate cases, this content is often made clearest by a consideration of the bivariate case (where graphs may be drawn and notation is not so intricate as to obscure meaning).

[6] σ, σ_1, σ_2 are used (respectively) to denote the positive square roots of σ^2, σ_1^2, σ_2^2.

A graph of the $N(0, 1)$ distribution is presented with Table 11, along with graphs of the $N(0, .4)$ and $N(0, 2.5)$ distributions.

Definition 4.5.2. A r.v. $X = (X_1, X_2)$ has the **(bivariate) normal** distribution $N(\mu_1, \mu_2; \sigma_1^2, \sigma_2^2, \rho)$ if (for some[6] $\sigma_1^2 > 0, \sigma_2^2 > 0, -1 < \rho < +1, -\infty < \mu_1 < +\infty, -\infty < \mu_2 < +\infty)$

$$f_{X_1, X_2}(x_1, x_2) = \frac{1}{2\pi\sigma_1\sigma_2\sqrt{1-\rho^2}} e^{-\frac{1}{2(1-\rho^2)}\left\{\left(\frac{x_1-\mu_1}{\sigma_1}\right)^2 - 2\rho\left(\frac{x_1-\mu_1}{\sigma_1}\right)\left(\frac{x_2-\mu_2}{\sigma_2}\right) + \left(\frac{x_2-\mu_2}{\sigma_2}\right)^2\right\}}$$

$$-\infty < x_1, x_2 < +\infty.$$

Example 4.5.3. It can be shown that if (X_1, X_2) has the **bivariate normal** distribution of Definition 4.5.2, then its p.d.f. $f_{X_1, X_2}(x_1, x_2)$ has its **largest value at the point** (μ_1, μ_2), where we find by simple evaluation that

$$f_{X_1, X_2}(\mu_1, \mu_2) = \frac{1}{2\pi\sigma_1\sigma_2\sqrt{1-\rho^2}}.$$

For any constant c between 0 and this maximum possible value of the joint p.d.f., **the locus of the points in the plane where** $f_{X_1, X_2}(x_1, x_2) = c$ **is an ellipse** (for details see Problem 14.14), and **the probability content of that ellipse is**

$$\iint_A f_{X_1, X_2}(x_1, x_2)\, dx_1\, dx_2 = 1 - 2\pi\sigma_1\sigma_2\sqrt{1-\rho^2}\, c,$$

where A denotes all points in the ellipse, that is,

$$A = \left\{(x_1, x_2): f_{X_1, X_2}(x_1, x_2) \geq c\right\}.$$

(A short table of this integral, which is trivial to calculate for given values of σ_1, σ_2, ρ, and c, is given in Problem 14.14.) In applications, if we choose

$$1 - 2\pi\sigma_1\sigma_2\sqrt{1-\rho^2}\, c = .95,$$

then A is the smallest area where we can be 95% sure the value of (X_1, X_2) will fall. Some graphs are given in Figure 4.5-1. You can show from these facts that (for $0 < L < 1$)

$$\iint_{\{(x_1, x_2): Q(x_1, x_2) \leq -2(1-\rho^2)\ln(1-L)\}} f_{X_1, X_2}(x_1, x_2)\, dx_1\, dx_2 = L$$

where

$$Q(x_1, x_2) = \left(\frac{x_1 - \mu_1}{\sigma_1} \right)^2 - 2\rho \left(\frac{x_1 - \mu_1}{\sigma_1} \right) \left(\frac{x_2 - \mu_2}{\sigma_2} \right) + \left(\frac{x_2 - \mu_2}{\sigma_2} \right)^2.$$

In Figure 4.5-1, we have chosen $L = .25$, $.50$, $.75$, and $.95$ [i.e., the contours shown have equal density height and inside them the density is higher than it is at any point outside the contour, and the probability content of the inner contour is .25 (of the next contour, .50; of the third contour, .75; and of the outer contour, .95)]. The values shown below the graphs are the four values of $-2(1 - \rho^2)\ln(1 - L)$ in that graph.

In Figure 4.5-2 we show three-dimensional plots of the surfaces that are defined by the density $f_{X_1, X_2}(x_1, x_2)$ corresponding to each of the cases in Figure 4.5-1. Cutting these surfaces by planes parallel to the (x_1, x_2) plane produces the contours shown in Figure 4.5-1.

Definition 4.5.4. A r.v. $X = (X_1, \ldots, X_n)$ has the **(multivariate) normal** distribution $N(\mu, \Sigma)$ where

$$\mu \equiv \begin{bmatrix} \mu_1 \\ \vdots \\ \mu_n \end{bmatrix}$$

is a vector of n real numbers and

$$\Sigma = \begin{bmatrix} \sigma_{11} & \sigma_{12} & \cdots & \sigma_{1n} \\ \sigma_{21} & \sigma_{22} & \cdots & \sigma_{2n} \\ \vdots & & & \\ \sigma_{n1} & \sigma_{n2} & \cdots & \sigma_{nn} \end{bmatrix}$$

is any $n \times n$ symmetric positive definite matrix of real numbers if [defining $x = (x_1, \ldots, x_n)'$]

$$f_X(x) = \frac{1}{(2\pi)^{n/2} \sqrt{|\Sigma|}} e^{-\frac{1}{2}(X-\mu)'\Sigma^{-1}(X-\mu)}$$

for all vectors x of real numbers.

After a review of vector and matrix algebra [e.g., Appendix II, pp. 387–405 of Scheffé (1959) or Appendix A of Siotani, Hayakawa, and Fujikoshi (1985)], you should be able to verify that (if $n = 2$) Definitions 4.5.2 and 4.5.4 are equivalent.

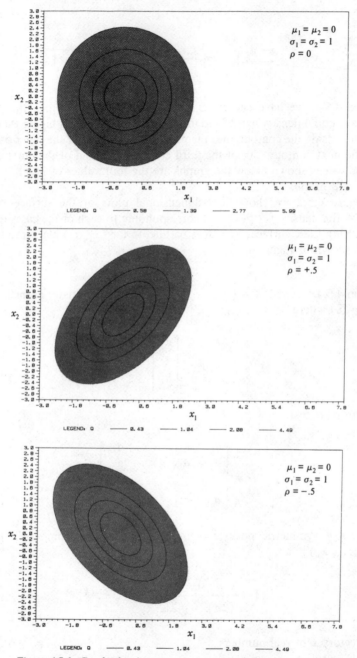

Figure 4.5-1. Graphs showing curves (contours) such that $f_{X_1, X_2}(x_1, x_2)$ $= c$ for various values of c when (X_1, X_2) has the bivariate normal distribution. (The shaded area A has probability content .95 and is the smallest such area.)

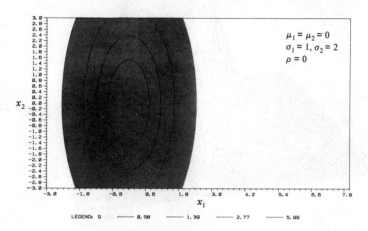

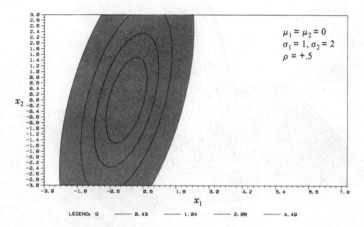

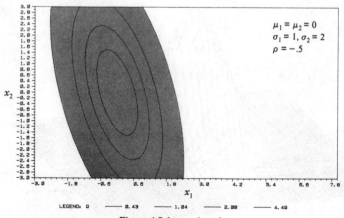

Figure 4.5-1. continued

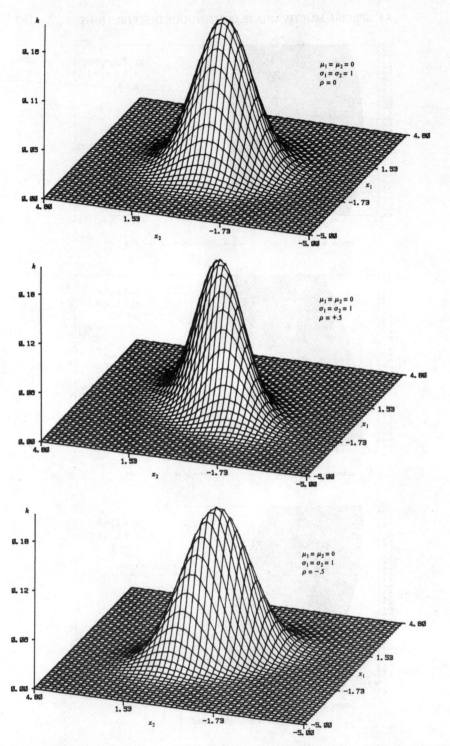

Figure 4.5-2. Graphs showing the surfaces defined by the density $f_{X_1, X_2}(x_1, x_2)$ over the (x_1, x_2) plane. (Cutting these surfaces by planes parallel to the (x_1, x_2) plane produces the contours shown in Figure 4.5-1.)

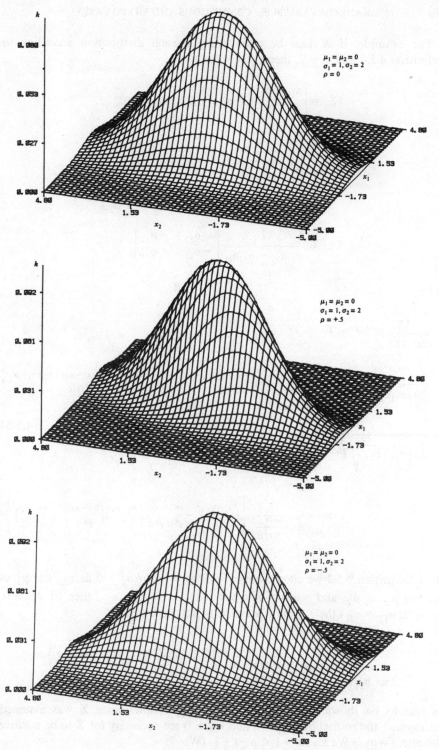

Figure 4.5-2. continued

For example, if X has the multivariate normal distribution according to Definition 4.5.4 and $n = 2$, then

$$|\Sigma| = \begin{vmatrix} \sigma_{11} & \sigma_{12} \\ \sigma_{21} & \sigma_{22} \end{vmatrix} = \sigma_{11}\sigma_{22} - \sigma_{12}\sigma_{21};$$

$$\Sigma^{-1} = \begin{bmatrix} \dfrac{\sigma_{22}}{\sigma_{11}\sigma_{22} - \sigma_{12}\sigma_{21}} & \dfrac{-\sigma_{12}}{\sigma_{11}\sigma_{22} - \sigma_{12}\sigma_{21}} \\ \dfrac{-\sigma_{21}}{\sigma_{11}\sigma_{22} - \sigma_{12}\sigma_{21}} & \dfrac{\sigma_{11}}{\sigma_{11}\sigma_{22} - \sigma_{12}\sigma_{21}} \end{bmatrix}$$

$$= \frac{1}{\sigma_{11}\sigma_{22} - \sigma_{12}\sigma_{21}} \begin{bmatrix} \sigma_{22} & -\sigma_{12} \\ -\sigma_{21} & \sigma_{11} \end{bmatrix};$$

$f_X(x)$

$$= \frac{1}{2\pi\sqrt{|\Sigma|}} e^{-\frac{1}{2}(X-\mu)'\Sigma^{-1}(X-\mu)}$$

$$= \frac{1}{2\pi\sqrt{\sigma_{11}\sigma_{22} - \sigma_{12}\sigma_{21}}} e^{-\frac{1}{2(\sigma_{11}\sigma_{22} - \sigma_{12}\sigma_{21})}\{\sigma_{22}(x_1-\mu_1)^2 - (\sigma_{12}+\sigma_{21})(x_1-\mu_1)(x_2-\mu_2) + \sigma_{11}(x_2-\mu_2)^2\}}$$

$$= \frac{1}{2\pi\sqrt{\sigma_{11}}\sqrt{\sigma_{22}}\sqrt{1 - \dfrac{\sigma_{12}\sigma_{21}}{\sigma_{11}\sigma_{22}}}} \tag{4.5.5}$$

$$\times e^{-\frac{1}{2\left(1 - \frac{\sigma_{12}\sigma_{21}}{\sigma_{11}\sigma_{22}}\right)}\left\{\left(\frac{x_1-\mu_1}{\sqrt{\sigma_{11}}}\right)^2 - \frac{\sigma_{12}+\sigma_{21}}{\sqrt{\sigma_{11}}\sqrt{\sigma_{22}}}\left(\frac{x_1-\mu_1}{\sqrt{\sigma_{11}}}\right)\left(\frac{x_2-\mu_2}{\sqrt{\sigma_{22}}}\right) + \left(\frac{x_2-\mu_2}{\sqrt{\sigma_{22}}}\right)^2\right\}}.$$

If in Definition 4.5.2 we choose our $\sigma_1^2 > 0$ as σ_{11}, our $\sigma_2^2 > 0$ as σ_{22}, our μ_1 as μ_1, our μ_2 as μ_2, and our $\rho(-1 < \rho < +1)$ as $\sigma_{12}/\sqrt{\sigma_{11}\sigma_{22}}$, then (if $\sigma_{11} > 0$, $\sigma_{22} > 0$, $\sigma_{12} = \sigma_{21}$) the $f_X(x)$ of equation (4.5.5) becomes

$$\frac{1}{2\pi\sigma_1\sigma_2\sqrt{1-\rho^2}} e^{-\frac{1}{2(1-\rho^2)}\left\{\left(\frac{x_1-\mu_1}{\sigma_1}\right)^2 - 2\rho\left(\frac{x_1-\mu_1}{\sigma_1}\right)\left(\frac{x_2-\mu_2}{\sigma_2}\right) + \left(\frac{x_2-\mu_2}{\sigma_2}\right)^2\right\}},$$

as was to be shown. The restriction $\sigma_{12} = \sigma_{21}$ follows since Σ was assumed symmetric; the restrictions $\sigma_{11} > 0$ and $\sigma_{22} > 0$ are necessary for Σ to be positive definite. (Why?) We know $-1 < \rho < +1$. (Why?)

PROBLEMS FOR SECTION 4.5

4.5.1 Let (X_1, X_2) have a bivariate normal distribution (see Definition 4.5.2).
(a) Find the marginal p.d.f.'s of X_1 and of X_2.
(b) Find the conditional p.d.f. of X_1 given $X_2 = x_2$, and the conditional p.d.f. of X_2 given $X_1 = x_1$.

4.5.2 Let (X_1, X_2) be a bivariate normal r.v. Show that if $\rho = 0$ then X_1 and X_2 are independent r.v.'s. (In fact the converse is also true, but is not as easy to show until after the discussion of expectations in Chapter 5, where this result is given in Theorem 5.3.25.)

4.5.3 Let (X_1, X_2) be a r.v. with joint p.d.f.

$$f_{X_1, X_2}(x_1, x_2) = \frac{1}{2\pi} e^{-(x_1^2 + x_2^2)/2}\left(1 + x_1 x_2 e^{-(x_1^2 + x_2^2 - 2)/2}\right)$$

for $-\infty < x_1 < \infty$ and $-\infty < x_2 < \infty$.
(a) Show that $f_{X_1, X_2}(x_1, x_2)$ is a p.d.f.
(b) Find the marginal p.d.f.'s $f_{X_1}(x_1)$ and $f_{X_2}(x_2)$ and show they are normal.
(c) Show that $f_{X_1, X_2}(x_1, x_2)$ is not bivariate normal. (Thus, normal marginal p.d.f.'s does not imply the joint p.d.f. is normal.)

4.5.4 Suppose that (X_1, X_2) is bivariate normal with $\mu_1 = \mu_2 = 0$, $\sigma_1 = \sigma_2 = 1$ and $\rho = 0$.
(a) Find c_1 such that

$$P\left(-c_1 \le X_1 \le c_1, -c_1 \le X_2 \le c_1\right) = .95.$$

(b) Find an ellipse (circle) such that

$$P\left(X_1^2 + X_2^2 \le c_2\right) = .95.$$

(c) Carefully graph the square of part (a) and the circle of part (b) on the same coordinate axes. [*Note:* Each region has probability .95 of containing the r.v. (X_1, X_2).]

4.6. DISTRIBUTIONS OF FUNCTIONS OF CONTINUOUS RANDOM VARIABLES

In Section 3.6, we considered the **distribution of a function** of a discrete r.v. and obtained a comprehensive formula. In the case of continuous r.v.'s the situation is more complicated; in this section some of the results are stated and motivated (and formulas for the comparable discrete case are given in a few instances to illustrate the difference).

Theorem 4.6.1. If $Y = aX + b$ and $a > 0$, then $F_Y(y) = F_X\left(\dfrac{y-b}{a}\right)$. If X is (absolutely) continuous, so is Y and

$$f_{aX+b}(y) = \frac{1}{a}f_X\left(\frac{y-b}{a}\right).$$

If X is discrete, so is Y and

$$p_{aX+b}(y) = p_X\left(\frac{y-b}{a}\right).$$

[*Note:* These results are for the case $a > 0$; if $a < 0$, similar results can be obtained.]

Proof: (Assuming $a > 0$.) First,

$$F_Y(y) = F_{aX+b}(y) = P[aX + b \le y] = P\left[X \le \frac{y-b}{a}\right] = F_X\left(\frac{y-b}{a}\right).$$

Differentiating this equation with respect to y, we find (in the case of absolutely continuous X)

$$\frac{d}{dy}F_Y(y) = \frac{d}{dy}F_X\left(\frac{y-b}{a}\right) = \frac{1}{a}f_X\left(\frac{y-b}{a}\right).$$

Let us call this function $f(y)$. The $f(y) \ge 0$ [since $f_X(x) \ge 0$ and $a > 0$] and

$$\int_{-\infty}^{\infty} f(y)\, dy = \int_{-\infty}^{\infty} \frac{1}{a}f_X\left(\frac{y-b}{a}\right) dy = \int_{-\infty}^{\infty} f_X(y)\, dy = 1,$$

so (by Definition 4.1.1) $f(y)$ is a p.d.f. However,

$$\int_{-\infty}^{z} f(y)\, dy = \int_{-\infty}^{z} \frac{1}{a}f_X\left(\frac{y-b}{a}\right) dy = \int_{-\infty}^{(z-b)/a} f_X(x)\, dx$$

$$= P\left[X \le \frac{z-b}{a}\right] = P[aX + b \le z] = P[Y \le z] = F_Y(z)$$

for all z. Hence (by Definition 4.1.1), Y is an absolutely continuous r.v. with p.d.f. $f(y)$.

In the discrete case, it is easy to see that

$$p_{aX+b}(y) = P[aX + b = y] = P\left[X = \frac{y-b}{a}\right] = p_X\left(\frac{y-b}{a}\right). \quad \blacksquare$$

Example 4.6.2. Suppose that X is $N(\mu, \sigma^2)$ and $Y = (X - \mu)/\sigma$. Then the p.d.f. of Y is, using Theorem 4.6.1,

$$f_Y(y) = f_{\frac{1}{\sigma}X + \frac{-\mu}{\sigma}}(y) = \frac{1}{\frac{1}{\sigma}}f_X\left(\frac{y - (-\mu/\sigma)}{1/\sigma}\right) = \sigma f_X(\sigma y + \mu)$$

$$= \sigma \frac{1}{\sqrt{2\pi}\,\sigma} e^{-\frac{1}{2}(\sigma y + \mu - \mu)^2/\sigma^2}$$

$$= \frac{1}{\sqrt{2\pi}} e^{-y^2/2},$$

from which we recognize (see Definition 4.2.18) that $Y = (X - \mu)/\sigma$ is a $N(0,1)$ r.v. [*Note*: Y is simply the "standardized" X, and we already knew from direct calculation in Theorem 4.2.20 that Y is $N(0,1)$.]

Example 4.6.3. Suppose that X is Poisson with parameter μ, so that (see Definition 3.2.11)

$$P(X = x) = p_X(x) = e^{-\mu}\frac{\mu^x}{x!} \qquad \text{(for } x = 0,1,2,\ldots)$$

(and otherwise $p_X(x) = 0$). Then the distribution of $Y = nX$ is, by Theorem 4.6.1,

$$p_Y(y) = p_{nX+0}(y) = p_X((y-0)/n) = p_X(y/n)$$

$$= \begin{cases} e^{-\mu}\dfrac{\mu^{y/n}}{(y/n)!}, & \text{if } y/n = 0,1,2,\ldots \\ 0, & \text{otherwise} \end{cases}$$

$$= \begin{cases} e^{-\mu}\dfrac{\mu^{y/n}}{(y/n)!}, & \text{if } y = 0,n,2n,3n,\ldots \\ 0, & \text{otherwise.} \end{cases}$$

Theorem 4.6.4. If $y = g(x)$ is differentiable for all x, and either $g'(x) > 0$ for all x or $g'(x) < 0$ for all x, and if X is (absolutely) continuous, then $Y = g(X)$ is (absolutely) continuous and

$$f_Y(y) = \begin{cases} f_X\big(g^{-1}(y)\big)\left|\dfrac{d}{dy}g^{-1}(y)\right|, & \text{if } \min\Big(\lim\limits_{x\to-\infty} g(x),\ \lim\limits_{x\to+\infty} g(x)\Big) \\ & \qquad < y < \max\Big(\lim\limits_{x\to-\infty} g(x),\ \lim\limits_{x\to+\infty} g(x)\Big) \\ 0, & \text{otherwise.} \end{cases}$$

Proof: As motivation, consider the fact that $F_Y(y) = P[Y \le y] = P[g(X) \le y] = P[X \in \{x: g(x) \le y\}]$.

Case I: $g'(x) > 0$. Then

$$F_Y(y) = P\big[X \le g^{-1}(y)\big] = F_X\big(g^{-1}(y)\big)$$

and by differentiation

$$f_Y(y) = f_X\big(g^{-1}(y)\big)\frac{d}{dy}g^{-1}(y).$$

As motivation, consider Figure 4.6-1.

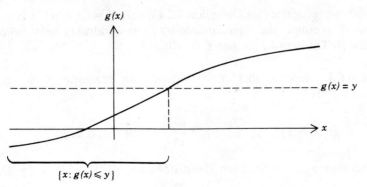

Figure 4.6-1.

Case II: $g'(x) < 0$. Then

$$F_Y(y) = P\left[X \geq g^{-1}(y)\right] = 1 - P\left[X < g^{-1}(y)\right]$$

$$= 1 - F_X\left(g^{-1}(y)\right) + P\left[X = g^{-1}(y)\right] = 1 - F_X\left(g^{-1}(y)\right)$$

and by differentiation

$$f_Y(y) = -f_X\left(g^{-1}(y)\right)\frac{d}{dy}g^{-1}(y).$$

As motivation, consider Figure 4.6-2.

Since $y = g(x)$, $x = g^{-1}(y)$ and

$$\frac{d}{dy}g^{-1}(y) = \frac{d}{d\left[g(x)\right]}x = \frac{1}{\dfrac{dg(x)}{dx}} = \frac{1}{g'(x)|_{x=g^{-1}(y)}} = \frac{1}{g'(x)},$$

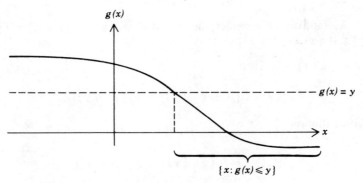

Figure 4.6-2.

which is > 0 if $g'(x) > 0$, and is < 0 if $g'(x) < 0$. Thus, we may combine cases I and II to obtain

$$f_Y(y) = f_X\big(g^{-1}(y)\big)\left|\frac{d}{dy}g^{-1}(y)\right|.$$

The range of positivity and validity of this formula is determined by consideration of where $F_Y(y)$ is 0 and 1.   ∎

Example 4.6.5. Suppose a r.v. X has the Weibull distribution with $\alpha > 0$ and $\beta > 0$ [see (4.2.40)]

$$f_X(x) = \begin{cases} \alpha\beta x^{\beta-1}e^{-\alpha x^\beta}, & x \geq 0 \\ 0, & x < 0. \end{cases}$$

Find the density of $Y = X^\beta$.

Here $y = g(x) = x^\beta$ is differentiable for all x, and $g'(x) = \beta x^{\beta-1} > 0$ for all $x > 0$. Also $g^{-1}(y) = x = y^{1/\beta}$, so

$$f_X\big(g^{-1}(y)\big) = f_X\big(y^{1/\beta}\big) = \alpha\beta y^{1-\frac{1}{\beta}}e^{-\alpha y}$$

and

$$\frac{d}{dy}g^{-1}(y) = \frac{d}{dy}y^{1/\beta} = \frac{1}{\beta}y^{\frac{1}{\beta}-1};$$

hence (by Theorem 4.6.4),

$$f_Y(y) = \begin{cases} \alpha e^{-\alpha y}, & \text{if } 0 < y < \infty \\ 0, & \text{otherwise.} \end{cases}$$

[*Note:* We have actually used a slight extension of Theorem 4.6.4, wherein now we talk only of x for which $f_X(x) > 0$; e.g., $g'(x) > 0$ for all x for which $f_X(x) > 0$, i.e., for all $x > 0$. Only a slight modification of the proof of Theorem 4.6.4 is needed in order to restrict attention throughout to $\{x\colon f_X(x) > 0\}$. We then also take limits of $g(x)$ with x in this set, of course.]

Thus, if X is Weibull, X^β is exponential. (And, **if Y is exponential, $Y^{1/\beta}$ is Weibull.**)

Example 4.6.6. If X has absolutely continuous d.f. $F(x)$, then $Y_1 = -\ln(F(x))$ is an exponential r.v., as is $Y_2 = -\ln(1 - F(X))$.

To show this for Y_1, first note that $Y_1 \geq 0$ (since $0 \leq F(x) \leq 1$, $\ln(F(x)) \leq 0$, and $-\ln(F(x)) \geq 0$), so that $F_{Y_1}(t) = 0$ for $t < 0$. For $t \geq 0$,

$$F_{Y_1}(t) = P(Y_1 \leq t) = P\big(-\ln(F(X)) \leq t\big) = P\big(F(X) \geq e^{-t}\big)$$

$$= P\big(X \geq F^{-1}(e^{-t})\big) = 1 - P\big(X \leq F^{-1}(e^{-t})\big)$$

$$= 1 - F\big(F^{-1}(e^{-t})\big) = 1 - e^{-t}.$$

Thus,

$$f_{Y_1}(t) = \frac{d}{dt} F_{Y_1}(t) = \begin{cases} e^{-t}, & \text{if } 0 \le t < \infty \\ 0, & \text{otherwise}, \end{cases}$$

which is (see Definition 4.2.10) the p.d.f. of an exponential r.v. with $A = 0$ and $\beta = 1$. (The result for Y_2 is left to Problem 4.6.1.)

Definition 4.6.7. If X is $N(\mu, \sigma^2)$, then the r.v. $Y = e^X$ is called a **lognormal random variable** [since its logarithm $\ln(Y) = \ln(e^X) = X$ is a normal r.v.].

Example 4.6.8. We now find the p.d.f. of a lognormal r.v. Y by using Theorem 4.6.4. First, note that $Y = e^X$ arises from $y = g(x)$ with $g(x) = e^x$, which is a differentiable function with $g'(x) = e^x > 0$ for all x. Since X is $N(\mu, \sigma^2)$, X is absolutely continuous and $f_Y(y)$ is given by the formula in the statement of Theorem 4.6.4. To simplify and evaluate that formula, note that

$$\min\left(\lim_{x \to -\infty} g(x), \lim_{x \to \infty} g(x) \right) = \min\left(\lim_{x \to -\infty} e^x, \lim_{x \to \infty} e^x \right) = \min(0, \infty) = 0$$

and

$$\max\left(\lim_{x \to -\infty} g(x), \lim_{x \to \infty} g(x) \right) = \max(0, \infty) = \infty,$$

while $y = g(x) = e^x$ solves to $x = \ln(y)$ or $g^{-1}(y) = \ln(y)$, hence

$$\frac{d}{dy} g^{-1}(y) = \frac{d}{dy} \ln(y) = \frac{1}{y}.$$

Thus,

$$f_Y(y) = \begin{cases} \left| f_X(g^{-1}(y)) \left| \frac{d}{dy} g^{-1}(y) \right| \right|, & \text{if } 0 < y < \infty \\ 0, & \text{otherwise} \end{cases}$$

$$= \begin{cases} f_X(\ln(y)) \dfrac{1}{|y|}, & \text{if } 0 < y < \infty \\ 0, & \text{otherwise} \end{cases}$$

and since $f_X(x)$ is the p.d.f. of a $N(\mu, \sigma^2)$ r.v.,

$$f_Y(y) = \begin{cases} \dfrac{1}{\sqrt{2\pi}\,\sigma y} e^{-(\ln(y)-\mu)^2/(2\sigma^2)}, & \text{if } 0 < y < \infty \\ 0, & \text{otherwise}. \end{cases}$$

The lognormal model for a p.d.f. arises commonly in biology and medicine, where the basic processes underlying phenomena are often multiplication of factors (e.g., growth a percentage of previous growth); the underlying causes are studied in the Central Limit Theorem in Chapter 6.

Definition 4.6.9. A Student's t-distribution with $n = 1$ degree of freedom is called a **Cauchy distribution**, thus (see Definition 4.2.26) a Cauchy r.v. X has p.d.f.

$$f_X(x) = \frac{1}{\pi(1 + x^2)}, \qquad -\infty < x < \infty.$$

(A more general Cauchy distribution is given in Theorem 5.5.64(v).)

Example 4.6.10. We now find the p.d.f. of $Y = X^2$ where X is a Cauchy r.v. Note that $y = g(x) = x^2$ has $g'(x) = 2x$, which is sometimes > 0 and sometimes < 0, so Theorem 4.6.4 cannot be used. Instead, we directly find $F_Y(t) = 0$ for $t \le 0$, and for $t > 0$

$$F_Y(t) = P(Y \le t) = P(X^2 \le t) = P(-\sqrt{t} \le X \le \sqrt{t}) = F_X(\sqrt{t}) - F_X(-\sqrt{t})$$

where

$$F_X(x) = \int_{-\infty}^{x} \frac{1}{\pi(1 + t^2)} \, dt.$$

Making the substitution $t = \tan\theta$ (so $dt = \sec^2\theta \, d\theta$), we find

$$F_X(x) = \int_{-\pi/2}^{\tan^{-1} x} \frac{\sec^2\theta}{\pi(1 + \tan^2\theta)} \, d\theta = \int_{-\pi/2}^{\tan^{-1} x} \frac{1/\cos^2\theta}{\pi(1 + \sin^2\theta/\cos^2\theta)} \, d\theta$$

$$= \int_{-\pi/2}^{\tan^{-1} x} \frac{1}{\pi} \, d\theta = \frac{1}{\pi}\left(\tan^{-1} x + \frac{\pi}{2}\right) = \frac{1}{\pi}\tan^{-1} x + \frac{1}{2}.$$

Note that

$$F_X(x) + F_X(-x) = \left(\frac{1}{\pi}\tan^{-1} x + \frac{1}{2}\right) + \left(\frac{1}{\pi}\tan^{-1}(-x) + \frac{1}{2}\right) = 1$$

(this can also be deduced from the fact that $f_X(x)$ is symmetric about 0; see the discussion following Example 4.2.21), hence for $t > 0$

$$F_Y(t) = 2F_X(\sqrt{t}) - 1 = 2\left(\frac{1}{\pi}\tan^{-1}\sqrt{t} + \frac{1}{2}\right) - 1 = \frac{2}{\pi}\tan^{-1}\sqrt{t},$$

so

$$F_Y(t) = \begin{cases} \dfrac{2}{\pi}\tan^{-1}\sqrt{t}, & \text{if } t > 0 \\ 0, & \text{otherwise} \end{cases}$$

and therefore

$$f_Y(t) = \frac{d}{dt}F_Y(t) = \begin{cases} \dfrac{2}{\pi(1 + t)} \cdot \dfrac{1}{2\sqrt{t}} = \dfrac{1}{\pi(1 + t)\sqrt{t}}, & \text{if } t > 0 \\ 0, & \text{otherwise.} \end{cases}$$

Definition 4.6.11. For any r.v. X, $Y = |X|$ is called the **folded** (at zero) **r.v.** X.

A folded r.v. X, $|X|$, arises when, for example, we look at the magnitude of a signal (but not at its sign).

Definition 4.6.12. A r.v. X is said to be **symmetrically distributed** about a point c if $F_X(c + x) + F_X(c - x) = 1$ for all x.

Note that Definition 4.6.12 generalizes the concept of a symmetric p.d.f. (Example 4.2.21) to the case of general r.v.'s (discrete, continuous, and mixed all included).

Example 4.6.13. If X is $N(\mu, \sigma^2)$, then X is symmetric about μ.

Example 4.6.14. **Folded Normal Distribution.** If X is $N(\mu, \sigma^2)$, then $|X|$ is said (see Definition 4.6.11) to have the folded normal distribution. To find the p.d.f. of $Y = |X|$, we have (first finding the d.f. directly, since $g(x)$ here has $g'(x)$, which can be both positive and negative) $F_Y(t) = 0$ for $t \leq 0$, and for $t > 0$

$$F_Y(t) = P(|X| \leq t) = P(-t \leq X \leq t)$$

$$= P\left(\frac{-t - \mu}{\sigma} \leq \frac{X - \mu}{\sigma} \leq \frac{t - \mu}{\sigma} \right)$$

$$= \Phi\left(\frac{t - \mu}{\sigma} \right) - \Phi\left(-\frac{t + \mu}{\sigma} \right) = \Phi\left(\frac{t - \mu}{\sigma} \right) - \left(1 - \Phi\left(\frac{t + \mu}{\sigma} \right) \right)$$

where we have "standardized X (which is $N(\mu, \sigma^2)$) to a $N(0, 1)$ r.v. as in Example 4.2.21, used $\Phi(z)$ to denote the area under the standard normal p.d.f. to the left of z (this is the area tabulated in Table 11), and used the symmetry of the $N(0, 1)$ r.v. about $c = 0$ (see Definition 4.6.12 and Example 4.6.13) to reexpress the next-to-last expression. Therefore

$$f_Y(t) = \begin{cases} \dfrac{1}{\sigma}\phi\left(\dfrac{\mu}{\sigma} + \dfrac{t}{\sigma} \right) + \dfrac{1}{\sigma}\phi\left(\dfrac{\mu}{\sigma} - \dfrac{t}{\sigma} \right), & \text{if } t > 0 \\ 0, & \text{otherwise,} \end{cases}$$

where $\phi(z)$ denotes the standard normal p.d.f. To summarize the new notation using $\Phi(z)$ and $\phi(z)$, we have for a $N(0, 1)$ r.v. Z

$$\Phi(z) \equiv F_Z(z) = P(Z \leq z) = \int_{-\infty}^{z} \frac{1}{\sqrt{2\pi}} e^{-t^2/2} \, dt = \int_{-\infty}^{z} \phi(t) \, dt,$$

$$\phi(z) \equiv \frac{1}{\sqrt{2\pi}} e^{-t^2/2}.$$

Theorem 4.6.15.* Let $Y = X_1 + X_2$. If (X_1, X_2) is (absolutely) continuous,

$$F_Y(y) = P[X_1 + X_2 \leq y] = \iint\limits_{\{(x_1, x_2):\ x_1 + x_2 \leq y\}} f_{X_1, X_2}(x_1, x_2)\, dx_1\, dx_2$$

$$= \int_{-\infty}^{\infty} \left[\int_{-\infty}^{y - x_1} f_{X_1, X_2}(x_1, x_2)\, dx_2 \right] dx_1$$

$$= \int_{-\infty}^{\infty} \left[\int_{-\infty}^{y} f_{X_1, X_2}(x_1, x_2' - x_1)\, dx_2' \right] dx_1.$$

Differentiating,

$$f_Y(y) = f_{X_1 + X_2}(y) = \int_{-\infty}^{\infty} f_{X_1, X_2}(x_1, y - x_1)\, dx_1 = \int_{-\infty}^{\infty} f_{X_1, X_2}(y - x_2, x_2)\, dx_2.$$

If X_1 and X_2 are independent,

$$f_{X_1 + X_2}(y) = \int_{-\infty}^{\infty} f_{X_1}(x) f_{X_2}(y - x)\, dx = \int_{-\infty}^{\infty} f_{X_1}(y - x) f_{X_2}(x)\, dx.$$

This theorem's statement actually contains its proof. Similarly, we may derive the following theorem.

Theorem 4.6.16. If (X_1, X_2) is (absolutely) continuous,

(i) $f_{X_1 - X_2}(y) = \int_{-\infty}^{\infty} f_{X_1, X_2}(y + x, x)\, dx = \int_{-\infty}^{\infty} f_{X_1, X_2}(x, x - y)\, dx;$

(ii) $f_{X_1 X_2}(y) = \int_{-\infty}^{\infty} \dfrac{1}{|x|} f_{X_1, X_2}\left(\dfrac{y}{x}, x\right) dx = \int_{-\infty}^{\infty} \dfrac{1}{|x|} f_{X_1, X_2}\left(x, \dfrac{y}{x}\right) dx;$

(iii) $f_{X_1/X_2}(y) = \int_{-\infty}^{\infty} |x| f_{X_1, X_2}(yx, x)\, dx.$

Example 4.6.17. Let X_1 and X_2 be independent $N(0, 1)$ r.v.'s. Then the p.d.f. of $Y = X_1 + X_2$ may be found using Theorem 4.6.15, as follows:

$$f_Y(y) = f_{X_1 + X_2}(y) = \int_{-\infty}^{\infty} f_{X_1}(x) f_{X_2}(y - x)\, dx$$

$$= \int_{-\infty}^{\infty} \frac{1}{\sqrt{2\pi}} e^{-x^2/2} \frac{1}{\sqrt{2\pi}} e^{-(y - x)^2/2}\, dx$$

$$= \int_{-\infty}^{\infty} \frac{1}{2\pi} e^{-x^2 + xy - y^2/2}\, dx$$

---

*The remainder of this section may be omitted if the instructor desires.

$$= \frac{1}{\sqrt{2\pi}\sqrt{2}}e^{-y^2/4}\int_{-\infty}^{\infty}\frac{1}{\sqrt{2\pi}\sqrt{\frac{1}{2}}}e^{-\frac{1}{2}\left(\frac{x-y/2}{\sqrt{1/2}}\right)^2}dx$$

$$= \frac{1}{\sqrt{2\pi}\sqrt{2}}e^{-y^2/4},$$

where the last integral was 1 since it is the integral of the $N(y/2, .5)$ p.d.f., and we now recognize the result as the $N(0, 2)$ p.d.f.

Example 4.6.17 shows what is called a **reproductive property** of the normal r.v.: that by adding two independent standard normal r.v.'s, one again obtains a normal r.v. Many of the most useful distributions of statistics possess such properties (e.g., the normal, gamma, exponential, Poisson, and binomial r.v.'s have such properties). In Chapter 5 we will introduce methods that will allow us to show these properties easily.

Theorem 4.6.18.[7] We wish to find the **joint density of** $Y_1 = g_1$ $(X_1, \ldots, X_n), \ldots, Y_m = g_m(X_1, \ldots, X_n)$ **where** $m \le n$ **and** $(X_1, \ldots, X_n)$ **is an (ab-solutely) continuous r.v.** Suppose we consider $Y_1, \ldots, Y_{m+1}, \ldots, Y_n$ where

$$Y_{m+1} = g_{m+1}(X_1, \ldots, X_n)$$

$$\vdots$$

$$Y_n = g_n(X_1, \ldots, X_n).$$

Suppose the functions $g_1(x_1, \ldots, x_n), \ldots, g_n(x_1, \ldots, x_n)$ have continuous first partial derivatives at all $(x_1, \ldots, x_n)$ and are such that at all $(x_1, \ldots, x_n)$ the **Jacobian**

$$J\left(\frac{y_1, \ldots, y_n}{x_1, \ldots, x_n}\right) \equiv \begin{vmatrix} \dfrac{\partial y_1}{\partial x_1} & \cdots & \dfrac{\partial y_1}{\partial x_n} \\ \dfrac{\partial y_2}{\partial x_1} & \cdots & \dfrac{\partial y_2}{\partial x_n} \\ \vdots & & \\ \dfrac{\partial y_n}{\partial x_1} & \cdots & \dfrac{\partial y_n}{\partial x_n} \end{vmatrix} \ne 0.$$

If the p.d.f. of $(X_1, \ldots, X_n)$ is continuous at all but a finite number of points

---

[7]A simplification of the conditions of this theorem results if we use the simple conditions of Varberg (1971). Since a substantial amount of mathematics is needed to understand this simplification, we leave it as an exercise for the mathematically well-prepared student.

$(x_1, \ldots, x_n)$, then $(Y_1, \ldots, Y_n)$ is (absolutely) continuous with

$$
f_{Y_1, \ldots, Y_n}(y_1, \ldots, y_n) = \begin{cases} f_{X_1, \ldots, X_n}(x_1, \ldots, x_n) \dfrac{1}{\left| J\left(\dfrac{y_1, \ldots, y_n}{x_1, \ldots, x_n} \right) \right|}, & \mathbf{y} \in C \\ 0, & \mathbf{y} \notin C, \end{cases}
$$

where C is the set of $\mathbf{y} = (y_1, \ldots, y_n)'$ such that the n equations

$$
\begin{cases} y_1 = g_1(x_1, \ldots, x_n), \\ \vdots \\ y_n = g_n(x_1, \ldots, x_n), \end{cases}
$$

possess at least one solution $(x_1, \ldots, x_n)$; the $(x_1, \ldots, x_n)$ are the unique solution, say

$$
\begin{cases} x_1 = g_1^{-1}(y_1, \ldots, y_n), \\ \vdots \\ x_n = g_n^{-1}(y_1, \ldots, y_n). \end{cases}
$$

Finally,

$$
f_{Y_1, \ldots, Y_m}(y_1, \ldots, y_m)
$$
$$
= \int_{-\infty}^{\infty} \cdots \int_{-\infty}^{\infty} f_{Y_1, \ldots, Y_m, Y_{m+1}, \ldots, Y_n}(y_1, \ldots, y_m, y_{m+1}, \ldots, y_n) \, dy_{m+1} \cdots dy_n.
$$

Note 4.6.19. $\quad \left| J\left(\dfrac{x_1, \ldots, x_n}{y_1, \ldots, y_n} \right) \right| = \left| J\left(\dfrac{y_1, \ldots, y_n}{x_1, \ldots, x_n} \right) \right|^{-1}$

but the right side is often easy to obtain, rather than solving for $x_1, \ldots, x_n$ in terms of $y_1, \ldots, y_n$ or differentiating implicitly.

Example 4.6.20. Let X_1, X_2 be independent r.v.'s, each with the exponential distribution with $\beta^{-1} = \lambda$, $A = 0$ (see Definition 4.2.10). Are the r.v.'s $X_1 + X_2$ and X_1/X_2 independent?

We know that

$$
f_{X_1}(x) = f_{X_2}(x) = \begin{cases} \lambda e^{-\lambda x}, & x > 0 \\ 0, & x \le 0, \end{cases}
$$

so that

$$
f_{X_1, X_2}(x_1, x_2) = \begin{cases} \lambda^2 e^{-\lambda(x_1 + x_2)}, & x_1 > 0 \text{ and } x_2 > 0 \\ 0, & \text{otherwise.} \end{cases}
$$

Let $Y_1 = X_1 + X_2$, $Y_2 = X_1/X_2$. If we find $f_{Y_1, Y_2}(y_1, y_2)$ and show it equals $f_{Y_1}(y_1) \cdot f_{Y_2}(y_2)$ for all y_1, y_2, then Y_1 and Y_2 are independent r.v.'s by Theorem 4.4.18. Now (since the conditions of Theorem 4.6.18 are satisfied)

$$f_{Y_1, Y_2}(y_1, y_2) = \begin{cases} f_{X_1, X_2}(x_1, x_2) \dfrac{1}{\left| J\left(\dfrac{y_1, y_2}{x_1, x_2} \right) \right|}, & \mathbf{y} \in C \\ 0, & \mathbf{y} \notin C. \end{cases}$$

(Here it is understood that x_1, x_2 are to be eliminated from the right side.) Since $y_1 = x_1 + x_2$ and $y_2 x_2 = x_1$,

$$\begin{cases} x_1 = \dfrac{y_1 y_2}{1 + y_2}, \\ x_2 = \dfrac{y_1}{1 + y_2}. \end{cases}$$

Also,

$$J\left(\frac{y_1, y_2}{x_1, x_2} \right) = \begin{vmatrix} \dfrac{\partial y_1}{\partial x_1} & \dfrac{\partial y_1}{\partial x_2} \\ \dfrac{\partial y_2}{\partial x_1} & \dfrac{\partial y_2}{\partial x_2} \end{vmatrix} = \begin{vmatrix} 1 & 1 \\ \dfrac{1}{x_2} & \dfrac{-x_1}{x_2^2} \end{vmatrix} = \frac{-x_1}{x_2^2} - \frac{1}{x_2}.$$

Thus, for $\mathbf{y} \in C$,

$$f_{Y_1, Y_2}(y_1, y_2) = \lambda^2 e^{-\lambda(x_1 + x_2)} \frac{1}{\left| -\dfrac{x_1}{x_2^2} - \dfrac{1}{x_2} \right|}$$

$$= \lambda^2 e^{-\lambda y_1} \frac{x_2^2}{x_1 + x_2} = \lambda^2 e^{-\lambda y_1} \frac{\dfrac{y_1^2}{(1 + y_2)^2}}{y_1}$$

$$= \lambda^2 y_1 e^{-\lambda y_1} \cdot \frac{1}{(1 + y_2)^2}.$$

Since $C = \{(y_1, y_2): y_1 > 0, \ y_2 > 0\}$, it follows easily that

$$f_{Y_1, Y_2}(y_1, y_2) = f_{Y_1}(y_1) f_{Y_2}(y_2), \qquad \text{all } y_1, y_2.$$

Example 4.6.21. Suppose that $X_1, \ldots, X_k$ are independent r.v.'s, each distributed as chi-square with n degrees of freedom $\chi_n^2(0)$ (see Definition 4.2.13). Define new random variables

$$Y_1 = \frac{X_2}{X_1}, \ Y_2 = \frac{X_3}{X_1}, \ldots, Y_{k-1} = \frac{X_k}{X_1}. \tag{4.6.22}$$

Find the joint density of $Y_1, \ldots, Y_{k-1}$.

First, since $X_1, \ldots, X_k$ are independent r.v.'s we have (using Definition 4.2.13)

$$f_{X_1, \ldots, X_k}(x_1, \ldots, x_k) = f_{X_1}(x_1) \ldots f_{X_k}(x_k)$$

$$= \prod_{i=1}^{k} \frac{1}{\Gamma\!\left(\dfrac{n}{2}\right) 2^{n/2}} x_i^{(n-2)/2} e^{-x_i/2} \tag{4.6.23}$$

$$= \frac{1}{\left(\Gamma\!\left(\dfrac{n}{2}\right)\right)^k 2^{nk/2}} x_1^{(n-2)/2} \ldots x_k^{(n-2)/2} e^{-\frac{1}{2}(x_1 + \cdots + x_k)}$$

when $x_1 > 0$ and ... and $x_k > 0$, and zero otherwise. We now wish to use Theorem 4.6.18; to do so we must define a Y_k (of no interest to us) in such a way that all k functions of $X_1, \ldots, X_k$ have continuous partial derivatives and $J \neq 0$. Let us try $Y_k = X_1 + \cdots + X_k$. Then our functions are

$$\begin{cases} y_1 = g_1(x_1, \ldots, x_k) = \dfrac{x_2}{x_1}, \\[2mm] y_2 = g_2(x_1, \ldots, x_k) = \dfrac{x_3}{x_1}, \\[2mm] \vdots \\[2mm] y_{k-1} = g_{k-1}(x_1, \ldots, x_k) = \dfrac{x_k}{x_1}, \\[2mm] y_k = g_k(x_1, \ldots, x_k) = x_1 + \cdots + x_k, \end{cases} \tag{4.6.24}$$

all of which have continuous first partial derivatives at all $(x_1, \ldots, x_k)$ [as in Example 4.6.5, we need only talk of $(x_1, \ldots, x_k)$ for which $f_{X_1, \ldots, X_k}(x_1, \ldots, x_k)$

> 0]. We now find the Jacobian

$$
J\left(\frac{y_1,\ldots,y_k}{x_1,\ldots,x_k}\right) =
\begin{vmatrix}
-\dfrac{x_2}{x_1^2} & \dfrac{1}{x_1} & 0 & 0 & \cdots & 0 & 0 \\[2ex]
-\dfrac{x_3}{x_1^2} & 0 & \dfrac{1}{x_1} & 0 & \cdots & 0 & 0 \\[2ex]
-\dfrac{x_4}{x_1^2} & 0 & 0 & \dfrac{1}{x_1} & \cdots & 0 & 0 \\[1ex]
\vdots & & & & & & \\[1ex]
-\dfrac{x_{k-1}}{x_1^2} & 0 & 0 & 0 & \cdots & \dfrac{1}{x_1} & 0 \\[2ex]
-\dfrac{x_k}{x_1^2} & 0 & 0 & 0 & \cdots & 0 & \dfrac{1}{x_1} \\[2ex]
1 & 1 & 1 & 1 & \cdots & 1 & 1
\end{vmatrix}
$$

$$
=
\begin{vmatrix}
0 & \dfrac{1}{x_1} & 0 & 0 & \cdots & 0 & 0 \\[2ex]
0 & 0 & \dfrac{1}{x_1} & 0 & \cdots & 0 & 0 \\[2ex]
0 & 0 & 0 & \dfrac{1}{x_1} & \cdots & 0 & 0 \\[1ex]
\vdots & & & & & & \\[1ex]
0 & 0 & 0 & 0 & \cdots & \dfrac{1}{x_1} & 0 \\[2ex]
0 & 0 & 0 & 0 & \cdots & 0 & \dfrac{1}{x_1} \\[2ex]
1 + \dfrac{x_2}{x_1} + \cdots + \dfrac{x_k}{x_1} & 1 & 1 & 1 & \cdots & 1 & 1
\end{vmatrix}
$$

$$
= \left(\frac{1}{x_1}\right)^{k-1}\left(1 + \frac{x_2}{x_1} + \cdots + \frac{x_k}{x_1}\right)
$$

$$
= \frac{x_1 + x_2 + \cdots + x_k}{x_1^k} \tag{4.6.25}
$$

(where we multiplied columns $2, 3, \ldots, k$ by $x_2/x_1, x_3/x_1, \ldots, x_k/x_1$, respectively, and added them to the first column). Hence,

$$
f_{Y_1, \ldots, Y_k}(y_1, \ldots, y_k)
$$

$$
= f_{X_1, \ldots, X_k}(x_1, \ldots, x_k) \left| J\!\left(\frac{y_1, \ldots, y_k}{x_1, \ldots, x_k} \right) \right|^{-1}
$$

(4.6.26)

$$
= \frac{1}{\left(\Gamma\!\left(\dfrac{n}{2}\right)\right)^{k} 2^{nk/2}} \; \frac{x_1^{(n-2)/2} \cdots x_k^{(n-2)/2} x_1^{k}}{x_1 + x_2 + \cdots + x_k} e^{-(x_1 + \cdots + x_k)/2}
$$

where $x_1, \ldots, x_k$ are to be replaced by their unique solutions [from system (4.6.24)] in terms of $y_1, \ldots, y_k$ [and where $f_{Y_1, \ldots, Y_k}(y_1, \ldots, y_k) = 0$ otherwise; i.e., unless $(y_1, \ldots, y_k)$ can arise from some $(x_1, \ldots, x_k)$]. Doing this replacement, we find

$$
f_{Y_1, \ldots, Y_k}(y_1, \ldots, y_k)
$$

$$
= \frac{1}{\left(\Gamma\!\left(\dfrac{n}{2}\right)\right)^{k} 2^{nk/2}} \; \frac{\displaystyle\prod_{i=1}^{k-1} y_i^{(n-2)/2}}{(1 + y_1 + \cdots + y_{k-1})^{nk/2}} y_k^{nk/2-1} e^{-y_k/2},
$$

(4.6.27)

where $0 < y_i < \infty$ $(i = 1, 2, \ldots, k)$. [Since $y_1 = x_2/x_1, \ldots, y_{k-1} = x_{k-1}/x_1$, we can clearly fix $y_1, \ldots, y_{k-1}$ (independently of each other) to any positive values. Can we then do similarly for y_k? Yes, for $y_k = x_1 + \cdots + x_k$
$= \left(1 + \dfrac{x_2}{x_1} + \cdots + \dfrac{x_k}{x_1}\right) x_1 = (1 + y_1 + \cdots + y_{k-1}) x_1$ and x_1 is still under our control.]

Now, however, recall that Y_k was an extraneous variable introduced for mathematical reasons. We complete this example by eliminating Y_k as follows:

$$
f_{Y_1, \ldots, Y_{k-1}}(y_1, \ldots, y_{k-1})
$$

$$
= \int_0^\infty f_{Y_1, \ldots, Y_{k-1}, Y_k}(y_1, \ldots, y_{k-1}, y_k) \, dy_k
$$

(4.6.28)

$$
= \frac{1}{\left(\Gamma\!\left(\dfrac{n}{2}\right)\right)^{k} 2^{nk/2}} \; \frac{\displaystyle\prod_{i=1}^{k-1} y_i^{(n-2)/2}}{(1 + y_1 + \cdots + y_{k-1})^{nk/2}} \int_0^\infty y_k^{nk/2-1} e^{-y_k/2} \, dy_k.
$$

Making the substitution $z = y_k/2$, the last integral becomes

$$
2^{nk/2} \int_0^\infty z^{nk/2-1} e^{-z} \, dz = 2^{nk/2} \Gamma\!\left(\frac{nk}{2}\right)
$$

[where we used Definition 4.1.9 of $\Gamma(n)$]. Hence,

$f_{Y_1,\ldots,Y_{k-1}}(y_1,\ldots,y_{k-1})$

$$= \begin{cases} \dfrac{\Gamma\left(\dfrac{kn}{2}\right)}{\left(\Gamma\left(\dfrac{n}{2}\right)\right)^k} \dfrac{\prod_{i=1}^{k-1} y_i^{(n-2)/2}}{(1+y_1+\cdots+y_{k-1})^{nk/2}}, & \text{if } 0 < y_1,\ldots,0 < y_{k-1} \\ 0, & \text{otherwise.} \end{cases} \quad (4.6.29)$$

[The problem of finding the density of $Y_1,\ldots,Y_{k-1}$ as specified in Example 4.6.21 arose in Bechhofer and Sobel (1954). In particular, our final result (4.6.29) is a special case of Equation (13) on their p. 277 (the case $t = 1$). One practical example of the class of problems they were considering would be the selection of that one of several effective drugs which has the least variability in its effects. Problems of this sort are called problems of "ranking and selection" and are studied in Chapter 11.]

PROBLEMS FOR SECTION 4.6

4.6.1 Let X have absolutely continuous d.f. $F(x)$. Show that $Y_2 = -\ln(1 - F(X))$ is an exponential r.v.

4.6.2 Show that if X is $N(0,1)$, Y is $\chi_n^2(0)$, and X and Y are independent r.v.'s, then $S = X/\sqrt{(Y/n)}$ has Student's t-distribution with n degrees of freedom.

4.6.3 Show that if X is a $\chi_{n_1}^2(0)$ r.v., Y is a $\chi_{n_2}^2(0)$ r.v., and X and Y are independent r.v.'s, then

$$G = \frac{X/n_1}{Y/n_2}$$

has an F-distribution with n_1 and n_2 degrees of freedom (respectively) in the numerator and denominator.

4.6.4 Let U_1 and U_2 be independent r.v.'s, each uniform on $(0,1)$. Show that $X_1 = \sqrt{-2\ln(U_1)} \sin(2\pi U_2)$ and $X_2 = \sqrt{-2\ln(U_1)} \cos(2\pi U_2)$ are independent r.v.'s, and that each is $N(0,1)$.

4.6.5 Let X have an F-distribution with n_1 and n_2 (numerator and denominator) degrees of freedom. Show that

$$Y = \frac{1}{1 + \left(\dfrac{n_1}{n_2}\right)X}$$

has a beta distribution, and find the parameters of this beta distribution.

4.6.6 Let X_1 and X_2 be independent r.v.'s, each $N(\mu, \sigma^2)$. Let $Y = X_1 + X_2$, $Z = X_1 - X_2$. Show that Y and Z are independent r.v.'s. [*Hint:* Use transformations to find the joint p.d.f. of (Y, Z), and then the independence.]

4.6.7 If X has an F-distribution with n_1 and n_2 degrees of freedom, show that $1/X$ is also an F r.v., with n_2 and n_1 degrees of freedom.

4.6.8 Let X_1 and X_2 be independent $N(0, 1)$ r.v.'s. Let $Y = X_1^2 + X_2^2$ and $Z = X_1/X_2$.
(a) Find the joint p.d.f. of (Y, Z).
(b) Show that Y and Z are independent r.v.'s.

4.6.9 Let (X_1, X_2) be a bivariate normal r.v. Let $X_i^* = (X_i - \mu_i)/\sigma_i$ for $i = 1, 2$, and $Y = X_1^* + X_2^*$, $Z = X_1^* - X_2^*$.
(a) Find the joint p.d.f. of (Y, Z).
(b) Find the marginal p.d.f.'s $f_Y(y)$ and $f_Z(z)$.
(c) Show that Y and Z are independent r.v.'s.

4.6.10 Let X_1 and X_2 be independent r.v.'s, each $N(\mu, \sigma^2)$. Let $Y = aX_1 + bX_2$, $Z = cX_1 + dX_2$. Show that the joint p.d.f. of (Y, Z) is bivariate normal with parameters

$$\mu_1 = (a + b)\mu, \mu_2 = (c + d)\mu,$$

$$\sigma_1^2 = (a^2 + b^2)\sigma^2, \sigma_2^2 = (c^2 + d^2)\sigma^2,$$

$$\rho = \frac{ac + bd}{\sqrt{(a^2 + b^2)(c^2 + d^2)}}.$$

4.6.11 If X is a beta r.v., $B(x|\alpha, \lambda)$, show that $Y = 1 - X$ is also a beta r.v.

4.6.12 Let $f_X(x) = 1/\pi$ for $-\pi/2 < x < \pi/2$ (and $= 0$ otherwise), and $Y = \tan(X)$. Find the p.d.f. and d.f. of Y.

4.6.13 Let X_1 and X_2 be independent $N(\mu, \sigma^2)$ r.v.'s. Find the p.d.f. of $Y = (X_1 + X_2)/2$.

4.6.14 Let X be uniform on $(0, 1)$. Find the d.f. and p.d.f. of (a) $1/X$; (b) X^2; (c) $aX + b$; (d) e^X.

4.6.15 Let $f_X(x) = 2/x^3$ for $1 < x < \infty$ (and $= 0$ otherwise).
(a) Find the d.f. of (i) $1/X$; (ii) e^X; (iii) $\ln(X)$; (iv) $aX + b$.
(b) If X_1 and X_2 are independent r.v.'s with the same p.d.f. as X, find the p.d.f. of (i) X_1/X_2; (ii) $X_1 X_2$.

4.6.16 Let $X_1, X_2, \ldots, X_n$ be independent r.v.'s, each with p.d.f. $f_X(x) = (1/\lambda)e^{-x/\lambda}$ for $x > 0$ (for some $\lambda > 0$), and $= 0$ otherwise. Let $Y_1 = X_1$, $Y_2 = X_1 + X_2$, and in general $Y_i = X_1 + \cdots + X_i$ ($i = 1, 2, \ldots, n$). Show that the p.d.f. of Y_i is a gamma density ($i = 1, 2, \ldots, n$).

4.6.17 Let $X_1, X_2, \ldots, X_n$ be independent r.v.'s, each with p.d.f.

$$f(x) = \frac{1}{\sqrt{2\pi}\,\sigma} e^{-(x-\mu)^2/(2\sigma^2)}, \quad -\infty < x < \infty$$

for some μ ($-\infty < \mu < \infty$) and σ ($\sigma > 0$). Consider the transformation

$$\overline{X}_i = \sum_{j=1}^{i} X_j/i \quad (i = 1, 2, \ldots, n).$$

Show that $\overline{X}_n$ is $N(\mu, \sigma^2/n)$.

4.6.18 Let $X_1, X_2, \ldots, X_n$ be independent chi-square r.v.'s, each with r degrees of freedom. Show that $Y = X_1 + X_2 + \cdots + X_n$ is chi-square with nr degrees of freedom.

4.6.19 Let X be an r.v. with strictly increasing d.f. $F_X(x)$. Show that $Y = -2\ln(1 - F_X(x))$ is chi-square with 2 degrees of freedom. [*Hint:* Note that the r.v. $F_X(X)$ is uniform on [0,1], because $F_X^{-1}(\cdot)$ exists due to the strictly increasing nature of $F_X(\cdot)$.]

4.6.20 Let $X_1, X_2, \ldots, X_n$ be independent r.v.'s, where X_i has strictly increasing d.f. $F_i(\cdot)$ $(i = 1, 2, \ldots, r)$. Show that

$$Z = -2 \sum_{i=1}^{r} \ln(1 - Y_i),$$

where $Y_i = F_i(X_i)$, has a chi-square distribution with $2r$ degrees of freedom. [*Hint:* Use Problems 4.6.18 and 4.6.19.]

4.7. COMPUTER GENERATION OF RANDOM VARIABLES

Today, simulation and Monte Carlo studies play an important and ever more significant role in virtually every field [for some references in such areas as job-shop scheduling, marketing, psychoanalysis, air pollution, chemistry, genetics, social conflict, housing policies, and parapsychology, see Chapter 1 of Dudewicz and Ralley (1981)]. Computer simulation is a powerful tool for gaining insight into complex systems (as well as simple ones) and allows one to build and test theories as well as to peer into the future. In fact, as can be seen from the professional statistical journals' current issues, today many statistical questions are being answered through simulation.

Since simulation involves running (inside a digital computer) a model of some real system, and since **randomness occurs in real systems in such instances as those where** items are neither completely predictable from, nor perfectly correlated with, available knowledge and accepted causes; items are unexpected; results of an experiment differ from the norm; and systems are not controllable in every detail, **therefore randomness must be incorporated into every simulation that is to be an adequate mirror of reality.** This randomness is usually provided by making the attributes and times (in the systems being studied) random variables with an appropriate statistical distribution. For example, cash requirements in an accounting system, priorities of jobs and routings through machines in a job-shop, rainfall amounts, service times, interarrival times, and times between storms are examples of such attributes and times. Thus, we will have some given d.f. $F(x)$ and desire (in order to provide input to the simulation) to produce independent r.v.'s $X_1, X_2, \ldots$ that have this d.f. (In some cases one does not know the d.f. and must estimate it; such problems are introduced in Section 4.8 and studied further in Chapter 7.)

Virtually all methods for producing a sequence of r.v.'s $X_1, X_2, \ldots$ that are independent with d.f. $F(x)$ involve use of a sequence of r.v.'s $U_1, U_2, \ldots$ that are

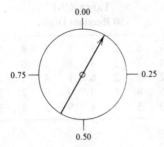

Figure 4.7-1. An observational random number generator.

independent and have the uniform distribution on $(0, 1)$ (see Definition 4.2.2). For this reason, in this section **we will first discuss how to obtain such a sequence** $U_1, U_2, \ldots$, **and then methods for using it to produce the desired** $X_1, X_2, \ldots$.

Although it was in the decade 1940–1949 that development of the first modern computers occurred, and that in turn led to extensive developments in the principles, techniques, and capabilities of simulation and Monte Carlo techniques, the simulation area was in existence in embryonic form even before the modern computer came on the scene. For example, in the second half of the nineteenth-century experimenters threw needles haphazardly onto a ruled board and used the observed number of needle-line intersections to estimate π (see Problem 4.7.1). In 1908, W. S. Gosset (writing under the pseudonym Student) used experimental sampling to seek out the distribution function of an estimate of the parameter ρ for a bivariate normal distribution, and also to bolster his shaky and incomplete theoretical analysis of what is now called the t-distribution. *At that time*, **random numbers** (the name given to the $U_1, U_2, \ldots$ that we are seeking) *were generated by* **observational methods** (*also called* **physical devices**) *such as rolling dice, drawing from a supposedly well-shuffled deck of cards, drawing from a supposedly well-stirred urn, or spinning a roulette wheel.* For example, if one spins a spinner as illustrated in Figure 4.7-1 in a certain manner, and if the circumference is marked off from 0.00 through 1.00, then it might be reasonable in some instances to assume the result is a random number between 0 and 1. Rather than go through the significant effort of such a process each time random numbers are needed, it seemed to make sense to construct such numbers and table them for others to use when needed. L. H. C. Tippett prepared the first such table in 1927, and it appears to have been the only such table until 1938. His table consisted of 41,600 digits collected from census reports. Each of the digits is one of the integers $0, 1, 2, 3, 4, 5, 6, 7, 8, 9$; a user takes several of these and adds a decimal point to form a random number between 0 and 1. Since 41,600 digits were an insufficient number for lengthy investigations even before the advent of the modern digital computer (e.g., one can form only 4160 ten-digit random numbers from such a collection), a table of 100,000 digits (from which one can form 10,000 ten-digit numbers) was published by Kendall and Babington-Smith

TABLE 4.7-1
50 Random Digits

1	8	6	2	8	5	2	8	2	4
4	4	7	1	3	8	4	0	3	7
2	2	3	2	6	1	4	3	7	5
4	6	8	6	8	0	9	7	7	8
5	0	3	7	4	9	3	8	7	3

in 1939. Those digits were produced mechanically. A number of other tables were also produced at about this time, including tables derived from telephone directory numbers and from logarithm tables (in particular, 15,000 random digits tabled by Fisher and Yates in 1938 from among the 15th to 19th digits in certain sections of a logarithm table). Tabling efforts seem to have ended with the publication of a monumental 1,000,000 random digits by the Rand Corporation in 1955; those digits were produced by an electronic roulette wheel constructed explicitly for this purpose. An example of such a table is given in Table 4.7-1, which contains 50 digits. To simulate flipping a coin with probability .95 of heads, for example, one chooses two digits from the table. If the digits are $01, 02, \ldots, 95$, say heads occurred (while if the digits are $96, 97, 98, 99, 00$, say tails occurred).

Since observational methods involve a number of dubious assumptions (e.g., if one derives one's numbers from telephone numbers, one may need to assume an assignment of numbers independent of names as well as ignoring the exchange), tables developed from them may often fail statistical tests of randomness (such tests are studied in Chapter 9). Even if they pass, however, one will have a large volume to store. These considerations led to the development of **internal numeric sources of random numbers**. These methods use a deterministic numeric process to produce sequences of numbers that can pass statistical tests for randomness (i.e., that cannot be distinguished from "true randomness"). The internal numeric source used almost exclusively at present is the **multiplicative congruential (or power residue) method**. *Such a method requires specification of three integers ρ, x_0,* and m, *called the* **multiplier**, **seed**, *and* **modulus** *of the random number generator.* One then operates iteratively setting the nth number x_n in the sequence via

$$x_n = \rho x_{n-1} \bmod m. \qquad (4.7.1)$$

Example 4.7.2.* If we use the multiplicative congruential random number generator with multiplier $\rho = 11$, $x_0 = 3$, and $m = 100$, find $x_1, x_2, x_3, x_4, x_5, x_6, x_7, x_8, x_9, x_{10}$.

*Material from this point up to Definition 4.7.5 may be omitted if the instructor desires.

Here, we find

$$x_1 = (11)(3) \bmod 100 = 33 \bmod 100 = 33$$

$$x_2 = (11)(33) \bmod 100 = 363 \bmod 100 = 63$$

$$x_3 = (11)(63) \bmod 100 = 693 \bmod 100 = 93$$

$$x_4 = (11)(93) \bmod 100 = 1023 \bmod 100 = 23$$

$$x_5 = (11)(23) \bmod 100 = 253 \bmod 100 = 53$$

$$x_6 = (11)(53) \bmod 100 = 583 \bmod 100 = 83$$

$$x_7 = (11)(83) \bmod 100 = 913 \bmod 100 = 13$$

$$x_8 = (11)(13) \bmod 100 = 143 \bmod 100 = 43$$

$$x_9 = (11)(43) \bmod 100 = 473 \bmod 100 = 73$$

$$x_{10} = (11)(73) \bmod 100 = 803 \bmod 100 = 3$$

$$x_{11} = (11)(3) \bmod 100 = 33 \bmod 100 = 33 = x_1.$$

Thus, the "mod" function gives the remainder when one divides by the modulus (or, the number left when one subtracts as many multiples of the modulus as possible without driving the number negative). This particular generator gives 10 terms and then cycles (since after $x_{11} = x_1$ one will next find $x_{12} = x_2$, and so on). This is unsuitable for any practical use and is just used here to illustrate the method.

It is also worth noting that this particular multiplicative congruential generator (with $\rho = 11$, $x_0 = 3$, and $m = 100$) always yields a "3" in the last digit. (Even if x_0 were different, the procedure would always yield the same last digit, that digit being the last digit of the value x_0 used.) Hence the ones digit of the resulting number is decidedly nonrandom. In the following example we note that **careful choice of ρ, x_0, and m can yield a multiplicative congruential generator with good properties.**

Example 4.7.3. A Good Random Number Generator. It can be shown that the choices $\rho = 663,608,941$, x_0 any odd integer number between 1 and 2^{32}, and $m = 2^{32}$ yield a good random number sequence. This generator was first proposed by J. H. Ahrens and V. Dieter, and was tested extensively in Dudewicz and Ralley (1981). Since generators of this type produce sequences of integers, to convert $x_1, x_2, x_3, \ldots$ to $U_1, U_2, U_3, \ldots$ we set

$$U_i = x_i/m \qquad (i = 1, 2, 3, \ldots). \qquad (4.7.4)$$

(Thus, in Example 4.7.2 we would have $x_1 = .33$ and $x_{10} = .03$.) Assembler

```
URN13  START 0              URN13(IX,X,NBATCH)
       USING *,15           USE REGISTER 15 AS BASE REGISTER
       STM 14,12,12(13)     STORE SAVE AREA
       L 14,0(1)            LOAD ADDRESS OF IX INTO REG. 14
       L 6,4(1)             LOAD ADDRESS OF X INTO REG. 6
       L 7,8(1)             LOAD ADDRESS OF NDIMX INTO REG. 7
       L 2,0(6)             LOAD CONTENTS OF X INTO REG. 2
       L 3,0(7)             LOAD CONTENTS OF NDIMX INTO REG. 3
LOOP   L 1,0(14)            LOAD CONTENTS OF IX INTO REG. 1
       M 0,FACTOR           X(I+1)=A*X(I)MOD(2**32) IN REG. 1
       ST 1,0(14)           IX=X(I+1)
       SLDL 0,24            SHIFT DBL. REG 0-1 LEFT BY 24 BITS
       STM 0,1,HOLD         STORE DOUBLE PRECISION MANTISSA IN HOLD
       MVI HOLD,X'40'       INSERT BIASED EXPONENT (TRUE EXPONENT ZERO)
       LD 0,HOLD            LOAD FLT PT REG. 0 WITH HOLD
       AD 0,ZERO            NORMALIZE REG. 0. IT NOW CONTAINS X(I+1).
       STE 0,0(6)           STORE INTO X(I)
       LA 6,4(6)             INCREMENT INDEX REGISTER
       BCT 3,LOOP           BRANCH TO TOP OF LOOP
       LM 14,12,12(13)      RESTORE SAVE AREA
       BR 14                BRANCH TO RETURN ADDRESS
HOLD   DS 1D                HOLD=ONE DOUBLE WORD
ZERO   DC D'0.0'            ZERO=DOUBLE PRECISION ZERO.
FACTOR DC X'278DDE6D'       THIS HEX FACTOR=663608941 IN DECIMAL
       END
```

Figure 4.7-2. Assembler computer code for the random number generator of Example 4.7.3.

language code for the present generator for IBM 370/470 and comparable machines (e.g., the Amdahl 470) is given in Figure 4.7-2. In that code, IX represents x_0, and X is an array of dimension NBATCH where one wishes the NBATCH random numbers which are generated to be stored. (It is faster to generate large batches of random numbers, rather than to generate one at a time.) An example of use of this code to produce and print 100 numbers with a FORTRAN program using the choice $x_0 = 524287$ is given in Figure 4.7-3.

Having seen how to produce a sequence of random numbers $U_1, U_2, \ldots$, *we now wish to consider* **how to produce the independent r.v.'s** $X_1, X_2, \ldots$ **that have d.f.** **F(x).** The most general method for accomplishing this involves the inverse distribution function $F^{-1}(\cdot)$ of $F(x)$.

Definition 4.7.5. If $F(x)$ is a d.f. the inverse function of which exists for all x, then that inverse function $F^{-1}(\cdot)$ is called the **inverse d.f.** of $F(x)$.

Example 4.7.6. If X has the exponential distribution with $\beta = 1$ and $A = 0$, then (see Example 4.2.11) for $x \geq 0$ we have $F_X(x) = 1 - e^{-x}$; hence, if we wish to solve for $F_X^{-1}(y)$ for any y [where $0 < y < 1$ since all possible values of $F_X(x)$

```
      DIMENSION X(10000)
C
      NBATCH = 100
      IX = 524287
C
      CALL URN13(IX,X,NBATCH)
C
      WRITE(6,100)
  100 FORMAT(' THESE ARE THE FIRST 100 NUMBERS FROM URN13',//)
      WRITE(6,110) (X(I),I=1,NBATCH)
  110 FORMAT(4F11.8)
      STOP
      END
```

```
      THESE ARE THE FIRST 100 NUMBERS FROM URN13

      0.79629713 0.84357864 0.04583855 0.14499283
      0.21417087 0.46331453 0.83064628 0.65813637
      0.52331352 0.91584021 0.29460627 0.20976347
      0.38656980 0.67632109 0.51638800 0.26010877
      0.21219134 0.44585949 0.64709449 0.70371783
      0.50613201 0.17664093 0.77622896 0.88482797
      0.67356128 0.06192477 0.96563065 0.92134291
      0.45709676 0.92837769 0.13887870 0.27490109
      0.19925541 0.46825200 0.51366544 0.50453782
      0.11662322 0.74890655 0.26463830 0.14144111
      0.77324426 0.43717241 0.10421008 0.62230128
      0.94072783 0.17606169 0.46883833 0.21875435
      0.03257476 0.55132008 0.99827367 0.90041912
      0.30022216 0.08532375 0.99527615 0.06902802
      0.97830731 0.69581914 0.55330104 0.10115176
      0.56664997 0.05700738 0.03965328 0.63701761
      0.43645358 0.30047154 0.62161005 0.55292171
      0.94822514 0.49344867 0.52301306 0.55473465
      0.26891392 0.33194447 0.69882894 0.33000124
      0.07576895 0.48619270 0.61517835 0.19613385
      0.33441490 0.03595783 0.82233423 0.18219954
      0.33864743 0.43318117 0.00818853 0.48180085
      0.19944656 0.42947173 0.21968776 0.21455050
      0.97070920 0.40593958 0.93973738 0.43363965
      0.59920037 0.54287410 0.70707458 0.31700009
```

Figure 4.7-3. FORTRAN computer code to call the assembler program of Figure 4.7-2 and produce 100 random numbers, with output.

are between 0 and 1], we find

$$y = 1 - e^{-x}$$
$$e^{-x} = 1 - y$$
$$- x = \ln(1 - y)$$
$$x = -\ln(1 - y),$$

hence we have

$$F_X^{-1}(y) = -\ln(1 - y).$$

That is, the value of x where the d.f. $F_X(x)$ attains value y is $-\ln(1 - y)$, as can easily now be verified:

$$F_X(-\ln(1 - y)) = 1 - e^{-(-\ln(1-y))}$$

$$= 1 - e^{\ln(1-y)} = 1 - (1 - y) = y.$$

If $F_X(x)$ has flat parts or jumps, then $F_X^{-1}(y)$ will not exist. However, it can be shown that there is a function $G(\cdot)$ with the properties we will need.

Theorem 4.7.7. Given a d.f. $F(x)$ with inverse d.f. $F^{-1}(\cdot)$, **the r.v. $F^{-1}(U)$ has d.f. $F(x)$**, where U is uniform on $(0, 1)$.

Proof: We wish to find the d.f. of the r.v. $F^{-1}(U)$, that is,

$$F_{F^{-1}(U)}(x) = P(F^{-1}(U) \leq x) = P(U \leq F(x)) = F(x),$$

which proves the result. ∎

Theorem 4.7.8. For any d.f. $F(x)$, there is a function $G(\cdot)$ such that $G(U)$ has d.f. $F(x)$, where U is uniform on $(0, 1)$.

We will not prove Theorem 4.7.8. If the inverse function of $F(x)$ exists, then $G(\cdot)$ is that inverse d.f. In the general case, $G(\cdot)$ simply chooses a unique point when there are many choices (as when there are flat parts of $F(x)$), and chooses the jump point when seeking $G(y)$ for a y that is "jumped over" by $F(x)$.

Using Theorem 4.7.7, we are now in a position to produce a sequence of r.v.'s $X_1, X_2, \ldots$ with d.f. $F(x)$ by simply using the inverse function.

Theorem 4.7.9. Let $U_1, U_2, \ldots$ be a sequence of independent r.v.'s that are uniform on $(0, 1)$, and let $F(x)$ be a d.f. with inverse d.f. $F^{-1}(\cdot)$. Then **the r.v.'s $X_1 = F^{-1}(U_1)$, $X_2 = F^{-1}(U_2), \ldots$ are independent and have d.f. $F(x)$.**

This result (the proof of which is direct and need not be stated separately) is easy to use whenever the inverse d.f. can be given in a simple form. In other cases, other methods are needed.

Example 4.7.10. Given a sequence $U_1, U_2, \ldots$ of independent uniform r.v.'s on $(0, 1)$, show how to produce a sequence of independent r.v.'s $X_1, X_2, \ldots$ that have the **exponential** distribution with arbitrary β and $A = 0$.

Here, as in Example 4.2.11, direct calculation yields (for $x \geq 0$)

$$F(x) = 1 - e^{-x/\beta},$$

and, as in Example 4.7.6, we find the inverse d.f. is

$$F^{-1}(y) = -\beta \ln(1 - y).$$

Thus, using Theorem 4.7.9, the desired sequence of independent r.v.'s, each with the exponential distribution with general β and $A = 0$, is

$$X_1 = -\beta \ln(1 - U_1)$$

$$X_2 = -\beta \ln(1 - U_2)$$

$$\vdots$$

When the inverse d.f. of the desired distribution that we want to generate does not exist in simple form, methods involving transformations (*discussed in Section 4.6*) are often of use; such results are often found in the literature of what are called **characterization theorems**.

Example 4.7.11. Given a sequence of independent r.v.'s $U_1, U_2, \ldots$ which are uniform on $(0, 1)$, produce a sequence of r.v.'s $X_1, X_2, \ldots$ that are $N(0, 1)$ and independent.

Here, from Problem 4.6.4, we know that $\sqrt{-2 \ln(U_i)} \sin(2\pi U_{i+1})$ will be $N(0, 1)$, hence we answer the question by taking

$$X_1 = \sqrt{-2 \ln(U_1)} \sin(2\pi U_2)$$

$$X_2 = \sqrt{-2 \ln(U_3)} \sin(2\pi U_4)$$

$$X_3 = \sqrt{-2 \ln(U_5)} \sin(2\pi U_6)$$

$$\vdots$$

Note that we *cannot* take $\sqrt{-2 \ln(U_1)} \sin(2\pi U_2)$, $\sqrt{-2 \ln(U_2)} \sin(2\pi U_3)$, $\sqrt{-2 \ln(U_3)} \sin(2\pi U_4), \ldots$ as the sequence: These r.v.'s are *not* independent since they involve some of the same uniform r.v.'s (even though they are each $N(0, 1)$).

PROBLEMS FOR SECTION 4.7

4.7.1 Buffon Needle Experiment. Consider the plane with a set of parallel lines at a distance d from one another. A needle of length $a < d$ is tossed "at random" onto the plane.

(a) Show that the probability that the needle will intersect one of the lines is $2a/(\pi d)$. [In interpreting the phrase "at random," assume that x is uniform on $(0, d/2)$ and that θ is uniform on $(-\pi/2, \pi/2)$. Here x is the distance from the center of the needle to the nearest line, and θ is the angle that a perpendicular from the center of the needle to the nearest line makes with the needle.]

(b) If the experiment in part (a) is performed n times and Y denotes the number of times that the needle intersects the line, then by the frequency definition of probability we expect that $Y/n \simeq 2a/(\pi d)$, hence that $\pi \simeq 2an/(dY)$. Perform this experiment with $n = 100$ and see how close the estimate $2an/(dY) = 200a/(dY)$ is to π.

4.7.2 For the random number generator

$$x_n = 663,608,941 x_{n-1} \bmod 2^{32},$$

$U_n = x_n/2^{32}$, of Example 4.7.3, take $x_0 = 1$. Show in detail the calculation of $x_1, U_1, x_2, U_2, x_3, U_3$.

4.7.3 Find the inverse d.f. $F^{-1}(\cdot)$ of a uniform distribution on (a, b), $a < b$. Hence display a function $G(U)$ of a uniform r.v. U on $(0, 1)$ such that $G(U)$ is uniform on (a, b).

4.7.4 Given $U_1, U_2, \ldots$ independent uniform $(0, 1)$ r.v.'s, display a function of these r.v.'s that is chi-square with 3 degrees of freedom. [Hint: Use Example 4.7.10, the fact that if $Z \sim N(0, 1)$ then $Z^2 \sim \chi_1^2(0)$, and Problem 4.6.18.]

4.7.5 Generation of Discrete r.v.'s. Suppose that X is binomial $B(3, .4)$. Then $F_X(x)$ has jumps and flat places, so an inverse function is not defined. However, let $G(y)$ for $0 \le y \le 1$ be defined by

(1) $G(0) = 0$;

(2) $G(y)$ equals the value of x for which $F_X(x) > y$ and $F_X(x^-) < y$ if it is never the case that $F_X(z) = y$ for any z (i.e., if $F_X(\cdot)$ jumps over height y);

(3) $G(y)$ equals inf $\{x: F_X(x) = y\}$ if there are many z such that $F_X(z) = y$ (i.e., $F_X(\cdot)$ has a flat place at height y).

(a) Graph $G(\cdot)$.

(b) Find the probability function of $G(U)$ where U is uniform on $(0, 1)$. Compare with the $B(3, .4)$ probability function.

4.8. ESTIMATION OF d.f.'s AND p.d.f.'s

As noted in Section 4.7, often you may have a set of data $Y_1, Y_2, \ldots, Y_n$ which are independent r.v.'s with d.f. $F(x)$, and you do not know $F(x)$. In this section we wish to begin study of the **estimation of $F(x)$** when it is unknown; this study, which is an important one in statistics, will be continued in Chapter 7.

Definition 4.8.1. Suppose that r.v.'s $Y_1, \ldots, Y_n$ are independent with d.f. $F(\cdot)$. The **empiric d.f.** or **sample d.f.** (based on $Y_1, \ldots, Y_n$) is defined for all x ($-\infty < x < \infty$) by

$$F_n(x \mid Y_1, \ldots, Y_n) = \frac{(\textbf{Number of } Y_1, \ldots, Y_n \textbf{ that are} \leq x)}{n}.$$

Recall that the true distribution function of $Y_1, \ldots, Y_n$ gives us such probabilities as $F(83.0)$, the probability that Y_i will be ≤ 83.0. Recalling the frequency definition of probability from equation (2.1.8), we see that we think of the probability $F(83.0)$ as the limit of the proportion of times Y_i is less than or equal to 83.0 in n trials, as $n \to \infty$. Thus, in a finite number n of trials, it seems natural to estimate $F(83.0)$ by $F_n(83.0 \mid Y_1, \ldots, Y_n)$, the empiric d.f. (That this estimator in fact has good properties is shown in Chapter 7, where this aspect is studied in more detail, as well as in Example 6.2.12 and Theorem 6.2.13.)

Example 4.8.2. The seasonal snowfall at Syracuse, New York, for the 41 seasons 1942–43 through 1982–83 is given in Table 4.8-1. For these $n = 41$ r.v.'s $Y_1, \ldots, Y_{41}$ calculate and plot the empiric d.f.

The plot of the empiric d.f. for this set of snowfall data is given in Figure 4.8-1. As is evident from examination of Figure 4.8-1, this plot was produced on a line printer as computer output. To do such statistical calculations, we can either write our own program or we can use a package of computer programs for statistical calculations that have been compiled by others. The first option (writing our own program) is preferable if we have the statistical, numerical, and computer programming knowledge needed to perform this task properly, and if we need to take this approach (e.g., this will often be the case when dealing with new statistical methods or new application areas, where the software for the task at hand may not yet exist). The second option (using a package of programs) is preferable in most cases, if a package exists that has the software we need and if we have assurance it is of high quality (of course, if it is user-friendly that is a plus). The two most widely used packages, both of which are generally of high quality, are BMDP and SAS. References that may be consulted for an introduction to these packages are, respectively, Dixon (1983) and SAS Institute (1982).

The BMDP programs (in a version called BMD) date from about 1961, though they have been extensively updated and expanded since that time. As one might expect from the date of their genesis, they are not very user-friendly, especially in their (lack of) ease of data-base manipulation. They are in wide use since statisticians tend to use what they know, and since they are of high quality (though, as with most packages, a careful user will not need to wait long to find problems in their more advanced analyses—as the field of statistics advances, software rapidly becomes obsolete, in the sense it is no longer at the cutting edge of the methodology).

The SAS package of software for data analysis dates from about 1966, and it has been in wide use since about 1975, at which time many hailed it as a new

TABLE 4.8-1
Seasonal Snowfall at Syracuse, New York, for
the 41 Seasons 1942–43 through 1982–83, in Inches

Season	Snowfall
1942–43	76.5
1943–44	66.5
1944–45	128.7
1945–46	67.8
1946–47	110.6
1947–48	75.5
1948–49	76.6
1949–50	118.0
1950–51	92.8
1951–52	100.5
1952–53	77.5
1953–54	85.9
1954–55	101.4
1955–56	146.8
1956–57	76.1
1957–58	141.1
1958–59	137.2
1959–60	134.8
1960–61	130.5
1961–62	77.3
1962–63	116.5
1963–64	83.8
1964–65	97.3
1965–66	118.8
1966–67	83.0
1967–68	81.2
1968–69	97.9
1969–70	125.5
1970–71	157.2
1971–72	133.7
1972–73	81.2
1973–74	123.2
1974–75	105.5
1975–76	95.8
1976–77	145.0
1977–78	161.2
1978–79	118.5
1979–80	93.4
1980–81	79.0
1981–82	123.1
1982–83	66.0

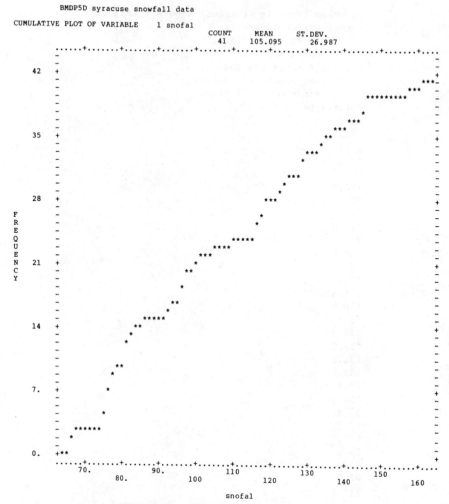

Figure 4.8-1. BMDP output for empiric d.f. plot.

generation of statistical software. It has ease of data-base manipulation, elements of report writing, and supports a graphics package and graphics options. At the current time, some have become dissatisfied with SAS, however, and effort is now starting on **expert statistical systems**, that is, computer programs that will incorporate the knowledge and approach of an expert statistician and be easy to use (e.g., it has been proposed that such systems should not have a manual; instead, the interactive package should have on-screen documentation of such a level that it *is* the manual). A number of such systems are currently being developed, and one called **ESS**™ (The *E*xpert *S*tatistical *S*ystem, from the NMR and Data Processing Laboratory at Syracuse University, in which one of the authors of this text is participating) **is now commercially available**.

The plot in Figure 4.8-1 was produced using the BMDP system of programs. The complete program for this analysis, given in Figure 4.8-2, consists of 9 lines

```
/problem title is 'syracuse snowfall data'.
/input variables are 1.
        format is '(1f5.1)'.
        cases are 41.
/variable names are snofal.
        maximum is (1) 161.2.
        minimum is (1) 66.0.
/plot type is cum.
/end
76.5
66.5
128.7
67.8
110.6
75.5
76.6
118.0
92.8
100.5
77.5
85.9
101.4
146.8
76.1
141.1
137.2
134.8
130.5
77.3
116.5
83.8
97.3
118.8
83.0
81.2
97.9
125.5
157.2
133.7
81.2
123.2
105.5
95.8
145.0
161.2
118.5
93.4
79.0
123.1
66.0
```

Figure 4.8-2. BMDP code for empiric d.f. plot.

of code (to which the data set is appended so the BMDP package can read it). The particular BMDP program that executes this code (and must be called) is the "5D" program (one of more than 30 that are in the BMDP package). The code is almost self-explanatory: There is one variable (snowfall), data on it is in the F5.1 format (those familiar with FORTRAN formats will understand what this means), there are 41 cases (data on 41 seasons of snowfall), and we state upper (161.2) and lower (66.0) limits on the range of the snowfall data. Plot type is needed, as 5D has several types of plots available.

The empiric d.f. has always played an important role in statistical thinking. Recently, it has become more so, with a new class of methods called **bootstrap statistics** being based on it. These important methods, which are discussed in Chapter 15, use Monte Carlo simulation methods to develop solutions to statistical problems of the types studied in Chapters 7ff.

Just as estimation of the d.f. is important when it is unknown, similarly, **estimation of the p.d.f. is important in cases where the d.f. is known to be absolutely continuous.** However, simply differentiating the empiric d.f. does *not* produce an estimator of the p.d.f., since that derivative is 0 at almost all points (since the empiric d.f. is the d.f. of a discrete r.v. that puts probability $1/n$ at each of the observed values $Y_1, \ldots, Y_n$). However, **there is a natural way to modify the empiric d.f. to an absolutely continuous d.f., the derivative of which is called the empiric p.d.f.**

Definition 4.8.3. Let $a \le \min(Y_1, \ldots, Y_n) \le \max(Y_1, \ldots, Y_n) \le b$ be given numbers. Let $Z_1, \ldots, Z_n$ denote the values of $Y_1, \ldots, Y_n$ in increasing numeric order. Define $Z_0 \equiv a$ and $Z_{n+1} \equiv b$. Then the **continuous-empiric d.f.** is the d.f. $G_n(x|a, Z_1, \ldots, Z_n, b)$, which is 0 if $x \le a$, 1 if $x \ge b$, and in between has the value of the straight line segments that join the successive midpoints of the successive bars that constitute the empiric d.f.; the midpoint of the leftmost bar is joined to the point $(a, 0)$, while the rightmost bar is joined to the point $(b, 1)$. The **empiric p.d.f.** is

$$g_n(x|a, Z_1, \ldots, Z_n, b) = G_n'(x|a, Z_1, \ldots, Z_n, b). \qquad (4.8.4)$$

Example 4.8.5. For the $n = 3$ seasonal snowfalls for the seasons 1980–81, 1981–82, and 1982–83 in Table 4.8-1, find and graph the empiric p.d.f.; use $a = 0$ and $b = 200$.

Here we successively find the empiric d.f. as in Figure 4.8-3, the continuous-empiric d.f. as in Figure 4.8-4, and the empiric p.d.f. as in Figure 4.8-5. Note that the empiric p.d.f. *is* a p.d.f., so the area under it must integrate to 1; we see from Figure 4.8-5 that the area is

$$(72.5 - 0.0)(.0045978) + (101.05 - 72.5)(.0116754)$$

$$+ (200.0 - 101.05)(.0033687)$$

$$= .3333 + .3333 + .3333 = 1.000;$$

$F_3(x \mid Y_1, Y_2, Y_3) = F_3(x \mid 79.0, 123.1, 66.0)$

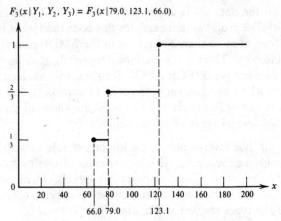

Figure 4.8-3. Empiric d.f. for the $n = 3$ data points of Example 4.8.5.

$G_3(x \mid a, Z_1, Z_2, Z_3, b) = G_3(x \mid 0.0, 66.0, 79.0, 123.1, 200.0)$

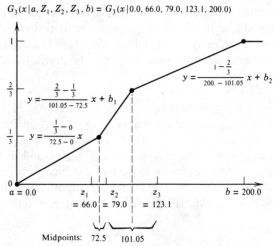

Figure 4.8-4. Continuous-empiric d.f. for the $n = 3$ data points of Example 4.8.5.

as is apparent from this sum, the probabilities that (in the empiric d.f.) are $\frac{1}{3}$ at each of three points, in the continuous-empiric p.d.f. are spread continuously over three ranges, with probability $\frac{1}{3}$ in each of the ranges.

Via elementary algebra, one can write down the general formula for $G_n(x \mid a, Z_1, \ldots, Z_n, b)$, which is a straight line segment over the range

$$\frac{Z_j + Z_{j-1}}{2} \le x \le \frac{Z_{j+1} + Z_j}{2}$$

for $j = 1, 2, \ldots, n$ (as we saw in Figure 4.8-4). Differentiating, we then obtain **the**

$g_3(x \mid a, Z_1, Z_2, Z_3, b) = g_3(x \mid 0.0, 66.0, 79.0, 123.1, 200.0)$

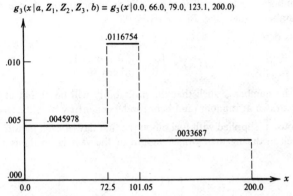

Figure 4.8-5. Empiric p.d.f. for the $n = 3$ data points of Example 4.8.5.

general formula for the empiric p.d.f. as

$$g_n(x \mid a, Z_1, \ldots, Z_n, b)$$

$$= \begin{cases} \dfrac{2}{n(Z_{j+1} - Z_{j-1})}, & \text{if } \dfrac{Z_j + Z_{j-1}}{2} \le x \le \dfrac{Z_{j+1} + Z_j}{2} \text{ for } j = 1, 2, \ldots, n \\ 0, & \text{otherwise.} \end{cases}$$

PROBLEMS FOR SECTION 4.8

4.8.1 The weights of $n = 5$ female Syracuse University students chosen at random were 116, 110, 118, 120, and 130 pounds. Find and graph the empiric d.f. of this data.

4.8.2 Find and graph the continuous-empiric d.f. for the $n = 5$ data points of Problem 4.8.1.

4.8.3 Find and graph the empiric p.d.f. for the data of Problem 4.8.1.

PROBLEMS FOR CHAPTER 4

4.1 If a r.v. X has density

$$f(x) = \begin{cases} 2x, & \text{if } 0 < x < 1 \\ 0, & \text{otherwise,} \end{cases}$$

find the probability that **(a)** $X < \frac{1}{2}$; **(b)** $\frac{1}{4} < X < \frac{1}{2}$; **(c)** $X > \frac{3}{4}$, given that $X > \frac{1}{2}$.

4.2 Define a density using $x(2 - x)$ over the set $0 < x < 2$. Find the probability that $a < X < b$ if **(a)** $0 < a < b < 2$; **(b)** $a < 0, 2 < b$. (X has the defined p.d.f.)

4.3 If a r.v. X has density

$$f(x) = \begin{cases} 4x^3, & \text{if } 0 < x < 1 \\ 0, & \text{otherwise,} \end{cases}$$

find the number a such that X is equally likely to be greater than a or less than a. Find the number b such that $P[X > b] = .05$.

4.4 A r.v. X has density

$$f(x) = \begin{cases} 1, & \text{if } 0 < x < 1 \\ 0, & \text{otherwise.} \end{cases}$$

Determine the number a such that the probability will be .9 that at least one of 4 values of X drawn at random (and hence independent r.v.'s) will exceed a.

4.5 A certain house is supplied with fuel oil on the first day of each month. If its monthly need for fuel oil during the "worst" month of the year is, in thousands of gallons, distributed as

$$f(x) = \begin{cases} 5(1 - x)^4, & 0 < x < 1 \\ 0, & \text{otherwise,} \end{cases}$$

what capacity tank is needed in order that the probability that its supply will be exhausted in a typical "worst" month will be **(a)** .01; **(b)** 0.

4.6 Suppose that a r.v. X has the $N(\mu, \sigma^2)$ distribution (see Definition 4.2.18). Express $F(z) = P[X \leq z]$ in terms of $\Phi(\cdot)$ where (for all x, $-\infty < x < +\infty$)

$$\Phi(x) = \int_{-\infty}^{x} \frac{1}{\sqrt{2\pi}} e^{-\frac{1}{2}y^2} \, dy.$$

[*Note:* $\Phi(\cdot)$ is tabled in Table 11.]

4.7 If

$$f_{X,Y}(x, y) = \begin{cases} e^{-(x+y)}, & x > 0 \text{ and } y > 0 \\ 0, & \text{otherwise,} \end{cases}$$

find $P(X > 1)$; $P(a < X + Y < b)$ if $0 < a < b$; and $P(X < Y | X < 2Y)$.

4.8 Suppose that the total length in minutes of intercontinental satellite long distance telephone calls is found to have d.f.

$$F(x) = \begin{cases} 0, & x \leq 0 \\ 1 - \frac{2}{3}e^{-x/3} - \frac{1}{3}e^{-[x/3]}, & x > 0, \end{cases}$$

where $[y]$ means the largest integer which is $\leq y$ (e.g., $[5.3] = 5$ and $[6] = 6$).
(a) Sketch the d.f.
(b) Is the d.f. absolutely continuous, discrete, singularly continuous, or a combination of these? (If a combination, specify c_1, c_2, c_3 as noted in Theorem 4.1.6.)
(c) What is the probability that the total length in minutes of a telephone call of this type will be > 6 minutes; < 4 minutes; $= 3$ minutes; between 4 and 7 minutes?
(d) What is the conditional probability that the total length in minutes of a telephone call of this type will be < 9 minutes, given that it has lasted more than 5 minutes?

4.9 The choice of a random point Y between 0 and 1 can be described as follows in terms of discrete r.v.'s. Let $Y_k(y)$ denote the kth decimal of y and, to avoid ambiguities, use terminating expansions when possible. Let the r.v. Y_k take values $0, 1, \ldots, 9$ with probability $1/10$ each. Suppose that $Y_1, Y_2, \ldots$ are independent r.v.'s.

Then

$$Y = \sum_{i=1}^{\infty} \frac{1}{10^i} Y_i,$$

which reduces the random choice of a point Y to choice of its successive decimals:

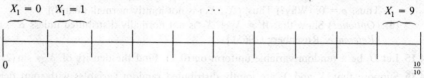

$X_1 = 0$ $X_1 = 1$ $\cdots$ $X_1 = 9$

0    $\frac{10}{10}$

Find the d.f. of $99Z$, where

$$Z = \sum_{k=2,4,\ldots} \frac{1}{10^k} Y_k = \sum_{y=1}^{\infty} \frac{1}{100^y} Y_{2y}.$$

[*Hint:* See Example 4.2.29.]

4.10 We define a function x^+, called the **positive part of** x, as

$$x^+ = \begin{cases} x, & \text{if } x \geq 0 \\ 0, & \text{if } x < 0. \end{cases}$$

Similarly the **negative part of** x, x^-, is

$$x^- = \begin{cases} 0, & x \geq 0 \\ -x, & x < 0. \end{cases}$$

[*Note:* $x = x^+ - x^-$ and $|x| = x^+ + x^-$.] If X is a random variable with d.f. $F_X(x)$, find the d.f. of $Y = X^+$.

4.11 Let X_1, X_2 be independent random variables, each with a uniform distribution on $(0, 1)$. Find and sketch the density functions of $X_1 + X_2$; $X_1 - X_2$; $|X_1 - X_2|$; $\max(X_1, X_2)$; $\min(X_1, X_2)$; $X_1 X_2$; X_1/X_2.

4.12 Prove the **theorem**: Let $(X_1, \ldots, X_n)$ be an n-dimensional (absolutely) continuous random variable with density function $f_{X_1, \ldots, X_n}(x_1, \ldots, x_n)$. Then, $X_1, \ldots, X_n$ are stochastically independent iff, for some functions $g_1(\cdot), \ldots, g_n(\cdot)$,

$$f_{X_1, \ldots, X_n}(x_1, \ldots, x_n) = g_1(x_1) \ldots g_n(x_n), \quad \text{for all } \mathbf{x} \in \mathscr{R}^n. \quad (*)$$

4.13 If $(*)$ holds in Problem 4.12, find $f_{X_1}(x_1)$ in terms of $g_1(\cdot), \ldots, g_n(\cdot)$.

4.14 Let $\mathbf{X} = (X_1, X_2)$ have the joint density function

$$f_{X_1, X_2}(x_1, x_2) = f_1(x_1) f_2(x_2) \{1 + \alpha[2F_1(x_1) - 1][2F_2(x_2) - 1]\}, \quad (*)$$

$|\alpha| \leq 1$, where

$$f_i(x_i) = \frac{1}{\sqrt{2\pi}} e^{-\frac{1}{2} x_i^2} \quad (i = 1, 2)$$

$$F_i(x_i) = \int_{-\infty}^{x_i} \frac{1}{\sqrt{2\pi}} e^{-\frac{1}{2} t^2} dt \quad (i = 1, 2).$$

(a) Verify that $\int_{-\infty}^{\infty} \int_{-\infty}^{\infty} f_{X_1, X_2}(x_1, x_2) \, dx_1 \, dx_2 = 1$.

(b) Find $f_{X_1}(x_1)$ and $f_{X_2}(x_2)$. What are these particular densities called?

(c) Is (X_1, X_2) jointly normal? [*Hint:* Consider two cases, $\alpha = 0$, $\alpha \neq 0$. In the case $\alpha \neq 0$, for (X_1, X_2) to be jointly normal it must be the case that $(*)$ equals the normal bivariate density with parameters $\mu_1 = \mu_2 = 0$, $\sigma_1^2 = \sigma_2^2 = 1$, and ρ. (Why?) This equality must hold for all (x_1, x_2), in particular for $(x_1, x_2) = (0,0)$. Thus, $\rho = 0$. (Why?) Thus, (X_1, X_2) is not jointly normal. (Why?)]

(d) (*Optional*) Show that $W = X_1 + X_2$ is not normally distributed unless $\alpha = 0$. [*Reference:* Rosenberg (1965).]

4.15 Let U be a random variable uniform on $(0,1)$. Find the density of $X = \sin(2\pi U)$.

4.16 Suppose that X and Y are jointly distributed random variables with joint density function

$$f_{X,Y}(x, y) = \begin{cases} e^{-(x+y)} & \text{if } x \geq 0 \text{ and } y \geq 0 \\ 0, & \text{otherwise.} \end{cases}$$

Find the density function of $Z = XY$.

4.17 Show that if a random variable X is exponential, that is, for some λ ($\lambda > 0$)

$$f_X(x) = \begin{cases} \lambda e^{-\lambda x}, & \text{for } x > 0 \\ 0, & \text{otherwise,} \end{cases}$$

then it has the **"lack of memory property."** That is, for all positive numbers x_1 and x_2,

$$P[X \geq x_1 + x_2 | X \geq x_1] = P[X \geq x_2].$$

4.18 Prove (see Example 4.2.6) that if Y is uniform on $(0,1)$, then (for $b < c$ fixed) $X = (c - b)Y + b$ is uniform on (b, c).

4.19 Supply the remaining details in the verification that (if $n = 2$) Definitions 4.5.2 and 4.5.4 are equivalent.

4.20 $X_1, \ldots, X_n$ are independent random variables distributed according to the uniform density on the interval from 0 to 1. Let $Z_n = \max(X_1, \ldots, X_n)$. Derive an expression for $P[Z_n \leq x]$, and use this to find how large n must be in order that $P[Z_n > .9] \geq .99$. (Your answer may be left in terms of logarithms, and so on.)

4.21 Suppose that X and Y are jointly distributed random variables with joint density function

$$f_{X,Y}(x, y) = \begin{cases} \frac{1}{4}\left(1 + xy(x^2 - y^2)\right), & \text{if } -1 \leq x, y \leq 1 \\ 0, & \text{otherwise.} \end{cases}$$

Find the density of X; of Y; of $X + Y$. Find

$$f(z) = \int_{-\infty}^{\infty} f_X(x) f_Y(z - x) \, dx$$

[called the **convolution** of $f_X(\cdot)$ and $f_Y(\cdot)$]. Interpret the results as in Example 3.6.10.

4.22 If X and Y have the joint density function

$$f_{X,Y}(x, y) = \begin{cases} \dfrac{1}{2\pi} e^{-\frac{1}{4\pi}x^2 - y}, & \text{if } -\infty < x < +\infty, y \geq 0 \\ 0, & \text{otherwise,} \end{cases}$$

find $f_X(x)$ and $f_Y(y)$. Are X and Y independent?

4.23 Suppose that X is a random variable with d.f. $F(x)(-\infty < x < +\infty)$. Find the d.f. of $Z = \sqrt{|X|}$. [*Hint:* First find the d.f. of $Y = |X|$; then find the d.f. of $Z = \sqrt{Y}$.]

4.24 Suppose that $X_1, \ldots, X_n$ are independent r.v.'s and that X_i has the exponential distribution

$$f_i(t) = \begin{cases} \alpha_i e^{-\alpha_i t}, & t \geq 0 \\ 0, & t < 0. \end{cases}$$

Find the distribution function and density function of $Y_1 = \min(X_1, \ldots, X_n)$. Find and plot the failure rate[8] (see Example 4.2.38) for Y_1 (which corresponds to a series system). Find the distribution function and density function of $Y_2 = \max(X_1, \ldots, X_n)$. What can you say about the failure rate[9] for Y_2 (which corresponds to a parallel system)?

4.25 Suppose that X and Y are independent r.v.'s, that X has the $\chi_m^2(0)$ distribution, and that Y has the $\chi_n^2(0)$ distribution (see Definition 4.2.13). Find the density of $U = X/(X + Y)$. Find the density of $V = X/Y$. (These will turn out to be distributions we have already discussed; find out which they are.)

4.26 Let $F(x, y)$ be the d.f. of some two-dimensional r.v. (X, Y), and let $F_1(x)$ and $F_2(y)$, respectively, be the marginal d.f.'s of X and of Y. Define functions

$$U(x, y) = \min\{F_1(x), F_2(y)\},$$

$$L(x, y) = \max\{F_1(x) + F_2(y) - 1, 0\}.$$

(a) Prove that $L(x, y)$ and $U(x, y)$ are each distribution functions and that their marginal distributions are the same as those of $F(x, y)$.

(b) Prove that $L(x, y) \leq F(x, y) \leq U(x, y)$. [This bound for a bivariate probability in terms of given marginals was attributed to a 1951 paper of Fréchet by Marshall and Olkin (1967); Professor Ingram Olkin has called attention to the fact that W. Hoeffding had this result in 1940.]

(c) Suppose that X and Y each are $N(0, 1)$ r.v.'s, but their joint distribution function is otherwise unknown. Graph (as a function of x) the bounds $L(x, y_0)$ and $U(x, y_0)$ on $F(x, y_0)$ of (b), for $y_0 = 0$. Also for $y_0 = -1$. Also for $y_0 = 1$.

4.27 Let X be a r.v. with d.f. $F_1(x)$. Let $F_2(y)$ denote the d.f. of $Y = g(X)$. Let $F(x, y)$ denote the d.f. of the two-dimensional r.v. (X, Y).

(a) Show that if $g(\cdot)$ is monotone increasing, then

$$F(x, y) = \min\{F_1(x), F_2(y)\}.$$

(b) Show that if $g(\cdot)$ is monotone decreasing, then

$$F(x, y) = \max\{F_1(x) + F_2(y) - 1, 0\}.$$

4.28 In Example 4.6.21 we were given the joint distribution of $X_1, X_2, \ldots, X_k$ and desired to find the joint density of $Y_1, \ldots, Y_{k-1}$ where

$$Y_1 = \frac{X_2}{X_1}, Y_2 = \frac{X_3}{X_1}, \ldots, Y_{k-1} = \frac{X_k}{X_1}.$$

---

[8] This failure rate is still the subject of research. For each, see Sarkar (1971), and the references therein.

[9] This failure rate exhibits unusual properties. For example, see Bryson (1971).

In order to use Theorem 4.6.18 we defined another r.v. $Y_k = X_1 + \cdots + X_k$, found the joint density of $Y_1, \ldots, Y_{k-1}, Y_k$, and then (integrating out Y_k) found the joint density of $Y_1, \ldots, Y_{k-1}$ as desired.

Many other possible choices of Y_k can be made, some of which will simplify (and some of which will complicate) the calculation of the joint density of $Y_1, \ldots, Y_{k-1}$ when the foregoing method is used. Solve the problem of finding the joint density of $Y_1, \ldots, Y_{k-1}$ by this method when Y_k is defined as $Y_k = X_1$ [hence, $y_k = g_k(x_1, \ldots, x_k) = x_1$ in system (4.6.24)]. Is it better to choose Y_k to be $X_1 + \cdots + X_k$ or to be X_1?

HONORS PROBLEMS FOR CHAPTER 4

4.1H Supply the details noted at the end of Example 4.2.29 on a singularly continuous d.f. in Section 4.2.

4.2H Give an example of a two-dimensional singularly continuous d.f. (It is not necessary to show a random variable that leads to this d.f., but it is necessary to prove that it is a d.f. and that it is singularly continuous.) [*Note:* If we construct a random variable X that has a singularly continuous d.f., we may be able to construct a two-dimensional analog.]

Give an example of a random variable that has a singularly continuous two-dimensional d.f. Try to do this so that, if $\mathbf{X} = (X_1, X_2)$ is the random variable, X_1 and X_2 are not independent. [*Reference:* Koopmans (1969). Additionally, see Brown (1969).]

4.3H An example of a singularly continuous $F(x)$ was given as equation (10) by Lamperti and Rudin (1967). Consult that article and supply the details.

4.4H Fix $n \geq 3$. Show that there exist r.v.'s $X_1, \ldots, X_n$ such that any two are pairwise independent (in fact any proper subset is a set of independent r.v.'s) but the set of n r.v.'s are not independent. [*Reference:* Dykstra and Pierce (1969).]

4.5H Find and plot (using a computer plotter if possible) the failure rate $q(x)$ [see (4.2.39)] for the $N(0, 1)$ distribution [see Definition 4.2.18].

4.6H The failure rate for the $N(\mu, \sigma^2)$ distribution, say $q_{\mu, \sigma^2}(x)$, has the property that

$$
q_{\mu, \sigma^2}(x) = \frac{\dfrac{1}{\sqrt{2\pi}\,\sigma} e^{-\frac{1}{2}\left(\frac{x-\mu}{\sigma}\right)^2}}{\displaystyle\int_x^\infty \dfrac{1}{\sqrt{2\pi}\,\sigma} e^{-\frac{1}{2}\left(\frac{y-\mu}{\sigma}\right)^2} dy}
$$

$$
= \frac{1}{\sigma} \frac{\dfrac{1}{\sqrt{2\pi}} e^{-\frac{1}{2}\left(\frac{x-\mu}{\sigma}\right)^2}}{\displaystyle\int_{(x-\mu)/\sigma}^\infty \dfrac{1}{\sqrt{2\pi}} e^{-\frac{1}{2}z^2} dz}
$$

$$
= \frac{1}{\sigma} q_{0,1}\left(\frac{x-\mu}{\sigma}\right) = \frac{1}{\sigma} q\left(\frac{x-\mu}{\sigma}\right).
$$

Thus, the failure rate for the $N(\mu, \sigma^2)$ distribution can be easily obtained from the $N(0, 1)$ distribution's failure rate. (An illustration of how this works, for an arbitrary function, is given below.)

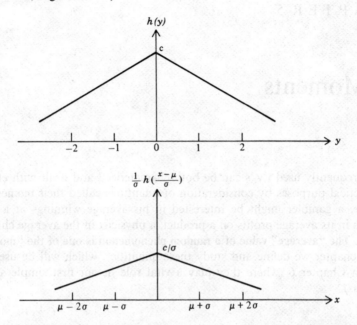

Prove that the $N(\mu, \sigma^2)$ distribution is an IFR distribution. [*Hint:* From Problem 4.5H we see that $q'_{\mu, \sigma^2}(x)$ is simply related to $q'_{0,1}(y)$. Then use equation (1.8) of Feller (1968), p. 175.]

CHAPTER 5

Moments

Many frequently used r.v.'s can be both characterized and dealt with effectively for practical purposes by consideration of quantities called their **moments**. (For example, a gambler might be interested in his average winnings at a game, a business in its average profits on a product, a physicist in the average charge of a particle. **The "average" value of a random phenomenon is one of the "moments."**) In this chapter we define and study these quantities, which will be used extensively in Chapter 6 (where they play a vital role in our first simple statistical problems).

5.1. EXPECTATION AND OTHER MOMENTS; MEDIAN

The definitions and results of this section are stated only for two cases: X a discrete r.v. and X an (absolutely) continuous r.v. These are the cases of most practical interest. They can be unified [and the definitions and results extended to a r.v. X with an arbitrary d.f. $F(x)$] by use of the Stieltjes (or Lebesgue-Stieltjes) integral, but this is not central to our theme and will be omitted. In any case, it will be transparent how we should deal with mixed discrete and (absolutely) continuous d.f.'s. [For details of these notions for arbitrary d.f.'s $F(x)$ see Tucker (1967).]

Definition 5.1.1. For a r.v. X we define its **expectation** [EX or $E(X)$] as $EX = \int_{-\infty}^{\infty} x f_X(x)\,dx$ [$EX = \Sigma x_i p_X(x_i)$] if X is absolutely continuous with density function $f_X(x)$ [if X is discrete with probability function $p_X(x)$], provided this integral (sum) exists[1] and is finite.

Theorem 5.1.2. If X is a r.v., then the expectation of the r.v. $g(X)$ exists iff $\int_{-\infty}^{\infty} |g(x)| f_X(x)\,dx < \infty$ when X is absolutely continuous [$\Sigma |g(x_i)| p_X(x_i) < \infty$

---

[1] This requires absolute convergence, that is, existence of $\int_{-\infty}^{\infty} |x| f_X(x)\,dx$ (or $\Sigma |x_i| p_X(x_i)$); see Corollary 5.1.3.

when X is discrete], in which case $Eg(X) = \int_{-\infty}^{\infty} g(x) f_X(x) dx$ $[Eg(X) = \Sigma g(x_i) p_X(x_i)]$.

Corollary 5.1.3. If X is a r.v., then EX exists iff $\int_0^{\infty} x f_X(x) dx$ and $\int_{-\infty}^0 x f_X(x) dx$ are finite when X is absolutely continuous [$\sum_{x_i \geq 0} x_i p_X(x_i)$ and $\sum_{x_i < 0} x_i p_X(x_i)$ are finite when X is discrete], in which case $EX = \int_{-\infty}^{\infty} x f_X(x) dx$ $[EX = \Sigma x_i p_X(x_i)]$.

Example 5.1.4. Suppose that X has the **Laplace distribution** of Example 4.1.3, that is,

$$f_X(x) = e^{\frac{-|x|}{2}}, \qquad -\infty < x < \infty.$$

Then the average value $E(X)$ exists since

$$\int_0^{\infty} x e^{-|x|} dx = \int_0^{\infty} x e^{-x} dx = 1$$

and

$$\int_{-\infty}^0 x e^{-|x|} dx = \int_{-\infty}^0 x e^x dx = -1$$

are finite, hence

$$E(X) = \int_{-\infty}^{\infty} x f_X(x) dx = \int_{-\infty}^0 x f_X(x) dx + \int_0^{\infty} x f_X(x) dx = 1 - 1 = 0.$$

Example 5.1.5. Suppose that X has the **Cauchy distribution** of Example 4.6.9. Then

$$\int_0^{\infty} x f_X(x) dx = \int_0^{\infty} x \frac{1}{\pi(1 + x^2)} dx = \int_0^{\infty} \frac{1}{2\pi} \frac{2x}{1 + x^2} dx$$

$$= \frac{1}{2\pi} (\ln(1 + x^2)) \Big|_0^{\infty} = \infty,$$

that is, this is a divergent integral (the area under the curve $2x/(1 + x^2)$ between 0 and infinity is infinite), hence **in this case, $E(X)$ is not defined** (see Definition 5.1.1). It is also easy to show that in this example

$$\int_{-\infty}^0 x f_X(x) dx = -\infty$$

and the positive and negative areas are "balanced" in the sense that

$$\lim_{M \to \infty} \int_{-M}^{M} x f_X(x) \, dx = 0.$$

Nevertheless, although in this case it might seem reasonable to take $E(X)$ to be equal to 0, we do *not* define $E(X)$ unless *both* of the integrals

$$\int_{-\infty}^{0} x f_X(x) \, dx \quad \text{and} \quad \int_{0}^{\infty} x f_X(x) \, dx$$

are finite (although if one is finite and the other is not, we do sometimes talk as though $E(X)$ were defined and equal to $-\infty$ or ∞).

Corollary 5.1.6. If X is a r.v. with d.f. $F(x)$, then [for any d.f. $F(x)$] EX exists iff $\int_{0}^{\infty} (1 - F(x)) \, dx$ and $\int_{-\infty}^{0} F(x) \, dx$ are finite, in which case

$$EX = \int_{0}^{\infty} (1 - F(x)) \, dx - \int_{-\infty}^{0} F(x) \, dx.$$

We will not prove Theorem 5.1.2, Corollary 5.1.3, or Corollary 5.1.6, although we note that Corollary 5.1.6 follows from Corollary 5.1.3 and integration by parts.

Suppose that X and $g(X)$ are both (absolutely) continuous r.v.'s. Then by Definition 5.1.1, $Eg(X) = \int_{-\infty}^{\infty} y f_{g(X)}(y) \, dy$, so that we will need to find $f_{g(X)}(y)$ (an onerous task, as we saw in Chapter 4). But Theorem 5.1.2 tells us that $Eg(X) = \int_{-\infty}^{\infty} g(x) f_X(x) \, dx$, a very useful result that allows us to bypass $f_{g(X)}(y)$. In Parzen (1960) this result is shown to be due to the fact that we define expectation only when our integrals are absolutely convergent (pp. 344–345), and an example is given where this result fails to hold if absolute convergence is not required in the definition of expectation (pp. 350–351). Parzen (p. 347) also notes the extension that, if $Y = g_1(X)$, then $Eg(Y) = \int_{-\infty}^{\infty} g(y) f_{g_1(X)}(y) \, dy$ $= \int_{-\infty}^{\infty} g(g_1(x)) f_X(x) \, dx$. [So, we can find $Eg(Y)$ without finding the probability distribution of Y, where $Y = g_1(X)$.]

Theorem 5.1.7. Properties of Expectation. If c is a constant and $g(X)$, $g_1(X)$, and $g_2(X)$ are functions whose expectations exist, then

(i) $E(c) = c$;
(ii) $E(cg(X)) = cEg(X)$;
(iii) $E(g_1(X) + g_2(X)) = Eg_1(X) + Eg_2(X)$;
(iv) $Eg_1(X) \leq Eg_2(X)$ if $g_1(x) \leq g_2(x)$ for all x;
(v) $|Eg(X)| \leq E|g(X)|$.

Proof: [Part (iii) for the case where X is (absolutely) continuous.]

$$E(g_1(X) + g_2(X))$$

$$= \int_{-\infty}^{\infty} (g_1(x) + g_2(x))f_X(x)\,dx$$

$$= \int_{-\infty}^{\infty} g_1(x)f_X(x)\,dx + \int_{-\infty}^{\infty} g_2(x)f_X(x)\,dx = Eg_1(X) + Eg_2(X). \quad \blacksquare$$

Example 5.1.8. Roulette. The expectation of a random variable is thought of as a long-term average. For example, a popular casino game is roulette. A roulette wheel has 18 red, 18 green, and 2 black "spots" (depressions in which a ball spun around the wheel may come to rest). To enter the game, one pays a fee such as $2 and wins $.50 if a red spot shows up, $1 if a green spot shows up, and $10 if a black spot shows up. What is the expected net profit after 1 play? What is the expected profit after 100 plays?

If X denotes the winnings after 1 play, then the probability function of X is

$$p_X(x) = \begin{cases} 18/38 & \text{if } x = .5 \\ 18/38 & \text{if } x = 1 \\ 2/38 & \text{if } x = 10 \\ 0 & \text{otherwise,} \end{cases}$$

hence

$$E(X) = (.5)(18/38) + (1)(18/38) + (10)(2/38) = \tfrac{47}{38}.$$

The net profit $Y = X - 2$, and by property (iii) of Theorem 5.1.7 [with $g_2(X) \equiv -2$, a constant], we find

$$E(Y) = E(X) - 2 = \tfrac{47}{38} - 2 = -\tfrac{29}{38} = -\$.76316.$$

This does not mean that a player who plays the game once will lose 76¢; in fact, it is clear that on one play of the game one will either lose $1.50, or lose $1.00, or win $8.00. Rather, if one plays for a "long" period, then *on the average play* one will lose 76¢. (This last statement is fully justified by the Weak Law of Large Numbers, Theorem 6.2.7.)

As seems intuitively clear, and is shown in Section 5.3, the mean of a sum (in this case of the profits over 100 plays) is the sum of the means, hence the expected profit in 100 plays will equal $(100)(-.763) = -\$76.32$. [Note that a game is called **fair** if the net profit Y has $E(Y) = 0$; $E(Y) < 0$ for all casino games.]

Example 5.1.9. Another property of expectation is that

$$E|g(X)| = 0 \Rightarrow g(x) = 0 \text{ for all } x \text{ with positive density (or probability).}$$

(This follows since for the integral of a nonnegative function to be zero, that function must be identically zero, and by assumption we have

$$E|g(X)| = \int_{-\infty}^{\infty} |g(x)|f_X(x)\, dx = 0$$

where the integrand is a nonnegative function since both $|g(x)|$ and $f_X(x)$ are nonnegative.) However, this should not be confused with the *false* statement that "$E[g(X)] = 0$ implies $g(x) = 0$ for all x." That this latter statement is false is illustrated by Example 5.1.4, where $g(X) = X$ has $E(X) = 0$, but X itself certainly can take on values other than 0.

Definition 5.1.10. Let X be a r.v. with d.f. $F(x)$. The **nth (noncentral) moment** of X is (if this expectation exists) $\mu'_n \equiv EX^n$.

Lemma 5.1.11. If the rth moment $E(X^r)$ of a r.v. X exists for some positive integer r, then $E(X^s)$ also exists for $s = 1, 2, \ldots, r - 1$.

A proof of Lemma 5.1.11 can be given using Hölder's Inequality (Theorem 5.1.13). (This proof takes X to be X^s, $Y = 1$, and $p = r$ in Hölder's Inequality.) In the following example, we show that **the converse of Lemma 5.1.11 is false**.

Example 5.1.12. Let X be a r.v. with p.d.f. $f(x) = 2/x^3$ for $1 < x < \infty$ (and 0 otherwise). Then $E(X)$ exists since

$$E(X) = \int_1^{\infty} x \frac{2}{x^3}\, dx = -\frac{2}{x}\Big|_1^{\infty} = 2,$$

but $E(X^r)$ does not exist for $r \geq 2$ since

$$E(X^r) = \int_1^{\infty} x^r f_X(x)\, dx \geq \int_1^{\infty} x^2 f_X(x)\, dx = E(X^2)$$

$$= \int_1^{\infty} \frac{2x^2}{x^3}\, dx = 2\ln(x)\Big|_1^{\infty} = \infty.$$

[Thus, the converse of Lemma 5.1.11 is false. However, note that the contrapositive of Lemma 5.1.11 states that if $E(X^s)$ does not exist, then neither does $E(X^t)$ for any $t > s$; this is a true statement and should be carefully distinguished from the converse (which is false as shown in this example).]

Theorem 5.1.13. Hölder's Inequality. Let X and Y be any two r.v.'s, and let p and q, $p > 1$ and $q > 1$, be such that $1/p + 1/q = 1$. Then

$$E|XY| \leq \big(E(|X|^p)\big)^{1/p}\big(E(|Y|^q)\big)^{1/q}.$$

Definition 5.1.14. Let X be a r.v. with d.f. $F(x)$. The **nth central moment** of X is (if this expectation exists) $\mu_n \equiv E(X - EX)^n$. The **variance** of X, denoted **Var**(X) or $\sigma^2(X)$, is μ_2 (the second central moment of X).

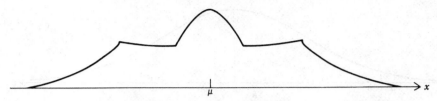

Figure 5.1-1. A typical symmetric density.

The *mean* (expectation) and variance of a r.v. X are usefully thought of as **measures of location** and **dispersion** (respectively) of the distribution of the r.v. X. The **mean** of an absolutely continuous r.v. X corresponds to the center of gravity of a bar with density $f_X(x)$. Then "the" **median** of X (if X is absolutely continuous) is any point m where

$$\int_{-\infty}^{m} f_X(x)\,dx = \tfrac{1}{2} = \int_{m}^{\infty} f_X(x)\,dx.$$

(For discrete and other distributions, this concept is not as easy to formulate, but may, nevertheless, be usefully thought of in this way.) The **mode** of X (if X is absolutely continuous) is the point where $f_X(x)$ is maximized; it may not be unique, and in fact may not exist. We now wish to investigate relations among the mean, median, and mode, all of which are in a sense measures of the location of a distribution. The following concepts will be useful in our discussion.

Definition 5.1.15. A density function $f_X(x)$ is **symmetric about** μ if (for all x) $f_X(\mu + x) = f_X(\mu - x)$. (See Figure 5.1-1.)

Definition 5.1.16. The 3rd moment about the mean, $\mu_3 = E(X - EX)^3$, divided by what is called the "standard deviation" (see Definition 5.1.20 below) cubed, is called the **skewness** of the distribution of X, and is often denoted by α_3:

$$\alpha_3 = \frac{\mu_3}{\sigma^3} = \frac{E(X - EX)^3}{\sigma^3}.$$

The skewness is a measure (one of many measures) of symmetry. It follows from Corollary 5.1.17 that for a symmetric distribution $\alpha_3 = 0$.

Corollary 5.1.17. If the distribution of X is symmetric, then

$$\mu_3 = E(X - EX)^3 = 0.$$

(See Figure 5.1-2.)

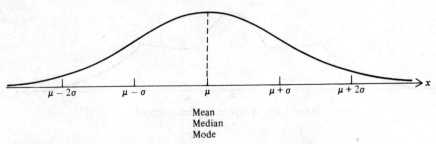

Mean
Median
Mode

Figure 5.1-2. Measures of location for the $N(\mu, \sigma^2)$ distribution (symmetric, so $\mu_3 = 0$).

Definition 5.1.18. The 4th moment about the mean, $\mu_4 = E(X - EX)^4$, divided by σ^4, is called the **kurtosis** of the distribution of X, and is often denoted by α_4:

$$\alpha_4 = \frac{\mu_4}{\sigma^4} = \frac{E(X - EX)^4}{\sigma^4}.$$

The kurtosis is used as a measure of how "heavy" the tails of a distribution are. Later in Chapter 5, we will see a use of skewness and kurtosis in fitting a p.d.f. to a set of data (see Example 5.2.11).

Lemma 5.1.19. If a r.v. X has a symmetric density, and if Mean (X) exists, then Mean (X) = Median (X).

Proof: Suppose X is symmetric about a, so that [letting $f_X(x)$ denote the density of X] $f_X(a + x) = f_X(a - x)$ for all x. We first show Median (X) = a. First,

$$P[X > a] = \int_a^\infty f_X(x)\, dx = \int_0^\infty f_X(a + y)\, dy,$$

where we wrote the probability $P(X > a)$ as an integral and made the change of variables $y = x - a$. Secondly, by similar methods we find that

$$P[X < a] = \int_{-\infty}^a f_X(x)\, dx = \int_{-\infty}^0 f_X(y + a)\, dy$$

$$= -\int_\infty^0 f_X(a - z)\, dz = \int_0^\infty f_X(a - z)\, dz.$$

By the symmetry of $f_X(x)$, it follows from these expressions that $P(X > a) = P(X < a)$. Since these probabilities add to 1 and are equal, each must be 0.5 so that (by definition of the median, given after Definition 5.1.14) the Median (X) = a.

We next prove that Mean(X) = a. To do so, we write $E(X)$ as an integral, then make a change of variables $y = x - a$ (which allows us to isolate the term "a" since the integral of any p.d.f. over the whole space is one), and finally use symmetry to show all other terms in the expression add to zero:

$$EX = \int_{-\infty}^{\infty} x f_X(x) \, dx = \int_{-\infty}^{\infty} (y + a) f_X(a + y) \, dy$$

$$= a + \int_{-\infty}^{\infty} y f_X(a + y) \, dy$$

$$= a + \int_{0}^{\infty} y f_X(a + y) \, dy + \int_{-\infty}^{0} y f_X(a + y) \, dy$$

$$= a + \int_{0}^{\infty} y f_X(a + y) \, dy - \int_{0}^{\infty} z f_X(a - z) \, dz = a.$$

Since we have shown that $\text{Median}(X) = a = \text{Mean}(X)$, it follows that the mean and the median are equal for an r.v. with a symmetric density, as was claimed in the statement of the lemma.   ∎

Many **common fallacies about the mean, median, mode, and symmetry** exist even in high quality reference works. For example, in Kendall and Stuart (1969), pp. 39, 85, we find the statements: "It is a useful mnemonic to observe that the mean, median and mode occur in the same order (or the reverse order) as in the dictionary; and that the median is nearer to the mean than to the mode, just as the corresponding words are nearer together in the dictionary" (shown totally false by the example of Figure 5.1-3) and "In a symmetrical population, mean, median and mode coincide" (true as to mean and median, but shown false as to mode by the example of Figure 5.1-4).

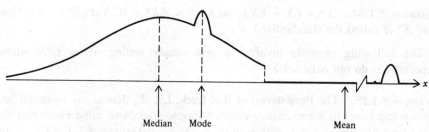

Figure 5.1-3. Measures of location for an altered $N(\mu, \sigma^2)$.

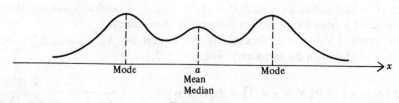

Figure 5.1-4.

Definition 5.1.20. Let us denote $\sigma^2(X)$ as, simply, σ^2. Then σ (the positive square root of σ^2) is called the **standard deviation** of X and is often written $\sigma(X)$.

Lemma 5.1.21. $\sigma^2(X) \geq 0$ with equality iff X is a constant with probability 1.

Lemma 5.1.22. $\text{Var}(X) = EX^2 - (EX)^2$.

Proof:

$$\text{Var}(X) = E(X - EX)^2$$
$$= E\{X^2 - 2XEX + (EX)^2\}$$
$$= EX^2 - 2(EX)^2 + (EX)^2$$
$$= EX^2 - (EX)^2. \qquad \blacksquare$$

Theorem 5.1.23. $\text{Var}(aX + b) = a^2 \text{Var}(X)$.

Proof:

$$\text{Var}(aX + b) = E[(aX + b) - E(aX + b)]^2$$
$$= E[a(X - EX)]^2$$
$$= a^2 E(X - EX)^2$$
$$= a^2 \text{Var}(X). \qquad \blacksquare$$

Theorem 5.1.24. $X^* = (X - EX)/\sigma(X)$ has $EX^* = 0$, $\text{Var}(X^*) = 1$. (Note that X^* is called the **standardized** X.)

The following example involves a very **simple setting where r.v.'s whose expectations do not exist arise.**

Example 5.1.25. The Persistence of Bad Luck. Let X_0 denote my financial loss (or waiting time) at some chance event. Suppose friends of mine encounter the same type of chance event, with results $X_1, X_2, \ldots$. Assume $X_0, X_1, X_2, \ldots$ are independent r.v.'s, each with the same distribution, and are (absolutely) continuous.

Let $N = $ first subscript n such that $X_n > X_0$ (i.e., a random quantity, the time it takes until a friend experiences worse luck than mine).

The event $\{N > n - 1\}$ occurs iff the largest of $X_0, X_1, \ldots, X_{n-1}$ is X_0. $P[N > n - 1] = 1/n$ by symmetry. For $n = 1, 2, \ldots,$

$$P[N = n] = P[N > n - 1] - P[N > n] = \frac{1}{n} - \frac{1}{n+1} = \frac{1}{n(n+1)}.$$

Now,

$$EN = \sum_{n=1}^{\infty} nP[N = n] = \sum_{n=1}^{\infty} \frac{1}{n+1} = +\infty.$$

Thus (although EN = 10,000 would be bad) the waiting time in fact has infinite expectation. However, the probability is only, for example, $\frac{1}{5}$ that you will have to wait longer than four friends until someone has worse luck than you. [This should give insight into the nature (and deficiencies) of the mean as a central value.]

As a final word on measures of location, we note the following concept of **concentration of a r.v.** at a point, which will prove useful in the chapters on statistics.

Definition 5.1.26. If X and Y are r.v.'s, X is said to be **more concentrated** about a than Y if (for all $r > 0$)

$$P[|X - a| \leq r] \geq P[|Y - a| \leq r].$$

Lemma 5.1.27.[2] If X is more concentrated than Y about μ, and if $EX = EY = \mu$, then $\text{Var}(X) \leq \text{Var}(Y)$.

PROBLEMS FOR SECTION 5.1

5.1.1 Let $f_X(x) = (1/\sqrt{2\pi})e^{-x^2/2}$, $-\infty < x < \infty$, and $f_Y(x) = (1/2)e^{-|x|}$, $-\infty < x < \infty$. For $r = .1(.1)3.0$, find and tabulate $P(|X| \leq r)$ and $P(|Y| \leq r)$. From this table, note that you have shown numerically that X is more concentrated about zero than is Y.

5.1.2 Let X be an r.v. with p.d.f. $f_X(x) = (r-1)/x^r$ for $x > 0$ (and $= 0$ otherwise) for some $r \geq 3$. Show that $E(X^s)$ exists for $s \leq r - 2$ and that $E(X^s)$ does not exist for $s \geq r - 1$.

5.1.3 An urn contains 4 red balls, 1 yellow ball, and 3 green balls. Balls are drawn successively at random, without replacement, until a green ball is drawn. Let X be the number of draws required. Compute $E(X)$ and $\text{Var}(X)$.

5.1.4 Let X be an r.v. having a "semitriangular" distribution given by p.d.f. $f_X(x) = 2(a - x)/a^2$ for $0 < x \leq a$ (and $= 0$ otherwise) for some $a > 0$. Find $E(X)$, $\text{Var}(X)$, and Median(X).

5.1.5 Let X be an r.v. with "parabolic" p.d.f. $f_X(x) = 3(a^2 - x^2)/(4a^3)$ if $|x| \leq a$ (and $= 0$ otherwise) for some $a > 0$. Find $E(X)$, $\text{Var}(X)$, and Median (X).

---

[2] This is easy to see intuitively. A rigorous proof is straightforward (but messy) and is omitted.

5.1.6 Let the r.v. X have p.d.f.

$$f_X(x) = \begin{cases} \dfrac{2(\beta + x)}{\beta(\alpha + \beta)} & \text{if } -\beta \leq x \leq 0 \\[2mm] \dfrac{2(\alpha - x)}{\alpha(\alpha + \beta)} & \text{if } 0 \leq x \leq \alpha \\[2mm] 0 & \text{otherwise} \end{cases}$$

for some $\alpha > 0$ and $\beta > 0$. Find the mean, median, mode, and variance of X.

5.1.7 For the following probability distributions, find $E(X)$ and $\text{Var}(X)$.

(a) $p_X(x) = \binom{5}{x}(.4)^x(.6)^{5-x}$, if $x = 0, 1, 2, 3, 4, 5$ (and $= 0$ otherwise).

(b) $p_X(x) = \binom{5}{x}\binom{15}{5-x}\Big/\binom{20}{5}$, if $x = 0, 1, 2, 3, 4, 5$ (and $= 0$ otherwise).

5.1.8 A discount airline sells tickets from city A to city B for \$100 in coach class and for \$150 in first class. Their standby ticket costs 60% of the coach class fare. If you arrive at the airport with a standby ticket and no standby seat is available, you must buy a first-class ticket. Based on previous experience, it is estimated that 20% of standbys do not get a standby seat on the plane. What ticket has the smallest expected cost: coach, first class, or standby?

5.1.9 A nationally known auto-transmission repair company offers a one-year warranty (free repair or replacement if the transmission fails). However, after collecting data for this company it is estimated that T, the time to failure, has p.d.f. $f_T(t) = (1/5)e^{-t/5}$ if $t > 0$ (and $= 0$ otherwise).

(a) Compute the average time to failure. Based on this computation, is the warranty valuable?

(b) Compute the probability of the transmission failing before its expected failure time.

5.1.10 Let X be the sum of the faces when we toss two fair six-sided dice independently and simultaneously. Find the mean and variance of $X/2$.

5.1.11 Random variable X is said to be **bounded** if, for some M $(0 < M < \infty)$, $P(|X| \leq M) = 1$. Show that if X is bounded then $E(X)$ exists.

5.1.12 Let X be an r.v. with $E(X) < \infty$ and $\text{Var}(X) < \infty$. Show that

$$\text{Var}(X) < E(X - a)^2$$

for all $a \neq E(X)$.

5.1.13 Let X be an r.v. with p.d.f. $f_X(x) = \sin(x)$ if $0 < x < \pi$ (and $= 0$ otherwise).
(a) Find the p.d.f. of $\cos(X)$. (b) Find the mean and variance of $\cos(X)$.

5.2. MEAN AND VARIANCE OF SPECIAL RANDOM VARIABLES

Theorem 5.2.1. If X has the **Bernoulli distribution** (see Definition 3.2.1)

$$p_X(x) = \begin{cases} p^x(1 - p)^{1-x}, & x = 0, 1 \\ 0, & \text{otherwise,} \end{cases}$$

then $EX = p$, $\text{Var}(X) = pq$.

Proof:

$$EX = 0 \cdot (1 - p) + 1 \cdot p = p.$$

$$EX^2 = 0^2 \cdot (1 - p) + 1^2 \cdot p = p.$$

$$\text{Var}(X) = EX^2 - (EX)^2 = p - p^2 = p(1 - p) = pq. \qquad \blacksquare$$

Theorem 5.2.2. If X has the **binomial distribution** (see Definition 3.2.3)

$$p_X(x) = \begin{cases} \binom{n}{x} p^x (1 - p)^{n-x}, & x = 0, 1, \ldots, n \\ 0, & \text{otherwise,} \end{cases}$$

then $EX = np$, $\text{Var}(X) = npq$.

Proof:

$$EX = \sum_{x=0}^{n} x \binom{n}{x} p^x (1 - p)^{n-x} = \sum_{x=1}^{n} n \binom{n-1}{x-1} p^x q^{n-x}$$

$$= np \sum_{x=1}^{n} \binom{n-1}{x-1} p^{x-1} q^{(n-1)-(x-1)}$$

$$= np \sum_{k=0}^{n-1} \binom{n-1}{k} p^k q^{(n-1)-k}$$

$$= np(p + q)^{n-1} = np.$$

$$EX^2 = \sum_{x=0}^{n} x^2 \binom{n}{x} p^x (1 - p)^{n-x} = \sum_{x=0}^{n} [x(x - 1) + x] \binom{n}{x} p^x (1 - p)^{n-x}$$

$$= \sum_{x=2}^{n} x(x - 1) \binom{n}{x} p^x (1 - p)^{n-x} + EX$$

$$= n(n - 1) \sum_{x=2}^{n} \binom{n-2}{x-2} p^x q^{n-x} + EX$$

$$= n(n - 1) p^2 \sum_{k=0}^{n-2} \binom{n-2}{k} p^k q^{(n-2)-k} + EX$$

$$= n(n - 1) p^2 (p + q)^{n-2} + np = n^2 p^2 + npq.$$

$$\text{Var}(X) = EX^2 - (EX)^2 = npq. \qquad \blacksquare$$

Theorem 5.2.3. If X has the **Poisson distribution** (see Definition 3.2.11)

$$p_X(x) = \begin{cases} \dfrac{e^{-\mu} \mu^x}{x!}, & x = 0, 1, 2, \ldots \\ 0, & \text{otherwise,} \end{cases}$$

then $EX = \mu$, $\text{Var}(X) = \mu$.

Proof:

$$EX = \sum_{x=0}^{\infty} x e^{-\mu} \frac{\mu^x}{x!} = e^{-\mu} \sum_{x=1}^{\infty} \frac{\mu^x}{(x-1)!}$$

$$= e^{-\mu} \mu \sum_{x=1}^{\infty} \frac{\mu^{x-1}}{(x-1)!} = e^{-\mu} \mu e^{\mu} = \mu.$$

$$EX^2 = \sum_{x=0}^{\infty} x^2 e^{-\mu} \frac{\mu^x}{x!} = \sum_{x=0}^{\infty} \{x(x-1) + x\} e^{-\mu} \frac{\mu^x}{x!}$$

$$= \sum_{x=2}^{\infty} e^{-\mu} \frac{\mu^x}{(x-2)!} + \mu = \mu^2 + \mu.$$

$$\mathrm{Var}(X) = EX^2 - (EX)^2 = \mu. \qquad \blacksquare$$

Theorem 5.2.4. If X has the **uniform distribution** (see Definition 4.2.5)

$$f_X(x) = \begin{cases} \dfrac{1}{c-b}, & b \le x \le c \\ 0, & \text{otherwise,} \end{cases}$$

then $EX = (b + c)/2$, $\mathrm{Var}(X) = (c - b)^2/12$.

Proof:

$$EX = \int_b^c x \frac{1}{c-b} \, dx = \frac{1}{2} \frac{1}{c-b} x^2 \Big|_b^c = \frac{b+c}{2}.$$

$$EX^2 = \int_b^c x^2 \frac{1}{c-b} \, dx = \frac{1}{3} \frac{1}{c-b} (c^3 - b^3) = \frac{c^2 + bc + b^2}{3}.$$

$$\mathrm{Var}(X) = EX^2 - (EX)^2 = \frac{(c-b)^2}{12}. \qquad \blacksquare$$

Theorem 5.2.5. If X has the **exponential distribution** (see Definition 4.2.10)

$$f_X(x) = \begin{cases} \dfrac{1}{\lambda} e^{-x/\lambda}, & 0 \le x < \infty \\ 0, & \text{otherwise,} \end{cases}$$

then $EX = \lambda$, $\mathrm{Var}(X) = \lambda^2$.

Proof:

$$EX = \int_0^\infty x \frac{1}{\lambda} e^{-x/\lambda} \, dx = \lambda \int_0^\infty y e^{-y} \, dy$$

$$= \lambda \Gamma(2) = \lambda(1!) = \lambda.$$

$$EX^2 = \int_0^\infty x^2 \frac{1}{\lambda} e^{-x/\lambda} \, dx = \lambda^2 \int_0^\infty y^2 e^{-y} \, dy = \lambda^2 \Gamma(3) = 2\lambda^2.$$

$$\text{Var}(X) = EX^2 - (EX)^2 = \lambda^2.$$ ∎

Theorem 5.2.6. If X has the **normal distribution** (see Definition 4.2.18)

$$f_X(x) = \frac{1}{\sqrt{2\pi}\,\sigma} e^{-\frac{1}{2}\left(\frac{x-\mu}{\sigma}\right)^2}, \qquad -\infty < x < +\infty,$$

then $EX = \mu$, $\text{Var}(X) = \sigma^2$.

Proof:

$$EX = \int_{-\infty}^\infty \frac{x}{\sqrt{2\pi}\,\sigma} e^{-\frac{1}{2}\left(\frac{x-\mu}{\sigma}\right)^2} \, dx = \int_{-\infty}^\infty \frac{\sigma y + \mu}{\sqrt{2\pi}\,\sigma} e^{-\frac{1}{2}y^2} \sigma \, dy$$

$$= \frac{\sigma}{\sqrt{2\pi}} \int_{-\infty}^\infty y e^{-\frac{1}{2}y^2} \, dy + \mu \int_{-\infty}^\infty \frac{1}{\sqrt{2\pi}} e^{-\frac{1}{2}y^2} \, dy$$

$$= 0 + \mu \cdot 1 = \mu.$$

$$EX^2 = \int_{-\infty}^\infty \frac{x^2}{\sqrt{2\pi}\,\sigma} e^{-\frac{1}{2}\left(\frac{x-\mu}{\sigma}\right)^2} \, dx = \int_{-\infty}^\infty \frac{(\sigma y + \mu)^2}{\sqrt{2\pi}\,\sigma} e^{-\frac{1}{2}y^2} \sigma \, dy$$

$$= \sigma^2 \int_{-\infty}^\infty \frac{y^2}{\sqrt{2\pi}} e^{-\frac{1}{2}y^2} \, dy + \frac{2\sigma\mu}{\sqrt{2\pi}} \int_{-\infty}^\infty y e^{-\frac{1}{2}y^2} \, dy + \mu^2 \int_{-\infty}^\infty \frac{1}{\sqrt{2\pi}} e^{-\frac{1}{2}y^2} \, dy$$

$$= \sigma^2 2 \int_0^\infty \frac{y^2}{\sqrt{2\pi}} e^{-\frac{1}{2}y^2} \, dy + 0 + \mu^2 \cdot 1$$

$$= \sigma^2 \frac{1}{\sqrt{2\pi}} 2 \int_0^\infty z^2 \frac{2}{1} e^{-z^2} \sqrt{2} \, dz + \mu^2$$

$$= \sigma^2 \frac{2}{\sqrt{\pi}} \Gamma\left(\frac{3}{2}\right) + \mu^2 = \sigma^2 \frac{2}{\sqrt{\pi}} \frac{1}{2} \sqrt{\pi} + \mu^2 = \sigma^2 + \mu^2.$$

$$\text{Var}(X) = EX^2 - (EX)^2 = \sigma^2.$$ ∎

Theorem 5.2.7. If X has the **gamma distribution** $G(x|\alpha, \beta, A = 0)$ (see Definition 4.2.7), then for $r > 0$

$$E(X^r) = \frac{\beta^r \Gamma(\alpha + r + 1)}{\Gamma(\alpha + 1)},$$

hence $EX = (\alpha + 1)\beta$, $\text{Var}(X) = (\alpha + 1)\beta^2$.

Proof:

$$E(X^r) = \int_0^\infty x^r \frac{x^\alpha}{\beta^{\alpha+1}\Gamma(\alpha + 1)} e^{-x/\beta}\, dx = \int_0^\infty \frac{x^{\alpha+r}}{\beta^{\alpha+1}\Gamma(\alpha + 1)} e^{-x/\beta}\, dx$$

$$= \frac{\beta^r \Gamma(\alpha + r + 1)}{\Gamma(\alpha + 1)} \int_0^\infty \frac{x^{\alpha+r}}{\beta^{\alpha+r+1}\Gamma(\alpha + r + 1)} e^{-x/\beta}\, dx$$

$$= \frac{\beta^r \Gamma(\alpha + r + 1)}{\Gamma(\alpha + 1)}.$$

Note that in the above equalities we recognized the integrand to be a gamma p.d.f. except for its multiplying constant. Hence, multiplying and dividing by the constants needed to make the integrand a gamma p.d.f., we obtained an integral that integrates to 1. Now, to complete the proof, we find (taking $r = 1$ and $r = 2$ in the above)

$$EX = \frac{\beta \Gamma(\alpha + 2)}{\Gamma(\alpha + 1)} = \frac{\beta(\alpha + 1)\Gamma(\alpha + 1)}{\Gamma(\alpha + 1)} = (\alpha + 1)\beta,$$

$$E(X^2) = \frac{\beta^2 \Gamma(\alpha + 3)}{\Gamma(\alpha + 1)} = (\alpha + 2)(\alpha + 1)\beta^2,$$

$$\text{Var}(X) = E(X^2) - (EX)^2 = (\alpha + 1)\beta^2. \qquad \blacksquare$$

Theorem 5.2.8. If X has the **beta distribution** $B(x|\alpha, \lambda)$ (see Definition 4.2.1), then for $r > 0$

$$E(X^r) = \frac{B(\alpha + r + 1, \lambda + 1)}{B(\alpha + 1, \lambda + 1)}.$$

Hence $EX = (\alpha + 1)/(\alpha + \lambda + 2)$, $\text{Var}(X) = ((\alpha + 1)(\lambda + 1))/((\alpha + \lambda + 2)^2(\alpha + \lambda + 3))$.

Proof:

$$E(X^r) = \int_0^1 \frac{x^r}{\beta(\alpha + 1, \lambda + 1)} x^\alpha (1 - x)^\lambda \, dx$$

$$= \frac{\beta(\alpha + r + 1, \lambda + 1)}{\beta(\alpha + 1, \lambda + 1)} \int_0^1 \frac{x^{r+\alpha}(1 - x)^\lambda}{\beta(\alpha + r + 1, \lambda + 1)} \, dx$$

$$= \frac{\beta(\alpha + r + 1, \lambda + 1)}{\beta(\alpha + 1, \lambda + 1)},$$

where we used the same technique as in the proof of Theorem 5.2.7 to perform the integration (in this case, multiplying to make the integrand a beta p.d.f., which must integrate to one). Hence, it now follows that

$$EX = \frac{\beta(\alpha + 2, \lambda + 1)}{\beta(\alpha + 1, \lambda + 1)} = \frac{\Gamma(\alpha + 2)\Gamma(\lambda + 1)}{\Gamma(\alpha + \lambda + 3)} \frac{\Gamma(\alpha + \lambda + 2)}{\Gamma(\alpha + 1)\Gamma(\lambda + 1)}$$

$$= \frac{\alpha + 1}{\alpha + \lambda + 2},$$

$$E(X^2) = \frac{\beta(\alpha + 3, \lambda + 1)}{\beta(\alpha + 1, \lambda + 1)} = \frac{\Gamma(\alpha + 3)\Gamma(\lambda + 1)}{\Gamma(\alpha + \lambda + 4)} \frac{\Gamma(\alpha + \lambda + 2)}{\Gamma(\alpha + 1)\Gamma(\lambda + 1)}$$

$$= \frac{(\alpha + 2)(\alpha + 1)}{(\alpha + \lambda + 3)(\alpha + \lambda + 2)},$$

$$\mathrm{Var}(X) = E(X^2) - (EX)^2 = \frac{(\alpha + 2)(\alpha + 1)}{(\alpha + \lambda + 3)(\alpha + \lambda + 2)} - \left(\frac{\alpha + 1}{\alpha + \lambda + 2}\right)^2$$

$$= \frac{(\alpha + 1)(\lambda + 1)}{(\alpha + \lambda + 2)^2(\alpha + \lambda + 3)}. \qquad \blacksquare$$

Example 5.2.9. A particular container of one brand of a certain food is labeled as containing 500 grams of food. Suppose it is known that the net weight of the food in a container selected at random is distributed as $N(500, 25)$. A container is considered to be underweight if its net food weight is less than 98% of the label claim, in this case less than 490 grams. If 1000 containers are chosen at random, how many should we expect to be underweight?

Let X_i denote the net food weight of the ith container selected ($1 \le i \le 1000$). Assuming $X_i \sim N(500, 25)$,

$$P(i\text{th container is underweight}) = P(X_i < 490)$$

$$= P\left(\frac{X_i - 500}{5} < -2\right) = \Phi(-2) = .0228.$$

If Y denotes the number of underweight containers out of the 1000, then assuming independence from container to container as to the characteristic of being underweight or not [which is reasonable due to the 1000 being selected at random from the output, which is known to have a $N(500, 25)$ net weight per container], Y is binomial $B(n = 1000, p = .0228)$. Hence

$$E(Y) = np = 22.8,$$

and we would "expect" approximately 23 containers out of the 1000 chosen to be underweight (i.e., to have net weight less than 490 grams).

Example 5.2.10. Cards are drawn one at a time, without replacement, from a standard deck of 52 cards until all 4 of the aces are drawn. How many cards are expected to be drawn in this process?

If X denotes the number of cards drawn in this process, $P(X = x) = 0$ unless $x \in \{4, 5, 6, \ldots, 52\}$, in which case

$$p_X(x) = \frac{\binom{4}{3}\binom{48}{x-4}}{\binom{52}{x-1}} \cdot \frac{1}{(52 - (x - 1))},$$

hence

$$E(X) = \sum_{x=4}^{52} x p_X(x) = \sum_{x=4}^{52} x \frac{\binom{4}{3}\binom{48}{x-4}}{\binom{52}{x-1}} \cdot \frac{1}{(52 - (x - 1))}$$

$$= \frac{4}{(52)(51)(50)(49)} \sum_{x=4}^{52} x(x - 1)(x - 2)(x - 3)$$

$$= \frac{4}{(52)(51)(50)(49)} \sum_{x=4}^{52} (x^4 - 6x^3 + 11x^2 - 6x)$$

$$= \frac{1}{1,624,350} (79,743,128 - 11,392,704 + 530,200 - 8,208)$$

$$= 42.399985.$$

Thus, we expect to need to draw about 43 cards to obtain all 4 aces.

Example 5.2.11. Generalized Lambda Distribution; Use for Fitting Probability Density Functions. In Section 4.7, we introduced the inverse d.f. of a r.v. in Definition 4.7.5 and found (in Theorem 4.7.7) that it was of great use in generating r.v.'s for computer simulation studies: If X has d.f. $F(x)$ and inverse d.f. $F^{-1}(y)$, then the r.v. $Z = F^{-1}(U)$ has d.f. $F(x)$ if U is a r.v. uniform on $(0, 1)$. Thus, if we can generate r.v.'s that are uniform, by a simple transformation of them we can obtain r.v.'s with the desired d.f. F (e.g., for computer simulation studies). Most distributions we have studied so far have been specified by formulas for their d.f.'s or p.d.f.'s (or, in the discrete case, point probability functions). The **generalized lambda distribution (GLD)** is, however, specified by its inverse d.f.

$$F^{-1}(p) = \lambda_1 + \frac{p^{\lambda_3} - (1-p)^{\lambda_4}}{\lambda_2} \qquad (0 \le p \le 1). \qquad (5.2.12)$$

It can be shown by differentiation that the p.d.f. corresponding to (5.2.12) is

$$f(x) = f(F^{-1}(p)) = \frac{\lambda_2}{\lambda_3 p^{\lambda_3 - 1} + \lambda_4 (1-p)^{\lambda_4 - 1}} \qquad (0 \le p \le 1). \qquad (5.2.13)$$

It can be shown that the moments of a r.v. X with a GLD are given by

$$E(X^k) = \lambda_2^{-k} \sum_{i=0}^{k} \binom{k}{i} (-1)^i \beta(\lambda_3(k-i) + 1, \lambda_4 i + 1), \qquad (5.2.14)$$

where we have used the beta function (recall Definition 4.1.8). It follows by some algebraic manipulation that the first four moments (in the form of mean, variance, skewness, and kurtosis) are (see Definitions 5.1.14, 5.1.16, and 5.1.18)

$$\mu = \lambda_1 + A/\lambda_2, \qquad (5.2.15)$$

$$\sigma^2 = (B - A^2)/\lambda_2^2, \qquad (5.2.16)$$

$$\alpha_3 = \mu_3/\sigma^3, \qquad \mu_3 = (C - 3AB + 2A^3)/\lambda_2^3, \qquad (5.2.17)$$

$$\alpha_4 = \mu_4/\sigma^4, \qquad \mu_4 = (D - 4AC + 6A^2B - 3A^4)/\lambda_2^4, \qquad (5.2.18)$$

where

$$A = 1/(1 + \lambda_3) - 1/(1 + \lambda_4),$$

$$B = 1/(1 + 2\lambda_3) + 1/(1 + 2\lambda_4) - 2\beta(1 + \lambda_3, 1 + \lambda_4),$$

$$C = 1/(1 + 3\lambda_3) - 3\beta(1 + 2\lambda_3, 1 + \lambda_4)$$

$$\qquad + 3\beta(1 + \lambda_3, 1 + 2\lambda_4) - 1/(1 + 3\lambda_4),$$

$$\qquad\qquad\qquad\qquad\qquad\qquad\qquad\qquad\qquad (5.2.19)$$

$$D = 1/(1 + 4\lambda_3) - 4\beta(1 + 3\lambda_3, 1 + \lambda_4) + 6\beta(1 + 2\lambda_3, 1 + 2\lambda_4)$$

$$\qquad - 4\beta(1 + \lambda_3, 1 + 3\lambda_4) + 1/(1 + 4\lambda_4).$$

[*Note:* Not every set of possible $\lambda_1, \lambda_2, \lambda_3, \lambda_4$ values yields a valid d.f., which must be nondecreasing from 0 to 1 and right continuous—see Theorems 3.1.3

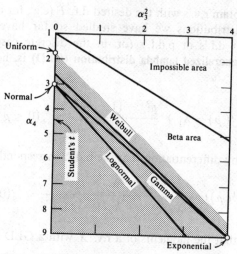

Figure 5.2-1. Characterization of distributions by
their skewness squared (α_3^2) and kurtosis (α_4); the
GLD covers the shaded region.

and 3.1.5. There are no restrictions on λ_1 and λ_2, but some are needed on λ_3
and λ_4; for details see Figure 4 of Ramberg, Tadikamalla, Dudewicz, and
Mykytka (1979).]

We know that a normal distribution can have any mean, any positive variance,
and has skewness 0 and kurtosis 3 ($\alpha_3 = 0$ and $\alpha_4 = 3$). **The GLD also can have
any mean and any positive variance, but can attain a whole region of possible α_3
and α_4 values as the $\lambda_1, \lambda_2, \lambda_3, \lambda_4$ values vary.** This is shown in Figure 5.2-1,
where we have also plotted the point corresponding to the normal distribution
($\alpha_3 = 0$ and $\alpha_4 = 3$). The shaded region can be attained by GLD's. (Points and
regions that other distributions can attain are also marked.) Note the region
marked "impossible," which cannot be attained for reasons such as those found
in Example 6.3.17, where we show that $\alpha_4 \geq 1$ for *every* distribution [just as
$\mathrm{Var}(X) \geq 0$ for all r.v.'s X]. Since the GLD can attain so many (mean, variance,
skewness, kurtosis) vectors, it is possible to reason as follows: If we do not know
a p.d.f. of a r.v., it is possible to estimate it as in Section 4.8 by the empiric p.d.f.
But, it would be easier to use (for instance, in simulation studies) if we had an
inverse d.f. for our fitted p.d.f. This is available for the GLD, so let us **fit a GLD
to our data** (i.e., choose $\lambda_1, \lambda_2, \lambda_3, \lambda_4$ values that make a GLD "close" to our
data). This can be done, and details are given in Ramberg, Tadikamalla,
Dudewicz, and Mykytka (1979), where the Method of Moments (which we will
cover in Chapter 7) was used to choose the GLD: $\lambda_1, \lambda_2, \lambda_3, \lambda_4$ were chosen so
that their GLD would have moments $\mu, \sigma^2, \alpha_3, \alpha_4$ (from equations (5.2.15–18)
equal to the estimates (such as $\overline{X}$ for μ) obtained from the data (discussed in
detail in Chapter 7). This has proven to be **a powerful method in applications, and
is in wide use.**

PROBLEMS FOR SECTION 5.2

5.2.1 Let $X \sim N(\mu, \sigma^2)$. Find the skewness and kurtosis of X. In particular, compute these values when $\mu = 0$ and $\sigma^2 = 1$.

5.2.2 Let $X \sim G(x|\alpha, \beta, 0)$. Find
(a) The skewness and kurtosis of X.
(b) The mean and variance of $Y = aX^2 + b$.
(c) For $\alpha = -1$, repeat parts (a) and (b).

5.2.3 Let $X \sim N(\mu, \sigma^2)$. Find the mean and variance of $Y = aX^2 + b$.

5.2.4 Let $X \sim B(x|\alpha, \lambda)$.
(a) Compute the skewness and kurtosis of X.
(b) Compute the mean and variance of $Y = aX^2 + b$.
(c) For $\alpha = -1$ and $\lambda = -1$, repeat parts (a) and (b).

5.2.5 Let $X \sim B(n, p)$, and $Y = n - X$. Find the mean and variance of Y.

5.2.6 A simple method of computing higher order moments for a discrete r.v. taking on values $0, 1, 2, 3, \ldots$ is to successively compute $E(X)$, $E(X(X - 1))$, $E(X(X - 1)(X - 2))$, $\ldots$. One then eliminates terms to obtain $E(X)$,

$$E(X^2) = E(X(X - 1)) + E(X),$$

$$E(X^3) = E(X(X - 1)(X - 2)) + 3E(X(X - 1)) + E(X),$$

and so on. Use this method to find the mean, variance, skewness, and kurtosis of X if X is (a) $B(n, p)$. (b) Poisson with parameter μ.

5.2.7 Use the method of Problem 5.2.6 to find the mean, variance, skewness, and kurtosis of a geometric r.v. with probability function $p_X(x) = q^{x-1}p$ if $x = 1, 2, 3, \ldots$ (and $= 0$ otherwise).

5.2.8 Recall that a chi-square r.v. is a special case of the gamma r.v. If $X \sim \chi_n^2(0)$, find its mean, variance, skewness, and kurtosis.

5.2.9 For the Laplace distribution (see Example 4.1.3 for a special case), $f_X(x) = (1/(2\lambda))e^{-|x-\mu|/\lambda}$ for $-\infty < x < \infty$, for some μ and λ ($-\infty < \mu < \infty, \lambda > 0$). Find the mean and variance of X.

5.2.10 Let the probability of heads on any toss of a certain coin be p. Suppose we toss this coin n times independently and X denotes the number of heads obtained, while Y denotes the number of tails in the n tosses. Compute the mean and variance of $X - Y$.

5.2.11 Let the r.v. X be distributed as **negative binomial** with probability function $p_X(x) = \binom{x-1}{r-1}p^r q^{x-r}$ if $x = r, r + 1, r + 2, \ldots$ (and $= 0$ otherwise). Show that

$$E(X) = \frac{rq}{p}, \qquad \text{Var}(X) = \frac{rq}{p^2}.$$

5.2.12 Let X be a hypergeometric r.v. Find $E(X)$ and $\text{Var}(X)$.

5.2.13 Let A be an event in some sample space Ω, with $P(A) = p$. Define

$$X(\omega) = \begin{cases} 1, & \text{if } \omega \in A \\ 0, & \text{if } \omega \in \overline{A}. \end{cases}$$

Compute $E(X^r)$, and in particular find $E(X)$ and $\text{Var}(X)$.

5.2.14 Let $X \sim N(\mu, \sigma^2)$. Let $Y = e^X$ (a **lognormal** random variable). Find $E(Y)$ and $\text{Var}(Y)$.

5.2.15 Let $X \sim N(\mu, \sigma^2)$. Recall that $|X|$ is called a **folded normal** r.v. Compute the mean and variance of $|X|$.

5.2.16 Suppose that $P(X \ge 0) = 1$, that is, X is a nonnegative r.v. Show that

$$\sqrt{E(X)} \ge E(\sqrt{X}).$$

[*Hint:* Note that $\text{Var}(X) \ge 0$ for any r.v.]

5.2.17 Consider the three statements

$$A: \quad P(X > Y) = 1$$

$$B: \quad E(X) > E(Y)$$

$$C: \quad F_X(z) > F_Y(z) \text{ for all } z.$$

Prove or give a counterexample for the implications **(a)** $A \Rightarrow B$; **(b)** $B \Rightarrow A$; **(c)** $A \Rightarrow C$; **(d)** $C \Rightarrow A$; **(e)** $B \Rightarrow C$; **(f)** $C \Rightarrow B$. Thus, **(g)** draw a Venn diagram of A, B, and C in the space of all pairs of r.v.'s (X, Y).

5.2.18 Let X be a Weibull r.v. with p.d.f. $f_X(x) = \beta x^{\beta-1} e^{-x^\beta}$ if $0 < x < \infty$ (and $= 0$ otherwise).
(a) Find $E(X^\beta)$.
(b) What conditions are necessary for both $E(X)$ and $E(X^2)$ to exist?

5.2.19 Let r.v. t_n have Student's t-distribution with n degrees of freedom. Find $E(t_n)$ and $\text{Var}(t_n)$. [*Hint:* t_n is symmetric about zero and $\text{Var}(t_n) = n/(n-2)$.]

5.2.20 To find the mean of an r.v. F with an F-distribution, note that F can be represented as

$$F_{n_1, n_2} = \frac{\dfrac{X}{n_1}}{\dfrac{Y}{n_2}},$$

where $X \sim \chi^2_{n_1}(0)$ and $Y \sim \chi^2_{n_2}(0)$ with X and Y independent r.v.'s. Thus

$$E\left(F_{n_1, n_2}\right) = E\left(\frac{\dfrac{X}{n_1}}{\dfrac{Y}{n_2}}\right) = \frac{n_2}{n_1} E(X) E\left(\frac{1}{Y}\right).$$

Compute $E(X)$ and $E(1/Y)$, and hence find $E(F)$.

5.2.21 Let r.v. X have p.d.f. $f(x) = (2/\pi)(1 + x^2)^{-2}$ for $-\infty < x < \infty$. Find $E(X)$ and $\text{Var}(X)$.

5.2.22 If $X \sim N(0,1)$, we know μ, σ^2, α_3, and α_4 (see Problem 5.2.1). Find a GLD with the same μ and σ^2, and "close" α_3 and α_4. [*Hint:* Try $\lambda_1 = 0$, $\lambda_2 = \sigma^{-1}$, and choose $\lambda_3 = \lambda_4 = c$ so that $B = 1$. What C and D then result? What α_3 and α_4 does this GLD possess?]

5.3. MULTIVARIATE MOMENTS

Section 5.1 considered moments for a single (i.e., one-dimensional) random variable X; in this section we deal with moments of several random variables (which, in general, are not independent—thus, they "affect" each other).

If $(X_1, \ldots, X_n)$ is an n-dimensional random variable, then $g(X_1, \ldots, X_n)$ is itself a random variable with some d.f. and hence its expectation has been defined (Definition 5.1.1) and various theorems relative to it have been stated in Section 5.1, for example, Corollary 5.1.3 and Corollary 5.1.6. We now wish to state without proof a result analogous to Theorem 5.1.2.

Theorem 5.3.1. If $(X_1, \ldots, X_n)$ is an n-dimensional r.v. and if $Eg(X_1, \ldots, X_n)$ exists, then

$$Eg(X_1, \ldots, X_n) = \int_{-\infty}^{\infty} \cdots \int_{-\infty}^{\infty} g(x_1, \ldots, x_n) f_{X_1, \ldots, X_n}(x_1, \ldots, x_n) \, dx_1 \cdots dx_n$$

when $(X_1, \ldots, X_n)$ is absolutely continuous, and

$$Eg(X_1, \ldots, X_n) = \sum \cdots \sum g(x_1, \ldots, x_n) p_{X_1, \ldots, X_n}(x_1, \ldots, x_n)$$

when $(X_1, \ldots, X_n)$ is discrete.

Although we do not give the proof of Theorem 5.3.1, we do prove the important special case:

Theorem 5.3.2. If (X_1, X_2) is a bivariate r.v. and if the means referred to exist, then $E(X_1 + X_2) = E(X_1) + E(X_2)$.

Proof: Since $Y = X_1 + X_2$ is a r.v., and its p.d.f. can be calculated from the joint p.d.f. of (X_1, X_2) as in Theorem 4.6.15, we have

$$E(Y) = \int_{-\infty}^{\infty} y f_Y(y) \, dy = \int_{-\infty}^{\infty} y f_{X_1 + X_2}(y) \, dy$$

$$= \int_{-\infty}^{\infty} y \left(\int_{-\infty}^{\infty} f_{X_1, X_2}(x_1, y - x_1) \, dx_1 \right) dy.$$

Interchanging the order of integration and making the change of variables

$x_2 = y - x_1$ on the inner integral, we obtain

$$E(Y) = \int_{-\infty}^{\infty} \left(\int_{-\infty}^{\infty} (x_1 + x_2) f_{X_1, X_2}(x_1, x_2) \, dx_2 \right) dx_1$$

$$= \int_{-\infty}^{\infty} \left(x_1 \int_{-\infty}^{\infty} f_{X_1, X_2}(x_1, x_2) \, dx_2 + \int_{-\infty}^{\infty} x_2 f_{X_1, X_2}(x_1, x_2) \, dx_2 \right) dx_1$$

$$= \int_{-\infty}^{\infty} \left(x_1 f_{X_1}(x_1) + \int_{-\infty}^{\infty} x_2 f_{X_1, X_2}(x_1, x_2) \, dx_2 \right) dx_1,$$

where to obtain the last line we noted that integrating the joint p.d.f. over all values of X_2 yields the marginal p.d.f. of X_1. Continuing, we will now recognize the first term as $E(X_1)$; on interchange of order of integration and recognition of the p.d.f. of X_2, the second term is seen to be $E(X_2)$:

$$E(Y) = \int_{-\infty}^{\infty} x_1 f_{X_1}(x_1) \, dx_1 + \int_{-\infty}^{\infty} x_2 \int_{-\infty}^{\infty} f_{X_1, X_2}(x_1, x_2) \, dx_1 \, dx_2$$

$$= E(X_1) \qquad\qquad + \int_{-\infty}^{\infty} x_2 f_{X_2}(x_2) \, dx_2$$

$$= E(X_1) \qquad\qquad + E(X_2).$$

Since $Y = X_1 + X_2$ by definition, we have shown the desired result that $E(X_1 + X_2) = E(X_1) + E(X_2)$. ∎

Although the proof we gave for Theorem 5.3.2 was for the case where (X_1, X_2) has a joint p.d.f., the result is true for all r.v.'s (whether discrete, continuous, mixed, or general). It can easily be generalized to the expectation of the sum of any finite number of r.v.'s. [For example, to show that $E(X_1 + X_2 + X_3) = E(X_1) + E(X_2) + E(X_3)$, one first uses Theorem 5.3.2 to note that $E(X_1 + (X_2 + X_3)) = E(X_1) + E(X_2 + X_3)$, and then a second time on $E(X_2 + X_3)$ to obtain the result.] Namely,

Corollary 5.3.3. If $(X_1, \ldots, X_n)$ is an n-dimensional r.v. and if the means referred to exist, then $E(X_1 + \cdots + X_n) = E(X_1) + \cdots + E(X_n)$.

Example 5.3.4. In the roulette example (Example 5.1.8), we noted that it was "intuitively clear" that the mean of the sum of the profits over 100 plays was the sum of the means. Letting Y_i denote the profit on play i of the game, and noting that the profit over the first 100 plays is $Y_1 + \cdots + Y_{100}$, it follows from Corollary 5.3.3 that

$$E(Y_1 + \cdots + Y_{100}) = E(Y_1) + \cdots + E(Y_{100}) = -76.32,$$

as was stated in Example 5.1.8. [*Note:* This holds no matter what the joint p.d.f. of the profits is, as long as their marginal distributions are not altered, since the marginal p.d.f. alone is used to find $E(Y_i)$.]

Definition 5.3.5. Let (X_1, X_2) be a two-dimensional r.v. For any n_1, n_2 (non-negative integers) we define $\mu'_{n_1, n_2} = E(X_1^{n_1} X_2^{n_2})$ (if this expectation exists). This is called a **joint moment of** (X_1, X_2) **of order** $n_1 + n_2$.

Example 5.3.6. Let (X_1, X_2) be a two-dimensional r.v. Then $\mu'_{1,0} = EX_1$, $\mu'_{0,1} = EX_2$, $\mu'_{2,0} = EX_1^2$, $\mu'_{0,2} = EX_2^2$, $\mu'_{1,1} = E(X_1 X_2)$. Note that $\mu'_{1,1}$ is called the **product moment**.

Definition 5.3.7. Let (X_1, X_2) be a two-dimensional r.v. For any n_1, n_2 (non-negative integers) we define $\mu_{n_1, n_2} = E\{(X_1 - EX_1)^{n_1}(X_2 - EX_2)^{n_2}\}$ (if this expectation exists). This is called a **joint central moment of** (X_1, X_2) **of order** $n_1 + n_2$.

Example 5.3.8. Let (X_1, X_2) be a two-dimensional r.v. Then $\mu_{1,0} = \mu_{0,1} = 0$, $\mu_{2,0} = \mathrm{Var}(X_1)$, $\mu_{0,2} = \mathrm{Var}(X_2)$, $\mu_{1,1} = E\{(X_1 - EX_1)(X_2 - EX_2)\}$. Note that $\mu_{1,1}$ is called the **covariance of** X_1 **and** X_2, denoted $\mathrm{Cov}(X_1, X_2)$.

Lemma 5.3.9. $\mathrm{Cov}(X_1, X_2) = E(X_1 X_2) - EX_1 EX_2$.

Proof:

$$\mathrm{Cov}(X_1, X_2) \equiv E\{(X_1 - EX_1)(X_2 - EX_2)\}$$

$$= E\{X_1 X_2 - X_2 EX_1 - X_1 EX_2 + EX_1 EX_2\}$$

$$= E(X_1 X_2) - 2EX_2 EX_1 + EX_1 EX_2$$

$$= E(X_1 X_2) - EX_1 EX_2. \qquad \blacksquare$$

Lemma 5.3.10[3]**.** $\mathrm{Var}(X_1 + X_2) = \mathrm{Var}(X_1) + \mathrm{Var}(X_2) + 2\,\mathrm{Cov}(X_1, X_2)$.

Proof:

$$\mathrm{Var}(X_1 + X_2)$$

$$= E(X_1 + X_2)^2 - (E(X_1 + X_2))^2$$

$$= EX_1^2 - (EX_1)^2 + EX_2^2 - (EX_2)^2 + 2\{EX_1 X_2 - EX_1 EX_2\}. \qquad \blacksquare$$

Thus, the variance of the sum of two r.v.'s is the sum of their variances plus two times the quantity called their "covariance" (a measure of how they are interrelated). If the r.v.'s are unrelated in the sense of zero covariance (or correlation), are they independent? This question will be studied below, with the final results being given in Theorem 5.3.19; related questions will also be considered. First, however, we give a useful extension of Lemma 5.3.10 to a sum of n r.v.'s and several examples.

---

[3] Note that we write $EX_1 X_2$ for $E(X_1 X_2)$ to simplify notation.

Lemma 5.3.11. $\text{Var}(X_1 + X_2 + \cdots + X_n) = \sum\limits_{i=1}^{n} \text{Var}(X_i) + 2\sum\limits_{i<j} \text{Cov}(X_i, X_j).$

The proof of Lemma 5.3.11 follows easily from Lemma 5.3.10 using mathematical induction (to start, note that $X_1 + X_2 + \cdots + X_n = X_1 + (X_2 + \cdots + X_n)$, a sum of two random variables, to which Lemma 5.3.10 may be directly applied). A useful result combining Corollary 5.3.3 and Lemma 5.3.11 is the following:

Corollary 5.3.12. Let $Y = a_1 X_1 + a_2 X_2 + \cdots + a_n X_n$, where $X_1, \ldots, X_n$ are r.v.'s with $E(X_i) = \mu_i$, $\text{Var}(X_i) = \sigma_i^2$, and $\text{Cov}(X_i, X_j) = \sigma_{ij}$ $(i, j = 1, \ldots, n;$ $i \neq j)$. Then

$$E(Y) = \sum_{i=1}^{n} a_i \mu_i,$$

and

$$\text{Var}(Y) = \sum_{i=1}^{n} a_i^2 \sigma_i^2 + 2\sum_{i<j} a_i a_j \sigma_{ij}.$$

Example 5.3.13. Let (X_1, X_2) be a 2-dimensional random variable with joint p.d.f.

$$f_{X_1, X_2}(x_1, x_2) = \begin{cases} \dfrac{1}{2x_1} & \text{if } 0 < x_2 < x_1, \quad 0 < x_1 < 2 \\ 0 & \text{otherwise.} \end{cases}$$

To find the moments up to second order and compute the correlation (by definition—see Definition 5.3.21—the **correlation** is the covariance $\text{Cov}(X_1, X_2)$ divided by the product of the standard deviations $\sigma(X_1)\sigma(X_2)$), we proceed as follows.

In general,

$$E(g(X_1)) = \int_{-\infty}^{\infty} \int_{-\infty}^{\infty} g(x_1) f_{X_1, X_2}(x_1, x_2) \, dx_1 \, dx_2$$

$$= \int_{-\infty}^{\infty} g(x_1) f_{X_1}(x_1) \, dx_1.$$

Thus, to find the individual moments, first find (check these) that

$$f_{X_1}(x_1) = \begin{cases} \frac{1}{2}, & \text{if } 0 < x_1 < 2 \\ 0, & \text{otherwise,} \end{cases}$$

and

$$f_{X_2}(x_2) = \begin{cases} \frac{1}{2}(\ln(2) - \ln(x_2)), & \text{if } 0 < x_2 < 2 \\ 0, & \text{otherwise.} \end{cases}$$

Thus

$$E(X_1) = \int_{-\infty}^{\infty} \int_{-\infty}^{\infty} x_1 f_{X_1, X_2}(x_1, x_2) \, dx_1 \, dx_2$$

$$= \int_{-\infty}^{\infty} x_1 f_{X_1}(x_1) \, dx_1 = \int_0^2 \frac{x_1}{2} \, dx_1 = 1,$$

$$E(X_1^2) = \int_0^2 \frac{x_1^2}{2} \, dx_1 = \tfrac{4}{3},$$

hence $\mu'_{1,0} = 1$, and

$$\mu_{2,0} = \sigma^2(X_1) = \text{Var}(X_1) = E(X_1^2) - (EX_1)^2 = \tfrac{1}{3}.$$

Similarly,

$$E(X_2) = \int_0^2 \frac{x_2}{2} (\ln(2) - \ln(x_2)) \, dx_2 = \frac{\ln(2)}{2} \frac{x_2^2}{2} \bigg|_0^2 - \frac{1}{2} \int_0^2 x_2 \ln(x_2) \, dx_2$$

$$= \ln(2) - \frac{1}{2} \int_{-\infty}^{\ln(2)} y e^{2y} \, dy = \ln(2) - \ln(2) + \tfrac{1}{2} = \tfrac{1}{2},$$

$$E(X_2^2) = \int_0^2 \frac{x_2^2}{2} (\ln(2) - \ln(x_2)) \, dx_2 = \tfrac{4}{9},$$

$$\text{Var}(X_2) = \tfrac{4}{9} - \tfrac{1}{4} = \tfrac{7}{36},$$

$$E(X_1 X_2) = \int_0^2 \int_0^{x_1} x_1 x_2 \frac{1}{2x_1} \, dx_2 \, dx_1 = \int_0^2 \int_0^{x_1} \frac{x_2}{2} \, dx_2 \, dx_1$$

$$= \int_0^2 \frac{x_1^2}{4} \, dx_1 = \frac{x_1^3}{12} \bigg|_0^2 = \tfrac{2}{3},$$

and the correlation (to be formally defined and discussed at and below Definition 5.3.21) is

$$\text{Corr}(X_1, X_2) = \frac{E(X_1 X_2) - E(X_1) E(X_2)}{\sqrt{\text{Var}(X_1) \text{Var}(X_2)}} = \frac{\text{Cov}(X_1, X_2)}{\sigma(X_1) \sigma(X_2)}$$

$$= \frac{\frac{2}{3} - (1)\left(\frac{1}{2}\right)}{\sqrt{\frac{1}{3}} \sqrt{\frac{7}{36}}} = \sqrt{\frac{3}{7}} = .65.$$

Example 5.3.14. Let (X_1, X_2) be a two-dimensional random variable with joint p.d.f.

$$f_{X_1, X_2}(x_1, x_2) = \begin{cases} a^2 e^{-ax_2}, & \text{if } 0 < x_1 < x_2 < \infty \\ 0, & \text{otherwise.} \end{cases}$$

To find all moments up to order 2 and the correlation between X_1 and X_2, we proceed as follows:

$$E(X_1^r) = \int_0^\infty \int_0^{x_2} x_1^r a^2 e^{-ax_2} \, dx_1 \, dx_2$$

$$= \int_0^\infty \frac{a^2 x_2^{r+1}}{r+1} e^{-ax_2} \, dx_2 = \frac{\Gamma(r+1)}{a^r} = \frac{r!}{a^r},$$

$$E(X_2^r) = \int_0^\infty \int_0^{x_2} a^2 x_2^r e^{-ax_2} \, dx_1 \, dx_2$$

$$= \int_0^\infty a^2 x_2^{r+1} e^{-ax_2} \, dx_2 = \frac{\Gamma(r+2)}{a^r} = \frac{(r+1)!}{a^r},$$

$$E(X_1 X_2) = \int_0^\infty \int_0^{x_2} x_1 x_2 a^2 e^{-ax_2} \, dx_1 \, dx_2$$

$$= \int_0^\infty \frac{a^2}{2} x_2^3 e^{-ax_2} \, dx_2 = \frac{3}{a^2}.$$

Now

$$E(X_1) = \frac{1}{a}, \; E(X_1^2) = \frac{2}{a^2}, \; \text{Var}(X_1) = \frac{2}{a^2} - \frac{1}{a^2} = \frac{1}{a^2},$$

$$E(X_2) = \frac{2}{a}, \; E(X_2^2) = \frac{6}{a^2}, \; \text{Var}(X_2) = \frac{6}{a^2} - \frac{4}{a^2} = \frac{2}{a^2},$$

$$\text{Cov}(X_1, X_2) = E(X_1 X_2) - E(X_1)E(X_2) = \frac{3}{a^2} - \left(\frac{1}{a}\right)\left(\frac{2}{a}\right) = \frac{1}{a^2},$$

and the correlation (defined in Definition 5.3.21) is

$$\rho(X_1, X_2) = \frac{\text{Cov}(X_1, X_2)}{\sigma(X_1)\sigma(X_2)}$$

$$= \frac{\frac{1}{a^2}}{\sqrt{\frac{1}{a^2} \frac{2}{a^2}}} = \frac{1}{\sqrt{2}}.$$

Example 5.3.15. Computation of Multivariate Moments in the Discrete Case. Let (X_1, X_2) be a two-dimensional discrete random variable with the probability function in Example 3.5.5. Find all moments up to order 2.

Here (see Example 3.5.5),

$$p_{X_1}(x_1) = \begin{cases} \frac{1}{6}, & \text{if } x_1 = 0 \\ \frac{2}{6}, & \text{if } x_1 = 1, \\ \frac{3}{6}, & \text{if } x_1 = 2 \end{cases} \qquad p_{X_2}(x_2) = \begin{cases} \frac{14}{60} = \frac{7}{30}, & \text{if } x_2 = 0 \\ \frac{20}{60} = \frac{1}{3}, & \text{if } x_2 = 1 \\ \frac{14}{60} = \frac{7}{30}, & \text{if } x_2 = 2 \\ \frac{12}{60} = \frac{1}{5}, & \text{if } x_2 = 3 \end{cases}$$

(with $p_{X_1}(x_1) = 0$ at all other x_1, and $p_{X_2}(x_2) = 0$ at all other x_2). Thus,

$$E(X_1) = \sum_{x_1} x_1 p_{X_1}(x_1) = 0 \cdot \tfrac{1}{6} + 1 \cdot \tfrac{2}{6} + 2 \cdot \tfrac{3}{6} = \tfrac{4}{3},$$

$$E(X_2) = \sum_{x_2} x_2 p_{X_2}(x_2) = \frac{(0)(14) + (1)(20) + (2)(14) + (3)(12)}{60} = \tfrac{84}{60} = \tfrac{7}{5},$$

$$E(X_1^2) = \sum_{x_1} x_1^2 p_{X_1}(x_1) = 0^2 \cdot \tfrac{1}{6} + 1^2 \cdot \tfrac{2}{6} + 2^2 \cdot \tfrac{3}{6} = \tfrac{7}{3},$$

$$E(X_2^2) = \sum_{x_2} x_2^2 p_{X_2}(x_2) = 0^2 \cdot \tfrac{14}{60} + 1^2 \cdot \tfrac{20}{60} + 2^2 \cdot \tfrac{14}{60} + 3^2 \cdot \tfrac{12}{60} = \tfrac{184}{60} = \tfrac{46}{15},$$

$$E(X_1 X_2) = \sum_{x_1} \sum_{x_2} x_1 x_2 p_{X_1, X_2}(x_1, x_2) = \tfrac{5}{3}.$$

Thus,

$$E(X_1) = \tfrac{4}{3}, \text{Var}(X_1) = \frac{7}{3} - \left(\frac{4}{3}\right)^2 = \tfrac{5}{9},$$

$$E(X_2) = \tfrac{7}{5}, \text{Var}(X_2) = \frac{46}{15} - \left(\frac{7}{5}\right)^2 = \tfrac{83}{75},$$

$$\text{Cov}(X_1, X_2) = E(X_1 X_2) - E(X_1)E(X_2) = \tfrac{5}{3} - \tfrac{4}{3} \cdot \tfrac{7}{5} = -\tfrac{1}{5},$$

and (see Definition 5.3.21)

$$\text{Corr}(X_1, X_2) = \frac{-1/5}{\sqrt{(5/9)(83/75)}} = -\frac{3\sqrt{3}}{\sqrt{(5)(83)}} = -.255069.$$

We now return to the question raised after Lemma 5.3.10 (and before an extension of that lemma and several examples); namely, **If r.v.'s are unrelated in the sense of zero covariance (or correlation), are they independent?**

Theorem 5.3.16. If X_1 and X_2 are **independent, then** [for any two functions $g_1(x)$ and $g_2(x)$]

$$Eg_1(X_1)g_2(X_2) = Eg_1(X_1)Eg_2(X_2)$$

if the expectations on the right side exist. (The obvious generalization to n r.v.'s $X_1, \ldots, X_n$ is also true.)

The proof of Theorem 5.3.16 may be easily shown, for example, for $n = 2$ in the absolutely continuous case. There, $f_{X_1, X_2}(x_1, x_2) = f_{X_1}(x_1)f_{X_2}(x_2)$ by independence and Theorem 4.4.6, and the integral defining $Eg_1(X_1)g_2(X_2)$ can easily be written as the product of the integrals defining $Eg_1(X_1)$ and $Eg_2(X_2)$. Now, two random variables X_1 and X_2 are called **uncorrelated** if $EX_1X_2 = EX_1EX_2$ [i.e., if the result of Theorem 5.3.16 holds for $g_1(x) = g_2(x) = x$]. We now wish to first study correlation and then its relation to independence. (Rephrasing the question asked following the proof of Lemma 5.3.10, we ask "Can uncorrelated r.v.'s fail to be independent?")

Lemma 5.3.17. X_1 and X_2 are uncorrelated iff $\text{Cov}(X_1, X_2) = 0$.

Proof: X_1 and X_2 are uncorrelated iff $EX_1X_2 = EX_1EX_2$,

iff $EX_1X_2 - EX_1EX_2 = 0$,

iff $\text{Cov}(X_1, X_2) = 0$,   by Lemma 5.3.9. ∎

Theorem 5.3.18. $\text{Var}(X_1 + X_2) = \text{Var}(X_1) + \text{Var}(X_2)$ iff X_1 and X_2 are uncorrelated.

Proof: By Lemma 5.3.10

$$\text{Var}(X_1 + X_2) = \text{Var}(X_1) + \text{Var}(X_2) + 2\text{Cov}(X_1, X_2),$$

the last term of which is zero by Lemma 5.3.17. ∎

Theorem 5.3.19.

(i) If X_1 and X_2 are independent, they are uncorrelated.
(ii) If X_1 and X_2 are uncorrelated, they are not necessarily independent.

Proof:

(i) This follows by Theorem 5.3.16 with $g_1(x) = g_2(x) = x$.
(ii) Let $X_1 = \sin(2\pi U)$, $X_2 = \cos(2\pi U)$ with U uniform on $(0, 1)$. We can show that X_1 and X_2 are then uncorrelated, but since $F_{X_1, X_2}(x_1, x_2) \neq F_{X_1}(x_1)F_{X_2}(x_2)$ for all x_1 and x_2, they are not independent. ∎

The previous theorem answers the question, raised following the proof of Lemma 5.3.10, as to whether covariance zero implies independence, while the following theorem gives a precise and complete statement of the relationship between correlation and independence. (Feller says: "As frequently happens, the history of the problem and the luster of partial results easily obscured the fact

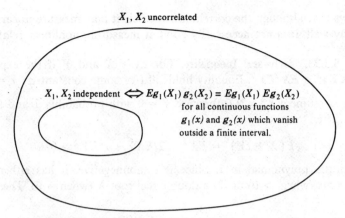

Figure 5.3-1. Relation between independence and correlation.

that the solution is extremely simple by modern methods. The following theorem contains various results proved in the literature by laborious methods.")

Theorem 5.3.20. X_1 and X_2 are independent iff $Eg_1(X_1)g_2(X_2) = Eg_1(X_1)$ $Eg_2(X_2)$ for all continuous functions $g_1(x)$ and $g_2(x)$ which vanish outside a finite interval. (See Figure 5.3-1.)

Definition 5.3.21. The **correlation coefficient** of two jointly distributed r.v.'s X_1 and X_2 is [if $\sigma^2(X_1) > 0$, $\sigma^2(X_2) > 0$ and $\sigma^2(X_1)$, $\sigma^2(X_2)$ are finite]

$$\text{Corr}(X_1, X_2) \equiv \rho(X_1, X_2) = \frac{\text{Cov}(X_1, X_2)}{\sigma(X_1)\sigma(X_2)}.$$

[*Note:* Details of computation of $\text{Corr}(X_1, X_2)$ were given in Examples 5.3.13, 5.3.14, and 5.3.15.]

Lemma 5.3.22. Suppose that $\rho(X_1, X_2)$ is defined.[4] Then X_1 and X_2 are uncorrelated iff $\rho(X_1, X_2) = 0$.

The correlation coefficient provides a measure of the **linear relationship** between two r.v.'s, that is, a measure of how good a prediction of the value of one of the r.v.'s can be formed by a linear function of an observation on the other. But suppose $X_1 = X$ and $X_2 = X^2$; then $X_2 = X_1^2$ and we have an exact **quadratic relationship** between X_1 and X_2; then $\text{Cov}(X_1, X_2) = EX^3 - EXEX^2$ and if $EX^3 = EXEX^2$ [e.g., if $X = -1, 1$ with probability $\frac{1}{2}$ each, or if X has any density symmetric about zero, e.g., the $N(0, \sigma^2)$ density], then $\text{Cov}(X_1, X_2) = 0$. However, given X_1 we can predict X_2 very well (if we know that $X_2 = X_1^2$).

---

[4]We see from Definition 5.3.21 that $\rho(X_1, X_2)$ fails to be defined iff at least one of X_1, X_2 has a constant value (variance zero). (Of course, it is also not defined if the moments it refers to do not all exist.)

This shows that although the correlation coefficient may measure linear relationships fairly well, it is not necessarily good at measuring nonlinear relationships.

Theorem 5.3.23. Schwarz' Inequality. For r.v.'s X and Y if the expectations exist, $(EXY)^2 \le EX^2 EY^2$. Equality holds iff (for some constant a) $Y = aX$.

Proof: Assume $EY^2 > 0$ (otherwise $Y = 0$ with probability 1 and the result is trivial). Then

$$E(X + tY)^2 = EX^2 + 2tEXY + t^2 EY^2 \ge 0$$

is a quadratic polynomial in t. Since it is nonnegative, it has either (1) two complex roots (when > 0) or (2) a double real root λ (when $= 0$). These are (or this is)

$$t = \frac{-2EXY \pm \sqrt{4(EXY)^2 - 4EX^2 EY^2}}{2EY^2}$$

So, we have case (1) iff $4(EXY)^2 - 4EX^2 EY^2 < 0$, that is, iff $(EXY)^2 < EX^2 EY^2$. We have case (2) iff $(EXY)^2 = EX^2 EY^2$; and this is the case $E(X + t_0 Y)^2 = 0$, so $X + t_0 Y = 0$ with probability 1 and $t_0 = -EXY/EY^2$. ∎

[*Note:* Schwarz' Inequality is the special case of Hölder's Inequality (Theorem 5.1.13) where $p = q = 2$.]

Theorem 5.3.24.

(i) $-1 \le \rho(X_1, X_2) \le 1$;

(ii) $\rho(X_1, X_2) = 1$ iff $\dfrac{X_2 - EX_2}{\sigma(X_2)} = \dfrac{X_1 - EX_1}{\sigma(X_1)}$;

and

(iii) $\rho(X_1, X_2) = -1$ iff $\dfrac{X_2 - EX_2}{\sigma(X_2)} = -\dfrac{X_1 - EX_1}{\sigma(X_1)}$.

Proof:
(i) Take (in Theorem 5.3.23) $X = X_1 - EX_1$, $Y = X_2 - EX_2$. Then

$$(EXY)^2 \le EX^2 EY^2;$$

$$[\text{Cov}(X_1, X_2)]^2 \le \text{Var}(X_1)\,\text{Var}(X_2);$$

$$|\text{Cov}(X_1, X_2)| \le \sigma(X_1)\sigma(X_2);$$

$$|\rho(X_1, X_2)| \le 1;$$

$$-1 \le \rho(X_1, X_2) \le 1.$$

(ii) and (iii)

$$(EXY)^2 = EX^2 EY^2 \quad \text{iff} \quad X = \frac{EXY}{EY^2}\,Y.$$

So,

$$|\rho(X_1, X_2)| = 1 \text{ iff } X_1 - EX_1 = \frac{E(X_1 - EX_1)(X_2 - EX_2)}{\sigma^2(X_2)}(X_2 - EX_2)$$

$$\text{iff } \frac{X_1 - EX_1}{\sigma(X_1)} = \frac{E(X_1 - EX_1)(X_2 - EX_2)}{\sigma(X_1)\sigma(X_2)}\frac{X_2 - EX_2}{\sigma(X_2)}$$

$$\text{iff } \frac{X_1 - EX_1}{\sigma(X_1)} = \rho(X_1, X_2)\frac{X_2 - EX_2}{\sigma(X_2)}. \quad \blacksquare$$

As an example, recall (Definition 4.5.2) that a r.v. $X = (X_1, X_2)$ has the bivariate normal distribution $N(\mu_1, \mu_2; \sigma_1^2, \sigma_2^2, \rho)$ if $(-\infty < x_1, x_2 < +\infty)$

$$f_{X_1, X_2}(x_1, x_2) = \frac{1}{2\pi\sigma_1\sigma_2\sqrt{1 - \rho^2}}e^{-\frac{1}{2(1-\rho^2)}\left\{\left(\frac{x_1-\mu_1}{\sigma_1}\right)^2 - 2\rho\left(\frac{x_1-\mu_1}{\sigma_1}\right)\left(\frac{x_2-\mu_2}{\sigma_2}\right) + \left(\frac{x_2-\mu_2}{\sigma_2}\right)^2\right\}}$$

Then, we may prove the following.

Theorem 5.3.25. Let X_1, X_2 be jointly normally distributed. Then $EX_1 = \mu_1$, $\text{Var}(X_1) = \sigma_1^2$, $EX_2 = \mu_2$, $\text{Var}(X_2) = \sigma_2^2$, $\rho(X_1, X_2) = \rho$. Also, X_1 and X_2 are uncorrelated iff they are independent.

Proof: We first note that if X_1, X_2 has the bivariate normal distribution, then

$$f_{X_1}(x_1) = \int_{-\infty}^{\infty} f_{X_1, X_2}(x_1, x_2)\, dx_2$$

$$= \frac{1}{2\pi\sigma_1\sigma_2\sqrt{1 - \rho^2}} \int_{-\infty}^{\infty} e^{-\frac{1}{2(1-\rho^2)}\left\{\left(\frac{x_1-\mu_1}{\sigma_1}\right)^2 - 2\rho\left(\frac{x_1-\mu_1}{\sigma_1}\right)\left(\frac{x_2-\mu_2}{\sigma_2}\right) + \left(\frac{x_2-\mu_2}{\sigma_2}\right)^2\right\}}\, dx_2$$

$$= \frac{1}{2\pi\sigma_1\sqrt{1 - \rho^2}} \int_{-\infty}^{\infty} e^{-\frac{1}{2(1-\rho^2)}\left\{\left(\frac{x_1-\mu_1}{\sigma_1}\right)^2 - 2\rho\left(\frac{x_1-\mu_1}{\sigma_1}\right)y + y^2\right\}}\, dy$$

$$= \frac{1}{2\pi\sigma_1\sqrt{1 - \rho^2}} \int_{-\infty}^{\infty} e^{-\frac{1}{2(1-\rho^2)}\left\{\left(\frac{x_1-\mu_1}{\sigma_1}\right)^2 - \rho^2\left(\frac{x_1-\mu_1}{\sigma_1}\right)^2 + \left(y - \rho\left(\frac{x_1-\mu_1}{\sigma_1}\right)\right)^2\right\}}\, dy$$

$$= \frac{1}{\sqrt{2}\,\pi\sigma_1} \int_{-\infty}^{\infty} e^{-\frac{1}{2}\left(\frac{x_1-\mu_1}{\sigma_1}\right)^2} e^{-z^2}\, dz$$

$$= \frac{1}{\sqrt{2}\,\pi\sigma_1} e^{-\frac{1}{2}\left(\frac{x_1-\mu_1}{\sigma_1}\right)^2}\Gamma\left(\tfrac{1}{2}\right) = \frac{1}{\sqrt{2\pi}\,\sigma_1} e^{-\frac{1}{2}\left(\frac{x_1-\mu_1}{\sigma_1}\right)^2},$$

where we made the substitution $y = (x_2 - \mu_2)/\sigma_2$, completed the square via

$$-2\rho\left(\frac{x_1-\mu_1}{\sigma_1}\right)y + y^2 = \left(y - \rho\left(\frac{x_1-\mu_1}{\sigma_1}\right)\right)^2 - \rho^2\left(\frac{x_1-\mu_1}{\sigma_1}\right)^2,$$

and made the substitution

$$z = \frac{y - \rho\left(\dfrac{x_1 - \mu_1}{\sigma_1}\right)}{\sqrt{2(1 - \rho^2)}}.$$

Thus, if X_1, X_2 has the bivariate normal distribution, then X_1 has the (univariate) normal distribution, which (see Theorem 5.2.6) shows that $EX_1 = \mu_1$ and $\mathrm{Var}(X_1) = \sigma_1^2$. Similarly, we find $EX_2 = \mu_2$, $\mathrm{Var}(X_2) = \sigma_2^2$. The remainder of this theorem's proof is left to Problem 5.4. Theorem 5.3.25 may be extended to the multivariate normal distribution of Definition 4.5.4; in particular, $X_1, \ldots, X_n$ **has an n-dimensional normal distribution iff every linear combination of $X_1, \ldots, X_n$ is normally distributed.** Note, however, that X_1 and X_2 must be *jointly* normal for their "normality" to imply independence iff $\rho(X_1, X_2) = 0$, as the following example shows.   ∎

Example 5.3.26. Let X be normal with mean 0. Let Y be independent of X and $P[Y = 1] = P[Y = -1] = \frac{1}{2}$. Define $Z = XY$. *Then* X and Z have marginal normal distributions, $\rho(X, Z) = 0$, *but* X and Z are dependent.

The crux of the argument is that the normal distribution is symmetric about its mean, so that $P[X < a] = P[X > -a]$ for all a. Then, since X and Y are independent,

$$P[Z < a] = P[XY < a]$$
$$= P[Y = 1]P[X < a] + P[Y = -1]P[X > -a]$$
$$= P[X < a],$$

that is, Z (as well as X) has a marginal normal distribution. Now $\rho(X, Z) = 0$ since $E(XZ) = E(X^2Y) = EX^2EY = 0$. But $Z = \pm X$, so Z and X are quite dependent.

As the final topic of this section, we consider **conditional expectation**. This is used to answer such questions as, if we know $X = x$, then what is EY, taking into account the information that $X = x$?

Definition 5.3.27. If $F_{Y|X}(y|x)$ is absolutely continuous or discrete, then (respectively) the **conditional mean of Y, given X** is

$$E(Y|X = x) = \int_{-\infty}^{\infty} y f_{Y|X}(y|x)\, dy$$

$$E(Y|X = x) = \sum y p_{Y|X}(y|x).$$

Thus, the definition of **conditional expectation** is almost the same as the definition of expectation (Definition 5.1.1), except that instead of a marginal density (or probability) function it **uses a conditional density** (or probability) function. We will see later that conditional expectation is one of the basic tools in estimation theory. In addition, in probability theory conditional expectation is of great importance in stochastic processes.

Theorem 5.3.28. If the quantities indicated exist, if $F_X(x)$ is absolutely continuous or discrete, then (respectively)

$$EY = \int_{-\infty}^{\infty} E(Y|X = x) f_X(x)\, dx,$$

$$EY = \sum E(Y|X = x) p_X(x).$$

Proof: Let us consider the discrete case. (The absolutely continuous case follows similarly on replacing summations by integrals.) Then by Definition 5.3.27,

$$E(Y|X = x) = \sum_y y p_{Y|X}(y|x)$$

so multiplying both sides by $p_X(x)$ we have

$$E(Y|X = x) p_X(x) = \sum_y y p_{Y|X}(y|x) p_X(x) = \sum_y y p_{X,Y}(x, y)$$

where the last equality follows since $p_{Y|X}(y|x) p_X(x) = p_{X,Y}(x, y)$. Now summing on x, we find

$$\sum_x E(Y|X = x) p_X(x) = \sum_x \sum_y y p_{X,Y}(x, y) = \sum_y y \left(\sum_x p_{X,Y}(x, y) \right)$$

$$= \sum_y y p_Y(y) = EY$$

(where we used Definition 3.4.14 to identify $\sum_x p_{X,Y}(x, y)$ as $p_Y(y)$, the marginal probability function of Y), which proves the theorem. ∎

Theorem 5.3.28 can be very useful in the calculation of expected values. Note that it is possible to define not only $E(Y|X = x)$, but also a r.v. $E(Y|X)$ (at least if EY exists). Then, our last result says that

$$E(E(Y|X)) = EY.$$

A useful extension of Theorem 5.3.28 says (in this last notation) that

$$E(g(Y)h(X)) = E(h(X)E(g(Y)|X)).$$

Example 5.3.29. Suppose that (X, Y) is a two-dimensional r.v. with density function

$$f_{X,Y}(x, y) = \begin{cases} 6, & \text{if } x^2 \le y \le x, 0 \le x \le 1 \\ 0, & \text{otherwise;} \end{cases}$$

that is, (X, Y) is uniformly distributed over the region shown in Figure 5.3-2. [Check that $f_{X,Y}(\cdot, \cdot)$ is a density function, that is, it is ≥ 0 and $\int_{-\infty}^{\infty} \int_{-\infty}^{\infty} f_{X,Y}(x, y)\, dx\, dy = 1$.] What is the average of Y in those cases in which X has value x_0 ($0 \le x_0 \le 1$)?

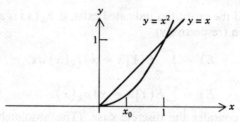

Figure 5.3-2. Region $x^2 \leq y \leq x, 0 \leq x \leq 1$.

The desired quantity is that made precise by Definition 5.3.27; namely, $E(Y|X = x_0)$. Now [see equation (4.4.5)]

$$E(Y|X = x_0) = \int_{-\infty}^{\infty} y f_{Y|X}(y|x_0)\, dy = \int_{-\infty}^{\infty} y \frac{f_{X,Y}(x_0, y)}{f_X(x_0)}\, dy. \quad (5.3.30)$$

We now pause to calculate $f_X(x_0)$:

$$f_X(x) = \int_{-\infty}^{\infty} f_{X,Y}(x, y)\, dy = \begin{cases} \int_{x^2}^{x} 6\, dy, & \text{if } 0 \leq x \leq 1 \\ 0, & \text{otherwise} \end{cases}$$

$$= \begin{cases} 6(x - x^2), & \text{if } 0 \leq x \leq 1 \\ 0, & \text{otherwise.} \end{cases}$$

Thus,

$$f_{Y|X}(y|x) = \frac{f_{X,Y}(x, y)}{f_X(x)} = \begin{cases} \dfrac{1}{x - x^2}, & \text{if } x^2 \leq y \leq x, 0 \leq x \leq 1 \\ 0, & \text{otherwise} \end{cases}$$

and

$$E(Y|X = x_0) = \int_{x_0^2}^{x_0} y \frac{1}{x_0 - x_0^2}\, dy = \frac{x_0(x_0 + 1)}{2}.$$

Note that $f_{Y|X}(y|x)$ is the uniform distribution on (x^2, x), so it follows immediately from Theorem 5.2.4 that $E(Y|X = x_0) = (x_0^2 + x_0)/2 = x_0(x_0 + 1)/2$. Also note that having found $E(Y|X = x_0)$, we can easily find $E(Y)$ via Theorem 5.3.28:

$$E(Y) = \int_{-\infty}^{\infty} E(Y|X = x_0) f_X(x_0)\, dx_0$$

$$= \int_{0}^{1} \frac{x^2 + x}{2} 6(x - x^2)\, dx$$

$$= \tfrac{2}{5}.$$

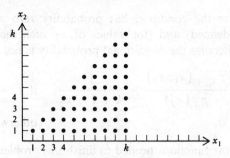

Figure 5.3-3. Points where $p_{X_1, X_2}(x_1, x_2)$ is positive $(k = 10)$.

Example 5.3.31. Let (X_1, X_2) be a two-dimensional discrete r.v. with probability function

$$p_{X_1, X_2}(x_1, x_2) = \begin{cases} \dfrac{2}{k(k+1)}, & \text{if } x_2 = 1, 2, \ldots, x_1 \text{ and } x_1 = 1, 2, \ldots, k \\ 0, & \text{otherwise} \end{cases}$$

for a given positive integer k. Find all moments up to second order, Corr(X_1, X_2), and $E(X_1 | X_2 = x_2)$, $E(X_2 | X_1 = x_1)$, Var$(X_1 | X_2 = x_2)$, Var$(X_2 | X_1 = x_1)$.

First, for insight note that the distribution of (X_1, X_2) is uniform over the points shown in Figure 5.3-3. We now proceed to calculate the marginal and conditional probability functions and moments as follows.

$$p_{X_1}(x_1) = \sum_{x_2=1}^{x_1} p_{X_1, X_2}(x_1, x_2) = \begin{cases} \dfrac{2x_1}{k(k+1)}, & \text{if } x_1 = 1, 2, \ldots, k \\ 0, & \text{otherwise,} \end{cases}$$

$$p_{X_2}(x_2) = \sum_{x_1=x_2}^{k} p_{X_1, X_2}(x_1, x_2) = \begin{cases} \dfrac{2(k+1-x_2)}{k(k+1)}, & \text{if } x_2 = 1, 2, \ldots, k \\ 0, & \text{otherwise.} \end{cases}$$

Having the joint and marginal probability functions, we are now in a position to compute the conditional probability functions

$$p_{X_2|X_1}(x_2|x_1) = \begin{cases} \dfrac{p_{X_1, X_2}(x_1, x_2)}{p_{X_1}(x_1)} = \dfrac{\dfrac{2}{k(k+1)}}{\dfrac{2x_1}{k(k+1)}} = \dfrac{1}{x_1}, & \text{if } x_2 = 1, 2, \ldots, x_1 \\ 0, & \text{otherwise,} \end{cases}$$

(the preceding holds only for values of x_1 such that $p_{X_1}(x_1) > 0$, i.e., $x_1 =$

$1, 2, \ldots, k$; otherwise the condition has probability zero and the conditional probability is not defined) and (for values of x_2 such that $p_{X_2}(x_2) > 0$, i.e., $x_2 = 1, 2, \ldots, k$; otherwise the conditional probability is not defined).

$$p_{X_1|X_2}(x_1|x_2) = \begin{cases} \dfrac{p_{X_1,X_2}(x_1, x_2)}{p_{X_2}(x_2)} = \dfrac{1}{k + 1 - x_2}, & \text{if } x_1 = x_2, x_2 + 1, \ldots, k \\ 0, & \text{otherwise.} \end{cases}$$

The above provide the functions needed to finish this problem by calculating the desired moments, as we now do:

$$E(X_1) = \sum_{x_1=1}^{k} \frac{2x_1}{k(k+1)} x_1 = \frac{2}{k(k+1)} \sum_{x_1=1}^{k} x_1^2$$

$$= \frac{2}{k(k+1)} \frac{k(k+1)(2k+1)}{6} = \frac{2k+1}{3}$$

$$E(X_1^2) = \sum_{x_1=1}^{k} \frac{2x_1^3}{k(k+1)} = \frac{2}{k(k+1)} \frac{k^2(k+1)^2}{4} = \frac{k(k+1)}{2}$$

$$\text{Var}(X_1) = \frac{k(k+1)}{2} - \frac{(2k+1)^2}{9} = \frac{k^2 + k - 2}{18}$$

$$E(X_2) = \sum_{x_2=1}^{k} \frac{2(k+1-x_2)}{k(k+1)} x_2 = \frac{k+2}{3}$$

$$E(X_2^2) = \sum_{x_2=1}^{k} \frac{2(k+1-x_2)}{k(k+1)} x_2^2 = \frac{(k+1)(k+2)}{6}$$

$$\text{Var}(X_2) = \frac{(k+1)(k+2)}{6} - \left(\frac{k+2}{3}\right)^2 = \frac{(k+2)(k-1)}{18}$$

$$E(X_1 X_2) = \sum_{x_1=1}^{k} \sum_{x_2=1}^{x_1} \frac{2}{k(k+1)} x_1 x_2 = \sum_{x_1=1}^{k} \frac{2x_1}{k(k+1)} \frac{x_1(x_1+1)}{2}$$

$$= \sum_{x_1=1}^{k} \frac{x_1^3 + x_1^2}{k(k+1)} = \frac{3k^2 + 7k + 2}{12}$$

$$\text{Cov}(X_1, X_2) = E(X_1 X_2) - E(X_1)E(X_2)$$

$$= \frac{3k^2 + 7k + 2}{12} - \frac{2k+1}{3} \frac{k+2}{3} = \frac{(k+2)(k-1)}{36}$$

and (if $k > 1$, since the denominator is zero when $k = 1$ and the correlation is not then defined)

$$\text{Corr}(X_1, X_2) = \frac{\dfrac{(k+2)(k-1)}{36}}{\sqrt{\dfrac{k^2+k-2}{18}\dfrac{(k+2)(k-1)}{18}}} = \frac{k-1}{2(k-1)} = \frac{1}{2}.$$

We have seen calculations similar to this before (e.g., in Examples 5.3.13, 5.3.14, and 5.3.15); we now move on to **calculation of the new quantities, the conditional expectations**:

$$E(X_1|X_2 = x_2) = \sum_{x_1} x_1 p_{X_1|X_2}(x_1|x_2)$$

$$= \sum_{x_1 = x_2}^{k} x_1 \frac{1}{k+1-x_2} = \frac{k(k+1) - x_2(x_2-1)}{2(k+1-x_2)}$$

if $x_2 = 1, 2, \ldots, k$ (note that this conditional expectation is not defined for any other values of x_2);

$$E(X_2|X_1 = x_1) = \sum_{x_2} x_2 p_{X_2|X_1}(x_2|x_1) = \sum_{x_2 = 1}^{x_1} x_2 \frac{1}{x_1} = \frac{x_1 + 1}{2}$$

if, $x_1 = 1, 2, \ldots, k$ (and the conditional expectation is not defined for any other values of x_1);

$$E(X_2^2|X_1 = x_1) = \sum_{x_2 = 1}^{x_1} x_2^2 p_{X_2|X_1}(x_2|x_1) = \frac{1}{x_1}\sum_{x_2 = 1}^{x_1} x_2^2 = \frac{(x_1+1)(2x_1+1)}{6}$$

if $x_1 = 1, 2, \ldots, k$;

$$\text{Var}(X_2|X_1 = x_1) = E(X_2^2|X_1 = x_1) - [E(X_2|X_1 = x_1)]^2$$

$$= \frac{(x_1+1)(2x_1+1)}{6} - \frac{(x_1+1)^2}{4} = \frac{x_1^2 - 1}{12}$$

if $x_1 = 1, 2, \ldots, k$;

$$E(X_1^2|X_2 = x_2) = \sum_{x_1 = x_2}^{k} x_1^2 \frac{1}{k+1-x_2}$$

$$= \frac{1}{k+1-x_2}\left(\frac{k(k+1)(2k+1) - (x_2-1)(x_2)(2x_2-1)}{6}\right)$$

if $x_2 = 1, 2, \ldots, k$; and

$$\text{Var}(X_1 | X_2 = x_2) = \frac{1}{k+1-x_2} \left(\frac{k(k+1)(2k+1) - x_2(x_2-1)(2x_2-1)}{6} \right.$$
$$\left. - \left(\frac{k(k+1) - x_2(x_2-1)}{2(k+1-x_2)} \right)^2 \right)$$

if $x_2 = 1, 2, \ldots, k$.

Note that, having found the $E(X_1 | X_2 = x_2)$, we are in a position to **derive** $E(X_1)$ **by the result of Theorem 5.3.28:**

$$E(X_1) = E(E(X_1 | X_2)) = E \frac{k(k+1) - X_2(X_2-1)}{2(k+1-X_2)}$$

$$= \sum_{x_2=1}^{k} \frac{k(k+1) - x_2(x_2-1)}{2(k+1-x_2)} \frac{2(k+1-x_2)}{k(k+1)}$$

$$= \sum_{x_2=1}^{k} \frac{k(k+1) - x_2^2 + x_2}{k(k+1)}$$

$$= \frac{2k+1}{3},$$

as we derived earlier in this example from the marginal distribution of X_1. [We leave it as an exercise to verify the result $E(X_2) = (k+2)/3$, which we found using the marginal distribution of X_2, via $E(X_2) = E(E(X_2 | X_1))$.]

PROBLEMS FOR SECTION 5.3

5.3.1 Let (X_1, X_2) be a two-dimensional r.v. (X_1 equals time to contract a certain terminal disease after exposure to its cause, and X_2 equals time to death after the disease exposure) with joint p.d.f. $f_{X_1, X_2}(x_1, x_2) = (2/\lambda^2)e^{-(x_1+x_2)/\lambda}$ for $0 < x_1 < x_2 < \infty$ (and $= 0$ otherwise) for some $\lambda > 0$.
   (a) Find the marginal p.d.f.'s of X_1 and X_2.
   (b) Find $E(X_1)$, $E(X_2)$, $\text{Var}(X_1)$, $\text{Var}(X_2)$, $\text{Cov}(X_1, X_2)$, and $\text{Corr}(X_1, X_2)$.
   (c) Compute $E(X_1 | X_2 = l)$ and $E(X_2 | X_1 = m)$.
   (d) Are X_1 and X_2 independent r.v.'s?
   (e) Compute $\text{Var}(X_1 | X_2 = l)$ and $\text{Var}(X_2 | X_1 = m)$.

5.3.2 Consider a two-dimensional r.v. (X_1, X_2) with joint p.d.f. $f_{X_1, X_2}(x_1, x_2) = x_1 + x_2$ if $0 \le x_1 \le 1$ and $0 \le x_2 \le 1$ (and $= 0$ otherwise).
   (a) Compute the marginal p.d.f.'s $f_{X_1}(x_1)$ and $f_{X_2}(x_2)$.
   (b) Compute $E(X_1)$, $E(X_2)$, $\text{Var}(X_1)$, $\text{Var}(X_2)$, $\text{Cov}(X_1, X_2)$, and $\rho(X_1, X_2)$.
   (c) Compute $E(X_1 | X_2 = l)$ and $E(X_2 | X_1 = m)$.

(d) Are X_1 and X_2 independent r.v.'s?

(e) Compute $\mathrm{Var}(X_1|X_2 = l)$ and $\mathrm{Var}(X_2|X_1 = m)$.

(f) Compute the variance of $3X_1 + 6X_2 - 12$.

5.3.3 Suppose the conditional p.d.f. of X_2, given $X_1 = x_1 > 0$, is $f_{X_2|X_1 = x_1}(x_2|x_1) = ((x_1 + x_2)/(x_1 + 1))e^{-x_2}$ if $x_2 > 0$ (and $y = 0$ otherwise) and that $f_{X_1}(x_1) = ((x_1 + 1)/2)e^{-x_1}$ if $x_1 > 0$ (and $= 0$ otherwise). Find $E(X_1|X_2 = x_2)$, $E(X_1)$, and $\mathrm{Corr}(X_1, X_2)$.

5.3.4 On n independent tosses of a coin with probability p of heads, let X denote the number of heads, and Y denote the number of tails. Compute $\mathrm{Corr}(X, Y)$. Are X and Y independent r.v.'s?

5.3.5 Let (X_1, X_2) be a two-dimensional discrete r.v. with joint probability function

x_1 \ x_2	$p_{X_1, X_2}(x_1, x_2)$	
	1	2
1	1/8	1/16
2	1/16	1/16
3	1/8	1/8
4	3/16	1/4

(a) Compute $\mathrm{Corr}(X_1, X_2)$.

(b) Are X_1 and X_2 independent r.v.'s?

5.3.6 Prove or disprove

(a) $E(1/X) = 1/E(X)$.

(b) If X and Y are independent r.v.'s, then $E(X/Y) = E(X)/E(Y)$.

5.3.7 Prove

(a) If $X_1, X_2, \ldots, X_n$ are r.v.'s each with finite mean and finite variance, $a_1, a_2, \ldots, a_n, b_1, b_2, \ldots, b_n$ are finite numbers, and $Y_1 = a_1 X_1 + \cdots + a_n X_n$, $Y_2 = b_1 X_1 + \cdots + b_n X_n$, then

$$\mathrm{Cov}(Y_1, Y_2) = \sum_{i=1}^{n} a_i b_i \mathrm{Var}(X_i) + \sum_{i<j} (a_i b_j + a_j b_i) \mathrm{Cov}(X_i, X_j).$$

(b) If in addition $X_1, X_2, \ldots, X_n$ are independent r.v.'s, then

$$\mathrm{Cov}(Y_1, Y_2) = \sum_{i=1}^{n} a_i b_i \mathrm{Var}(X_i).$$

5.3.8 Let (X_1, X_2) be a two-dimensional r.v. with joint probabilities given by

$$f_{X_1|X_2}(x_1|x_2) p_{X_2}(x_2) = \frac{\Gamma(\alpha + \lambda + 2)}{\Gamma(\alpha + 1)\Gamma(\lambda + 1)} x_1^{\alpha}(1 - x_1)^{\beta} \binom{n}{x_2} p^{x_2} q^{n - x_2}$$

if $0 \le x_1 \le 1$ and $x_2 = 0, 1, 2, \ldots, n$ (and $= 0$ otherwise). Compute

(a) $\mathrm{Corr}(X_1, X_2)$.

(b) $\text{Var}(3X_1 + 4X_2 - 9)$ and $\text{Var}(2X_1 - 6X_2 + 12)$.

(c) $\text{Cov}(3X_1 + 4X_2, 2X_1 - 6X_2)$.

5.3.9 If (X_1, X_2) has a bivariate normal distribution with $\mu_1 = \mu_2 = 0$, $\sigma_1^2 = \sigma_2^2 = 1$, and correlation coefficient ρ, show that $Y = X_1/X_2$ has p.d.f.

$$f_Y(y) = \frac{\sqrt{1 - \rho^2}}{\pi(1 - 2\pi y + y^2)}, \quad -\infty < y < \infty.$$

Does $E(Y)$ exist? (If so, compute it.)

5.3.10 Let X_1 and X_2 be independent r.v.'s, each $N(\mu, \sigma^2)$. For what values of θ are the r.v.'s

$$Y = X_1\cos(\theta) + X_2\sin(\theta), \qquad Z = X_1\cos(\theta) - X_2\sin(\theta)$$

independent?

5.3.11 In Problem 5.3.10 suppose $X_1 \sim N(\mu_1, \sigma_1^2)$ and $X_2 \sim N(\mu_2, \sigma_2^2)$ with X_1 and X_2 independent. Compute $\text{Corr}(Y, Z)$.

5.3.12 In Problem 5.3.10 let $W = X_2\cos(\theta) - X_1\sin(\theta)$. Show that

$$\text{Corr}(Y, W) = 1 - \frac{4\sigma_1^2\sigma_2^2}{4\sigma_1^2\sigma_2^2 + \left(\sigma_1^2 - \sigma_2^2\right)^2\sin^2(2\theta)}.$$

5.3.13 Let X be an r.v. with $E(X) < \infty$ and $\text{Var}(X) < \infty$. Let r.v.'s be defined by $X_1 = X$, $X_2 = \rho X_1$, $X_3 = \rho X_2, \ldots, X_i = \rho X_{i-1}, \ldots$. Compute $\text{Corr}(X_n, X_1)$.

5.3.14 Consider $2n$ r.v.'s $X_1, X_2, \ldots, X_{2n}$ such that $\text{Var}(X_i) = \sigma^2 < \infty$ and $\text{Corr}(X_i, X_j) = \rho$ $(i \neq j)$. Show that if $Y = X_1 + \cdots + X_n$ and $Z = X_{n+1} + \cdots + X_{2n}$, then

$$\text{Corr}(Y, Z) = \frac{n\rho}{1 + (n-1)\rho}.$$

5.3.15 Compute the conditional expectation $E(Y|X = x)$ for the following distributions.
(a) $f_{X,Y}(x, y) = (y/(1 + x)^4)e^{-y/(1+x)}$ if $x \geq 0$ and $y \geq 0$ (and $= 0$ otherwise).
(b) $f_{X,Y}(x, y) = 4.5(1 + x + y)/((1 + x)^4(1 + y)^4)$ if $x \geq 0$ and $y \geq 0$ (and $= 0$ otherwise).

5.3.16 Let X be an exponential r.v. with p.d.f. $f_X(x) = (1/\lambda)e^{-x/\lambda}$ for $x > 0$ (and $= 0$ otherwise). **(a)** Compute $E(X|X > 1)$. **(b)** Compute $E(X|X < 2)$. [*Hint:* Use truncated r.v.'s.]

5.3.17 Show that the correlation coefficient between r.v.'s X and Y can be expressed as

$$\rho(X, Y) = \frac{\text{Var}(X) + \text{Var}(Y) - \text{Var}(X - Y)}{2\sqrt{\text{Var}(X)\,\text{Var}(Y)}}.$$

5.3.18 If $\text{Corr}(X, Y) > 0$, show that **(a)** $\text{Corr}(X, -Y) < 0$; **(b)** $\text{Corr}(-X, -Y) > 0$.

5.3.19 Let X and Y be r.v.'s with means 0, variances 1, and $\text{Corr}(X, Y) = \rho$. Show that $E(\max(X^2, Y^2)) \leq 1 + \sqrt{1 - \rho^2}$. [*Hint:* Note that $\max(X^2, Y^2) = (X^2 + Y^2)/2 + |X^2 - Y^2|/2$, and $(E|X^2 - Y^2|)^2 \leq E(X - Y)^2E(X + Y)^2$.]

5.3.20 Show that, for any function $g(\cdot)$,

$$E(g(X)Y) = E(g(X)E(Y|X)).$$

5.3.21 Let $g(\cdot, \cdot)$ be any function of two variables. Show that
(a) $E(g(X, Y)|Y = y) = E(g(X, y)|Y = y)$.
(b) $E(XY|Y = y) = yE(X|Y = y)$.

5.3.22 Let (X_1, X_2) be a two-dimensional r.v. with joint p.d.f. $f_{X_1, X_2}(x_1, x_2)$. Show that
(a) $\mathrm{Var}(X_2|X_1 = x_1) = E((X_2 - E(X_2|X_1 = x_1))^2|X_1 = x_1)$
$\qquad = E(X_2^2|X_1 = x_1) - (E(X_2|X_1 = x_1))^2$.
(b) $\mathrm{Var}(X_2) = E(\mathrm{Var}(X_2|X_1)) + \mathrm{Var}(E(X_2|X_1))$.

5.3.23 Let $X_1, X_2, \ldots, X_n$ be n r.v.'s with means μ_i and variances σ_i^2 $(i = 1, 2, \ldots, n)$. Let $\mathrm{Corr}(X_i, X_j) = \rho_{ij}$. Consider, for any real numbers $a_1, a_2, \ldots, a_n$, $b_1, b_2, \ldots, b_n$, $Y = a_1 X_1 + \cdots + a_n X_n$ and $Z = b_1 X_1 + \cdots + b_n X_n$. Show that

$$\mathrm{Cov}(Y, Z) = \sum_{i=1}^{n} \sum_{j=1}^{n} a_i b_j \sigma_i \sigma_j \rho_{ij}.$$

5.3.24 If in Problem 5.3.23 the r.v.'s $X_1, X_2, \ldots, X_n$ were independent $N(\mu, \sigma^2)$, find the conditions under which Y and Z would be independent r.v.'s.

5.3.25 Let $(X_1, X_2, \ldots, X_k)$ be a multinomial r.v. with cell probabilities $(p_1, p_2, \ldots, p_k)$. Show that $E(X_i) = np_i$, $\mathrm{Var}(X_i) = np_i q_i$, and $\mathrm{Cov}(X_i, X_j) = -np_i p_j$.

5.4. MEANS AND VARIANCES OF SUMS OF INDEPENDENT RANDOM VARIABLES

Often in applications, one is interested in the mean (average value) and **variance** (variability about the average value) **of a sum of random variables**, such as $S_n = X_1 + X_2 + \cdots + X_n$, where n is a positive integer.

Example 5.4.1. The total amount of sales (in dollars) to the customers of a certain market are independent random variables with average sales per customer of \$25.00 and variance of sales per customer of 20.00 (standard deviation \$4.47). If $n = 100$ customers come to the market on a certain day, then total sales on that day will be $S_{100} = X_1 + X_2 + \cdots + X_{100}$, where X_i represents the amount of sales to the ith customer $(i = 1, \ldots, 100)$. We are then interested in $E(S_{100})$ and $\mathrm{Var}(S_{100})$.

From Corollary 5.3.3 and Lemma 5.3.11, we are immediately able to find the result needed to solve the problem in Example 5.4.1:

Theorem 5.4.2. If $X_1, X_2, \ldots, X_n$ are independent random variables, and $S_n = X_1 + X_2 + \cdots + X_n$, then

$$E(S_n) = E(X_1) + E(X_2) + \cdots + E(X_n),$$

$$\mathrm{Var}(S_n) = \mathrm{Var}(X_1) + \mathrm{Var}(X_2) + \cdots + \mathrm{Var}(X_n).$$

If $X_1, X_2, \ldots, X_n$ also have the same mean $E(X_1)$ and the same variance $\text{Var}(X_1)$, then

$$E(S_n) = nE(X_1), \qquad \text{Var}(S_n) = n\text{Var}(X_1).$$

Example 5.4.3. In Example 5.4.1, we may now use Theorem 5.4.2 to find the average sales on a day with 100 customers as

$$E(S_{100}) = 100E(X_1) = (100)(25.00) = 2500,$$

and the variance of the average sales on a day with 100 customers as

$$\text{Var}(S_{100}) = 100\,\text{Var}(X_1) = (100)(20.00) = 2000.$$

Thus, sales on a 100-customer day average $2500.00 and have a standard deviation of $44.72 (the square root of the variance of 2000).

The above discussion answers the practical question when the number n of random variables is known, but **in some applications n is also a random variable, which we will then denote by N**, so that $S_N = X_1 + X_2 + \cdots + X_N$ is now a sum with a random number of terms.

Example 5.4.4. Sales to each customer of a certain market are random, with average sales per customer of $25.00 and variance of sales per customer of 20.00 (standard deviation $4.47). Sales are independent from customer to customer. The number of customers on any day is not known in advance, but it is known to follow a Poisson distribution with a mean of 100 customers, that is,

$$P[N = i] = e^{-100}(100)^i/i! \qquad (i = 0, 1, 2, \ldots).$$

We are interested in the mean and variance of the sales in a day, namely $E(S_N)$ and $\text{Var}(S_N)$ where $S_N = X_1 + X_2 + \cdots + X_N$ with $N, X_1, X_2, \ldots$ independent random variables (we are also assuming that sales are independent of the number of customers).

One might conjecture that $E(S_N) = E(N)E(X_1)$ as a generalization of Theorem 5.4.2 to the case when n is replaced by a random variable. We will see that this conjecture is valid. The corresponding conjecture for $\text{Var}(S_N)$, namely $E(N)\text{Var}(X_1)$, is, however, *not* valid; intuitively, one may think of the situation as one in which there is more variability since there is variability in the sales of a customer, *and* also in the number of customers... while the conjectured quantity $E(N)\text{Var}(X_1)$ does not take account of the variability in the number of customers and would yield the same $\text{Var}(S_N)$ if we always had $N = 100$ as if we had N extremely variable. [Thus, we expect the $\text{Var}(S_N)$ will be larger than $E(N)\text{Var}(X_1)$.]

To find $E(S_N)$ and $\text{Var}(S_N)$, we will make use of the material on conditional expectation developed as the last topic in Section 5.3.

Theorem 5.4.5. If $N, X_1, X_2, \ldots$ are independent random variables where N takes on nonnegative integers as values, and if $E(X_1) = E(X_2) = \cdots$, $\text{Var}(X_1) = \text{Var}(X_2) = \cdots$, $S_N = X_1 + X_2 + \cdots + X_N$, then

$$E(S_N) = E(N)E(X_1), \qquad \text{Var}(S_N) = E(N)\,\text{Var}(X_1) + \text{Var}(N)(EX_1)^2.$$

Proof: We first find the conditional expectation of S_N, given the value of N, as

$$
\begin{aligned}
E(S_N | N = n) &= E(X_1 + \cdots + X_N | N = n) \qquad \text{by definition of } S_N \\
&= E(X_1 + \cdots + X_n | N = n) \\
&= E(X_1 + \cdots + X_n) \qquad \text{since } N \text{ and } X_1 + \cdots + X_n \\
&\qquad\qquad\qquad\qquad\qquad \text{are independent} \\
&= E(X_1) + \cdots + E(X_n) \qquad \text{by Theorem 5.4.2} \\
&= nE(X_1) \qquad \text{since } E(X_1) = E(X_2) = \cdots \qquad \text{by assumption.}
\end{aligned}
$$

Now, using Theorem 5.3.28, we find

$$
\begin{aligned}
E(S_N) &= \sum_n E(S_N | N = n) P[N = n] \\
&= \sum_n nE(X_1) P[N = n] = E(X_1) \sum_n nP[N = n] \\
&= E(X_1)E(N) = E(N)E(X_1),
\end{aligned}
$$

that is, we have shown the mean of S_N as in the statement of the theorem.

For the second part of the theorem, we first find the second conditional moment of S_N,

$$
\begin{aligned}
E(S_N^2 | N = n) \\
&= E\left((X_1 + \cdots + X_N)^2 | N = n \right) \\
&= E\left((X_1 + \cdots + X_n)^2 | N = n \right) = E\left((X_1 + \cdots + X_n)^2 \right) \\
&= E\left(X_1^2 + \cdots + X_n^2 + 2\sum_{i<j} X_i X_j \right) = nE(X_1^2) + n(n-1)(EX_1)^2 \\
&= n\left(E(X_1^2) - (EX_1)^2 \right) + n^2(EX_1)^2 = n\,\text{Var}(X_1) + n^2(EX_1)^2.
\end{aligned}
$$

Now,

$$\text{Var}(S_N) = E(S_N^2) - (E(S_N))^2$$

$$= \sum_n E(S_N^2 | N = n) P(N = n) - (ENE(X_1))^2$$

$$= \sum_n \left(n \text{Var}(X_1) + n^2(EX_1)^2 \right) P[N = n] - (EN)^2(E(X_1))^2$$

$$= \text{Var}(X_1) \sum_n nP[N = n] + (EX_1)^2 \sum_n n^2 P[N = n] - (EN)^2(E(X_1))^2$$

$$= \text{Var}(X_1) E(N) + (EX_1)^2 E(N^2) - (EN)^2(E(X_1))^2$$

$$= E(N) \text{Var}(X_1) + \left(E(N^2) - (EN)^2 \right)(E(X_1))^2$$

$$= E(N) \text{Var}(X_1) + \text{Var}(N)(EX_1)^2,$$

as was to be shown.   ∎

Example 5.4.6. In Example 5.4.4, we have $S_N = X_1 + \cdots + X_N$ with $X_1, X_2, \ldots$ each having mean \$25.00 and variance 20, N being Poisson with mean 100, and $N, X_1, X_2, \ldots$ being independent random variables. Then it follows by Theorem 5.4.5 that

$$E(S_N) = E(N)E(X_1) = (100)(25.00) = 2500.$$

Thus, mean sales per day are \$2500 when an average of 100 customers come to the store per day, just as they were in Example 5.4.3 when we knew there were 100 customers on a particular day.

For the variance, it also follows from Theorem 5.4.5 that

$$\text{Var}(S_N) = E(N) \text{Var}(X_1) + \text{Var}(N)(EX_1)^2$$

$$= (100)(20) + (100)(25.00)^2$$

$$= 64,500.$$

Thus, the variance is much greater with the variability in how many customers visit the store each day [we now have $\text{Var}(S_N) = 64,500$ vs. 2000 in Example 5.4.3 where we knew there had been 100 customers]. Thus, the standard deviation is now \$253.97 for a day's receipts vs. \$44.72 when we knew the number of customers. This information can be useful in accounting. [As we will see in Chapter 6, it is very unusual for a random variable to be more than 3 standard deviations from its mean value, hence a daily receipts not within (3)(253.97) = \$761.91 of the mean of \$2500 is cause for suspicion, e.g., that there has been skimming of the cash; similar applications arise with toll-road receipts, lottery sales, and the like.]

PROBLEMS FOR SECTION 5.4

5.4.1 A certain company competes independently for each of 100 contracts in a year. It has probability .15 of winning on each contract. A contract it does not win is worth $0 to it, while the profit from a contract it wins is approximately normally distributed with a mean of $10,000 and a standard deviation of $1000. Let Z denote the company's total profit next year. Find $E(Z)$, $\text{Var}(Z)$, and $E(Z) \pm 3\sqrt{\text{Var}(Z)}$.

5.4.2 As in Problem 5.4.1, but now each contract lost costs the company $1000 (costs to prepare the bid).

5.4.3 One-hundred agricultural pests independently lay 100 eggs each on a farmer's field and then die. Each egg has probability .01 of producing a mature pest in the next year's growing season. Let Y denote the number of pests the farmer has to contend with next year. Find $E(Y)$, $\sqrt{\text{Var}(Y)}$, and $E(Y) \pm 3\sqrt{\text{Var}(Y)}$.

5.4.4 As in Problem 5.4.3, but now suppose the number of eggs laid by each pest is a Poisson r.v. with mean 100.

5.4.5 Suppose the number of automobile accidents in a certain area in a week is a random variable with mean μ_1 and variance σ_1^2. The number of persons injured in each accident is independent from accident to accident and has mean μ_2 and variance σ_2^2. Let W denote the number of persons injured in automobile accidents in this area in a week. Find $E(W)$, $\text{Var}(W)$, and $E(W) \pm 3\sqrt{\text{Var}(W)}$.

5.5. MOMENT-GENERATING FUNCTIONS AND CHARACTERISTIC FUNCTIONS

In this section, we introduce and study **moment-generating functions (m.g.f.'s)** and **characteristic functions (ch.f.'s)**. These will allow us to prove theorems of fundamental importance in statistics (e.g., in Chapter 6, the Central Limit Theorem). We first introduce the conceptually simpler m.g.f., and then the ch.f.[5]

Definition 5.5.1.   The **moment-generating function** of a r.v. X is defined for every real number t by $\psi_X(t) = Ee^{tX}$.

[Thus, the **m.g.f.** is a function of a real variable t. Of course, it is only defined for values t for which Ee^{tX} exists. Recall that we spoke previously of expected values of functions of random variables, $Eg(X)$. Here $g(X) = e^{tX}$.]

Theorem 5.5.2.   If the m.g.f. $\psi_X(t)$ of the r.v. X exists for $|t| \leq T$ (for some $T > 0$), then EX^n exists ($n = 1, 2, 3, \ldots$) and

$$EX^n = \psi_X^{(n)}(0) \equiv \left. \frac{d^n}{dt^n} \psi_X(t) \right|_{t=0}.$$

---

[5] The ch.f. is included for completeness and because some instructors prefer to use it. Only the m.g.f. need be studied at this point.

Proof: We know that (by definition) $\psi_X(t) = Ee^{tX}$, and for the function e^y we have the series expansion $e^y = 1 + y + \dfrac{y^2}{2!} + \dfrac{y^3}{3!} + \cdots$. Replacing y by tX and taking the expectation of both sides, we then have (for $|t| < T$, where the expectation exists by the hypotheses of the theorem)

$$\psi_X(t) = Ee^{tX} = E\left(1 + tX + (tX)^2/2! + (tX)^3/3! + \cdots\right)$$

$$= E\left(1 + Xt + X^2\frac{t^2}{2!} + X^3\frac{t^3}{3!} + \cdots\right)$$

$$= 1 + (EX)t + (EX^2)\frac{t^2}{2!} + \cdots + (EX^n)\frac{t^n}{n!} + \cdots.$$

If we differentiate both sides with respect to t and evaluate at $t = 0$, we find

$$\psi_X'(0) = \left(0 + EX + (EX^2)t + (EX^3)\frac{t^2}{2!} + \cdots + (EX^n)\frac{t^{n-1}}{(n-1)!} + \cdots\right)\Bigg|_{t=0}$$

$$= EX,$$

which is the result claimed in the statement of the theorem for the case $n = 1$. The results for $n = 2, 3, \ldots$ follow on successive differentiation and evaluation at $t = 0$. (We have omitted the proof that the expected value, of this infinite sum of terms, equals the sum of the expected values.) The result follows by differentiation (where we also omit the proof that the derivative, of this infinite sum of terms, equals the sum of the derivatives of the individual terms). ∎

Note that we can therefore readily obtain EX^n for any $n = 1, 2, \ldots$ if we can obtain a power series expansion of $\psi_X(t)$; EX^n will simply be the coefficient of $t^n/n!$ in the power series expansion.

Alternate Proof: Since $\psi_X(t)$ exists for $|t| < T$, we may (we omit the proof) form its successive derivatives by successively differentiating "under the integral sign." Thus,

$$\psi_X^{(n)}(t) = \frac{d^n}{dt^n}\psi_X(t) = E\left[\frac{\partial}{\partial t}\frac{d^{n-1}}{dt^{n-1}}e^{tX}\right] = E[X^n e^{tX}].$$

Setting $t = 0$, $\psi_X^{(n)}(0) = EX^n$. ∎

In the following four examples, we compute m.g.f.'s for several commonly encountered r.v.'s, and use them to compute moments.

Example 5.5.3. If X is a **Poisson r.v.** (see Definition 3.2.11) with parameter λ, then its m.g.f. is

$$\psi_X(t) = E(e^{tX}) = \sum_{x=0}^{\infty} e^{tx} e^{-\lambda} \lambda^x / x!$$

$$= e^{-\lambda} \sum_{x=0}^{\infty} (\lambda e^t)^x / x! = e^{-\lambda} e^{\lambda e^t} = e^{\lambda(e^t-1)}.$$

[*Note:* This m.g.f. exists for all values of t.] We may now compute the first two moments and variance of X from its m.g.f. as follows:

$$E(X) = \frac{d}{dt}\psi_X(t)\Big|_{t=0} = e^{\lambda(e^t-1)}\lambda e^t\Big|_{t=0} = \lambda,$$

$$E(X^2) = \frac{d^2}{dt^2}\psi_X(t)\Big|_{t=0} = \frac{d}{dt}\left(\frac{d}{dt}\psi_X(t)\right)\Big|_{t=0} = \frac{d}{dt}\left(e^{\lambda(e^t-1)}\lambda e^t\right)\Big|_{t=0}$$

$$= \left(e^{\lambda(e^t-1)}\lambda^2 e^{2t} + e^{\lambda(e^t-1)}\lambda e^t\right)\Big|_{t=0} = \lambda^2 + \lambda,$$

$$\mathrm{Var}(X) = E(X^2) - (EX)^2 = \lambda.$$

(Recall that these same results were derived directly from the definition of expectation in Theorem 5.2.3.)

Example 5.5.4. Suppose (as in Theorem 5.2.7) that X has the **gamma distribution** $G(x|\alpha, \beta, A = 0)$. Then the m.g.f. of X is

$$\psi_X(t) = Ee^{tX} = \int_0^{\infty} e^{tx} \frac{x^{\alpha}}{\beta^{\alpha+1}\Gamma(\alpha+1)} e^{-x/\beta}\, dx$$

$$= \int_0^{\infty} \frac{x^{\alpha} e^{-x(1-\beta t)/\beta}}{\Gamma(\alpha+1)\beta^{\alpha+1}}\, dx = \frac{1}{(1-\beta t)^{\alpha+1}} \int_0^{\infty} \frac{y^{\alpha} e^{-y/\beta}}{\Gamma(\alpha+1)\beta^{\alpha+1}}\, dy$$

$$= \frac{1}{(1-\beta t)^{\alpha+1}}$$

as long as $|t| < 1/\beta$ (outside of this range, the integral may not be defined; e.g., it is divergent when $t = 1/\beta$). Since (see Theorem 5.5.2) the m.g.f. need only exist for all $|t| < T$ for some $T > 0$ in order for us to use it to find moments, we are now able to find

$$E(X) = \psi'_X(0) = -(\alpha+1)(-\beta)(1-\beta t)^{-\alpha-2}\Big|_{t=0} = (\alpha+1)\beta,$$

$$E(X^2) = \psi''_X(0) = (\alpha+1)(\alpha+2)\beta^2(1-\beta t)^{-\alpha-3}\Big|_{t=0} = (\alpha+1)(\alpha+2)\beta^2,$$

$$\mathrm{Var}(X) = E(X^2) - (EX)^2 = (\alpha+1)\beta^2.$$

[*Note:* These agree with moments already found directly from the definition of moments in Theorem 5.2.7.]

If we choose $\alpha = 0$, then X has the exponential distribution with parameter β. Thus, for an **exponential r.v.**, the m.g.f., mean, and variance are

$$\psi_X(t) = \frac{1}{1 - \beta t} \quad \text{for } |t| < 1/\beta, \, E(X) = \beta, \, \text{Var}(X) = \beta^2.$$

(Recall that the mean and variance of the exponential distribution were first found in Theorem 5.2.5 by direct methods.)

If we choose $\alpha = \dfrac{n}{2} - 1$ and $\beta = 2$, then (see Definition 4.2.13) X has the chi-square distribution with n degrees of freedom. Hence, the m.g.f., mean, and variance of a $\chi_n^2(0)$ r.v. are

$$\psi_X(t) = \frac{1}{(1 - 2t)^{n/2}} \quad \text{for } |t| < 1/2, \, E(X) = n, \, \text{Var}(X) = 2n.$$

Example 5.5.5. If X has the **normal distribution** (as in Theorem 5.2.6), then

$$\psi_X(t) = \int_{-\infty}^{\infty} e^{xt} \frac{1}{\sqrt{2\pi}\,\sigma} e^{-(x-\mu)^2/(2\sigma^2)} \, dx$$

$$= \int_{-\infty}^{\infty} \frac{1}{\sqrt{2\pi}\,\sigma} \exp\left\{ -\left(x^2 + \mu^2 - 2x\mu - 2\sigma^2 tx\right) / (2\sigma^2) \right\} dx$$

$$= \int_{-\infty}^{\infty} \frac{1}{\sqrt{2\pi}\,\sigma} \exp\left\{ -\left(x^2 - 2(\mu + \sigma^2 t)x + (\mu + \sigma^2 t)^2\right) / (2\sigma^2) \right\}$$

$$\cdot \exp\left\{ \left((\mu + \sigma^2 t)^2 - \mu^2\right) / (2\sigma^2) \right\} dx$$

$$= e^{(2\mu\sigma^2 t + \sigma^4 t^2)/(2\sigma^2)}$$

$$\cdot \int_{-\infty}^{\infty} \frac{1}{\sqrt{2\pi}\,\sigma} \exp\left\{ -0.5\left(x - (\mu + \sigma^2 t)\right)^2 \Big/ \sigma^2 \right\} dx$$

$$= e^{\mu t + \frac{1}{2}\sigma^2 t^2},$$

and hence (also see Theorem 5.2.6 for these moments)

$$E(X) = \psi_X'(0) = \left(e^{\mu t + 0.5\sigma^2 t^2}(\mu + \sigma^2 t) \right)\Big|_{t=0} = \mu,$$

$$E(X^2) = \psi_X''(0) = \left(e^{\mu t + 0.5\sigma^2 t^2}(\mu + \sigma^2 t)^2 + e^{\mu t + 0.5\sigma^2 t^2}\sigma^2 \right)\Big|_{t=0}$$

$$= \mu^2 + \sigma^2,$$

$$\text{Var}(X) = E(X^2) - (EX)^2 = \sigma^2.$$

Example 5.5.6. A r.v. X is said to have the **Pareto distribution** with parameters α and β if

$$f_X(x) = \begin{cases} \beta \dfrac{\alpha^\beta}{x^{\beta+1}}, & \text{if } x \geq \alpha > 0, \ \beta > 0 \\ 0, & \text{otherwise.} \end{cases}$$

Note that

$$Ee^{tX} = \beta\alpha^\beta \int_\alpha^\infty \frac{e^{tx}}{x^{\beta+1}} \, dx$$

does not exist (since e^{tx} grows faster than $x^{\beta+1}$ at such a rate that $e^{tx}/x^{\beta+1} \to \infty$ as $x \to \infty$). Hence, **the m.g.f. does not always exist** (in particular, does not exist for the Pareto distribution). However, some **moments of X may still exist**. In this case, for $r < \beta$ we have

$$E(X^r) = \int_\alpha^\infty x^r \frac{\beta\alpha^\beta}{x^{\beta+1}} \, dx = \beta\alpha^\beta \int_\alpha^\infty x^{-\beta-1+r} \, dx$$

$$= -\beta\alpha^\beta \frac{x^{-\beta+r}}{\beta-r} \Bigg|_\alpha^\infty = \frac{\beta\alpha^r}{\beta-r}$$

(since the integral converges as long as $r < \beta$). In particular, **the mean and variance exist as long as $\beta > 2$**, in which case

$$E(X) = \frac{\alpha\beta}{\beta-1}, \quad E(X^2) = \frac{\alpha^2\beta}{\beta-2},$$

$$\mathrm{Var}(X) = E(X^2) - (EX)^2 = \frac{\beta\alpha^2}{(\beta-1)^2(\beta-2)}$$

For the same reasons, the integral

$$\int_{-\infty}^\infty \frac{e^{tx}}{\pi(1+x^2)} \, dx$$

does not converge, hence **the m.g.f. of a Cauchy r.v.** (Example 4.6.9) **does not exist**. In this case (recall Example 5.1.5) the moments also do not exist.

Lemma 5.5.7. $\psi_{aX+b}(t) = e^{bt}\psi_X(at)$.

Proof: We have, by definition of the moment-generating function of $aX + b$,

$$\psi_{aX+b}(t) = E(e^{(aX+b)t}) = E(e^{atX}e^{bt}) = e^{bt}E(e^{(at)X})$$

$$= e^{bt}\psi_X(at),$$

which completes the proof. ∎

[*Note:* By Lemma 5.5.7, if we know the moment-generating function of X, then we know the moment-generating function of any linear function of X.]

The notion of the m.g.f. can be extended to several r.v.'s:

Definition 5.5.8. The **joint m.g.f.** of $X_1, \ldots, X_n$ is defined for real numbers $t_1, \ldots, t_n$ by

$$\psi_{X_1, \ldots, X_n}(t_1, \ldots, t_n) = Ee^{t_1 X_1 + \cdots + t_n X_n}.$$

We will simply note informally that as in Theorem 5.6.2, we may obtain expressions like

$$\psi_{X_1, X_2}(t_1, t_2) = \sum_{n_1=0}^{\infty} \sum_{n_2=0}^{\infty} \frac{t_1^{n_1}}{n_1!} \frac{t_2^{n_2}}{n_2!} E(X_1^{n_1} X_2^{n_2}).$$

These can then be used to prove results such as the following:

$$E(X_1) = \frac{\partial}{\partial t_1} \psi_{X_1, X_2}(0,0),$$

$$E(X_1^2) = \frac{\partial^2}{\partial t_1^2} \psi_{X_1, X_2}(0,0),$$

$$E(X_1 X_2) = \frac{\partial^2}{\partial t_1 \, \partial t_2} \psi_{X_1, X_2}(0,0),$$

$$\mathrm{Var}(X_1) = \frac{\partial^2}{\partial t_1^2} \psi_{X_1 - EX_1, X_2 - EX_2}(0,0),$$

$$\mathrm{Cov}(X_1, X_2) = \frac{\partial^2}{\partial t_1 \, \partial t_2} \psi_{X_1 - EX_1, X_2 - EX_2}(0,0).$$

If we have a r.v. X, then its probability distribution is completely specified by its d.f. $F_X(x)$ $(-\infty < x < +\infty)$ and this always exists. Alternatively, its probability distribution is completely specified by $P[X \in S]$ (all $S \subseteq \{x: -\infty < x < +\infty\}$), and this always exists. [In the absolutely continuous and discrete cases, respectively, we may give its density function $f_X(x)$ $(-\infty < x < +\infty)$ and its probability function $p_X(x)$ $(-\infty < x < +\infty)$.] The m.g.f., of course, does not have this property, since it does not always exist. We will now show that $F_X(x)$ $(-\infty < x < +\infty)$ and $P[X \in S]$ $(S \subseteq \{x: -\infty < x < +\infty\})$ share a common property. (The **characteristic function**, to be introduced in Definition 5.5.46 after we complete discussion of the m.g.f., also serves to specify the probability distribution of a r.v.)

Lemma 5.5.9. Both the probability function $P[X \in S]$ for sets S, and the d.f. $F_X(x)$ $(-\infty < x < +\infty)$, can be regarded as expectations.

Proof: Let the **indicator function** of the set S be defined by

$$I_S(x) = \begin{cases} 1, & \text{if } x \in S \\ 0, & \text{if } x \notin S. \end{cases} \tag{5.5.10}$$

Then $P[X \in S] = 1 \cdot P[X \in S] + 0 \cdot P[X \notin S] = E\{I_S(X)\}$, proving our first result.

Secondly, define a function $I_y(x)$ of a real variable x $(-\infty < x < +\infty)$ by

$$I_y(x) = \begin{cases} 1, & \text{if } x \leq y \\ 0, & \text{if } x > y. \end{cases} \tag{5.5.11}$$

Then $F_X(y) = E\{I_y(X)\}$, proving our second result. [Another proof could be given by simply noting that $F_X(y) = P[X \in S]$, itself an expectation, when $S = (-\infty, x)$.] ∎

As we saw in the cases of the Pareto and Cauchy distributions (Example 5.5.6), the moment generating function does not always exist. However, when it does exist it is unique, as stated in the following theorem.

Theorem 5.5.12.   Uniqueness Theorem for m.g.f.'s.

   (i) If two r.v.'s have m.g.f.'s that exist and are equal, then they have the same d.f.

   (ii) If two r.v.'s have the same d.f., then (if it exists) they have the same m.g.f.

[For a proof, see Widder (1961), pp. 460–467.]

So far we have calculated (when they existed) the m.g.f.'s of several given r.v.'s. However, as shown in Problem 5.2H, different distributions may have all their moments the same. Thus, we are led to **the moment problem**, which considers the question:

Suppose a r.v. X has d.f. $F(x)$ and that all moments EX, EX^2, EX^3, $EX^4, \ldots$ (which we called $\mu'_1, \mu'_2, \mu'_3, \mu'_4, \ldots$) exist—when do $\mu'_1, \mu'_2, \mu'_3, \ldots$ uniquely determine $F(x)$? [See Feller (1966) for an extensive treatment.] The following results are available.

Theorem 5.5.13.   Carleman's Theorem*. A d.f. $F(x)$ is uniquely determined by its moments $\mu'_1, \mu'_2, \mu'_3, \ldots$ (which are assumed to exist) iff

$$\sum_{n=1}^{\infty} (M_n)^{-1/n} = \infty,$$

where $M_n = E|X|^n$.

---

*May be omitted if instructor desires.

Theorem 5.5.14. Hausdorff's Theorem*. A sequence of numbers $\mu'_0, \mu'_1, \ldots$ represents the moments of some d.f. $F(x)$ concentrated on $[0,1]$ [i.e., such that $F(1) = 1$ and $F(0) = 0 + P[X = 0]$] iff

$$E\left(X^k (1 - X)^r \right) \geq 0, \qquad \mu'_0 = 1.$$

In such a case the d.f. $F(x)$ is unique, and at each point t where $F(x)$ is a continuous function,

$$F(t) = \lim_{n \to \infty} \sum_{k \leq nt} \binom{n}{k} E\left\{ X^k (1 - X)^{n-k} \right\}.$$

Lemma 5.5.15. The following criterion may be substituted in Carleman's theorem (Theorem 5.5.13):

$$\sum_{n=1}^{\infty} \left(\mu'_{2n} \right)^{-1/2n} = \sum_{n=1}^{\infty} \frac{1}{\left(\mu'_{2n} \right)^{1/2n}} = \infty.$$

Example 5.5.16. From Example 5.5.5, we know that if X is a standard (i.e., mean $\mu = 0$ and variance $\sigma^2 = 1$) normal r.v., then the m.g.f. of X is

$$\psi_X(t) = e^{0.5t^2}.$$

If we use the series expansion for the function e^y, we then find that

$$e^{0.5t^2} = 1 + \left(\frac{t^2}{2} \right) + \frac{1}{2!}\left(\frac{t^2}{2} \right)^2 + \frac{1}{3!}\left(\frac{t^2}{2} \right)^3 + \frac{1}{4!}\left(\frac{t^2}{2} \right)^4 + \cdots$$

$$= 1 + (0)t + (1)\frac{t^2}{2!} + (0)\frac{t^3}{3!} + (3)\frac{t^4}{4!} + (0)\frac{t^5}{5!} + (15)\frac{t^6}{6!} + \cdots.$$

It follows from Theorem 5.5.2 that $E(X) = E(X^3) = E(X^5) = \cdots = 0$ (the odd moments are zero—as we know from the symmetry of the distribution about zero also), while $E(X^2) = 1$, $E(X^4) = 3$, $E(X^6) = 15$, and so on; the general pattern for the even moments can be seen to be such that

$$E(X^k) = \begin{cases} \dfrac{k!}{2^{k/2}(k/2)!}, & \text{if } k = 2, 4, 6, \ldots \\ 0, & \text{if } k = 1, 3, 5, \ldots. \end{cases}$$

To show that the standard normal distribution is the *only* distribution that has these moments, it is (see Lemma 5.5.15) necessary to show that

$$\sum_{n=1}^{\infty} \left(\frac{1}{\mu'_{2n}} \right)^{1/2n} = \infty,$$

*May be omitted if instructor desires.

namely that

$$\sum_{n=1}^{\infty} \left(\frac{2^{2n/2}(2n/2)!}{(2n)!} \right)^{1/2n} = \sqrt{2} \sum_{n=1}^{\infty} \left(\frac{n!}{(2n)!} \right)^{1/2n} = \infty.$$

From the Uniqueness Theorem for m.g.f.'s (Theorem 5.5.12), we know that if two r.v.'s have the same m.g.f., then they have the same d.f. Thus, **when two r.v.'s have the same moments but different d.f.'s**—as in Problem 5.2H—**if follows that** *either* **they have different m.g.f.'s also** (in which case the infinite series given in the proof of Theorem 5.5.2 would *not* give the m.g.f.'s, since then they would be equal since they have the same moments) *or* **they do not exist.** Our next theorem implies the latter is the case—and indeed, it is easy to verify in Problem 5.2H that the m.g.f. does not exist, as the integral diverges.

Theorem 5.5.17. If the m.g.f. $\psi_X(t)$ of the r.v. X exists for $|t| \le T$ (for some $T > 0$), then EX^n exists (for $n = 1, 2, 3, \dots$) and $\psi_X(t)$ can be expanded in a neighborhood of $t = 0$ as follows:

$$\psi_X(t) = 1 + \frac{EX}{1!}t + \frac{EX^2}{2!}t^2 + \cdots + \frac{EX^k}{k!}t^k + o(t^k),$$

where

$$\lim_{t \to 0} \frac{o(t^k)}{t^k} = 0.$$

This seems a natural place to note that such series expansions can be used to derive **approximations to means and variances of functions of a r.v. X.** This is of use in practice since, although the moments of a r.v. X whose d.f. is known are easily expressed (e.g., as an integral involving the p.d.f. in the continuous case—see Theorem 5.1.2), those expressions can be difficult to evaluate in practice. In particular, we will demonstrate the result of the following theorem, and then consider an example before continuing with the development of uses of m.g.f.'s.

Theorem 5.5.18. If X is a r.v. for which the kth moment $\mu_k = E(X - \mu)^k$ exists [where $\mu = E(X)$ and $\sigma^2 = E(X - \mu)^2$], and if $g(\cdot)$ is a k-times differentiable function, then

$$Eg(X) = g(\mu) + g^{(2)}(\mu)\frac{\sigma^2}{2} + g^{(3)}(\mu)\frac{\mu_3}{6} + g^{(4)}(\mu)\frac{\mu_4}{24}$$

$$+ \cdots + g^{(k-1)}(\mu)\frac{\mu_{k-1}}{(k-1)!} + \frac{1}{k!}Eg^{(k)}(\xi)(X - \mu)^k.$$

Proof: Since $g(x)$ is k-times differentiable, by Taylor's Theorem with Remainder we may expand it about μ as

$$g(x) = g(\mu) + \frac{g^{(1)}(\mu)}{1!}(x - \mu) + \frac{g^{(2)}(\mu)}{2!}(x - \mu)^2$$

$$+ \cdots + \frac{g^{(k-1)}(\mu)}{(k-1)!}(x - \mu)^{k-1} + \frac{g^{(k)}(\xi)}{k!}(x - \mu)^k$$

where $0 < \xi < x - \mu$ (or, if $x - \mu < 0$, $x - \mu < \xi < 0$). Evaluating at X and taking the expectation, recalling Definition 5.1.14 [so $E(X - \mu) = 0$, $E(X - \mu)^2 = \sigma^2$, and $E(X - \mu)^i = \mu_i$], we obtain the result claimed. ∎

Corollary 5.5.19. Taking $k = 2$ in Theorem 5.5.18, we have the approximation

$$Eg(X) = g(\mu) + g^{(2)}(\mu)\frac{\sigma^2}{2}.$$

Corollary 5.5.20. The variance may be approximated by

$$\mathrm{Var}\,(g(X)) = \left(g^{(1)}(\mu)\right)^2\sigma^2.$$

Proof of Corollaries 5.5.19 and 5.5.20: Corollary 5.5.19 follows directly on taking $k = 2$ in Theorem 5.5.18 and dropping the remainder term. If we apply Corollary 5.5.19 to the function $g^2(\cdot)$, whose first derivative is $2g(\cdot)g^{(1)}(\cdot)$ and whose second derivative is $2(g(\cdot)g^{(2)}(\cdot) + (g^{(1)}(\cdot))^2)$, we find the approximation

$$Eg^2(X) = g^2(\mu) + \left(\left(g^{(1)}(\mu)\right)^2 + g(\mu)g^{(2)}(\mu)\right)\sigma^2,$$

hence the variance is approximated by

$$\mathrm{Var}\,(g(X)) = Eg^2(X) - (Eg(X))^2$$

$$= g^2(\mu) + \left(\left(g^{(1)}(\mu)\right)^2 + g(\mu)g^{(2)}(\mu)\right)\sigma^2$$

$$- \left(g(\mu) + g^{(2)}(\mu)\frac{\sigma^2}{2}\right)^2$$

$$= \left(g^{(1)}(\mu)\right)^2\sigma^2 - \left(g^{(2)}(\mu)\right)^2\frac{\sigma^4}{4} \approx \left(g^{(1)}(\mu)\right)^2\sigma^2. ∎$$

Example 5.5.21. An electrical circuit has a constant voltage of $e = 120$ volts coming into it, and its resistance R is a normal random variable with mean 12 ohms and standard deviation of 3 ohms. The standard electrical theory states that the amperes in this setting is given by $I = e/R$, and a first "naive" estimate is to approximate $E(I)$ by $e/E(R) = 120/12 = 10$ amperes.

Using Corollary 5.5.19, we estimate the amperes with the function $g(r) = e/r$ as

$$E(e/R) = g(\mu) + g^{(2)}(\mu)\frac{\sigma^2}{2} = \frac{e}{\mu} + \frac{2e}{\mu^3}\frac{(3)^2}{2}$$

$$= \frac{120}{12} + \frac{1080}{(12)^3} = 10 + .625 = 10.63 \text{ amperes.}$$

The variance of the current output (for which we do not have a "naive" estimate) is estimated by Corollary 5.5.20 as

$$\text{Var}(e/R) = \left(g^{(1)}(\mu)\right)^2 \sigma^2 = \left(\frac{-e}{\mu^2}\right)^2 (3)^2 = (1.2)^2(9) = 12.96,$$

so the standard deviation of the current is 3.6 amperes.

Special Note. In Example 5.5.21, it is easy to show that (as in Example 5.1.5) $E(X)$ does not exist [so, $\text{Var}(X)$ does not exist]. So, **have we just estimated items that do not exist?** The answer to this question in terms of the formal problem statement is, *yes*, and a mathematician would stop here. However, a statistician must go further and delve into the realities behind the problem statement. Now, in fact, engineers would often give the problem statement of Example 5.5.21 when they actually mean to state that R has a distribution that is like the normal $N(12, 3^2)$, *but* that it takes on values only between $12 - 9$ and $12 + 9$ (these are the mean of 12, plus and minus 3 standard deviations; in later chapters we will see why this is a reasonable specification). However, for this new density, which is

$$f_{R*}(r) = \begin{cases} \dfrac{f_R(r)}{\displaystyle\int_{12-9}^{12+9} f_R(r)\, dr}, & \text{if } 12 - 9 \leq r \leq 12 + 9 \\[12pt] 0, & \text{otherwise,} \end{cases} \qquad (5.5.22)$$

it is easy to show that all moments exist, and that the estimates already given are the correct ones [there is a change since the correct density $f_{R*}(r)$ differs from $f_R(r)$, but the change is negligible since the denominator in equation (5.5.22) is $1 - (2)(.0013) = .9974$]. Thus, the answer for the problem the engineer should have asked us (and, that is the one we should find and provide the answer to) is, *no*: **We have not estimated items that do not exist, but rather have estimated the items of real interest in the problem.**

When they exist, **m.g.f.'s play a fundamental role in the study of distributions** (called **distribution theory**). Recall that two r.v.'s are said to be independent (see Lemma 3.4.9) iff their joint distribution function can be written as the product of their marginal d.f.'s. A similar characterization of independence of two r.v.'s can also be given in terms of the joint (Definition 5.5.8) and marginal m.g.f.'s:

Theorem 5.5.23. Suppose the joint m.g.f. of (X_1, X_2) exists. Then X_1 and X_2 are independent r.v.'s iff $\psi_{X_1, X_2}(t_1, t_2) = \psi_{X_1}(t_1)\psi_{X_2}(t_2)$.

Proof: If X_1 and X_2 are independent r.v.'s, then

$$\psi_{X_1, X_2}(t_1, t_2) = E(e^{t_1 X_1 + t_2 X_2}) = E(e^{t_1 X_1} e^{t_2 X_2})$$

$$= E(e^{t_1 X_1})E(e^{t_2 X_2}) = \psi_{X_1}(t_1)\psi_{X_2}(t_2)$$

(where we used Theorem 5.3.16 to show the expected value of the product is the product of the expected values), as was to be shown.

Conversely,

$$\psi_{X_1, X_2}(t_1, t_2) = E(e^{t_1 X_1 + t_2 X_2}) \tag{5.5.24}$$

is the joint m.g.f. of (X_1, X_2). Let Y_1 and Y_2 be independent r.v.'s, where the marginal d.f. of Y_1 is the same as the marginal d.f. of X_1, and the marginal d.f. of Y_2 is the same as the marginal d.f. of X_2. Then the joint m.g.f. of (Y_1, Y_2) is

$$\psi_{Y_1, Y_2}(t_1, t_2) = E(e^{t_1 Y_1 + t_2 Y_2}) = E(e^{t_1 Y_1} e^{t_2 Y_2})$$

$$= E(e^{t_1 Y_1})E(e^{t_2 Y_2}) = E(e^{t_1 X_1})E(e^{t_2 X_2}) \tag{5.5.25}$$

$$= \psi_{X_1}(t_1)\psi_{X_2}(t_1)$$

where we used Theorem 5.3.16 to show the factorization of the joint m.g.f. of (Y_1, Y_2), and the fact that each of X_1, X_2 has the same marginal d.f. as each of Y_1, Y_2 (respectively). Now by hypothesis, equations (5.5.24) and (5.5.25) are equal. By uniqueness of the m.g.f. (Theorem 5.5.12's extension to joint m.g.f.'s), it follows that (X_1, X_2) and (Y_1, Y_2) have the same distribution, hence X_1 and X_2 are independent r.v.'s when their joint m.g.f. factors into the product of their individual m.g.f.'s.   ∎

We will now use Theorem 5.5.23 to obtain a simple technique for finding the distribution of a sum of independent and identically distributed r.v.'s, then giving some examples of the technique.

Theorem 5.5.26. Let $X_1, \ldots, X_n$ be independent and identically distributed r.v.'s and let $Y = a_1 X_1 + \cdots + a_n X_n$. Then the m.g.f. of Y is

$$\psi_Y(t) = E(e^{tY}) = E(e^{t(a_1 X_1 + \cdots + a_n X_n)}) = E(e^{a_1 X_1 t + \cdots + a_n X_n t})$$

$$= E(e^{a_1 X_1 t} \ldots e^{a_n X_n t}) = E(e^{a_1 X_1 t}) \ldots E(e^{a_n X_n t})$$

$$= \psi_{X_1}(a_1 t) \ldots \psi_{X_n}(a_n t) = \prod_{i=1}^{n} \psi_{X_1}(a_i t).$$

If also $a_1 = \cdots = a_n$, then

$$\psi_Y(t) = \left(\psi_{X_1}(a_1 t)\right)^n.$$

Example 5.5.27. Let $X_1, \ldots, X_n$ be independent Poisson r.v.'s with parameter λ. Find the distribution of $Y = X_1 + \cdots + X_n$. Here, we know the m.g.f. of each of the X_i's (from Example 5.5.3), hence by Theorem 5.5.26 we have the m.g.f. of Y as

$$\psi_Y(t) = \left(e^{\lambda(e^t - 1)} \right)^n = e^{n\lambda(e^t - 1)}.$$

As we now recognize this as the m.g.f. of a Poisson r.v. with parameter $n\lambda$, it follows that Y is Poisson with parameter (mean) $n\lambda$.

Example 5.5.28. Let $X_1, \ldots, X_n$ be independent r.v.'s with the gamma distribution $G(x | \alpha_i, \beta, A = 0)$, and let $Y = X_1 + \cdots + X_n$. Then (using the m.g.f. of X_i from Example 5.5.4) the m.g.f. of Y is, by Theorem 5.5.26,

$$\psi_Y(t) = \prod_{i=1}^n \psi_{X_i}(t) = \prod_{i=1}^n \frac{1}{(1 - \beta t)^{\alpha_i + 1}} = \frac{1}{(1 - \beta t)^{\Sigma \alpha_i + n}},$$

hence Y has the gamma distribution $G\left(x \,\middle|\, \sum_{i=1}^n \alpha_i + n - 1, \beta, A = 0 \right)$: A sum of independent gamma r.v.'s with the same β-parameter is again a gamma r.v.

As a special case, if $\alpha_i = n_i/2 - 1$ so that X_i is $\chi^2_{n_i}(0)$, then

$$\psi_Y(t) = \frac{1}{(1 - 2t)^{\Sigma n_i/2}},$$

so that Y is $\chi^2_{\Sigma n_i}(0)$: A sum of independent chi-square r.v.'s is chi-square with degrees of freedom the sum of the respective degrees of freedom. This result is very useful in applications.

Example 5.5.29. Let $X_1, \ldots, X_n$ be independent and X_i a $N(\mu_i, \sigma_i^2)$ r.v. Then

$$Y = \sum_{i=1}^n a_i X_i \sim N\left(\sum_{i=1}^n a_i \mu_i, \sum_{i=1}^n a_i^2 \sigma_i^2 \right),$$

since the m.g.f. of Y is (see Example 5.5.5 for the normal m.g.f.)

$$\psi_Y(t) = \prod_{i=1}^n \psi_{X_i}(a_i t) = \prod_{i=1}^n e^{\mu_i a_i t + \frac{1}{2}\sigma_i^2 a_i^2 t^2}$$

$$= e^{(\Sigma a_i \mu_i)t + \frac{1}{2}(\Sigma a_i^2 \sigma_i^2)t^2},$$

which we recognize as the m.g.f. of a normal r.v. with mean $\Sigma a_i \mu_i$ and variance $\Sigma a_i^2 \sigma_i^2$.

Example 5.5.30. If X_1 and X_2 are independent normal random variables, then their joint m.g.f. is (by Theorem 5.5.23)

$$\psi_{X_1, X_2}(t_1, t_2) = \psi_{X_1}(t_1)\psi_{X_2}(t_2) = e^{t_1 \mu_1 + t_2 \mu_2 + \frac{1}{2}(t_1^2 \sigma_1^2 + t_2^2 \sigma_2^2)}.$$

It is easy to see (from Definition 4.5.4 and Theorem 5.3.25) that (X_1, X_2) is then bivariate normal with $\rho = 0$. If (X_1, X_2) is bivariate normal with $\rho \neq 0$, we leave it as an exercise to show that

$$\psi_{X_1, X_2}(t_1, t_2) = e^{t_1\mu_1 + t_2\mu_2 + \frac{1}{2}(t_1^2\sigma_1^2 + 2\rho\sigma_1\sigma_2 t_1 t_2 + t_2^2\sigma_2^2)}. \tag{5.5.31}$$

Note that since

$$\psi_{X_1}(t_1) = \psi_{X_1, X_2}(t_1, 0) = e^{t_1\mu_1 + \frac{1}{2}t_1^2\sigma_1^2},$$

it follows that X_1 is still $N(\mu_1, \sigma_1^2)$ in this case [and similarly, X_2 is still $N(\mu_2, \sigma_2^2)$]. We know (by a slight extension of Example 4.6.17) that $Y = a_1 X_1 + a_2 X_2$ is $N(a_1\mu_1 + a_2\mu_2, a_1^2\sigma_1^2 + a_2^2\sigma_2^2)$ when X_1 and X_2 are independent normal variables; now, in the general bivariate normal case with $\rho \neq 0$, it follows from the definition of the joint m.g.f. and equation (5.5.31) that

$$\psi_Y(t) = E(e^{a_1 X_1 t_1 + a_2 X_2 t_2}) = e^{(a_1\mu_1 + a_2\mu_2)t + \frac{t^2}{2}(a_1^2\sigma_1^2 + 2\rho a_1 a_2 \sigma_1 \sigma_2 + a_2^2\sigma_2^2)},$$

so that Y is $N(a_1\mu_1 + a_2\mu_2, a_1^2\sigma_1^2 + 2\rho a_1 a_2 \sigma_1 \sigma_2 + a_2^2\sigma_2^2)$; thus, **every linear combination of a general bivariate normal r.v. has a univariate normal distribution.**

Conversely, suppose that (X_1, X_2) is a bivariate r.v. with $E(X_i) = \mu_i$, $\mathrm{Var}(X_i) = \sigma_i^2$, $\mathrm{Cov}(X_1, X_2) = \rho\sigma_1\sigma_2$, and that every linear combination of (X_1, X_2) is normally distributed. For a general linear combination $Y = a_1 X_1 + a_2 X_2$,

$$E(Y) = a_1\mu_1 + a_2\mu_2$$

$$\mathrm{Var}(Y) = a_1^2\sigma_1^2 + a_2^2\sigma_2^2 + 2a_1 a_2 \rho\sigma_1\sigma_2$$

and (since Y is a normal r.v. by assumption)

$$\psi_Y(t) = e^{(a_1\mu_1 + a_2\mu_2)t + \frac{t^2}{2}(a_1^2\sigma_1^2 + a_2^2\sigma_2^2 + 2a_1 a_2 \rho\sigma_1\sigma_2)}$$

for every t. Now

$$\psi_{X_1, X_2}(a_1, a_2) = E(e^{a_1 X_1 + a_2 X_2})$$

$$= \psi_Y(1) = e^{a_1\mu_1 + a_2\mu_2 + \frac{1}{2}(a_1^2\sigma_1^2 + 2\rho\sigma_1\sigma_2 a_1 a_2 + a_2^2\sigma_2^2)},$$

so by equation (5.5.31) and m.g.f. uniqueness (X_1, X_2) has a bivariate normal distribution, and we have proved the following theorem characterizing bivariate normal r.v.'s.

Theorem 5.5.32. A bivariate r.v. (X_1, X_2) is jointly normally distributed if and only if every linear combination of X_1 and X_2 is normally distributed.

A natural extension of Theorem 5.5.32 is to the p-variate case (recall the p-variate normal distribution was given in Definition 4.5.4), which we state without proof.

Theorem 5.5.33. Let $(X_1, X_2, \ldots, X_p)$ be a p-variate random variable. $(X_1, \ldots, X_p)$ is p-variate normal iff every linear combination of the X_i's is normally distributed. Thus,

(i) If $(X_1, \ldots, X_p)$ is p-variate normal with means μ_i, variances σ_i^2, and covariances σ_{ij} $(i \neq j)$, then $Y = \sum\limits_{i=1}^{p} a_i X_i$ has a univariate normal distribution with

$$E(Y) = \sum_{i=1}^{p} a_i \mu_i,$$

$$\mathrm{Var}\,(Y) = \sum_{i=1}^{p} a_i^2 \sigma_i^2 + 2 \sum_{j=2}^{p} \sum_{i=1}^{j-1} a_i a_j \sigma_{ij},$$

and,

(ii) If $X_1, X_2, \ldots, X_p$ are independent and each normal $N(\mu, \sigma^2)$ (hence p-variate normal with $\mathrm{Cov}\,(X_i, X_j) = 0$, $i \neq j$), the random variable

$$\overline{X}_p = \frac{X_1 + X_2 + \cdots + X_p}{p}$$

has a univariate normal distribution with mean μ and variance σ^2/p.

As an application and extension of some of the results in Theorems 5.5.32 and 5.5.33, we now show that, if $X_1, \ldots, X_n$ are independent $N(\mu, \sigma^2)$ r.v.'s, then the variables

$$\overline{X}_n = \sum_{i=1}^{n} \frac{X_i}{n} \quad \text{and} \quad s_n^2 = \sum_{i=1}^{n} \frac{\left(X_i - \overline{X}_n\right)^2}{n-1}$$

are independent, and $(n-1)s_n^2/\sigma^2$ is $\chi_{n-1}^2(0)$. [We already know from Example 4.2.22 and Example 5.5.28 that if $U_1, \ldots, U_k$ are independent $N(0, 1)$ r.v.'s, then U_i^2 is $\chi_1^2(0)$ for $i = 1, \ldots, k$ and $U_1^2 + \cdots + U_k^2$ is $\chi_k^2(0)$.] The proof given is an improved version [due to Stigler (1984)] of Kruskal's proof.

Theorem 5.5.34. If $X_1, \ldots, X_n$ are independent $N(\mu, \sigma^2)$ r.v.'s, then

(i) $\overline{X}_n$ is $N(\mu, \sigma^2/n)$.
(ii) $(n-1)s_n^2/\sigma^2$ is $\chi_{n-1}^2(0)$.
(iii) $\overline{X}_n$ and s_n^2 are independent r.v.'s.

Proof: (i) was proved in Theorem 5.5.33. We now prove (ii) and (iii) by induction. First, consider the case $n = 2$ where

$$\overline{X}_2 = \frac{X_1 + X_2}{2},$$

$$s_2^2 = \sum_{i=1}^{2} \frac{\left(X_i - \overline{X}_2\right)^2}{2-1} = \frac{\left(X_1 - X_2\right)^2}{2}.$$

Now $X_1 + X_2$ and $X_1 - X_2$ are independent r.v.'s (to see this directly, find the joint m.g.f. of $X_1 + X_2$ and $X_1 - X_2$, and note it equals the product of their individual normal m.g.f.'s), thus $\overline{X}_2$ and s_2^2 are independent. Also,

$$(n-1)\frac{s_n^2}{\sigma^2} = \frac{(X_1 - X_2)^2}{2\sigma^2} \sim \chi_1^2(0) \qquad \text{since} \quad \frac{X_1 - X_2}{\sqrt{2}\,\sigma} \sim N(0,1).$$

Thus results (ii) and (iii) are true for $n = 2$. We now suppose (ii) and (iii) hold for any specific n, and show it follows they also hold for $n + 1$ (hence by mathematical induction they hold for all n). First,

$$\overline{X}_{n+1} = \left(n\overline{X}_n + X_{n+1}\right)/(n + 1)$$

and

$$ns_{n+1}^2 = \sum_{i=1}^{n+1} \left(X_i - \overline{X}_{n+1}\right)^2 = \sum_{i=1}^{n+1} \left(X_i - \overline{X}_n + \overline{X}_n - \overline{X}_{n+1}\right)^2$$

$$= \sum_{i=1}^{n+1} \left(X_i - \overline{X}_n\right)^2 + 2\left(\overline{X}_n - \overline{X}_{n+1}\right)\sum_{i=1}^{n+1}\left(X_i - \overline{X}_n\right) + (n+1)\left(\overline{X}_n - \overline{X}_{n+1}\right)^2$$

$$= \sum_{i=1}^{n} \left(X_i - \overline{X}_n\right)^2 + \Big[\left(X_{n+1} - \overline{X}_n\right)^2 + 2\left(\overline{X}_n - \overline{X}_{n+1}\right)\left(X_{n+1} - \overline{X}_n\right)$$

$$+ (n+1)\left(\overline{X}_n - \overline{X}_{n+1}\right)^2\Big]$$

$$= (n-1)s_n^2 + \frac{n}{n+1}\left(X_{n+1} - \overline{X}_n\right)^2$$

(where we replaced $\overline{X}_{n+1}$ by $\left(n\overline{X}_n + X_{n+1}\right)/(n+1)$ in $[\ldots]$ and simplified algebraically). Since $\sqrt{n/(n+1)}\,\left(X_{n+1} - \overline{X}_n\right) \sim N(0, \sigma^2)$, it follows that

$$\frac{n}{n+1}\,\frac{\left(X_{n+1} - \overline{X}_n\right)^2}{\sigma^2} \sim \chi_1^2(0).$$

Also, by the induction hypothesis $(n-1)s_n^2/\sigma^2 \sim \chi_{n-1}^2(0)$ and $\overline{X}_n$ is independent of s_n^2. Since X_{n+1} is independent of $\overline{X}_n$ and s_n^2, (ii) follows:

$$n\frac{s_{n+1}^2}{\sigma^2} \sim \chi_n^2(0).$$

It remains to show that $\overline{X}_{n+1}$ and s_{n+1}^2 are independent r.v.'s. Now $\overline{X}_{n+1} = (n\overline{X}_n + X_{n+1})/(n + 1)$ is independent of both s_n^2 and $X_{n+1} - \overline{X}_n$, hence $\overline{X}_{n+1}$ is independent of s_{n+1}^2 as it is a function of s_n^2 and $X_{n+1} - \overline{X}_n$. ∎

For another method of proof (via Helmert's transformation), see Lemma 9.5.15. The converse of part (iii) of Theorem 5.5.34 is also true [for a proof see

Laha and Lukacs (1964), pp. 79–81], hence we have

Theorem 5.5.35. $X_1, X_2, \ldots, X_n$ are independent $N(\mu, \sigma^2)$ r.v.'s iff $\overline{X}_n$ and s_n^2 are independent.

Before leaving m.g.f.'s, we note that **sometimes variants of the m.g.f. (i.e., other generating functions) are used to compute moments.** These include the **probability generating function** or **factorial moment generating function** and the **cumulant** [the last is not discussed here; see Kendall and Stuart (1969), p. 67].

Definition 5.5.36. The **factorial moment-generating function (f.m.g.f.)** of a random variable X is defined (if it exists) as

$$\eta_X(t) = E(t^X), \qquad -\infty < t < \infty.$$

Note that

$$\psi_X(\ln(t)) = E(e^{X \ln(t)}) = E\left(e^{\ln(t^X)}\right) = E(t^X) = \eta_X(t),$$

hence factorial moment-generating functions and m.g.f.'s have a simple relationship. In many discrete cases when X takes on only nonnegative integer values, it is easier to use the f.m.g.f. For example, we will use it in the case of the Poisson and binomial r.v.'s as illustrations; first, note the formulas:

$$\frac{d}{dt}\eta_X(t)\bigg|_{t=1} = E\left(\frac{\partial}{\partial t}t^X\right)\bigg|_{t=1} = E(Xt^{X-1})\big|_{t=1} = E(X), \quad (5.5.37)$$

$$\frac{d^2}{dt^2}\eta_X(t)\bigg|_{t=1} = E(X(X-1)), \qquad (5.5.38)$$

$$\vdots$$

$$\frac{d^k}{dt^k}\eta_X(t)\bigg|_{t=1} = E(X(X-1)(X-2)\ldots(X-k+1)), \qquad (5.5.39)$$

which we now use in the Poisson and binomial cases as promised.

Example 5.5.40. If X is a Poisson r.v. with parameter λ, we can use the f.m.g.f. to find its mean and variance as follows.

$$\eta_X(t) = E(t^X) = \sum_{x=0}^{\infty} t^x \frac{e^{-\lambda}\lambda^x}{x!} = \sum_{x=0}^{\infty} \frac{(t\lambda)^x e^{-\lambda}}{x!} = e^{-\lambda}e^{t\lambda} = e^{\lambda(t-1)},$$

hence

$$\eta_X'(1) = e^{\lambda(t-1)}\lambda\big|_{t=1} = \lambda = E(X),$$

$$\eta_X''(1) = e^{\lambda(t-1)}\lambda^2\big|_{t=1} = \lambda^2 = E(X(X-1)),$$

$$\mathrm{Var}(X) = E(X^2) - (EX)^2 = E(X(X-1)) + E(X) - (EX)^2$$

$$= \lambda^2 + \lambda - \lambda^2 = \lambda.$$

(Compare with Example 5.5.3, where the m.g.f. was used to find the same moments.)

Example 5.5.41. If X is binomial with n trials and probability of success p, then

$$\eta_X(t) = \sum_{x=0}^{n} t^x p^x \binom{n}{x} q^{n-x} = \sum_{x=0}^{n} \binom{n}{x}(tp)^x q^{n-x} = (tp+q)^n,$$

hence

$$\eta_x'(1) = n(q+tp)^{n-1}p\big|_{t=1} = np = E(X),$$

$$\eta_X''(1) = n(n-1)(q+tp)^{n-2}p^2\big|_{t=1} = n(n-1)p^2 = E(X(X-1)),$$

$$\mathrm{Var}(X) = E(X^2) - (EX)^2 = E(X(X-1)) + E(X) - (EX)^2$$

$$= n(n-1)p^2 + np - n^2p^2 = np(1-p) = npq.$$

As a final note on the binomial, the m.g.f. can easily be found as

$$\psi_X(t) = E(e^{tX}) = E\big((e^t)^X\big) = \eta_X(e^t)$$

$$= (e^t p + q)^n. \qquad (5.5.42)$$

In the remainder of this section **we introduce and study the characteristic function**, which we introduce as an answer to a question. (Although the m.g.f. does not always exist, the characteristic function does, and this is its chief advantage. Its disadvantage is that its proper use requires some complex variable knowledge, which is also summarized in what follows. Because of this complexity, *this material is not used extensively in later chapters, and at your instructor's discretion, may be skipped over at this point.*)

Question: Do other families of functions on the real line, besides those of form (5.5.10) and (5.5.11), exist such that (when evaluated at X) knowledge of their expectations is sufficient to determine the probability distribution of X?
Answer: Yes, the **complex exponential functions.**

Definition 5.5.43. For a function $g(x)$ that (for $-\infty < x < +\infty$) takes values from among the complex numbers, we define

$$Eg(X) = E\{\text{Re } g(X)\} + iE\{\text{Im } g(X)\},$$

where "Re z" means "real part of z" and "Im z" means "imaginary part of z." [Any complex number z may be written as $z = x + iy$, where x and y are real numbers. Then Re $z = x$, Im $z = y$, $|z| = \sqrt{x^2 + y^2}$, and $\bar{z} = x - iy$ (called the **complex conjugate** of z).] We say $Eg(X)$ exists if $E|g(X)| < \infty$. [Of course, $i = \sqrt{-1}$ and $i^2 = -1$.]

Corollary 5.5.44. All the usual properties of expectation hold for complex-valued functions whose expectations exist (under Definition 5.5.43).

Theorem 5.5.45. $|Eg(X)| \le E|g(X)|$; that is,

$$\sqrt{(E \text{ Re } g(X))^2 + (E \text{ Im } g(X))^2} \le E\sqrt{(\text{Re } g(X))^2 + (\text{Im } g(X))^2}.$$

Definition 5.5.46. The **characteristic function (ch.f.)** of a r.v. X is given by (for all real numbers t)

$$\phi_X(t) = Ee^{itX} = E\{\cos(tX) + i\sin(tX)\} = E\cos(tX) + iE\sin(tX).$$

Theorem 5.5.47.

(i) The ch.f. of a r.v. X always exists.

(ii) $|\phi_X(t)| \le 1$ for all real numbers t.

(iii) $\phi_X(0) = 1$ and $\phi_X(t) = \overline{\phi_X(-t)}$.

(iv) $\phi_X(t)$ is continuous (in fact uniformly continuous) as a function of $t(-\infty < t < +\infty)$.

Proof:

(i) $E|e^{itX}| = E(1) = 1 < \infty$ since $|e^{itx}|^2 = [\cos(tx)]^2 + [\sin(tx)]^2 = 1$.

(ii) $|Ee^{itX}| \le E|e^{itX}| = 1$.

(iii) $\phi_X(0) = Ee^0 = 1$; $Ee^{itX} = \overline{(Ee^{-itX})}$.

(iv) This is beyond the scope of this book; see, for example, Lukacs (1960). ∎

Theorem 5.5.48. $\phi_{aX+b}(t) = e^{ibt}\phi_X(at)$.

Proof:

$$\phi_{aX+b}(t) = Ee^{it(aX+b)} = e^{itb}Ee^{i(at)X}. \qquad ∎$$

Theorem 5.5.49. If EX^k exists, then $\phi_X(t)$ can be expanded in a neighborhood of $t = 0$ as follows:

$$\phi_X(t) = 1 + \frac{iEX}{1!}t + \frac{i^2EX^2}{2!}t^2 + \cdots + \frac{i^kEX^k}{k!}t^k + o(t^k),$$

where $\lim_{t \to 0} \dfrac{o(t^k)}{t^k} = 0.$

Proof: If $h(x)$ is k-times differentiable, then by Taylor's Theorem with Remainder,

$$h(x) = h(0) + \frac{h^{(1)}(0)}{1!}x + \frac{h^{(2)}(0)}{2!}x^2 + \cdots + \frac{h^{(k-1)}(0)}{(k-1)!}x^{k-1} + \frac{h^{(k)}(\xi)}{k!}x^k,$$

with $0 < \xi < x$ (or, if $x < 0$, $x < \xi < 0$). In our case, since EX^k exists, the differentiations may be taken under the integral sign (yielding our coefficients). The error term follows by continuity of $\phi_X^{(k)}(t)$ for all real t (which we will not prove). ■

Theorem 5.5.50. Uniqueness Theorem

(i) Two ch.f.'s that are equal at all (except a countable number of) points are the ch.f.'s of the same d.f.

(ii) Two d.f.'s that are equal at all (except a countable number of) points give rise to the same ch.f.

Corollary 5.5.51. If EX^k exists, then $EX^k = \phi_X^{(k)}(0)/i^k$.

Proof: Use Theorem 5.5.49. ■

Example 5.5.52. If X has the binomial distribution (see Definition 3.2.3)

$$p_X(x) = \begin{cases} \binom{n}{x}p^x(1-p)^{n-x}, & x = 0,1,\ldots,n \\ 0, & \text{otherwise,} \end{cases}$$

then

$$\phi_X(t) = Ee^{itX} = \sum_{k=0}^{n}\binom{n}{k}p^k q^{n-k}e^{itk}$$

$$= \sum_{k=0}^{n}\binom{n}{k}(pe^{it})^k q^{n-k}$$

$$= (pe^{it} + q)^n.$$

Example 5.5.53. If X has the Poisson distribution (see Definition 3.2.11)

$$p_X(x) = \begin{cases} \dfrac{e^{-\mu}\mu^x}{x!}, & x = 0,1,2,\ldots \\ 0, & \text{otherwise,} \end{cases}$$

then

$$\phi_X(t) = Ee^{itX} = \sum_{k=0}^{\infty} e^{-\mu} \frac{\mu^k}{k!} e^{itk}$$

$$= e^{-\mu} \sum_{k=0}^{\infty} \frac{(\mu e^{it})^k}{k!} = e^{-\mu} e^{\mu e^{it}}$$

$$= e^{\mu(e^{it}-1)}.$$

Example 5.5.54. If $P[X = c] = 1$ for some constant c, then

$$\phi_X(t) = Ee^{itX} = e^{itc}.$$

We will now state, without proof, several more ch.f's of important distributions of r.v.'s.

Example 5.5.55. If X has the normal distribution (see Definition 4.2.18)

$$f_X(x) = \frac{1}{\sqrt{2\pi}\,\sigma} e^{-\frac{1}{2}\left(\frac{x-\mu}{\sigma}\right)^2}, \quad -\infty < x < +\infty,$$

then

$$\phi_X(t) = e^{\mu it - \frac{1}{2}\sigma^2 t^2}.$$

[So, if X is standard normal with $\mu = 0$ and $\sigma^2 = 1$, then $\phi_X(t) = e^{-\frac{1}{2}t^2}$. Letting $Y = aX + b$ and using Theorem 5.5.48, the general result follows from this special one.]

Example 5.5.56. If X has the uniform distribution (see Definition 4.2.6)

$$f_X(x) = \begin{cases} \dfrac{1}{b-a}, & a \le x \le b \\ 0, & \text{otherwise,} \end{cases}$$

then

$$\phi_X(t) = \frac{e^{itb} - e^{ita}}{it(b-a)}.$$

Example 5.5.57. If X has the exponential distribution (see Definition 4.2.10)

$$f_X(x) = \begin{cases} \lambda e^{-\lambda x}, & 0 \le x < \infty \\ 0, & \text{otherwise,} \end{cases}$$

then

$$\phi_X(t) = \left(1 - \frac{it}{\lambda}\right)^{-1}.$$

Example 5.5.58. If X has the gamma distribution (see Definition 4.2.7) $G(x|\alpha = r - 1, \beta = 1/\lambda, A = 0)$, that is

$$f_X(x) = \begin{cases} \dfrac{\lambda}{\Gamma(r)}(\lambda x)^{r-1}e^{-\lambda x}, & x \geq 0 \\ 0, & \text{otherwise,} \end{cases}$$

then

$$\phi_X(t) = \left(1 - \frac{it}{\lambda}\right)^{-r}.$$

Example 5.5.59. Generating Moments. Suppose X has the binomial distribution of Example 5.5.50. Then, by Corollary 5.5.51,

$$EX = \frac{\phi_X^{(1)}(0)}{i^1} = \frac{1}{i}\frac{d}{dt}\{(pe^{it} + q)^n\}\Big|_{t=0}$$

$$= \frac{1}{i}n(pe^{it} + q)^{n-1}ipe^{it}\Big|_{t=0}$$

$$= \frac{1}{i}n(p + q)^{n-1}ip1 = np.$$

Example 5.5.60. Determining Distributions. Suppose that $X_1, \ldots, X_n$ are independent r.v.'s, each with the exponential distribution of Example 5.5.57. What is the distribution of $Y = X_1 + \cdots + X_n$?

To find the distribution of Y, we could use the methods of Chapter 4. However, this can also be found as follows. The characteristic function of Y is

$$\phi_Y(t) = Ee^{itY} = Ee^{it(X_1 + \cdots + X_n)}$$

$$= E(e^{itX_1}\cdots e^{itX_n}), \quad \text{and by Theorem 5.3.16}$$

$$= (Ee^{itX_1})\ldots(Ee^{itX_n})$$

$$= \phi_{X_1}(t)\ldots\phi_{X_n}(t), \quad \text{and by Example 5.5.57}$$

$$= \left(1 - \frac{it}{\lambda}\right)^{-1}\ldots\left(1 - \frac{it}{\lambda}\right)^{-1}$$

$$= \left(1 - \frac{it}{\lambda}\right)^{-n},$$

and by Theorem 5.5.50 and Example 5.5.58 we know Y has the gamma distribution $G(x|\alpha = n - 1, \beta = 1/\lambda, A = 0)$. (Note that Theorem 5.3.16's use needed the independence of $X_1, \ldots, X_n$.) Thus, use of characteristic functions can yield simple determinations of the distributions of functions of r.v.'s (*if* we can recognize the relevant characteristic functions). This is studied in more detail below.

Example 5.5.61. Suppose that X is a discrete r.v. with distribution given by $P[X = -1] = P[X = +1] = \frac{1}{3}$, $P[X = 0] = P[X = 6] = \frac{1}{6}$. Find $E(X)$, $E(X^2)$, $\text{Var}(X)$, $E(e^{itX})$.

$$E(X) = (-1) \cdot \tfrac{1}{3} + (1) \cdot \tfrac{1}{3} + (0) \cdot \tfrac{1}{6} + (6) \cdot \tfrac{1}{6} = 1.$$

$$E(X^2) = (-1)^2 \cdot \tfrac{1}{3} + (1)^2 \cdot \tfrac{1}{3} + (0)^2 \cdot \tfrac{1}{6} + (6)^2 \cdot \tfrac{1}{6} = 6\tfrac{2}{3}.$$

$$\text{Var}(X) = E(X^2) - (EX)^2 = 6\tfrac{2}{3} - 1 = 5\tfrac{2}{3}.$$

$$E(e^{itX}) = \tfrac{1}{6}\{2e^{-it} + 2e^{it} + e^{6it} + 1\}.$$

In the Uniqueness Theorem (Theorem 5.5.50) we saw that if we could identify the ch.f. of a r.v. Y, we would know its d.f. We show below how this may be done in some special cases, and we then give some examples.

Note that if X_1 and X_2 are independent r.v.'s, then the d.f. of $Z = X_1 + X_2$ is called the **convolution** of the d.f.'s $F_{X_1}(x)$ and $F_{X_2}(x)$:

$$F_{X_1 + X_2}(z) = \int_{-\infty}^{\infty} F_{X_1}(z - x) f_{X_2}(x)\, dx$$

[if $F_{X_2}(x)$ has a density]. We then write $F_{X_1 + X_2} = F_{X_1} * F_{X_2}$, $F^{2*} = F * F$, and F convoluted with itself $n - 1$ times is called F^{n*}.

Theorem 5.5.62. Let $X_1, \ldots, X_n$ be r.v.'s that are independent. Then

$$\phi_{X_1 + \cdots + X_n}(t) = \phi_{X_1}(t) \ldots \phi_{X_n}(t).$$

Proof:

$$\phi_{X_1 + \cdots + X_n}(t) = Ee^{it(X_1 + \cdots + X_n)}$$

$$= E(e^{itX_1} \cdots e^{iX_n}), \text{ and by independence}[6]$$

$$= Ee^{itX_1} \cdots Ee^{itX_n} = \phi_{X_1}(t) \ldots \phi_{X_n}(t). \quad \blacksquare$$

[6] A slight strengthening of Theorem 5.3.16 is needed here, since we are using complex-valued functions.

Theorem 5.5.63. Let $X_1, \ldots, X_n$ be r.v.'s that are independent and identically distributed. Then

$$\phi_{X_1 + \cdots + X_n}(t) = \left[\phi_{X_1}(t) \right]^n.$$

Proof: By Theorem 5.5.62,

$$\phi_{X_1 + \cdots + X_n}(t) = \phi_{X_1}(t) \ldots \phi_{X_n}(t),$$

and by identical distribution

$$= \phi_{X_1}(t) \ldots \phi_{X_1}(t)$$

$$= \left[\phi_{X_1}(t) \right]^n. \qquad \blacksquare$$

Theorem 5.5.64. Let $X_1, \ldots, X_n$ be independent r.v.'s. Let $S_n = X_1 + \cdots + X_n$.

(i) If X_k is $N(\mu_k, \sigma_k^2)$ [Definition 4.2.18 and Example 5.5.55] (for $k = 1, \ldots, n$), then S_n is $N(\mu_1 + \cdots + \mu_n, \sigma_1^2 + \cdots + \sigma_n^2)$.

(ii) If X_k is binomial [Definition 3.2.3 and Example 5.5.52] with n_k, p (for $k = 1, \ldots, n$), then S_n is binomial with $n_1 + \cdots + n_n, p$.

(iii) If X_k is Poisson [Definition 3.2.11 and Example 5.5.53] with λ_k (for $k = 1, \ldots, n$), then S_n is Poisson with $\lambda_1 + \cdots + \lambda_n$.

(iv) If X_k is $\chi_{n_k}^2(0)$ [Definition 4.2.13] (for $k = 1, \ldots, n$), then S_n is $\chi_{n_1 + \cdots + n_k}^2(0)$.

(v) X is said to be **Cauchy** with $a(-\infty < a < +\infty)$ and $b > 0$ if

$$f_X(x) = \frac{1}{\pi b} \left[1 + \left(\frac{x - a}{b} \right)^2 \right]^{-1}, \qquad -\infty < x < +\infty.$$

[*Note:* If $a = 0$, $b = 1$, then X is Student's t with $n = 1$ degrees of freedom; see Definition 4.2.26.] If X_k is Cauchy with a_k and b_k (for $k = 1, \ldots, n$), then S_n is Cauchy with $a_1 + \cdots + a_n, b_1 + \cdots + b_n$.

Proof: We will prove only part **(i)** since parts **(ii)** through **(v)** are proved similarly.

$$\phi_{S_n}(t) = \phi_{X_1}(t) \ldots \phi_{X_n}(t)$$

$$= e^{it\mu_1 - \frac{1}{2}\sigma_1^2 t^2} \cdots e^{it\mu_n - \frac{1}{2}\sigma_n^2 t^2}$$

$$= e^{it(\mu_1 + \cdots + \mu_n) - \frac{1}{2}(\sigma_1^2 + \cdots + \sigma_n^2)t^2}.$$

By the Uniqueness Theorem, S_n is $N(\mu_1 + \cdots + \mu_n, \sigma_1^2 + \cdots + \sigma_n^2)$. $\qquad \blacksquare$

PROBLEMS FOR SECTION 5.5

5.5.1 Let the r.v.'s $X_1, X_2, \ldots, X_k$ be independent with $X_i \sim \chi^2_{n_i}(0)$, $i = 1, 2, \ldots, k$. Show that $Y = X_1 + \cdots + X_k \sim \chi^2_N(0)$, where $N = n_1 + \cdots + n_k$.

5.5.2 Let X be an r.v. with $\psi_X(t) = e^{2t + t^2}$. Find:
(a) $P(0 < X < 2)$.
(b) $P(-1 < X < 3)$.
(c) $E(X)$ and $\text{Var}(X)$.

5.5.3 Let X be an r.v. with $\psi_X(t) = e^{4(e^t - 1)}$. Find:
(a) $P(X \le 1)$.
(b) $P(2 < X \le 8)$.
(c) $E(X)$ and $\text{Var}(X)$.

5.5.4 Let X be an r.v. with $\psi_X(t) = 1/(1 - 2\beta)$. Find:
(a) $E(X)$ and $\text{Var}(X)$.
(b) $P(1.2 \le X < 9)$.

5.5.5 If X has m.g.f. $\psi_X(t) = 1/(1 - 2t)^8$, then:
(a) Find c such that $P(X > c) = .975$.
(b) Find c such that $P(X < c) = .50$.

5.5.6 Let X be uniform on (a, b), $a < b$, so that the p.d.f. of X is $f_X(x) = 1/(b - a)$ if $a < x < b$ (and $= 0$ otherwise). Find $\psi_X(t)$, and using its derivatives compute $E(X)$ and $\text{Var}(X)$.

5.5.7 Compute the m.g.f. of a chi-square r.v. with r degrees of freedom directly.

5.5.8 Let $X \sim B(n, p)$. Compute $\psi_X(t)$ and use it to find $E(X)$ and $\text{Var}(X)$. [*Hint:* $\psi_X(t) = (q + pe^t)^n$.]

5.5.9 Let $X_i \sim B(n_i, p)$, $i = 1, 2, \ldots, k$, with the X_i's independent r.v.'s. Find the distribution of $Y = \sum_{i=1}^{k} a_i X_i$, where the a_i's are nonnegative integers (not all zero).

5.5.10 In Problem 5.5.9, let X_i be Poisson with parameter λ_i, $i = 1, 2, \ldots, k$. Assume the X_i's are independent. Find the distribution of Y if all $a_i > 0$.

5.5.11 Let X and Y be independent r.v.'s, each $N(0, 1)$. Show that $XY \sim \chi^2_1(0)$.

5.5.12 Let (X_1, X_2) be a bivariate normal r.v. with parameters $\mu_1, \mu_2, \sigma_1^2, \sigma_2^2$, and ρ. Show, using moment generating functions, that Y and Z, given by

$$Y = X_1 - \mu_1, \qquad Z = (X_2 - \mu_2) - \rho \frac{\sigma_2}{\sigma_1}(X_1 - \mu_1),$$

are independent r.v.'s, and that Y and Z are each normal r.v.'s.

5.5.13 If the m.g.f. of the r.v. X exists and X has moments as given here, find $\psi_X(t)$ and identify the distribution of X:
(a) $E(X^n) = n!$.
(b) $E(X^n) = n!/(n/2)!$ if $n = 2k$ for $k = 1, 2, \ldots$ (and $= 0$ otherwise).

5.5.14 let X_1 and X_2 be independent r.v.'s, $X_i \sim B(n_i, p)$ for $i = 1, 2$. Use m.g.f.'s to find the distribution of $X_1 - X_2 + n_2$.

5.5.15 Use the series in the proof of Theorem 5.2.2 to find $\psi_X(t)$ for $X \sim B(x|\alpha, \lambda)$.

5.5.16 If X has p.d.f. $f_X(x) = (1/(2\beta))e^{-|x-\alpha|/\beta}$ for $-\infty < x < \infty$ for some α $(-\infty < \alpha < \infty)$ and $\beta > 0$, show that $\psi_X(t) = e^{\alpha t}/(1 - (\beta t)^2)$.

5.5.17 Find $\psi_X(t)$ for X a geometric r.v. with probability function $p_X(x) = q^x p$ if $x = 0,1,2,\ldots$ (and $= 0$ otherwise). Use $\psi_X(t)$ to find $E(X)$ and $\text{Var}(X)$.

5.5.18 Let X be a negative binomial r.v. with probability function $p_X(x) = \binom{r+x-1}{x}p^r q^x$ if $x = 0,1,2,\ldots$ (and $= 0$ otherwise). Show that

$$\psi_X(t) = \left(\frac{p}{1 - qe^t}\right)^r$$

and use it to find $E(X)$ and $\text{Var}(X)$.

5.5.19 Let X_i $(i = 1,\ldots,k)$ be independent r.v.'s, with probability functions $p_{X_i}(x)$ $= \binom{r_i+x-1}{x}p^{r_i}q^x$ if $x = 0,1,2,\ldots$ (and $= 0$ otherwise). Show that $\sum_{i=1}^{k} X_i$ has a negative binomial distribution.

5.5.20 Show that a sum of independent geometric r.v.'s is a negative binomial r.v.

5.5.21 let X_1 and X_2 be independent $N(0,1)$ r.v.'s, and let $Y = X_1 + X_2$, $Z = X_1^2 + X_2^2$.
(a) Show that the joint m.g.f. of (Y, Z) is

$$\psi_{Y,Z}(t_1, t_2) = \frac{e^{t_1^2(1-2t_2)}}{1 - 2t_2}.$$

(b) Find $\text{Corr}(Y, Z)$.

5.5.22 Let X be a lognormal r.v. Find $\psi_Y(t)$, where $Y = \ln(X)$.

5.6. ORDER STATISTICS

Order statistics, which have applications in many areas of statistical inference (e.g., nonparametric statistics, estimation theory, and selection theory) are also often used to estimate moments. Hence, in this section we introduce order statistics and discuss some of their properties. (More advanced aspects are covered later, e.g., limiting distributions of some extreme order statistics are covered in Chapter 6.) Applications to estimation and statistical inference are made often in the remainder of the text.

Definition 5.6.1. let $X_1, X_2,\ldots, X_n$ be a **random sample** (i.e., a set of independent and identically distributed r.v.'s) of size n from a population with d.f. $F_X(x)$. The **rth order statistic** is the rth smallest value in the sample, say Y_r. Also, $Y_1 \leq Y_2 \leq \cdots \leq Y_{r-1} \leq Y_r \leq \cdots \leq Y_n$ are called the **order statistics**.

Definition 5.6.2. If $X_1, X_2,\ldots, X_n$ are any r.v.'s (not necessarily independent or identically distributed) the **order statistics** are still as in Definition 5.6.1.

Unlike the parent r.v.'s $X_1, \ldots, X_n$, the order statistics $Y_1, \ldots, Y_n$ are neither independent nor identically distributed. **In the following example, we find the distribution of any Y_r ($1 \le r \le n$).**

Example 5.6.3. Let $X_1, \ldots, X_n$ be a random sample of size n, each with d.f. $F(x)$ and p.d.f. $f(x)$. Let Y_r be the rth order statistic from this sample. Then

$$F_{Y_r}(y) = P(Y_r \le y) = P \text{ (At least r of $X_1, \ldots, X_n$ are $\le y$)}$$

$$= \sum_{j=r}^{n} P \text{ (Exactly j of $X_1, \ldots, X_n$ are $\le y$)}$$

$$= \sum_{j=r}^{n} \binom{n}{j}(F(y))^j (1 - F(y))^{n-j} \qquad (5.6.4)$$

$$= r\binom{n}{r} \int_0^{F(y)} t^{r-1}(1 - t)^{n-r} \, dt,$$

where the last step follows from repeated integration by parts, as

$$r\binom{n}{r} \int_0^{F(y)} t^{r-1}(1 - t)^{n-r} \, dt$$

$$= r\binom{n}{r} \left(\frac{t^r}{r}(1 - t)^{n-r} \Big|_0^{F(y)} + \int_0^{F(y)} (n - r)(1 - t)^{n-r-1} \frac{t^r}{r} \, dt \right)$$

$$= \binom{n}{r}(F(y))^r (1 - F(y))^{n-r} + \binom{n}{r}(n - r) \int_0^{F(y)} (1 - t)^{n-r-1} t^r \, dt$$

$$= \binom{n}{r}(F(y))^r (1 - F(y))^{n-r} + (r + 1)\binom{n}{r+1} \int_0^{F(y)} t^r (1 - t)^{n-r-1} \, dt.$$

Differentiating (5.6.4), we find

$$f_{Y_r}(y) = \frac{d}{dy} F_{Y_r}(y) = r\binom{n}{r}(F(y))^{r-1}(1 - F(y))^{n-r} f(y). \qquad (5.6.5)$$

The formula for the d.f. of Y_r in equation (5.6.4) uses what is called the **incomplete beta function**. Note that equation (5.6.4) is valid for both continuous and discrete distributions.

Example 5.6.6. The Distribution of the Smallest Order Statistic. Let $X_1, \ldots, X_n$ be a random sample of size n, each with d.f. $F(x)$ and p.d.f. $f(x)$. The distribution of $Y_1 = \min(X_1, \ldots, X_n)$ can be found from (5.6.4) and (5.6.5) with

$r = 1$, or directly as follows:

$$F_{Y_1}(t) = P\big(\min(X_1,\ldots,X_n) \le t\big) = 1 - P\big(\min(X_1,\ldots,X_n) > t\big)$$

$$= 1 - P(X_1 > t,\, X_2 > t,\ldots, X_n > t)$$

$$= 1 - \prod_{i=1}^{n} P(X_i > t), \quad \text{by independence}$$

$$= 1 - \prod_{i=1}^{n}(1 - P(X_i \le t)) = 1 - \prod_{i=1}^{n}(1 - F(t)),$$

$$\text{by identical distribution}$$

$$= 1 - (1 - F(t))^n,$$

hence

$$f_{Y_1}(t) = \frac{d}{dt} F_{Y_1}(t) = n(1 - F(t))^{n-1} f(t).$$

Example 5.6.7. Find the probability that in a random sample of size 4 from the beta distribution $B(x|1,1)$ (see Definition 4.2.1) the largest value is less than 0.9. Let X_1, X_2, X_3, X_4 denote the random sample of size 4. Let $Y_4 = \max(X_1, X_2, X_3, X_4)$, the largest value from the sample. Then

$$P(Y_4 < .9) = P\big(\max(X_1, X_2, X_3, X_4) < .9\big)$$

$$= P(X_1 < .9, X_2 < .9, X_3 < .9, X_4 < .9)$$

$$= \prod_{i=1}^{4} P(X_i < .9) = \prod_{i=1}^{4} F_{X_i}(.9) = \big(F_{X_1}(.9)\big)^4$$

where $F_{X_1}(\cdot)$ is the given common beta d.f. Since

$$F_{X_1}(.9) = \int_0^{.9} 6x(1-x)\, dx = 6\left(\frac{x^2}{2} - \frac{x^3}{3}\right)\bigg|_{x=.9} = (.9)^2(3 - (2)(.9)) = .972,$$

$$P(Y_4 < .9) = \big(F_{X_1}(.9)\big)^4 = (.972)^4 = .8926168.$$

The median (first introduced in the case where there is a p.d.f.—just after Definition 5.1.7—and now to be defined in general) and the variance are often estimated using order statistics, especially the **sample median** and **sample midrange** in the case of the median, and (a multiple of) the **sample range** in the case of the standard deviation (especially in quality control). The definitions are as follows.

Definition 5.6.8. If X has d.f. $F(x)$, then m is said to be **a median** of X if $P(X < m) \leq 1/2$ and $P(X \leq m) \geq 1/2$. If there is only one such m, it is called **the median.**

Definition 5.6.9. Let $Y_1, Y_2, \ldots, Y_n$ be the order statistics obtained from a random sample $X_1, \ldots, X_n$ of size n, each with d.f. $F(x)$ and p.d.f. $f(x)$. Then the **sample range** is $Y_n - Y_1$, the **sample midrange** is $(Y_n + Y_1)/2$, and the **sample median** is

$$M_n = \begin{cases} Y_k, & \text{if } n = 2k + 1 \\ \dfrac{Y_k + Y_{k+1}}{2}, & \text{if } n = 2k. \end{cases}$$

To find the distribution of the sample range, sample midrange, and sample median, we first find the distribution of the order statistics.

Theorem 5.6.10. Let $X_1, \ldots, X_n$ be a random sample of size n, each with d.f. $F(x)$ and p.d.f. $f(x)$, and let $Y_1 \leq Y_2 \leq \cdots \leq Y_n$ denote the order statistics. Then

$$f_{Y_1, Y_2, \ldots, Y_n}(y_1, y_2, \ldots, y_n) = \begin{cases} n! \displaystyle\prod_{i=1}^{n} f(y_i), & \text{if } -\infty < y_1 < y_2 < \cdots < y_n < \infty \\ 0, & \text{otherwise.} \end{cases}$$

Proof:* Let

$$\Lambda = \{\lambda \colon \lambda \text{ is a permutation of the integers } \{1, 2, \ldots, n\}\},$$

that is, Λ is the set of all permutations of the first n positive integers. Note that there are $n!$ such permutations, that is, $|\Lambda| = n!$. Denote $Y = (Y_1, \ldots, Y_n)$, $X = (X_1, \ldots, X_n)$, $y = (y_1, \ldots, y_n)$, and $x = (x_1, \ldots, x_n)$. Note that

$$f_X(x) = \prod_{i=1}^{n} f(x_i).$$

Now Euclidean n-dimensional space can be split into $n!$ mutually exclusive and exhaustive sets A_λ, one for each permutation λ in Λ, by taking

$$A_\lambda = \{(x_1, \ldots, x_n) \colon x_{\lambda(1)} < x_{\lambda(2)} < \cdots < x_{\lambda(n)}\}.$$

[Thus, A_λ is the set of points in n-space where the $\lambda(1)$ coordinate is the smallest in the vector, the $\lambda(2)$ coordinate is the next to smallest in the vector,..., and the $\lambda(n)$ coordinate is the largest in the vector.] Then the Jacobian of the transformation from $(X_1, \ldots, X_n)$ to $(Y_1, \ldots, Y_n)$ is ± 1 over each of the sets A_λ,

---

*This proof may be skipped at a first reading, as it involves advanced concepts not needed elsewhere in this text.

and in general maps $n!$ permutations of a vector x into the same vector y. Hence, by a generalization of Theorem 4.4.6,

$$f_Y(y) = \sum_{\lambda \in \Lambda} \frac{1}{|J_\lambda|} f_X(y) = \sum_{\lambda \in \Lambda} f_X(y) = n! f_X(y) \qquad \text{for } y_1 < y_2 < \cdots < y_n,$$

as was to be shown. ∎

Integrating over all variables except y_i and y_j $(i < j)$ in Theorem 5.6.10, we find

Corollary 5.6.11. The (marginal) joint distribution of (Y_i, Y_j), $i < j$, is

$$f_{Y_i, Y_j}(y_i, y_j) = \frac{n!}{(i-1)!(j-i-1)!(n-j)!} (F(y_i))^{i-1} (F(y_j) - F(y_i))^{j-i-1}$$

$$\cdot (1 - F(y_j))^{n-j} f(y_i) f(y_j) \qquad \text{for } y_i < y_j$$

(and zero elsewhere).

Using Corollary 5.6.11, we can find the distribution of the sample range, sample midrange, and median. We illustrate this for the sample range, leaving the others to the problems.

Example 5.6.12. Distribution of the Sample Range. Let $X_1, \ldots, X_n$ be a random sample each with d.f. $F(x)$ and p.d.f. $f(x)$, and let $Y_1, \ldots, Y_n$ denote the order statistics. Find the distribution of the sample range $R = Y_n - Y_1$.

The joint distribution of Y_1, Y_n is (see Corollary 5.6.11)

$$f_{Y_1, Y_n}(y_1, y_n) = \begin{cases} n(n-1)(F(y_n) - F(y_1))^{n-2} f(y_1) f(y_n), & \text{if } y_1 < y_n \\ 0, & \text{otherwise.} \end{cases}$$

Letting $R = Y_n - Y_1 > 0$ and $V = Y_n$, we have $Y_n = V$ and $Y_1 = Y_n - R = V - R$, hence the Jacobian of the transformation is

$$J = \begin{vmatrix} -1 & 1 \\ 0 & 1 \end{vmatrix}$$

which has $|J| = 1$. Therefore (see Theorem 4.6.18)

$$f_{R,V}(r, v) = n(n-1)(F(v) - F(v-r))^{n-2} f(v-r) f(v), \qquad \text{if } 0 < r$$

and

$$f_R(r) = \int_{-\infty}^{\infty} f_{R,V}(r, v)\, dv$$

$$= \int_{-\infty}^{\infty} n(n-1)(F(v) - F(v-r))^{n-2} f(v-r) f(v)\, dv, \qquad \text{if } 0 < r.$$

As a special case, suppose the X_i are uniform on $(0, 1)$ or $B(x|0, 0)$ (see Example 4.2.3). Then

$$f_R(r) = \int_r^1 n(n - 1)[v - (v - r)]^{n-2} \, dv$$

$$= n(n - 1)r^{n-2} \int_r^1 dv = n(n - 1)r^{n-2}(1 - r), \quad \text{for } 0 < r < 1.$$

For a sample of size 10 from the uniform on $(0, 1)$, the probability that the range of the values in the sample is larger than 0.8 is

$$P(R > .8) = \int_{.8}^1 90r^8(1 - r) \, dr = 90\left(\frac{r^9}{9} - \frac{r^{10}}{10}\right)\Bigg|_{.8}^1$$

$$= (10 - 9) - (.8)^9(10 - (9)(.8)) = .62419.$$

Similarly, for a sample of size 8 from the uniform on $(0, 1)$, the probability that the sample range is less than .9 is

$$P(R < .9) = \int_0^{.9} 8(8 - 1)r^6(1 - r) \, dr = 56\left(\frac{r^7}{7} - \frac{r^8}{8}\right)\Bigg|_0^{.9} = .81310.$$

PROBLEMS FOR SECTION 5.6

5.6.1 Let $X_1, X_2, \ldots, X_n$ be a random sample of size n from a continuous distribution with d.f. $F_X(x)$ and p.d.f. $f_X(x)$. Let $Y_1, Y_2, \ldots, Y_n$ be the order statistics associated with the sample.

(a) Show that $F_X(Y_r)$ has a beta distribution with parameters $\alpha = r + 1$, $\lambda = n - r + 1$, and that for any integer $k > 0$

$$E\big(F_X^k(Y_r)\big) = \frac{\Gamma(n + 1)\Gamma(r + k)}{\Gamma(r)\Gamma(n + k + 1)}.$$

(b) If $U_r = F_X(Y_r)$, deduce from part (a) that $E(U_r) = r/(n + 1)$ and $\text{Var}(U_r) = r(n - r + 1)/((n + 1)^2(n + 2))$.

(c) For $i < j$, show that U_{j-i} and $U_j - U_i$ have the same p.d.f.

(d) Let $W_i = (Y_i/Y_{i+1})^i$ for $i = 1, 2, \ldots, n - 1$, and $W_n = Y_n$. Show that the W_i's are independent and identically distributed uniform r.v.'s on $(0, 1)$.

5.6.2 If X is a continuous r.v. with p.d.f. $f_X(x) = 1/x^2$ for $1 \leq x < \infty$ (and $= 0$ otherwise), find a transformation $Y = g(X)$ such that Y has a uniform distribution on the interval $(0, 1)$.

5.6.3 Find the distribution of the range R of a random sample of size n from the exponential distribution with p.d.f. $f_X(x) = \lambda e^{-\lambda x}$ for $x \geq 0$ (and $= 0$ otherwise) for some $\lambda > 0$. Compute $P(R < 2\lambda)$.

5.6.4 The "order statistics" in Definition 5.6.1 are defined in discrete cases as well as in continuous cases. Suppose we have a random sample of size 4 from the discrete uniform distribution $p_X(x) = 1/6$ for $x = 1, 2, 3, 4, 5, 6$ (and $= 0$ otherwise).
(a) Find the probability function of Y_1 (the first order statistic).
(b) Find the probability function of Y_4 (the largest order statistic).

5.6.5 A random sample of size 10 is taken from a uniform distribution on $(0, 1)$.
(a) Find $P(Y_{10} < .9)$.
(b) Find c such that $P(Y_1 > c) = .5$.

5.6.6 Let $X_1, X_2, \ldots, X_n$ be a random sample of size n from the p.d.f. $f_X(x) = (1/\lambda)e^{-(x-A)/\lambda}$ for $x > A$ (and $= 0$ otherwise) for some $\lambda > 0$. Let $Y_1, Y_2, \ldots, Y_n$ denote the order statistics. Show that $Y_1, Y_2 - Y_1, Y_3 - Y_2, \ldots, Y_n - Y_{n-1}$ are independent r.v.'s.

5.6.7 Let $X_1, X_2, \ldots, X_n$ be a random sample of size n from the p.d.f. $f_X(x) = \alpha x^{\alpha-1}$ if $0 < x < 1$ (and $= 0$ otherwise) for some $\alpha > 0$. Show that Y_i/Y_n, $i = 1, 2, \ldots,$ $n - 1$ and Y_n are independent r.v.'s.

5.6.8 Let $X_1, X_2, \ldots, X_n$ be a random sample of size n from a continuous distribution with d.f. $F_X(x)$. If $E|X| < \infty$, show that $E|Y_r| < \infty$, for all r ($1 \le r \le n$), and compute $E(Y_n)$.

5.6.9 **A Characterization of the Exponential Distribution.** Let $X_1, X_2, \ldots, X_n$ be a random sample from a continuous d.f. Show that Y_1 is exponential with parameter $n\lambda$ iff each X_i is exponential with parameter λ.

5.6.10 Let X_1, X_2, X_3 be a random sample of size 3 from the triangular p.d.f. $f_X(x) = 2(2 - x)$ if $1 \le x \le 2$ (and $= 0$ otherwise). Find $P(Y_2 > m)$, where m is the median of the parent distribution $f_X(x)$.

5.6.11 Let $X_1, X_2, \ldots, X_n$ be a random sample of size n from a continuous d.f. $F_X(x)$. Calculate (a) $P(Y_1 \ge m)$, and (b) $P(Y_n \le m)$, where m is the median of the parent d.f. $F_X(x)$.

5.6.12 Find the distribution of $Y_n = \max(X_1, X_2, \ldots, X_n)$, and also the distribution of $Y_1 = \min(X_1, X_2, \ldots, X_n)$, where $X_1, X_2, \ldots, X_n$ is a random sample of size n from a continuous d.f. $F_X(x)$.

5.6.13 Let $\tilde{X}$ be the median of a random sample of size 11 from the beta distribution with $\alpha = 3$ and $\lambda = 2$. Find the probability that $\tilde{X}$ will exceed $1/2$.

5.6.14 Let $X_1, X_2, \ldots, X_{2k+1}$ be an odd-size random sample from a $N(\mu, \sigma^2)$ distribution. Find the distribution of the sample median, and show that it is symmetric about μ, hence has mean μ.

5.6.15 As in Problem 5.6.14 for an even sample size.

5.6.16 Let $X_1, X_2, \ldots, X_n$ be a random sample from a continuous d.f. $F_X(x)$. Let $Y_1 \le Y_2 \le \cdots \le Y_n$ be the associated order statistics. Show that

$$E(Y_n) = E(Y_{n-1}) + \int_0^\infty F_X^{n-1}(x)(1 - F_X(x)) \, dx$$

for $n = 2, 3, 4, \ldots$. Use this formula to find $E(Y_n)$ if
(a) X_1 is exponential with parameter λ.
(b) X_1 is uniform on $(0, 1)$.

PROBLEMS FOR CHAPTER 5

5.1 **(a)** Let $X_0, X_1, X_2, \ldots$ be independent and identically distributed absolutely continuous random variables. Let

$$N_1 = \text{The first subscript } n \text{ such that } X_n > X_0;$$

$$N_2 = \text{The first subscript } n \text{ such that } X_n < X_0.$$

[Intuitively, we may think of N_1 as the number of the first person to experience worse luck, and N_2 as the number of the first person to experience better luck.]
Find $E(N_1)$; $E(N_2)$; $E\min(N_1, N_2)$; $E[\min(N_1, N_2)]^2$; $\text{Var}[\min(N_1, N_2)]$.
(b) If $P[X = 1] = 1$, find $E(X)$ and $\text{Var}(X)$.
(c) Suppose $P[X = n] = 1/(n^2 + n)$ for $n = 1, 2, \ldots$. Find $E(X)$.

5.2 Show that random variables X and Y may be uncorrelated and yet nonindependent.

5.3 Consider the following gambling game. A player bets \$1 on a number i_0 ($1 \le i_0 \le 6$), where i_0 is an integer. Two fair dice are then tossed. If two i_0's show, the player receives \$3; if one i_0 shows, the player receives \$2; and if no i_0's show, the player receives \$0.
(a) Let $X_1 = $ the number of i_0's that appear in a single play of this game. Find the probability distribution of X_1 and $E(X_1)$.
(b) Suppose each *winning* payoff is increased by \$1. Then what is $E(X_1)$?
(c) Let $W_1 = $ the player's winnings on a single play of the original game. Find $E(W_1)$.
(d) Suppose that 100 plays of the game are made, but that rather than being independent they are such that

$$\rho(W_i, W_{i+1}) = 1 - \frac{1}{2^i} \qquad (i = 1, 2, \ldots)$$

$$\rho(W_i, W_j) = 0 \qquad\qquad (j > i + 1).$$

Find $E(W_1 + \cdots + W_{100})$.

5.4 Prove that, if X_1, X_2 has the bivariate normal distribution, then $\rho(X_1, X_2) = \rho$. Deduce that X_1 and X_2 are then uncorrelated iff they are independent. (This completes the proof of Theorem 5.3.25.)

5.5 Show that, if X is a r.v. that has the $\chi_n^2(0)$ distribution (see Definition 4.2.13) and $n \ge 2$, then $EX = n$ and the mode of the distribution of X is $n - 2$. Find EX and the mode when $n = 1$.

5.6 **(a)** Prove that $e^{5it - 10t^2 + 6(e^{it} - 1)}$ is a characteristic function.
(b) Prove that $e^{4it + t^2}$ is not a characteristic function.

5.7 If random variables $X_1, X_2, \ldots, X_n$ are independent and identically distributed with common density function $f(x)$, and if

$$Q = \frac{1}{n} \sum_{i=1}^{n} \sin X_i,$$

$$R = (\sin X_1)(\sin X_2) \ldots (\sin X_n),$$

show that

(a) $E(Q) = \int_{-\infty}^{\infty} (\sin x) f(x)\, dx.$

(b) $E(R) = \{ \int_{-\infty}^{\infty} (\sin x) f(x)\, dx \}^n.$

5.8 Prove that

$$\left(\tfrac{1}{10} e^{it} + 1 \right) \cdot e^{5(e^{it} - 1)} \cdot e^{5it - t^2}$$

is not a characteristic function.

5.9 Let $X_1, \ldots, X_n$ be independent random variables with $E(X_i) = \mu_i$ and $\mathrm{Var}(X_i) = a_i \sigma^2$ $(i = 1, \ldots, n)$. Find $E(S_n^2)$, where $S_n = X_1 + \cdots + X_n$.

5.10 It is sometimes the case that a sequence (say $Y_1, Y_2, \ldots$) of random variables cannot be observed, although we can observe results of the values of $Y_1, Y_2, \ldots$ (say $X_1, X_2, \ldots$).

Let $Y_1, Y_2, \ldots$ be independent and identically distributed random variables. Let a be a fixed number $(-\infty < a < +\infty)$. For $i = 1, 2, \ldots$ define

$$X_i = \begin{cases} 1, & \text{if } Y_i \geq a \\ 0, & \text{if } Y_i < a. \end{cases}$$

Define $p = P[Y_1 \geq a]$, $q = 1 - p$, $S_n = X_1 + \cdots + X_n$. (Note that S_n is the number of $Y_1, \ldots, Y_n$ that exceed a.)

(a) Define the characteristic function, say $\phi_X(t)$, of a random variable X.
(b) Find $\phi_{X_1}(t)$.
(c) Find $\phi_{S_n}(t)$.
(d) Show that $P[S_n = j] = \binom{n}{j} p^i q^{n-i}$ for $j = 0, 1, \ldots, n$.

5.11 Lemma 5.3.10 stated that

$$\mathrm{Var}(X_1 + X_2) = \mathrm{Var}(X_1) + \mathrm{Var}(X_2) + 2\,\mathrm{Cov}(X_1, X_2).$$

Extending this to n r.v.'s, show that

$$\mathrm{Var}(X_1 + \cdots + X_n) = \sum_{i=1}^{n} \mathrm{Var}(X_i) + 2 \sum_{i<j} \mathrm{Cov}(X_i, X_j).$$

[*Hint:* Use mathematical induction on n.]

5.12 (*Due to J. Keilson*) Let $X_1, X_2, \ldots$ be a sequence of r.v.'s and let $p_i \geq 0$ $(i = 1, 2, \ldots)$ with $\sum_{i=1}^{\infty} p_i = 1$. Prove that

$$\sigma\left(\sum_{i=1}^{\infty} p_i X_i \right) \leq \sum_{i=1}^{\infty} p_i \sigma(X_i) \leq \sqrt{\sum_{i=1}^{\infty} p_i \sigma^2(X_i)}.$$

5.13 Let $X_1, X_2, \ldots, X_n$ be n r.v.'s. Prove that

$$\mathrm{Var}\left(\frac{X_1 + \cdots + X_n}{n} \right) \leq \frac{\sum_{i=1}^{n} \mathrm{Var}(X_i)}{n}.$$

5.14 Let X, Y, Z be r.v.'s, and let a, b be constants. Prove that

(a) $\text{Cov}(X, aY + b) = a \, \text{Cov}(X, Y)$;

(b) $\text{Cov}(X, Y + Z) = \text{Cov}(X, Y) + \text{Cov}(X, Z)$;

(c) $\rho(X, aY + b) = \rho(X, Y)$ for $a > 0$;

(d) $\rho(X, Y + Z) = \dfrac{\sigma(Y)}{\sigma(Y + Z)} \rho(X, Y) + \dfrac{\sigma(Z)}{\sigma(Y + Z)} \rho(X, Z)$.

5.15 Let X_1, X_2, X_3 be three independent r.v.'s each with variance σ^2. If we define new r.v.'s W_1, W_2, W_3 by

$$W_1 = X_1,$$

$$W_2 = \frac{\sqrt{3} - 1}{2} X_1 + \frac{3 - \sqrt{3}}{2} X_2,$$

$$W_3 = (\sqrt{2} - 1) X_2 + (2 - \sqrt{2}) X_3,$$

show that

$$\rho(W_i, W_{i+1}) = \tfrac{1}{2} \quad (i = 1, 2)$$

$$\rho(W_i, W_j) = 0 \quad (j > i + 1).$$

5.16 Suppose that Z_1, Z_2, Z_3 are independent random variables with $\text{Var}(Z_i) = \sigma_i^2 > 0$ $(i = 1, 2, 3)$. Let $X = Z_1 + Z_2$, $Y = Z_1 + Z_3$. Find the correlation coefficient $\rho(X, Y)$. What is the value of $\rho(X, Y)$ when $\sigma_1^2 = \sigma_2^2 = \sigma_3^2 > 0$? What is the range of possible values of $\rho(X, Y)$ as σ_1^2, σ_2^2, σ_3^2 vary?

5.17 Let X_1 and X_2 be two jointly discrete r.v.'s whose joint probability function assigns probability $1/17$ to each of the following 17 pairs of values.

$$(86, 100), \ (75, 98), \ (93, 98), \ (92, 95),$$

$$(95, 93), \ (87, 91), \ (81, 83), \ (81, 79),$$

$$(66, 66), \ (67, 64), \ (78, 63), \ (94, 58),$$

$$(95, 56), \ (88, 53), \ (98, 33), \ (87, 31),$$

$$(54, 5).$$

Find EX_1, EX_2, $E|X_1 - EX_1|$, $\rho(X_1, X_2)$, and the smallest d such that $P[|X_1 - EX_1| \leq d] \geq .75$. [The 17 pairs of values actually represent the scores of 17 students on two examinations. As discussed briefly following Lemma 5.3.22, $\rho(X_1, X_2)$ is a measure of how well a quantity such as $aX_1 + b$ can predict the score X_2 on the second test.]

5.18 Suppose a given event occurs (success) with probability p (and therefore fails to occur with probability $q = 1 - p$), and independent trials are conducted. Let X denote the number of trials needed to obtain a total of k successes. Find $\text{Var}(X)$. [*Hint:* Show that we can express X as $X = Y_1 + \cdots + Y_k$ where $Y_1, \ldots, Y_k$ are independent r.v.'s and Y_i has the geometric distribution of Definition 3.2.20. Then use Problem 5.10 and Theorem 5.3.19.]

5.19 Suppose that X is an (absolutely) continuous random variable with density function given by

$$f_X(y) = \begin{cases} 5e^{-5y}, & \text{if } 0 \le y < \infty \\ 0, & \text{otherwise.} \end{cases}$$

Find $E(X)$, $E(X^2)$, $\text{Var}(X)$, mode of X, median of X.

5.20 A die is tossed $n + 2$ times. After each toss a "$+$" is recorded if a 4, 5, or 6 occurs; and a "$-$" is recorded if a 1, 2, or 3 occurs. We thus form an ordered sequence of signs. Let (for $i = 2, \ldots, n + 1$)

$$X_{i-1} = \begin{cases} 1, & \text{if sign } i - 1 \text{ and sign } i + 1 \text{ both differ from sign } i \\ 0, & \text{otherwise.} \end{cases}$$

We thus define random variables $X_1, X_2, \ldots, X_n$. (For example, if $n = 3$ and we observe dice outcomes 4, 3, 1, 6, 5, then the sign sequence is $+ - - + +$ and $X_1 = 0$, $X_2 = 0$, $X_3 = 0$.) Let $Y = X_1 + \cdots + X_n$. Find $E(Y)$ and $\text{Var}(Y)$.

5.21 Assume r balls ($r \ge 1$, r an integer) are distributed at random into n cells ($n \ge 1$); thus, each assignment vector has probability $1/n^r$. Let

$$p_m(r, n) = \text{probability of finding exactly } m \text{ cells empty.}$$

In Feller (1966) we find that

$$p_m(r, n) = \binom{n}{m} \sum_{v=0}^{n-m} (-1)^v \binom{n-m}{v} \left(1 - \frac{m+v}{n}\right)^r; \tag{1}$$

direct numerical evaluation of (1) is limited to the case of relatively small n and r. However, the following is true:

Limit Theorem: If $n \to \infty$ and $r \to \infty$ in such a way that $\lambda = ne^{-r/n}$ remains bounded, then for each fixed m

$$p_m(r, n) - e^{-\lambda} \frac{\lambda^m}{m!} \to 0. \tag{2}$$

Recall that if a random variable $\tilde{M}$ is such that $P[\tilde{M} = m] = e^{-\lambda}\lambda^m/m!$ ($m = 0, 1, 2, \ldots$), then $E(\tilde{M}) = \lambda$. (Poisson distribution.)

Suppose that r balls are placed at random into n cells; r is known, but n is unknown and we desire to estimate it. We observe the random variable $n - M$, the number of cells with at least 1 ball, and find value c (say).

Because of Limit Theorem (2), we might (for "large" r and n, and "moderate" $\lambda = ne^{-r/n}$) hope that

$$E(M) \approx E(\tilde{M}) = \lambda = ne^{-r/n}, \tag{3}$$

or

$$E(n - M) \approx E(n - \tilde{M}) = n(1 - e^{-r/n}). \tag{4}$$

If we also assume that the observed value c of $n - M$ is "close" to $E(n - M)$, from (4) we obtain

$$n(1 - e^{-r/n}) \approx c. \tag{5}$$

We could solve (5) numerically for an estimate of the (unknown) number n of cells, obtaining (say)

$$\hat{n}_1(c, r). \tag{6}$$

Alternatively, we could also assume (as a first approximation)

$$n \approx c \tag{7}$$

and, using (7) in (5), obtain a second more easily computed estimate of n, say

$$\hat{n}_2(c, r) = \frac{c}{1 - e^{-r/c}}. \tag{8}$$

(a) In general, $E\hat{n}_2(c, r)$ will be difficult to calculate. For the case $r = 1$, find $\{p_m(r, n)\}$: $p_0(1, n)$, $p_1(1, n)$, $p_2(1, n), \ldots, p_{n-1}(1, n)$, $p_n(1, n)$. Then calculate $E\hat{n}_2(c, 1)$.

(b) Show that

$$\hat{n}_2(c, r) \leq \frac{\min(r, n)}{1 - e^{-r/\min(r, n)}}.$$

(c) Show that, if $r \leq n$, $\hat{n}_2(c, r) \leq (1 - e^{-1})^{-1}r$. Does this mean that we should try to have $r \geq (1 - e^{-1})n$ when using $\hat{n}_2$ as an estimator? Why or why not?

(d) If $r = 9000$, $n = 1000$, we have (by the Poisson approximation) the approximate probabilities

$p_m(9000, 1000)$	.8869	.1064	.0064	.0003	$\ldots$
m	0	1	2	3	$\ldots$

Find, using these approximate probabilities, $E\hat{n}_2(c, 9000)$. What is an "ideal" value for $\hat{n}_2(c, r)$?

x	4.50	4.51	4.52	4.53	4.54
e^{-x}	.011	.011	.011	.011	.011

x	9.00	9.05	9.10	9.15	9.20
e^{-x}	.0001	.0001	.0001	.0001	.0001

5.22 Let $X_1, X_2, \ldots, X_n$ be independent random variables such that $P[X_i = 1] = P[X_i = -1] = \frac{1}{2}(i = 1, \ldots, n)$. Let $a_1, a_2, \ldots, a_n$ be constants. Find the characteristic function of X_1; of $Y_n = a_1 X_1 + \cdots + a_n X_n$. Let $a_1 = 1/2$, $a_2 = 1/2^2$, $a_3 = 1/2^3, \ldots$. What is $\phi_n(t)$, the characteristic function of Y_n, in this case? Show that $\lim_{n \to \infty} \phi_n(t)$
$$= \frac{\sin(t)}{t}. \; [\textit{Hint:} \sin(x) = (e^{ix} - e^{-ix})/(2i) \text{ and } \cos(x) = (e^{ix} + e^{-ix})/2.]$$

5.23 Suppose that (X, Y) is a two-dimensional r.v. with density function

$$f_{X,Y}(x, y) = \begin{cases} 1, & \text{if } 0 \leq y \leq x, 0 \leq x \leq \sqrt{2} \\ 0, & \text{otherwise;} \end{cases}$$

that is, (X, Y) is uniformly distributed over a certain triangle. Find $E(Y|X = x_0)$ $(0 \le x_0 \le \sqrt{2})$ and $E(Y)$.

5.24 Suppose that (for $i = 1, 2$) the r.v. X_i has the exponential density

$$f_{X_i}(x) = \begin{cases} (1/\beta_i) e^{-x/\beta_i}, & x > 0 \\ 0, & x \le 0 \end{cases}$$

where $\beta_i > 0$, and that X_1 and X_2 are independent r.v.'s. Show that the density function of $Y = X_1/X_2$ is

$$f_Y(y) = \begin{cases} \alpha/(y + \alpha)^2, & y > 0 \\ 0, & y \le 0 \end{cases}$$

where $\alpha = \beta_1/\beta_2$. Show that, for $\delta \ge 1$, EY^δ does not exist. [This distribution was discussed by Lachenbruch and Brogan (1971).]

HONORS PROBLEMS FOR CHAPTER 5

5.1H Prove Corollary 5.1.6.

5.2H Let α be fixed, $0 < \alpha < 1$. Show that

$$f(x) = \begin{cases} \dfrac{1}{24} e^{-\sqrt[4]{x}} \left(1 - \alpha \sin \sqrt[4]{x}\right), & 0 \le x \\ 0, & \text{otherwise} \end{cases}$$

is a density function. Show that the moments $\mu_1' = EX$, $\mu_2' = EX^2$, $\mu_3' = EX^3, \ldots$ do not depend on α $(0 < \alpha < 1)$. What does this imply (via Carleman's theorem) about the value of

$$\sum_{n=1}^{\infty} \left\{ \int_{-\infty}^{\infty} |x|^n f(x)\, dx \right\}^{-1/n} ? \qquad (*)$$

Evaluate $(*)$ explicitly.

5.3H Let $X_1, X_2, X_3, \ldots$ be a sequence of independent random variables, each with d.f. $F(x)$. Can you construct a sequence of functions of $X_1, X_2, X_3, \ldots$ (say $W_1, W_2, W_3, \ldots$) such that

$$\rho(W_i, W_{i+1}) = 1 - \frac{1}{2^i} \qquad (i = 1, 2, \ldots)$$

$$\rho(W_i, W_j) = 0 \qquad (j > i + 1)?$$

[*Hint:* See Problems 5.15 and 5.4H.]

5.4H Let $-1 \le \rho_{ij} \le 1$ $(1 \le i, j \le n)$ be n^2 numbers and let (ρ_{ij}) be an $n \times n$ matrix whose entry in row i and column j is ρ_{ij}. Give a necessary and sufficient condition for (ρ_{ij}) to be the matrix of correlation coefficients of some n random variables $Z_1, \ldots, Z_n$.

5.5H For the random variable X defined in Problem 2.8H, find $E(X)$ as a general formula. Evaluate this formula for $n = 100$, $N = 200$ and $m = 1, 2, 3, \ldots, 100$. [If you are unable to solve this problem analytically, you may try a simulation approach. Namely, write a computer program that—via use of pseudorandom numbers—distributes $N = 200$ balls into $n = 100$ cells and records the number of balls in each cell. Then let $S(i)$ be the number of cells that have more than m balls in them if $m = i$; record $S(1), S(2), \ldots, S(100)$. Then do the experiment over again and add the new results $S(i)$ to the old ones, and so on, performing the experiment $t = 1000$ times. Then $S(i)/1000$ is an estimate of $E(X)$ when $m = i$.]

Even if you were able to solve the problem analytically, try the simulation approach (which is often used when analytic solutions cannot be obtained). How should t be chosen? Why do you expect $E(X) \approx S(i)/1000$? (Recall the relative frequency interpretation of probabilities.) A reference is Naylor, Balintfy, Burdick, and Chu (1966).

5.6H Construct a probability distribution for a random variable $X \geq 0$ such that

(a) EX does not exist.

(b) EX^δ does not exist for any $\delta > 0$.

(c) EX^δ does not exist for $\delta = -1$.

(d) EX^δ does not exist for any $\delta < 0$.

(e) EX^δ exists iff $\delta = 0$.

5.7H Let $A_1, \ldots, A_n$ be $n \geq 2$ events and define (for $i = 1, \ldots, n$) indicator r.v.'s by

$$I_{A_i} = \begin{cases} 1, & \text{if } A_i \text{ occurs} \\ 0, & \text{otherwise.} \end{cases}$$

We know (see Boole's Inequality, Theorem 2.1.16) that it is always the case that

$$P(A_1 \cup \cdots \cup A_n) \leq P(A_1) + \cdots + P(A_n).$$

What can be said about $P(A_1 \cap \cdots \cap A_n)$ [usually written $P(A_1 \cdots A_n)$]? More specifically,

(a) Prove that $P(A_1 \cdots A_n) = P(A_1) \ldots P(A_n)$ if $A_1, \ldots, A_n$ are independent events.

(b) Prove that $P(A_1 A_2) \geq P(A_1)P(A_2)$ iff $\text{Cov}(I_{A_1}, I_{A_2}) \geq 0$.

(c) Prove that $P(A_1 \ldots A_n) \geq P(A_1) \ldots P(A_n)$ if $\text{Cov}(I_{A_j}, I_{A_1 \ldots A_{j-1}}) \geq 0$ for $j = 2, \ldots, n$.

(d) R.v.'s $X_1, \ldots, X_n$ (e.g., $I_{A_1}, \ldots, I_{A_n}$) are said to be **associated** if, for all nondecreasing functions f and g, $\text{Cov}(f(X_1, \ldots, X_n), g(X_1, \ldots, X_n)) \geq 0$. [See Esary, Proschan, and Walkup (1967) for further details.] Try to use this concept to provide a theorem giving a condition C such that it is true that "$P(A_1 \cdots A_n) \geq P(A_1) \cdots P(A_n)$ iff C."

CHAPTER 6

Sums of Random Variables, Probability Inequalities, and Limit Laws

To this point, we have usually been dealing with situations where the exact distribution function is known (one exception being our considerations of estimating a p.d.f. in Chapter 5). However, in real-world problems one often has little or no knowledge about the distribution underlying samples (such as industrial response variables or sociological, psychological, and business survey variables). In such cases, knowledge of the distribution of the sum (or average) of the response variables is often of great use. Finding such knowledge, when little or nothing is known of the underlying distribution, is the main topic of this chapter.

In probability problems, the distribution of the random variables $X_1, \ldots, X_n$ is assumed to be known. In such a case, if we desire to make probability statements about the sum $X_1 + \cdots + X_n$, we can (since the d.f. of $(X_1, \ldots, X_n)$ is known) use the techniques of Section 4.6 to determine the d.f. of $X_1 + \cdots + X_n$. However, this is a hard task (as we saw in Chapter 4), and in real-world problems we may not know the d.f. of $(X_1, \ldots, X_n)$.

In a statistical approach, we start with partial or no information about the d.f. of $(X_1, \ldots, X_n)$. In Section 6.1 we study bounds that can be given (for example) on the probability that $X_1 + \cdots + X_n$ is "large." In Section 6.2 we study convergence of r.v.'s, such as what happens to the d.f. of $X_1 + \cdots + X_n$ as n grows large. This study culminates in Section 6.3, where we prove the Central Limit Theorem (CLT) and give statistical applications. The Central Limit Theorem is one of the most central results of statistics, far-reaching in both its theoretical and applied implications, and has even been called the premier modern contribution not only of mathematical statistics, but also of all mathematics, dwarfing in its beauty and applicability even the combined results of algebra, analysis, topology, and classical applied mathematics. It is our great fortune to be able to study this result in a modern, streamlined form that is both general in its assumptions and (hence) simple in its applicability.

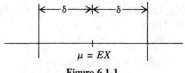

Figure 6.1-1.

6.1. CHEBYSHEV, MARKOV, AND OTHER PROBABILITY INEQUALITIES

Theorem 6.1.1. **Chebyshev's Inequality.** Let $\delta > 0$ be fixed. Let X be a r.v. with mean μ and variance σ^2. Then

$$P[|X - \mu| \geq \delta] \leq \frac{\sigma^2}{\delta^2}.$$

Proof: Consider the diagram of Figure 6.1-1. Now $\sigma^2 = E(X - EX)^2 \geq \delta^2 P[|X - EX| \geq \delta]$, which proves the theorem. In this inequality, we have first neglected the integral from $\mu - \delta$ to $\mu + \delta$, then replaced the integrand on the remaining integral (which ranges from $-\infty$ to $\mu - \delta$, and from $\mu + \delta$ to $+\infty$) by its minimal value δ^2. Note that $P[|X - EX| \geq \delta]$ is the probability mass outside the interval from $\mu - \delta$ to $\mu + \delta$: $P[X \in S] = \int_{x \in S} f(x)\, dx$, where $S = \{x : |x - \mu| \geq \delta\}$.

In summary, the proof in equation form (with justifications as just presented) is

$$\sigma^2 = E(X - \mu)^2 = \int_{-\infty}^{\infty} (x - \mu)^2 f(x)\, dx$$

$$\geq \int_{-\infty}^{\mu - \delta} (x - \mu)^2 f(x)\, dx + \int_{\mu + \delta}^{\infty} (x - \mu)^2 f(x)\, dx$$

$$\geq \int_{-\infty}^{\mu - \delta} \delta^2 f(x)\, dx + \int_{\mu + \delta}^{\infty} \delta^2 f(x)\, dx = \delta^2 \left(\int_{-\infty}^{\mu - \delta} f(x)\, dx + \int_{\mu + \delta}^{\infty} f(x)\, dx \right)$$

$$= \delta^2 (P(X \leq \mu - \delta) + P(X \geq \mu + \delta))$$

$$= \delta^2 (P(X - \mu \leq -\delta) + P(X - \mu \geq \delta)) = \delta^2 P(|X - \mu| \geq \delta). \qquad \blacksquare$$

Example 6.1.2. **Equality may be achieved in Chebyshev's Inequality.** For example, let $P[X = c] = 1$. Then Chebyshev's Inequality states that $P[|X - c| \geq \delta] \leq 0/\delta^2 = 0$, and in fact equality holds for all $\delta > 0$.

Corollary 6.1.3. Let $\delta > 0$ be fixed. Let X be a r.v. with mean μ and variance $\sigma^2 > 0$. Then

$$P\left[\left| \frac{X - \mu}{\sigma} \right| \geq \delta \right] \leq \frac{1}{\delta^2}.$$

Proof: By Chebyshev's Inequality, for any $t > 0$, $P[|X - \mu| \geq t] \leq \sigma^2/t^2$. Let $t = \delta\sigma$, which is > 0. Then

$$P[|X - \mu| \geq \delta\sigma] \leq \frac{\sigma^2}{(\delta\sigma)^2},$$

that is,

$$P\left[\left|\frac{X - \mu}{\sigma}\right| \geq \delta\right] \leq \frac{1}{\delta^2}. \qquad \blacksquare$$

Example 6.1.4. **Equality may be achieved in Chebyshev's Inequality with $\sigma^2 > 0$.** For example, let $P[X = -1] = P[X = 1] = \frac{1}{2}$. Then $\mu = 0$, $\sigma^2 = 1$, and Chebyshev's Inequality states that $P[|X| \geq \delta] \leq 1/\delta^2$. This is an equality when $\delta = 1$.

Theorem 6.1.5. **Chebyshev's Inequality.** Let $t > 0$ be fixed. Let Y be a r.v. such that $P[Y \geq 0] = 1$. Then $P[Y \geq t] \leq EY^2/t^2$. (This implies Chebyshev's inequality in the form of Theorem 6.1.1 on taking $Y = |X - \mu|$.)

Proof: Essentially as in Theorem 6.1.1; that is, $EY^2 \geq t^2 P[Y \geq t]$, q.e.d. $\qquad \blacksquare$

Theorem 6.1.6. **Markov's Inequality.** Let $t > 0$, $a \geq 0$ be fixed. Let Y be a r.v. such that $P[Y \geq 0] = 1$. Then $P[Y \geq t] \leq EY^a/t^a$.

Proof: As in Theorem 6.1.5. $\qquad \blacksquare$

Note: A reference to these (and more general) inequalities is Loève (1963), p. 158. An interesting and readable application is made by Samuelson (1968).

Example 6.1.7. A newspaper stand has observed that, over the course of 10 days, the numbers of newspapers demanded were $X_1, X_2, \ldots, X_{10}$, respectively. If we assume that these are independent and identically distributed observations of demand, what bound can be put on the probability that their average $\overline{X} = (X_1 + \cdots + X_{10})/10$ is more than 3σ newspapers from the (unknown) average demand μ? We have $E\overline{X} = \mu$, $\text{Var}(\overline{X}) = \sigma^2/10$, so by Corollary 6.1.3,

$$P[|\overline{X} - \mu| \geq 3\sigma] = P\left[\left|\frac{\overline{X} - \mu}{\sigma/\sqrt{10}}\right| \geq 3\sqrt{10}\right] \leq \frac{1}{(3\sqrt{10})^2} = \frac{1}{90}.$$

Recall that we have already made use of some probability inequalities other than those of Chebyshev and Markov just studied; that use was in Chapter 5 (Hölder's Inequality in Theorem 5.1.13 and Schwarz' Inequality in Theorem 5.3.15). There are a number of other probability inequalities, and their generalizations to the multivariate case; however, we will study only one in addition to the above: Jensen's Inequality* (which requires the concept of a "convex" function and will be used in Chapter 12 in our study of statistical decision theory).

---

*This material may be omitted at this time, and studied when it is needed (e.g., in Chapter 12).

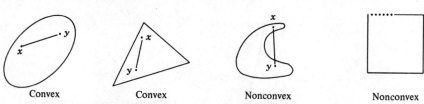

| Convex | Convex | Nonconvex | Nonconvex |

Figure 6.1-2. Some convex and nonconvex sets.

Recall that the set of all **vectors x** of k real numbers $x_1, \ldots, x_k$ is denoted by $\mathscr{R}^k$, and that we write vectors as columns

$$\mathbf{x} = \begin{pmatrix} x_1 \\ x_2 \\ \vdots \\ x_k \end{pmatrix}.$$

The **transpose** of $\mathbf{x}$, say $\mathbf{x}'$, is a row vector $(x_1, \ldots, x_k)$. The **inner product** is $\mathbf{x}'\mathbf{y} = x_1 y_1 + \cdots + x_k y_k = \sum_{i=1}^{k} x_i y_i$. The **origin** is the zero vector $\mathbf{0} = (0, 0, \ldots, 0)$.

Also, a subset S of the set of vectors $\mathscr{R}^k$ is **closed** if every limit point of S is a point in S. The **distance** from $\mathbf{x}$ to $\mathbf{y}$ (if $\mathbf{x}, \mathbf{y} \in \mathscr{R}^k$) is

$$\sqrt{(x_1 - y_1)^2 + (x_2 - y_2)^2 + \cdots + (x_n - y_n)^2} = \sqrt{(\mathbf{x} - \mathbf{y})'(\mathbf{x} - \mathbf{y})}.$$

The **sphere**[1] of radius $\alpha > 0$ about $\mathbf{a}$ is $\{\mathbf{x}: \mathbf{x} \in \mathscr{R}^k, (\mathbf{x} - \mathbf{a})'(\mathbf{x} - \mathbf{a}) \le \alpha^2\}$.

Definition 6.1.8. A subset S of $\mathscr{R}^k$ is called **convex** if $\mathbf{x}, \mathbf{y} \in S$ implies $\lambda \mathbf{x} + (1 - \lambda)\mathbf{y} \in S$ for all λ with $0 < \lambda < 1$. (This means S is convex if all of the line joining each two points of S, is itself in S. See Figure 6.1-2.)

Definition 6.1.9. A function $f(\mathbf{x})$, which has values in $\mathscr{R}$ and is defined for all $\mathbf{x}$ in some convex subset S of $\mathscr{R}^k$, is called **convex** if (for all $0 < \beta < 1$, $\mathbf{x} \in S$, $\mathbf{y} \in S$)

$$f(\beta \mathbf{x} + (1 - \beta)\mathbf{y}) \le \beta f(\mathbf{x}) + (1 - \beta)f(\mathbf{y}).$$

Figure 6.1-3 illustrates the convex function $f(x) = 1/x$ on $S = \{x: x \in \mathscr{R}, x > 0\}$. Of course, $f(x)$ is not defined for $x = 0$ and is not convex if points $x < 0$ are allowed in S; but it is only claimed that, on this particular $S = \{x: x \in \mathscr{R}, x > 0\}$, $f(x) = 1/x$ is a convex function.

---

[1] Or "ball," or "solid sphere," or "spherical cell."

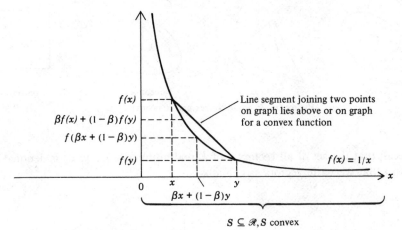

$$S \subseteq \mathscr{R}, S \text{ convex}$$

Figure 6.1-3. Convex function $f(x) = 1/x$ on $S = \{x : x \in \mathscr{R}, x > 0\}$.

Theorem 6.1.10. Jensen's Inequality. If $f(\mathbf{x})$ is a convex function defined on $S \neq \varnothing$, $S \subseteq \mathscr{R}^k$, and if $\mathbf{Z}$ is a k-dimensional r.v. such that $E\mathbf{Z}$ exists[2] and $P[\mathbf{Z} \in S] = 1$, then $E\mathbf{Z} \in S$ and (provided $Ef(\mathbf{Z})$ exists)

$$f(E\mathbf{Z}) \leq Ef(\mathbf{Z}).$$

Example 6.1.11. It is relatively easy to show (check this) that $f(x) = x^2$ is a convex function on the real line. Therefore, by Jensen's Inequality, for any r.v. X we have $f(EX) \leq Ef(X)$, namely $(EX)^2 \leq E(X^2)$. We already know this fact, since it follows from $\text{Var}(X) = E(X^2) - (EX)^2 \geq 0$.

Example 6.1.12. It can be shown (check this) that $f(x) = e^x$ is a convex function on the real line. Therefore, by Jensen's Inequality, for any r.v. X we have $f(EX) \leq Ef(X)$, namely

$$e^{EX} \leq E(e^X) \tag{6.1.13}$$

or (taking logarithms of each side)

$$E(X) \leq \ln\left(E(e^X)\right). \tag{6.1.14}$$

This fact (which is not obvious or easily proven by other methods) is important

---

[2] In Chapter 5, moments were discussed with regard to only a univariate r.v. X (which was allowed to be a function of, say, $\mathbf{Y} = (Y_1, \ldots, Y_n)$). By such a notation as $E\mathbf{Z}$, we simply mean $(EZ_1, \ldots, EZ_k)$; similarly, $\text{Var}(\mathbf{Z})$ simply means $(\text{Var}(Z_1), \ldots, \text{Var}(Z_k))$, and so on. [*Note:* The notation $\text{Var}(\mathbf{Z})$ is often used to denote the variance-covariance matrix, though we do not do so in this book.]

in advanced statistical theory (e.g., in proving the consistency of maximum likelihood estimators (Dudewicz (1976), p. 199)).

PROBLEMS FOR SECTION 6.1

6.1.1 Let X be an r.v. with mean μ and variance σ^2. Let $k > 0$ be fixed. Show that

(a) $P(|X - \mu| \geq k\sigma) \leq \dfrac{1}{k^2}$.

(b) $P(|X - \mu| < k\sigma) > 1 - \dfrac{1}{k^2}$.

(The above are alternate versions of Chebyshev's Inequality, Theorem 6.1.1.)

6.1.2 Let r.v. X have probability function

$$p_X(x) = \begin{cases} 1/8 & \text{if } x = -1 \\ 6/8 & \text{if } x = 0 \\ 1/8 & \text{if } x = +1 \\ 0 & \text{otherwise.} \end{cases}$$

Using this distribution, show that the bound for Chebyshev's Inequality cannot (without additional assumptions on the distribution of X) be improved.

6.1.3 For the following distributions, compute the exact probabilities $P(|X - \mu| < k\sigma)$ for $k = 1, 2, 3$, and compare them with the Chebyshev bounds.

(a) $X \sim N(0, \sigma^2)$.

(b) $f_X(x) = (1/\sqrt{2\pi})e^{-x^2/2}$ for all x.

(c) $X \sim B(n = 10, p = .3)$.

(d) $X \sim B(n = 10, p = .4)$.

(e) $X \sim B(n = 10, p = .5)$.

(f) $X \sim B(n = 10, p = .6)$.

(g) X Poisson with mean 4.

(h) $f_X(x) = (1/2)e^{-|x|}$ for all x.

(i) $X \sim \chi_9^2(0)$.

(j) $X \sim \chi_{25}^2(0)$.

6.1.4 Let $X_1, X_2, \ldots, X_k$ be independent and identically distributed r.v.'s with probability function $p_X(x) = 1/n$ if $x = 1, 2, \ldots, n$ (and $= 0$ otherwise). Let $Y_k = \max(X_1, \ldots, X_k)$ and $Y_1 = \min(X_1, \ldots, X_k)$. Show that $E(Y_1 + Y_k) = n + 1$.

6.1.5 Use Markov's Inequality for $a = 1, 2, 3$ to compute upper bounds for $P(X \geq k\mu)$, $k = 1, 2, 3, \ldots$ where X is a strictly positive r.v. and $E(X^r) < \infty$ for $r = 1, 2, 3$.

6.1.6 Let $X_1, X_2, \ldots, X_n$ be independent and identically distributed r.v.'s, each distributed as discrete uniform over the set $\{1, 2, 3, \ldots, n\}$. Let X denote one of $X_1, X_2, \ldots, X_n$ chosen at random. Note that

$$E(X|X_1, \ldots, X_n) = \frac{X_1 + X_2 + \cdots + X_n}{n} = \sum_{i=1}^{n} X_i/n = \overline{X}_n,$$

$$\text{Var}(X|X_1, \ldots, X_n) = \sum_{i=1}^{n} \left(X_i - \overline{X}_n\right)^2/n = s_n^{*2}.$$

Compute the Chebyshev bound for $P(|X - \overline{X}_n| > ks_n^* | X_1, \ldots, X_n)$ and for $P(|X - \overline{X}_n| > ks_n^*)$.

6.1.7 Let $X_1, X_2, \ldots, X_n$, X be independent and identically distributed r.v.'s. Consider a Chebyshev-type inequality for $P(|X - \overline{X}_n| > ks_n^*)$.

6.2.   CONVERGENCE CONCEPTS; LAWS OF LARGE NUMBERS

Let $Z_1, \ldots, Z_n$ be a sequence of jointly distributed r.v.'s (for $n \geq 1$) defined on the same sample space Ω. Let Z be another r.v. defined on this same space. We will consider now what can be meant by Z_n "tending (or converging) to" Z.

Definition 6.2.1.   We say Z_n **converges to Z with probability one (w.p. 1)** if $P[\lim_{n \to \infty} Z_n = Z] = 1$. (This is also called **almost sure (a.s.) convergence**, or **almost everywhere (a.e. or p.p.) convergence**, or **strong convergence**.)

Definition 6.2.2.   We say Z_n **converges to Z in probability** $(Z_n \overset{P}{\to} Z)$ if for every $\varepsilon > 0$

$$\lim_{n \to \infty} P[|Z_n - Z| > \varepsilon] = 0.$$

(This is also called **stochastic convergence**, or **convergence in measure**, or **weak convergence**.)

Definition 6.2.3.   We say Z_n **converges to Z in mean square** if

$$\lim_{n \to \infty} E(Z_n - Z)^2 = 0.$$

(We also say $Z_n \to Z$ in $\mathscr{L}_2$, or $Z_n \overset{2}{\to} Z$.)

Definition 6.2.4.   We say Z_n **converges to Z in distribution or in law** $(Z_n \overset{d}{\to} Z)$ if

$$\lim_{n \to \infty} F_{Z_n}(t) = F_Z(t)$$

at each point t where $F_Z(\cdot)$ is continuous. In such a case, we also say that $F_n(t) \equiv F_{Z_n}(t)$ **converges weakly**[3] to $F(t) \equiv F_Z(t)$ and write $F_n \to F$.

The relationships among these various types of convergence are given in the following theorem. For our purposes, which are statistical, convergence in probability and in distribution are the central concepts.

---

[3] This is also called **complete convergence** as well as **weak convergence**.

Theorem 6.2.5.

$$(Z_n \to Z \text{ w.p. } 1) \qquad\qquad (Z_n \overset{d}{\to} Z)$$

$$\searrow \qquad \nearrow$$

$$(Z_n \not\to Z)$$

$$\nearrow \qquad\qquad \searrow$$

$$(Z_n \to Z \text{ in } \mathscr{L}_2) \qquad\qquad \begin{pmatrix} \text{There is a subsequence} \\ n_k \text{ such that} \\ Z_{n_k} \to Z \text{ w.p. } 1 \end{pmatrix}$$

We omit the proof of Theorem 6.2.5 (parts of which involve advanced material) and give an example.

Example 6.2.6. Let X_n be a sequence of r.v.'s defined by

$$X_n = \begin{cases} 0, & \text{with probability } 1 - \left(\tfrac{1}{2}\right)^n \\ 1, & \text{with probability } \left(\tfrac{1}{2}\right)^n \end{cases}$$

for $n = 1, 2, 3, \ldots$. Then it can be shown that $P(\lim_{n \to \infty} X_n = 0) = 1$, hence $X_n \to 0$ w.p. 1. Since (for all n) $E(X_n) = \left(\tfrac{1}{2}\right)^n$, $E(X_n^2) = \left(\tfrac{1}{2}\right)^n$, and $\text{Var}(X_n) = (2^n - 1)/2^{2n}$, by Markov's Inequality we have that (for every $\varepsilon > 0$)

$$P\left(|X_n| \geq \varepsilon\right) \leq \frac{1}{2^n \varepsilon^2},$$

hence

$$\lim_{n \to \infty} P\left(|X_n| \geq \varepsilon\right) = 0$$

and thus the sequence X_n converges in probability to a r.v. X that is "degenerate at zero" (i.e., takes on value 0 with probability 1). Finally, also note that

$$E(X_n - X)^2 = E\left(X_n^2\right) = \left(\tfrac{1}{2}\right)^n \to 0,$$

so that $X_n \to X$ in $\mathscr{L}_2$.

In later chapters we will see that the most important types of convergence in statistics are convergence in probability and in distribution. (Both of these convergence concepts are called "weak" types of convergence, and are in general easier to prove than the less useful types called "strong" convergences, such as that in Definition 6.2.1.) We now give a theorem called *a* Weak Law of Large Numbers, which asserts that in many cases the sample mean $(X_1 + \cdots + X_n)/n$ converges in probability to $E(X_1 + \cdots + X_n)/n$, which furnishes a general method for proving weak convergence; we follow this with several examples.

Theorem 6.2.7. Weak Law of Large Numbers (WLLN). Let $X_1, \ldots, X_n$ be independent random variables such that $EX_i = a$, $\sigma^2(X_i) = b^2$ $(i = 1, \ldots, n)$.

Let $\delta > 0$ and $\varepsilon > 0$ be arbitrary. Then there exists $M(\varepsilon, \delta)$ such that for all $n > M(\varepsilon, \delta)$

$$P\left[\left|\frac{X_1 + \cdots + X_n}{n} - a\right| > \delta\right] < \varepsilon.$$

$\left(\text{More concisely, } \dfrac{X_1 + \cdots + X_n}{n} \twoheadrightarrow a.\right)$

Proof: Let $Z_n = (X_1 + \cdots + X_n)/n$. Then

$$EZ_n = \frac{1}{n}na = a, \qquad \sigma^2(Z_n) = \frac{1}{n^2}n\sigma^2(X_1) = \frac{b^2}{n},$$

and by Chebyshev's Inequality

$$P\left[\left|\frac{X_1 + \cdots + X_n}{n} - a\right| > \delta\right] \leq \frac{\sigma^2(Z_n)}{\delta^2} = \frac{b^2}{n\delta^2}.$$

Let $M(\varepsilon, \delta)$ be the smallest positive integer n such that $b^2/(n\delta^2) < \varepsilon$ and the theorem follows.   ∎

Note that the proof of Theorem 6.2.7 illustrates **a general method for proving stochastic convergence.** Let $X_1, \ldots, X_n$ be any r.v.'s such that their means and variances exist. Let $S_n/n = (X_1 + \cdots + X_n)/n$. We say $X_1, \ldots, X_n$ obey the WLLN if $S_n/n - E(S_n/n) \twoheadrightarrow 0$. By Chebyshev's Inequality,

$$P\left[\left|\frac{S_n}{n} - E\left(\frac{S_n}{n}\right)\right| > \delta\right] \leq \frac{\sigma^2(S_n/n)}{\delta^2}. \tag{6.2.8}$$

Thus, $\sigma^2(S_n/n) \to 0$ will imply the WLLN for $X_1, \ldots, X_n$.

Example 6.2.9. Suppose a coin has probability $p (0 < p < 1)$ of turning up heads when flipped in a certain manner, and we flip it independently n times. Let (for $i = 1, \ldots, n$)

$$X_i = \begin{cases} 1, & \text{if the } i\text{th toss yields a head} \\ 0, & \text{otherwise.} \end{cases}$$

Then we may decide to estimate p by

$$\frac{S_n}{n} = \frac{X_1 + \cdots + X_n}{n},$$

and we desire to know in what sense is this close to p. The WLLN provides one answer. Also, our general method will allow us to consider the question: If our trials are correlated, how "large" can the correlation be and yet have $S_n/n \not\xrightarrow{P} p$? [We are interested in convergence as $n \to \infty$ because, even though the actual n is "small" or "moderate" in many cases, it is helpful to know your procedure would behave well for n very large $(n \to \infty)$. We intuitively feel that if a procedure cannot do well with lots of observations it probably is not very good with just a few.]

Example 6.2.10. Let $X_1, X_2, \ldots$ be a sequence of independent r.v.'s, each with exponential p.d.f. $f(x) = (1/\lambda)\exp(-x/\lambda)$ for $x > 0$. Then $\overline{X} \not\xrightarrow{P} \lambda$.

To see this, recall that $E(X_i) = \lambda = \sqrt{\text{Var}(X_i)}$ $(i = 1, 2, \ldots)$ with $0 < \lambda < \infty$, hence by Chebyshev's Inequality

$$P\left(\left|\overline{X} - \lambda\right| \geq \varepsilon\right) \leq \sigma_{\overline{X}}^2/\varepsilon^2$$

for $\varepsilon > 0$. Since $E(\overline{X}) = \lambda$ and $\text{Var}(\overline{X}) = \sigma_{\overline{X}}^2 = \lambda^2/n$, it follows that

$$\lim_{n \to \infty} P\left(\left|\overline{X} - \lambda\right| \geq \varepsilon\right) \leq \lim_{n \to \infty} \lambda^2/(n\varepsilon) = 0,$$

that is, $\overline{X} \xrightarrow{P} \lambda$. (Alternatively, this result follows directly from Theorem 6.2.7, the WLLN.)

The implications of the WLLN are strong for both theoretical and applied statistics, since it implies that *if* one takes a random sample of size n from *any* population with mean μ and finite variance, *then* as n increases the sample mean "gets closer and closer to the population mean."

As in Example 6.2.10, we can also show that

(i) If $X_1, X_2, \ldots$ are independent Poisson r.v.'s with mean μ, then $\overline{X} \xrightarrow{P} \mu$.
(ii) If $X_1, X_2, \ldots$ are independent $N(\mu, \sigma^2)$ r.v.'s, then $\overline{X} \xrightarrow{P} \mu$; and so forth.

Note that in the WLLN the r.v.'s do *not* have to be identically distributed, they just need to have the same mean and the same finite variance. (Later we give an even more general WLLN.)

Chebyshev's Inequality is a very strong tool for showing weak convergence, as we see in the following example.

Example 6.2.11. Let $X_1, X_2, \ldots, X_n$ be independent $N(\mu, \sigma^2)$ r.v.'s. Recall (Theorem 5.5.34) that for

$$s_n^2 = \sum_{i=1}^{n} \frac{\left(X_i - \overline{X}_n\right)^2}{n-1}, \qquad \overline{X}_n = \sum_{i=1}^{n} X_i/n$$

we know that $(n-1)s_n^2/\sigma^2 = \sum_{i=1}^{n}(X_i - \overline{X}_n)^2/\sigma^2$ has the chi-square distribution with $n - 1$ degrees of freedom, and (Example 5.5.5)

$$E\left(\frac{(n-1)s_n^2}{\sigma^2}\right) = n - 1 \quad \left(\text{or } E\left(s_n^2\right) = \sigma^2\right)$$

and

$$\text{Var}\left(\frac{(n-1)s_n^2}{\sigma^2}\right) = 2(n-1) \quad \left(\text{or } \text{Var}\left(s_n^2\right) = 2\sigma^4/(n-1)\right).$$

Therefore, by Chebyshev's Inequality for any given $\varepsilon > 0$

$$P\left(\left|s_n^2 - \sigma^2\right| \geq \varepsilon\right) \leq \frac{1}{\varepsilon^2}\frac{2\sigma^4}{n-1} \to 0 \text{ as } n \to \infty.$$

Hence $s_n^2 \overset{P}{\to} \sigma^2$. (In fact, it can be shown that $s_n^2 \to \sigma^2$ in $\mathcal{L}_2$.)

Example 6.2.12. Convergence in Probability of the Empiric d.f. Suppose that $X_1, \ldots, X_n$ are independent r.v.'s, each with d.f. $F(x)$. Often $F(x)$ is unknown, and in Definition 4.8.1 we introduced a way to estimate it called the **empiric d.f.**:

$$F_n(x|X_1,\ldots,X_n) = \frac{(\text{Number of } X_1,\ldots,X_n \text{ that are } \leqslant x)}{n}.$$

We will now show that $F_n(x) \to F(x)$ in $\mathcal{L}_2$ [and hence, by Theorem 6.2.5, $F_n(x) \overset{P}{\to} F(x)$], where we have abbreviated $F_n(x|X_1,\ldots,X_n)$ to $F_n(x)$. Now let (for $i = 1,\ldots,n$)

$$W_i = \begin{cases} 1, & \text{if } X_i \leq x \\ 0, & \text{if } X_i > x. \end{cases}$$

Then $W_1,\ldots,W_n$ are independent r.v.'s (since $X_1,\ldots,X_n$ are independent r.v.'s), each with $P(W_i = 1) = P(X_i \leq x) = F(x)$ and $P(W_i = 0) = P(X_i > x) = 1 - P(X_i \leq x) = 1 - F(x)$, so that

$$E(W_i) = 1 \cdot F(x) + 0 \cdot (1 - F(x)) = F(x),$$

$$E(W_i^2) = 1^2 \cdot F(x) + 0^2 \cdot (1 - F(x)) = F(x),$$

$$\text{Var}(W_i) = E(W_i^2) - (EW_i)^2 = F(x) - (F(x))^2 = F(x)(1 - F(x)).$$

Since

$$F_n(x) = \frac{W_1 + \cdots + W_n}{n},$$

we have that

$$E(F_n(x)) = F(x), \qquad \text{Var}(F_n(x)) = \frac{F(x)(1 - F(x))}{n}.$$

Therefore,

$$E(F_n(x) - F(x))^2 = \text{Var}(F_n(x)) = \frac{F(x)(1 - F(x))}{n} \to 0$$

as $n \to \infty$, that is, $F_n(x) \to F(x)$ in $\mathscr{L}_2$ as was to be shown.

In fact, the result we have given can be strengthened considerably to show that the biggest difference between $F_n(x)$ and $F(x)$ over all x, goes to zero as n increases. This result is sometimes called the **Fundamental Theorem of Statistics**:

Theorem 6.2.13. Glivenko-Cantelli Theorem. Suppose that independent r.v.'s $Y_1, \ldots, Y_n$ each have d.f. $F(\cdot)$. Then for any $\varepsilon > 0$, as $n \to \infty$,

$$P\left[\sup_x |F_n(x \mid Y_1, \ldots, Y_n) - F(x)| < \varepsilon\right] \to 1. \qquad (6.2.14)$$

[That is, $\sup_x |F_n(x \mid Y_1, \ldots, Y_n) - F(x)| \overset{P}{\to} 0$.] In fact, the weak convergence of (6.2.14) can be replaced by strong convergence (see Definitions 6.2.1 and 6.2.2 for details of these two notions).

Note 6.2.15. The expressions "**sup**" and "**inf**" (abbreviations for "**supremum**" and "**infimum**," respectively) will be used throughout the following chapters. They are essentially "max" and "min" (for "maximum" and "minimum," respectively), with the following proviso. The maximum of a specified set of numbers may not exist (e.g., $\max_{0 < x < 1} x$ does not, since there is *no* largest number x between 0 and 1), but there will be a least number $\geq$ all numbers in the set (e.g., 1 in the case of $\max_{0 < x < 1} x$). We therefore usually write $\sup_{0 < x < 1} x$ (which must exist) instead of $\max_{0 < x < 1} x$ (which often, as in this case, does not exist). (Similarly for inf.) The student not familiar with these notions can simply read "max" for "sup" and "min" for "inf" with little loss.

The following example shows how certain problems have solutions that involve the d.f. $F(x)$, and how the empiric d.f. may be utilized when $F(x)$ is unknown.

Example 6.2.16. A newsboy wishes to determine how many newspapers to purchase from a distributor. He is allowed to purchase $0, 1, 2, \ldots, U$ papers on a specified day, and while each one costs him \$p, each will fetch \$r from a customer (if it sells) and will fetch \$s from a scrappaper dealer (if it fails to sell). Now our newsboy does not know how many newspapers (say X) he will be able to sell today, but on the past n days he could have sold respectively $X_1, X_2, \ldots, X_n$ copies. He is willing to assume that $X_1, X_2, \ldots, X_n$ are independent r.v.'s with some common d.f. (distribution function of demand) $F(\cdot)$, and that today's demand will be independent of past demands, but will have the same d.f. as did past demands.

The boy's father, a statistician, reasons as follows. If my son buys K papers from the distributor, his profit will be (on the average) $E\{P(K, X)\}$ where $P(K, X)$ (the profit if K papers are bought and demand is X) is

$$P(K, X) = \begin{cases} -pK + rX + s(K - X), & \text{if } K \geq X \\ -pK + rK, & \text{if } K < X. \end{cases}$$

Hence, the expected profit is [denoting $P[X = x]$ by $f(x)$ and assuming $\sum_{x=0}^{\infty} f(x) = 1$]

$$\overline{P}_K \equiv E\{P(K, X)\} = \sum_{x=0}^{\infty} P(K, x)f(x)$$

$$= \sum_{x=0}^{K} \{(s - p)K + (r - s)x\}f(x) + \sum_{x=K+1}^{\infty} (r - p)Kf(x)$$

$$= (s - p)K \sum_{x=0}^{K} f(x) + (r - s) \sum_{x=0}^{K} xf(x) + (r - p)K \sum_{x=K+1}^{\infty} f(x) \qquad (6.2.17)$$

$$= (s - p)KF(K) + (r - s) \sum_{x=0}^{K} xf(x) + (r - p)K[1 - F(K)].$$

Now we may wish to choose K so as to maximize $\overline{P}_K$; then we simply use equation (6.2.17) to find the appropriate value of K *if* we know $F(\cdot)$. Here we do not know $F(\cdot)$, but we do have information about it in the form of $X_1, \ldots, X_n$, independent observations with the same d.f. $F(\cdot)$. One approach [suggested by Weiss (1961), pp. 134–135] is to replace $F(\cdot)$ by $F_n(\cdot | X_1, \ldots, X_n)$. Other approaches have also been suggested [e.g., see Hayes (1971)]. The newsboy problem is a special case of a statistical decision problem; we will study such problems in detail in Chapter 12.

Note that logic requires $s < p < r$ (if $s \geq p$, he can buy all U papers and either make a profit by selling them for scrap ($s > p$) or at least break even on unsold papers by selling them for scrap ($s = p$); if $p \geq r$, selling to customers is a losing proposition and he should either go out of business or sell papers for scrap). Of course, logic does not always prevail; thus, during the 1960s in the United States, certain coins cost, for example, $1 at the bank but could be melted down in large quantities and sold as metal for $1.25.

In our next several examples we concentrate on convergence in distribution (whereas to this point our examples have concentrated on convergence w.p. 1, in probability, and in mean square).

Example 6.2.18. Let $X_1, \ldots, X_n$ be independent r.v.'s with p.d.f. uniform on $(0, \theta)$ where θ is positive. Let $Y_n = \max(X_1, \ldots, X_n)$, and define the r.v. Z by $P(Z = \theta,) = 1$. Then $Y_n \overset{d}{\to} Z$.

To show this, note that

$$F_{Y_n}(t) = P(Y_n \le t) = P(\max(X_1, \ldots, X_n) \le t) = (P(X_1 \le t))^n$$

$$= \left(\int_{-\infty}^{t} f_{X_1}(x) \, dx \right)^n$$

$$= \begin{cases} 1, & \text{if } t \ge \theta \\ \left(\dfrac{t}{\theta} \right)^n, & \text{if } 0 \le t < \theta \\ 0, & \text{if } t < 0, \end{cases}$$

so that

$$\lim_{n \to \infty} F_{Y_n}(t) = \begin{cases} 1, & \text{if } t \ge \theta \\ 0, & \text{if } t < \theta \end{cases}$$

which equals the d.f. of Z, hence by Definition 6.2.4 $Y_n \overset{d}{\to} Z$.

Example 6.2.19. Let $X_1, X_2, \ldots, X_n$ be independent r.v.'s with p.d.f. $f(x)$, let $Y_n = \max(X_1, X_2, \ldots, X_n)$, and define

$$Z_n = n \left(1 - \int_{-\infty}^{Y_n} f(x) \, dx \right) = n(1 - F(Y_n)).$$

Find Z such that $Z_n \overset{d}{\to} Z$.

Here, for $0 < t < n$,

$$F_{Z_n}(t) = P(Z_n \le t) = P \left(\int_{-\infty}^{Y_n} f(x) \, dx \ge 1 - \frac{t}{n} \right)$$

$$= P \left(F(Y_n) \ge 1 - \frac{t}{n} \right) = P \left(Y_n \ge F^{-1} \left(1 - \frac{t}{n} \right) \right)$$

$$= 1 - P \left(Y_n \le F^{-1} \left(1 - \frac{t}{n} \right) \right) = 1 - \left(P \left[X_1 \le F^{-1} \left(1 - \frac{t}{n} \right) \right] \right)^n$$

$$= 1 - \left(1 - \frac{t}{n} \right)^n,$$

so that

$$F_{Z_n}(t) = \begin{cases} 1, & \text{if } t \ge n \\ 1 - \left(1 - \dfrac{t}{n} \right)^n, & \text{if } 0 \le t < n \\ 0, & \text{if } t < 0. \end{cases}$$

Hence

$$\lim_{n \to \infty} F_{Z_n}(t) = \begin{cases} 1 - e^{-t}, & \text{if } t \geq 0 \\ 0, & \text{if } t < 0 \end{cases}$$

which is the d.f. of an exponential random variable with mean 1, hence $Z_n \xrightarrow{d} Z$ for Z an exponential r.v. with mean 1.

Example 6.2.20. Let $X_1, X_2, \ldots, X_n$ be independent $N(0, \sigma^2)$ r.v.'s, and $Z_n = \sqrt{n}\, \overline{X}_n = \sqrt{n} \sum_{i=1}^{n} \dfrac{X_i}{n}$. Then $Z_n \xrightarrow{d} Z$, where Z is a $N(0, \sigma^2)$ r.v.

To see this, we note that each independent X_i is $N(0, \sigma^2)$, hence $\overline{X}_n$ is $N(0, \sigma^2/n)$, and $\sqrt{n}\, \overline{X}_n$ is $N(0, \sigma^2)$. As this distribution does not involve n, $Z_n = \sqrt{n}\, \overline{X}_n$ achieves its limiting distribution for every value of n.

Example 6.2.21. Suppose that in Example 6.2.20 we take $Z_n = \overline{X}_n$. Then Z_n is $N(0, \sigma^2/n)$, hence

$$F_{\overline{X}_n}(t) = P(\overline{X}_n \leq t) = \Phi\left(\frac{\sqrt{n}\, t}{\sigma}\right)$$

where $\Phi(\cdot)$ denotes the standard normal d.f. (see Problem 4.6), and

$$\lim_{n \to \infty} F_{\overline{X}_n}(t) = \lim_{n \to \infty} \Phi\left(\frac{\sqrt{n}\, t}{\sigma}\right) = \begin{cases} 1, & \text{if } t > 0 \\ \frac{1}{2}, & \text{if } t = 0 \\ 0, & \text{if } t < 0. \end{cases}$$

This limit is not a distribution function [because it is not continuous from the right; see Theorem 3.1.3, part (iii)]. However, let r.v. U put the probability mass of 1 at zero. Then $\overline{X}_n \xrightarrow{d} U$.

The general point is that, since by definition $Z_n \xrightarrow{d} Z$ iff $F_{Z_n}(t) \to F_Z(t)$ at each point **where $F_Z(t)$ is continuous**, therefore points such as $t = 0$ where $\lim_{n \to \infty} F_{\overline{X}_n}(0) = \frac{1}{2}$ are not a problem because $F_U(t)$ is not continuous at $t = 0$.

Not all sequences Z_n of r.v.'s converge to a limit, as the following example illustrates.

Example 6.2.22. Consider the sequence of r.v.'s Z_n with d.f.'s

$$F_n(x) = \begin{cases} 1, & \text{if } x \geq n \\ 0, & \text{if } x < n. \end{cases}$$

[Note that Z_n has $P(Z_n = n) = 1$.] Then for all x

$$\lim_{n \to \infty} F_n(x) = 0,$$

which is not a distribution function of any r.v. In such a case we also say that the probability has **escaped to infinity**. (We also say this if the limit is 1 for all x.) Thus, **it is quite possible for a sequence of distribution functions to converge to a limit that is not a distribution function. In addition $F_n(x)$ may not converge at all** (e.g., if Z_n is $N(0, 1)$ for n odd and $N(1, 1)$ for n even this will occur). **However, it can be shown that some subsequence always converges and that in the case of boundedness it converges to a d.f.** [For further details, which are beyond the scope of this book, see Feller (1966), p. 261.]

In the foregoing we directly found $\lim_{n \to \infty} F_{Z_n}(x)$ in several examples where we sought to show $Z_n \xrightarrow{d} Z$. **A second technique of obtaining the limit uses moment-generating functions.** In Chapter 5, we showed how to obtain the distributions of sums and averages of r.v.'s using m.g.f.'s (see Theorem 5.5.26ff) since (see Uniqueness Theorem 5.5.12) m.g.f.'s are unique (when they exist) and characterize the d.f.

For use in limiting cases we now give Lévy's Continuity Theorem for characteristic functions, and a version for m.g.f.'s.

Theorem 6.2.23. Lévy's Continuity Theorem. Let $Z_1, Z_2, \ldots$ be a sequence of r.v.'s; let the d.f. of Z_n be F_n and let the ch.f. of Z_n be ϕ_n. Then $F_n \to F$ (a d.f.) iff $\phi_n(t) \to \phi(t)$ for every point t and $\phi(t)$ is continuous at $t = 0$. (In either case ϕ is the ch.f. of F, and the convergence $\phi_n \to \phi$ is uniform in every finite interval.)

Theorem 6.2.24. Continuity Theorem for m.g.f.'s. Let $Z_1, Z_2, \ldots$ be a sequence of r.v.'s; let the d.f. of Z_n be F_n and let the m.g.f. of Z_n be $\psi_{Z_n}(t)$ which exists for $|t| < \varepsilon$ ($\varepsilon > 0$) for every n. Then $F_n \to F$ (a d.f.) iff $\psi_{Z_n}(t) \to \psi_Z(t)$ for every point $t > 0$ and $\psi_Z(t) \to 1$ as $t \to 0$. Here $\psi_Z(t)$ is the m.g.f. of F and exists for $|t| \le \varepsilon_1 < \varepsilon$, for some $\varepsilon_1 > 0$.

As an application of the Continuity Theorem for m.g.f.'s we now obtain a **second general method for proving stochastic convergence** of a r.v. to a constant (the first method was given by the method of Chebyshev's Inequality—see the discussion at equation (6.2.8)). As an illustration we prove Khinchin's Theorem and then consider some illustrative examples.

Corollary 6.2.25. A r.v. $X_n \xrightarrow{P} c$ (a constant) iff the d.f. of X_n, $F_n \to F$ where $F(x) = 0$ for $x < c$ and $F(x) = 1$ for $x \ge c$; this occurs iff $\psi_{X_n}(t) \to e^{ct}$ for all t.

Proof: (1a) Suppose that $X_n \xrightarrow{P} c$ (a constant). Then for any $\delta > 0$, $P[|X_n - c| \ge \delta] \to 0$. Hence, $F_n(x) = P[X_n \le x] \to 0$ for $x < c$, and $F_n(x) = P[X_n \le x] \to 1$ for $x > c$. Thus, $F_n \to F$ as stated.

(1b) Suppose $F_n \to F$ with $F(x) = 0$ for $x < c$ and $F(x) = 1$ for $x \ge c$. Then for any $\delta > 0$, we have

$$P[|X_n - c| \ge \delta] = P[X_n \le c - \delta] + P[X_n \ge c + \delta]$$

$$= P[X_n \le c - \delta] + 1 - P[X_n < c + \delta]$$

$$\to 0 + 1 - 1 = 0,$$

so $X_n \xrightarrow{P} c$.

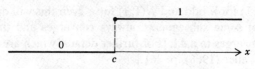

Figure 6.2-1. $F(x)$ for Corollary 6.2.25.

(2) The specified d.f., $F(x)$ with $F(x) = 0$ for $x < c$ and $F(x) = 1$ for $x \geq c$ (see Figure 6.2-1), corresponds to a r.v. X such that $P(X = c) = 1$. Such a r.v. X has moment-generating function $\psi_X(t) = Ee^{tX} = e^{ct}$, for which $\psi_X(t) \to 1$ as $t \to 0$. By the Continuity Theorem, $F_n \to F$ iff $\psi_{X_n}(t) \to \psi_X(t)$ for all $t > 0$ and $\psi_X(t) \to 1$ as $t \to 0$. Hence, the second "iff" of the corollary follows. ∎

Theorem 6.2.26. Khinchin's Theorem. If $X_1, X_2, \ldots$ are independent and identically distributed r.v.'s and EX_1 exists ($EX_1 = a$, say), then

$$\frac{X_1 + \cdots + X_n}{n} \xrightarrow{P} a.$$

Proof:

$$\psi_{\frac{X_1 + \cdots + X_n}{n}}(t) = \psi_{\frac{X_1}{n} + \cdots + \frac{X_n}{n}}(t)$$

$$= \left[\psi_{X_1/n}(t) \right]^n, \quad \text{by Theorem 5.5.26}$$

$$= \left[\psi_{X_1}\left(\frac{t}{n}\right) \right]^n, \quad \text{by Definition 5.5.1}$$

$$= \left[1 + \frac{EX_1}{1!} \frac{t}{n} + o\left(\frac{t}{n}\right) \right]^n, \quad \text{by Theorem 5.5.17}$$

$$= \left[1 + \frac{at + no(t/n)}{n} \right]^n$$

$$\to e^{at}, \quad \text{as } n \to \infty.$$

The result then follows by Corollary 6.2.25. Note that we have not used the well-known result

$$\lim_{n \to \infty} \left(1 + \frac{a}{n} \right)^n = e^a,$$

but rather its slight generalization (see Problem 6.3H)

$$\lim_{n \to \infty} \left(1 + \frac{a_n}{n} \right)^n = e^{\lim_{n \to \infty} a_n}.$$ ∎

Note that Khinchin's Theorem is *a* Weak Law of Large Numbers, just as Theorem 6.2.7 was: Both assert conditions under which $\overline{X} \overset{P}{\to} c$ for some constant c. Khinchin's form of the WLLN is a very strong result; while our proof of it requires that the m.g.f.'s involved exist (and hence that all moments exist), essentially the same proof using the ch.f. shows the result in full generality.

Example 6.2.27. Convergence in Probability of the Empiric d.f. In Example 6.2.12 we showed that if $X_1, \ldots, X_n$ are independent r.v.'s each with d.f. $F(x)$ then $F_n(x) \overset{P}{\to} F(x)$, where $F_n(x)$ is the empiric d.f. $F_n(x|X_1, \ldots, X_n)$. In that example we used the *first* (Chebyshev's Inequality) method of proof. Now, we use the *second* method's result (Khinchin's Theorem).

Let x be fixed but arbitrary. Let $W_i = 1$ if $X_i \leq x$ (and zero otherwise) for $i = 1, \ldots, n$. Then $W_1, \ldots, W_n$ are independent r.v.'s, each binomial with success probability $P(X_i \leq x) = F(x)$. Hence, $EW_1 = F(x)$ and (by Khinchin's Theorem)

$$\frac{W_1 + \cdots + W_n}{n} \overset{P}{\to} F(x).$$

But

$$\frac{W_1 + \cdots + W_n}{n} = \frac{(\text{Number of } X_1, \ldots, X_n \text{ that are } \leq x)}{n}$$

$$= F_n(x|X_1, \ldots, X_n),$$

so the result follows.

Example 6.2.28. Let $X_1, X_2, \ldots, X_n, \ldots$ be r.v.'s, each with gamma d.f. $G(x|n, \beta, 0)$. Show that X_n/n converges in probability to a constant c, and find c.

The m.g.f. of $Y_n = X_n/n$ is (see Example 5.5.4)

$$\psi_{Y_n}(t) = E(e^{tY_n}) = E(e^{X_n t/n}) = \frac{1}{\left(1 - \beta\dfrac{t}{n}\right)^{n+1}},$$

for which

$$\lim_{n \to \infty} \psi_{Y_n}(t) = \lim_{n \to \infty} \frac{1}{\left(1 - \dfrac{\beta t}{n}\right)^n} \lim_{n \to \infty} \frac{1}{\left(1 - \dfrac{\beta t}{n}\right)} = e^{\beta t} \cdot 1 = e^{\beta t},$$

hence by the Continuity Theorem for m.g.f.'s (Theorem 6.2.24) $Y_n \overset{P}{\to} \beta$.

Example 6.2.29. Let $X_1, \ldots, X_n, \ldots$ be independent Poisson r.v.'s with mean

$\mu > 0$, and let $Y_n = \sqrt{n}\,(\overline{X}_n - \mu)/\sqrt{\mu}$. Show that $Y_n \overset{d}{\to} N(0, 1)$.
Here

$$\psi_{Y_n}(t) = E\big(e^{t\sqrt{n}(\overline{X}_n-\mu)/\sqrt{\mu}}\big) = e^{-\sqrt{n\mu}\,t} \cdot E\big(e^{\sqrt{n}\,\overline{X}_n(t/\sqrt{\mu})}\big)$$

$$= e^{-\sqrt{n\mu}\,t} E\left(e^{\sum_{i=1}^{n} X_i \frac{t}{\sqrt{n\mu}}}\right)$$

$$= e^{-\sqrt{n\mu}\,t}\big(E(e^{X_1 t/\sqrt{n\mu}})\big)^n \qquad \text{by Theorem 5.5.26}$$

$$= e^{-\sqrt{n\mu}\,t}\big(e^{\mu(e^{t/\sqrt{n\mu}}-1)}\big)^n \qquad \text{by Example 5.5.3}$$

$$= e^{-\sqrt{n\mu}\,t} e^{n\mu(e^{t/\sqrt{n\mu}}-1)}.$$

As $n \to \infty$ this m.g.f. becomes an indeterminate form. Although we could rearrange the terms and use l'Hospital's rule, we note and use another method of proceeding that is especially helpful when exponents are involved. We first take the natural logarithm of both sides, and then take the limit:

$$\ln \psi_{Y_n}(t) = -\sqrt{n\mu}\,t + n\mu\big(e^{t/\sqrt{n\mu}} - 1\big)$$

$$= -\sqrt{n\mu}\,t + n\mu\left(1 + \frac{t}{\sqrt{n\mu}} + \frac{t^2}{n\mu}\cdot\frac{1}{2!} + \frac{t^3}{(n\mu)^{3/2}3!} + \cdots - 1\right)$$

$$= \frac{t^2}{2!} + \frac{t^3}{(n\mu)^{1/2}3!} + \frac{t^4}{(n\mu)\cdot 4!} + \cdots$$

for which

$$\lim_{n\to\infty}\big(\ln \psi_{Y_n}(t)\big) = t^2/2,$$

hence

$$\lim_{n\to\infty}\psi_{Y_n}(t) = e^{t^2/2} \equiv \psi(t),$$

which is (see Example 5.5.5) the m.g.f. of a $N(0, 1)$ r.v., hence $Y_n \overset{d}{\to} N(0, 1)$, as was to be shown.

Example 6.2.30. In Section 3.3 we showed that, for large n and small p such that $np = \lambda$ (a constant), the $P(X = k)$ for X a binomial r.v. with n trials and success probability p tends to $P(Y = k)$ for Y a Poisson r.v. with λ as its parameter. We will now show via m.g.f.'s that if $X_n \sim B(n, p)$, then $X_n \overset{d}{\to} X$, a Poisson r.v. with mean λ, provided that np is held constant at value λ.
We have (see equation (5.5.24))

$$\psi_{X_n}(t) = \big(q + pe^t\big)^n = \big(1 - p + pe^t\big)^n = \big(1 - p(1 - e^t)\big)^n,$$

hence (with $\lambda = np$ held constant)

$$\lim_{n \to \infty} \psi_{X_n}(t) = \lim_{n \to \infty} \left(1 + \frac{-\lambda(1 - e^t)}{n}\right)^n = e^{\lambda(e^t - 1)}$$

where we used the result of Problem 6.3H (see the proof of Theorem 6.2.26 also). This limit is (see Example 5.5.3) the m.g.f. of a Poisson r.v. with parameter λ.

As a final note on convergence in distribution, we note that convergence of p.d.f.'s implies convergence in distribution.

Theorem 6.2.31. If X_n has d.f. $F_n(x)$ and p.d.f. $f_n(x)$; X has d.f. $F(x)$ and p.d.f. $f(x)$; and $\lim_{n \to \infty} f_n(x) = f(x)$ for all[4] x, then $F_n \to F$ (i.e., $X_n \overset{d}{\to} X$).

Proof: See Scheffé (1947).

Converses of this result [which state that, under some conditions, if $F_n \to F$ then $f_n(x) \to f(x)$ for all x and that in fact the maximal difference between $f_n(x)$ and $f(x)$ goes to 0 as $n \to \infty$] have also been studied; for details, see Boos (1985). ∎

Example 6.2.32. Let X_n be "displaced exponential" with p.d.f.

$$f_n(x) = \begin{cases} \lambda e^{-\lambda(x-\theta/n)}, & \text{if } x > \theta/n \\ 0, & \text{otherwise} \end{cases}$$

where $\lambda > 0$, so that its d.f. is

$$F_n(x) = \begin{cases} 1 - e^{-\lambda(x-\theta/n)}, & \text{if } x > \theta/n \\ 0, & \text{if } x \le \theta/n. \end{cases}$$

Then

$$\lim_{n \to \infty} f_n(x) = \lambda e^{-\lambda x} \quad (x > 0),$$

the p.d.f. of an exponential r.v. with mean $1/\lambda$, hence by Theorem 6.2.31 $X_n \overset{d}{\to} X$, an exponential r.v. with mean $1/\lambda$. (Note that we can also show directly that $F_n \to F$, hence that $X_n \overset{d}{\to} X$.)

PROBLEMS FOR SECTION 6.2

6.2.1 Let $X_1, X_2, \ldots$ be a sequence of independent and identically distributed r.v.'s with finite mean μ and variance. Show that

(a) $\dfrac{2}{n(n+1)} \sum_{i=1}^{n} iX_i \overset{p}{\to} \mu$.

(b) $\dfrac{6}{n(n+1)(2n+1)} \sum_{i=1}^{n} i^2 X_i \overset{p}{\to} \mu$.

[4] If this limit does not hold for some x values, say for x in the set C, the result is still true as long as $P(X \text{ in } C) = 0$.

6.2.2 Let $X_1, X_2, \ldots$ be a sequence of independent r.v.'s, each with probability distribution $P(X_i = i) = P(X_i = -i) = 1/2$. Show that $\sum_{i=1}^{n} X_i/n$ does not converge in probability to $\mu = 0$.

6.2.3 Let $f_n(x)$ be the p.d.f. of a Student's-t r.v. with n degrees of freedom, and let $\phi(x)$ denote the p.d.f. of a standard normal r.v. Show that $\lim_{n \to \infty} f_n(x) = \phi(x)$ for all x.

6.2.4 Let $X_n \sim \chi_n^2(0)$ and $Y_n = X_n/n$. Show that $\psi_{Y_n}(t) \to e^t$ as $n \to \infty$. (Hence the limiting distribution of Y_n is degenerate at 1.)

6.2.5 Consider the uniform distribution on the interval $[0, \theta]$ for some $\theta > 0$. Show that $Y_n \xrightarrow{P} \theta$, where Y_n is the largest order statistic in a random sample of size n from this distribution.

6.2.6 If $X_1, X_2, X_3, \ldots$ is a sequence of geometric r.v.'s with respective probabilities of success $p, p/2, p/3, \ldots$ ($0 < p < 1$), determine whether $X_n/n \xrightarrow{d} X$ for some r.v. X; if so, find the distribution of X.

6.2.7 Let X be an r.v. with population median M. Let $X_1, X_2, \ldots, X_n$ be a random sample of size n, and $\tilde{X}_n$ the sample median. Show that $\tilde{X}_n \xrightarrow{P} M$.

6.2.8 Let X be a continuous r.v. with d.f. $F(x)$. Show that $nF(Y_2) \xrightarrow{d} G(x|1,1,0)$ where Y_2 is the next-to-smallest order statistic in a random sample of size n.

6.2.9 **A Generalized WLLN.** Let $X_1, X_2, \ldots$ be a sequence of r.v.'s (not necessarily independent or identically distributed) with $\mathrm{Corr}(X_i, X_j) = 0$ ($i \neq j$). Let $E(X_i) = \mu_i$ with $|\mu_i| < \infty$ and $\mathrm{Var}(X_i) < \infty$, and consider

$$\overline{X}_n = \frac{1}{n} \sum_{i=1}^{n} X_i, \qquad \overline{\mu}_n = \frac{1}{n} \sum_{i=1}^{n} \mu_i.$$

Show that

$$\overline{X}_n - \overline{\mu}_n \xrightarrow{P} 0.$$

6.2.10 Let $X_1, X_2, \ldots$ be independent r.v.'s, X_i having an exponential distribution with mean $2^{-i/2}$. Prove or disprove: the Generalized WLLN of Problem 6.2.9 holds for this sequence of r.v.'s.

6.2.11 Let $X_1, X_2, X_3, \ldots$ be a sequence of independent and identically distributed r.v.'s, each uniform on $[0, 1]$. For the geometric mean

$$G_n = (X_1 X_2 \ldots X_n)^{1/n},$$

show that $G_n \xrightarrow{P} c$ for some finite number c. Find c.

6.2.12 Let $X_1, X_2, \ldots$ be independent and identically distributed r.v.'s with finite mean μ and finite variance σ^2, and let $\overline{X}_n = \sum_{i=1}^{n} X_i/n$. Show that $\overline{X}_n \xrightarrow{2} \mu$ (i.e., $\overline{X}_n \to \mu$ in $\mathcal{L}_2$).

6.2.13 Let $X_1, X_2, \ldots$ be independent and identically distributed r.v.'s (not necessarily normal) with $E(X_1^4) < \infty$ and $\mathrm{Var}(X_1) = \sigma^2$. If s_n^2 is as in Example 6.2.11 and $s_n^{*2} = ((n-1)/n)s_n^2$, show that

$$s_n^2 \xrightarrow{P} \sigma^2, \qquad s_n^{*2} \xrightarrow{P} \sigma^2.$$

6.2.14 Let $X_1, X_2, \ldots$ be a sequence of independent Bernoulli r.v.'s with respective success probabilities $p_1, p_2, \ldots$. Show that

$$\frac{1}{n}\left(S_n - \sum_{i=1}^{n} p_i\right) \rightsquigarrow 0,$$

where S_n denotes the total number of successes in the first n trials.

6.2.15 In the setting of Problem 6.2.8, show that

$$n(1 - F(Y_n) + F(Y_1)) \xrightarrow{d} G(x|1,1,0).$$

6.3. CENTRAL LIMIT THEOREM, OTHER LIMIT LAWS, AND THEIR APPLICATIONS

The Central Limit Theorem (CLT) states when the distribution of $\overline{X}$ is "approximately normal." As noted in the introduction to this chapter, the CLT is the premier result of all mathematics, and its applications occur throughout theoretical and applied statistics. We prove this result for a simple case, and state (without proof) versions for more general settings, as well as some of their applications.

Some properties of mixed convergence (i.e., convergence in probability and in distribution mixed) are given, and Slutsky's famous theorem is noted.

Definition 6.3.1. A sequence of jointly distributed r.v.'s $X_1, \ldots, X_n$ with finite means and variances is said to obey the (classical) **central limit theorem (CLT)** iff Z_n, defined by

$$Z_n = \frac{S_n - E(S_n)}{\sigma(S_n)}, \qquad S_n = X_1 + \cdots + X_n,$$

converges in distribution to a r.v. that is normally distributed with mean 0 and variance 1. [That is, by the Continuity Theorem for m.g.f.'s (Theorem 6.2.24), $\{X_n\}$ obeys the CLT iff (for all t)

$$\psi_{Z_n}(t) \to e^{\frac{1}{2}t^2}.]$$

We now prove a result which indicates that this is a common (or "normal") situation.

Theorem 6.3.2. Central Limit Theorem. Let $X_1, X_2, \ldots$ be independent and identically distributed r.v.'s with $EX_1 = \mu$ and $\mathrm{Var}(X_1) = \sigma^2 > 0$ (both finite). Then (for all z, $-\infty < z < +\infty$) as $n \to \infty$,

$$P\left[\frac{(X_1 - \mu) + \cdots + (X_n - \mu)}{\sqrt{n}\,\sigma} < z\right] \to \frac{1}{\sqrt{2\pi}}\int_{-\infty}^{z} e^{-\frac{1}{2}y^2}\,dy.$$

Proof: (Note that since this proof uses m.g.f.'s, it is necessary to assume that they exist. However, essentially the same proof goes through, line by line, using ch.f.'s instead; hence, the assumptions given in the statement of the theorem are sufficient for the result to hold, although this version of proof requires additional assumptions for its validity.) As in the proof of Theorem 6.2.26 (Khinchin's Theorem), we find

$$\psi_{\frac{(X_1-\mu)+\cdots+(X_n-\mu)}{\sqrt{n}\,\sigma}}(t) = \psi_{\frac{(X_1-\mu)}{\sqrt{n}\,\sigma}+\cdots+\frac{(X_n-\mu)}{\sqrt{n}\,\sigma}}(t)$$

$$= \left[\psi_{\frac{X_1-\mu}{\sqrt{n}\,\sigma}}(t)\right]^n, \quad \text{by Theorem 5.5.26}$$

$$= \left[\psi_{X_1-\mu}\left(\frac{t}{\sqrt{n}\,\sigma}\right)\right]^n, \quad \text{by Definition 5.5.1}$$

$$= \left[1 + \frac{E(X_1-\mu)}{1!}\frac{t}{\sqrt{n}\,\sigma} + \frac{E(X_1-\mu)^2}{2!}\frac{t^2}{n\sigma^2}\right.$$

$$\left. + o\left(\frac{t^2}{n\sigma^2}\right)\right]^n, \quad \text{by Theorem 5.5.17}$$

$$= \left[1 + \frac{1}{2}\frac{t^2}{n} + o\left(\frac{t^2}{n\sigma^2}\right)\right]^n$$

$$= \left[1 + \frac{\frac{1}{2}t^2 + no\left(\frac{t^2}{n\sigma^2}\right)}{n}\right]^n$$

$$\to e^{\frac{1}{2}t^2}, \quad \text{as } n \to \infty.$$

The result then follows by Corollary 6.2.25. ∎

This CLT also goes under the name of the **Lindberg-Levy Theorem**. It can be rephrased to state that

$$\frac{\sqrt{n}\,(\overline{X}_n - \mu)}{\sigma} \overset{d}{\to} N(0,1). \tag{6.3.3}$$

[*Note:* Since $F_n \to F$, F being a d.f. which is continuous everywhere, it follows that F_n converges uniformly to F. (This is called **Polya's Theorem**; for details see Theorem 7.4.6.) This means that we may say "the distribution of Z_n looks more and more like the normal distribution."]

We now give several examples that involve applications of the CLT.

Example 6.3.4. As a first application of the CLT, we prove one of the earliest versions of the central limit theorem, that due to DeMoivre and Laplace for Bernoulli r.v.'s.

Consider a sequence of Bernoulli r.v.'s $X_1, X_2, \ldots$ that are independent and each with success probability p. Then $E(X_1) = p$ and $\mathrm{Var}(X_1) = pq$ (where $q = 1 - p$), and by the Lindberg-Levy CLT

$$\frac{\sqrt{n}\,(\bar{X}_n - p)}{\sqrt{pq}} \xrightarrow{d} N(0, 1)$$

or

$$\frac{\sum_{i=1}^{n} X_i - np}{\sqrt{npq}} \xrightarrow{d} N(0, 1).$$

Since $S_n \equiv \sum_{i=1}^{n} X_i \sim B(n, p)$, it follows that for large n a simple approximation for binomial probabilities can be obtained using $S_n \sim N(np, npq)$.

Example 6.3.5. A casino has a coin and wishes to estimate p, the probability of a head on any toss, in such a way that they can be 99% confident that their estimate ($\hat{p}$, say) is within .01 of p.

They take n independent tosses, which yield $X_1, \ldots, X_n$ with (for $i = 1, \ldots, n$)

$$X_i = \begin{cases} 1, & \text{if a head occurs on the } i\text{th toss} \\ 0, & \text{otherwise.} \end{cases}$$

If they decide to use $\hat{p} = \bar{X} \equiv (X_1 + \cdots + X_n)/n$ to estimate p, then *how large* must n be? *Approximately how large* must n be?

By the WLLN, Theorem 6.2.7, $\bar{X} \xrightarrow{P} p$, so **there is a smallest sample size n_0 that will "do the job,"** that is, such that for $n = n_0$, $P[|\bar{X} - p| < .01] \geq .99$. (In fact, there is an n_0 such that for $n \geq n_0$ we know $P[|\bar{X} - p| < .01] \geq .99$.)* Now

$$P[|\bar{X} - p| < .01] = P[-.01 < \bar{X} - p < .01]$$

$$= P[p - .01 < \bar{X} < p + .01]$$

$$= P[n(p - .01) < X_1 + \cdots + X_n < n(p + .01)]$$

$$= \sum_{j \in J(n, p)} \binom{n}{j} p^j (1 - p)^{n-j}$$

---

*At a first reading, the rest of this paragraph may be skipped, and you may proceed to the next paragraph, where an approximation to n_0 is developed.

where the summation runs from

$$j = \max\left(\left[n(p - .01)\right] + \left(1 - \delta_{[n(p-.01)],\, n(p-.01)}\right), 0\right)$$

to $j = \min\left(\left[n(p + .01)\right], n\right)$ and δ_{xy} is 0 if $x \neq y$ and 1 if $x = y$. We have called this set of values $J(n, p)$. If we show that, whatever value n may have, $P[|\overline{X} - p| < .01]$ is a minimum when $p = .5$, then we simply calculate $P_{p = .5}$ $[|\overline{X} - p| < .01]$ for $n = 1, 2, 3, \ldots$ and choose n_0 as the first n for which this probability is at least .99. (See Honors Problem 6.4H.)

We now seek an approximation to n_0. We have

$$P[|\overline{X} - p| < .01] = P[n(p - .01) < X_1 + \cdots + X_n < n(p + .01)]$$

$$= P[-.01n < X_1 + \cdots + X_n - np < .01n]$$

$$= P\left[\frac{-.01n}{\sqrt{npq}} < \frac{X_1 + \cdots + X_n - np}{\sqrt{npq}} < \frac{.01n}{\sqrt{npq}}\right]$$

$$= P\left[-.01\sqrt{\frac{n}{pq}} < \frac{X_1 + \cdots + X_n - np}{\sqrt{npq}} < .01\sqrt{\frac{n}{pq}}\right]$$

$$\approx P\left[-.01\sqrt{\frac{n}{pq}} < Y < .01\sqrt{\frac{n}{pq}}\right],$$

where Y is a $N(0, 1)$ r.v. [This follows by the CLT, Theorem 6.3.2; here $EX_1 = p$, $\mathrm{Var}(X_1) = pq$.] Now this approximation is a function of p and is clearly minimized when $pq = p(1 - p)$ is maximized, which occurs at $p = \frac{1}{2}$ (so $pq = \frac{1}{4}$). We will now find n, such that

$$P[-.02\sqrt{n} < Y < .02\sqrt{n}] \approx .99.$$

Let $\Phi(z) \equiv P[Y \leq z]$, $-\infty < z < +\infty$ (the area under the normal density to the left of z). Of course $\Phi(0) = \frac{1}{2}$. Then we wish to set n by

$$.99 = P[-.02\sqrt{n} < Y < .02\sqrt{n}]$$

$$= \Phi(.02\sqrt{n}) - \Phi(-.02\sqrt{n})$$

$$= \Phi(.02\sqrt{n}) - [1 - \Phi(.02\sqrt{n})]$$

$$= 2\Phi(.02\sqrt{n}) - 1$$

so $\Phi(.02\sqrt{n}) = .995$ and $.02\sqrt{n} = 2.58$, or $n = (129)^2 \approx (130)^2 = 16,900$. So our approximation to n_0 is $n_0 = 16,900$.

Example 6.3.6. A standard process is known to yield about 80% acceptable items. A new process has been found to yield 85 acceptable items out of its first 100. Is the superiority of the new process well established?

If the new process' probability of producing an acceptable item (p_2, say) is less than or equal to the old process' probability of producing an acceptable item (p_1, say), how large can the probability of obtaining 85 acceptables in a sample of 100 from the new process be? Denote the 100 items by $X_1, \ldots, X_{100}$, where

$$X_i = \begin{cases} 1, & \text{if the } i\text{th unit is acceptable} \\ 0, & \text{otherwise.} \end{cases}$$

Then $X_1, \ldots, X_{100}$ will be assumed independent with $P[X_i = 1] = p_2$ ($i = 1, \ldots, 100$). We wish to study

$$P_{p_2}[X_1 + \cdots + X_{100} \geq 85]$$

$$= P_{p_2}\left[\frac{(X_1 + \cdots + X_{100}) - 100p_2}{\sqrt{100}\sqrt{p_2(1 - p_2)}} \geq \frac{85 - 100p_2}{\sqrt{100}\sqrt{p_2(1 - p_2)}}\right]$$

$$\approx 1 - \Phi\left(\frac{85 - 100p_2}{10\sqrt{p_2(1 - p_2)}}\right), \qquad \text{by the CLT.}$$

For $p_2 \leq p_1 = .80$, this is maximized when $\Phi\left(\dfrac{85 - 100p_2}{10\sqrt{p_2(1 - p_2)}}\right)$ is a minimum, that is, when $\dfrac{85 - 100p_2}{10\sqrt{p_2(1 - p_2)}}$ is a minimum. Since the derivative of this expression with respect to p_2 is negative for $0 \leq p_2 \leq 1$, the minimum for $p_2 \leq .80$ occurs at $p_2 = .80$. (Alternatively, looking at the exact binomial probability sum for $P_{p_2}[X_1 + \cdots + X_{100} \geq 85]$, we see that the derivative with respect to p_2 is ≥ 0 if $p_2 \leq .85$, so the maximum for $p_2 \leq .80$ is at $p_2 = .80$.) Now

$$1 - \Phi\left(\frac{85 - 80}{10\sqrt{(.8)(.2)}}\right) = 1 - \Phi(1.25)$$

$$= 1 - .8944 = .1056 \approx .11.$$

So, there is at most 1 chance in 10 of obtaining 85 or more acceptable out of 100 if, in fact, $p_2 \leq p_1 = .80$.

We could decide to switch to the new process based on this evidence, or we could decide to wait for more evidence, or we could decide to reject the new process. (For example, we might in advance have decided to reject on observing 75 or fewer acceptable out of 100, wait for more evidence on observing $76, \ldots, 90$ acceptable out of 100, and accept on observing 91 or more acceptable out of 100.) Reaching a realistic decision rule involves consideration of cost of observations, loss suffered by not switching to a better process, loss suffered by switching to an inferior process, and so on, and is studied in statistical decision theory [see, for example, Weiss (1961) and Chapter 12].

Recall (see (6.3.3)) that

$$\frac{S_n - ES_n}{\sigma(S_n)} = \frac{\bar{X} - \mu}{\sigma/\sqrt{n}} = \frac{\sqrt{n}}{\sigma}(\bar{X} - \mu),$$

so that approximate normality of the former implies approximate normality of the latter. The latter form is often encountered.

Example 6.3.7.   Our tables of the chi-square distribution (Table 10) go up to $n = 100$ degrees of freedom. We now obtain a simple approximation for large n (outside the range of Table 10) and illustrate its accuracy for $n = 100$.

Let $X_1, \ldots, X_n$ be independent r.v.'s, each $\chi_1^2(0)$. Then $E(X_1) = 1$, $\mathrm{Var}(X_1) = 2$, and $S_n = X_1 + \cdots + X_n$ is (see Theorem 5.5.64 (iv)) $\chi_n^2(0)$ by reproductivity of the chi-square. By the Lindberg-Levy CLT,

$$\frac{S_n - n}{\sqrt{2n}} \xrightarrow{d} N(0,1),$$

and S_n, which is $\chi_n^2(0)$, can be approximated by $N(n, 2n)$:

$$P(S_n \le a) = P\left(\frac{S_n - n}{\sqrt{2n}} \le \frac{a - n}{\sqrt{2n}}\right) \approx \Phi\left(\frac{a - n}{\sqrt{2n}}\right).$$

For example, if $n = 100$ and we wish to approximate a such that $P(\chi_{100}^2(0) \le a) = .95$, we set

$$\Phi\left(\frac{a - 100}{\sqrt{200}}\right) = .95$$

or

$$\frac{a - 100}{\sqrt{200}} = 1.645, \qquad a = 100 + 1.645\sqrt{200} = 123.2638.$$

From Table 10 (which goes up to $n = 100$) the exact value is $a = 124.342$.

Example 6.3.8.   Numbers in decimal form are often approximated by the closest integer. In the process, if n numbers $X_1, \ldots, X_n$ are each approximated by closest integers, their sum $X_1 + \cdots + X_n$ is altered. If X_i is the ith true number and J_i is the nearest integer, then the error made by the rounding process is $U_i = X_i - J_i$. Suppose that $U_1, \ldots, U_n$ are independent, and each is uniform on the interval $(-.5, .5)$. What is the probability that the true sum is within a units of the approximate sum?

This problem can be solved exactly by using the methods of Section 4.6, however that solution is extremely complicated for n large, so we will seek an approximate solution. Denote the true sum by

$$S_n = \sum_{i=1}^{n} X_i$$

and the approximate sum by

$$K_n = \sum_{i=1}^{n} J_i.$$

Then the desired probability is

$$P(|S_n - K_n| \le a) = P\left(-a \le \sum_{i=1}^{n}(X_i - J_i) \le a\right)$$

$$= P\left(-a \le \sum_{i=1}^{n} U_i \le a\right).$$

Since $U_1, \ldots, U_n$ are independent and uniform on $(-1/2, 1/2)$, $E(U_1) = 0$, $\text{Var}(U_1) = 1/12$, and by the Lindberg-Levy CLT

$$\frac{\sum_{i=1}^{n} U_i - 0}{\sqrt{n/12}} \xrightarrow{d} N(0,1),$$

or $\sum_{i=1}^{n} U_i \sim N(0, n/12)$ for large n. Thus,

$$P(|S_n - K_n| \le a) = P\left(\frac{-a-0}{\sqrt{n/12}} \le \frac{\sum_{i=1}^{n} U_i - 0}{\sqrt{n/12}} \le \frac{a}{\sqrt{n/12}}\right)$$

$$\approx \Phi\left(a\sqrt{12/n}\right) - \Phi\left(-a\sqrt{12/n}\right) = 2\Phi\left(a\sqrt{12/n}\right) - 1.$$

If $n = 300$ terms are added, the probability the approximate sum is within 5 of the true sum ($a = 5$) is

$$P(|S_{300} - K_{300}| \le 5) \approx 2\Phi(1) - 1 = .6826.$$

Note that we can also find a such that we are 95% sure the approximation is within a units of the true:

$$2\Phi\left(a\sqrt{12/n}\right) - 1 = .95$$

$$\Phi\left(a\sqrt{12/n}\right) = 1.95/2 = .975$$

$$a\sqrt{12/n} = 1.96$$

$$a = 1.96\sqrt{n/12} = 1.96\sqrt{300/12} = (1.96)(5) = 9.8.$$

Note that when adding 300 terms with an error of between $-.5$ and $.5$ per term, the total error could be as large as $(300)(.5) = 150$; however, we have shown that (under reasonable assumptions) the error in fact will not exceed 10 is absolute value in such circumstances. (More precisely stated, we have shown that the error will be at most 10 in 19 out of 20 times this process is used, i.e., in 95% of uses of the process.)

As noted in the introduction to this section, we will now give (without proof) versions of the CLT for some more general settings.* First, we note that the generalization of Theorem 6.3.2 to the multivariate case is valid.

Theorem 6.3.9. Multivariate Lindberg-Levy CLT. Let $X_1, X_2, \ldots$ be independent and identically distributed **p-dimensional r.v.'s**, each with mean vector $E(X_1) = \mu$, and variance-covariance matrix Σ. Then the limiting distribution of

$$\frac{(X_1 - \mu) + (X_2 - \mu) + \cdots + (X_n - \mu)}{\sqrt{n}}$$

is the p-variate normal of Definition 4.5.4, with mean vector $\mathbf{0}$ and the same variance-covariance matrix Σ.

The other direction of generalization of the CLT (Theorem 6.3.2) that we will examine, is to let the X_i's have different distributions (recall that in Theorem 6.3.2 they were both independent *and* identically distributed). Here one of the most powerful results is:

Theorem 6.3.10. Lindeberg's Condition CLT. Let $X_1, X_2, \ldots$ be independent (one-dimensional) r.v.'s, where X_i has d.f. $F_i(\cdot)$ with $E(X_i) = \mu_i$ and $\operatorname{Var}(X_i) = \sigma_i^2$. Let

$$Y_n = \frac{(X_1 - \mu_1) + (X_2 - \mu_2) + \cdots + (X_n - \mu_n)}{\left(\sigma_1^2 + \sigma_2^2 + \cdots + \sigma_n^2\right)^{0.5}}.$$

We say **Lindeberg's condition holds** if, for every fixed $t > 0$, as $n \to \infty$

$$\frac{E(X_1^* - \mu_1)^2 + \cdots + E(X_n^* - \mu_n)^2}{\sigma_1^2 + \cdots + \sigma_n^2} \to 0, \qquad (6.3.11)$$

where (for $i = 1, 2, \ldots$)

$$X_i^* = \begin{cases} 1, & \text{if } |X_i - \mu_i| > t\left(\sigma_1^2 + \cdots + \sigma_n^2\right)^{0.5} \\ 0, & \text{otherwise.} \end{cases}$$

(i) If the Lindeberg condition holds, then $Y_n \overset{d}{\to} N(0,1)$.
(ii) If $Y_n \overset{d}{\to} N(0,1)$ and

$$\sigma_1^2 + \cdots + \sigma_n^2 \to \infty, \qquad \frac{\sigma_n^2}{\sigma_1^2 + \cdots + \sigma_n^2} \to 0,$$

then the Lindeberg condition holds.

---

*This material is not used extensively in what follows, and instructors skipping it may move ahead to properties of mixed convergence at Theorem 6.3.12.

Thus, we now have conditions that are essentially necessary and sufficient for a limiting normal distribution for independent r.v.'s whose means and variances all exist. (We say "essentially" since with violation of the limits in part (ii) we can still have a limiting non-standard-normal distribution—that is, a normal distribution with variance other than 1. Also, in situations where means and variances do not exist, similar results sometimes hold if $\sqrt{n}$ is replaced with other quantities.)

As promised, we now conclude this section with a study of properties of mixed convergence (i.e., convergence in probability and convergence in distribution mixed). One of the most general results available, and one from which all the special results we will need follow, is

Theorem 6.3.12. Let $X_1, X_2, \ldots$ be r.v.'s, and let $t_1 = t_1(X_1, \ldots, X_n), \ldots, t_r = t_r(X_1, \ldots, X_n)$ be r functions of the r.v.'s. Suppose that $t_1 \overset{P}{\to} a_1, \ldots, t_r \overset{P}{\to} a_r$ (as $n \to \infty$) for some constants $a_1, \ldots, a_r$. Suppose $g(\cdot, \ldots, \cdot)$ is a continuous function such that $|g(a_1, \ldots, a_r)| < \infty$. Then

$$g(t_1, \ldots, t_r) \overset{P}{\to} g(a_1, \ldots, a_r).$$

[In the special case where $g(\cdot, \ldots, \cdot)$ is a *rational function* (i.e., a ratio of polynomials), this result is known as **Slutsky's Theorem**.]

Although a proof of Theorem 6.3.12 is beyond the scope of this text (see Problem 7.3H for references), many consequences of Theorem 6.3.12 and of the definitions of convergence in probability and in distribution are easy to show from first principles. Some important results are the following.

Corollary 6.3.13.

(i) $X_n \overset{P}{\to} X$ if and only if $X_n - X \overset{P}{\to} 0$.
(ii) $X_n \overset{P}{\to} X$ and $Y_n \overset{P}{\to} X$ imply that $X_n - Y_n \overset{P}{\to} 0$.
(iii) $X_n \overset{P}{\to} X$ and $Y_n \overset{P}{\to} Y$ imply that (a) $X_n \pm Y_n \overset{P}{\to} X \pm Y$, and (b) $X_n Y_n \overset{P}{\to} XY$.
(iv) $X_n \overset{P}{\to} X$ and $g(\cdot)$ a continuous function imply that $g(X_n) \overset{P}{\to} g(X)$.

From the case where X and Y are constants in Corollary 6.3.13, we immediately find properties of convergence in probability to a constant.

Corollary 6.3.14. If $X_n \overset{P}{\to} a$, $Y_n \overset{P}{\to} b$, and $g(\cdot)$ is a continuous function, then

(i) $X_n \pm Y_n \overset{P}{\to} a \pm b$.
(ii) $X_n Y_n \overset{P}{\to} ab$.
(iii) $X_n / Y_n \overset{P}{\to} a/b$, provided $b \neq 0$.
(iv) $g(X_n) \overset{P}{\to} g(a)$.

Note that, since convergence in probability implies convergence in distribution, the results claimed in (i) through (iv) of Corollary 6.3.14 still hold if convergence in probability is replaced by convergence in distribution in the conclusions stated.

Our final results on mixed convergence are contained in the following theorem.

Theorem 6.3.15.

(i) If $X_n \overset{d}{\to} X$ and $X_n - Y_n \overset{p}{\to} 0$, then $Y_n \overset{d}{\to} X$.

(ii) If $X_n \overset{d}{\to} X$, $X_n - Y_n \overset{p}{\to} 0$, and $g(\cdot)$ is a continuous function, then $g(X_n) - g(Y_n) \overset{p}{\to} 0$.

In the following three results, c is a constant.

(iii) If $X_n \overset{d}{\to} X$ and $Y_n \overset{p}{\to} c$, then $X_n \pm Y_n \overset{d}{\to} X \pm c$.

(iv) If $X_n \overset{d}{\to} X$ and $Y_n \overset{p}{\to} c$, then $X_n Y_n \overset{d}{\to} cX$ if $c \neq 0$,   and $X_n Y_n \overset{p}{\to} 0$ if $c = 0$.

(v) If $X_n \overset{d}{\to} X$ and $Y_n \overset{p}{\to} c$, then $X_n / Y_n \overset{d}{\to} X/c$ if $c \neq 0$.

Example 6.3.16. Let $X_1, X_2, \ldots$ be a sequence of independent r.v.'s, each $N(\mu, \sigma^2)$. Then we know that (Example 6.2.11)

$$s_n^2 = \sum_{i=1}^{n} \frac{(X_i - \bar{X}_n)^2}{n - 1} \overset{p}{\to} \sigma^2 \quad (\text{as } n \to \infty),$$

that (Theorem 5.5.34) $\bar{X}_n$ and s_n^2 are independent, and that

$$T_{n-1} = \frac{\dfrac{\sqrt{n}\,(\bar{X}_n - \mu)}{\sigma}}{\sqrt{\dfrac{(n-1)s_n^2}{\sigma^2}\Big/(n-1)}} = \frac{\sqrt{n}\,(\bar{X}_n - \mu)}{s_n}$$

has Student's t-distribution with $n - 1$ degrees of freedom (since by Problem 4.6.2 a Student's t r.v. is the ratio of an independent standard normal r.v. and the square root of a chi-square r.v. divided by its degrees of freedom). We claim that (as $n \to \infty$)

$$T_{n-1} \overset{d}{\to} N(0, 1).$$

Since $T_{n-1} = Z_n / Y_n$ where

$$Z_n = \frac{\sqrt{n}\,(\bar{X}_n - \mu)}{\sigma} \sim N(0,1) \equiv Z, \ Y_n = \sqrt{s_n^2/\sigma^2} \overset{p}{\to} 1,$$

by Theorem 6.3.15(v)

$$T_{n-1} = \frac{Z_n}{Y_n} \overset{d}{\to} \frac{Z}{1} = Z.$$

Thus, **for large degrees of freedom** (e.g., beyond the range of Table 13) **the t-distribution can be approximated by a standard normal distribution.**

Example 6.3.17. Let $X_1, X_2, \ldots$ be independent and identically distributed r.v.'s with mean μ, variance σ^2, and $\mu_4 = E(X_1 - \mu)^4 = \alpha_4 \sigma^4$ with $\alpha_4 > 1$. [Recall (Definition 5.1.18) that α_4 is called the **kurtosis** of the distribution of X_1. Note that $\alpha_4 \geq 1$ in all cases.] Then

$$s_n^2 \overset{P}{\nrightarrow} \sigma^2.$$

Further,

$$\sqrt{n}\left(s_n^2 - \sigma^2\right) \overset{d}{\to} N\left(0, (\alpha_4 - 1)\sigma^4\right).$$

(Note that unlike the situation in Example 6.2.11, we do *not* now assume normality of the X_i's.)

First, if we let

$$s_n^{*2} = \sum_{i=1}^{n} (X_i - \mu)^2 / n,$$

then

$$\frac{\sum_{i=1}^{n} (X_i - \bar{X}_n)^2}{n} - s_n^{*2} = \frac{1}{n}\left(\sum_{i=1}^{n} (X_i - \bar{X}_n)^2 - \sum_{i=1}^{n} (X_i - \mu)^2 \right)$$

$$= \frac{1}{n}\left(-n\bar{X}_n^2 - n\mu^2 + 2n\mu\bar{X}_n\right)$$

$$= -\left(\bar{X}_n - \mu\right)^2 \overset{P}{\nrightarrow} 0$$

by the WLLN (Theorem 6.2.7), thus

$$\frac{n-1}{n} s_n^2 - s_n^{*2} \overset{P}{\nrightarrow} 0,$$

and (since $(n-1)/n \overset{P}{\nrightarrow} 1$) by Corollary 6.3.13 $s_n^2 - s_n^{*2} \overset{P}{\nrightarrow} 0$. *Now* s_n^{*2} has mean and variance

$$E\left(s_n^{*2}\right) = E\left(\sum_{i=1}^{n} (X_i - \mu)^2 / n \right) = \sigma^2,$$

$$\mathrm{Var}\left(s_n^{*2}\right) = E\left(s_n^{*2}\right)^2 - \sigma^4 = E\left(\sum_{i=1}^{n} (X_i - \mu)^2 / n \right)^2 - \sigma^4$$

$$= \frac{1}{n^2}\left(\sum_{i=1}^{n} E(X_i - \mu)^4 + 2 \sum_{\substack{i,j=1 \\ i<j}}^{n} E(X_i - \mu)^2 E(X_j - \mu)^2 \right) - \sigma^4$$

$$= \frac{1}{n}\alpha_4\sigma^4 + \frac{n(n-1)}{n^2}\sigma^4 - \sigma^4 = \frac{1}{n}(\alpha_4 - 1)\sigma^4.$$

(Note that since $\text{Var}(Z) \geq 0$ for any r.v. Z, we have shown $\alpha_4 \geq 1$.) Therefore by Chebyshev's Inequality, for any $\varepsilon > 0$

$$P\left(\left|s_n^{*2} - \sigma^2\right| \geq \varepsilon\right) \leq \frac{\text{Var}\left(s_n^{*2}\right)}{\varepsilon^2} = (\alpha_4 - 1)\sigma^4/(n\varepsilon^2)$$

which $\to 0$ as $n \to \infty$, hence $s_n^{*2} \xrightarrow{P} \sigma^2$. Since we already showed $s_n^2 - s_n^{*2} \xrightarrow{P} 0$, by Corollary 6.3.13 (iii) $s_n^2 \xrightarrow{P} \sigma^2$.

We now study **the limiting distribution of** $\sqrt{n}\,(s_n^2 - \sigma^2)$. Noting that

$$\sqrt{n}\left(s_n^{*2} - \sigma^2\right) = \sqrt{n}\left(\frac{\sum\limits_{i=1}^{n}(X_i - \mu)^2}{n} - \sigma^2\right) = \sqrt{n}\left(\overline{Y}_n - \sigma^2\right)$$

where $Y_1 = (X_1 - \mu)^2$, $Y_2 = (X_2 - \mu)^2, \ldots, Y_n = (X_n - \mu)^2$ are independent and identically distributed r.v.'s with mean $E(Y_1) = \sigma^2$ and variance $\text{Var}(Y_1) = (\alpha_4 - 1)\sigma^4$, it follows from the Central Limit Theorem that

$$\sqrt{n}\left(s_n^{*2} - \sigma^2\right) \xrightarrow{d} N\left(0, (\alpha_4 - 1)\sigma^4\right).$$

Now from previous calculations in this example, we have that

$$\sqrt{n}\left(s_n^{*2} - \sigma^2\right) - \sqrt{n}\left(\sum_{i=1}^{n}(X_i - \overline{X}_n)^2/n - \sigma^2\right)$$

$$= \sqrt{n}\left(s_n^{*2} - \sum_{i=1}^{n}(X_i - \overline{X}_n)^2/n\right) = \sqrt{n}\left(\overline{X}_n - \mu\right)^2 = \left(n^{0.25}(\overline{X}_n - \mu)\right)^2$$

which $\xrightarrow{P} 0$ by Corollary 6.3.14(iv) since $n^{0.25}(\overline{X}_n - \mu) \xrightarrow{P} 0$ follows (show this) from the CLT. Thus, since

$$\sqrt{n}\left(s_n^{*2} - \sigma^2\right) \xrightarrow{d} N\left(0, (\alpha_4 - 1)\sigma^4\right)$$

and

$$\sqrt{n}\left(s_n^{*2} - \sigma^2\right) - \sqrt{n}\left(\frac{n-1}{n}s_n^2 - \sigma^2\right) \xrightarrow{P} 0,$$

by Theorem 6.3.15(i)

$$\sqrt{n}\left(\frac{n-1}{n}s_n^2 - \sigma^2\right) \xrightarrow{d} N\left(0, (\alpha_4 - 1)\sigma^4\right).$$

As

$$\sqrt{n}\left(s_n^2 - \sigma^2\right) - \sqrt{n}\left(\frac{n-1}{n}s_n^2 - \sigma^2\right) = \frac{\sqrt{n}}{n}s_n^2 = \frac{s_n^2}{\sqrt{n}} \xrightarrow{P} 0,$$

another use of Theorem 6.3.15(i) yields the desired result that

$$\sqrt{n}\left(s_n^2 - \sigma^2\right) \overset{d}{\to} N\left(0, (\alpha_4 - 1)\sigma^4\right).$$

Situations often arise where we know the limiting distribution of X_n; for example, we may know that $\sqrt{n}(X_n - \theta) \overset{d}{\to} N(0, \sigma^2)$, but the real interest is in a function $g(X_n)$. The **limiting distribution** of $\sqrt{n}(g(X_n) - g(\theta))$ is considered in the following theorem.

Theorem 6.3.18. * Suppose that $\sqrt{n}(X_n - \theta) \overset{d}{\to} N(0, \sigma^2)$, and that $g(x)$ is a function for which $g'(x)$ exists and is continuous in some neighborhood of θ. Then

$$\sqrt{n}\left(g(X_n) - g(\theta)\right) \overset{d}{\to} N\left(0, [g'(\theta)]^2\sigma^2\right).$$

Proof: By the Mean Value Theorem of calculus,

$$g(X_n) - g(\theta) = (X_n - \theta)g'(\xi_n)$$

with $\theta < \xi_n < X_n$ (or, if $X_n < \theta$, $X_n < \xi_n < \theta$). Since $\sqrt{n}(X_n - \theta) \overset{d}{\to} N(0, \sigma^2)$ implies $X_n - \theta \overset{P}{\to} 0$, by Corollary 6.3.14(iv) $g(X_n) - g(\theta) \overset{P}{\to} 0$. Since $|\xi_n - \theta| < |X_n - \theta|$, $X_n \overset{P}{\to} \theta$ implies $\xi_n \overset{P}{\to} \theta$, and, by Corollary 6.3.14(iv) $g'(\xi_n) \overset{P}{\to} g'(\theta)$. Since

$$\sqrt{n}\left[g(X_n) - g(\theta)\right] = \sqrt{n}(X_n - \theta) \cdot \left(\frac{g'(\xi_n)}{g'(\theta)}g'(\theta)\right),$$

by Theorem 6.3.15(iv) the right side converges in distribution to $N(0, [g'(\theta)]^2\sigma^2)$. ∎

Example 6.3.19. We know from Example 6.3.17 that if $X_1, X_2, \ldots$ are independent and identically distributed r.v.'s with mean μ, variance σ^2, and $\mu_4 = E(X_1 - \mu)^4 = \alpha_4\sigma^4$ with $\alpha_4 > 1$, then $\sqrt{n}(s_n^2 - \sigma^2) \overset{d}{\to} N(0, (\alpha_4 - 1)\sigma^4)$. We now seek the limiting distribution of s_n (which might be used to estimate σ).

Since we know the limiting distribution of s_n^2 and seek the limiting distribution of s_n, we take $g(x) = \sqrt{x}$. This is differentiable with continuous derivative for all positive values of x. Hence by Theorem 6.3.18,

$$\sqrt{n}\left(g(s_n^2) - g(\sigma^2)\right) \overset{d}{\to} N\left(0, [g'(\sigma^2)]^2(\alpha_4 - 1)\sigma^4\right),$$

that is,

$$\sqrt{n}\left(s_n - \sigma\right) \overset{d}{\to} N\left(0, \frac{1}{4\sigma^2}(\alpha_4 - 1)\sigma^4\right) = N\left(0, (\alpha_4 - 1)\sigma^2/4\right).$$

As a special case, if $X_1, X_2, \ldots$ are $N(\mu, \sigma^2)$, then $\alpha_4 = 3$ and

$$\sqrt{n}\left(s_n - \sigma\right) \overset{d}{\to} N\left(0, \sigma^2/2\right).$$

*May be omitted if the instructor desires.

Definition 6.3.20. If X is a r.v. with mean μ and variance σ^2, then the **coefficient of variation** is defined as

$$\text{C.V.}(X) = \frac{\sigma}{\mu}.$$

The **signal-to-noise ratio** is defined as

$$\text{S.N.}(X) = \frac{\mu}{\sigma}.$$

Example 6.3.21. Limiting Distribution of an Estimate of the C.V. Let $X_1, \ldots, X_n$ be independent and identically distributed r.v.'s with mean μ and variance σ^2. The **sample coefficient of variation** is defined as $s_n / \overline{X}_n$. Is it "near" σ/μ? What is its limiting distribution?

Since $\overline{X}_n \overset{p}{\to} \mu$ and $s_n \overset{p}{\to} \sigma$, by Corollary 6.3.14(iii)

$$\frac{s_n}{\overline{X}_n} \overset{p}{\to} \frac{\sigma}{\mu}.$$

For the limiting distribution, note that

$$\sqrt{n}\left(\frac{s_n}{\overline{X}_n} - \frac{\sigma}{\mu}\right) = \frac{\sqrt{n}}{\overline{X}_n}(s_n - \sigma) + \frac{\sqrt{n}}{\overline{X}_n}\left(\sigma - \frac{\sigma \overline{X}_n}{\mu}\right)$$

$$= \frac{\sqrt{n}}{\overline{X}_n}(s_n - \sigma) + \frac{\sigma}{\overline{X}_n \mu}\left(\sqrt{n}\left(\mu - \overline{X}_n\right)\right),$$

and recall that we know (or can easily show) that

$$\sqrt{n}(s_n - \sigma) \overset{d}{\to} N\left(0, (\alpha_4 - 1)\sigma^2/4\right), \qquad \sqrt{n}\left(\mu - \overline{X}_n\right) \overset{d}{\to} N(0, \sigma^2),$$

$$\frac{1}{\overline{X}_n} \overset{p}{\to} \frac{1}{\mu}, \qquad \frac{\sigma}{\overline{X}_n \mu} \overset{p}{\to} \frac{\sigma}{\mu^2}.$$

Hence by Theorem 6.3.15,

$$\sqrt{n}\left(\frac{s_n}{\overline{X}_n} - \frac{\sigma}{\mu}\right) \overset{d}{\to} N\left(0, \frac{(\alpha_4 - 1)\sigma^2}{4\mu^2}\right) + N\left(0, \frac{\sigma^4}{\mu^4}\right).$$

If the X_i's are also assumed to be *normal* (in which case s_n^2 and $\overline{X}_n$ are independent),

$$\sqrt{n}\left(\frac{s_n}{\overline{X}_n} - \frac{\sigma}{\mu}\right) \overset{d}{\to} N\left(0, \frac{\sigma^2}{2\mu^2} + \frac{\sigma^4}{\mu^4}\right).$$

PROBLEMS FOR SECTION 6.3

6.3.1 Let $X_1, X_2, \ldots$ be independent and identically distributed r.v.'s with p.d.f. $f(x) = x^{\mu-1} e^{-x} / \Gamma(\mu)$ if $x > 0$ (and $= 0$ otherwise) for some μ with $0 < \mu < \infty$. Let $\overline{X}_n = (X_1 + X_2 + \cdots + X_n)/n$. Show that, as $n \to \infty$,

$$\frac{\sqrt{n}\,(\overline{X}_n - \mu)}{\sqrt{\overline{X}_n}} \overset{d}{\to} N(0,1).$$

[*Hint:* Use Theorem 6.3.15 and the CLT.]

6.3.2 Let $X_1, X_2, \ldots$ be independent and identically distributed r.v.'s with exponential p.d.f. $f(x) = (1/\lambda)e^{-x/\lambda}$ if $x > 0$ (and $= 0$ otherwise) for some λ with $0 < \lambda < \infty$.

(a) Show that $\sqrt{n}\,(\overline{X}_n - \lambda)/\overline{X}_n \overset{d}{\to} N(0,1)$ as $n \to \infty$.
[*Hint:* Use Theorem 6.3.15 and the CLT.]

(b) Let $\beta = 1/\lambda$. Show that $\sqrt{n}\,(\beta\overline{X}_n - 1) \overset{d}{\to} N(0,1)$ as $n \to \infty$.
[*Hint:* $\sqrt{n}\,(\beta\overline{X}_n - 1) = \sqrt{n}\,(\overline{X}_n - 1/\beta)/(1/\beta)$.]

6.3.3 Let $X_1, X_2, \ldots$ be independent $N(1,1)$ r.v.'s. Prove or disprove:

$$\sqrt{n}\,(\overline{X}_n^2 - 1) \overset{d}{\to} N(0,1) \text{ as } n \to \infty.$$

6.3.4 Let $X_1, X_2, \ldots$ and $Y_1, Y_2, \ldots$ be sequences of r.v.'s with $E(X_m) = \mu$, $E|X_m| < \infty$, $\operatorname{Var}(X_m) = \sigma^2 < \infty$, $\sqrt{n}\,(X_m - \mu) \overset{d}{\to} X$, and $Y_m \overset{p}{\to} c$ (finite). Prove or disprove: $\sqrt{n}\,(X_m Y_m - c\mu) \overset{d}{\to} cX$.

6.3.5 Let $X_1, X_2, \ldots$ and $Y_1, Y_2, \ldots$ be sequences of r.v.'s such that $X_m \overset{d}{\to} X$ and $Y_m \overset{d}{\to} X$. Prove or disprove: $X_m - Y_m \overset{d}{\to} 0$.

6.3.6 Find an approximation to the probability $P(175 \leq \chi^2_{200}(0) \leq 225)$.

6.3.7 Let $X_1, X_2, \ldots, X_{n_1}$ be a random sample of size n_1 from a $N(\mu_1, \sigma^2)$ distribution, and $Y_1, Y_2, \ldots, Y_{n_2}$ a random sample of size n_2 from a $N(\mu_2, \sigma^2)$ distribution, with $\sigma^2 > 0$. If $\overline{X}_{n_1} = (X_1 + \cdots + X_{n_1})/n_1$, $\overline{Y}_{n_2} = (Y_1 + \cdots + Y_{n_2})/n_2$, and

$$s_P^2 = \frac{\displaystyle\sum_{i=1}^{n_1} \left(X_i - \overline{X}_{n_1}\right)^2 + \sum_{j=1}^{n_2} \left(Y_j - \overline{Y}_{n_2}\right)^2}{n_1 + n_2 - 2},$$

then prove that

(a) $\overline{X}_{n_1} - \overline{Y}_{n_2} \overset{p}{\to} \mu_1 - \mu_2$ as $\min(n_1, n_2) \to \infty$.

(b) $s_P^2 \overset{p}{\to} \sigma^2$ as $\min(n_1, n_2) \to \infty$.

(c) $((\overline{X}_{n_1} - \overline{Y}_{n_2}) - (\mu_1 - \mu_2))/\sqrt{s_P^2(1/n_1 + 1/n_2)} \overset{d}{\to} N(0,1)$ as $\min(n_1, n_2) \to \infty$.

6.3.8 A cereal box is supposed to contain 500 grams of cereal, with a standard deviation of 10 grams. If we sample 100 such boxes at random, what is the (approximate) probability that the average of their cereal contents will be

(a) At most 495 grams.

(b) At least 503 grams.

(c) Between 499 and 506 grams.

6.3.9 If X is a Poisson r.v. with mean 81, find (using the CLT) the approximate probability $P(X \geq 75)$.

6.3.10 Let $X_1, X_2, \ldots$ be independent Bernoulli r.v.'s, each with probability of success p. Let $Y_n = X_1 + \cdots + X_n$ so that $Y_n \sim B(n, p)$, and let $\hat{p}_n = Y_n/n$.
(a) Show that $\hat{p}_n(1 - \hat{p}_n) \twoheadrightarrow p(1 - p)$ as $n \to \infty$.
(b) Use Theorem 6.3.15 to show that

$$\frac{\hat{p}_n - p}{\sqrt{\dfrac{\hat{p}_n(1 - \hat{p}_n)}{n}}} \xrightarrow{d} N(0,1) \text{ as } n \to \infty.$$

6.3.11 Let $X_1, X_2, \ldots$ be independent Bernoulli r.v.'s with mean p_1, and independently let $Y_1, Y_2, \ldots$ be independent Bernoulli r.v.'s with mean p_2. Let $\hat{p}_{1, n_1} = (X_1 + \cdots + X_{n_1})/n_1$ and $\hat{p}_{2, n_2} = (Y_1 + \cdots + Y_{n_2})/n_2$. Prove that

$$\frac{(\hat{p}_{1, n_1} - \hat{p}_{2, n_2}) - (p_1 - p_2)}{\sqrt{\dfrac{\hat{p}_{1, n_1}(1 - \hat{p}_{1, n_1})}{n_1} + \dfrac{\hat{p}_{2, n_2}(1 - \hat{p}_{2, n_2})}{n_2}}} \xrightarrow{d} N(0,1) \text{ as } n \to \infty,$$

where $n = \min(n_1, n_2)$.

6.3.12 If r.v. X has d.f. $F(x)$, $F(x)$ is said to be **infinitely divisible** if (for every n) it can be represented as the d.f. of a sum of n independent nondegenerate identically distributed r.v.'s; that is, if $X = X_1 + X_2 + \cdots + X_n$, where $X_1, \ldots, X_n$ are independent and identically distributed nondegenerate r.v.'s. Show that
(a) If X is Poisson with mean μ, then X is infinitely divisible.
(b) If $X \sim N(\mu, \sigma^2)$, then X is infinitely divisible.

6.3.13 A certain jet airliner seats up to 350 passengers and also accommodates their luggage (checked and carry-on). Suppose the weight of a passenger is an r.v. with mean 70 kilograms and standard deviation 10 kilograms, while the weight of a passenger's luggage is an r.v. with mean 45 kilograms and standard deviation 5 kilograms. If the airliner's load (passengers plus luggage weight) at takeoff must not exceed 45,000 kilograms, what is the probability (assuming independence) that
(a) On a given full flight (i.e., each of the 350 seats are occupied) the combined weight will exceed the limit.
(b) On a given full flight the combined weight will be between 42,000 and 43,000 kilograms.

6.3.14 An Olympic-class sprinter covers on the average 140 centimeters, with a standard deviation of 5 centimeters, in each stride. What is the approximate probability that this runner will cover the 100-meter distance in 70 steps? 72 steps? 75 steps?

6.3.15 Let $X_1, X_2, \ldots, X_n$ be independent and identically distributed r.v.'s with mean μ and variance σ^2 (both finite).
(a) How large a value of n will guarantee that $\overline{X}_n$ (the sample mean) is within k units of the population mean μ with probability at least P^*?

(b) As in part (a) with σ unknown and estimated by s, where $s^2 = \sum\limits_{i=1}^{n} (X_i - \overline{X}_n)^2/(n - 1)$.

6.3.16 A fair six-sided die is rolled independently 1000 times. Let X denote the number of 6's on the 1000 rolls. Compute the probability
(a) $P(X > 200)$. (b) $P(X \leq 175)$.

6.3.17 One-hundred fair six-sided dice are rolled independently and simultaneously. Let $\overline{X}_{100}$ denote the average of the 100 face numbers that show. Compute the (approximate) probability
(a) $P(\overline{X}_{100} \leq 3.5)$.
(b) $P(2.3 \leq \overline{X}_{100} < 3.4)$.

6.3.18 Let $X_1, X_2, \ldots$ be a sequence of independent r.v.'s with $X_i \sim N(0, a^{-i/2})$ for some $a > 0$, for $i \geq 1$. Is the Lindeberg condition (6.3.11) valid for this sequence?

6.3.19 Let $X_1, X_2, \ldots$ be a sequence of r.v.'s with

$$p_{X_n}(x) = \begin{cases} \dfrac{1}{2^{n+1}}, & \text{if } x = \pm 2^n \\ \dfrac{1}{2} - \dfrac{1}{2^{n+1}} & \text{if } x = \pm 1 \\ 0 & \text{otherwise.} \end{cases}$$

Let $T_n = X_1 + X_2 + \cdots + X_n$. Find the limiting distribution of T_n using the Lindeberg's condition CLT (Theorem 6.3.10).

6.3.20 Let $X_1, X_2, \ldots$ be a sequence of independent r.v.'s with probability function as specified. Determine whether Lindeberg's condition holds or not.
(a) $p_{X_n}(x) = 1/2$ if $x = \pm 2^n$ (and $= 0$ otherwise).
(b) $p_{X_n}(x) = 1/2$ if $x = \pm 1/2^n$ (and $= 0$ otherwise).
(c) $p_{X_n}(x)$ as in Problem 6.3.19.

PROBLEMS FOR CHAPTER 6

6.1 Let Y be a random variable which is always ≥ 0. Prove that (for any $t > 0$)

$$P[Y \geq t] \leq \min\left(\frac{EY^2}{t^2}, 1\right).$$

6.2 Let Y be a random variable such that $Y \geq 0$. Show that (for any $t > 0$)

$$P[Y \geq t] \leq \frac{EY}{t}.$$

Prove that the Chebyshev bound EY^2/t^2 is better iff

$$\frac{EY^2}{EY} < t.$$

6.3 Let X be a discrete random variable taking on values $0, 1, \ldots, n$. Assume that $E(X) = 1$ and $\text{Var}(X) = 1$. For $k = 2, 3, \ldots, n$ prove that

$$P[X \geq k] \leq \frac{1}{(k-1)^2}.$$

6.4 Suppose given a sequence of n independent tosses of a coin with probability p $(0 \leq p \leq 1)$ of heads. Let T_n = number of times in n tosses that a head is followed by a tail. Prove that

$$\frac{T_n}{n} \rightsquigarrow c,$$

where c is some constant, and find c. [*Hint:* Use Chebyshev's Inequality.]

6.5 Approximately how many independent flips n of a fair coin are needed in order that

$$P[.49 \leq (\text{Proportion of heads in } n \text{ tosses}) \leq .51] \geq .99?$$

6.6 A country has estimated that the probability that any particular nuclear weapon will explode unintentionally in a given decade is .00001. If this country has 100,000 nuclear weapons, let us consider the probability that exactly j or more explode unintentionally between 1988 and 1998. Give **(a)** an exact expression, **(b)** the Poisson approximation, and **(c)** the normal approximation. Evaluate **(b)** and **(c)** for $j = 1$; for $j = 2$.

6.7 A fair die is thrown 1000 times independently. Let X = the number of 6's that occur. Find an exact expression for $P[X \geq 170]$. Use the normal approximation to evaluate $P[X \geq 170]$.

6.8 It costs \$1 to play a certain slot machine in Las Vegas. The machine is set by the house to pay \$2 with probability .45 (and to pay nothing with probability .55). Let X_i be the house's net winnings on the ith play of the machine. Then $S_n = \sum_{i=1}^{n} X_i$ equals the house's winnings after n plays of the machine. Assuming that successive plays are independent, find

(a) $E(S_n)$;

(b) $\text{Var}(S_n)$;

(c) The approximate probability that after 10,000 plays of the machine the house's winnings are between \$800 and \$1100. Express your answer as a decimal.

6.9 Let $X_1, \ldots, X_n$ be n independent and identically distributed random variables with $E(X_1) = \mu (-\infty < \mu < +\infty)$, $\text{Var}(X_1) = \sigma^2 (0 \leq \sigma^2 < +\infty)$, and $E(X_1 - \mu)^4 = \sigma^4 + 1$.

(a) State the Weak Law of Large Numbers.

(b) It is the case that, as $n \to \infty$,

$$\frac{X_1^2 + X_2^2 + \cdots + X_n^2}{n} \rightsquigarrow c$$

for some constant $c (0 \leq c < +\infty)$. Find c.

(c) State the Central Limit Theorem.

(d) Find $\lim\limits_{n\to\infty} P\left[\sigma^2 - \dfrac{1}{\sqrt{n}} \le \dfrac{(X_1 - \mu)^2 + \cdots + (X_n - \mu)^2}{n} \le \sigma^2 + \dfrac{1}{\sqrt{n}}\right].$

6.10 (Refer to Problem 5.3.)

(a) Suppose that 100 plays of this game are made independently, yielding winnings $W_1, \ldots, W_{100}$. What does Chebyshev's Inequality say about

$$P\left[\left|\dfrac{W_1 + \cdots + W_{100}}{100} + \dfrac{13}{36}\right| > \dfrac{1}{2}\sqrt{\dfrac{1235}{1296}}\right]?$$

Can you improve on this statement?

(b) Prove that $\dfrac{W_1 + \cdots + W_n}{n} \xrightarrow{P} -\dfrac{13}{36}$ by using

(1) Chebyshev's Inequality;
(2) Lévy's Continuity Theorem;
(3) The Weak Law of Large Numbers;
(4) Khinchin's Theorem.

6.11 The random variables $X_1, X_2, \ldots$ are such that $EX_k = 0$, $P[|X_k| < 4] = 1$ ($k = 1, 2, \ldots$), and

$$\operatorname{Var}\left(\dfrac{X_1 + \cdots + X_n}{n}\right) \to \dfrac{1}{2}, \quad \text{as } n \to \infty.$$

($X_1, X_2, \ldots$ are not necessarily identically distributed.)

(a) Prove that the X's cannot all be independent.
(b) Prove that the Law of Large Numbers does not hold for the X's.

6.12 Let $X_1, \ldots, X_n$ be independent r.v.'s with $P[X_i = 1] = p$ and $P[X_i = 0] = 1 - p$ for $i = 1, \ldots, n$, where p is unknown and $0 \le p \le 1$. Let $S_n = X_1 + \cdots + X_n$. Fix $t > 0$.

(a) Using Chebyshev's Inequality, how large an n will guarantee

$$P\left[\left|\dfrac{S_n}{n} - p\right| \ge t\right] \le .01$$

no matter what value the (unknown) p may have? (Note that your n cannot depend on the unknown p.)

(b) Using the Central Limit Theorem, the approximate n needed so that

$$\min_{0 \le p \le 1} P\left[-t \le \dfrac{S_n}{n} - p \le t\right] \ge \dfrac{99}{100}$$

is what?

(c) Compare the answers to (a) and (b) when $t = .01$.

6.13 Let $X_1, \ldots, X_n$ be independent random variables, each $N(\mu, \sigma^2)$ where μ is unknown ($-\infty < \mu < +\infty$) and $\sigma^2 > 0$ is known. Let $\bar{X} \equiv (X_1 + \cdots + X_n)/n$.

Only some pairs of real numbers (d_1, d_2) will be such that (irrespective of the value of μ)

$$P[\bar{X} - d_1 \le \mu \le \bar{X} + d_2] = .99; \tag{$*$}$$

if (d_1, d_2) is such a pair then the interval of real numbers $(\overline{X} - d_1, \overline{X} + d_2)$ is called a **confidence interval** for μ with **confidence coefficient** .99.

(a) Specify precisely which pairs (d_1, d_2) satisfy (∗).

(b) Among all pairs (d_1, d_2) that satisfy (∗), which one minimizes $d_1 + d_2$? (That is, which pair minimizes the length of the confidence interval?)

6.14 Show that in Problem 5.22 when $a_i = 1/2^i$ $(i = 1, 2, 3, \ldots)$ the r.v. $a_1 X_1 + a_2 X_2 + \cdots$ has a uniform distribution on $(-1, 1)$. [*Hint:* Use the results of Problem 5.22 and Lévy's Continuity Theorem (Theorem 6.4.2).]

HONORS PROBLEMS FOR CHAPTER 6

6.1H In the literature of **ESP** and of **Parapsychology** much reference is made to probability and statistics: It is used and misused to justify conclusions. [See, for example, Feller (1968), p. 56, footnote 20; p. 407, footnote 16; and the articles referred to in those footnotes.]

(a) Read the articles referred to in Feller's book. Summarize them, with your analysis, in a well-written essay.

(b) Read one recent article in the *Journal of Parapsychology* and write a report on it. Read and report on Hansel (1966); and Christopher (1970).

6.2H Suppose $F_n \to L$ in the sense of Definition 6.2.4, but without any restrictions on L. When must L be ≥ 0 and monotonic? Show by example that L need not be a d.f.

6.3H Prove that

$$\lim_{n \to \infty} \left(1 + \frac{a_n}{n}\right)^n = e^{\lim_{n \to \infty} a_n}.$$

6.4H Let $\Phi(x) = P[Z \leq x]$ where Z is a $N(0, 1)$ r.v. Let X_1 be a $N(0, 1/n)$ r.v., let X_2 be a $N(1, 1/n)$ r.v., and suppose that X_1 and X_2 are independent.

(a) If a new r.v. Y is a result of choosing from the values $\{X_1, X_2\}$ at random with probability $1 - 1/n$ of choosing X_1 and probability $1/n$ of choosing X_2, show that

$$P[Y \leq x] = \left(1 - \frac{1}{n}\right)\Phi(\sqrt{n}\, x) + \frac{1}{n}\Phi\left(\sqrt{n}\,(x - 1)\right).$$

Find $\phi_Y(t) = Ee^{itY}$.

(b) Suppose that $Y_1, \ldots, Y_n$ are independent r.v.'s with the same distribution as Y in (a). Show that

$$\lim_{n \to \infty} \phi_{Y_1 + \cdots + Y_n}(t) = e^{-\frac{1}{2}t^2 + e^{it} - 1}.$$

(Note that the common d.f. of $Y_1, \ldots, Y_n$ changes as n changes.) How could we obtain a r.v. with this characteristic function? [*Hint:* If T_1 is a $N(0, 1)$ r.v. and T_2 is a Poisson r.v., what is the characteristic function of $T_1 + T_2$ if T_1 and T_2 are independent r.v.'s?] Express

$$\lim_{n \to \infty} P[Y_1 + \cdots + Y_n \leq x]$$

as an infinite series.

6.5H Suppose that $X_1, X_2, \ldots$ is a sequence of r.v.'s such that

$$X_n \not\to X(\theta) \qquad\qquad (*)$$

for a specified r.v. $X(\theta)$ for all θ in a specified set Θ. (The r.v.'s $X_1, X_2, \ldots$ are not necessarily either independent or identically distributed, and in general their d.f. depends on $\theta \in \Theta$.) *We then ask*: Does there always exist a subsequence n_k such that for all $\theta \in \Theta$

$$X_{n_k} \to X(\theta) \text{ w.p. 1?} \qquad\qquad (**)$$

[From Theorem 6.2.5 it does not follow that $(**)$ holds, but only that there is a subsequence $n_k(\theta)$ such that $X_{n_k(\theta)} \to X(\theta)$ w.p. 1. $(**)$ asserts we can find a subsequence that "works" for all θ simultaneously.] A reference is Simons (1971).

CHAPTER 7

Point Estimation

In this chapter we introduce the basic concepts of statistical estimation (Section 7.1) and then discuss the methods of **maximum likelihood** due to R. A. Fisher (Section 7.2) and of **moments** due to Karl Pearson (Section 7.3). The chapter concludes with considerations of **goodness of estimators** (Sections 7.4 and 7.5).

7.1. STATISTICAL POINT ESTIMATION: CONCEPTS

The basic situation in point estimation is as follows. We observe r.v.'s $X_1, \ldots, X_n$ (not necessarily independent or identically distributed); the d.f. of $X_1, \ldots, X_n$ depends on an unknown parameter θ (e.g., the mean of a normal distribution can be unknown) that is known to be in some given set Θ. The problem of estimating θ is a problem of **point estimation**. [We have a basic sample space Ω, the experiment essentially chooses an $\omega \in \Omega$, the observations are $X_1(\omega) = x_1, \ldots, X_n(\omega) = x_n$, and the d.f. of $X_1, \ldots, X_n$ is, say, $F_{X_1, \ldots, X_n}(y_1, \ldots, y_n | \theta)$. We then wish to estimate θ.] Of course, we estimate θ by some (appropriate) function of the observations $X_1, \ldots, X_n$; such a function being called a "statistic" or an "estimator":

Definition 7.1.1. Any function of the random variables that are being observed, say $t_n(X_1, \ldots, X_n)$, is called a **statistic**. It is also called an **estimator of** θ; since $X_1, \ldots, X_n$ are r.v.'s, it is a r.v. A particular value of the estimator, say $t_n(x_1, \ldots, x_n)$, is called an **estimate of** θ.

We would like our estimator of θ to be exactly θ on the average, and if it is we call it an "unbiased" estimator of θ.

Definition 7.1.2. We say $t_n(X_1, \ldots, X_n)$ is an **unbiased estimator** of θ if

$$E_\theta t_n(X_1, \ldots, X_n) \stackrel{\theta}{\equiv} \theta, \qquad \text{all } \theta \in \Theta.$$

[The subscript θ on the expectation sign indicates which d.f. $F_{X_1, \ldots, X_n}$

336

$(y_1, \ldots, y_n | \theta)$ is to be used in the evaluation. Recall that the notation " $\overset{\theta}{\equiv}$ " means "identically equal to." Thus, " $a(\theta) \overset{\theta}{\equiv} b(\theta)$ " is used to denote that $a(v) = b(v)$ for every value v of θ.]

However, many estimators are not unbiased, so we also define a measure of the difference between our estimator and θ.

Definition 7.1.3. (Bias of t_n) = $E_\theta t_n(X_1, \ldots, X_n) - \theta \equiv b_n(\theta)$.

Often an estimator t_n will not be unbiased, but its bias will go to 0 as n increases (e.g., if $t_n = s_n + 1/n$ where s_n is unbiased, then t_n is biased but asymptotically unbiased); we now formalize this notion.

Definition 7.1.4. We say $t_n(X_1, \ldots, X_n)$ is an **asymptotically unbiased** estimator of θ if

$$\lim_{n \to \infty} b_n(\theta) = 0, \qquad \text{all } \theta \in \Theta.$$

Another property we would like to have in estimators of θ is that they converge in probability to θ (i.e., their probability "collects" close to θ) as the number of observations $n \to \infty$.

Definition 7.1.5. If $X_1, \ldots, X_n$ are r.v.'s to be observed and they have d.f. $F_{X_1, \ldots, X_n}(y_1, \ldots, y_n | \theta)$ where the unknown $\theta \in \Theta$, then a sequence $t_1, t_2, \ldots$ is called **a consistent sequence of estimators of** θ iff (as $n \to \infty$)

$$t_n(X_1, \ldots, X_n) \overset{P}{\to} \theta, \qquad \text{all } \theta \in \Theta.$$

Example 7.1.6. Let $X_1, X_2, \ldots, X_n$ be independent and identically distributed r.v.'s with mean μ and variance σ^2, where $\mu \in \mathscr{R}$ (defined in Definition 3.1.1) and $\sigma^2 \in \mathscr{R}^+ \equiv \{x: x > 0\}$. If we consider the statistics

$$\overline{X}_n = \frac{X_1 + X_2 + \cdots + X_n}{n}, \ s_n^2 = \sum_{i=1}^{n} \frac{\left(X_i - \overline{X}_n\right)^2}{n-1}, \ u_n^2 = \sum_{i=1}^{n} \frac{\left(X_i - \overline{X}_n\right)^2}{n},$$

we find $E(\overline{X}_n) = \mu$,

$$E(s_n^2) = \frac{1}{n-1} E\left(\sum_{i=1}^{n} X_i^2 - n\overline{X}^2 \right) = \frac{1}{n-1} \left(n(\mu^2 + \sigma^2) - n\left(\frac{\sigma^2}{n} + \mu^2 \right) \right) = \sigma^2,$$

and

$$E(u_n^2) = \frac{n-1}{n} E(s_n^2) = \frac{n-1}{n} \sigma^2.$$

Thus $\overline{X}_n$ and s_n^2 are respective unbiased estimators of μ and σ^2. u_n^2 is not an unbiased estimator of σ^2, but since

$$\left(\text{Bias of } u_n^2\right) = b_n(\sigma^2) = E\left(u_n^2\right) - \sigma^2 = \frac{n-1}{n}\sigma^2 - \sigma^2$$

$$= -\frac{\sigma^2}{n} \to 0 \text{ as } n \to \infty,$$

u_n^2 is an asymptotically unbiased estimator of σ^2.

We have already shown that $\overline{X}_n \xrightarrow{P} \mu$ (Khinchin's WLLN, Theorem 6.2.26), and $s_n^2 \xrightarrow{P} \sigma^2$ (Example 6.3.17), and by Corollary 6.3.13(iii) **(b)** $u_n^2 \xrightarrow{P} \sigma^2$. Thus $\{\overline{X}_n\}$ is a consistent sequence of estimators for μ, and $\{s_n^2\}$ and $\{u_n^2\}$ are each consistent sequences of estimators of σ^2.

Remark 7.1.7. It is very often convenient to express the point probability function (discrete r.v. case) and p.d.f. (continuous r.v. case) using the indicator function (5.5.10) of the set of possible values of the r.v. This is especially useful when the range of the r.v. depends on the value of a parameter (which may be unknown).

Example 7.1.8. **(a)** If X has the (displaced) exponential distribution with p.d.f.

$$f_X(x) = \begin{cases} \dfrac{1}{\lambda}e^{-(x-\theta)/\lambda}, & \text{if } x > \theta \\ 0, & \text{otherwise} \end{cases}$$

then, since the indicator function $I_S(t)$ of a set S is (see equation (5.5.10))

$$I_S(t) = \begin{cases} 1, & \text{if } t \in S \\ 0, & \text{if } t \notin S, \end{cases}$$

we can write

$$f_X(x) = \frac{1}{\lambda}e^{-(x-\theta)/\lambda}I_{(\theta,\infty)}(t).$$

(b) If $X \sim N(\mu, \sigma^2)$, then

$$f_X(x) = \frac{1}{\sqrt{2\pi}\,\sigma}e^{-(x-\mu)^2/(2\sigma^2)}I_{\mathscr{R}}(x).$$

(c) If X is uniform on $(0, \theta)$, then $f_X(x) = I_{(0,\theta)}(x)/\theta$.

(d) If $X \sim B(x|\alpha, \lambda)$, then

$$f_X(x) = \frac{1}{\beta(\alpha+1, \lambda+1)}x^\alpha(1-x)^\lambda I_{[0,1]}(x).$$

(e) If $X \sim B(n, p)$, then $p_X(x) = \binom{n}{x}p^x q^{n-x}I_{\{0,1,2,\ldots,n\}}(x)$.

(f) If X is Poisson with parameter λ, then

$$p_X(x) = e^{-\lambda}\lambda^x/x! \cdot I_{Z_0^+}(x)$$

where $Z_0^+ = \{0, 1, 2, \dots\}$, the set of nonnegative integers and zero.

In Definitions 5.1.10 and 5.1.14, for any r.v. X for which these quantities exist, we talked about the **population moments** $\mu_k' = \mu_k'(X) = EX^k$ (kth noncentral[1] moment) and $\mu_k = \mu_k(X) = E(X - \mu_1')^k$ (kth central moment), and their importance became clear in Chapters 5 and 6. Often they are unknown and are **estimated by sample moments**. For instance, in Example 7.1.6 $\bar{X}_n$ and u_n^2 are called the first noncentral sample moment and the second central sample moment, respectively. After general definitions of the sample moments, we consider why the m_k' and m_k are called *sample moments*, and then proceed to consider their bias and consistency as estimators of the population moments μ_k' and μ_k.

Definition 7.1.9. Let $X_1, \dots, X_n$ be n r.v.'s (not necessarily independent or identically distributed). Their **kth (noncentral) sample moment** is

$$m_k' = \frac{X_1^k + \cdots + X_n^k}{n};$$

their **kth central sample moment** is

$$m_k = \frac{(X_1 - m_1')^k + \cdots + (X_n - m_1')^k}{n}.$$

Example 7.1.10. The $k = 1$st (noncentral) sample moment is

$$m_1' = \frac{X_1 + \cdots + X_n}{n} \equiv \bar{X}(n) \equiv \bar{X} \equiv \bar{X}_n,$$

called the **sample mean**, and we will use the **notations $\bar{X}(n)$, $\bar{X}$, and $\bar{X}_n$** (instead of m_1') quite extensively.

Example 7.1.11. Suppose we perform an experiment and obtain results $X_1 = x_1, \dots, X_n = x_n$. Let a r.v. Z be such that $P[Z = x_i] = 1/n$ ($i = 1, \dots, n$). Then

$$EZ = m_1', \quad EZ^k = m_k', \quad E(Z - EZ)^k = \frac{(x_1 - \bar{x})^k + \cdots + (x_n - \bar{x})^k}{n},$$

which justifies the name sample moments (moments of the sample). (Problem 5.17 involved the calculation of some sample moments.)

---

[1]Of course $E(X - a)^k$ is a "noncentral" moment as long as $a \neq \mu_1'$. However, the term is usually reserved for the case $a = 0$.

340   POINT ESTIMATION

Theorem 7.1.12. Let $X_1, \ldots, X_n$ be independent and identically distributed r.v.'s, each with d.f. $F(x|\theta)$ for some fixed $\theta \in \Theta$. (Suppose that any moment mentioned exists.) Then, by definition,

$$\mu_k' = EX_1^k, \qquad \mu_k = E(X_1 - \mu_1')^k$$

$$m_k' = \frac{X_1^k + \cdots + X_n^k}{n}, \qquad m_k = \frac{(X_1 - \bar{X})^k + \cdots + (X_n - \bar{X})^k}{n}.$$

We will prove that

(i) $Em_k' \equiv \mu_k'$, but $Em_k \not\equiv \mu_k$; and

(ii) $m_k' \overset{P}{\to} \mu_k'$, and $m_k \overset{P}{\to} \mu_k$.

Proof of (i).   First, we easily show $Em_k' \equiv \mu_k'$ as follows:

$$Em_k' = E\left(\frac{X_1^k + \cdots + X_n^k}{n}\right) = \frac{EX_1^k + \cdots + EX_n^k}{n} = \frac{n\mu_k'}{n} = \mu_k';$$

we used identical distribution, but not independence.

Second, we show with some algebra that $Em_k \not\equiv \mu_k$. Consider the case $k = 2$. Then $\mu_k = E(X_1 - \mu_1')^2 = \sigma^2$ (say) is called the variance of the distribution of the X_i's. Here

$$m_2 = \frac{\displaystyle\sum_{i=1}^{n}(X_i - \bar{X})^2}{n},$$

and

$$\begin{aligned}
Enm_2 &= E\sum_{i=1}^{n}\left[(X_i - \mu_1') - (\bar{X} - \mu_1')\right]^2 \\
&= E\left[\sum(X_i - \mu_1')^2 + n(\bar{X} - \mu_1')^2 - 2\sum(\bar{X} - \mu_1')(X_i - \mu_1')\right] \\
&= n\sigma^2 + \sigma^2 - 2\sigma^2 = (n-1)\sigma^2,
\end{aligned}$$

where (because it is obvious) we have written $\sum$ for $\displaystyle\sum_{i=1}^{n}$ (this will sometimes be done below without further mention); the second term gave

$$En\left(\frac{(X_1 - \mu_1') + \cdots + (X_n - \mu_1')}{n}\right)^2 = 0 + \frac{n}{n^2}n\sigma^2 = \sigma^2$$

(cross-products had expected value 0, using independence); a typical last term gave

$$E\left(\frac{(X_1 - \mu_1') + \cdots + (X_n - \mu_1')}{n}\right)(X_1 - \mu_1') = \frac{\sigma^2}{n}.$$

(cross-products had expected value 0, except when they had the same index), so the last term yielded $-2\sigma^2$; and we introduced μ_1' since $E(X_i - \mu_1') = 0$ [hence, $E(\overline{X} - \mu_1') = 0$]. Thus,

$$Em_2 = \frac{n-1}{n}\sigma^2 = \frac{n-1}{n}\mu_2 \neq \mu_2.$$

However, $E\dfrac{n}{n-1}m_2 = \sigma^2 = \mu_2$, so

$$E\frac{\displaystyle\sum_{i=1}^{n}\left(X_i - \overline{X}\right)^2}{n-1} = \sigma^2. \tag{7.1.13}$$

The quantity $\displaystyle\sum_{i=1}^{n}(X_i - \overline{X})^2/(n-1)$, an unbiased estimator of σ^2, is usually used instead of m_2. [Of course, if we knew $EX_1 = \mu$ (say), we could use $\displaystyle\sum_{i=1}^{n}(X_i - \mu)^2/n$ as an unbiased estimator of σ^2. Since we do not know μ, we in effect replace it by $\overline{X}$, and this requires division by $n - 1$ instead of by n in order to achieve unbiasedness; this is called a **loss of 1 degree of freedom**, for reasons that will become apparent later.] ∎

Proof of (ii). First, the fact that $m_k' \overset{P}{\to} \mu_k'$ follows on applying Khinchin's Theorem (Theorem 6.2.26) (a law of large numbers) to $X_1^k, \ldots, X_n^k$.

Second, we wish to prove that $m_k \overset{P}{\to} \mu_k$. Now $\mu_k = E(X_1 - \mu_1')^k$; if we expand $(X_1 - \mu_1')^k$ by the binomial theorem and use properties of expectation (e.g., the expected value of a sum equals the sum of the expected values—see Theorem 5.1.7),

$$\mu_k = \Pi(\mu_1', \ldots, \mu_k'),$$

that is, μ_k is a polynomial in $\mu_1', \ldots, \mu_k'$. We now claim that

$$m_k = \Pi(m_1', \ldots, m_k'), \tag{7.1.14}$$

that is, m_k is *the same* polynomial in $m_1', \ldots, m_k'$. Consider any set of observations $X_1 = x_1, \ldots, X_n = x_n$ and let D be a r.v. such that $P[D = x_i] = 1/n$ ($i = 1, \ldots, n$). Then $\mu_k(D) = m_k$; hence, $m_k = \Pi(m_1', \ldots, m_k')$ for any observations $x_1, \ldots, x_n$. Since equation (7.1.14) holds for any fixed numbers $x_1, \ldots, x_n$, it also holds for random numbers (r.v.'s) $X_1, \ldots, X_n$. But we already proved that

$$m_k' \overset{P}{\to} \mu_k',$$

and a polynomial Π is a jointly continuous function of its arguments. Hence, by Theorem 6.3.12,

$$m_k = \Pi(m_1', \ldots, m_k') \overset{P}{\to} \Pi(\mu_1', \ldots, \mu_k') = \mu_k. \qquad ∎$$

We will now give two examples which show that if we have more than one unbiased estimator, then we have infinitely many unbiased estimators, but that we need not have even one unbiased estimator. [Two questions arise.[2] First, if there are many unbiased estimators, how should we choose one of them to use? Some possible answers (maximum likelihood[3] and so on) are studied in this chapter. Second, if there are no unbiased estimators, which sorts of biased estimators should we use? This question is only treated implicitly (maximum likelihood, and so on).]

Example 7.1.15. Suppose that we observe random variables $X_1, \ldots, X_n$ (not necessarily independent or identically distributed) and that their joint d.f. depends on an unknown $\theta \in \Theta$. Further, suppose that we find functions of $X_1, \ldots, X_n$ (statistics) $t_1(X_1, \ldots, X_n), \ldots, t_k(X_1, \ldots, X_n)$ such that

$$E_\theta t_i(X_1, \ldots, X_n) \stackrel{\theta}{\equiv} \theta, \qquad \text{all } \theta \in \Theta \qquad (7.1.16)$$

(i.e., $t_1, \ldots, t_k$ are each unbiased estimators of θ). Then suppose $w_1, \ldots, w_k$ are k fixed constants ($-\infty < w_i < +\infty$). We have

$$E_\theta\{w_1 t_1(X_1, \ldots, X_n) + \cdots + w_k t_k(X_1, \ldots, X_n)\} \stackrel{\theta}{\equiv} (w_1 + \cdots + w_k)\theta$$

$$(\theta \in \Theta), \quad (7.1.17)$$

so $\sum_{i=1}^{k} w_i t_i(X_1, \ldots, X_n)$ is an unbiased estimator of θ iff $w_1 + \cdots + w_k = 1$. There are infinitely many such $w_1, \ldots, w_k$. Also, if t_1 is an unbiased estimator of θ, then so is $t_1 + s_1$ if $E_\theta s_1 \stackrel{\theta}{\equiv} 0$.

Example 7.1.18. Suppose that $X_1, X_2, \ldots$ are independent r.v.'s, each with $P[X_i = 1] = p$ and $P[X_i = 0] = q \equiv 1 - p$ for some unknown p ($0 \leq p \leq 1$) (this is the Bernoulli distribution of Definition 3.2.1). Let N be the number of observations we need to make to obtain our first success (then $N - 1$ has the negative binomial distribution of Definition 3.2.23 with $r = 1$ success). Hence, $X_1 = X_2 = \cdots = X_{N-1} = 0$ and $X_N = 1$. Also, $P[N = l] = q^{l-1}p$ for $l = 1, 2, 3, \ldots$.

We now wish to find all functions ζ of N alone that are unbiased estimators of p [so, such functions as $\zeta(N) + X_1 - X_2$ are excluded]. Our requirement is

$$E_p \zeta(N) \stackrel{p}{\equiv} p; \qquad (7.1.19)$$

---

[2] A third question could arise: "Does an estimator possess any advantage simply by virtue of being unbiased?" For us, lack of bias is appealing in itself. (However, biased estimators can sometimes possess desirable properties that unbiased ones lack.)
[3] This is not the only (or even the most important) context in which maximum likelihood is important.

that is [taking the expected value in (7.1.19)],

$$\sum_{j=1}^{\infty} \zeta(j) q^{j-1} p \stackrel{p}{\equiv} p. \tag{7.1.20}$$

If $q = 1$ (so $p = 0$), equation (7.1.20) becomes $0 = 0$. If $q \neq 1$ (so $p \neq 0$), on division by p (7.1.20) becomes

$$\sum_{j=1}^{\infty} \zeta(j) q^{j-1} \stackrel{p}{\equiv} 1. \tag{7.1.21}$$

Now it is well-known that **two power series** $\sum_0^{\infty} a_j x^j$ **and** $\sum_0^{\infty} b_j x^j$ **have the same value for every** x **in some interval iff** $a_0 = b_0$, $a_1 = b_1, \ldots$. Thus, from (7.1.21), $\zeta(1) = 1$ and $\zeta(j) = 0$ for $j > 1$. Hence, exactly one unbiased estimator $\zeta(N)$ exists, namely

$$\zeta(N) = \begin{cases} 1, & \text{if } N = 1 \\ 0, & \text{if } N > 1. \end{cases} \tag{7.1.22}$$

Note that this absurd estimator need only observe X_1; in fact, $P[\zeta(N) = X_1] = 1$. If we require that $P[\zeta(N) = X_1] \neq 1$, no unbiased estimators exist.

We now wish to introduce (in addition to bias and consistency) a third concept and to study its relation to the other two.

Definition 7.1.23. We say $t_n(X_1, \ldots, X_n)$ is **consistent in mean square** (or **consistent in quadratic mean**) if

$$E_\theta (t_n - \theta)^2 \to 0 \quad \text{as } n \to \infty \quad (\text{all } \theta \in \Theta). \tag{7.1.24}$$

The quantity $E(t_n - \theta)^2$ is called the **mean squared error** of estimator t_n.

Theorem 7.1.25. $t_n(X_1, \ldots, X_n)$ is consistent in mean square iff (1) $\text{Var}_\theta (t_n) \to 0$ as $n \to \infty$, and (2) t_n is asymptotically unbiased.

Proof: Since $EX^2 = \text{Var}(X) + (EX)^2$, we have

$$E_\theta (t_n - \theta)^2 = \text{Var}_\theta (t_n - \theta) + [E_\theta (t_n - \theta)]^2$$

$$= \text{Var}_\theta (t_n) + [b_n(\theta)]^2,$$

which will $\to 0$ iff both of its (positive) terms $\to 0$. ∎

Theorem 7.1.26. If $E_\theta(t_n - \theta)^2 \to 0$ (all θ), then $t_n \xrightarrow{P} \theta$ (all θ).

Proof: For any $\varepsilon > 0$, Chebyshev's Inequality (Theorem 6.1.1) states that

$$P[|t_n - \theta| \leq \varepsilon] \geq 1 - \frac{E(t_n - \theta)^2}{\varepsilon^2},$$

which (by the hypotheses of our theorem) $\to 1$ as $n \to \infty$. ∎

Note that Theorem 7.1.26 essentially states that convergence in $\mathscr{L}_2$ implies convergence in probability; this was a result stated (without proof) in Theorem 6.2.5.

We now end this section with an example.

Example 7.1.27. It is sometimes the case that a sequence (say $Y_1, Y_2, \ldots$) of r.v.'s cannot be observed, although we can observe some results of the values of $Y_1, Y_2, \ldots$ (say $X_1, X_2, \ldots$). Let $Y_1, Y_2, \ldots$ be independent and identically distributed r.v.'s. Let a be a fixed number ($-\infty < a < +\infty$). For $i = 1, 2, \ldots$ define

$$X_i = \begin{cases} 1, & \text{if } Y_i \geq a \\ 0, & \text{if } Y_i < a. \end{cases}$$

Define $p = P(Y_1 \geq a)$, $q = 1 - p$. [For example, if a manufacturing process produces parts with strength Y_i that are tested to see if they can withstand stress a, then X_i denotes whether the strength is at least a (in which case the part does not fail and $X_i = 1$) or the strength is less than a (in which case the part fails and $X_i = 0$). In such a case, we cannot directly observe the strength Y_i of the ith part, but we can observe whether it breaks in a stress test.]

Here X_1 has mean p and variance pq, and we may wish to estimate these. $S_n = X_1 + X_2 + \cdots + X_n$ is binomial $B(n, p)$, and we see that $E(S_n/n) = p$; that is, S_n/n is an **unbiased** estimator of p. It is also easy to show that $E(1 - S_n/n) = q$; that is, $1 - S_n/n$ is an **unbiased** estimator of $1 - p = q$. However, $(S_n/n)(1 - S_n/n)$ is **not** an unbiased estimator of pq since

$$E\left(\frac{S_n}{n}\left(1 - \frac{S_n}{n}\right)\right) = E\left(\frac{S_n}{n}\right) - E\left(\frac{S_n^2}{n^2}\right) = p - \frac{1}{n^2}E(S_n^2)$$

$$= p - \frac{1}{n^2}(n^2p^2 + npq) = p(1 - p) - \frac{pq}{n} = pq\frac{n-1}{n}.$$

The bias of $(S_n/n)(1 - S_n/n)$ as an estimator of pq is thus

$$\left(\text{Bias of } \frac{S_n}{n}\left(1 - \frac{S_n}{n}\right)\right) = pq\frac{n-1}{n} - pq = -\frac{pq}{n}$$

which $\to 0$ as $n \to \infty$, hence $(S_n/n)(1 - S_n/n)$ is an **asymptotically unbiased estimator** of pq.

Since

$$E\left(\frac{S_n}{n} - p\right)^2 = \text{Var}\left(\frac{S_n}{n}\right) = \frac{pq}{n} \to 0 \text{ as } n \to \infty,$$

it follows that S_n / n is consistent in mean square as an estimator of p.

That $(S_n / n)(1 - S_n / n)$ is a consistent estimator of pq follows from Corollary 6.3.11 (ii). (This can also be shown directly by showing that we have consistency in mean square, and then appealing to Theorem 6.2.5. However, this method is messy since in showing that

$$E\left(\frac{S_n}{n}\left(1 - \frac{S_n}{n}\right) - pq\right)^2$$

$\to 0$ as $n \to \infty$, we need to find the first 4 moments of S_n. This may be done using m.g.f.'s, as we know the m.g.f. of a binomial $B(n, p)$ r.v. S_n, and is left as an exercise.)

PROBLEMS FOR SECTION 7.1

7.1.1 Let $X_1, X_2, \ldots, X_n$ be independent and identically distributed Bernoulli r.v.'s with probability of success p, and denote $T_n = X_1 + X_2 + \cdots + X_n$, with $\overline{X}_n$ and s_n^2 as in Example 7.1.6. Show that
   (a) $T_n(T_n - 1)/c_n$ with $c_n = n(n - 1)$ is an unbiased estimator of p^2.
   (b) $T_n(T_n - 1)(T_n - 2)/d_n$ with $d_n = n(n - 1)(n - 2)$ is an unbiased estimator of p^3.
   (c) Investigate the consistency of the estimators in parts (a) and (b).
   (d) Find an unbiased estimator of $p - q$ where $q = 1 - p$.

7.1.2 Let T_n and T_n' be two independent r.v.'s, unbiased and consistent estimators of a parameter θ.
   (a) Find an unbiased estimator of θ^2.
   (b) Find an unbiased estimator of $\theta(\theta - 1)$.
   (c) Are the estimators in parts (a) and (b) consistent?

7.1.3 Let $X_1, X_2, \ldots$ be independent and identically distributed $N(\mu, \mu)$ r.v.'s for some $\mu > 0$. Find a consistent unbiased estimator of μ^2. [*Hint:* $E(\overline{X}_n) = \mu$ and $E(s_n^2) = \mu$; consider $T_n = \overline{X}_n s_n^2$.]

7.1.4 Let $X_1, X_2, \ldots, X_n$ be a random sample of size n from the p.d.f. $f(x) = ((1 - \theta) + \theta/(2\sqrt{x}))I_{[0,1]}(x)$ for some $\theta \in [0, 1]$.
   (a) Show that $\overline{X}_n$ is a biased estimator of θ, and find its bias $b_n(\theta)$.
   (b) Does $\lim_{n \to \infty} b_n(\theta) = 0$ for all θ?
   (c) Is $\overline{X}_n$ consistent in mean square?

7.1.5 Let $X_1, X_2, \ldots, X_n$ be independent and identically distributed Poisson r.v.'s with parameter λ. Show that $T_n = \overline{X}_n^2 - \overline{X}_n$ is a biased estimator of λ^2, find its bias $b_n(\lambda)$, and hence find an unbiased estimator of λ^2. Does $\lim_{n \to \infty} b_n(\lambda) = 0$ for all λ?

7.1.6 Let $X_1, X_2, \ldots, X_n$ be independent r.v.'s, each with the same "displaced Laplace" p.d.f. $f(x) = (1/2)e^{-|x-\theta|}I_{(-\infty,\infty)}(x)$, for some θ ($-\infty < \theta < \infty$). If $Y_1 \leq Y_2 \leq \cdots \leq Y_n$ are the order statistics, show that $T_n = (Y_1 + Y_n)/2$ is an unbiased estimator of θ.

7.1.7 Let $X_1, X_2, \ldots, X_n$ be independent r.v.'s, each with p.d.f. $f(x) = (1/\theta)I_{(\theta, 2\theta)}(x)$ for some $\theta > 0$. If $Y_1 \leq Y_2 \leq \cdots \leq Y_n$ are the order statistics, then
  (a) Show that Y_1 and Y_n are both biased estimators of θ, and find their respective biases. Do these biases converge to zero as $n \to \infty$?
  (b) Based on part (a), find unbiased estimators of θ based on Y_1 alone, Y_n alone, and a linear combination of Y_1 and Y_n.
  (c) Show that the intuitive estimators $T_n = Y_n - Y_1$ and $T_n' = (2Y_n + Y_1)/3$ are also biased estimators of θ.

7.1.8 (a) Let X have p.d.f. $f_X(x) = (2/(1-\theta)^2)(x-\theta)I_{(\theta,1)}(x)$ for some θ ($0 < \theta < 1$). Show that $E(X - \theta) = 2(1-\theta)/3$, and hence find an unbiased estimator of θ based on a sample of size 1.
  (b) If $X_1, X_2, \ldots, X_n$ is a random sample of size n from the density in part (a), find a function of $\overline{X}_n$ that is unbiased for θ, and also find the bias of $\overline{X}_n$.
  (c) Let $Y_1 \leq Y_2 \leq \cdots \leq Y_n$ be the order statistics in part (b). Find $E(Y_1)$.

7.1.9 Let T_{1n} and T_{2n} be independent unbiased estimators of θ, with $\text{Var}(T_{1n}) = \sigma_{1n}^2$ and $\text{Var}(T_{2n}) = \sigma_{2n}^2$, for which $\lim_{n \to \infty} \sigma_{1n}^2 = 0 = \lim_{n \to \infty} \sigma_{2n}^2$. For $\alpha \in [0,1]$ show that $T_{3n} = \alpha T_{1n} + (1-\alpha)T_{2n}$ is an unbiased sequence of estimators of θ. Find the value of α for which $\text{Var}(T_{3n})$ is a minimum.

7.1.10 Let $X_1, X_2, \ldots, X_n$ be independent r.v.'s, each $G(x|\alpha - 1, \beta)$, with $\alpha > 1$ known. Let $T_n(X_1, X_2, \ldots, X_n) = \overline{X}_n/\alpha$.
  (a) Show that T_n is unbiased and consistent in mean square for β.
  (b) Show that $(X_1^2 + X_2^2 + \cdots + X_n^2)/(\alpha(\alpha+1)n)$ is unbiased and consistent as an estimator of β^2.

7.1.11 Let $X_1, X_2, \ldots, X_n$ be independent r.v.'s, each $N(\mu, 1)$. Find an unbiased estimator of μ^2 that is a function of $\overline{X}_n$. [*Hint:* Consider $\overline{X}_n^2 - 1/n$.]

7.1.12 Let $X_1, X_2, \ldots, X_n$ be independent r.v.'s, each with p.d.f. $f(x) = \lambda e^{-\lambda x}I_{[0,\infty)}(x)$ for some $\lambda > 0$. Note that $E(X_1) = 1/\lambda$.
  (a) An intuitive estimator of λ is $1/\overline{X}_n$. Show that this estimator is biased, and compute its bias $b_n(\lambda)$.
  (b) Based on part (a), find an unbiased estimator of λ.

7.1.13 Let $X_1, X_2, \ldots, X_n$ be independent and identically distributed r.v.'s, with mean μ and variance σ^2. Show that s^2 is unbiased for σ^2, and that $\overline{X}$ is unbiased for μ.

7.1.14 Let $X_1, X_2, \ldots, X_n$ be a random sample from the triangular p.d.f.

$$f(x) = \begin{cases} \dfrac{x-a}{c}, & \text{if } a \leq x \leq \dfrac{a+b}{2} \\[2mm] \dfrac{b-x}{c}, & \text{if } \dfrac{a+b}{2} \leq x \leq b \\[2mm] 0 & \text{otherwise} \end{cases}$$

for some $a < b$, where $c = (b-a)^2/4$. Show that $\overline{X}_n$ is an unbiased estimator of $E(X_1)$ (the parent mean) and that $\text{Var}(\overline{X}_n) = (b-a)^2/(24n)$.

7.1.15 In Problem 7.1.9, suppose that $\mathrm{Corr}\,(T_{1n}, T_{2n}) = \rho$. Find the value of α for which $\mathrm{Var}\,(T_{3n})$ is a minimum.

7.2. MAXIMUM-LIKELIHOOD ESTIMATION

In Section 7.1, we noted several properties (unbiasedness, consistency, and their variants) that seem desirable in the context of point estimation. Thus, we would like to check a proposed estimator to see if it is consistent, unbiased, and so on. However, faced with a new point-estimation problem, where can we start to look for estimators? It would be convenient to have one (or several) intuitively reasonable methods of generating possibly good estimators to study for our problem; in particular, a method that often gives good results (i.e., generates "good" estimators often) would be desirable. In this section we introduce one such method, that of **maximum likelihood**, which will be studied in or related to much of the rest of Chapters 7 and 8.

Definition 7.2.1. Let $X_1, \ldots, X_n$ be n r.v.'s (not necessarily independent or identically distributed) with d.f. $F(x_1, \ldots, x_n|\theta)$ where $\theta \in \Theta$ is unknown. The **likelihood function** is

$$L(\theta) = \begin{cases} f(X_1, \ldots, X_n|\theta), & \text{if } F \text{ has a density } f \\ p(X_1, \ldots, X_n|\theta), & \text{if } F \text{ has a probability function } p. \end{cases} \quad (7.2.2)$$

[*Note:* The density f or probability function p is evaluated at the random point provided by the observations $X_1, \ldots, X_n$ and is considered as a function of θ (which may be a vector).] Any $\hat{\theta} = \hat{\theta}_n(X_1, \ldots, X_n) \in \Theta$ such that

$$L(\hat{\theta}) = \sup\{L(\theta): \theta \in \Theta\} \quad (7.2.3)$$

is called a **maximum-likelihood estimator (MLE)** of θ. [There may be none, one, or many such $\hat{\theta}$'s for any given problem. Fortunately, there is often one with "good" properties.]

In the past, we usually held θ fixed and let $x_1, \ldots, x_n$ vary in a density $f(x_1, \ldots, x_n|\theta)$; here we hold $x_1, \ldots, x_n$ fixed and let θ vary [in which case $f(x_1, \ldots, x_n|\theta)$ is called the likelihood function].

Note that (1) if $X_1, \ldots, X_n$ are independent r.v.'s and X_i has density $f_i(x|\theta)$ $(i = 1, \ldots, n)$, then

$$L(\theta) = f_1(X_1|\theta) \ldots f_n(X_n|\theta), \quad \theta \in \Theta; \quad (7.2.4)$$

(2) if in addition $f_1 = f_2 = \cdots = f_n = f$ (say), of course the subscripts on $f_1, \ldots, f_n$ in equation (7.2.4) can be deleted; and (3):

Lemma 7.2.5. Those $\hat{\theta}$'s that maximize $L(\theta)$ are precisely those that maximize $\ln L(\theta)$ [this latter form is often easier to deal with].

TABLE 7.2-1
Lion's Appetite Distribution

i	0	1	2	3	4
$p(i\|\theta_1)$	.00	.05	.05	.80	.10
$p(i\|\theta_2)$	.05	.05	.80	.10	.00
$p(i\|\theta_3)$	.90	.08	.02	.00	.00

Proof: This follows since $L(\theta_1) < L(\theta_2)$ iff $\ln L(\theta_1) < \ln L(\theta_2)$ (for all $\theta_1, \theta_2 \in \Theta$). ∎

The following example should help clarify why, intuitively, we might think an MLE would be a "good" estimator of θ.

Example 7.2.6. A certain lion has three possible states of activity each night; they are "very active" (denoted by θ_1), "moderately active" (denoted by θ_2), and "lethargic" (denoted by θ_3). Also, each night this lion eats people; it eats i people with probability $p(i|\theta)$, $\theta \in \Theta = \{\theta_1, \theta_2, \theta_3\}$. (Of course, the probability distribution of the number of people eaten depends on the lion's activity state $\theta \in \Theta$.) The numerical values are given in Table 7.2-1.

If we are told $X = x_0$ people were eaten last night, how should we estimate the lion's activity state (θ_1, θ_2, or θ_3)? One seemingly reasonable method is to **estimate θ as that θ in Θ for which $p(x_0|\theta)$ is largest (the $\theta \in \Theta$ that provides the largest probability of observing what we did observe)**. That is, $\hat{\theta} = \hat{\theta}(X)$, the MLE of θ based on X. We have, of course, $\hat{\theta}(0) = \theta_3$, $\hat{\theta}(1) = \theta_3$, $\hat{\theta}(2) = \theta_2$, $\hat{\theta}(3) = \theta_1$, $\hat{\theta}(4) = \theta_1$. (Note that we *must* have $\theta = \theta_1$ in order to observe $X = 4$.)

Suppose, as a slight modification, that we know $\theta \in \Theta' = \{\theta_1, \theta_2\}$. Then the MLE is no longer unique, for although $\hat{\theta}(0) = \theta_2$, $\hat{\theta}(2) = \theta_2$, $\hat{\theta}(3) = \theta_1$, $\hat{\theta}(4) = \theta_1$, still $\hat{\theta}(1)$ can be *either* θ_1 or θ_2 [since $p(1|\theta_1) = p(1|\theta_2) = .05$].

We now wish to illustrate the workings of the method in a number of problems and to compare the resulting estimators with previously developed ones. We first consider the problem of Example 7.1.18, where we found that the only unbiased estimator was absurd.

Example 7.2.7. Suppose we observe N and that $P_p[N = l] = q^{l-1}p$ ($l = 1, 2, 3, \ldots$) for some $p \in \Theta = \{x: 0 \le x \le 1\}$.[4] What is "the" MLE of p? Our likelihood function is $L(p) = q^{N-1}p$, which has a derivative

$$\frac{dL(p)}{dp} = q^{N-1} - (N-1)q^{N-2}p;$$

this is ≥ 0 iff $p \le 1/N$. Hence, $L(p)$ is maximized uniquely by $\hat{p} = \hat{p}(N) =$

[4]Recall that $q = 1 - p$.

$1/N$. This estimator says "if it took you N trials to observe 1 success, estimate the probability of a success as $1/N$." The absurd estimator of Example 7.1.18, which was unbiased, said "If it took you N trials to observe 1 success, estimate the probability of a success as 1 if $N = 1$ and as 0 if $N > 1$."

Example 7.2.8. Suppose we observe $X_1, \ldots, X_n$, independent r.v.'s each $N(\theta, 1)$ (see Definition 4.2.18) with θ unknown. What is "the" MLE of θ? (Here, since it is not stated what Θ is, it is to be taken as all possible θ, that is, since $-\infty < \theta < +\infty$, $\Theta = \{x: -\infty < x < +\infty\}$.) Here [see equation (7.2.4)]

$$L(\theta) = \prod_{i=1}^{n} f(X_i|\theta) = \prod_{i=1}^{n} \left\{ \frac{1}{\sqrt{2\pi}} e^{-.5(X_i - \theta)^2} \right\}$$

$$= \left(\frac{1}{\sqrt{2\pi}} \right)^n e^{-.5 \sum_{i=1}^{n} (X_i - \theta)^2} \tag{7.2.9}$$

and it is convenient (see Lemma 7.2.5) to take

$$\ln L(\theta) = -n \ln (\sqrt{2\pi}) - .5 \sum_{i=1}^{n} (X_i - \theta)^2. \tag{7.2.10}$$

Now we wish to maximize $\ln L(\theta)$ in (7.2.10) with respect to θ (see Definition 7.2.1); this is equivalent to minimizing $g(\theta) = \sum_{i=1}^{n} (X_i - \theta)^2$. Now

$$g'(\theta) \equiv \frac{dg(\theta)}{d\theta} = -2 \sum_{i=1}^{n} (X_i - \theta),$$

$$g''(\theta) = 2 \sum_{i=1}^{n} 1 = 2n.$$

Hence, solving $g'(\theta) = 0$, we find $\theta = \left(\sum_{i=1}^{n} X_i \right) \Big/ n$. We denote this MLE by $\hat{\theta}$; $\sum_{i=1}^{n} X_i/n$ is simply the sample mean $\overline{X}$, so $\hat{\theta} = \overline{X}$. Since $g''(\theta) > 0$ for all θ, in particular $g''(\hat{\theta}) > 0$, which proves (see Theorem 7.2.11) that $g(\theta)$ has a relative minimum [and hence $L(\theta)$ has a relative maximum] at $\hat{\theta}$. Since $\theta \in \Theta = \{x: -\infty < x < +\infty\}$ and $\lim_{|\theta| \to \infty} g(\theta) = +\infty$, $\hat{\theta}$ yields the absolute minimum of $g(\theta)$ [and hence the absolute maximum of $L(\theta)$]. We previously studied the sample mean as an estimator of the population mean (Theorem 7.1.12), and in this case it is both unbiased and consistent.

Theorem 7.2.11. Let $g(x)$ be continuous and twice differentiable in some open interval I containing a. If $g'(a) = 0$, then $g(x)$ has a relative maximum at $x = a$ if $g''(a) < 0$, and has a relative minimum at $x = a$ if $g''(a) > 0$. The set $\{a:$

$g'(a) = 0$} is called the set of **critical points** of $g(x)$. The only possible maxima and minima of $g(x)$ for $c \le x \le d$ are at the critical points between c and d, and at c and at d.

Proof: See any calculus book; for example, Thomas (1960), Chapter 3. ■

Example 7.2.12. We obtain the same MLE $\hat{\theta} = \overline{X}$ if, in Example 7.2.8, each of the r.v.'s is $N(\theta, \sigma^2)$ where $\sigma^2 > 0$ is known.

Example 7.2.13. Suppose we observe $X_1, \ldots, X_n$, independent r.v.'s each $N(\mu, \sigma^2)$ with μ known, and σ^2 unknown. What is the MLE of $\theta = \sigma^2$? (Here $\Theta = \{x: x > 0\}$ since $0 < \sigma^2 < +\infty$.) Now

$$L(\sigma^2) = \prod_{i=1}^{n} \left\{ \frac{1}{\sqrt{2\pi}\,\sigma} e^{-.5((X_i - \mu)/\sigma)^2} \right\}$$

$$= \left(\frac{1}{\sqrt{2\pi}\,\sigma} \right)^n e^{-.5 \sum_{i=1}^{n} ((X_i - \mu)/\sigma)^2}$$

and

$$\ln L(\sigma^2) = -n \ln(\sqrt{2\pi}) - n \ln(\sigma) - .5 \sum_{i=1}^{n} \left(\frac{X_i - \mu}{\sigma} \right)^2.$$

Choosing σ^2 to maximize $\ln L(\sigma^2)$ is equivalent to choosing σ^2 to minimize

$$g(\sigma^2) = n \ln(\sigma) + .5 \sum_{i=1}^{n} \left(\frac{X_i - \mu}{\sigma} \right)^2. \tag{7.2.14}$$

Now, it would be easier to differentiate with respect to σ in equation (7.2.14) (instead of with respect to σ^2). We will do this [and thus essentially seek the MLE of σ, say $\hat{\sigma}$, instead of the MLE of σ^2, say $\widehat{(\sigma^2)}$; we will prove later that, under conditions satisfied here, $(\hat{\sigma})^2 = \widehat{(\sigma^2)} \ldots$ an *invariance* property of MLE's (see Theorem 7.2.15)]. Hence, we find

$$\frac{dg(\sigma^2)}{d\sigma} = \frac{n}{\sigma} - \frac{\sum_{i=1}^{n} (X_i - \mu)^2}{\sigma^3},$$

$$\frac{d^2 g(\sigma^2)}{d\sigma^2} = -\frac{n}{\sigma^2} + 3 \frac{\sum_{i=1}^{n} (X_i - \mu)^2}{\sigma^4}.$$

Setting the first derivative to zero, we find the unique solution

$$\hat{\sigma} = \sqrt{\frac{\sum_{i=1}^{n}(X_i - \mu)^2}{n}},$$

and

$$(\hat{\sigma})^2 = \frac{\sum_{i=1}^{n}(X_i - \mu)^2}{n}$$

(which is an unbiased and consistent estimator of σ^2, as may be easily verified). At $\hat{\sigma}$, the second derivative is

$$\left.\frac{d^2g(\sigma^2)}{d\sigma^2}\right|_{\sigma=\hat{\sigma}} = \left(\frac{1}{\hat{\sigma}}\right)^2\{-n + 3n\} > 0,$$

so we have minimized $g(\sigma^2)$ [and hence maximized the likelihood $L(\sigma^2)$]. The case of μ and σ^2 both unknown will be covered in the problems.

In many applied problems, it is desired to estimate not the parameter θ itself, but rather a function of the parameter. For example, if X and Y are independent r.v.'s with $X \sim N(\mu, \sigma^2)$ and $Y \sim N(\nu, \sigma^2)$, the **overlapping coefficient** (the area that is under **both** the p.d.f.'s) is defined [see Mishra, Shah, and Lefante (1986)] as

$$\Delta = 2\Phi\left(-\frac{|\mu - \nu|}{2\sigma}\right).$$

(For example, if we compare the income distributions of two cities, Δ is the percentage of overlap in the income distributions.) To estimate Δ, we have to estimate not only μ, ν, and σ, but also a function of these three parameters. The following theorem's **invariance principle of maximum-likelihood estimation** aids us in this (as well as in situations such as that of Example 7.2.13).

Theorem 7.2.15. (i) Suppose we have likelihood function $L(\theta) = f(X_1, \ldots, X_n|\theta)$, $\theta \in \Theta$. Suppose $\hat{\theta}$ is an MLE of θ. If $g(\theta)$ is a one-to-one function [i.e., $g(\theta_1) = g(\theta_2) \Leftrightarrow \theta_1 = \theta_2$], then $g(\hat{\theta})$ is an MLE of $g(\theta)$ [i.e., $g(\hat{\theta})$ is a value of $g(\theta)$ at which $L(\theta)$ is maximized].

(ii) The result that $g(\hat{\theta})$ is an MLE of $g(\theta)$ [i.e., $g(\hat{\theta})$ is a value of $g(\theta)$ at which $L(\theta)$ is maximized] holds even if $g(\cdot)$ is not a one-to-one function, and even if θ is a vector.

Proof: (i) By $\overline{g(\theta)}$ we mean a value of $g(\theta)$ at which $L(\theta)$ is maximized. However, in general several θ's (some of which do not maximize $L(\theta)$) correspond to one value of $g(\theta)$. With a one-to-one function $g(\cdot)$ this cannot occur, so $\overline{g(\theta)} = g(\hat{\theta})$.

Formally, $L(\theta) = L(g^{-1}(g(\theta)))$ are both maximized by "the" same $\hat{\theta}$, so $\hat{\theta} = g^{-1}(\overline{g(\theta)})$, or $g(\hat{\theta}) = \overline{g(\theta)}$.

(ii) Even if several values of θ (some of which do *not* maximize $L(\theta)$) correspond to one value of $g(\theta)$, still $\hat{\theta}$ [which maximizes $L(\theta)$ by hypothesis] is one of the θ values leading to value $g(\hat{\theta})$ for $g(\cdot)$, hence $g(\hat{\theta})$ corresponds to maximizing $L(\cdot)$ as claimed.   ∎

We now illustrate Theorem 7.2.15 in several examples.

Example 7.2.16. Let $X_1, X_2, \ldots, X_n$ be independent r.v.'s, each Bernoulli with probability of success p. Then (see Example 7.1.27 where we considered estimation of p and pq) $E(X_1) = p$ and $\text{Var}(X_1) = p(1 - p)$. Consider MLE's of the mean and variance. [*Note:* $\text{Var}(X_1) = p(1 - p)$ is not a one-to-one function of p.]

Here

$$L(p) = p^{\sum X_i}(1 - p)^{n - \sum X_i},$$

$$\ln L(p) = \sum X_i \ln(p) + \left(n - \sum X_i\right)\ln(1 - p),$$

and

$$\frac{\partial}{\partial p}\ln L(p) = \frac{\sum X_i}{p} - \frac{n - \sum X_i}{1 - p}, \quad \frac{\partial^2}{\partial p^2}\ln L(p) = -\frac{\sum X_i}{p^2} - \frac{n - \sum X_i}{(1 - p)^2}.$$

Setting the first derivative to zero and solving, we find

$$\hat{p} = \frac{\sum X_i}{n} = \overline{X}.$$

Since the second derivative is negative at $\hat{p}$, this is the MLE of the mean. By Theorem 7.2.15 (ii), the variance's MLE is $g(\hat{p}) = \overline{X}(1 - \overline{X})$.

Example 7.2.17. In medical applications one often encounters r.v.'s X such that the logarithm of X has a normal distribution (i.e., the observation has the log-normal distribution of Definition 4.6.7). Let $X_1, X_2, \ldots, X_n$ be independent r.v.'s, each with the same lognormal distribution. Thus $Y_i = \ln X_i \sim N(\mu, \sigma^2)$. Our interest here is in finding maximum likelihood estimators of $E(X_i)$ and $\text{Var}(X_i)$, where

$$\nu = E(X_i) = \int_{-\infty}^{\infty} \frac{e^u e^{-(u-\mu)^2/(2\sigma^2)}}{\sqrt{2\pi}\,\sigma} \, du$$

$$= \int_{-\infty}^{\infty} e^{(-\mu^2 + (\mu + \sigma^2)^2)/(2\sigma^2)} \frac{e^{-(u - (\mu + \sigma^2))^2/(2\sigma^2)}}{\sqrt{2\pi}\,\sigma} \, du$$

$$= e^{\mu + \sigma^2/2}$$

and we leave it as an exercise to show that

$$\tau^2 = \text{Var}(X_i) = e^{2\mu + \sigma^2}(e^{\sigma^2} - 1).$$

If μ and σ^2 are unknown, then (see Problem 7.6) the MLE of (μ, σ^2) is $(\hat{\mu}, \hat{\sigma}^2)$ with

$$\hat{\mu} = \overline{Y}, \qquad \hat{\sigma}^2 = \sum_{i=1}^{n} (Y_i - \overline{Y})^2 / n.$$

Hence, by Theorem 7.2.15, the MLE's of $E(X_i)$ and $\text{Var}(X_i)$ are

$$\hat{\nu} = e^{\overline{Y} + \sum (Y_i - \overline{Y})^2 / (2n)}$$

and

$$\hat{\tau}^2 = e^{2\overline{Y} + \sum (Y_i - \overline{Y})^2 / n} \left(e^{\sum (Y_i - \overline{Y})^2 / n} - 1 \right).$$

In the previous examples, differentiation of the likelihood function with respect to θ has been used to find MLE's. However, such differentiation is not always possible [$L(\theta)$ may not be differentiable]. **We now illustrate techniques for determining MLE's in such cases.** We reemphasize that $L(\theta)$ is a function of θ, and the X_i's (after they have been observed) are **held fixed** in the entire process of finding MLE's.

Example 7.2.18. Let $X_1, X_2, \ldots, X_n$ be a random sample of size n from the displaced exponential distribution with p.d.f.

$$f(x|\theta) = e^{-(x-\theta)} I_{[\theta, \infty)}(x).$$

We wish to find $\hat{\theta}$, an MLE of θ.

Here

$$L(\theta) = e^{-\left(\sum X_i - n\theta \right)} I_{[\theta, \infty)}(X_1) I_{[\theta, \infty)}(X_2) \ldots I_{[\theta, \infty)}(X_n),$$

which is not differentiable with respect to θ. To find an MLE of θ, note that

$$L(\theta) = e^{-\sum X_i + n\theta} I_{[\theta, \infty)}(Y_1)$$

where $Y_1 = \min(X_1, \ldots, X_n)$. This $L(\theta)$ is the product of an increasing function of θ and an indicator function that is 1 for $\theta \le Y_1$ (0 otherwise), and hence is maximized at

$$\hat{\theta} = Y_1 = \min(X_1, X_2, \ldots, X_n).$$

[This is intuitively reasonable, since when we are sampling from a distribution that has possible values in the range $[\theta, \infty)$, we cannot observe any X_i's that are smaller than θ. Hence the MLE results from taking the θ small enough to "explain" all of the X_i's observed (but no smaller).]

Example 7.2.19. Suppose that $X_1, \ldots, X_n$ are independent r.v.'s, each with the uniform distribution on $[-d, d]$, where d is unknown, $d \in \Theta = \{x : x > 0\}$. Find the MLE of d. Here, for $i = 1, \ldots, n$,

$$f(X_i|d) = \begin{cases} \dfrac{1}{2d}, & \text{if } -d \le X_i \le d \\ 0, & \text{otherwise.} \end{cases}$$

Hence,

$$L(d) = \begin{cases} \left(\dfrac{1}{2d}\right)^n, & \text{if}^5 \; -d \le X_1, \ldots, X_n \le d \\ 0, & \text{otherwise.} \end{cases}$$

This $L(d)$ will be maximized by the smallest possible d that keeps $L(d) > 0$. But^6 $d \ge (-X_1, \ldots, -X_n, X_1, \ldots, X_n)$ iff $d \ge (|X_1|, \ldots, |X_n|)$, so

$$\hat{d} = \max(|X_1|, \ldots, |X_n|).$$

[This $\hat{d}$ is the "smallest" d that can explain the data (i.e., for which the data can occur).] Note that if we had a uniform distribution centered at a (a known) of width $2d$, that is, uniform on $[a - d, a + d]$, the $X_i - a$ would be uniform on $[-d, +d]$ and an analysis like the foregoing (with center $a = 0$) would apply, yielding

$$\hat{d} = \max(|X_1 - a|, \ldots, |X_n - a|).$$

Example 7.2.20. Suppose that $X_1, \ldots, X_n$ are independent r.v.'s, each with the uniform distribution on $[c - d, c + d]$, where d is known ($d > 0$), c is unknown, and $c \in \Theta = \{x : -\infty < x < +\infty\}$. Find the MLE of c. Here,

$$L(c) = \begin{cases} \left(\dfrac{1}{2d}\right)^n, & \text{if } c - d \le X_1, \ldots, X_n \le c + d \\ 0, & \text{otherwise.} \end{cases}$$

Hence any c such that $L(c) > 0$, is an MLE. The restriction is

$$c - d \le X_1, \ldots, X_n \le c + d, \text{ or } X_1 - d, \ldots, X_n - d \le c \le d + X_1, \ldots, d + X_n,$$

$$\text{or } \max(X_1, \ldots, X_n) - d \le \hat{c} \le \min(X_1, \ldots, X_n) + d.$$

---

^{5}"$-d \le X_1, \ldots, X_n \le d$" means "$-d \le X_1 \le d, \ldots, -d \le X_n \le d$."
^{6}"$d \ge (a, b, c, \ldots, x)$" means "$d \ge a, d \ge b, d \ge c, \ldots, d \ge x$." Similar notation occurs later.

We thus have another example of a nonunique MLE (the other being in Example 7.2.6).

Example 7.2.21. We now complete the trilogy whose first two parts were Examples 7.2.19 and 7.2.20. Let $X_1, \ldots, X_n$ be as in Example 7.2.20, but now with (c, d) unknown, $(c, d) \in \Theta = \{(x, y): -\infty < x < +\infty, y > 0\}$. Find the MLE of (c, d). Since

$$L(c, d) = \begin{cases} \left(\dfrac{1}{2d}\right)^n, & \text{if } c - d \le X_1, \ldots, X_n \le c + d \\ 0, & \text{otherwise,} \end{cases}$$

for any fixed c, $L(c, d)$ is maximized by the smallest d that yields $L(c, d) > 0$, that is, the smallest d such that

$$c - d \le X_1, \ldots, X_n \le c + d$$

$$\max(X_1, \ldots, X_n) - d \le c \le \min(X_1, \ldots, X_n) + d$$

$$c - \min(X_1, \ldots, X_n) \le d, \text{ and } \max(X_1, \ldots, X_n) - c \le d$$

$$d \ge \max\left[-\min(X_1 - c, \ldots, X_n - c), \max(X_1 - c, \ldots, X_n - c)\right]$$

that is,

$$d = \begin{cases} \max(X_1 - c, \ldots, X_n - c), \\ \quad \text{if } \max(X_1 - c, \ldots, X_n - c) \ge -\min(X_1 - c, \ldots, X_n - c) \\ -\min(X_1 - c, \ldots, X_n - c), \\ \quad \text{if } \max(X_1 - c, \ldots, X_n - c) \le -\min(X_1 - c, \ldots, X_n - c) \end{cases}$$

$$= \begin{cases} \max(X_1, \ldots, X_n) - c, \\ \quad \text{if } c \le (\max(X_1, \ldots, X_n) + \min(X_1, \ldots, X_n))/2 \\ -\min(X_1, \ldots, X_n) + c, \\ \quad \text{if } c \ge (\max(X_1, \ldots, X_n) + \min(X_1, \ldots, X_n))/2. \end{cases}$$

In either case, it is

$$c = \frac{\max(X_1, \ldots, X_n) + \min(X_1, \ldots, X_n)}{2}$$

which allows d to be minimized. Hence, we obtain

$$(\hat{c}, \hat{d}) = \left(\frac{\max(X_1, \ldots, X_n) + \min(X_1, \ldots, X_n)}{2}, \frac{\max(X_1, \ldots, X_n) - \min(X_1, \ldots, X_n)}{2}\right).$$

In Definition 7.2.1, we defined an MLE as any $\hat{\theta} \in \Theta$ such that $L(\hat{\theta}) = \sup\{L(\theta): \theta \in \Theta\}$. In Examples 7.2.6 and 7.2.20 we saw that such a $\hat{\theta}$ need not be unique. It may also not exist, as was noted at equation (7.2.3) and will arise again in Problems 7.5 and 7.6. There are a number of important **cases where the maximum likelihood estimator is not unique, or does not exist, or even worse is not consistent** [for a recent example in reliability distributions similar to those of Example 4.2.38, see Boyles, Marshall, and Proschan (1985)]. However, as we will see later (Section 7.4), in many situations the MLE exists uniquely and is consistent; where it does not, techniques such as that of moments (Section 7.3) are often used.

Our next two examples illustrate further the methods used to find an MLE when the unknown parameter has more than one component.

Example 7.2.22. Suppose that $X_1, \ldots, X_n$ are independent r.v.'s, each with the exponential distribution

$$f(x) = \begin{cases} \dfrac{1}{\theta_1} e^{-(x-\theta_2)/\theta_1}, & x \geq \theta_2 \\ 0, & x < \theta_2 \end{cases}$$

where $-\infty < \theta_2 < +\infty$ and $\theta_1 > 0$ are both unknown (see Definition 4.2.10; a slight generalization of Theorem 5.2.5 shows that $EX_1 = \theta_1 + \theta_2$). Find the MLE of (θ_1, θ_2), say $(\hat{\theta}_1, \hat{\theta}_2)$. Find $E\hat{\theta}_1$ and $E\hat{\theta}_2$.

Here

$$L(\theta_1, \theta_2) = f(X_1) \ldots f(X_n) = \begin{cases} \dfrac{1}{\theta_1^n} e^{-\sum\limits_{i=1}^{n}(X_i-\theta_2)/\theta_1}, & \min(X_1, \ldots, X_n) \geq \theta_2 \\ 0, & \min(X_1, \ldots, X_n) < \theta_2. \end{cases}$$

Now for any fixed $\theta_1 > 0$, $L(\theta_1, \theta_2)$ is maximized by choosing θ_2 as large as possible such that $L(\theta_1, \theta_2) > 0$, so

$$\hat{\theta}_2 = \min(X_1, \ldots, X_n).$$

Next, if we set $\dfrac{\partial \ln L(\theta_1, \hat{\theta}_2)}{\partial \theta_1}$ to zero, we find

$$\frac{\partial \ln L(\theta_1, \hat{\theta}_2)}{\partial \theta_1} = \frac{\partial}{\partial \theta_1}\left\{ -n \ln \theta_1 - \frac{\sum\limits_{i=1}^{n}(X_i - \hat{\theta}_2)}{\theta_1} \right\} = 0,$$

$$-\frac{n}{\theta_1} + \frac{\sum\limits_{i=1}^{n}(X_i - \hat{\theta}_2)}{\theta_1^2} = 0,$$

$$\hat{\theta}_1 = \overline{X} - \min(X_1, \ldots, X_n).$$

This yields a maximum since

$$\frac{\partial^2}{\partial \theta_1^2} \ln L(\theta_1, \hat{\theta}_2) = \frac{n}{\theta_1^2} - 2\frac{\sum\limits_{i=1}^{n}(X_i - \hat{\theta}_2)}{\theta_1^3}$$

is < 0 iff $\theta_1 < 2\hat{\theta}_1$. [To complete the proof, we should note that $L(\theta_1, \theta_2) \to 0$ as $\theta_1 \to 0$ and also as $\theta_1 \to +\infty$.]

Now to find $E\hat{\theta}_1$ and $E\hat{\theta}_2$ we need to find $E\overline{X}$ and $E \min(X_1, \ldots, X_n)$. First, $E(\overline{X}) = E(X_1) = \theta_1 + \theta_2$. Next, the distribution function of $\min(X_1, \ldots, X_n)$ $(x \geq \theta_2)$ is

$$P[\min(X_1, \ldots, X_n) \leq x] = 1 - P[\min(X_1, \ldots, X_n) > x]$$

$$= 1 - P[X_1 > x] \ldots P[X_n > x] = 1 - (P[X_1 > x])^n$$

$$= 1 - (1 - P[X_1 \leq x])^n = 1 - e^{-n\left(\frac{x - \theta_2}{\theta_1}\right)};$$

hence the density function of $\min(X_1, \ldots, X_n)$ is (via differentiation)

$$g(x) = \begin{cases} \dfrac{n}{\theta_1} e^{-n\left(\frac{x - \theta_2}{\theta_1}\right)}, & x \geq \theta_2 \\ 0, & x < \theta_2. \end{cases}$$

Thus,

$$E \min(X_1, \ldots, X_n) = \int_{\theta_2}^{\infty} y g(y)\, dy$$

$$= \int_{\theta_2}^{\infty} y \frac{n}{\theta_1} e^{-n\left(\frac{y - \theta_2}{\theta_1}\right)}\, dy = \int_{0}^{\infty} (\theta_2 + x) \frac{n}{\theta_1} e^{-nx/\theta_1}\, dx$$

$$= \theta_2 + \int_{0}^{\infty} x \frac{n}{\theta_1} e^{-nx/\theta_1}\, dx = \theta_2 + \frac{\theta_1}{n} \int_{0}^{\infty} z e^{-z}\, dz$$

$$= \theta_2 + \frac{\theta_1}{n}.$$

Hence, $E\hat{\theta}_1 = (\theta_1 + \theta_2) - (\theta_2 + \theta_1/n) = \theta_1(1 - 1/n)$, and $E\hat{\theta}_2 = \theta_2 + \theta_1/n$.

Example 7.2.23. Suppose that $X_1, \ldots, X_n$ are independent r.v.'s, each with the distribution

$$p(x) = \begin{cases} \theta, & \text{if } x = 1 \\ (1 - \theta)/(k - 1), & \text{if } x = 2, \ldots, k \\ 0, & \text{otherwise,} \end{cases}$$

where θ $(0 \leq \theta \leq 1)$ and k $(k = 1, 2, \ldots)$ are unknown. What is the MLE of

(θ, k)? [This distribution arose in Example 3.1.17 as the distribution of the number of microorganisms per clump on a surface. Thus, if n such clumps have been examined independently and respective numbers of organisms $X_1, \ldots, X_n$ found in each, what is the MLE of (θ, k), where θ is the probability a clump consists of one microorganism and k is the maximum possible number of microorganisms?]

Here, if we let Z represent the number of $X_1, \ldots, X_n$ that are one, then

$$L(\theta, k) = \begin{cases} \dfrac{\theta^Z (1 - \theta)^{n - Z}}{(k - 1)^{n - Z}}, & \text{if } 0 \le \theta \le 1, \ k \ge X_1, \ldots, k \ge X_n \\ 0, & \text{otherwise.} \end{cases}$$

Since (subject to $k \ge X_1, \ldots, k \ge X_n$) $(k - 1)^{n - Z}$ is minimized by $k = \max(X_1, \ldots, X_n)$ [unless $Z = n$, in which case $(k - 1)^{n - Z}$ is constant for all k] and since $\theta^Z (1 - \theta)^{n - Z}$ is maximized by $\theta = Z/n$, the MLE of (θ, k) is

$$(\hat{\theta}, \hat{k}) = \begin{cases} \left(\dfrac{Z}{n}, \max(X_1, \ldots, X_n) \right), & \text{if } 0 \le Z < n \\ (1, 1) \text{ or } (1, 2) \text{ or} \ldots & \text{if } Z = n. \end{cases}$$

That is, θ is estimated by the proportion of $X_1, \ldots, X_n$ that were one, and k is (except when $Z = n$, where the MLE is not unique) estimated by the largest number of microorganisms observed.

The next two examples explore further cases where simple differentiation is not sufficient.

Example 7.2.24. Consider Example 3.2.10 on wildlife sampling. The problem here is to estimate the size of the wildlife population of a certain species. We know from Example 3.2.10 that the number of tagged animals in a sample of size n has the hypergeometric distribution

$$p_X(x) = \frac{\dbinom{a}{x} \dbinom{N - a}{n - x}}{\dbinom{N}{n}}.$$

In order to estimate N via an MLE, we seek that value of N which maximizes the likelihood function $L(N) = p_X(X)$ as a function of N. Denote by $r(N)$ the ratio

$$\frac{L(N)}{L(N - 1)} = \frac{N - n}{N} \cdot \frac{N - a}{N - a - n + X}.$$

Then $r(N) < 1$ iff $(N - n)(N - a) < N(N - a - n + X)$; that is, iff $na < NX$, that is, iff

$$N > \frac{na}{X}$$

(and $r(N) > 1$ iff $N < na/X$). Thus, $L(N)$ is increasing for $N < na/X$, decreasing for $N > na/X$, and $L(N) = L(N-1)$ if $N = na/X$. Hence $L(N)$ is maximized by $N = na/X$ and the MLE is

$$\hat{N} = \frac{na}{X}.$$

(If this is not an integer, then let $N^- =$ (Largest integer $\leq \hat{N}$) and $N^+ =$ (Smallest integer $\geq \hat{N}$). The MLE is then that one of N^- and N^+ for which $L(N)$ is larger.)

Example 7.2.25. (This example illustrates cases where the likelihood equations need to be solved numerically.) Let $X_1, X_2, \ldots, X_n$ be independent r.v.'s, each $G(x | \alpha - 1, \beta, 0)$ (see Definition 4.2.7). Find the maximum likelihood estimator of (α, β).

Here

$$L(\alpha, \beta) = \left(\frac{1}{\Gamma(\alpha)\beta^\alpha} \right)^n e^{-\sum X_i/\beta} (X_1 X_2 \ldots X_n)^{\alpha - 1},$$

hence

$$\ln L(\alpha, \beta) = -n \ln(\Gamma(\alpha)) - n\alpha \ln(\beta) - \sum X_i/\beta + (\alpha - 1)\sum \ln(X_i).$$

To find values of α and β that maximize $\ln L(\alpha, \beta)$, we seek (by the generalization of Theorem 7.2.11 to functions of two variables) solutions of the equations

$$\frac{\partial}{\partial \alpha} \ln L(\alpha, \beta) = 0, \quad \frac{\partial}{\partial \beta} \ln L(\alpha, \beta) = 0,$$

that is, solutions of the two equations

$$n \frac{\Gamma'(\alpha)}{\Gamma(\alpha)} + n \ln(\beta) - \sum \ln(X_i) = 0, \tag{7.2.26}$$

$$n\beta\alpha - \sum X_i = 0. \tag{7.2.27}$$

Calling the solution $(\hat{\alpha}, \hat{\beta})$, from equation (7.2.27) we have that $\hat{\beta} = \overline{X}/\hat{\alpha}$. Using this in equation (7.2.26), we find we need to seek the solution of

$$n \frac{\Gamma'(\hat{\alpha})}{\Gamma(\hat{\alpha})} + n \ln(\overline{X}/\hat{\alpha}) - \sum \ln(X_i) = 0 \tag{7.2.28}$$

where (from differentiating $\Gamma(\alpha)$ in Definition 4.1.9 with respect to α)

$$\Gamma'(\hat{\alpha}) = \int_0^\infty x^{\hat{\alpha}-1} \ln(x) e^{-x} \, dx.$$

Simplifying equation (7.2.28), we find

$$\frac{\Gamma'(\hat{\alpha})}{\Gamma(\hat{\alpha})} + \ln(\bar{X}/\hat{\alpha}) - \frac{1}{n}\sum \ln(X_i) = 0,$$

or

$$\frac{\Gamma'(\hat{\alpha})}{\Gamma(\hat{\alpha})} - \ln(\hat{\alpha}) + \ln(\bar{X}) - \ln\left((X_1 X_2 \ldots X_n)^{1/n}\right) = 0,$$

or

$$\frac{\Gamma'(\hat{\alpha})}{\Gamma(\hat{\alpha})} - \ln(\hat{\alpha}) - \ln\left(\frac{(X_1 X_2 \ldots X_n)^{1/n}}{\bar{X}}\right) = 0. \qquad (7.2.29)$$

The solution $\hat{\alpha}$ of equation (7.2.29) can be obtained numerically, after which one computes $\hat{\beta} = \bar{X}/\hat{\alpha}$.

In fact, the relationship between $\hat{\alpha}$ and $1/(1 - R)$ where R is the ratio of the geometric mean of $X_1, \ldots, X_n$ to the arithmetic mean of $X_1, \ldots, X_n$ (which arose in equation (7.2.29)) has been tabled by Wilk, Gnanadesikan, and Huyett (1962). (Note that we have omitted considerations of whether the critical point found in this example is in fact a global maximum, as is in fact the case.) A short excerpt is:

$1/(1-R)$	1.0000	1.100	1.20	2.00	5.00	10.00	50.00
$\hat{\alpha}$	.00000	.28928	.37165	.84957	2.39414	4.90608	24.91457

PROBLEMS FOR SECTION 7.2

7.2.1 Let $X_1, X_2, \ldots, X_n$ be a random sample from the uniform p.d.f. $f(x|\theta) = (1/\theta)I_{(0,\theta)}(x)$ for some $\theta > 0$. Find the MLE of θ, say T_n. Show that T_n is a consistent sequence of estimators.

7.2.2 Let $X_1, X_2, \ldots, X_n$ be a random sample of size n from the $N(\theta, \theta^2)$ distribution for some $\theta \in (0, \infty)$. Find the MLE of θ. Is this estimator consistent?

7.2.3 Let $X_1, X_2, \ldots, X_m$ be a random sample of size m from a $N(\mu, \sigma^2)$ distribution, and let $Y_1, Y_2, \ldots, Y_n$ be a random sample (independent of $X_1, X_2, \ldots, X_m$) of size n from a $N(\nu, \sigma^2)$ distribution. Find the maximum likelihood estimator of the overlapping coefficient Δ defined before Theorem 7.2.15. Show that the MLE, say $\hat{\Delta}$, is consistent for Δ as $\min(m, n) \to \infty$. Also find MLE's of μ, ν, and σ^2. [*Hint:* See Mishra, Shah, and Lefante (1986).]

7.2.4 Let $X_1, X_2, \ldots, X_n$ be a random sample of size n from p.d.f. $f(x|\alpha, \lambda) = \Gamma^{-1}(\lambda)(\lambda/\alpha)^\lambda e^{-\lambda x/\alpha} x^{\lambda-1} I_{(0,\infty)}(x)$ for some $\alpha > 0$ and $\lambda > 0$. Find the MLE of (α, λ). (Assume, for large values of x, that

$$\frac{\partial}{\partial x}(\ln \Gamma(x)) \doteq \ln(x) - \frac{1}{2x}.)$$

7.2.5 Let $X_1, X_2, \ldots, X_n$ be a random sample of size n from a double exponential (Laplace) distribution with p.d.f. $f(x|\theta) = (1/2)e^{-|x-\theta|}$. Find the MLE of θ. [*Hint:* See Norton (1984) for consideration of use of derivatives to find the MLE. Note that direct consideration of the likelihood is an easier method in this case.]

7.2.6 Let $X_1, X_2, \ldots, X_n$ be a random sample of size n from a Poisson distribution with unknown mean μ. Find an MLE of $p(0) + p(1)$. Show that this estimator is consistent.

7.2.7 Let $X_1, X_2, \ldots, X_m$ be a random sample of size m from a $N(\mu, \sigma_1^2)$ distribution, and independently let $Y_1, Y_2, \ldots, Y_n$ be a random sample of size n from a $N(\mu, \sigma_2^2)$ distribution. Find the MLE's of μ, σ_1^2, and σ_2^2. Find the variance of these estimators.

7.2.8 Let $X_1, X_2, \ldots, X_n$ be a random sample of size n from the truncated Laplace p.d.f. $f(x|\theta) = (1/(2(1 - e^{-\theta})))e^{-|x|}I_{(-\theta, \theta)}(x)$ for some $\theta > 0$. Find an MLE of θ. Is this estimator unbiased? Consistent?

7.2.9 Let $X_1, X_2, \ldots, X_n$ be a random sample of size n from the beta p.d.f. $f(x|\alpha) = (\Gamma(\alpha + \lambda)/(\Gamma(\alpha)\Gamma(\lambda)))x^{\alpha-1}(1 - x)^{\lambda-1}I_{(0,1)}(x)$ with λ known and α unknown.
(a) Find the MLE of α if $\lambda = 1$.
(b) Find the MLE of α if $\lambda = 2$.
(c) Find the MLE of $\alpha/(\alpha + 1)$ in each of cases (a) and (b).

7.2.10 Let $f_1(x)$ be a p.d.f. with mean μ_1 and variance σ_1^2, and $f_2(x)$ a p.d.f. with mean μ_2 and variance σ_2^2. Consider Z_1, Z_2, a random sample of size 2 from the mixture p.d.f.

$$f(x|\theta) = \theta f_1(x) + (1 - \theta)f_2(x)$$

for some θ, $0 \le \theta \le 1$. If $\mu_1, \mu_2, \sigma_1^2, \sigma_2^2$ are all known, find an MLE of θ.

7.2.11 Let $X_1, X_2, \ldots, X_n$ be a random sample of size n from the discrete uniform distribution $p(x|\theta) = 1/\theta$ for $x = 1, 2, \ldots, \theta$ (and $= 0$ otherwise) with θ an unknown positive integer. Find the MLE of θ, and its mean. Is this MLE unbiased?

7.2.12 Let $X_1, X_2, \ldots, X_n$ be a random sample of size n from a Poisson distribution with unknown mean λ.
(a) Find an MLE of $e^{-\lambda}$.
(b) Find an unbiased estimator of $e^{-\lambda}$.

7.2.13 Let $X, X_2, \ldots, X_n$ be a random sample of size n from a Bernoulli distribution with probability of success p, and let $T_n = X_1 + X_2 + \cdots + X_n$.
(a) Find an MLE of pq, where $q = 1 - p$.
(b) Show that $T_n(n - T_n)/(n(n - 1))$ is unbiased for pq.
(c) Show that the MLE is biased for pq, but is asymptotically unbiased.
(d) Show that the unbiased estimator for pq has smaller variance than the MLE for pq.

7.2.14 Let $(X_{11}, X_{21}), (X_{12}, X_{22}), \ldots, (X_{1n}, X_{2n})$ be a random sample of size n from a bivariate normal distribution with means μ_1, μ_2, variances σ_1^2, σ_2^2, and correlation coefficient ρ. Find the MLE of ρ if
(a) $\mu_1, \mu_2, \sigma_1^2, \sigma_2^2$ are all known.
(b) $\mu_1, \mu_2, \sigma_1^2, \sigma_2^2$ are all unknown.

7.2.15 Let $X_1, X_2, \ldots, X_n$ be a random sample of size n from the logistic p.d.f. $f(x|\alpha) = \beta e^{-(\alpha + \beta x)}(1 + e^{-(\alpha + \beta x)})^{-2}$ for $-\infty < x < \infty$. Find the MLE of α if β is known.

7.2.16 Let $X_1, X_2, \ldots, X_m$ be a random sample from a $N(\mu, \sigma^2)$ distribution, and independently let $Y_1, Y_2, \ldots, Y_n$ be a random sample of size n from a $N(\mu, \lambda\sigma^2)$ distribution with $\lambda > 0$ unknown. Find the MLE of λ if
(a) μ and σ^2 are known.
(b) μ and σ^2 are unknown, and also find MLE's of μ and σ^2.

7.2.17 Let $X_1 \sim B(n_1, p)$, $X_2 \sim B(n_2, p), \ldots, X_k \sim B(n_k, p)$ be independent r.v.'s. Find the MLE of p.

7.2.18 Let $(X_1, X_2, \ldots, X_k)$ be a multinomial r.v. with probabilities $(p_1, p_2, \ldots, p_k)$, $p_1 + p_2 + \cdots + p_k = 1$, and n trials (so $X_1 + X_2 + \cdots + X_k = n$). Find the MLE's of $p_1, p_2, \ldots, p_k$.

7.2.19 Let $X_1, X_2, \ldots, X_n$ be a random sample from a $N(\mu, \sigma^2)$ distribution, where μ and σ^2 are both unknown. Compute the MLE of $P(X_1 > c)$, where c is some known constant, and show that it is consistent.

7.2.20 Let $X_1, X_2, \ldots, X_n$ be a random sample from the p.d.f. $f(x|\theta) = (\theta/x^2)I_{[\theta, \infty)}(x)$ for some $\theta > 0$.
(a) Find the MLE of θ.
(b) If $n = 5$ and $X_1 = 2.9$, $X_2 = 1.48$, $X_3 = 5.62$, $X_4 = 4.0$, $X_5 = 1.22$, find the MLE of $P(X_1 < c)$ where c is a known fixed number. Show that the estimator is consistent.

7.2.21 Let $X_1, X_2, \ldots, X_n$ be a random sample of size n from the displaced exponential p.d.f. $f(x|\theta, \lambda) = (1/\lambda)e^{-(x-\theta)/\lambda}I_{[\theta, \infty)}(x)$ for some $\lambda > 0$ and $-\infty < \theta < \infty$. The MLE's of θ and λ were found in Example 7.2.22. If a random sample of size 5 is as in Problem 7.2.20(b), find the MLE of the probability $P(X_1 > 3.0)$.

7.2.22 Let $X_1, X_2, \ldots, X_n$ be a random sample of size n from the geometric distribution $p(x|p) = (1 - p)^{x-1}p$ for $x = 1, 2, \ldots$ (and $= 0$ for all other x).
(a) Find the maximum likelihood estimator of p.
(b) A state has 36 counties. Assume that each county has equal proportions of people who favor a certain gun control proposal. In each of 8 randomly selected counties, we find how many people we need to sample to find the first person who favors the proposal. The results are

$$3, 8, 9, 6, 4, 5, 3, 2$$

(e.g., in the first county sampled, the first two persons sampled were opposed, the third was in favor). Based on this data, compute the MLE of $P(X_1 \geq 5)$.

7.3. METHOD OF MOMENTS ESTIMATION (MME)

In this section, we introduce a second method of estimation known as the **method of moments**, which is due to Karl Pearson. This method, like that of maximum likelihood (see Section 7.2), generates *possibly good* estimators. As with the method of maximum likelihood, under appropriate conditions certain good properties result for the estimators produced; this is discussed in Section 7.4.

Definition 7.3.1. Let $X_1, \ldots, X_n$ be independent and identically distributed r.v.'s, each with d.f. $F(x|\theta)$ for some fixed $\theta \in \Theta \subseteq \mathscr{R}^r$. If the moments indicated exist, then the **method of moments estimators** of $\theta_1, \ldots, \theta_r$ are the solutions of the equations

$$\mu'_k = m'_k \quad (k = 1, \ldots, r). \tag{7.3.2}$$

[Recall that $\mu'_k = EX_1^k$ is the kth noncentral population moment, whereas m'_k is the kth noncentral sample moment (see Definition 7.1.9).] Thus, **the method of moments attempts to equate the first r population moments to the first r sample moments (each noncentral) and take the resulting solution in $\theta_1, \ldots, \theta_r$ (if one exists) as an estimator of $\theta_1, \ldots, \theta_r$.**

Example 7.3.3. Suppose that $X_1, \ldots, X_n$ $(n \geq 2)$ are independent, each being a $N(\mu, \sigma^2)$ r.v. with $\mu(-\infty < \mu < +\infty)$ and $\sigma^2(\sigma^2 > 0)$ both unknown. Find the method of moments estimators of μ and σ^2.

Here the $r = 2$ equations to be solved are

$$\begin{cases} \mu'_1 = m'_1, \\ \mu'_2 = m'_2, \end{cases} \tag{7.3.4}$$

or

$$\begin{cases} \mu = EX_1 = \dfrac{\sum\limits_{i=1}^{n} X_i}{n}, \\[4mm] \sigma^2 + \mu^2 = EX_1^2 = \dfrac{\sum\limits_{i=1}^{n} X_1^2}{n}. \end{cases} \tag{7.3.5}$$

Solving system (7.3.5) yields

$$\begin{cases} \hat{\mu} = \bar{X}, \\[4mm] \hat{\sigma}^2 = \dfrac{\sum\limits_{i=1}^{n} X_i^2}{n} - \hat{\mu}^2 = \dfrac{\sum\limits_{i=1}^{n} (X_i - \bar{X})^2}{n}. \end{cases} \tag{7.3.6}$$

The estimators of (7.3.6) are also (see Problem 7.6) the maximum-likelihood estimators. This is often the case.

Method of moments estimation sometimes yields estimates easily in comparison with maximum likelihood estimation. For example, with the gamma distribution in Example 7.2.25, MLE's required numerical methods. In Example 7.3.7 we examine the same problem and find MME's for α and β.

Example 7.3.7. Let $X_1, X_2, \ldots, X_n$ be a random sample of size n from the $G(x|\alpha - 1, \beta, 0)$ distribution with $\alpha > 1$ and $\beta > 0$. Since (see Theorem 5.2.7)

$$E(X) = \alpha\beta$$

and

$$E(X^2) = \alpha^2\beta^2 + \alpha\beta^2,$$

MME's of α and β result from solving the system of equations

$$\hat{\alpha}\hat{\beta} = \frac{\sum X_i}{n} = \overline{X}, \qquad \hat{\alpha}^2\hat{\beta}^2 + \hat{\alpha}\hat{\beta}^2 = \frac{\sum X_i^2}{n}.$$

Thus $\hat{\alpha} = \overline{X}\hat{\beta}^{-1}$, $\overline{X}^2 + \overline{X}\hat{\beta} = \sum X_i^2/n$, and

$$\hat{\beta} = \frac{1}{\overline{X}}\left(\sum \frac{X_i^2}{n} - \overline{X}^2\right) = \frac{1}{\overline{X}}\frac{\sum(X_i - \overline{X})^2}{n} = \frac{\hat{\sigma}^2}{\overline{X}}, \qquad \hat{\alpha} = \overline{X}^2/\hat{\sigma}^2,$$

where we have denoted $\sum(X_i - \overline{X})^2/n$ by $\hat{\sigma}^2$. (Note that this same quantity arose in Example 7.3.3.)

Although the basic MME technique is as given in Definition 7.3.1 and requires solving as many equations as there are unknown parameters, sometimes this technique fails. The following example illustrates this and shows a modification that can be used in such cases.

Example 7.3.8. Consider the Laplace distribution centered at the origin and with shape parameter β, which for all x ($-\infty < x < \infty$) has the p.d.f.

$$f(x|\beta) = \frac{1}{2\beta}e^{-|x|/\beta}$$

where $\beta > 0$. (A special case of this distribution was considered in Example 5.1.4.) If X has this p.d.f., then $E(X) = 0$. If $X_1, X_2, \ldots, X_n$ is a random sample of size n from this distribution, then the equation $E(X) = \overline{X}$ does not yield an estimate of the single unknown parameter β.

However, we can find that $E(X^2) = 2\beta^2$, which is a function of β. Hence, setting $E(X^2)$ equal to $\sum X_i^2/n$ yields

$$\hat{\beta} = \left(\tfrac{1}{2}\sum X_i^2/n\right)^{0.5}. \tag{7.3.9}$$

(We leave it as an exercise to check that **the MLE in this example is not the same as the MME,** but rather is

$$\beta^* = \sum |X_i|/n. \tag{7.3.10}$$

Although both of these estimates are nonnegative (as is β), they differ.)

As a final example in this section, we investigate the dependence of MME's on known transformations of the data.

Example 7.3.11. Let $X_1, X_2, \ldots, X_n$ be independent r.v.'s, each with the lognormal distribution $\ln N(\mu, \sigma^2)$ for which MLE's of μ and σ^2 were found in Example 7.2.17. We now wish to find MME's of μ and σ^2.

Method 1:   Since (see Example 7.2.17)

$$E(X) = e^{\mu + \sigma^2/2}$$

and

$$E(X^2) = \left(e^{\mu + \sigma^2/2}\right)^2 e^{\sigma^2},$$

by equating the first two population and sample noncentral moments, we obtain

$$e^{\hat{\mu}_0 + \hat{\sigma}_0^2/2} = \overline{X}, \qquad \left(e^{\hat{\mu}_0 + \hat{\sigma}_0^2/2}\right)^2 e^{\sigma_0^2} = \sum X_i^2/n. \tag{7.3.12}$$

This system of equations implies (check this)

$$\hat{\sigma}_0^2 = \ln\left(\frac{1}{\overline{X}^2}\sum X_i^2/n\right), \qquad \hat{\mu}_0 = \ln(\overline{X}) - \frac{1}{2}\ln\left(\frac{1}{\overline{X}^2}\sum X_i^2/n\right)$$
$$= \ln\left(\sqrt{n}\,\overline{X}^2 \Big/ \sqrt{\sum X_i^2}\,\right). \tag{7.3.13}$$

Method 2:   Since X_i is $\ln N(\mu, \sigma^2)$, $\ln(X_i)$ is $N(\mu, \sigma^2)$, hence (see Example 7.3.3) based on the random sample $\ln(X_1), \ln(X_2), \ldots, \ln(X_n)$ the MME's are

$$\hat{\mu}_l = \sum \frac{\ln(X_i)}{n}, \qquad \hat{\sigma}_l^2 = \sum \frac{\left(\ln(X_i) - \hat{\mu}_l\right)^2}{n}. \tag{7.3.14}$$

Example 7.3.15. Although an extensive study of the two different sets of estimators of μ and σ^2 produced in Example 7.3.11 is beyond the scope of this text (see Cohen and Whitten (1981) for some comparisons of these and other estimators), we will now note what differences arise in one numerical example.

By the methods of Section 4.7, we have obtained a random sample of size $n = 10$ from a $\ln N(\mu, \sigma^2)$ distribution, for some μ and σ^2. We now wish to estimate μ and σ^2. The data $X_1, X_2, \ldots, X_{10}$ are

19.885682, 6.0496473, 12.807104, 42.521082, 42.73422,

69.407852, 12.30493, 9.6794008, 16.776851, 5.3121678.

Here $\sum X_i/n = 23.747894$ and $\sum X_i^2/n = 960.25503$, hence *(Method 1)* in the original observations we find the estimators

$$\hat{\mu}_0 = \ln\left(\sqrt{n}\,\overline{X}^2\Big/\sqrt{\sum X_i^2}\right), \qquad \hat{\sigma}_0^2 = \ln\left(\frac{1}{\overline{X}^2}\sum X_i^2/n\right)$$

$$= 2.9013883 \qquad\qquad = .5322112.$$

Using *Method 2*, we find

$$\hat{\mu}_l = \frac{\sum(\ln X_i)}{n}, \qquad \hat{\sigma}_0^2 = \frac{\sum\left(\ln(X_i) - \hat{\mu}_l\right)^2}{n}$$

$$= 2.8355 \qquad\qquad = .6616422.$$

For comparison, note that the original data were generated by taking $N(3,1)$ r.v.'s and exponentiating them (hence the data are lognormal), thus the true values are $\mu = 3$ and $\sigma^2 = 1$ in this example.

PROBLEMS FOR SECTION 7.3

7.3.1 Let $X_1, X_2, \ldots, X_n$ be a random sample of size n from the p.d.f. $f(x|\theta) = (1/\theta)I_{[0,\theta]}(x)$ for some $\theta > 0$.
(a) Find the MME of θ.
(b) Show that the MME is a biased estimator of θ. Find an unbiased function of the MME.
(c) Show that the unbiased function found in (b) is also a consistent estimator of θ.

7.3.2 Let $X_1, X_2, \ldots, X_n$ be a random sample of size n from the beta distribution $B(x|\alpha, \lambda)$. Find the MME's of α and λ.

7.3.3 Let $X_1, X_2, \ldots, X_n$ be independent r.v.'s, each with p.d.f. $f(x|\theta) = (1/(2\theta))$ $\cdot I_{[-\theta,\theta]}(x)$ for some $\theta > 0$. Find the MME of θ, and show that it is a biased estimator.

7.3.4 Let $X_1, X_2, \ldots, X_n$ be a random sample of size n from a $N(\theta, \theta^2)$ distribution for some $\theta \in (0, \infty)$. Find an MME of θ.

7.3.5 Let $X_1, X_2, \ldots, X_n$ be a random sample of size n from the geometric distribution $p(x|p) = q^{x-1}p$ if $x = 1, 2, 3, \ldots$ (and $= 0$ otherwise). Find an MME of p. Show that $\overline{X}_n$ is unbiased for $1/p$.

7.3.6 Let $X_1, X_2, \ldots, X_n$ be a random sample from the "displaced" exponential p.d.f. $f(x|\alpha, \lambda) = (1/\lambda)e^{-(x-\alpha)/\lambda}I_{(\alpha,\infty)}(x)$. Find the MME's of α and λ, and investigate their unbiasedness and consistency.

7.3.7 Let $X_1, X_2, \ldots, X_n$ be a random sample of size n from the discrete uniform distribution $p(x|\theta) = (1/\theta)I_{\{1,2,3,\ldots,\theta\}}(x)$. Find the MME of θ.

7.3.8 Let $f_1(x)$ be a p.d.f. with known mean μ_1, and $f_2(x)$ another p.d.f. with known mean μ_2. Consider the contaminated p.d.f.

$$f(x|\theta) = \theta f_1(x) + (1 - \theta)f_2(x)$$

for some θ, $0 \leq \theta \leq 1$. Let $X_1, X_2, \ldots, X_n$ be a random sample of size n from $f(x|\theta)$. Find the MME of θ.

7.3.9 Let $X_1, X_2, \ldots, X_n$ be a random sample of size n from the p.d.f. $f(x|\alpha, \lambda) = \Gamma^{-1}(\lambda)(\lambda/\alpha)^\lambda e^{-(\lambda/\alpha)x} x^{\lambda-1} I_{(0,\infty)}(x)$. Find MME's of α and λ.

7.3.10 Let $X_1, X_2, \ldots, X_n$ be independent Bernoulli r.v.'s, each with success probability p. Find the MME of p.

7.3.11 Let $X_1, X_2, \ldots, X_n$ be a random sample of size n from the p.d.f. $f(x|\theta) = (\theta/x^2) I_{[\theta, \infty)}(x)$ for some $\theta > 0$. Find the MME of θ.

7.3.12 Let $X_1, X_2, \ldots, X_n$ be independent Poisson r.v.'s, each with mean λ. Find the method of moments estimator of λ.

7.3.13 Let $X_1, X_2, \ldots, X_n$ be a random sample of size n from the $N(0, \sigma^2)$ p.d.f. Find the MME of σ^2, and show that it is consistent for σ^2.

7.4. "GOODNESS" PROPERTIES OF ESTIMATORS

In Section 7.1 we defined and discussed **bias** and **consistency** properties of point estimators, both of which are **goodness** criteria for estimators. In Sections 7.2 and 7.3 we discussed two methods of finding *possibly*-good estimators of parameters (and functions of parameters). We now consider **how to select one estimator from a number of possible estimators.**

First, we need a criterion of goodness for comparing two estimators. With an eye toward this need, in Definition 5.1.26 we introduced the notion of **concentration of a r.v. about a point**, namely that t_1 is said to be more concentrated about θ than t_2 if (for all $r > 0$)

$$P[|t_1 - \theta| \leq r] \geq P[|t_2 - \theta| \leq r]. \tag{7.4.1}$$

Now, if (7.4.1) holds for all $r > 0$, we ought [at least if in addition

$$P[|t_1 - \theta| \leq r] > P[|t_2 - \theta| \leq r]$$

for at least one $r > 0$] to prefer t_1 to t_2 as an estimator of θ, since in a quite reasonable and general sense it is "closer" to θ.

Now, in general, it will *not* be the case that t_1 is more concentrated than t_2, and also it will not be the case that t_2 is more concentrated than t_1 (the relation between $P[|t_1 - \theta| \leq r]$ and $P[|t_2 - \theta| \leq r]$ will vary, depending on the value of r). However, in one special case the relation is simple:

Theorem 7.4.2. If t_1 and t_2 are (respectively) $N(\theta, \sigma_1^2)$ and $N(\theta, \sigma_2^2)$ r.v.'s, then t_1 is more concentrated about θ than t_2 iff $\sigma_1^2 \leq \sigma_2^2$.

Proof: If t_i is $N(\theta, \sigma_i^2)$ $(i = 1, 2)$, then for any $r > 0$,

$$P[|t_i - \theta| \leq r] = P[-r \leq t_i - \theta \leq r]$$

$$= P\left[-\frac{r}{\sigma_i} \leq \frac{t_i - \theta}{\sigma_i} \leq \frac{r}{\sigma_i}\right] = 2\Phi\left(\frac{r}{\sigma_i}\right) - 1,$$

where $\Phi(x)$ is (review Example 6.3.5) the area under the $N(0,1)$ density to the left of x. Hence,

$$P[|t_1 - \theta| \le r] \ge P[|t_2 - \theta| \le r]$$

$$\Leftrightarrow 2\Phi\left(\frac{r}{\sigma_1}\right) - 1 \ge 2\Phi\left(\frac{r}{\sigma_2}\right) - 1$$

$$\Leftrightarrow \quad \Phi\left(\frac{r}{\sigma_1}\right) \ge \Phi\left(\frac{r}{\sigma_2}\right)$$

$$\Leftrightarrow \quad \frac{r}{\sigma_1} \ge \frac{r}{\sigma_2}$$

$$\Leftrightarrow \quad \sigma_1 \le \sigma_2$$

$$\Leftrightarrow \quad \sigma_1^2 \le \sigma_2^2. \qquad \blacksquare$$

Thus, if our competing estimators of θ, t_1 and t_2 (say), both had normal distributions with mean θ, it would be easy to choose between them. Generally life is not so simple; but $t_1 = t_1(X_1, \ldots, X_n)$ and $t_2 = t_2(X_1, \ldots, X_n)$ are functions of the number of observations n, and we have already seen some cases (see the CLT, Theorem 6.3.2) where as $n \to \infty$ a r.v. has a distribution that is approximately normal (and in fact—see the note following the CLT—the distribution "looks more and more like the $N(0,1)$ distribution" as $n \to \infty$). *We will now illustrate use of these considerations in selection of a better estimator with an example,* for which we need the following theorem (which is presented without proof; for a proof, see Dudewicz (1976), pp. 181–184); recall that the sample median M_n was introduced in Definition 5.6.8.

Theorem 7.4.3. Let $X_1, \ldots, X_n$ be independent r.v.'s, each with d.f. $F(x|\theta)$, $\theta \in \Theta$. Then (supposing $E_\theta X_1$ exists)

(i) $\overline{X}$ is an unbiased and consistent estimator of $E_\theta X_1$; and
(ii) M_n is a consistent (generally not unbiased) estimator of the population median, $\nu_\theta = \nu$ (say).
(iii) M_n is an unbiased estimator of ν if X_1 has a p.d.f. that is symmetric about ν.

Example 7.4.4. Let $X_1, X_2, \ldots, X_n$ be independent r.v.'s, each $N(\mu, \sigma^2)$ with σ^2 known. Recall (see Lemma 5.1.19) that the population mean μ equals the population median. Both the sample mean $\overline{X}$ and the sample median M_n are unbiased and consistent estimators of μ in this case. Further, note that $\overline{X}$ is $N(\mu, \sigma^2/n)$, while we will see later in this section that M_n is (for large n) close to the $N(\mu, (\pi/2)\sigma^2/n)$ distribution. Thus (for large n) $\overline{X}$ is more concentrated about μ than is M_n.

Similarly, the sample mean based on a sample of size n is more concentrated about μ than is the sample mean based on any smaller number of observations, so we would always use all of our observations—unless we had reason to believe that some of our observations were in error.

Before proceeding to develop our methods for comparing estimators, we note some facts about consistency of MLE's and MME's. It follows from results of Problem 7.6 and Theorem 7.1.12(i) that MLE's need not be unbiased estimators. However, MLE's, the likelihood function (see equation (7.2.2)), and related quantities are central to a large part of statistics. Although not unbiased in general, MLE's are usually consistent. Although a full statement of the conditions under which this is true is beyond the scope of this text (see Section 8.3 of Dudewicz (1976)), we will state the following theorem.

Theorem 7.4.5. Under reasonable assumptions, the MLE is consistent.

It may be helpful to give a brief **heuristic proof** of the consistency of the MLE. In seeking a maximum-likelihood estimator of θ, we seek to maximize (over θ)

$$L(\theta) = \prod_{i=1}^{n} f(X_i|\theta);$$

this is equivalent to maximizing $1/n$th the logarithm of $L(\theta)$, namely

$$\frac{\sum_{i=1}^{n} \ln f(X_i|\theta)}{n},$$

which is of the form $\overline{Y} = (Y_1 + \cdots + Y_n)/n$, with $Y_1, \ldots, Y_n$ independent and identically distributed r.v.'s (where $Y_i = \ln f(X_i|\theta)$, $i = 1, \ldots, n$). Hence, by the WLLN (for any θ)

$$\frac{\sum_{i=1}^{n} \ln f(X_i|\theta)}{n} \xrightarrow{P} E_{\theta_0} \ln f(X|\theta),$$

where θ_0 is the true parameter point. But $E_{\theta_0} \ln f(X|\theta)$ is *maximized* by $\theta = \theta_0$ (it is largest when θ is the true value), which intuitively allows us to distinguish between θ_0 and any other value θ. However, by *continuity*, we expect a little change in θ to result in a little change in $E_{\theta_0} \ln f(X|\theta)$. Hence, since $\left(\sum_{i=1}^{n} \ln f(X_i|\theta) \right) \Big/ n$ is "close" to $E_{\theta_0} \ln f(X|\theta)$, its maximum should be "close" to the true θ_0. (The full proof of Theorem 7.4.5 embodies this intuitive use of the WLLN, maximization at θ_0, and continuity, to prove consistency of the MLE.)

As one might expect, by a similar heuristic proof (based on Theorem 7.1.12), MME's are also consistent in most cases arising in practice.

We will now develop precisely this **method of comparing estimators**, and see how the MLE fits into the scheme of things.

Recall (Definition 6.2.4) that we say a sequence of d.f.'s $F_1, F_2, \ldots$ converges to a d.f. F (written $F_n \to F$) if $F_n(x) \to F(x)$ at each point x at which $F(x)$ is a continuous function. As we noted after the CLT (Theorem 6.3.2), for large n $F_n(x)$ is within δ of $F(x)$ for all x, that is:

Theorem 7.4.6. Polya's Theorem. Let $F, F_1, F_2, \ldots$ be d.f.'s. If $F_n \to F$ and F is continuous, then the convergence is uniform; that is,

$$\lim_{n \to \infty} \sup_x |F_n(x) - F(x)| = 0.$$

Hence, if we have two estimators t_1 and t_2 of θ (say), and can prove that the d.f.'s F_n of t_1 and G_n of t_2 satisfy $F_n \to F_1$ and $G_n \to F_2$ (with F_1 and F_2 each continuous d.f.'s), **we will be able to compare t_1 and t_2 by comparing the concentrations of F_1 and F_2 about θ.** Reality is slightly more complex, for if $t_1 \xrightarrow{P} \theta$ and $t_2 \xrightarrow{P} \theta$, then $F_1(x) = F_2(x)$ is 0 for $x < \theta$ and 1 if $x \geq \theta$. We will therefore find it necessary to "blow up" the difference between t_i and θ in order to obtain the continuous limiting distribution of t_i about θ ($i = 1, 2$). We now make the following definition:

Definition 7.4.7. If an estimator φ_n is such that $\sqrt{n}(\varphi_n - \theta)$ is asymptotically $N(0, J^2(\theta))$ for some function $J^2(\theta)$, it is called a **consistent asymptotically normal (CAN)** estimator.

In Definition 7.4.7, of course, $\varphi_n = \varphi_n(X_1, \ldots, X_n)$, where $X_1, \ldots, X_n$ are some observed (not necessarily independent or identically distributed) r.v.'s and θ is an unknown parameter with $\theta \in \Theta$ for some set $\Theta \subseteq \mathcal{R}$. By the phraseology "$\sqrt{n}(\varphi_n - \theta)$ is asymptotically $N(0, J^2(\theta))$" we mean that the d.f. F_n of $\sqrt{n}(\varphi_n - \theta)$ satisfies $F_n \to F$ where F is the d.f. of a $N(0, J^2(\theta))$ r.v., that is, of a normal r.v. with mean zero and variance that may depend on θ, $J^2(\theta)$.

Before proceeding, **we give two examples of CAN estimators to clarify the concept.**

Example 7.4.8. Let $X_1, X_2, \ldots, X_n$ be a random sample from a d.f. with mean μ, variance σ^2, and kurtosis α_4. Show that method of moments estimators (MME's) of μ and σ^2 are CAN estimators.

Here, as in Example 7.3.3, we find the MME's are

$$\hat{\mu} = \overline{X}_n, \qquad \hat{\sigma}^2 = \sum (X_i - \overline{X}_n)^2 / n.$$

The WLLN implies that $\hat{\mu} \xrightarrow{P} \mu$ and $\hat{\sigma}^2 \xrightarrow{P} \sigma^2$ (see Example 6.2.11 and Corollary 6.3.14(ii)), and by the CLT

$$\sqrt{n}(\hat{\mu} - \mu) \xrightarrow{d} N(0, \sigma^2)$$

and (Example 6.3.17)

$$\sqrt{n}\left(\hat{\sigma}^2 - \sigma^2\right) \xrightarrow{d} N\left(0, (\alpha_4 - 1)\sigma^4\right).$$

Thus, $\hat{\mu}$ is a CAN estimator with $J^2 = \sigma^2$, and $\hat{\sigma}^2$ is a CAN estimator with $J^2 = (\alpha_4 - 1)\sigma^4$. (If $X_1, X_2, \ldots, X_n$ are each normal, then $\hat{\mu}$ and $\hat{\sigma}^2$ are CAN estimators in that special case also.)

Example 7.4.9. Let $X_1, X_2, \ldots, X_n$ be independent Bernoulli r.v.'s, each with probability of success p. Then the MLE of p (see Example 7.2.16), and the MME of p (check this), are each $\hat{p} = \Sigma X_i/n$ (the proportion of successes observed in the n trials). We know (from Example 6.3.4) that

$$\sqrt{n}\left(\hat{p} - p\right) \xrightarrow{d} N(0, pq),$$

hence $\hat{p}$ is a CAN estimator of p with $J^2 = pq$.

The following theorem (see Dudewicz (1976), p. 208, for details of conditions and proof) establishes that **the MLE is a CAN estimator.**

Theorem 7.4.10. Under "regularity" conditions, the MLE $\hat{\theta}_n = \hat{\theta}_n(X_1, \ldots, X_n)$ is a CAN estimator with $J^2(\theta) = 1/I(\theta)$; that is,

$$\sqrt{n}\left(\hat{\theta}_n - \theta\right) \xrightarrow{d} N(0, 1/I(\theta)),$$

where $I(\theta)$ (known as **Fisher's Information**) is

$$I(\theta) \equiv E_\theta\left(\frac{\partial \ln f(X|\theta)}{\partial \theta}\right)^2. \tag{7.4.11}$$

Example 7.4.12. In Example 7.4.8, the Fisher Information for μ is

$$I(\mu) = \frac{1}{\sigma^2},$$

while the Fisher Information for σ^2 is

$$I(\sigma^2) = \frac{1}{(\alpha_4 - 1)\sigma^4}.$$

In Example 7.4.9, the Fisher Information for p is

$$I(p) = \frac{1}{pq}.$$

We will have occasion to compare our MLE $\hat{\theta}_n$ to other estimators φ_n. We noted (at the beginning of this section) that which of two proposed estimators t_1 and t_2 is preferable is usually not clear. Now if an estimator, say t, is a CAN estimator, then (letting $r = r(n)$ and $r^* = \lim_{n \to \infty} rn^{1/2}$)

$$P_\theta[|t - \theta| \le r] = P_\theta\left[\frac{\sqrt{n}|t - \theta|}{J(\theta)} \le \frac{rn^{1/2}}{J(\theta)}\right] \to 2\Phi\left(\frac{r^*}{J(\theta)}\right) - 1. \quad (7.4.13)$$

Hence, our concentration would $\to 1$ as $n \to \infty$ for all fixed r, for any CAN estimator t [for then $rn^{1/2} \to +\infty$ and $\Phi(+\infty) = 1$]; yet if $r = r(n)$ tends to zero at the proper rate, we get a limit that is strictly between 0 and 1. Since this rate is independent of which CAN estimator is being considered, it makes sense to compare CAN estimators by using $r = kn^{-1/2}$ for $k > 0$ fixed. However, by Theorem 7.4.2, the better CAN estimator will be the one with the lower $J^2(\theta)$. Hence, it makes sense to give the following:

Definition 7.4.14. If t_1 and t_2 are two CAN estimators of θ with respective $J^2(\theta)$'s of $J_1^2(\theta)$ and $J_2^2(\theta)$, t_1 is **asymptotically more concentrated about** θ if $J_1^2(\theta) \le J_2^2(\theta)$ for all θ (with $<$ for at least one θ).

Since by Theorem 7.4.10 we know that (for many densities $f(x|\theta)$) **the MLE is a CAN estimator**, $\sqrt{n}(\hat{\theta}_n - \theta)$ being asymptotically $N(0, I^{-1}(\theta))$, $\hat{\theta}_n$ will be asymptotically more concentrated about θ than another CAN estimator φ_n [for which, e.g., $\sqrt{n}(\varphi_n - \theta)$ is asymptotically $N(0, J^2(\theta))$] iff

$$\frac{1}{I(\theta)} \le J^2(\theta) \qquad (7.4.15)$$

for all θ (with $<$ for at least one θ). Now a program of R. A. Fisher was to show that **(for many densities $f(x|\theta)$) equation (7.4.15) holds, that is, the MLE is, for large n, the most concentrated about θ of all CAN estimators.** If this were true, then we would have (for all θ)

$$\frac{1/I(\theta)}{J^2(\theta)} \le 1;$$

this ratio might be called a measure of efficiency of $\hat{\theta}_n$ versus φ_n, as in the following:

Definition 7.4.16. The **asymptotic relative efficiency** of two CAN estimators t_1 and t_2 (with respective $J^2(\theta)$'s of $J_1^2(\theta)$ and $J_2^2(\theta)$) is

$$e_\theta(t_1, t_2) = \frac{J_1^2(\theta)}{J_2^2(\theta)}.$$

Example 7.4.17. In Example 7.4.4, for $t_1 = \overline{X}$ and $t_2 = M_n$ we have

$$e_\mu(t_1, t_2) = \frac{\sigma^2}{\frac{\pi}{2}\sigma^2} = \frac{2}{\pi} < 1,$$

that is, the MLE $\bar{X}$ is superior to the median M_n for large n. $e_\theta(t_1, t_2)$ is, in a very reasonable sense, **a measure of the relative efficiency of t_1 and t_2 (both CAN estimators) for large n** when θ is the true value of the unknown parameter.

Lemma 7.4.18. If t_1 is $N(\theta, J_1^2(\theta)/n_1)$ and t_2 is $N(\theta, J_2^2(\theta)/n_2)$ with $J_1^2(\theta) < J_2^2(\theta)$, the number of observations n_2 that will make t_2's variance as small as the variance $J_1^2(\theta)/n_1$ of t_1 must satisfy

$$\frac{J_2^2(\theta)}{n_2} = \frac{J_1^2(\theta)}{n_1},$$

or

$$\frac{J_1^2(\theta)}{J_2^2(\theta)} = \frac{n_1}{n_2}.$$

Lemma 7.4.18 is obvious. **The lemma itself justifies defining an efficiency for normally distributed unbiased estimators of θ** $e_\theta(t_1, t_2) = J_1^2(\theta) / J_2^2(\theta)$ and not, say, $J_1(\theta)/J_2(\theta)$ or some other quantity; for example, if $J_1^2(\theta)/J_2^2(\theta) = \frac{1}{2}$, then $n_2 = 2n_1$ observations are needed by t_2 to achieve the same variance that t_1 achieves with only n_1 observations. The same definition for CAN estimators (given in Definition 7.4.14) is also justified since for n_1 and n_2 large, we can act as though t_1 and t_2 are normally distributed (in which case, by Theorem 7.4.2, variance is *the* measure of concentration about the mean). Efficiency of estimators is considered further in Section 7.5.

We will now conclude this section by giving the result (used in Example 7.4.4) that allows us to find the asymptotic distribution of the sample median. In fact, the result is true in much greater generality, for what are called **quantiles** of a distribution (the median is one of these). If some random variable X of interest to us has an unknown distribution function $F(x)$, we are sometimes interested (for a given p) in estimating the (a) point ξ such that $P[X \le \xi] = p$. (For example, if $p = .95$ and X is the level of methyl mercury in a certain type of fish, then estimating the point ξ such that $P[X \le \xi] = .95$ means estimating the level of contamination that is exceeded by 5% of such fish.) Such a ξ is called a quantile:

Definition 7.4.19. For any p ($0 < p < 1$), the (a) **quantile of order p** of the d.f. $F(x)$ is any root of the equation

$$F(\xi) = p.$$

We will often call such a root ξ_p, or simply ξ, and will usually consider only cases where it is unique.

Definition 7.4.20. For n r.v.'s $X_1, \ldots, X_n$ let $Y_1, \ldots, Y_n$ denote the ordered X_i's (i.e., the X_i's ordered so that $Y_1 \le \cdots \le Y_n$; if several X_i's are equal, we can choose one at random for a place Y_i). The **sample quantile of order p** ($0 < p < 1$)

is

$$Z_p = Y_{[np]+1}$$

(where $[np]$ denotes the largest integer $< np$).

Note that (taking $p = .5$ in Definition 7.4.20) this definition takes, as the sample quantile of order .5, $Y_{(n+1)/2}$ if n is odd, and $Y_{n/2}$ if n is even. This differs slightly (when n is even) from the definition of the sample median; the difference is of no consequence when n is "large." (See Problem 7.10H.)

We now note that Z_p is a CAN estimator of ξ_p, that is (see Definition 7.4.7), $\sqrt{n}\,(Z_p - \xi_p)$ is asymptotically $N(0, J^2)$. It will be slightly simpler to show (which is an equivalent statement) that $\sqrt{n}\,(Z_p - \xi_p)/J$ is asymptotically $N(0,1)$. (The CAN nature of Z_p will allow us to compare it readily with other estimators.) (For traditional "messy," and modern, proofs of this result, see Dudewicz (1976), pp. 215–221.)

Theorem 7.4.21. Fix p $(0 < p < 1)$. Let $X_1, \ldots, X_n$ be independent r.v.'s with d.f. $F(x)$ and density $f(x)$. Suppose that $f(x)$ is continuous and positive at $x = \xi_p$. Then the following three (equivalent) results hold.

(i) Z_p is a CAN estimator of ξ_p with $J^2 = pq/f^2(\xi_p)$.

(ii) $\sqrt{\dfrac{n}{pq}}\, f(\xi_p)(Z_p - \xi_p)$ is asymptotically $N(0,1)$.

(iii) For all $y_1 < y_2$,

$$\lim_{n \to \infty} P\left[y_1 < \sqrt{\frac{n}{pq}}\, f(\xi_p)(Z_p - \xi_p) < y_2 \right] = \frac{1}{\sqrt{2\pi}} \int_{y_1}^{y_2} e^{-y^2/2}\, dy.$$

Example 7.4.22. Continuing Example 7.4.4, we now have justification that

$$\sqrt{n}\,(M_n - \mu) \text{ is asymptotically } N\left(0, \frac{pq}{f^2(\xi_p)}\right)$$

so

$$e_\mu\left(\overline{X}, M_n\right) = \frac{\sigma^2}{\dfrac{pq}{f^2(\xi_p)}} = \frac{\sigma^2}{\dfrac{\left(\frac{1}{2}\right)\left(\frac{1}{2}\right)}{f^2(\mu)}}$$

$$= \frac{4\sigma^2}{\left(\dfrac{1}{\sqrt{2\pi}\,\sigma} e^{-.5(\mu-\mu)^2/\sigma^2} \right)^{-2}} = \frac{4\sigma^2}{2\pi\sigma^2} = \frac{2}{\pi} < 1.$$

Since $2/\pi = .64$, $\overline{X}$ can (in large samples) estimate μ as well with $.64n$ observations as M_n can with n observations [assuming we have independent $N(\mu, \sigma^2)$ observations]. Estimation of μ by M_n nevertheless *is* performed in some cases, for the following reason. If one or several of $X_1, \ldots, X_n$ may contain gross errors (e.g., in practice this occurs when gauges are misread, when decimal points are misplaced, and when computers malfunction) $\overline{X}$ may be affected to a much larger degree (since it averages the gross observations with all the others) than is M_n (which depends only on which are the one or two middle observations and what are their values).

Another reason for use of M_n instead of $\overline{X}$ is that often we want to estimate not the mean EX_1, but rather $\xi_{.5}$ (the population median). In general, $\xi_{.5} \neq EX_1$, so M_n is an appropriate estimator and $\overline{X}$ is not. Theorem 7.4.21 tells us that under very general conditions M_n is a CAN estimator of $\xi_{.5}$.

Example 7.4.23. For the first 88 observations of seasonal snowfall (say $X_1, X_2, \ldots, X_{88}$) given in Problem 7.6, we find $\overline{X} = 79.7$ and $M_n = M_{88} = (75.8 + 76.4)/2 = 76.1$.

PROBLEMS FOR SECTION 7.4

7.4.1 Let $X_1, X_2, \ldots, X_n$ be independent and identically distributed r.v.'s from each of the following distributions, and let T_n be the MLE of θ based on a random sample of size n. Show in each case that T_n is a CAN estimator of θ, and find the Fisher Information.
   (a) Poisson with parameter θ.
   (b) Geometric with parameter $\theta = 1/p$.

7.4.2 Let $X_1, X_2, \ldots, X_n$ be a random sample of size n from a uniform distribution on $(0, \theta)$, and let T_n be the MLE of θ. Show that T_n is not a CAN estimator. Find the limiting distribution of $n(\theta - T_n)$.

7.4.3 Let $X_1, X_2, \ldots, X_n$ be a random sample of size n from the beta p.d.f. $f(x|\theta) = \theta(1 + \theta)(1 - x)x^{\theta-1}$ if $0 < x < 1$ (and $= 0$ otherwise) for some $\theta > 0$ (i.e., $B(x|\alpha = \theta - 1, \lambda = 1)$).
   (a) Show that the MME of θ is $2\overline{X}_n/(1 - \overline{X}_n)$. Call this estimator T_n.
   (b) Show that T_n [see part (a)] is a CAN estimator, and find the Fisher Information $I(\theta)$.

7.4.4 Let $X_1, X_2, \ldots, X_n$ be a random sample of size n from a $N(\mu, \sigma^2)$ distribution, so the MLE's are $\hat{\mu} = \overline{X}_n$, $s_n = \sqrt{\sum_{i=1}^{n} (X_i - \overline{X}_n)^2/(n - 1)}$. Show that s_n^2 is a CAN estimator of σ^2, and find the Fisher Information $I(\sigma^2)$. Find the Fisher Information $I(\sigma)$; is s_n a CAN estimator of σ?

7.4.5 Let $X_1, X_2, \ldots, X_n$ be a random sample of size n from the distribution of X given below. Independently, let $Y_1, Y_2, \ldots, Y_n$ be a random sample of size n from another distribution (that of Y) given below.
   (a) $X \sim N(\mu_1, \sigma_1^2)$, $Y \sim N(\mu_2, \sigma_2^2)$. Show that the difference between the MLE's, $\hat{\mu}_1 - \hat{\mu}_2$, is a CAN estimator of $\mu_1 - \mu_2$. Find $I(\mu_1 - \mu_2)$.

(b) $X \sim B(1, p_1)$, $Y \sim B(1, p_2)$. Show that the difference between the MLE's, $\hat{p}_1 - \hat{p}_2$, is a CAN estimator of $p_1 - p_2$. Find $I(p_1 - p_2)$.

7.4.6 Let $X_1, X_2, \ldots, X_n$ be a random sample of size n from a $N(\mu, \sigma^2)$ distribution. Consider the two estimators $\hat{\mu}_n = \overline{X}_n$ and $\hat{\mu}_n^* = n\overline{X}_n/(n + 1)$. Show that $\hat{\mu}_n$ and $\hat{\mu}_n^*$ are both CAN estimators. Compute the asymptotic relative efficiency of $\hat{\mu}_n$ and $\hat{\mu}_n^*$; which estimator should you choose, and why?

7.5. CRAMÉR-RAO (INFORMATION) INEQUALITY AND EFFICIENCY OF ESTIMATION

In Section 7.4 we discussed concentration of estimators, asymptotic normality, and asymptotic efficiency in some detail, and saw that the MLE was conjectured to be the "best" CAN estimator; that conjecture, although not always true, holds in many cases (and in generality for an extension of MLE's that is beyond the scope of this text; see Dudewicz (1976), pp. 211–214).

The Information (or Cramér-Rao) Inequality considered in this section is generally attributed to Cramér's work in 1946 and Rao's work in 1945, though it was apparently first given by M. Fréchet in 1937–38 in French. This inequality is a lower bound on the variance of an unbiased estimator. The fact that an unbiased estimator has a variance equal to this bound means it has the best (smallest) variance of a large class of estimators (not all estimators—and perhaps some important estimators are excluded by the conditions under which the inequality is true—but many estimators are beaten). Relations with the MLE are also covered in this section. The lower bound is defined in terms of Fisher Information (7.4.11).

In this section *we will be dealing with the case where* $X_1, X_2, \ldots, X_n$ *are* independent r.v.'s, each with the same d.f. $F(x|\theta)$ *as a r.v.* X. *It will be assumed that this is what is called a "regular estimation case,"* that is, that $F(x|\theta)$ and any estimator t_n we are considering satisfy certain technical conditions (listed in, e.g., Dudewicz (1976), pp. 223–225). These conditions are such that, for example, they are not usually satisfied if the set of possible values of the r.v. X depends on the value of the unknown parameter θ. In general, they cannot be verified easily in practical cases, and are specified instead since they are needed to give full proof of the result desired. (Our proofs below require these regularity conditions, but the level of technical detail given is such that we will not need to consider them further in most instances we consider. The conditions guarantee that integration and differentiation can be interchanged, that derivatives exist and are integrable, that $I(\theta) \neq 0$, and the like.) We will need

Lemma 7.5.1. Let $X, X_1, X_2, \ldots, X_n$ be independent r.v.'s, each with the same d.f. with p.d.f. $f(x|\theta)$ (or, in the discrete case, point probability function $f(x|\theta)$). Then the Fisher Information in the sample $X_1, \ldots, X_n$ equals n times the

Fisher Information in the r.v. X:

$$E_\theta \left(\frac{\partial}{\partial \theta} \ln f_{X_1,\ldots,X_n}(X_1,\ldots,X_n|\theta) \right)^2 = nE_\theta \left(\frac{\partial}{\partial \theta} \ln f(X|\theta) \right)^2 = nI(\theta).$$

Proof: Using the independence of the r.v.'s, we have

$$E_\theta \left(\frac{\partial}{\partial \theta} \ln f_{X_1,\ldots,X_n}(X_1,\ldots,X_n|\theta) \right)^2$$

$$= E_\theta \left(\frac{\partial}{\partial \theta} \ln \prod_{i=1}^n f(X_i|\theta) \right)^2$$

$$= E_\theta \left(\frac{\partial}{\partial \theta} \sum_{i=1}^n \ln f(X_i|\theta) \right)^2 = E_\theta \left(\sum_{i=1}^n \frac{\partial}{\partial \theta} \ln f(X_i|\theta) \right)^2$$

$$= \sum_{i=1}^n E_\theta \left(\frac{\partial}{\partial \theta} \ln f(X_i|\theta) \right)^2 + 2\sum_{i<j} E_\theta \left(\frac{\partial}{\partial \theta} \ln f(X_i|\theta) \cdot \frac{\partial}{\partial \theta} \ln f(X_j|\theta) \right)$$

$$= nI(\theta) + 0 = nI(\theta)$$

since X_i and X_j are independent r.v.'s (hence $E(g(X_i)h(X_j)) = (Eg(X_i))(Eh(X_j))$) and

$$E_\theta \left(\frac{\partial}{\partial \theta} \ln f(X_i|\theta) \right) = \int_{-\infty}^{\infty} \frac{\frac{\partial}{\partial \theta} f(x|\theta)}{f(x|\theta)} f(x|\theta) \, dx = \int_{-\infty}^{\infty} \frac{\partial}{\partial \theta} f(x|\theta) \, dx$$

$$= \frac{\partial}{\partial \theta} \int_{-\infty}^{\infty} f(x|\theta) \, dx = \frac{\partial}{\partial \theta}(1) = 0. \qquad \blacksquare$$

Lemma 7.5.2. For any r.v.'s $X_1,\ldots,X_n$,

$$\frac{\partial}{\partial \theta} \prod_{i=1}^n f(x_i|\theta) = \left(\frac{\partial}{\partial \theta} \ln \left(\prod_{i=1}^n f(x_i|\theta) \right) \right) \left(\prod_{i=1}^n f(x_i|\theta) \right).$$

Proof: This follows since

$$\frac{d}{dy} \ln h(y) = \frac{h'(y)}{h(y)}. \qquad \blacksquare$$

Theorem 7.5.3. Cramér-Rao Inequality. In a regular estimation case, let $X_1, X_2,\ldots, X_n$ be independent r.v.'s, each with p.d.f. $f(x|\theta)$ (or each with point probability function $f(x)|\theta)$). Let $t_n(X_1,\ldots, X_n)$ be an estimator of some function of θ, say $g(\theta)$, and let $b_n(\theta)$ be the bias of t_n: $b_n(\theta) = E(t_n) - g(\theta)$. Then the following hold.

(i) Cramér-Rao Inequality for Functions of θ.

$$E_\theta\big(t_n - g(\theta)\big)^2 \geq \frac{\big(g'(\theta) + b_n'(\theta)\big)^2}{nI(\theta)}.$$

(ii) Cramér-Rao Inequality for Unbiased Estimators of Functions of θ.

If t_n is an unbiased estimator of $g(\theta)$, we have

$$\text{Var}_\theta\,(t_n) \geq \frac{\big(g'(\theta)\big)^2}{nI(\theta)}.$$

(iii) Cramér-Rao Inequality for Unbiased Estimators of θ.

If t_n is an unbiased estimator of θ, we have

$$\text{Var}_\theta\,(t_n) \geq \frac{1}{nI(\theta)}.$$

Proof: By definition of the bias of t_n as an estimator of $g(\theta)$, we have

$$g(\theta) + b_n(\theta) = E_\theta(t_n)$$

$$= \int_{-\infty}^{\infty} \cdots \int_{-\infty}^{\infty} t_n(x_1,\ldots,x_n)\left(\prod_{i=1}^{n} f(x_i|\theta)\right) dx_1 \ldots dx_n,$$

and differentiating with respect to θ we find (using Lemma 7.5.2)

$$g'(\theta) + b_n'(\theta) = \int_{-\infty}^{\infty} \cdots \int_{-\infty}^{\infty} t_n(x_1,\ldots,x_n)\left(\frac{\partial}{\partial\theta}\prod_{i=1}^{n} f(x_i|\theta)\right) dx_1 \ldots dx_n$$

$$= \int_{-\infty}^{\infty} \cdots \int_{-\infty}^{\infty} t_n(x_1,\ldots,x_n)\left(\frac{\partial}{\partial\theta}\ln\left(\prod_{i=1}^{n} f(x_i|\theta)\right)\right)$$

$$\times \left(\prod_{i=1}^{n} f(x_i|\theta)\right) dx_1 \ldots dx_n \quad (7.5.4)$$

$$= \int_{-\infty}^{\infty} \cdots \int_{-\infty}^{\infty} (t_n - g(\theta))\left(\frac{\partial}{\partial\theta}\ln\left(\prod_{i=1}^{n} f(x_i|\theta)\right)\right)$$

$$\times \left(\prod_{i=1}^{n} f(x_i|\theta)\right) dx_1 \ldots dx_n,$$

where we were able to introduce the $g(\theta)$ term since it integrates to zero as

$$\int_{-\infty}^{\infty} \cdots \int_{-\infty}^{\infty} g(\theta)\left(\frac{\partial}{\partial\theta}\ln\left(\prod_{i=1}^{n}f(x_i|\theta)\right)\right)\left(\prod_{i=1}^{n}f(x_i|\theta)\right)dx_1\ldots dx_n$$

$$= g(\theta)\int_{-\infty}^{\infty} \cdots \int_{-\infty}^{\infty}\frac{\partial}{\partial\theta}\left(\prod_{i=1}^{n}f(x_i|\theta)\right)dx_1\ldots dx_n$$

$$= g(\theta)\frac{\partial}{\partial\theta}\int_{-\infty}^{\infty} \cdots \int_{-\infty}^{\infty}f(x_1|\theta)\ldots f(x_n|\theta)\,dx_1\ldots dx_n = g(\theta)\frac{\partial}{\partial\theta}(1) = 0.$$

Rewriting equation (7.5.4), we now have

$$g'(\theta) + b_n'(\theta) = E_\theta\left((t_n - g(\theta))\left(\frac{\partial}{\partial\theta}\ln\prod_{i=1}^{n}f(X_i|\theta)\right)\right)$$

$$\leq \left(E_\theta(t_n(X_1,\ldots,X_n) - g(\theta))^2\right)^{0.5}\left(E_\theta\left(\frac{\partial}{\partial\theta}\ln\prod_{i=1}^{n}f(X_i|\theta)\right)^2\right)^{0.5}$$

by Schwarz' Inequality (Theorem 5.3.23). Similarly,

$$-g'(\theta) - b_n'(\theta) = E_\theta\left((g(\theta) - t_n)\left(\frac{\partial}{\partial\theta}\ln\prod_{i=1}^{n}f(X_i|\theta)\right)\right)$$

has the same upper bound (since $E(Z)^2 = E(-Z)^2$ for $Z = t_n - g(\theta)$). Using Lemma 7.5.1, we then have

$$|g'(\theta) + b_n'(\theta)| \leq \left(E_\theta(t_n(X_1,\ldots,X_n) - g(\theta))^2\right)^{0.5}(nI(\theta))^{0.5},$$

from which the most general form of the present theorem follows on squaring each side and dividing by $nI(\theta)$. When t_n is unbiased $b_n = 0$ (hence $b_n' = 0$) and $E_\theta(t_n - g(\theta))^2 = \text{Var}_\theta(t_n)$, hence form (ii) of the theorem follows. Finally, when $g(\theta) = \theta$ we have $g'(\theta) = 1$ and form (iii) of the theorem follows. ∎

Corollary 7.5.5. We have equality in the Cramér-Rao Inequality iff

$$\frac{\partial}{\partial\theta}\ln\left(\prod_{i=1}^{n}f(x_i|\theta)\right) = k_n(\theta)(t_n(x_1,\ldots,x_n) - g(\theta))$$

for some constant $k_n(\theta)$.

Proof: From the proof of the Cramér-Rao Inequality we see that it will be an equality iff we have equality in Schwarz' Inequality, for which the necessary and sufficient condition was given in Theorem 5.3.23. ∎

Note that the Cramér-Rao Inequality remains valid if $X_1, \ldots, X_n$ are each multivariate r.v.'s (instead of univariate r.v.'s as above), the proof being essentially unchanged. The inequality is attributed variously to Cramér, Rao, Fréchet, and others; we have used the name by which it is most widely known. It is of most use in forms (ii) and (iii) of Theorem 7.5.3, when it furnishes a bound on the variance of any estimator that is unbiased (in the other form, the bound depends on the estimator through the derivative of the bias of t_n, b_n'). If an estimator achieves this lower bound, it is the best of the unbiased regular estimators in the sense of having a smallest possible variance.

We will now give several examples of the inequality and its uses.

Example 7.5.6. Suppose that $X_1, \ldots, X_n$ are n (≥ 3) independent r.v.'s, each Poisson with mean λ. Then $t_1(X_1, \ldots, X_n) = \overline{X}_n$ is an unbiased estimator of λ, with $\mathrm{Var}(\overline{X}_n) = \lambda/n$. A second unbiased estimator of λ is

$$t_2(X_1, \ldots, X_n) = \frac{1}{2} \sum_{i=1}^{n-1} \frac{X_i}{n-1} + \frac{X_n}{2},$$

with $\mathrm{Var}(t_2) = (n/(n-1))\lambda/4$.

In this case, we have $g(\lambda) = \lambda$, $g'(\lambda) = 1$, and

$$I(\lambda) = E_\lambda\left(\frac{\partial}{\partial\lambda}\ln f(X|\lambda)\right)^2 = E_\lambda\left(\frac{\partial}{\partial\lambda}\ln\left(\frac{e^{-\lambda}\lambda^X}{X!}\right)\right)^2$$

$$= E_\lambda\left(\frac{X}{\lambda} - 1\right)^2 = \frac{1}{\lambda^2}E_\lambda(X - \lambda)^2 = \lambda/\lambda^2 = \frac{1}{\lambda},$$

hence by the Cramér-Rao Inequality (assuming this is a regular estimation case) for any unbiased estimator $t(X_1, \ldots, X_n)$ of λ we have

$$\mathrm{Var}(t) \geq \frac{1}{n(1/\lambda)} = \frac{\lambda}{n}. \tag{7.5.7}$$

Estimator t_1 achieves equality in (7.5.7). Note that, by Corollary 7.5.5, equality implies that

$$k_n(\lambda)(t - \lambda) = \frac{\partial}{\partial\lambda}\left(\ln\prod_{i=1}^{n} f(X_i|\lambda)\right) = \frac{\partial}{\partial\lambda}\left(\sum_{i=1}^{n}\ln f(X_i|\lambda)\right)$$

$$= \sum_{i=1}^{n}\frac{\partial}{\partial\lambda}\ln f(X_i|\lambda) = \sum_{i=1}^{n}\left(\frac{X_i}{\lambda} - 1\right) = \frac{n}{\lambda}(\overline{X}_n - \lambda),$$

or

$$t(X_1, \ldots, X_n) = \frac{n}{k_n(\lambda)\lambda}\overline{X}_n + \lambda\left(1 - \frac{n}{k_n(\lambda)\lambda}\right)$$

which equals t_1 when $k_n(\lambda) = n/\lambda$. Note that $\text{Var}(t_2) > \lambda/n$ since $(n-2)^2 > 0$. Note that (since $\overline{X}_n$ varies) there is no other estimator that can achieve equality in the Cramér-Rao Inequality in this example (as making the constant term independent of λ, as it must be for an estimator of the unknown λ, requires $k_n(\lambda) = n/\lambda$).

Finally in this example we will find an unbiased estimator of a function of λ, $g(\lambda) = e^{-\lambda}(1 + \lambda)$. If

$$\psi(X_i) = \begin{cases} 1, & \text{if } X_i = 0 \text{ or } X_i = 1 \\ 0, & \text{otherwise,} \end{cases}$$

then

$$E(\psi(X_i)) = 1 \cdot P(X_i = 0 \text{ or } X_i = 1) + 0$$
$$= e^{-\lambda}\lambda^0/0! + e^{-\lambda}\lambda^1/1! = e^{-\lambda}(1 + \lambda),$$

hence $t_3(X_1,\ldots,X_n) = \Sigma\psi(X_i)/n$, the proportion of observations from a sample of size n that are either 0 or 1, is an unbiased estimator of $g(\lambda)$ with

$$\text{Var}(t_3) = \text{Var}(\psi(X_1))/n = \left(E(\psi^2(X_1)) - (E(\psi(X_1)))^2\right)/n$$
$$= \left(e^{-\lambda}(1 + \lambda) - e^{-2\lambda}(1 + \lambda)^2\right)/n.$$

The Cramér-Rao bound here is

$$\frac{(g'(\lambda))^2}{nI(\lambda)} = \frac{\lambda^3 e^{-2\lambda}}{n},$$

and it is an exercise to show that t_3 does not achieve this bound. In fact, by Corollary 7.5.5, equality would be achieved by an estimator t iff (check this)

$$t(X_1,\ldots,X_n) = \frac{n}{k_n(\lambda)\lambda}\overline{X}_n + \left(e^{-\lambda}(1 + \lambda) - \frac{n}{k_n(\lambda)}\right).$$

For the constant term to be independent of λ requires

$$k_n(\lambda) = \frac{n}{e^{-\lambda}(1 + \lambda)},$$

in which case the random part would still be a function of the unknown λ, hence for the function $g(\lambda)$ chosen there is *no* estimator that achieves the Cramér-Rao bound.

Example 7.5.8. Suppose that $X_1,\ldots,X_n$ are $n(\geq 2)$ independent r.v.'s, each $N(\mu, \sigma^2)$, where μ is known and $\sigma^2(\sigma^2 > 0)$ is unknown. Suppose that this is a regular estimation case; find the Cramér-Rao bound on the variance of any regular unbiased estimator φ_n of σ^2.

Here we have

$$E_{\sigma^2}\left(\frac{\partial \ln f(X|\sigma^2)}{\partial \sigma^2}\right)^2 = E_{\sigma^2}\left(\frac{\partial}{\partial \sigma^2}\ln\left\{\frac{1}{\sqrt{2\pi}\,\sigma}e^{-\frac{1}{2}\left(\frac{X-\mu}{\sigma}\right)^2}\right\}\right)^2$$

$$= E_{\sigma^2}\left(\frac{\partial}{\partial \sigma^2}\left\{-.5\ln(2\pi\sigma^2) - \frac{(X-\mu)^2}{2\sigma^2}\right\}\right)^2$$

$$= E_{\sigma^2}\left(-\frac{1}{2\sigma^2} + \frac{(X-\mu)^2}{2\sigma^4}\right)^2$$

$$= E_{\sigma^2}\left(\frac{1}{4\sigma^4} - \frac{(X-\mu)^2}{2\sigma^6} + \frac{(X-\mu)^4}{4\sigma^8}\right)$$

$$= \frac{1}{4\sigma^4} - \frac{1}{2\sigma^4}E(Y^2) + \frac{1}{4\sigma^4}EY^4$$

$$= \frac{1}{4\sigma^4} - \frac{1}{2\sigma^4}\cdot(1) + \frac{1}{4\sigma^4}\cdot(3)$$

$$= \frac{1}{2\sigma^4},$$

where Y is a $N(0,1)$ r.v. (since $(X-\mu)/\sigma$ is $N(0,1)$) and EY^4 was evaluated using the gamma function (see Definition 4.1.9). Thus, for any regular unbiased estimator φ_n,

$$\text{Var}_{\sigma^2}(\varphi_n) \geq \frac{2\sigma^4}{n}. \tag{7.5.9}$$

Recall that the MLE of σ^2 was (see Example 7.2.13)

$$\hat{\sigma}^2 = \frac{\sum_{i=1}^{n}(X_i-\mu)^2}{n} \tag{7.5.10}$$

and was unbiased. We may easily show that $\text{Var}_{\sigma^2}(\hat{\sigma}^2) = 2\sigma^4/n$, so we have an estimator with the minimal variance.

Example 7.5.11. (This example demonstrates that unbiased estimators may beat the Cramér-Rao bound, since it does not hold in cases that are not regular.) Let $X_1, X_2, \ldots, X_n$ be independent r.v.'s, each with p.d.f.

$$f(x|\theta) = \begin{cases} 1/\theta, & \text{if } 0 \leq x \leq \theta \\ 0, & \text{otherwise,} \end{cases}$$

for some $\theta > 0$. Here $Y_n = \max(X_1, X_2, \ldots, X_n)$ is the MLE of θ, and $E(Y_n) = n\theta/(n+1)$. Thus although Y_n is not an unbiased estimator of θ, $(n+1)Y_n/n$ is an unbiased estimator of θ, and has

$$\mathrm{Var}\left(\frac{n+1}{n}Y_n\right) = \frac{\theta^2}{n(n+2)}.$$

Also, since $E(X_1) = \theta/2$, $2\overline{X}_n$ is also an unbiased estimator of θ, and has

$$\mathrm{Var}\left(2\overline{X}_n\right) = \frac{\theta^2}{3n}.$$

Since

$$I(\theta) = E_\theta\left(\frac{\partial}{\partial\theta}\ln f(X|\theta)\right)^2 = E_\theta\left(\frac{\partial}{\partial\theta}(-\ln(\theta))\right)^2 = \frac{1}{\theta^2},$$

the Cramér-Rao bound for the variance of unbiased estimators is θ^2/n, which both of our unbiased estimators $(n+1)Y_n/n$ and $2\overline{X}_n$ beat. As noted at the beginning of this section, the regularity conditions are generally not satisfied when the possible values of X depend on the value of θ.

In any regular case, the lower bound may be used to evaluate unbiased estimators by comparing their variances to the bound. Thus, we make the

Definition 7.5.12. In any regular estimation case, the **efficiency** of an unbiased regular estimator $\varphi_n(X_1, \ldots, X_n)$ is

$$e_\theta(\varphi_n) = \frac{1\left/\left\{nE_\theta\left(\frac{\partial\ln f(X|\theta)}{\partial\theta}\right)^2\right\}\right.}{\mathrm{Var}_\theta(\varphi_n)}. \tag{7.5.13}$$

If $e_\theta(\varphi_n) \equiv 1$, then φ_n is called **efficient** and a **best regular unbiased estimator** (BRUE).

Corollary 7.5.14. In any regular estimation case, $0 \le e_\theta(\varphi_n) \le 1$. We have $e_\theta(\varphi_n) \equiv 1$ iff $\mathrm{Var}_\theta(\varphi_n)$ achieves the lower bound for all θ.

Definition 7.5.15. In any regular estimation case, the **asymptotic efficiency** of an unbiased regular estimator $\varphi_n(X_1, \ldots, X_n)$ is $\lim_{n\to\infty} e_\theta(\varphi_n)$.

Note that efficiency and asymptotic efficiency (defined in this section) should not be confused with the asymptotic relative efficiency (of two CAN estimators) introduced in Definition 7.4.16.

Example 7.5.16. Let $X_1, X_2, \ldots, X_n$ be independent r.v.'s, each exponential with p.d.f.

$$f(x|\lambda) = \frac{1}{\lambda} e^{-x/\lambda} I_{(0,\infty)}(x),$$

for which $E(X_1) = \lambda$ and $\text{Var}(X_1) = \lambda^2$. Here $\overline{X}_n$ is the MLE of λ, with $E(\overline{X}_n) = \lambda$, $\text{Var}(\overline{X}_n) = \lambda^2/n$. The Cramér-Rao lower bound on the variance of unbiased estimators of λ is

$$\frac{1}{nI(\lambda)} = \frac{1}{nE\left(\dfrac{\partial}{\partial \lambda} \ln f(X|\lambda)\right)^2} = \frac{1}{nE\left(\dfrac{\partial}{\partial \lambda}(-\ln(\lambda) - X/\lambda)\right)^2}$$

$$= \frac{1}{nE(-1/\lambda + X/\lambda^2)^2} = \frac{\lambda^4}{nE(X - \lambda)^2} = \frac{\lambda^4}{n\lambda^2} = \frac{\lambda^2}{n},$$

which equals $\text{Var}(\overline{X}_n)$. Thus (assuming regularity, which holds here) $\overline{X}_n$ is a BRUE and efficient for λ.

PROBLEMS FOR SECTION 7.5

7.5.1 Let $X_1, X_2, \ldots, X_n$ be a random sample of size n from a Bernoulli distribution with success probability p, let $T_n = X_1 + \cdots + X_n$ and $\hat{p}_n = T_n/n$.
   (a) Show that $\hat{p}_n$ is a BRUE for p.
   (b) Show that the function $T_n(n - T_n)(n - 1 - T_n)$ is an unbiased estimator of pq^2, and find the Cramér-Rao lower bound for the variance of this unbiased estimator.
   (c) Show that $T_n(n - T_n)/(n(n - 1))$ is an unbiased estimator of pq and has smaller variance than the MLE of pq, which is $\hat{p}\hat{q}$.

7.5.2 (a) Let $X_1, X_2, \ldots, X_n$ be a random sample of size n from a $N(\mu, 1)$ distribution and let T_{1n} be the maximum likelihood estimator of μ^2 and T_{2n} an unbiased estimator of μ^2. Compute the Cramér-Rao lower bound for the variance of these two estimators. Using consistency and unbiasedness, discuss why you should choose one estimator over the other.
   (b) Find the Cramér-Rao lower bound for the unbiased estimator of the probability $P(X > 2\mu)$.

7.5.3 Let $X_1, X_2, \ldots, X_n$ be a random sample of size n from a $G(x|\alpha, \lambda)$ distribution, let T_{1n} be an unbiased estimator of α where λ is known, and let T_{2n} be an unbiased estimator of λ when α is known. Find the Cramér-Rao lower bound for the variance of these two estimators. Are these estimators BRUE's?

7.5.4 Show that

$$E\left(\frac{\partial}{\partial \theta} \ln f(X|\theta)\right)^2 = -E\left(\frac{\partial^2}{\partial \theta^2} \ln f(X|\theta)\right).$$

7.5.5 Let $X_1, X_2, \ldots, X_n$ be a random sample of size n from the p.d.f. $f(x|\theta) = \theta(1 + x)^{-(1+\theta)}$ if $x > 0$ (and $= 0$ otherwise) for some $\theta > 0$. Find the Cramér-Rao lower bound for the unbiased estimator of
(a) $\theta^2 + 2$; (b) e^θ; (c) $1/\theta$.

7.5.6 Let $X_1, X_2, \ldots, X_n$ be a random sample of size n from the p.d.f. of Problem 7.1.4. Find the lower bound for $E(\overline{X}_n - \theta)^2$. [*Hint:* $\overline{X}_n$ is a biased estimator of θ.]

7.5.7 Let $X_1, X_2, \ldots, X_n$ be a random sample of size n from a Poisson distribution with parameter λ, and let $T_n = \overline{X}_n^2 - \overline{X}_n$. Find the lower bound for $E(T_n - \lambda^2)^2$. Find a function of T_n that is unbiased for λ^2 and find the lower bound for the variance of this function. [*Hint:* T_n is biased for λ^2.]

7.5.8 Let $X_1, X_2, \ldots, X_n$ be a random sample of size n from a $N(\mu, \mu)$ distribution, $\mu > 0$. Find the lower bound for $E(\overline{X}_n s_n^2 - \mu^2)^2$.

7.5.9 Let $X_1, X_2, \ldots, X_n$ be a random sample of size n from the p.d.f. $f(x|\theta) = e^{-(x-\theta)-e^{-(x-\theta)}}$. Find the Cramér-Rao lower bound for the variance of an unbiased estimator of
(a) θ^2; (b) e^θ; (c) θ; (d) $\theta^2 + \theta$.

7.5.10 Let $X_1, X_2, \ldots, X_n$ be independent $N(\mu, \sigma^2)$ r.v.'s with μ and σ^2 unknown. Three possible estimators of σ^2 are $t_1 = \Sigma(X_i - \overline{X})^2/(n - 1)$, $t_2 = \Sigma(X_i - \overline{X})^2/n$, and $t_3 = \Sigma(X_i - \overline{X})^2/(n + 1)$. Compare these estimators on each of bias and mean squared error $E(t_i - \sigma^2)^2$. Also find the variance of each estimator.

PROBLEMS FOR CHAPTER 7

7.1 Let $X_1, \ldots, X_n$ be independent and identically distributed r.v.'s. Assume that (for all $c, -\infty < c < +\infty$) $P[X_1 = c] < 1$. Prove that $\max(X_1, \ldots, X_n)$ is not an unbiased estimator of $\theta^* = EX_1$. [*Hint:*

$$\max(a, b) = \frac{a + b}{2} + \frac{|a - b|}{2}.]$$

7.2 Let X_1, X_2 be independent and identically distributed r.v.'s. Prove that $\max(X_1, X_2)$ is an unbiased estimator of $\theta^* = EX_1$ iff (for some $c, -\infty < c < +\infty$) $P[X_1 = c] = 1$. [*Note:* Since Example 7.1.27, we have been talking of unbiased estimators of $g(\theta)$ for $\theta \in \Theta$, which is a slightly more general concept than that given in Definition 7.1.2. The same applies to asymptotic unbiasedness, consistency, and so on, and is usually assumed without so stating in works on statistics. Note that in Problems 7.1 and 7.2, $g(\theta) = \theta^*$ and $\Theta = \{F(\cdot): F(\cdot)$ is a d.f. whose expected value exists$\}$. Thus, EX_1 should more properly be written $E_\theta X_1$ (or, if we denote a typical member of Θ by F, $E_F X_1$). Since *many* distributions F have the *same* $E_F X_1$, it does *not* suffice to let EX_1 index Θ.]

7.3 (a) Find $Em_3 = E \dfrac{\sum\limits_{i=1}^{n} (X_i - \overline{X})^3}{n}$.

(b) In part (a) you found $Em_3 = c(n)\mu_3$. How can you use this fact to find an unbiased estimator of μ_3?

7.4 Consider the newsboy of Example 6.2.16 who wishes to set K $(0 \leq K \leq U)$ to maximize the average profit $\bar{P}_K$.

(a) If $s < p < r$ and demand X is known to have a uniform distribution on $0, 1, 2, \ldots, M$, what is the best K? (First assume $M \leq U$; then do not assume $M \leq U$.) What is the value of K if $M = 200$, $U = 200$, $s = 5$, $p = 8$, and $t = 10$?

(b) Suppose $s = 5$, $p = 8$, $r = 10$, $U = 200$, and X is known to have a Poisson distribution with mean 100. Compute (via slide rule, desk calculator, or computer) the best K. Compare this with the value found in part (a) [both (a) and (b) specify $EX = 100$].

7.5 Suppose that $X_1, \ldots, X_n$ are independent r.v.'s, each having the Poisson distribution (see Definition 3.2.11) with unknown mean (see Theorem 5.2.3) $\lambda \in \Theta = \{x: x > 0\}$.

(a) Find "the" MLE of λ. Does an MLE of λ exist for all possible values of $X_1, \ldots, X_n$? If not, how could you alter Θ so that the MLE would always exist?

(b) The correct answer to the last question in part (a) is undesirable, in that it allows our MLE $\hat{\lambda}$ to take on a value *known* to be false. One attempt sometimes made to solve this problem is to define any $\hat{\theta} = \hat{\theta}_n(X_1, \ldots, X_n) \in \Theta$ such that (for some $\varepsilon > 0$)

$$L(\hat{\theta}) \geq (1 - \varepsilon) \sup \{ L(\theta): \theta \in \Theta \}$$

to be an ε-**MLE of** θ (i.e., it comes within ε of maximizing the likelihood). Find all the ε-MLE's of λ. (Specify your answer implicitly, involving the solution of a certain equation. Specify it explicitly for the case $X_1 = X_2 = \cdots = X_n = 0$.)

7.6 Suppose that $X_1, \ldots, X_n$ are independent r.v.'s, each $N(\mu, \sigma^2)$ with both μ and σ^2 unknown, $(\mu, \sigma^2) \in \Theta = \{(x, y): -\infty < x < +\infty, y > 0\}$.

(a) Suppose $n \geq 2$. Find the MLE of (μ, σ^2). [*Hint:* Show that, regardless of σ^2, $L(\mu, \sigma^2)$ may be maximized by setting $\mu = \hat{\mu}$ for a certain $\hat{\mu}$; then maximize $L(\hat{\mu}, \sigma^2)$ with respect to σ^2.]

(b) Suppose $n = 1$. Does the MLE of (μ, σ^2) exist? (Compare with Examples 7.2.8 and 7.2.13.) Can the ε-MLE of Problem 7.5 be used here? Why or why not?

(c) Suppose that $n = 97$ and that $X_1, \ldots, X_{97}$ are taken to be the seasonal snowfalls observed at Rochester, New York, since the 1884–85 winter that are given in Table 7.P-1. Find the numerical values of $\hat{\mu}$ and $\hat{\sigma}^2$ for this set of data.

7.7 Suppose that we observe r.v.'s $Y_1, \ldots, Y_n$ and we know that (for $i = 1, \ldots, n$)

$$Y_i = \alpha + \beta x_i + V_i,$$

where $x_1, \ldots, x_n$ are known constants, α and β are unknown constants, and $V_1, \ldots, V_n$ are independent r.v.'s, each $N(0, \sigma^2)$ with σ^2 known. Find the MLE of (α, β).

7.8 Suppose that X and Y are independent r.v.'s, each with a normal distribution, and that $EX = \theta$, $EY = 3\theta$, $\text{Var}(X) = \text{Var}(Y) = 1$. Here $\theta \in \Theta = \{x: -\infty < x < +\infty\}$ is unknown.

(a) Find the MLE of θ.

(b) If an estimator of the form $aX + bY$ is to be used to estimate θ, what restrictions must the constants a and b satisfy in order that the estimator be unbiased?

TABLE 7.P-1
Seasonal Snowfall (in Inches) at Rochester, New York

Winter	Amount	Winter	Amount	Winter	Amount
1884–85	90.3	1917–18	79.3	1949–50	81.7
1885–86	64.7	1918–19	36.0	1950–51	75.8
1886–87	72.6	1919–20	97.5	1951–52	75.8
1887–88	50.7	1920–21	61.3	1952–53	41.7
1888–89	82.2	1921–22	59.7	1953–54	77.5
1889–90	65.8	1922–23	102.5	1954–55	69.2
1890–91	84.6	1923–24	65.6	1955–56	121.4
1891–92	77.1	1924–25	60.8	1956–57	79.2
1892–93	96.6	1925–26	55.3	1957–58	130.8
1893–94	102.4	1926–27	80.6	1958–59	140.6
1894–95	93.4	1927–28	68.5	1959–60	161.7
1895–96	123.8	1928–29	55.1	1960–61	89.4
1896–97	66.5	1929–30	59.5	1961–62	65.6
1897–98	91.0	1930–31	77.3	1962–63	76.4
1898–99	96.0	1931–32	75.7	1963–64	92.0
1899–1900	131.3	1932–33	29.2	1964–65	71.1
1900–01	141.5	1933–34	77.1	1965–66	103.2
1901–02	79.0	1934–35	49.5	1966–67	74.0
1902–03	68.3	1935–36	90.0	1967–68	76.7
1903–04	95.7	1936–37	65.9	1968–69	79.8
1904–05	68.3	1937–38	54.7	1969–70	119.6
1905–06	44.3	1938–39	79.1	1970–71	142.7
1906–07	63.7	1939–40	54.5	1971–72	105.1
1907–08	67.3	1940–41	73.7	1972–73	73.0
1908–09	66.5	1941–42	66.3	1973–74	99.1
1909–10	84.9	1942–43	70.6	1974–75	91.2
1910–11	107.4	1943–44	46.1	1975–76	86.2
1911–12	62.0	1944–45	94.7	1976–77	92.1
1912–13	59.2	1945–46	49.5	1977–78	160.9
1913–14	86.7	1946–47	75.5	1978–79	138.5
1914–15	60.8	1947–48	63.4	1979–80	72.2
1915–16	106.9	1948–49	50.9	1980–81	94.4
1916–17	92.9				

(c) Of all unbiased estimators of θ that have the form $aX + bY$, which one has the smallest variance? (This estimator is called a *best* (or *minimum variance*) *linear unbiased estimator*, usually abbreviated to BLUE or MVLUE.)

7.9 Prove that any CAN estimator is consistent.

7.10 Prove that, if an estimator t_n of θ is such that $n^\delta(t_n - \theta)$ is asymptotically $N(0, J^2(\theta))$ for some $\delta > 0$, then t_n is consistent.

7.11 Let t_n be an estimator of θ such that $n^\delta(t_n - \theta)$ is asymptotically $N(0, J^2(\theta))$ for some $\delta > 0$. Show that (in a reasonable sense that you should define) such an estimator is (a) more efficient than any CAN estimator if $\delta > \frac{1}{2}$; (b) a CAN estimator if $\delta = \frac{1}{2}$; (c) less efficient than any CAN estimator if $0 < \delta < \frac{1}{2}$.

7.12 Let X_n be a r.v. with d.f. $F_n(\cdot)$, and let X be a r.v. with d.f. $F(\cdot)$. Give examples where $F_n \to F$ and

(a) $\lim\limits_{n \to \infty} \text{Var}(X_n) = +\infty$ while $\text{Var}(X) = 1$.

(b) $\lim\limits_{n \to \infty} \text{Var}(X_n) = \sigma^2 > 1$ while $\text{Var}(X) = 1$.

7.13 Suppose we observe $X_1, \ldots, X_n$, independent r.v.'s each $N(\mu, \sigma^2)$ with μ known and σ^2 unknown. The MLE $\hat{\theta}_n$ of $\theta = \sigma^2$ was found in Example 7.2.13. Show that $\sqrt{n}(\hat{\theta}_n - \theta)$ is asymptotically normal.

7.14 Suppose that $X_1, \ldots, X_n$ are independent r.v.'s, each with the uniform distribution on $[\theta - \frac{1}{2}, \theta + \frac{1}{2}]$ where θ is unknown. Any $t_n = t_n(X_1, \ldots, X_n)$ such that

$$\max(X_1, \ldots, X_n) - \tfrac{1}{2} \le t_n \le \min(X_1, \ldots, X_n) + \tfrac{1}{2}$$

was found (in Example 7.2.19) to be an MLE.

(a) For the particular choice of t_n as $t_n^* = \{\max(X_1, \ldots, X_n) + \min(X_1, \ldots, X_n)\}/2$, find the limiting distribution of $n(t_n^* - \theta)$.

(b) Compare t_n^* to any CAN estimator t_n'. Which is preferable (for large n) and why? Give an example of such a CAN estimator t_n'. [*Hint:* Try $\overline{X}$.]

(c) For a general MLE t_n, find the limiting distribution of $n(t_n - \theta)$.

7.15 Let $X_1, \ldots, X_n$ be independent $N(\mu, \sigma^2)$ r.v.'s. Show that the sample mean $\overline{X}$ is a CAN estimator of μ by using the CLT. Next, show that $\overline{X}$ is a CAN estimator of μ by using footnote 7 of Problem 7.9H (which can be used to determine that $\overline{X}$ is $N(\mu, \sigma^2/n)$).

7.16 In the proof of Theorem 7.5.3 we used the relation

$$\frac{dw(\theta)}{d\theta} = \frac{d \ln w(\theta)}{d\theta} w(\theta) \qquad (*)$$

for any positive function $w(\theta)$. Now in the application made, $w(\theta) = f(x|\theta)$ is a nonnegative function (not a positive function), that is, sometimes $f(x|\theta) = 0$. How can we justify our use of relation $(*)$ in this case?

7.17 Let $X_1, \ldots, X_n$ be $n(\ge 1)$ independent r.v.'s, each Poisson with parameter $\lambda > 0$ unknown. In Example 7.5.6 we showed that $\overline{X}$ is an efficient estimator of λ. Show that $\sqrt{n}(\overline{X} - \lambda)$ is asymptotically $N(0, \lambda)$; hence, $\overline{X}$ is a CAN estimator.

7.18 Let $X_1, \ldots, X_n$ be $n(\ge 1)$ independent r.v.'s, with $P[X_i = 1] = p$ and $P[X_i = 0] = 1 - p$ $(i = 1, \ldots, n)$ where $p(0 \le p \le 1)$ is unknown. Suppose that this is a regular estimation case, and find the lower bound (Theorem 7.5.3) on the variance of any regular unbiased estimator φ_n of p.

Find the MLE of p, and show that $\sqrt{n}(\text{MLE} - p)$ is asymptotically $N(0, \sigma^2(p))$ (and hence is a CAN estimator). Compare $\sigma^2(p)$ with

$$1/E_p\left(\frac{\partial \ln f(X|p)}{\partial p}\right)^2.$$

7.19 Let $X_1, \ldots, X_n$ be independent r.v.'s, each with density

$$f(x|\theta) = \begin{cases} \dfrac{x}{\theta} e^{-.5x^2/\theta}, & x > 0 \\ 0, & x \le 0, \end{cases}$$

where θ is unknown, $\theta \in \Theta = \{z: z > 0\}$. [This is called the **Rayleigh distribution**.] Find the method of moments estimator of θ.

7.20 As in Problem 7.19, but with $f(x|\theta)$ the uniform density on $(0, \theta)$.

HONORS PROBLEMS FOR CHAPTER 7

7.1H Suppose that $X_1, \ldots, X_n$ are independent and identically distributed r.v.'s (and that all moments referred to do exist). We defined (Definition 7.1.9)

$$m_k = \frac{\sum\limits_{i=1}^{n} (X_i - \overline{X})^k}{n},$$

and of course $\mu_k = E(X_i - \mu_1')^k$.

(a) Find $E m_4$.

(b) Find A and B such that $E(A m_4 + B m_2^2) = \mu_4$. [*Note:* In principle A and B may be functions of $X_1, \ldots, X_n$, say $A(X_1, \ldots, X_n)$ and $B(X_1, \ldots, X_n)$; however, they may not be functions of any population moments μ_k, since the latter are unknown. This problem claims we can, in fact, choose A and B as functions of n only, independent of $X_1, \ldots, X_n$.]

(c) Find $\mathrm{Var}(m_2)$ and $\mathrm{Var}\left(\sum\limits_{i=1}^{n} (X_i - \mu_1)^2/n \right)$.

7.2H In the newsboy problem (Example 6.2.16), suppose we wish to set K ($0 \le K < +\infty$) to maximize the average profit $\overline{P}_K$. Suppose that X is known to have a uniform distribution on the integers $L, L+1, \ldots, L+Q-1$ (Q possible demands), and that $s < p < r$. Show that

$$\overline{P}_K = \begin{cases} (r-p)K, & \text{if } K < L \\ (r-p)K + \dfrac{r-s}{2Q}[K(K+1) - L(L-1)] \\ \qquad + K(s-r)\dfrac{K-L+1}{Q}, & \text{if } L \le K \le L+Q-1 \\ (r-p)K + \dfrac{r-s}{2Q}[(L+Q-1)(L+Q) \\ \qquad -(L-1)L] + K(s-r), & \text{if } K > L+Q-1. \end{cases}$$

Hence, deduce that the K which maximizes $\overline{P}_K$ is the integer closest to $Q(r-p)/(r-s) + L - .5$.

7.3H In the proof that $m_k \overset{P}{\to} \mu_k$ (Theorem 7.1.12) we concluded from the fact of continuity of a polynomial Π jointly in its arguments that stochastic convergence of its arguments implied stochastic convergence of the polynomial itself (to the same polynomial evaluated at the limits of its arguments). Prove that this is so as formalized below in parts (a), (b), and (c).

Let $X_1, X_2, \ldots$ be any r.v.'s (not necessarily independent or identically distributed). Let $t_1 = t_1(X_1, \ldots, X_n), \ldots, t_r = t_r(X_1, \ldots, X_n)$ be r statistics. Suppose $t_1 \leadsto a_1, \ldots, t_r \leadsto a_r$ (as $n \to \infty$) with $a_1, \ldots, a_r$ constants.

(a) $\Pi(t_1, \ldots, t_r) \leadsto \Pi(a_1, \ldots, a_r)$ for any polynomial $\Pi(\cdot, \ldots, \cdot)$.

(b) $R(t_1, \ldots, t_r) \leadsto R(a_1, \ldots, a_r)$ for any rational function R of r variables with $|R(a_1, \ldots, a_r)| < +\infty$.

(c) $g(t_1, \ldots, t_r) \leadsto g(a_1, \ldots, a_r)$ if $g(\cdot, \ldots, \cdot)$ is a continuous function of r variables and $|g(a_1, \ldots, a_r)| < +\infty$.

Notes: (1) (c) $\Rightarrow$ (b) $\Rightarrow$ (a). (2) (b) is called **Slutsky's Theorem** [e.g., see Fisz (1963), p. 238, or Wilks (1962), p. 104]. (3) (c) may be generalized to the case where $a_1, \ldots, a_r$ are r.v.'s (see, e.g., p. 103 of Wilks). Note that if we also have a random parameter to contend with, things are a bit more complex; thus, Wilks' 4.3.8 on p. 105 is slightly wrong (see Suzuki (1964–1965), pp. 221–224; this is in Japanese with an English summary).

For a broad generalization of (c), see Sverdrup (1952).

7.4H Prove that the sample median M_n is a consistent estimator of the population median ν by using the Glivenko-Cantelli Theorem in any form.

7.5H In Theorem 7.2.15(i), we noted that it makes sense to talk of "the MLE of $g(\theta)$" if $g(\theta)$ is a one-to-one function, and that $\overline{g(\theta)} = g(\hat{\theta})$. Zehna (1966) and Berk (1967) propose to call $g(\hat{\theta})$ an MLE anyway. But Dudewicz (1971) proposes a different solution.

(a) Why does Zehna call $g(\hat{\theta})$ an MLE of $g(\theta)$? (Include the **"induced likelihood function"** in your discussion.)

(b) Why does Berk (who says Zehna "misses the point") wish to call $g(\hat{\theta})$ an MLE of $g(\theta)$?

(c) Why does Dudewicz think Berk's reasoning questionable? Study the **IMLE** of Dudewicz in a case not covered by his paper, and compare it with $g(\hat{\theta})$.

7.6H In Definition 7.1.5, we defined *consistency* of an estimator in terms of a "convergence in probability" or "weak convergence" (see Definition 6.2.2). We can similarly define **strong consistency** by replacing the requirement of "weak convergence" in Definition 7.1.5 by a requirement of "strong convergence" (see Definition 6.2.1). In fact, in his original article Wald (1949) actually proved strong consistency of the MLE. His proof is the same as the proof of Theorem 7.4.5 up to a certain point. Find that point and give in detail the remainder of his proof of strong consistency of the MLE.

7.7H Let X_n be a r.v. with d.f. F_n ($n = 1, 2, \ldots$) and suppose $F_n \to F$ where F is a d.f. of some r.v. X. If $0 = E(X_1) = E(X_2) = \cdots$, does $E(X) = 0$?

7.8H (a) For the MLE $\hat{d}$ of d in Example 7.2.19, find $E(\hat{d})$. Is $\hat{d}$ an unbiased estimator of d? Can you find a function of n, say $a(n)$, such that $a(n)\hat{d}$ is an unbiased estimator of d?

(b) In Example 7.2.20 we found that any $\hat{c}$ such that $L(X_1, \ldots, X_n) \leq \hat{c} \leq U(X_1, \ldots, X_n)$ is an MLE of c; here

$$L(X_1, \ldots, X_n) = \max(X_1, \ldots, X_n) - d,$$

$$U(X_1, \ldots, X_n) = \min(X_1, \ldots, X_n) + d.$$

Consider those $\hat{c}$'s that have the form

$$\hat{c} = a(n)L + b(n)U. \qquad (*)$$

What restrictions on $a(n)$ and $b(n)$ are necessary and sufficient for $\hat{c}$ to be an unbiased MLE? Consider all $\hat{c}$'s of the form $(*)$; what restrictions on $a(n)$ and $b(n)$ are necessary and sufficient for $\hat{c}$ to be unbiased? Among all such unbiased $\hat{c}$'s, which one has the smallest variance? Find that smallest variance.
   (c) In Example 7.2.21 find $E(\hat{c})$. Is $\hat{c}$ an unbiased estimator of c?

7.9H   (a) Let U, V, W be independent r.v.'s whose respective distributions are $N(0, \theta)$, $N(0, 1)$, $N(0, 1)$ where $\theta > 0$ is unknown. Let $X = U + V$ and $Y = U + W$. Show[7] that the joint distribution of (X, Y) is bivariate normal with $EX = EY = 0$, $\text{Var}(X) = \text{Var}(Y) = 1 + \theta$, and $\text{Cov}(X, Y) = \theta$ (hence $\rho(X, Y) = \theta/(1 + \theta)$).

   (b) Let $(X_1, Y_1), \ldots, (X_n, Y_n)$ be n independent pairs of r.v.'s where (X_i, Y_i) have the bivariate normal distribution found in part (a). Find the MLE of $\lambda = 1/(1 + 2\theta)$ based on $(X_1, Y_1), \ldots, (X_n, Y_n)$. Find the MLE of θ.

   (c) For the MLE of θ, say $\hat{\theta}$, found in part (b) find the exact probability distribution. [*Hint:* $(a + b)^2 = a^2 + 2ab + b^2$.]

7.10H Suppose Definition 7.4.20 is modified to let

$$Z_p = \begin{cases} Y_{[np]+1}, & \text{if } np \text{ is not an integer} \\ aY_{np} + (1 - a)Y_{np+1}, & \text{if } np \text{ is an integer} \end{cases}$$

where a is fixed $(0 < a \leq 1)$. Show that Theorem 7.4.20 is still valid for this definition of Z_p. Find a natural choice of a. [*Hint:* Why do we choose $a = .5$ in the case $p = .5$?]

7.11H Fix p $(0 < p < 1)$. Let $X_1, \ldots, X_n$ be independent r.v.'s with d.f. $F(x)$ and density $f(x)$. Suppose that

$$\lim_{x \uparrow F^{-1}(p)} f(x) = A > 0 \qquad \text{and} \qquad \lim_{x \downarrow F^{-1}(p)} f(x) = B > 0$$

with $A \neq B$. (The case $A = B$ was dealt with in Theorem 7.4.21.) Find the limiting distribution of

$$\sqrt{n}\left(Z_p - F^{-1}(p)\right).$$

[*Hint:* This is a nonstandard case. Two references are Moore (1969) and Weiss (1970).] Note that this study involves the case of a discontinuity of $f(x)$ at $F^{-1}(p) = \xi_p$.

---

[7]This result is a special case of the result [e.g., see Fisz (1963), p. 162] that: If $(X_1, \ldots, X_n)$ has a **multivariate normal distribution, then so does** $(Y_1, \ldots, Y_r)$ where $Y_1, \ldots, Y_r$ are $r \leq n$ linear functions of $X_1, \ldots, X_n$. Here you are to prove this result directly in a special case.

CHAPTER 8

Data Reduction and Best Estimation (Sufficiency, Completeness, UMVUE's)

In Chapter 7 we discussed basic concepts of statistical estimation and the two important techniques of MLE's and MME's. In Section 8.1 we introduce data reduction via **sufficiency** and its relevance in estimation. Basically, the idea of sufficiency is to compress given data (sometimes to a single number) without losing any information about the parameter(s) involved. For example, if we have a random sample of size n and the goal is to estimate the population mean μ, then sometimes $X_1 + \cdots + X_n$ contains as much information about μ as does the entire data set $\{X_1, \ldots, X_n\}$; in such a case we call ΣX_i a **sufficient statistic** for μ. A sufficient statistic is not itself necessarily a good estimator of the parameter under study; functions of a sufficient statistic provide a class of estimators that includes all good estimators.

For the goal of obtaining a function of a sufficient statistic that is a "good" estimator, the **completeness** concept is useful (Section 8.2). Finally, in Section 8.3 we use completeness and sufficiency to discuss *u*niformly *m*inimum *v*ariance *u*nbiased *e*stimators **(UMVUE's)**, also known as *b*est *u*nbiased *e*stimators **(BUE's)**. Such an estimator is an unbiased function of a **complete sufficient statistic** (if such a function for the given parameter exists).

Note that a thorough understanding of Chapters 7 through 11 will give you a basis for study of almost any modern statistical analyses.

8.1. SUFFICIENCY

The idea of sufficiency is that if we observe a r.v. X whose distribution depends on an unknown parameter θ [e.g., often $X = (X_1, \ldots, X_n)$ where $X_1, \ldots, X_n$ are independent and identically distributed r.v.'s, each having density function $f(x|\theta)$ where θ is unknown, $\theta \in \Theta$], **often X can be reduced via a function without losing any information about θ;** for example, $t(X) = t(X_1, \ldots, X_n) = (X_1 + \cdots + X_n)/n$, the sample mean, may in some cases contain all relevant information about θ, and in that case $t(X)$ is called a **sufficient statistic**. [*Note:* $t(X)$ may also be a random vector; e.g., the order statistics.] **We can then simply**

base our inference about θ on $t(X)$, which can be considerably simpler than X (e.g., one number $\overline{X}$ versus n numbers $X_1, \ldots, X_n$). The formal definition is as follows.

Definition 8.1.1. A statistic $t(X_1, \ldots, X_n)$ is **sufficient (for θ)** iff

$$P_\theta\big[(X_1, \ldots, X_n) \in \mathscr{U} | t(X_1, \ldots, X_n) = c\big] = l(\mathscr{U}|c) \qquad (8.1.2)$$

for all θ and all $\mathscr{U} \subseteq \mathscr{R}^n$, that is, iff the left side of equation (8.1.2) is a function of $\mathscr{U}$ and c, say $l(\mathscr{U}|c)$, but *not* a function of θ. [Here θ and c may be vectors.]

This definition of a "sufficient" statistic means that $t(X_1, \ldots, X_n)$ is a "sufficient" statistic if, once you are told the value of $t(\ )$ at $(X_1, \ldots, X_n)$, a more exact specification of where $(X_1, \ldots, X_n)$ lies in $\mathscr{R}^n$ has no information about θ (in the sense that the conditional distribution is independent of θ). More precisely, $\{(x_1, \ldots, x_n): t(x_1, \ldots, x_n) = c\}$ is a subset of $\mathscr{R}^n$ called a **hypersurface**. If we are told the value of $t(\ )$, we only know that *some* point on this hypersurface was the result of our experiment. The left side of equation (8.1.2) is the conditional probability of having obtained a value $(X_1, \ldots, X_n)$ in a certain subset of $t(\ ) = c$, given a value in $t(\ ) = c$ was obtained. (See Figure 8.1-1.) If this is not dependent on θ, then further specification of the point obtained contains no information about θ—that is why we call $t(\ )$ "sufficient." We now give two examples to clarify this concept.

Example 8.1.3. Let $X_1, X_2, \ldots, X_n$ be independent r.v.'s, each Bernoulli with success probability p. Let $t(X_1, X_2, \ldots, X_n) = \sum_{i=1}^{n} X_i$. Then (if $x_1, \ldots, x_n$ are each 0 or 1 and sum to $c \leq n$)

$$P\big[(X_1, X_2, \ldots, X_n) = (x_1, x_2, \ldots, x_n) | t(X_1, X_2, \ldots, X_n) = c\big]$$

$$= \frac{P\big[(X_1, X_2, \ldots, X_n) = (x_1, x_2, \ldots, x_n), t(X_1, X_2, \ldots, X_n) = c\big]}{P\big[t(X_1, X_2, \ldots, X_n) = c\big]}$$

$$= \frac{P\left[(X_1, X_2, \ldots, X_n) = (x_1, x_2, \ldots, x_n), X_n + \sum_{i=1}^{n-1} X_i = c\right]}{P\left[\sum_{i=1}^{n} X_i = c\right]}$$

$$= \frac{P\left[X_1 = x_1, X_2 = x_2, \ldots, X_{n-1} = x_{n-1}, X_n = c - \sum_{i=1}^{n-1} x_i\right]}{P\left[\sum_{i=1}^{n} X_i = c\right]}$$

$$= \frac{\prod_{i=1}^{n-1}\left\{p^{x_i}(1-p)^{1-x_i}\right\} \cdot p^{c-\sum_{i=1}^{n-1} x_i}(1-p)^{1-c+\sum_{i=1}^{n-1} x_i}}{\binom{n}{c}p^c(1-p)^{n-c}} = \frac{1}{\binom{n}{c}},$$

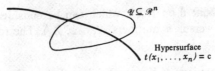

Figure 8.1-1.

which is independent of p. Hence, for any value of c $(0, 1, 2, \ldots, n$ are the only ones for which the conditional probability is defined) for which (8.1.2) is defined,

$$P\left[(X_1, \ldots, X_n) = (x_1, \ldots, x_n) | t(X_1, \ldots, X_n) = c\right]$$

$$= \begin{cases} \dfrac{1}{\dbinom{n}{c}}, & \text{if } x_1, \ldots, x_n \text{ are each 0 or 1 and sum to } c \\[2mm] 0, & \text{otherwise,} \end{cases}$$

and

$$P\left[(X_1, \ldots, X_n) \varepsilon \mathcal{U} | t(X_1, \ldots, X_n) = c\right]$$

$$= \frac{\left(\begin{array}{l} \text{Number of vectors } (x_1, \ldots, x_n) \text{ in } \mathcal{U} \text{ whose components} \\ \text{are nonnegative integers that sum to } c \end{array}\right)}{\dbinom{n}{c}}$$

$$= l(\mathcal{U}|c),$$

that is, is a function only of $\mathcal{U}$ and c (and not of p). Hence $t(X_1, X_2, \ldots, X_n)$ $= \sum_{i=1}^{n} X_i$ is a sufficient statistic for p.

Note that the conditional distribution of the original data given $t(X_1, \ldots, X_n)$ $= c$ is uniform, and there are exactly $\binom{n}{c}$ ways to assign 1 for success on c trials. For example, if $n = 2$ and $c = 1$, then $(1, 0)$ and $(0, 1)$ carry exactly the same amount of information about p, and the conditional distribution of which of these occurred is independent of p (and in this case, uniform, though that is not important for sufficiency—it is the independence of p of this distribution that is crucial).

Also note that our previous work (e.g., in Example 7.1.27) shows that $t = \sum X_i$ is *not* a good estimator of p, though a function of it (i.e., t/n) is, and we need only know t in order to calculate this function's value.

Example 8.1.4. Let $X_1, X_2, \ldots, X_n$ be independent r.v.'s, each uniform on $(0, \theta)$. Let $Y_n = \max(X_1, \ldots, X_n)$ and $Y_1 = \min(X_1, \ldots, X_n)$. Then (if $x_1, \ldots, x_n$

are all ≥ 0 and $\leq \theta$ with $y_n = \max(x_1, \ldots, x_n))$

$$f_{X_1, X_2, \ldots, X_n | Y_n = y_n}(x_1, x_2, \ldots, x_n | y_n)$$

$$= \frac{f_{X_1, X_2, \ldots, X_n, Y_n}(x_1, x_2, \ldots, x_n, y_n)}{f_{Y_n}(y_n)} = \frac{f_{X_1, X_2, \ldots, X_n}(x_1, x_2, \ldots, x_n)}{f_{Y_n}(y_n)}$$

$$= \frac{1/\theta^n}{ny_n^{n-1}/\theta^n} = \frac{1}{ny_n^{n-1}},$$

which is independent of θ. As in Example 8.1.3 (here integrating over $\mathcal{U}$ instead of summing), it follows that Y_n is a sufficient statistic for θ. However, since (if $x_1, \ldots, x_n$ are all ≥ 0 and $\leq \theta$ with $y_1 = \min(x_1, \ldots, x_n))$

$$f_{X_1, \ldots, X_n | Y_1 = y_1}(x_1, \ldots, x_n | y_1) = \frac{f_{X_1, \ldots, X_n, Y_1}(x_1, \ldots, x_n, y_1)}{f_{Y_1}(y_1)}$$

$$= \frac{f_{X_1, \ldots, X_n}(x_1, \ldots, x_n)}{f_{Y_1}(y_1)} = \frac{(1/\theta)^n}{n(\theta - y_1)^{n-1}/\theta^n}$$

$$= \frac{1}{n(\theta - y_1)^{n-1}}$$

which is not independent of θ, it similarly follows that Y_1 is *not* a sufficient statistic for θ.

Thus, although both Y_n and Y_1 each reduce the data to a single number, here Y_n does not lose any information about the parameter θ, while Y_1 does lose information.

Although Definition 8.1.1 is easy to understand intuitively, it is usually difficult to verify, and another criterion is needed. The following notation (unifying the discrete and continuous cases) will aid us in stating such a criterion.

Notation 8.1.5. Suppose that $(X_1, \ldots, X_n)$ is a r.v. with d.f. $F(x_1, \ldots, x_n | \theta) = P_\theta[X_1 \leq x_1, \ldots, X_n \leq x_n]$ where $\theta = (\theta_1, \ldots, \theta_r) \in \Theta \subseteq \mathcal{R}^r$. Assume $F(x_1, \ldots, x_n | \theta)$ is either absolutely continuous [in which case let $f(x_1, \ldots, x_n | \theta)$ denote its density at $(x_1, \ldots, x_n)$] or discrete [in which case let $f(x_1, \ldots, x_n | \theta)$ denote $P_\theta[X_1 = x_1, \ldots, X_n = x_n]$].

Theorem 8.1.6. Neyman Factorization Theorem. In Notation 8.1.5, $t(X_1, \ldots, X_n)$ is a sufficient statistic (for θ) iff

$$f(x_1, \ldots, x_n | \theta) = h(x_1, \ldots, x_n) g(t(x_1, \ldots, x_n) | \theta) \qquad (8.1.7)$$

for all $x_1, \ldots, x_n$, θ for some functions $h(\ )$ and $g(\ )$.

Proof: [We will give the proof only for the case of a r.v. $X = (X_1, \ldots, X_n)$, which assumes values $x = (x_1, \ldots, x_n)$ in a set containing at most denumerably many points; this is to be the same set for every $\theta \in \Theta$.][1]

First, suppose $t(X_1, \ldots, X_n)$ is a sufficient statistic (i.e., Definition 8.1.1 holds). Let X denote $(X_1, \ldots, X_n)$, and let x denote $(x_1, \ldots, x_n)$. Let $S = \{ x : f(x|\theta) > 0$ for some $\theta \in \Theta \}$, the set of values that X can assume.

We suppose S contains at most denumerably many points. Now (by (8.1.2))

$$P_\theta[X = x|t(X) = c] = l(\{x\}|c) \tag{8.1.8}$$

is not a function of $\theta \in \Theta$. Now let x_0 be an arbitrary member of S, and denote $t(x_0)$ by c_0. Then

$$\begin{aligned} f(x_0|\theta) = P_\theta[X = x_0] &= \sum_d P_\theta[t(X) = d] P_\theta[X = x_0|t(X) = d] \\ &= P_\theta[t(X) = c_0] P_\theta[X = x_0|t(X) = c_0] \\ &= P_\theta[t(X) = c_0] l(\{x_0\}|t(x_0)), \end{aligned} \tag{8.1.9}$$

where we used the Theorem of Total Probabilities (Theorem 2.3.7), the fact that $P_\theta[X = x_0|t(X) = d]$ is zero unless $d = c_0$, and equation (8.1.8). But now in (8.1.9) the factor $l(\{x_0\}|t(x_0))$ is a function of x_0 alone, say $h(x_0)$; and $P_\theta[t(X) = c_0]$ is a function of $t(x_0)$ and θ, say $g(t(x_0)|\theta)$. Hence, equation (8.1.7) follows, and since $x_0 \in S$ was arbitrary, this part of the theorem [sufficiency implies equation (8.1.7)] is proven.

Next, to prove the converse, suppose that equation (8.1.7) holds (i.e., the density, or probability function, factors). Then, if x_0 is an arbitrary member of S, we have

$$f(x_0|\theta) = h(x_0)g(t(x_0)|\theta). \tag{8.1.10}$$

Hence (denoting $t(x_0)$ by c_0)

$$\begin{aligned} & P_\theta[X = x_0|t(X) = c_0] \\ &= \frac{P_\theta[X = x_0, t(X) = c_0]}{P_\theta[t(X) = c_0]} = \frac{P_\theta[X = x_0]}{\displaystyle\sum_{d \ni t(d) = c_0} P_\theta[X = d]} \\ &= \frac{h(x_0)g(c_0|\theta)}{\displaystyle\sum_{d \ni t(d) = c_0} h(d)g(c_0|\theta)} = \frac{h(x_0)}{\displaystyle\sum_{d \ni t(d) = c_0} h(d)}, \end{aligned} \tag{8.1.11}$$

---

[1]For the general case see, for example, Lehmann (1959), pp. 49–50. This treatment requires understanding of the concepts mentioned in Problems 2.4H and 3.1H, but the basic ideas involved are the same as for the discrete case covered by our proof.

which is a function only of x_0 and c_0, say $l(\{x_0\}|c_0)$. Since x_0 was arbitrary and, in a denumerable case, $P_\theta[X \in \mathcal{U}|t(X) = c]$ is simply a sum of such terms (8.1.11) (each of which we have shown is independent of θ), the left side of equation (8.1.2) is independent of θ, hence proving the theorem. [Note that in equation (8.1.11) we ignored the possibility $P_\theta[t(X) = c_0] = 0$ and the possibility of considering $P_\theta[X = x_0|t(X) = c]$ with $c \neq c_0$. This is easily taken care of, and comprises Problem 8.1.] ∎

We now give some **examples of the use of Theorem 8.1.6**. Note that $t(\ )$ may be a vector in both Definition 8.1.1 and Theorem 8.1.6.

Example 8.1.12. Let $X_1, X_2, \ldots, X_n$ be a random sample from the displaced exponential distribution, so (for $i = 1, 2, \ldots, n$)

$$f_{X_i}(x) = e^{-(x-\theta)}I_{(\theta,\infty)}(x).$$

Then the joint p.d.f. of $X_1, X_2, \ldots, X_n$ is

$$
\begin{aligned}
f(x_1, x_2, \ldots, x_n|\theta) &= e^{-\sum_{i=1}^{n}(x_i-\theta)}\prod_{i=1}^{n}I_{(\theta,\infty)}(x_i) \\
&= e^{-\sum_{i=1}^{n}x_i}e^{n\theta} \cdot \begin{cases} 1, & \text{if } \min(x_1, \ldots, x_n) > \theta \\ 0, & \text{otherwise} \end{cases} \\
&= e^{-\sum_{i=1}^{n}x_i}e^{n\theta}I_{(\theta,\infty)}(y_1) \\
&= h(x_1, \ldots, x_n)g(t(x_1, \ldots, x_n)|\theta)
\end{aligned}
$$

where $y_1 = \min(x_1, \ldots, x_n)$ and we have chosen $h(x_1, \ldots, x_n) = \exp\{-\Sigma x_i\}$ and $g(z|\theta) = e^{n\theta}I_{(\theta,\infty)}(z)$. Thus (by the Neyman Factorization Theorem) $Y_1 = \min(X_1, X_2, \ldots, X_n)$ is a sufficient statistic for θ.

In the following example we have a multiparameter case.

Example 8.1.13. Let $X_1, X_2, \ldots, X_n$ be independent r.v.'s, each with the gamma distribution $G(x|\alpha, \beta, 0)$. Seeking to reduce the data for (α, β) (a two-dimensional parameter), the joint p.d.f. of $X_1, \ldots, X_n$ is

$$
\begin{aligned}
f(x_1, x_2, \ldots, x_n|\alpha, \beta) &= \left(\frac{1}{\beta^{\alpha+1}\Gamma(\alpha+1)}\right)^n (x_1 x_2 \ldots x_n)^\alpha e^{-\sum_{i=1}^{n}x_i/\beta} \\
&= h(x_1, \ldots, x_n)g\left(\prod_{i=1}^{n}x_i, \sum_{i=1}^{n}x_i \middle| \alpha, \beta\right)
\end{aligned}
$$

where we have chosen $h(x_1, \ldots, x_n) = 1$ (a constant function) and $g(y, z|\alpha, \beta) = (\beta^{\alpha+1}\Gamma(\alpha+1))^{-n}y^\alpha e^{-z/\beta}$. Hence (by the Neyman Factorization Theorem) $\left(\prod_{i=1}^{n}X_i, \sum_{i=1}^{n}X_i\right)$ is a (jointly) sufficient statistic for the vector parameter (α, β).

Note that the MLE of (α, β), studied in Example 7.2.25, was a function of the sufficient statistic we have just found.

(Note that "joint" sufficiency for (α, β) does *not* mean that $\prod_{i=1}^{n} X_i$ is sufficient for α or that $\sum_{i=1}^{n} X_i$ is sufficient for β. Also, the sufficient statistic is not itself (in most cases) the best estimator of the parameter; rather functions of the sufficient statistic (as studied in Section 8.3) are candidates for best estimator. In fact, **the next example involves a case where the parameter is a scalar (one-dimensional), while the sufficient statistic turns out to be multidimensional**—hence it clearly cannot be an estimator of the parameter.)

Example 8.1.14. Let $X_1, X_2, \ldots, X_n$ be independent r.v.'s, each uniform on $[-\theta, \theta]$ for some $\theta > 0$. Here, seeking a sufficient statistic for θ by the Neyman Factorization Theorem, we find the joint p.d.f. of $X_1, X_2, \ldots, X_n$ is

$$f(x_1, x_2, \ldots, x_n | \theta) = \left(\frac{1}{2\theta}\right)^n \prod_{i=1}^{n} I_{[-\theta, \theta]}(x_i)$$

$$= \left(\frac{1}{2\theta}\right)^n \prod_{i=1}^{n} I_{(-\infty, \theta]}(x_i) \cdot \prod_{i=1}^{n} I_{[-\theta, \infty)}(x_i)$$

$$= \left(\frac{1}{2\theta}\right)^n I_{(-\infty, \theta]}(y_n) I_{[-\theta, \infty)}(y_1)$$

where $y_1 = \min(x_1, x_2, \ldots, x_n)$ and $y_n = \max(x_1, x_2, \ldots, x_n)$. Letting $h(x_1, x_2, \ldots, x_n) = 1$ and $g(y, z | \theta) = I_{(-\infty, \theta]}(z) I_{[-\theta, \infty)}(y)$, $f(x_1, x_2, \ldots, x_n | \theta) = h(x_1, \ldots, x_n) g(y_1, y_n | \theta)$, so by the Neyman Factorization Theorem (Y_1, Y_n) is jointly sufficient for θ.

Note [see Definition 8.1.1 and equation (8.1.2)] that what makes a statistic $t(X_1, \ldots, X_n)$ sufficient is a property of sets of points $\{(x_1, \ldots, x_n): t(x_1, \ldots, x_n) = c\}$, that is, of sets of points to which $t(\ )$ assigns the same value [and hence, which $t(\ )$ chooses to "lump together" or not distinguish from each other]. **Thus, any one-to-one function of t, say $k(t)$, is also a sufficient statistic** (see Problem 8.2.1); **for example, if $t(\ )$ is sufficient, then so is $10 + t(\ )$.** [Hence, of course, $t(\ )$ itself may not be a proper (i.e., good) estimator of θ; rather, any good estimator of θ needs only the information in $(X_1, \ldots, X_n)$ about θ, that $t(X_1, \ldots, X_n)$ contains, and hence can be based solely on $t(X_1, \ldots, X_n)$.] It is useful to call the hypersurface of points $(x_1, \ldots, x_n)$ where a sufficient statistic has a specified value a **contour of $t(\ )$**. Then, all that matters about a sufficient statistic is not its specified values, but its contours; a function [which $t(\ )$ is] unites points onto contours, and any other statistic that unites the same points in the same way is essentially the same (see Figure 8.1-2).

To sum up, in an experiment we find a value of $X = (X_1, \ldots, X_n)$. If we are told the value of $t(X)$, that is, which contour of $t(\ )$ the observed point lies on,

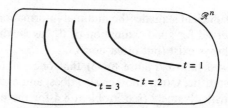

Figure 8.1-2. Contours of a sufficient statistic.

and further specification of the location of the observed point can shed no light on the value of θ (this was formalized in Definition 8.1.1, via independence of θ of the conditional distribution on the contour), then knowledge of the contour alone is *sufficient*. Intuitively, then, **if there exists a sufficient statistic $t(\ )$, any estimator of θ should be a function of $t(\ )$ only.** Hence, once we agree on what $f(x_1, \ldots, x_n | \theta)$ is, we need not report or record all our data $X = (X_1, \ldots, X_n)$; rather, $t(X_1, \ldots, X_n)$ is a sufficient summary of the data.

We have thus seen that it is desirable to have a sufficient statistic $t(X_1, \ldots, X_n)$. In fact **at least one sufficient statistic always exists, namely the identity statistic** $I(X_1, \ldots, X_n) = (X_1, \ldots, X_n)$; the proof of sufficiency is trivial from Definition 8.1.1, since the conditional distribution is independent of θ due to there being only one point on each contour, whose conditional probability is 1. But **suppose there is more than one sufficient statistic: which should we choose?** If there are two, say $t(\ )$ and $\varphi(\ )$, which are the same except as illustrated in Figure 8.1-3, then we should prefer $\varphi(\ )$ because it unites more points (i.e., summarizes the data more) but is still sufficient. Note that in fact $\varphi(\ ) = k(t(\ ))$, that is $\varphi(\ )$ is a function of $t(\ )$ (this is not true for every pair of sufficient statistics). Thus, **if we are seeking a best sufficient statistic, it should be the one with the largest contours.** We now formalize this notion.

Definition 8.1.15. $T(X_1, \ldots, X_n)$ is a **minimal sufficient statistic** if $T(\ )$ is a sufficient statistic and a function of every other sufficient statistic; that is,

$$T(X_1, \ldots, X_n) = k_t\big(t(X_1, \ldots, X_n)\big) \qquad (8.1.16)$$

for every sufficient statistic $t(\ )$.

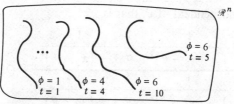

Figure 8.1-3. Two sufficient statisties' contours.

Thus, a minimal sufficient statistic [the minimal information about $(X_1, \ldots, X_n)$ which must ve preserved for good estimation of θ] **has maximal contours.** Such a statistic need not always exist (but often does).

We already showed (above Figure 8.1-3) that one sufficient statistic always exists, the identity statistic. Often another also does, and each of these is called a **trivial sufficient statistic.** Namely (see Problem 8.4 for the proof), the following.

Theorem 8.1.17.   In Notation 8.1.5, if $X_1, \ldots, X_n$ are independent and identically distributed r.v.'s, then the order statistic $t(X_1, \ldots, X_n) = (Y_1, \ldots, Y_n)$ [see Definition 5.6.1] is a sufficient statistic.

Next, we wish to show that **sometimes only trivial sufficient statistics exist.** For this we need the following lemma.

Lemma 8.1.18.   (We use Notation 8.1.5.) $f(x|\theta)/f(y|\theta)$ is independent of θ if $t(x) = t(y)$ for some sufficient statistic $t(\ )$ (i.e., if $x = (x_1, \ldots, x_n)$ and $y = (y_1, \ldots, y_n)$ are on the same contour of some sufficient statistic).

Proof: By the Neyman Factorization Theorem, since $t(\ )$ is sufficient and $t(x) = t(y)$,

$$\frac{f(x|\theta)}{f(y|\theta)} = \frac{h(x)g(t(x)|\theta)}{h(y)g(t(y)|\theta)} = \frac{h(x)}{h(y)},$$

which is independent of θ, hence proving the lemma.   ■

Example 8.1.19.   Suppose we have $n = 2$ independent observations from the Cauchy distribution (see Theorem 5.6.4) with $a = \theta$ and $b = 1$, that is, from density

$$f_X(x) = \frac{1}{\pi} \frac{1}{1 + (x - \theta)^2}, \qquad -\infty < x < +\infty. \qquad (8.1.20)$$

Show that no nontrivial sufficient statistic exists. (Note that the Cauchy distribution is essentially the Student's t-distribution of Definition 4.2.26 with 1 degree of freedom.)

Suppose there were a nontrivial sufficient statistic $t(\ )$. Then for some two points $x = (x_1, x_2)$ and $y = (y_1, y_2)$ [which are not permutations of each other] we would have $t(x) = t(y)$. From Lemma 8.1.18 it would then follow that $f(x|\theta)/f(y|\theta)$ is independent of θ, that is,

$$\frac{f(x|\theta)}{f(y|\theta)} = \frac{\dfrac{1}{\pi} \dfrac{1}{1 + (x_1 - \theta)^2} \cdot \dfrac{1}{\pi} \dfrac{1}{1 + (x_2 - \theta)^2}}{\dfrac{1}{\pi} \dfrac{1}{1 + (y_1 - \theta)^2} \cdot \dfrac{1}{\pi} \dfrac{1}{1 + (y_2 - \theta)^2}} = Q(x_1, x_2, y_1, y_2)$$

or

$$\left(1 + (x_1 - \theta)^2\right)\left(1 + (x_2 - \theta)^2\right)Q(x_1, x_2, y_1, y_2)$$
$$= \left(1 + (y_1 - \theta)^2\right)\left(1 + (y_2 - \theta)^2\right). \tag{8.1.21}$$

must hold for all θ; but by multiplying out the terms in equation (8.1.21) and collecting them all on one side equation (8.1.21) becomes

$$P_4(\theta) \overset{\theta}{\equiv} 0, \tag{8.1.22}$$

where $P_4(\theta)$ is a polynomial of degree 4 (i.e., $a + b\theta + c\theta^2 + d\theta^3 + e\theta^4$) in θ. Since such a polynomial can have only (at most) 4 real roots, equation (8.1.22) cannot be true for all θ; hence, there cannot be a nontrivial sufficient statistic $t(\ )$ in this case. (Also see Problem 8.5.)

We now wish to consider **how to find a minimal sufficient statistic.**

Theorem 8.1.23. (We use Notation 8.1.5.) Define a statistic $t(\ )$ as follows: Only **put x and y on the same contour iff $f(x|\theta)/f(y|\theta)$ is independent of θ. Then $t(\ )$ is a minimal sufficient statistic.**

Proof: [We will give the proof for the case of a r.v. $X = (X_1, \ldots, X_n)$ that assumes values $x = (x_1, \ldots, x_n)$ in a set containing at most denumerably many points;[2] this is to be the same set for every $\theta \in \Theta$. This is the same case for which we proved the Neyman Factorization Theorem.] Note that (Lemma 8.1.18) we previously showed the ratio $f(x|\theta)/f(y|\theta)$ to be independent of θ if $t(x) = t(y)$ for some sufficient statistic $t(\ )$.

First suppose that the statistic $t(\ )$ defined in the statement of the theorem is sufficient. Then it is minimal sufficient. For, if $s(\ )$ is another sufficient statistic and $s(w) = s(z)$, then (by Lemma 8.1.18) $f(w|\theta)/f(z|\theta)$ is independent of θ, and [by the definition of $t(\ )$] $t(w) = t(z)$. Hence, $t(\ )$ is a function of $s(\ )$ and (by Definition 8.1.15) is minimal sufficient.

Next, we wish to show $t(\ )$ is sufficient. Now for an arbitrary x_0 [denoting $t(x_0)$ by c_0],

$$P_\theta\left[X = x_0 | t(X) = c_0\right]$$

$$= \frac{P_\theta\left[X = x_0, t(X) = c_0\right]}{P\left[t(X) = c_0\right]} = \frac{P_\theta\left[X = x_0\right]}{\sum_{d \ni t(d) = c_0} P_\theta\left[X = d\right]} \tag{8.1.24}$$

$$= 1 \bigg/ \left\{ \sum_{d \ni t(d) = c_0} \left(f(d|\theta)/f(x_0|\theta)\right) \right\}.$$

---

[2] For the general case see pp. 327–337 of Lehmann and Scheffé (1950). The basic ideas (but not the mathematical details) are the same as for the discrete case covered by our proof.

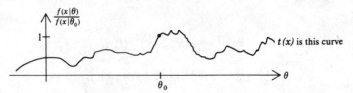

Figure 8.1-4. A typical $t(x)$ if $\Theta = \mathscr{R}$.

But since $t(d) = c_0$ and $t(x_0) = c_0$, d and x_0 have been put on the same contour; hence, it must have been the case that $f(d|\theta)/f(x_0|\theta)$ was independent of θ. Hence, equation (8.1.24) is independent of θ. As following equation (8.1.11), this proves $P_\theta[X \in \mathscr{U}|t(X) = c]$ is independent of θ; hence, $t(\ )$ is a sufficient statistic. ∎

In the following theorem we give **a statistic that is minimal sufficient in general.****

Theorem 8.1.25. Dynkin's Theorem. (Use Notation 8.1.5.) Let θ_0 be any fixed possible value of θ. Then

$$\left\{ \left(\theta, \frac{f(X|\theta)}{f(X|\theta_0)} \right) : \theta \in \Theta \right\} = t(X) \text{ (say)} \qquad (8.1.26)$$

is a minimal sufficient statistic for θ.

Proof: First, if we define

$$\begin{cases} h(x_1, \ldots, x_n) = f(x_1, \ldots, x_n|\theta_0), \\ g(t(x_1, \ldots, x_n)|\theta) = \dfrac{f(x_1, \ldots, x_n|\theta)}{f(x_1, \ldots, x_n|\theta_0)} \end{cases} \qquad (8.1.27)$$

then sufficiency follows by the Neyman Factorization Theorem.

Next we will show that $t(X)$ is a minimal sufficient statistic, by showing that if $s(X)$ is any other sufficient statistic, then $t(X)$ is a function of $s(X)$. To show this, it suffices to show that, whenever $s(x) = s(y)$, also $t(x) = t(y)$. Note that $t(x)$ is a function; for example, if $\Theta = \mathscr{R}$, a typical value of $t(x)$ is an entire function (see Figure 8.1-4). Now, since the other statistic $s(X)$ is sufficient, by the Neyman Factorization Theorem,

$$f(x|\theta) = h^*(x)g^*(s(x)|\theta) \qquad (8.1.28)$$

for some functions $h^*(\ )$ and $g^*(\ )$. Now suppose $s(x) = s(y)$; then (by Lemma 8.1.18) $f(x|\theta)/f(y|\theta)$ is independent of θ. We wish to show $t(x) = t(y)$; by

---

*Theorem 8.1.25 and Example 8.1.29 are our most advanced considerations of sufficiency and may (without loss of continuity) be skipped over.

equation (8.1.26), this will follow iff we can show (for all θ)

$$\frac{f(x|\theta)}{f(x|\theta_0)} = \frac{f(y|\theta)}{f(y|\theta_0)},$$

that is, (using (8.1.28)) iff for all θ

$$\frac{h^*(x)g^*(s(x)|\theta)}{h^*(x)g^*(s(x)|\theta_0)} = \frac{h^*(y)g^*(s(y)|\theta)}{h^*(y)g^*(s(y)|\theta_0)},$$

that is, iff for all θ

$$g^*(s(x)|\theta)g^*(s(y)|\theta_0) = g^*(s(x)|\theta_0)g^*(s(y)|\theta).$$

This is true since $s(x) = s(y)$. ∎

Example 8.1.29. Suppose that $\Theta = \{\theta_0, \theta_1\}$ where $\theta_0 \neq \theta_1$. What then is the sufficient statistic provided by Dynkin's Theorem (Theorem 8.1.25)?

Here we need to evaluate and specify

$$t(X) = \left\{ \left(\theta, \frac{f(X|\theta)}{f(X|\theta_0)} \right) : \theta \in \Theta \right\}$$

$$= \left\{ \left(\theta_0, \frac{f(X|\theta_0)}{f(X|\theta_0)} \right), \left(\theta_1, \frac{f(X|\theta_1)}{f(X|\theta_0)} \right) \right\};$$

but this is equivalent to specifying the quantity $f(X|\theta_1)/f(X|\theta_0)$, called the **likelihood-ratio statistic**.

In Chapter 7, considerable attention has been paid to maximum-likelihood estimators, and to the method of maximum likelihood as a way of generating possibly good estimators. Since we have seen in this section that a good estimator need only be based on any sufficient statistic, the question arises: **How are MLE's related to sufficient statistics?**

Theorem 8.1.30. (Use Notation 8.1.5.) If $t(X_1, \ldots, X_n)$ is a sufficient statistic for θ and a unique MLE $\hat{\theta}$ of θ exists, then $\hat{\theta}$ is a function of $t(X_1, \ldots, X_n)$. If any MLE exists, an MLE $\hat{\theta}$ can be found that is a function of $t(X_1, \ldots, X_n)$.

Proof: Since $t(X_1, \ldots, X_n)$ is a sufficient statistic for θ, by the Neyman Factorization Theorem (Theorem 8.1.6) it follows that for all $x_1, \ldots, x_n$, θ and for some functions $h(\ )$ and $g(\ )$ we have

$$f(x_1, \ldots, x_n|\theta) = h(x_1, \ldots, x_n)g(t(x_1, \ldots, x_n)|\theta). \qquad (8.1.31)$$

In seeking an MLE we hold $x_1, \ldots, x_n$ fixed and seek to find a $\hat{\theta}(x_1, \ldots, x_n)$ that maximizes quantity (8.1.31). Thus, if there is a unique MLE, it will maximize

$g(t(x_1,\ldots,x_n)|\theta)$ and hence be a function of $t(x_1,\ldots,x_n)$. In any case, if any MLE exists, an MLE can be found that is a function only of $t(x_1,\ldots,x_n)$. ∎

Note that Theorem 8.1.31 does *not* say that "any MLE must be a function of any sufficient statistic"; that remark need not be true if the MLE is not unique (for then the class of MLE's includes some that depend on other information about $X_1,\ldots,X_n$ than the information provided by $t(X_1,\ldots,X_n)$). This was first noted by Moore (1971), and a simple example is given in Problem 8.1.18. The erroneous statement occurs in many books.

We now conclude this section with **several examples involving minimal sufficient statistics.**

Example 8.1.32. Suppose $X_1,\ldots,X_n$ are independent r.v.'s each $N(\theta,\sigma^2)$ where θ is unknown $(-\infty < \theta < +\infty)$ and $\sigma^2 > 0$ is known. Find a minimal sufficient statistic for θ.

Here, we have

$$
\begin{aligned}
f(x_1,\ldots,x_n|\theta) &= \prod_{i=1}^{n} f(x_i|\theta) = \prod_{i=1}^{n}\left\{\frac{1}{\sqrt{2\pi}\,\sigma}e^{-\frac{1}{2\sigma^2}(x_i-\theta)^2}\right\} \\
&= \left(\frac{1}{\sqrt{2\pi}\,\sigma}\right)^n e^{-\frac{1}{2\sigma^2}\sum_{i=1}^{n}(x_i-\theta)^2} \qquad (8.1.33) \\
&= \left(\frac{1}{\sqrt{2\pi}\,\sigma}\right)^n e^{-\frac{1}{2\sigma^2}\sum_{i=1}^{n}x_i^2} e^{-\frac{1}{2\sigma^2}\left\{-2\theta\sum_{i=1}^{n}x_i + n\theta^2\right\}},
\end{aligned}
$$

from which it follows via the Neyman Factorization Theorem (Theorem 8.1.6) taking

$$
\begin{cases}
h(x_1,\ldots,x_n) = \left(\dfrac{1}{\sqrt{2\pi}\,\sigma}\right)^n e^{-\frac{1}{2\sigma^2}\sum_{i=1}^{n}x_i^2}, \\[2mm]
g(x_1 + \cdots + x_n|\theta) = e^{-\frac{1}{2\sigma^2}\left\{2\theta(x_1+\cdots+x_n)+n\theta^2\right\}},
\end{cases}
$$

that $t(X_1,\ldots,X_n) = X_1 + \cdots + X_n$ is a sufficient statistic for θ. Hence (see the discussion following the proof of the Neyman Factorization Theorem), so is any one-to-one function of $X_1 + \cdots + X_n$; for example, $\overline{X} = (X_1 + \cdots + X_n)/n$. Recall (see Example 7.2.12) that $\overline{X}$ was found to be the unique MLE of θ in this case.

We now turn our attention to finding a *minimal* sufficient statistic. By Theorem 8.1.23, if we set $t(x) = t(y)$ iff $f(x|\theta)/f(y|\theta)$ is independent of θ, then $t(\ )$ will be a minimal sufficient statistic. But using (8.1.33) we find

$$
\frac{f(x|\theta)}{f(y|\theta)} = e^{-\frac{1}{2\sigma^2}\left\{\sum_{i=1}^{n}x_i^2 - \sum_{i=1}^{n}y_i^2\right\}} e^{-2\theta\left\{\sum_{i=1}^{n}x_i - \sum_{i=1}^{n}y_i\right\}}, \qquad (8.1.34)
$$

which is independent of θ iff $\sum_{i=1}^{n}x_i = \sum_{i=1}^{n}y_i$. Hence $t(X_1, X_2,\ldots,X_n) = \sum_{i=1}^{n}X_i$ is a minimal sufficient statistic for θ.

We next seek a minimal sufficient statistic for (θ, σ^2) when θ and σ^2 are both unknown. From (8.1.34) we see that $f(x)/f(y)$ is independent of (θ, σ^2) iff

$$\left\{ \sum_{i=1}^{n} x_i = \sum_{i=1}^{n} y_i \quad \text{and} \quad \sum_{i=1}^{n} x_i^2 = \sum_{i=1}^{n} y_i^2 \right\}.$$

Hence, $t(X_1, \ldots, X_n) = \left(\sum_{i=1}^{n} X_i, \sum_{i=1}^{n} X_i^2 \right)$ is a minimal sufficient statistic for (θ, σ^2). [Note that this $t(\ )$ puts x and y on the same contour iff $\left\{ \sum_{i=1}^{n} x_i = \sum_{i=1}^{n} y_i \text{ and } \sum_{i=1}^{n} x_i^2 = \sum_{i=1}^{n} y_i^2 \right\}.$] [One could verify from the Neyman Factorization Theorem that $(\Sigma X_i, \Sigma X_i^2)$ is a sufficient statistic for (θ, σ^2), but not the fact that it is minimal, that is, cannot be further reduced without losing information about (θ, σ^2).]

Note that in Example 7.2.17 we saw that $(\overline{X}, \hat{\sigma}^2 = \Sigma(X_i - \overline{X})^2/n)$ is the unique MLE of (θ, σ^2). This is a function of the minimal sufficient statistic $(\Sigma X_i, \Sigma X_i^2)$: $\overline{X} = \Sigma X_i/n$, and $\hat{\sigma}^2 = (\Sigma X_i^2 - (\Sigma X_i)^2/n)/n$.

Example 8.1.35. Let X be a single observation from the point probability function

$$f(x|\theta) = \begin{cases} \dfrac{\theta}{2} & \text{if } x = -3 \\[2mm] \dfrac{\theta}{3} & \text{if } x = 0 \\[2mm] \dfrac{1 - 2\theta}{3} & \text{if } x = 6, 13, 52 \\[2mm] \theta^2 + \dfrac{\theta}{6} & \text{if } x = 60 \\[2mm] \theta - \theta^2 & \text{if } x = 68, \end{cases}$$

where $0 < \theta < 1/2$. Find a minimal sufficient statistic for θ.

Of course, X itself is a sufficient statistic for θ (the identity statistic; see the discussion before Definition 8.1.15). To find a minimal sufficient statistic, by Theorem 8.1.23 we put on the same contour a set of points such that, for every pair of points (y, z) in the set, $f(y|\theta)/f(z|\theta)$ does not depend on θ. Thus, we partition the sample space into the sets $\{-3, 0\}$, $\{6, 13, 52\}$, $\{60\}$, $\{68\}$, and a minimal sufficient statistic is

$$t(X) = \begin{cases} c_1 & \text{if } X = -3 \text{ or } 0 \\ c_2 & \text{if } X = 6 \text{ or } 13 \text{ or } 52 \\ c_3 & \text{if } X = 60 \\ c_4 & \text{if } X = 68 \end{cases}$$

where c_1, c_2, c_3, c_4 are distinct constants (*any* distinct constants). The probability distribution of $t(X)$ (to be used in Section 8.2) is

$$
p_{t(X)}(w) = P[t(X) = w] = \begin{cases} \dfrac{5\theta}{6} & \text{if } w = c_1 \\[2mm] 1 - 2\theta & \text{if } w = c_2 \\[2mm] \theta^2 + \dfrac{\theta}{6} & \text{if } w = c_3 \\[2mm] \theta - \theta^2 & \text{if } w = c_4. \end{cases}
$$

The following example is similar to the preceding, but **deals with a bivariate random variable.**

Example 8.1.36. Let (X_1, X_2) be a bivariate r.v. obtained as follows. We find X_1 with $P[X_1 = 1] = p$, $P[X_1 = 0] = q = 1 - p$. If $X_1 = 1$, we find X_2 with $P[X_2 = 1] = p$, $P[X_2 = 0] = q$; while if $X_1 = 0$, we find X_2 with $P[X_2 = 1] = P[X_2 = 0] = 1/2$. Here $p \in [0, 1]$ is unknown. Find a minimal sufficient statistic for p.

Clearly, (X_1, X_2) is a sufficient statistic for p. To find a minimal sufficient statistic, note that

$$
p_{X_1, X_2}(x_1, x_2) = \begin{cases} \dfrac{q}{2} & \text{if } (x_1, x_2) = (0,0) \text{ or } (0,1) \\[2mm] pq & \text{if } (x_1, x_2) = (1,0) \\[2mm] p^2 & \text{if } (x_1, x_2) = (1,1). \end{cases}
$$

Now, as in Example 8.1.35, the minimal sufficient statistic is

$$
t(X_1, X_2) = \begin{cases} c_1 & \text{if } (X_1, X_2) = (0,0) \text{ or } (0,1) \\ c_2 & \text{if } (X_1, X_2) = (1,0) \\ c_3 & \text{if } (X_1, X_2) = (1,1), \end{cases}
$$

where c_1, c_2, c_3 are any three different constants. The probability distribution of $t = t(X_1, X_2)$ is

$$
p_{t(X_1, X_2)}(w) = \begin{cases} q & \text{if } w = c_1 \\ pq & \text{if } w = c_2 \\ p^2 & \text{if } w = c_3. \end{cases}
$$

In the final example of this section, **we investigate the minimal sufficient statistic in a case where the range of the r.v. depends on the parameters.**

Example 8.1.37. Let $X_1, X_2, \ldots, X_n$ be independent r.v.'s, each with the truncated and displaced exponential p.d.f.

$$f(x|L, \beta, U) = \frac{1}{\beta(1 - e^{-(U-L)/\beta})} e^{-(x-L)/\beta} I_{[L,U]}(x)$$

where $L < U$.

Then the joint p.d.f. of $X_1, X_2, \ldots, X_n$ is

$$f(x_1, x_2, \ldots, x_n | L, \beta, U)$$

$$= \left(\frac{1}{\beta(1 - e^{-(U-L)/\beta})} \right)^n e^{-\sum_{i=1}^n (x_i - L)/\beta} \prod_{i=1}^n I_{[L,U]}(x_i)$$

$$= \left(\frac{1}{\beta(1 - e^{-(U-L)/\beta})} \right)^n e^{-\sum_{i=1}^n x_i/\beta} e^{nL/\beta} \prod_{i=1}^n I_{(-\infty, U]}(x_i) \cdot \prod_{i=1}^n I_{[L,\infty)}(x_i)$$

$$= \left(\frac{e^{L/\beta}}{\beta(1 - e^{-(U-L)/\beta})} \right)^n e^{-\sum x_i/\beta} I_{(-\infty, U]}(x_{(n)}) I_{[L,\infty)}(x_{(1)})$$

where $x_{(1)} = \min(x_1, x_2, \ldots, x_n)$ and $x_{(n)} = \max(x_1, x_2, \ldots, x_n)$. Using Theorem 8.1.23 to seek a minimal sufficient statistic, we put vectors $x = (x_1, \ldots, x_n)$ and $y = (y_1, \ldots, y_n)$ in the sample space on the same contour of $t(\ )$ iff $f(x|L, \beta, U)/f(y|L, \beta, U)$ is independent of (L, β, U). Here

$$\frac{f(x|L, \beta, U)}{f(y|L, \beta, U)} = e^{-\left(\sum x_i - \sum y_i \right)/\beta} \frac{I_{(-\infty, U]}(x_{(n)})}{I_{(-\infty, U]}(y_{(n)})} \frac{I_{[L,\infty)}(x_{(1)})}{I_{[L,\infty)}(y_{(1)})},$$

which is independent of (L, β, U) iff $\sum x_i = \sum y_i$, and $x_{(n)} = y_{(n)}$, and $x_{(1)} = y_{(1)}$. Hence $t(X_1, X_2, \ldots, X_n) = (\sum X_i, X_{(1)}, X_{(n)})$ is a minimal sufficient statistic for (L, β, U).

As a final result on sufficiency, we note the following, which is useful in showing various statistics are not sufficient: **A statistic T is not sufficient if any conditional distribution given t depends on θ.**

Theorem 8.1.38. A statistic $T(X_1, \ldots, X_n)$ is sufficient iff the conditional distribution of every statistic $S(X_1, \ldots, X_n)$ given T is independent of θ.

Although we do not give the details of the proof of Theorem 8.1.38, it follows easily from results already shown. First, if T is sufficient, then by Definition 8.1.1 we can show that the d.f. of S given T does not depend on θ. Conversely, if the d.f. of S given T is independent of θ for all S, then by choosing S to be the indicator function of the set $\mathscr{U}$ in Definition 8.1.1 we easily find that (8.1.2) holds for all $\mathscr{U}$, hence T is sufficient.

PROBLEMS FOR SECTION 8.1

8.1.1   Let $X_1, X_2, \ldots, X_n$ be a random sample of size n from a $N(\theta, \theta)$ distribution for some $\theta > 0$. Find **(a)** A sufficient statistic for θ; **(b)** A minimal sufficient statistic for θ.

8.1.2   Let $X_1, X_2, \ldots, X_n$ be a random sample of size n from a $N(\theta, \theta^2)$ distribution. Find **(a)** A sufficient statistic for θ; **(b)** A minimal sufficient statistic for θ.

8.1.3   Let X be a single observation from the probability function

$$p(x|\theta) = \begin{cases} \theta^2 & \text{if } x = -1, 3 \\[2mm] \dfrac{1}{2} - \dfrac{\theta^2}{2} & \text{if } x = 0 \\[2mm] -\dfrac{\theta^2}{2} + \dfrac{\theta}{2} & \text{if } x = 2, 4 \\[2mm] \dfrac{1}{2} - \dfrac{\theta^2}{2} - \theta & \text{if } x = 1, \end{cases}$$

where θ is an unknown number between zero and $\sqrt{2} - 1$. Find a minimal sufficient statistic for θ.

8.1.4   Let $X_1, X_2, \ldots, X_n$ be a random sample of size n from a $G(x|\alpha, \beta)$ distribution. Find sufficient and minimal sufficient statistics for
(a) α if β is known;
(b) β if α is known;
(c) Show that MLE's in parts **(a)** and **(b)** are functions of the statistics stated in your answers.

8.1.5   Let $X_1, X_2, \ldots, X_n$ be a random sample of size n from a Poisson distribution with mean λ. Use the basic definition (via conditioning) of a sufficient statistic to show that $X_1 + X_2 + \cdots + X_n$ is a sufficient statistic for λ. Also show that $\sum_{i=1}^{n} X_i$ is minimal sufficient, and that the MLE of λ is a function of this statistic.

8.1.6   Let $X_1, X_2, \ldots, X_n$ be a random sample of size n from a $B(x|\alpha, \lambda)$ distribution. Find a minimal sufficient statistic (possibly a vector) for:
(a) α if λ is known;
(b) λ if α is known;
(c) α and λ (when both are unknown).
(d) Are the MLE's of α and λ functions of the sufficient statistics in parts **(a)** and **(b)**?

8.1.7   Let $X_1, X_2, \ldots, X_n$ be a random sample of size n from a geometric point probability function $p(x|p) = q^{x-1}p$ if $x = 1, 2, \ldots$ (and $= 0$ otherwise). Show that $\sum_{i=1}^{n} X_i$ is a minimal sufficient statistic for p. Show that the MLE of p is a function of this sufficient statistic.

8.1.8   Let $X_1, X_2, \ldots, X_n$ be a random sample of size n from the discrete uniform distribution $p(x|\theta) = (1/\theta) I_{\{1,2,\ldots,\theta\}}(x)$. Show that Y_n, the largest order statistic, is minimal sufficient, and find its point probability function. (Recall that Y_n is also the MLE of θ.)

8.1.9 Let $X_1, X_2, \ldots, X_n$ be a random sample of size n from a $N(0, \sigma^2)$ distribution.
(a) If $n = 1$ (i.e., we have a sample of size $n = 1$), show that X_1^2 is a minimal sufficient statistic (and hence a sufficient statistic) for σ^2.
(b) If $n > 1$, find a sufficient statistic for σ^2.

8.1.10 Let $X_1, X_2, \ldots, X_n$ be a random sample of size n from the "displaced Laplace" distribution $f(x|\theta) = e^{-|x-\theta|}/2$, $-\infty < x < \infty$ for some unknown θ ($-\infty < \theta < \infty$). Show that the order statistic vector $(Y_1, Y_2, \ldots, Y_n)$ is minimal sufficient for θ. Is the MLE of θ, $\hat{\theta} = \text{median}(X_1, \ldots, X_n)$, a function of this sufficient statistic?

8.1.11 Let $X_1, X_2, \ldots, X_n$ be a random sample of size n from a lognormal distribution with p.d.f. $f(x|\mu, \sigma^2) = e^{-(\ln(x)-\mu)^2/(2\sigma^2)}/(x\sigma\sqrt{2\pi}) \cdot I_{(0,\infty)}(x)$. Find the joint sufficient statistics for (μ, σ^2), and show that MLE's of μ and σ^2 are respectively functions of this joint sufficient statistic.

8.1.12 Let $X_1, X_2, \ldots, X_n$ be a random sample of size n from the p.d.f. $f(x|\theta) = \theta(1 + x)^{-1-\theta}I_{(0,\infty)}(x)$ for some unknown $\theta > 0$. Show that $\prod_{i=1}^{n}(1 + X_i)$ is a minimal sufficient statistic for θ, and that the MLE of θ is a function of this sufficient statistic.

8.1.13 Let X be a single observation from a beta distribution $B(x|\theta, \theta)$. Show that the only minimal sufficient statistic for θ is the trivial sufficient statistic.

8.1.14 Let $X_1, X_2, \ldots, X_n$ be a random sample from the Laplace p.d.f. $f(x|\theta) = e^{-|x|/\theta}/(2\theta) \cdot I_{(-\infty,\infty)}(x)$ for some unknown $\theta > 0$. Find a sufficient statistic for θ.

8.1.15 Let $X_1, X_2, \ldots, X_k$ be a random sample of size k from a $B(n, p)$ distribution. Show that $\sum_{i=1}^{k} X_i$ is a minimal sufficient statistic, and that the MLE of p is a function of this minimal sufficient statistic.

8.1.16 Let $X_1, X_2, \ldots, X_n$ be a random sample of size n from the "displaced exponential" p.d.f. $f(x|\alpha, \beta) = e^{-(x-\alpha)/\beta}/\beta \cdot I_{(\alpha,\infty)}(x)$. Let $Y_1 \leq Y_2 \leq \cdots \leq Y_n$ be the order statistics, and $S = \sum_{i=1}^{n} (X_i - Y_1)$. Show that (Y_1, S) is jointly minimal sufficient for (α, β).

8.1.17 Prove Theorem 8.1.38.

8.1.18 Let X be a random variable with

$$p_X(x) = \begin{cases} 1/4, & \text{if } x = 1, 2 \\ 1/4 + \theta/4, & \text{if } x = 3 \\ 1/4 - \theta/4, & \text{if } x = 4 \\ 0, & \text{otherwise,} \end{cases}$$

for some θ with $0 \leq \theta \leq 1$.
(a) Show that $t(X)$ is a minimal sufficient statistic if and only if $t(1) = t(2) = a$, $t(3) = b$, $t(4) = c$ where a, b, c are any three different real numbers.
(b) Show that $\hat{\theta}$ is an MLE of θ if and only if $\hat{\theta}(3) = 1$ and $\hat{\theta}(4) = 0$.
(c) Find an MLE of θ that is not a function of the sufficient statistic $t(X)$. Why doesn't this contradict Theorem 8.1.30?
[This example is due to Levy (1985).]

8.2. COMPLETENESS

In Section 8.1 we discussed reduction of the data to a smaller set of numbers without losing information about the parameters. In this section we discuss the concept of **completeness**. As we will see in Section 8.3, this property (when it holds for a sufficient statistic) allows us to obtain "best" estimators.

For what is called the **exponential class** or **Koopman-Darmois family** of probability distributions, a minimal sufficient statistic is easy to find and (under certain "regularity" conditions) is complete. We conclude the section with the concept of **ancillary** statistics and their relation to (i.e., independence of) sufficient statistics.

Definition 8.2.1. (We use Notation 8.1.5.) The family of density or probability functions $f(x|\theta)$, $\theta \in \Theta$, is called **complete** if, for every function $u(x)$, the identity

$$E_\theta u(X) \overset{\theta}{\equiv} 0 \qquad (8.2.2)$$

implies $u(x) = 0$ at all x (more precisely, at all x for which $f(x|\theta) > 0$ for some θ).

Note that (see Definition 7.1.2) completeness can be rephrased as meaning that **"the only unbiased estimator of zero is zero itself."**

Definition 8.2.3. If a sufficient statistic T in some problem has a family of density or probability functions $g(x|\theta)$ that is complete, then T is called a **complete sufficient statistic**.

The following examples illustrate these concepts.

Example 8.2.4. Suppose that $X_1, X_2, \ldots, X_n$ are independent r.v.'s, each with the Poisson distribution with unknown parameter $\mu > 0$. Find a minimum sufficient statistic for μ, and check if it is complete.

The joint point probability function of $X_1, X_2, \ldots, X_n$ is

$$f(x_1, x_2, \ldots, x_n|\mu) = \prod_{i=1}^{n} \left(\frac{e^{-\mu}\mu^{x_i}}{x_i!} I_{\{0,1,2,\ldots\}}(x_i) \right)$$

$$= \left(\prod_{i=1}^{n} \left(\frac{1}{x_i!} I_{\{0,1,2,\ldots\}}(x_i) \right) \right) \left(e^{-n\mu}\mu^{x_1 + x_2 + \cdots + x_n} \right),$$

hence by the Neyman Factorization Theorem (Theorem 8.1.6) $\sum_{i=1}^{n} X_i$ is a sufficient statistic. Further, it can be shown easily (using Theorem 8.1.23) that ΣX_i is minimal sufficient.

Since the probability function of ΣX_i is

$$f_{\Sigma X_i}(x|\mu) = e^{-n\mu}(n\mu)^x/x! \cdot I_{\{0,1,2,\ldots\}}(x),$$

ΣX_i is Poisson with mean $n\mu$. Hence, showing that the family of probability functions of the minimal sufficient statistic ΣX_i is complete is equivalent to showing that the Poisson family is complete. Let $u(\cdot)$ be any function. Then

$$E_\mu u(X) \equiv 0 \qquad (8.2.5)$$

means

$$\sum_{k=0}^{\infty} u(k)\frac{e^{-\mu}\mu^k}{k!} \equiv 0. \qquad (8.2.6)$$

Since $e^{-\mu} > 0$, this holds iff

$$\sum_{k=0}^{\infty} \frac{u(k)}{k!}\mu^k \equiv 0. \qquad (8.2.7)$$

Since two power series are equal iff their coefficients are equal (see the discussion following equation (7.1.21)), it follows that $u(k) = 0$ for $k = 0, 1, 2, \ldots$. Hence the Poisson family of distributions is complete, and therefore ΣX_i is a complete minimal sufficient statistic for μ.

Example 8.2.8. Let $X_1, X_2, \ldots, X_n$ be independent r.v.'s, each uniform on $[0, \theta]$ where $\theta > 0$. We know (see Example 8.1.4) that $Y_n = \max(X_1, X_2, \ldots, X_n)$ is a sufficient statistic for θ and has p.d.f.

$$f_{Y_n}(x) = \frac{nx^{n-1}}{\theta^n}I_{[0,\theta]}(x).$$

To investigate completeness of this family, let $u(\cdot)$ be any arbitrary function. Then

$$E_\theta u(Y_n) \equiv 0 \qquad (8.2.9)$$

means

$$\int_0^\theta \frac{u(x)nx^{n-1}}{\theta^n}\, dx \equiv 0,$$

which (multiplying both sides by θ^n/n which is > 0) holds iff

$$\int_0^\theta u(x)x^{n-1}\, dx \equiv 0. \qquad (8.2.10)$$

Differentiating both sides of (8.2.10) with respect to θ, we obtain

$$u(\theta)\theta^{n-1} \equiv 0,$$

hence $u(\theta) \equiv 0$ for all θ, or in other words $u(x) \equiv 0$ for all $x > 0$ as was to be shown. Therefore, Y_n is a complete sufficient statistic for θ. (In fact, it is also minimal sufficient.)

In Example 8.2.8, we needed to differentiate an integral and used the Fundamental Theorem of Integral Calculus, part of which states that

$$\frac{d}{dx} \int_0^x f(y)\, dy = f(x).$$

Sometimes the limits and the integrand all depend on θ, and then Leibniz' theorem (see Whittaker and Watson (1965), p. 67) may be used:

Theorem 8.2.11. Leibniz' Theorem. If $f(x, \theta)$ is integrable with respect to x, and $\dfrac{\partial f(x, \theta)}{\partial \theta}$ is a continuous function of both variables x and θ, then

$$\frac{d}{d\theta} \int_{a(\theta)}^{b(\theta)} f(x, \theta)\, dx = f(b(\theta), \theta) \frac{db(\theta)}{d\theta} - f(a(\theta), \theta) \frac{da(\theta)}{d\theta}$$

$$+ \int_{a(\theta)}^{b(\theta)} \frac{\partial f(x, \theta)}{\partial \theta}\, dx.$$

Note that if $b(\theta)$ is $+\infty$ (or $a(\theta)$ is $-\infty$), the result continues to hold if we interpret $db(\theta)/d\theta$ as zero $(da(\theta)/d\theta$ as zero), dropping the first (second) term, as long as $\displaystyle\int_{a(\theta)}^{\infty} f(x, \theta)\, dx \left(\int_{-\infty}^{b(\theta)} f(x, \theta)\, dx \right)$ converges uniformly (see p. 74 of Whittaker and Watson (1965)).

We now introduce the **exponential class** (or **Koopman-Darmois family**) of distributions, for which minimal sufficiency and completeness are fairly easy to show; many of the most useful statistical distributions belong to this class.

Definition 8.2.12. (We use Notation 8.1.5.) The density of $(X_1, \ldots, X_n)$ is said to be a member of the **exponential class** [or a member of the **Koopman-Darmois class**; or is said to have **Koopman-Darmois form**] if

$$f(x_1, \ldots, x_n | \theta) = e^{\sum_{i=1}^{r} \varphi_i(x_1, \ldots, x_n) c_i(\theta) + c_0(\theta) + \varphi_0(x_1, \ldots, x_n)} \tag{8.2.13}$$

for all $\theta = (\theta_1, \ldots, \theta_r) \in \Theta \subseteq \mathscr{R}^r$. [Here $\varphi_0(x_1, \ldots, x_n), \ldots, \varphi_r(x_1, \ldots, x_n)$ are some functions of $x_1, \ldots, x_n$; and $c_0(\theta), \ldots, c_r(\theta)$ are some functions of $\theta = (\theta_1, \ldots, \theta_r)$. If $n = 1$ we talk of a **univariate exponential family**, while if $r = 1$ we talk of a **one-parameter exponential family**.]

Example 8.2.14. Show that if $X_1, \ldots, X_n$ are independent r.v.'s, each $N(\mu, \sigma^2)$ where $\mu(-\infty < \mu < +\infty)$ and $\sigma^2(\sigma^2 > 0)$ are both unknown, then $(X_1, \ldots, X_n)$ is a member of the two-parameter exponential family.

Starting from equation (8.1.33) (a result in Example 8.1.32, in which we also studied this $(X_1, \ldots, X_n)$ and found a minimal sufficient statistic for (μ, σ^2)) we have

$$f(x_1, \ldots, x_n | \mu, \sigma^2) = \left(\frac{1}{\sqrt{2\pi}\,\sigma} \right)^n e^{-\frac{1}{2\sigma^2} \left\{ \sum_{i=1}^{n} x_i^2 - 2\mu \sum_{i=1}^{n} x_i + n\mu^2 \right\}}$$

$$= e^{\left(\sum_{i=1}^{n} x_i \right) \frac{\mu}{\sigma^2} + \left(\sum_{i=1}^{n} x_i^2 \right) \left(\frac{-1}{2\sigma^2} \right) + \left\{ -\frac{n\mu^2}{2\sigma^2} - n \ln (\sqrt{2\pi}\,\sigma) \right\}},$$

(8.2.15)

which is clearly of form (8.2.13) for all $(\mu, \sigma^2) \in \Theta = \{(x, y): -\infty < x < +\infty, y > 0\}$ if we take

$$\begin{cases} \varphi_1(x_1, \ldots, x_n) = \sum_{i=1}^{n} x_i, \quad c_1(\mu, \sigma^2) = \frac{\mu}{\sigma^2}, \\[2mm] \varphi_2(x_1, \ldots, x_n) = \sum_{i=1}^{n} x_i^2, \quad c_2(\mu, \sigma^2) = \frac{-1}{2\sigma^2}, \\[2mm] c_0(\mu, \sigma^2) = \frac{-n\mu^2}{2\sigma^2} - n \ln (\sqrt{2\pi}\,\sigma) \\[2mm] \varphi_0(x_1, \ldots, x_n) = 0. \end{cases}$$

(8.2.16)

From Example 8.2.14 it appears that $(\varphi_1(X_1, \ldots, X_n), \ldots, \varphi_r(X_1, \ldots, X_n))$ will be our minimal sufficient statistic for $\theta = (\theta_1, \ldots, \theta_r)$, and this is the case (Problem 8.12). The question then arises: If we have a nontrivial sufficient statistic, must our $(X_1, \ldots, X_n)$ be a member of the exponential class? As is shown by Example 8.1.4 and Problem 8.5H, the answer is "no." However, under certain conditions of "regularity" the answer is "yes" [for references see Dudewicz (1976), p. 244].

Example 8.2.17. For a random sample of size n, $(X_1, X_2, \ldots, X_n)$, the joint p.d.f. (or point probability function) and its exponential class representation are as follows for some of the commonly encountered distributions:

Bernoulli $\quad f(x_1, x_2, \ldots, x_n | p) = p^{\sum x_i} (1 - p)^{n - \sum x_i}$

$$= e^{\sum x_i (\ln (p) - \ln (1-p)) + n \ln (1-p)}$$

Poisson $\quad f(x_1, x_2, \ldots, x_n | \mu) = \dfrac{e^{-n\mu} \mu^{\sum x_i}}{\prod x_i!}$

$$= e^{\sum x_i \ln (\mu) - n\mu - \sum \ln (x_i!)}$$

Gamma $G(x|\alpha, \beta, 0)$ $f(x_1, x_2, \ldots, x_n|\alpha, \beta)$

$$= \left(\frac{1}{\Gamma(\alpha + 1)\beta^{\alpha+1}} \right)^n \left(\prod x_i^{\alpha} \right) e^{-\sum x_i/\beta}$$

$$= e^{-\sum x_i \frac{1}{\beta} + \alpha \sum \ln(x_i) + \delta},$$

$$\delta = -n \ln \left(\Gamma(\alpha + 1) \right) - n(\alpha + 1) \ln(\beta).$$

The following theorem formalizes the discussion following Example 8.2.14, as to how one can obtain a complete minimal sufficient statistic for the parameter when the joint distribution belongs to the exponential class. (The proof uses uniqueness of the Laplace transform, and is omitted; for details, see Lehmann (1959), pp. 132–133.)

Theorem 8.2.18. Let $(X_1, X_2, \ldots, X_n)$ be a r.v. in the exponential class, that is, with density

$$f(x_1, x_2, \ldots, x_n|\theta) = e^{\sum_{i=1}^{r} T_i(x_1, x_2, \ldots, x_n)c_i(\theta) + c_0(\theta) + \varphi_0(x_1, x_2, \ldots, x_n)}$$

for all $\theta = (\theta_1, \theta_2, \ldots, \theta_r) \in \Theta \subseteq \mathscr{R}^r$. Then $T = (T_1(X_1, \ldots, X_n), \ldots, T_r(X_1, \ldots, X_n))$ is a minimal sufficient statistic for $(\theta_1, \theta_2, \ldots, \theta_r)$. T is also complete as long as Θ contains all θ in *some* r-dimensional rectangle.

In situations where one does not know what family the d.f. belongs to (which are called **"nonparametric"** situations), estimation is still of interest (e.g., estimation of the d.f. as we studied in Example 6.2.12 and Theorem 6.2.13). We already know that **the order statistic vector is sufficient in any such setting** (see Theorem 8.1.17); **we now see that it is also complete when the set of possible d.f.'s is large** (for the proof, which is omitted, see Lehmann (1959), p. 133):

Theorem 8.2.19. Let $X_1, X_2, \ldots, X_n$ be independent r.v.'s, each with d.f. F, where F is unknown and $F \in \Theta \equiv \{$all continuous d.f.'s$\}$. Then the order statistic $(Y_1, Y_2, \ldots, Y_n)$ is a complete sufficient statistic for F.

We now give two examples using **Theorem 8.2.18**. (Theorem 8.2.19 will be used in later chapters.)

Example 8.2.20. Let $X_1, X_2, \ldots, X_n$ be independent r.v.'s, each $N(\mu, \sigma^2)$ with μ and σ^2 unknown. By Example 8.2.14 and Theorem 8.2.18, it follows that $T(X_1, X_2, \ldots, X_n) = (\Sigma X_i, \Sigma X_i^2)$ is a complete minimal sufficient statistic for (μ, σ^2).

Example 8.2.21. Continuing Example 8.2.17, if $X_1, X_2, \ldots, X_n$ are independent r.v.'s each with the same distribution, which is either Bernoulli, Poisson, or gamma with unknown parameters, then the respective complete sufficient statistics are:

$\sum X_i$ for p in the Bernoulli case
$\sum X_i$ for μ in the Poisson case
$(\sum X_i, \sum \ln(X_i))$ for (α, β) in the gamma case.

We conclude this section with introduction and discussion of the concept of an "**ancillary**" **statistic** and its independence of any complete sufficient statistic.

Definition 8.2.22. A statistic $U(X_1, \ldots, X_n)$ is called **first-order ancillary** if $E_\theta U(X_1, \ldots, X_n)$ is a constant independent of θ. $U(X_1, \ldots, X_n)$ is called an **ancillary statistic** for θ if the d.f. of $U(X_1, \ldots, X_n)$ does not depend on θ.

Thus, unlike a sufficient statistic, **an ancillary statistic does not contain any information about the parameter** θ. In such cases, intuition suggests that (since the sufficient statistic $T(X_1, \ldots, X_n)$ contains all the information about θ) the ancillary statistic should be independent of $T(X_1, \ldots, X_n)$. If T is complete this is true, as was first proved by D. Basu in 1955:

Theorem 8.2.23. Basu's Theorem. Let $T(X_1, \ldots, X_n)$ be a complete sufficient statistic and $U(X_1, \ldots, X_n)$ an ancillary statistic. Then T and U are independent r.v.'s.

Proof: Fix u as an arbitrary value of U. Let $g(t) = P[U = u | T = t]$. Then

$$E_\theta g(T) = \sum_t P[U = u | T = t] P[T = t] = \sum_t P[U = u, T = t] = P[U = u],$$

so

$$E_\theta(g(T) - P[U = u]) \equiv 0.$$

By completeness of T, $g(t) - P[U = u] = 0$ for all t, that is,

$$P[U = u | T = t] = P[U = u] \quad \text{for all } t$$

(and for all u since u was arbitrary), hence U and T are independent r.v.'s. (Although we have written summations above, the general case follows similarly, e.g. with integrals in the continuous case.) ∎

Example 8.2.24. Let X_1 and X_2 be independent r.v.'s, each $N(\mu, \sigma^2)$ with σ^2 known and μ unknown. Let

$$T(X_1, X_2) = X_1 + X_2, \qquad U(X_1, X_2) = X_1 - X_2.$$

Then $U(X_1, X_2)$ is $N(0, 2\sigma^2)$ and its distribution does not depend on μ (hence it is an ancillary statistic for μ). Since $T(X_1, X_2)$ is a complete sufficient statistic, it follows from Theorem 8.2.23 that $X_1 - X_2$ and $X_1 + X_2$ are independent r.v.'s.

Example 8.2.25. Let $X_1, X_2, \ldots, X_n$ be a random sample of size n from the uniform distribution on $[0, \theta]$, and let $Y_1 \le Y_2 \le \cdots \le Y_n$ denote the corresponding order statistics. Show that Y_1/Y_n are Y_n are independent r.v.'s.

Since Y_n is a complete sufficient statistic for θ, it suffices (by Theorem 8.2.23) to show that the distribution of Y_1/Y_n does not depend on θ (i.e., that Y_1/Y_n is an ancillary statistic), which follows since (for $0 < t \le 1$)

$$F_{Y_1/Y_n}(t) = P(Y_1/Y_n \le t) = P(Y_1 \le tY_n)$$

$$= \int_0^\theta P(Y_1 \le ty) f_{Y_n}(y)\, dy$$

$$= \int_0^\theta \left(1 - \left(1 - \frac{ty}{\theta}\right)^n\right) \frac{ny^{n-1}}{\theta^n}\, dy$$

$$= \int_0^\theta \frac{ny^{n-1}}{\theta^n}\, dy - \int_0^\theta \left(1 - t\frac{y}{\theta}\right)^n n\left(\frac{y}{\theta}\right)^{n-1} \frac{1}{\theta}\, dy$$

$$= 1 - n\int_0^1 (1 - tx)^n x^{n-1}\, dx$$

(where we made the change of variables $x = y/\theta$).

PROBLEMS FOR SECTION 8.2

8.2.1 Let $X_1, X_2, \ldots, X_n$ be a random sample of size n from a $N(\mu, \sigma^2)$ distribution with σ^2 known. Use Theorem 8.2.23 (Basu's Theorem) to show that $\bar{X}_n$ and $s_n^2 = \sum_{i=1}^n (X_i - \bar{X}_n)^2/(n-1)$ are independent r.v.'s. Does the result hold if σ^2 is also unknown?

8.2.2 Show that the minimal sufficient statistic $t(X)$ found in Example 8.1.35 is complete.

8.2.3 Show that the minimal sufficient statistic $t(X_1, X_2)$ found in Example 8.1.36 is a complete minimal sufficient statistic.

8.2.4 (a) Let X_1, X_2 be a random sample of size 2 from the p.d.f. $f(x|\theta) = (1/\theta)e^{-x/\theta}I_{(0,\infty)}(x)$. Show that

$$T_1(X_1, X_2) = X_1 + X_2, \qquad T_2(X_1, X_2) = \frac{X_1}{X_1 + X_2}$$

are independent r.v.'s. [*Hint:* Use Theorem 8.2.23 (Basu's Theorem).]

(b) Generalize the result in part (a) by proving the following. If $X_1, X_2, \ldots, X_n$ is a random sample of size n from the p.d.f. of part (a), show that $S_n = X_1 + X_2 + \cdots + X_n$ and $T_i = X_i/S_n$ are (for any fixed $i = 1, 2, \ldots, n$) independent r.v.'s.

8.2.5 Consider a random sample of size n from a uniform distribution on $(0, \theta)$, and let Y_n be the largest-order statistic of this sample. Show that the distribution of

$\sum_{i=1}^{n} X_i/Y_n = T_n$ does not depend on θ, and that hence T_n is independent of Y_n. [*Hint:* Show the result for $n = 2$, and then proceed by mathematical induction.]

8.2.6 (a) Show that the $N(\theta, \theta^2)$ distribution belongs to the exponential class of distributions, and hence find a minimal sufficient complete statistic for θ ($-\infty < \theta < \infty$).
  (b) As in part (a), but for the $N(\theta, \theta)$ distribution ($0 < \theta < \infty$).

8.2.7 Is the minimal sufficient statistic of Problem 8.1.3 complete?

8.2.8 Let $X_1, X_2, \ldots, X_n$ be a random sample of size n from the geometric point probability function $p(x|p) = q^{x-1}p$ if $x = 1, 2, 3, \ldots$ (and $= 0$ otherwise) for some p, $0 \le p \le 1$.
  (a) Show that this distribution is a member of the exponential family of distributions, and hence find a complete minimal sufficient statistic for p.
  (b) Using the definition of completeness, show that $X_1 + X_2 + \cdots + X_n$ is complete.

8.2.9 In Problem 8.1.8, $Y_n = \max(X_1, X_2, \ldots, X_n)$ was found to be minimal sufficient. Show that Y_n has a distribution which is complete.

8.2.10 In Problem 8.1.11, show that the lognormal distribution is a member of the exponential class, and find a complete minimal sufficient statistic for (μ, σ^2).

8.2.11 In Problem 8.1.12, find a complete minimal sufficient statistic for θ.

8.2.12 (a) Let $(X_1, X_2, \ldots, X_n)$ be a random sample of size n from the beta distribution $B(x|\alpha, \lambda)$. Show that this distribution is a member of the exponential class of distributions, and find a minimal complete sufficient statistic for (α, λ).
  (b) As in part (a), for the $B(x|\theta, \theta)$ distribution.

8.2.13 In Problem 8.1.14, find a complete minimal sufficient statistic for θ.

8.2.14 Let X_1, X_2 be a random sample of size 2 from a $N(\mu, \sigma^2)$ distribution. Show that (X_1, X_2) is a sufficient statistic but is not complete. [*Hint:* Consider $U(\mathbf{X}) = X_1 - X_2$.]

8.2.15 Let $X_1, X_2, \ldots, X_n$ be a random sample of size n from the truncated Poisson probability function $p(x|\mu) = e^{-\mu}\mu^x/(x!(1 - e^{-\mu})) \cdot I_{\{1,2,3,\ldots\}}(x)$.
  (a) Show that the joint distribution of $X_1, X_2, \ldots, X_n$ is a member of the exponential class.
  (b) Find a complete minimal sufficient statistic for μ.

8.2.16 Let $X_1, X_2, \ldots, X_n$ be a random sample of size n from a uniform distribution on (θ_1, θ_2), $\theta_1 < \theta_2$. Show that (Y_1, Y_n) is a complete sufficient statistic for (θ_1, θ_2), where $Y_1 \le Y_2 \le \cdots \le Y_n$ are the order statistics.

8.2.17 Let $X_1, X_2, \ldots, X_n$ be independent r.v.'s, each $N(\mu, \sigma^2)$. Show that $\overline{X}_n$ and $\sum_{i=1}^{n} a_i X_i$ are independent r.v.'s if $\sum_{i=1}^{n} a_i = 0$. [*Hint:* Use Basu's Theorem.]

8.2.18 Let $X_1, X_2, \ldots, X_n$ be a random sample of size n from the p.d.f. $f(x|\theta) = (x + 1)/(\theta(\theta + 1)) \cdot e^{-x/\theta}I_{(0, \infty)}(x)$ for some $\theta > 0$. Show that this p.d.f. is a member of the exponential class, and find a complete sufficient statistic for θ.

8.2.19 Let $X_1, X_2, \ldots, X_n$ be a random sample of size n from the p.d.f. $f(x|\theta) = (2x/\theta^2)I_{(0, \infty)}(x)$ for some $\theta > 0$. Find a complete sufficient statistic for θ.

8.2.20 Let $X_1, X_2, \ldots, X_n$ be a random sample of size n from the p.d.f. $f(x|\theta) = \theta x^{\theta-1} I_{(0,1)}(x)$. Find a complete sufficient statistic for θ, and the distribution of the statistic you find.

8.3. BEST UNBIASED ESTIMATION (UMVUE's)

We introduced unbiased estimation in Section 7.1 and gave some basic examples. This sets the stage for **optimal** unbiased estimation with **uniformly minimum variance** unbiased estimators (or UMVUE's). Such an estimator has the minimum variance among all possible unbiased estimators. Although a UMVUE does not always exist (as we saw in Example 7.1.18, it may be the case that *no* unbiased estimators exist), often it does and achieves the Cramér-Rao lower bound on the variance of an unbiased estimator (Theorem 7.5.3). We discuss **a method of finding UMVUE's: by finding an unbiased function of a complete sufficient statistic;** and, its variant of conditioning an unbiased function with a complete sufficient statistic.

Definition 8.3.1. (*We use Notation* 8.1.5.) Suppose that (for $i = 1, \ldots, r$) $E_\theta t_i \stackrel{\theta}{\equiv} \theta_i$ and, among all unbiased estimators of θ_i, t_i has the smallest variance for each possible value of θ. Then t_i is called a **best unbiased estimator (BUE)** or **uniformly minimum variance unbiased estimator (UMVUE)** of θ_i. We also call t a BUE (or a UMVUE) of θ.

We will now state and prove the Rao-Blackwell Theorem, which gives a technique for obtaining, from a given unbiased estimator Y, a new unbiased estimator $\varphi(X)$ of θ such that $\varphi(X)$ has uniformly smaller variance than does Y.

Theorem 8.3.2. Rao-Blackwell Theorem. Let X and Y be r.v.'s with $E(Y) = \mu$ and $\mathrm{Var}(Y) = \sigma_Y^2 < +\infty$. Let $\varphi(x) = E(Y|X = x)$. Then $E\varphi(X) = \mu$, and $\mathrm{Var}\,\varphi(X) \leq \sigma_Y^2$ with equality iff $P[Y = \varphi(X)] = 1$.

Proof: [We will only give the proof for the case where the distribution of (X, Y) is absolutely continuous. You should review conditional densities (equation (4.4.5)) and conditional expectation (Theorem 5.3.8) at this point.] Let $f(x, y)$ denote the joint density of (X, Y), $f_1(x)$ the density of X, $f_2(y)$ the density of Y, and $h(y|x)$ the conditional density of Y given $X = x$.

We will *first* show that $E\varphi(X) = \mu$. For since

$$E(Y|X = x) = \int_{-\infty}^\infty yh(y|x)\,dy = \frac{\int_{-\infty}^\infty yf(x, y)\,dy}{f_1(x)} \equiv \varphi(x),$$

we have $\int_{-\infty}^{\infty} yf(x, y)\, dy = \varphi(x)f_1(x)$. Thus,

$$E\varphi(X) = \int_{-\infty}^{\infty} \varphi(x)f_1(x)\, dx = \int_{-\infty}^{\infty} \left[\int_{-\infty}^{\infty} yf(x, y)\, dy \right] dx$$

$$= \int_{-\infty}^{\infty} y \left[\int_{-\infty}^{\infty} f(x, y)\, dx \right] dy = \int_{-\infty}^{\infty} yf_2(y)\, dy = \mu. \tag{8.3.3}$$

We will *next* show that $\operatorname{Var}\varphi(X) \le \sigma_Y^2$ with equality iff $P[Y = \varphi(X)] = 1$. For,

$$\sigma_Y^2 = E(Y - \mu)^2 = E\left[(Y - \varphi(X)) + (\varphi(X) - \mu) \right]^2$$

$$= E(Y - \varphi(X))^2 + E(\varphi(X) - \mu)^2 + 2E(Y - \varphi(X))(\varphi(X) - \mu) \tag{8.3.4}$$

$$= E(Y - \varphi(X))^2 + \operatorname{Var}\varphi(X) + 0.$$

Hence,

$$\operatorname{Var}\varphi(X) = \sigma_Y^2 - E(Y - \varphi(X))^2 \le \sigma_Y^2, \tag{8.3.5}$$

with equality iff $E(Y - \varphi(X))^2 = 0$; the last holds iff $P[Y = \varphi(X)] = 1$ (the simple proof being similar to that of Lemma 5.1.21).

Note that we must still show (for equation (8.3.4) to be demonstrated) that $E(Y - \varphi(X))(\varphi(X) - \mu) = 0$. However,

$$E(Y - \varphi(X))(\varphi(X) - \mu)$$

$$= \int_{-\infty}^{\infty} \int_{-\infty}^{\infty} (y - \varphi(x))(\varphi(x) - \mu)f(x, y)\, dy\, dx$$

$$= \int_{-\infty}^{\infty} (\varphi(x) - \mu) \left[\int_{-\infty}^{\infty} (y - \varphi(x))f(x, y)\, dy \right] dx$$

$$= \int_{-\infty}^{\infty} (\varphi(x) - \mu) \left[\int_{-\infty}^{\infty} (y - \varphi(x))h(y|x)\, dy \right] f_1(x)\, dx$$

$$= 0$$

because $\int_{-\infty}^{\infty} (y - \varphi(x))h(y|x)\, dx = 0$ since $\varphi(x)$ is $\int_{-\infty}^{\infty} yh(y|x)\, dy$. ∎

The application of the Rao-Blackwell Theorem to reduce the variance of an unbiased estimator by using a sufficient statistic will now be given. (Recall from the discussion above Figure 8.1-3 that at least one sufficient statistic always exists.) For now we obtain an *improved* unbiased estimator (later we tie this result to UMVUE's); for this reason, Lemma 8.3.6 is sometimes called the **Rao-Blackwell Improvement Theorem**.

Lemma 8.3.6.   (We use Notation 8.1.5.) Let T be a sufficient statistic for θ and U an unbiased estimator of θ (which is not a function of T alone). Then

$$\varphi_\theta(t) = E_\theta(U|T = t) \qquad (8.3.7)$$

is in fact not a function of θ (hence we could use $\varphi(T)$ as an estimator of θ) and: $E_\theta\varphi(T) = \theta$, $\text{Var}_\theta \varphi(T) < \text{Var}_\theta U$.

Proof: First, $\varphi_\theta(t) = E_\theta(U|T = t) = \int_{-\infty}^{\infty} ug(u|t)\,du$. But $g(u|t) = f(u, t|\theta)/h(t|\theta)$ is independent of θ because T is a sufficient statistic (recall Definition 8.1.1). Hence, $\varphi_\theta(t)$ is in fact not a function of θ.

Next, applying the Rao-Blackwell Theorem (Theorem 8.3.2) with $X = T$ and $Y = U$, it follows that in fact $\varphi(T)$ is an unbiased estimator of θ ($E_\theta\varphi(T) = \theta$) with reduced variance compared to U ($\text{Var}_\theta \varphi(T) < \text{Var}_\theta U$). ∎

We can now state and prove our general BUE result (which furnishes a **method of obtaining BUE's** in many cases).

Theorem 8.3.8.   Let T be a complete sufficient statistic for θ. If $E_\theta\varphi(T) \equiv \theta$ for some function $\varphi(\cdot)$, then $\varphi(T)$ **(i)** is unique; and **(ii)** has smaller variance than any other unbiased estimator of θ (i.e., is a UMVUE).

Proof: First, to show that $\varphi(\cdot)$ is unique, let $\psi(T)$ be any other function of T alone, such that $E_\theta\psi(T) \equiv \theta$. Then

$$E_\theta[\varphi(T) - \psi(T)] \equiv 0, \qquad (8.3.9)$$

so (by the completeness of T) $\varphi(t) = \psi(t)$ for all t (more precisely, for all t for which $g(t|\theta) > 0$ for some θ).

Second, to show that $\varphi(T)$ has smaller variance than any other unbiased estimator of θ (whether based on T alone or not) we proceed as follows. Now $\varphi(T)$ is, by our first result, the only function of T alone that is an unbiased estimator of θ. Hence, if another unbiased estimator exists, say U, it is not a function of T alone. By the Rao-Blackwell Improvement Theorem (Lemma 8.3.6), the estimator defined by $\psi(t) = E_\theta(U|T = t)$ is unbiased and $\text{Var}_\theta \psi(T) < \text{Var}_\theta U$; and by our first result $\psi(\cdot) \equiv \varphi(\cdot)$. Hence, $\text{Var}_\theta \varphi(T) < \text{Var}_\theta U$. ∎

We now give **a number of examples of best unbiased estimation.**

Example 8.3.10.   Let $X_1, X_2, \ldots, X_n$ be independent r.v.'s, each $N(\mu, \sigma^2)$ with both μ and σ^2 unknown. Find BUE's of μ and σ^2.

We know (from Example 8.2.20) that $(\Sigma X_i, \Sigma X_i^2)$ is a complete sufficient statistic for (μ, σ^2). Also, $\bar{X}_n = \Sigma X_i/n$ and $s_n^2 = \Sigma(X_i - \bar{X}_n)/(n-1)$ are unbiased functions of the complete sufficient statistic: $E(\bar{X}_n) = \mu$, $E(s_n^2) = \sigma^2$. Therefore $\bar{X}_n$ is a UMVUE for μ, and s_n^2 is a UMVUE for σ^2.

Recall that the MLE of μ is $\bar{X}_n$, and the MLE of σ^2 is $((n-1)/n)s_n^2$ (which is biased), and these estimators are consistent and asymptotically normal. Further, these estimators also achieve the Cramér-Rao lower bound. Although statisticians differ on whether to use s_n^2 or $((n-1)/n)s_n^2$, as long as n is not small (say $n \geq 15$) it does not matter in practice which we use since they are numerically close to each other (e.g., there is a 7% difference when $n = 15$, since then $(n-1)/n = 14/15 = .93$).

Example 8.3.11. In Example 8.2.4 we showed that if $X_1, X_2, \ldots, X_n$ is a random sample of size n from a Poisson distribution with parameter μ, then $\sum\limits_{i=1}^{n} X_i$ is a complete sufficient statistic for μ. Find a UMVUE of μ.

Method 1. Finding an Unbiased Function of a Complete Sufficient Statistic. Since we know (or, suppose we can guess and then verify) that $\overline{X}_n = \Sigma X_i/n$ is an unbiased function of a complete sufficient statistic, $\overline{X}_n$ is a UMVUE of μ.

Method 2. Conditioning an Unbiased Function with a Complete Sufficient Statistic. Suppose that we do not know (or cannot guess and verify) that $\overline{X}_n$ is a function of ΣX_i which is unbiased (and hence by Method 1 is UMVUE). In many cases, we will still be able to find an unbiased function (though it will not be a function of the complete sufficient statistic); here, we let $U(X_1, X_2, \ldots, X_n) = X_1$, and U is an unbiased estimator of μ, that is, $E(U) = E(X_1) = \mu$. We can therefore obtain a UMVUE as the conditional expectation of X_1 given the complete sufficient statistic ΣX_i: $E(X_1 | \Sigma X_i)$. To find this, we first seek the conditional probability distribution of X_1 given ΣX_i, and then find its mean. For $0 \leq i \leq s$,

$$P\left(X_1 = i \mid \sum X_i = s\right) = \frac{P\left(X_1 = i, \sum X_i = s\right)}{P\left(\sum X_i = s\right)}$$

$$= \frac{P(X_1 = i)P(X_2 + \cdots + X_n = s - i)}{P(X_1 + \cdots + X_n = s)}$$

$$= \frac{\dfrac{e^{-\mu}\mu^i}{i!}\dfrac{e^{-(n-1)\mu}((n-1)\mu)^{s-i}}{(s-i)!}}{\dfrac{e^{-n\mu}(n\mu)^s}{s!}}$$

$$= \frac{s!}{i!(s-i)!}\left(\frac{n-1}{n}\right)^{s-i}\left(\frac{1}{n}\right)^i$$

which we recognize as the binomial distribution $B(s, 1/n)$. Therefore

$$E\left(X_1 \mid \sum X_i = s\right) = s\frac{1}{n} = \frac{s}{n},$$

hence $\Sigma X_i/n = \overline{X}_n$ is the UMVUE of μ.

Example 8.3.12. In Example 8.3.11 (dealing with a Poisson random sample), find a UMVUE of the function of μ, $g(\mu) = e^{-\mu}(1 + \mu)$. Recall from Example 7.5.6 that

$$g(\mu) = P(X = 0) + P(X = 1).$$

Now we can **(Method 1)** guess a function of the complete sufficient statistic ΣX_i that is unbiased for $g(\mu)$, and then it will be a UMVUE. We know that

$$t_3(X_1, X_2, \ldots, X_n) = \sum \psi(X_i)/n$$

$$= \{\text{Proportion of } X_1, X_2, \ldots, X_n \text{ that are 0 or 1}\}$$

where

$$\psi(X_i) = \begin{cases} 1, & \text{if } X_i = 0 \text{ or } X_i = 1 \\ 0, & \text{otherwise}, \end{cases}$$

is an unbiased estimator of $g(\mu)$. However, this is *not* a function simply of ΣX_i (i.e., if we know ΣX_i, we do not have enough information to determine what proportion of the X_i were 0 or 1). Thus, Method 1 will not work (unless we can guess or divine an unbiased estimator of $g(\mu)$ that is a function just of ΣX_i). As one method of trying to find a function of ΣX_i that is unbiased, we may look at the MLE, which here is (using Theorem 7.2.15)

$$\overline{g(\mu)} = g(\hat{\mu}) = e^{-\overline{X}}(1 + \overline{X}).$$

Since (with some work) we may show that

$$E\left(e^{-\overline{X}}(1 + \overline{X})\right) \neq e^{-\mu}(1 + \mu),$$

this approach to making Method 1 work does not succeed.

In **Method 2**, we seek an unbiased estimator of $g(\mu)$ and its conditional expectation given ΣX_i is UMVUE. Since $\Sigma \psi(X_i)/n$ is unbiased, we may try to compute $E(\Sigma \psi(X_i)/n | \Sigma X_i)$, but this is a difficult task. Since *any* unbiased function of the data is usable with this method, let us try a simpler function in hopes it may yield a more tractable conditional expectation computation. In particular, note that $\psi(X_1)$ itself is an unbiased estimator of $g(\mu)$. Thus, $E(\psi(X_1)|\Sigma X_i)$ is a UMVUE of $g(\mu)$. We will find this conditional expectation by finding the conditional probability distribution in three cases.

Case (i): s = 0.   Here

$$P\left(\psi(X_1) = 0 \Big| \sum X_i = 0\right) = P\left(X_1 > 1 \Big| \sum X_i = 0\right) = 0,$$

$$P\left(\psi(X_1) = 1 \Big| \sum X_i = 0\right) = P\left(X_1 = 0 \Big| \sum X_i = 0\right) = 1,$$

and hence

$$E\left(\psi(X_1)\Big| \sum X_i = 0\right) = 1.$$

Case (ii): s = 1.   Here

$$P\big(\psi(X_1) = 0 \big| \sum X_i = 1\big) = P\big(X_1 > 1 \big| \sum X_i = 1\big) = 0,$$

$$P\big(\psi(X_1) = 1 \big| \sum X_i = 1\big) = 1,$$

and

$$E\big(\psi(X_1) \big| \sum X_i = 1\big) = 1.$$

Case (iii): s > 1.   Using the fact (from Example 8.3.11) that X_1 given $\sum X_i$ is $B(s, 1/n)$ we have

$$P\big(\psi(X_1) = 1 \big| \sum X_i = s\big) = P\big(X_1 = 0 \text{ or } X_1 = 1 \big| \sum X_i = s\big)$$

$$= P\big(X_1 = 0 \big| \sum X_i = s\big) + P\big(X_1 = 1 \big| \sum X_i = s\big)$$

$$= \left(\frac{n-1}{n}\right)^s + s\left(\frac{n-1}{n}\right)^{s-1}\left(\frac{1}{n}\right)^1$$

$$= \frac{(n-1)^{s-1}(n-1+s)}{n^s},$$

hence

$$E\big(\psi(X_1) \big| \sum X_i = s\big) = \frac{(n-1)^{s-1}(n-1+s)}{n^s}.$$

Combining cases **(i)**, **(ii)**, and **(iii)**, we find that the UMVUE of $g(\mu) = e^{-\mu}(1 + \mu)$ is given by

$$\varphi(s) = E\big(\psi(X_1) \big| \sum X_i = s\big) = \begin{cases} 1, & \text{if } s = 0 \text{ or } s = 1 \\ \dfrac{(n-1)^{s-1}(n-1+s)}{n^s}, & \text{if } s \geq 2, \end{cases}$$

which may be simplified to the formula

$$\varphi\big(\sum X_i\big) = \frac{(n-1)^{\sum X_i - 1}(n-1+\sum X_i)}{n^{\sum X_i}}.$$

To compare with the MLE, note that we may write this in the form

$$\varphi\big(\sum X_i\big) = \left(\frac{n-1}{n}\right)^{\sum X_i} \frac{(n-1) + \sum X_i}{(n-1)n} n = \left(\frac{n-1}{n}\right)^{n\bar{X}}\left(\frac{n-1}{n} + \bar{X}\right)\frac{n}{n-1}$$

which may for large n (since

$$\lim_{n \to \infty} \frac{n-1}{n} = 1, \quad \lim_{n \to \infty} \left(1 + \frac{-1}{n}\right)^n = e^{-1})$$

be seen to be close to

$$e^{-\overline{X}}(1 + \overline{X}),$$

which is the MLE.

Example 8.3.13. Let $X_1, X_2, \ldots, X_n$ be independent r.v.'s, each uniform on $[0, \theta]$ for some $\theta > 0$. Since (see Example 8.2.8) $Y_n = \max(X_1, X_2, \ldots, X_n)$ is a complete sufficient statistic for θ, and

$$E(Y_n) = \int_0^\theta \frac{nx^n}{\theta^n}\, dx = \frac{n}{n+1}\theta,$$

$\dfrac{n+1}{n} Y_n$ is an unbiased estimator and a function of a complete sufficient statistic for θ, hence is the unique UMVUE of θ. (Recall that the MLE of θ was Y_n.)

Remark 8.3.14. Although in many important cases the MLE and the UMVUE are the same, in other cases we see that the UMVUE is a function of the MLE—sometimes a simple function (as in Example 8.3.13), sometimes not very simple. (Of course the UMVUE may not be a function of the MLE at all, and a UMVUE may not exist: As we noted earlier, there may be *no* unbiased estimators.)

Example 8.3.15. Let $X_1, X_2, \ldots, X_n$ be independent Bernoulli r.v.'s with probability of success p. If $g(p) = 1/p$, show there are no UMVUE's of $g(p)$.

Here (see Example 8.2.21) ΣX_i is a complete sufficient statistic for p. However, no function of ΣX_i is unbiased for $1/p$. To see this, suppose that $U(\Sigma X_i)$ is unbiased. Then $E(U(\Sigma X_i)) \equiv 1/p$, that is,

$$\sum_{x=0}^{n} U(x)\binom{n}{x}p^x(1-p)^{n-x} \equiv \frac{1}{p} \qquad (8.3.16)$$

since ΣX_i is $B(n, p)$. However, as $p \to 0$

$$\sum_{x=0}^{n} U(x)\binom{n}{x}p^x(1-p)^{n-x} \to U(0)$$

and $1/p \to \infty$. Since the left and right sides of equation (8.3.16) would approach different limits as $p \to 0$, no such $U(\cdot)$ exists, hence no UMVUE exists. (Recall that the MLE

$$\left(\widehat{\frac{1}{p}}\right) = \frac{1}{\hat{p}} = \frac{1}{\dfrac{\sum X_i}{n}} = \frac{n}{\sum X_i}$$

does exist.)

Remark 8.3.17. Although unbiasedness is an intuitively desirable property, sometimes no unbiased estimator exists. In such cases, consistent and "slightly biased" estimators may serve our estimation needs well. (Of course, a large bias would be undesirable. In Chapter 15 we consider techniques that serve to reduce bias.)

PROBLEMS FOR SECTION 8.3

8.3.1 Let $X_1, X_2, \ldots, X_n$ be a random sample of size n, each Bernoulli with unknown probability of success p.
   (a) Find a UMVUE for p by
      (i) Using the Rao-Blackwell Improvement Theorem.
      (ii) Finding an unbiased function of the complete sufficient statistic.
   (b) Find a UMVUE for pq.
   (c) Find a UMVUE for p^s, $0 < s < n$.
   (d) Find a UMVUE for $p^s + (1 - p)^{n-s}$, $0 < s < n$.
   (e) Show that both of the estimators in part (a), and the estimator in part (b), are consistent.
   (f) Compute the variance of the estimators in parts (a) and (b), and compare them with the Cramér-Rao lower bounds.

8.3.2 Let $X_1, X_2, \ldots, X_n$ be a random sample from a Poisson distribution with unknown $\mu > 0$. Find
   (a) A UMVUE for $e^{-\mu}$.
   (b) A UMVUE for $e^{-\mu}(1 + \mu + \mu^2/2)$.

8.3.3 Let $X_1, X_2, \ldots, X_n$ be a random sample of size n from a $N(\mu, \sigma^2)$ distribution.
   (a) Find a UMVUE for μ if σ^2 is known, and show that this estimator is consistent and CAN.
   (b) Find a UMVUE for σ^2 if μ is known, and show that this estimator is consistent and CAN.

8.3.4 In Example 8.1.35 (also see Problem 8.2.2), find the UMVUE for θ.

8.3.5 In Example 8.1.36 (also see Problem 8.2.3), find the BUE for p.

8.3.6 Let $X_1, X_2, \ldots, X_n$ be a random sample of size n from a $G(x \mid \alpha - 1, \beta, 0)$ distribution.
   (a) Find the BUE for $\alpha\beta$.
   (b) Show that the BUE for $\alpha\beta$ is CAN.

8.3.7 Let $X_1, X_2, \ldots, X_n$ be a random sample of size n from the exponential p.d.f. $f(x|\theta) = \theta e^{-\theta x} I_{(0, \infty)}(x)$ for some $\theta > 0$. Show that $(n - 1)/\sum_{i=1}^{n} X_i$ is the unique MVUE for θ.

8.3.8 Let $X_1, X_2, \ldots, X_n$ be a random sample of size n from a $N(\mu, \sigma^2)$ distribution. Find the BUE of $P(X_1 \leq c)$, where c is known.

8.3.9 In Problem 8.2.15, find a BUE of $\mu/(1 - e^{-\mu})$, and of $1 - e^{-\mu}$.

8.3.10 In Problem 8.2.16
    (a) Show that a UMVUE for $(\theta_1 + \theta_2)/2$ is $(Y_n + Y_1)/2$.
    (b) Show that a UMVUE for $\theta_2 - \theta_1$ is $((n + 1)/(n - 1))(Y_n - Y_1)$.

8.3.11 Let X be a single observation from a Poisson distribution with unknown parameter μ.
    (a) Find a BUE for μ^2. [*Hint:* Note that $E(X(X - 1)) = \mu^2$.]
    (b) If we have a random sample of size n, find the BUE for μ^2.
    (c) Based on a sample of size 1, find the BUE for μ^r, $r > 1$. [*Hint:* Compute $E(X(X - 1)(X - 2)\ldots(X - r + 1))$.]

8.3.12 Let $X_1, X_2, \ldots, X_n$ be a random sample of size n from the p.d.f. $f(x|\beta) = \Gamma^{-1}(\alpha)\beta^{-\alpha}e^{-x/\beta}x^{\alpha-1}I_{(0, \infty)}(x)$, α known. Note that X_1/α is an unbiased estimator of β. Use this fact and the Rao-Blackwell Improvement Theorem to obtain the BUE for β. (Recall that this distribution belongs to the exponential class, hence a complete sufficient statistic is easy to obtain.)

8.3.13 Let $X_1, X_2, \ldots, X_m$ be independent r.v.'s sampled respectively from $B(n_i, p)$, $i = 1, 2, \ldots, m$, distributions. Find the unique BUE of p.

8.3.14 Let $X_1, X_2, \ldots, X_n$ be a random sample of size $n > 3$ from a $N(\mu, \sigma^2)$ distribution. Find
    (a) A BUE for μ/σ^2.
    (b) A BUE for μ^2/σ^2.

[*Hint:* Note that $\left(\sum_{i=1}^{n} X_i, \sum_{i=1}^{n} X_i^2\right)$ is a complete minimal sufficient statistic for (μ, σ^2),

$$E\left(\frac{\overline{X}^2}{s^2}\right) = E(\overline{X}^2)E\left(\frac{1}{s^2}\right) = \left(\frac{\sigma^2}{n} + \mu^2\right)E\left(\frac{1}{s^2}\right),$$

and $E(1/s^2) = ((n - 1)/(n - 3))/\sigma^2$.]

8.3.15 Let $X_1, X_2, \ldots, X_n$ be independent and identically distributed $N(\mu, \sigma^2)$ r.v.'s. Show that the MLE of σ^2, $\sum_{i=1}^{n}(X_i - \overline{X}_n)^2/n$, has smaller mean squared error than the BUE of σ^2, which is $\sum_{i=1}^{n}(X_i - \overline{X}_n)^2/(n - 1)$.

8.3.16 Let $X_1, X_2, \ldots, X_n$ be a random sample of size n from the p.d.f. $f(x|\theta) = (\theta/x^2)I_{(\theta, \infty)}(x)$. Find the UMVUE of θ.

8.3.17 Let $X_1, X_2, \ldots, X_n$ be a random sample of size n from the p.d.f. $f(x|\theta) = \theta/(1 + x)^{1+\theta} \cdot I_{(0, \infty)}(x)$.
    (a) Find a BUE of θ (if one exists).
    (b) Find a BUE of $1/\theta$ (if one exists).

8.3.18 Let $X_1, X_2, \ldots, X_n$ be a random sample of size n from the displaced exponential p.d.f. $f(x|\theta) = e^{-(x-\theta)}I_{(\theta,\infty)}(x)$. Find the UMVUE of θ. Is this estimator consistent?

8.3.19 Let $X_1, X_2, \ldots, X_n$ be a random sample of size n from the p.d.f. $f(x|\theta) = \theta e^{-x\theta}I_{(0,\infty)}(x)$. Find the unique BUE of $P(X_1 > k) = e^{-k\theta}$. [*Hint:* Define $g(X_1) = 1$ if $X_1 > k$ (and $= 0$ otherwise); then $Eg(X_1) = e^{-k\theta}$.]

8.3.20 Let $X_1, X_2, \ldots, X_n$ be a random sample of size n from the p.d.f. $f(x|\theta) = ((x+1)/(\theta(\theta+1)))e^{-x/\theta}I_{(0,\infty)}(x)$ for some $\theta > 0$.
(a) Find the UMVUE of $g(\theta) = \theta(2\theta + 1)/(\theta + 1)$.
(b) Find the MLE of θ, and hence the MLE of $g(\theta)$.

8.3.21 In Problem 8.2.20, find the BUE of θ.

8.3.22 In Problem 8.2.19, find the BUE of θ (if it exists).

8.3.23 In Problem 8.2.9 (also see Problem 8.1.8), show that

$$T_n = \frac{Y_n^{n+1} - (Y_n - 1)^{n+1}}{Y_n^n - (Y_n - 1)^n}$$

is the unique UMVUE of θ.

8.3.24 Let $X_1, X_2, \ldots, X_n$ be a random sample of size n from a $N(\theta, \theta^2)$ distribution. Find the BUE of θ.

8.3.25 Let X be a truncated binomial r.v. with probability function $p(x|p) = \binom{n}{x}p^x \cdot (1-p)^{n-x}/(1-q^n)$ if $x = 1, 2, \ldots, n$ (and $= 0$ otherwise). Find the UMVUE of $p/(1 - q^n)$.

8.3.26 Let $X_1, X_2, \ldots, X_n$ be a random sample of size n from a $N(\theta, \theta)$ distribution. Find the unique BUE of θ (if it exists). (Note that $\overline{X}_n$ is unbiased.)

8.3.27 Let $X_1, X_2, \ldots, X_n$ be a random sample of size n from the p.d.f. $f(x|\theta) = (1/(2\theta))e^{-|x|/\theta}$. Find the BUE of θ (if it exists).

PROBLEMS FOR CHAPTER 8

8.1 In our proof of the Neyman Factorization Theorem (Theorem 8.1.6), equation (8.1.11) was developed by excluding the cases $t(X) = c \neq c_0$ and $P_\theta[t(X) = c_0] = 0$. Complete the proof by showing how to handle these cases.

8.2 Formally prove that if $t(\ )$ is a sufficient statistic, then so is $k(t(\ ))$ for any one-to-one function $k(\ )$. [*Hint:* See the paragraph after Example 8.1.14.]

8.3 Use the Neyman Factorization Theorem to prove that (under Notation 8.1.5) the identity statistic is a sufficient statistic. (See the paragraph preceding Definition 8.1.15.)

8.4 Prove Theorem 8.1.17. [*Hint:* If there are no ties among $X_1, \ldots, X_n$, then $n!$ possible orderings exist and the conditional distribution on any contour assigns probability $1/n!$ to each ordering.]

8.5 At the end of Example 8.1.19 we claimed (8.1.22) could hold for at most 4 values of θ. However, it holds for all θ in the special case $b = c = d = e = 0$. Show the latter is true iff (x_1, x_2) is a permutation of (y_1, y_2) (which was excluded at the start of the example).

8.6 Develop considerations, for the proof of Theorem 8.1.23, like those developed in Problem 8.1 for the proof of the Neyman Factorization Theorem.

8.7 In the case of Example 8.1.32, show that $\left(\sum X_i \right)^3$ is sufficient for θ.

8.8 In the case of Example 8.2.8, show Y_n is a minimal sufficient statistic for θ.

8.9 In the case of Example 8.1.32, use the Neyman Factorization Theorem to show that
$$t(X_1, \ldots, X_n) = \left(\sum_{i=1}^{n} X_i, \sum_{i=1}^{n} X_i^2 \right) \text{ is a sufficient statistic for } (\mu, \sigma^2).$$

8.10 In Example 8.1.29 the likelihood-ratio statistic was not well-defined since we did not take account of the possibility that $f(x|\theta_0) = 0$. Take account of this in the course of using a Neyman Factorization Theorem argument to show that the likelihood-ratio statistic is a sufficient statistic.

8.11 Suppose $X_1, \ldots, X_n$ are independent r.v.'s, each with the uniform distribution on $[\theta - \frac{1}{2}, \theta + \frac{1}{2}]$, where θ is unknown, $\theta \in \Theta = \{x: -\infty < x < +\infty\}$.
   (a) Show that $t(X_1, \ldots, X_n) = (\min(X_1, \ldots, X_n), \max(X_1, \ldots, X_n))$ is a sufficient statistic for θ.
   (b) In Example 7.2.20 we found that the MLE of θ was not unique, but that any $\hat{\theta}$ such that
$$\max(X_1, \ldots, X_n) - \frac{1}{2} \le \hat{\theta}(X_1, \ldots, X_n) \le \min(X_1, \ldots, X_n) + \frac{1}{2}$$

is an MLE. Show how to choose an MLE that is not a function of $t(X_1, \ldots, X_n)$. (For example, Moore (1971) gives one.)

8.12 Show that if $(X_1, \ldots, X_n)$ is a member of the exponential class (see Definition 8.2.12), then $(\varphi_1(X_1, \ldots, X_n), \ldots, \varphi_r(X_1, \ldots, X_n))$ is a minimal sufficient statistic for θ.

8.13 Show that, if equality holds in the Cramér-Rao Inequality for unbiased estimators, then $(X_1, \ldots, X_n)$ is of one-parameter Koopman-Darmois form.

8.14 Prove that if we have $n > 2$ independent observations from the Cauchy distribution (8.1.20), then no nontrivial sufficient statistic exists. (Example 8.1.19 proved this for the case $n = 2$.)

8.15 If X has the Poisson distribution with unknown parameter $\mu \ge 0$, prove that no nontrivial sufficient statistic exists.

8.16 If $X_1, X_2, \ldots, X_n$ are independent and each $N(\mu, \sigma^2)$ with μ and σ^2 unknown, prove that (for $n \ge 2$) $\left(\sum_{i=1}^{n} X_i/n, \sum_{i=1}^{n} (X_i - \overline{X})^2/(n-1) \right)$ is a minimal sufficient statistic for (μ, σ^2).

8.17 Let $X_1, \ldots, X_n$ be independent r.v.'s, each Bernoulli (see Definition 3.2.1) with unknown probability of success $p(0 \le p \le 1)$. Prove that: $\sum_{i=1}^{n} X_i$ is a sufficient statistic; $\sum_{i=1}^{n} X_i/n$ is a sufficient statistic; $\left(\sum_{i=1}^{n} X_i \right)^2$ is a sufficient statistic; and $\sum_{i=1}^{n} X_i$ is a minimal sufficient statistic.

8.18 Let $X_1, \ldots, X_n$ be independent r.v.'s, each with $P[X_j = z_i] = p_i (i = 1, \ldots, k; \ j = 1, \ldots, n)$, where $0 \le p_1, \ldots, p_k \le 1$, $p_1 + \cdots + p_k = 1$, and no two of $z_1, \ldots, z_k$ are equal. Find a minimal sufficient statistic for $(p_1, \ldots, p_k)$, the unknown vector of probabilities. [*Hint:* Compare with the multinomial distribution of Definition 3.5.1, which bears essentially the same relation to these $X_1, \ldots, X_n$ as the binomial distribution bears to Bernoulli r.v.'s.]

8.19 Show that the family of uniform distributions on $(0, \theta)$ (where $\theta > 0$ is unknown) is complete.

8.20 If X has the Bernoulli distribution with unknown probability of success $p (0 \le p \le 1)$, find: a complete sufficient statistic T; the unique MVU estimator $\varphi(T)$ of p; and $\text{Var}_\theta \, \varphi(T)$, using the Rao-Blackwell Theorem.

8.21 As in Problem 8.20, but with X having a uniform distribution on $(0, \theta)$ where $\theta > 0$ is unknown.

8.22 Suppose we observe $X = (X_1, \ldots, X_n, Y_1, \ldots, Y_m)$, where $X_1, \ldots, X_n, Y_1, \ldots, Y_m$ are independent r.v.'s, and X_i is $N(\mu, \sigma_1^2)(1 \le i \le n)$ while Y_j is $N(\mu, \sigma_2^2)(1 \le j \le m)$. Show that (assuming μ, σ_1^2, σ_2^2 are unknown with $-\infty < \mu < +\infty$, $\sigma_1^2 > 0$, $\sigma_2^2 > 0$) $T = (X_1 + \cdots + X_n, X_1^2 + \cdots + X_n^2, Y_1 + \cdots + Y_m, Y_1^2 + \cdots + Y_m^2)$ is a sufficient statistic. Show that T is not a complete sufficient statistic. [*Hint:* Consider $u(T) = \overline{X} - \overline{Y}$.]

HONORS PROBLEMS FOR CHAPTER 8

8.1H In Dynkin's Theorem (Theorem 8.1.25) we did not completely define $t(X)$, since we did not consider what to do if $f(X|\theta_0) = 0$. Show how to handle this problem. [*Hint:* First modify (8.1.27) appropriately. You may wish to consult Dynkin (1961).]

8.2H Show that with $n = 1$ neither the Cauchy distribution nor the uniform distribution on $(0, \theta)$ are members of the univariate one-parameter exponential family. [*Hint:* First prove that if X_1 is a member of the univariate one-parameter exponential family, then $(X_1, \ldots, X_n)$ where $X_1, \ldots, X_n$ are independent r.v.'s with the same distribution as X_1 is a member of the one-parameter exponential family.]

8.3H In our proof of Theorem 8.3.2 (the Rao-Blackwell Theorem) we wrote $h(y|x)$ as $f(x, y)/f_1(x)$; however, if $f_1(x) = 0$, then $h(y|x) = 0$ by definition. Revise the proof to allow for $f_1(x) = 0$, and show that this causes no problems.

8.4H Show that if $(X_1, \ldots, X_n)$ is a member of the exponential class, then (under certain conditions, which you should specify) $(\varphi_1(X_1, \ldots, X_n), \ldots, \varphi_r(X_1, \ldots, X_n))$ is a complete sufficient statistic. [*Hint:* See Problem 8.12. Problem 8.22 gives a counterexample to the statement that $(\varphi_1(X_1, \ldots, X_n), \ldots, \varphi_r(X_1, \ldots, X_n))$ is complete without any conditions being needed.]

8.5H Let $X_1, \ldots, X_n$ be independent r.v.'s, each with the same density $f(x|\theta)$ where $\theta \in \Theta = \{f(\cdot): f(\cdot) \text{ is a density function}\}$ (and $f(x|\theta)$ is the density function specified by θ). In Theorem 8.1.17 we showed that the order statistic $(Y_1, \ldots, Y_n)$ is a sufficient statistic in another context. Show that here, also, $(Y_1, \ldots, Y_n)$ is a sufficient statistic. [This is a distinct case since here Θ is not a subset of $\mathcal{R}^r$.] Prove that $(Y_1, \ldots, Y_n)$ is also a complete sufficient statistic. [*Hint:* See Lehmann (1959), p. 133.]

8.6H In Definition 8.2.1 we defined a *complete* family. A *family is called* **boundedly complete** *if* (*for every bounded function* $u(x)$) (8.2.2) *implies* $u(x) = 0$ *at all* x. Show that a family may be boundedly complete without being complete.

8.7H Construct a collection of probability distributions, indexed by a parameter θ, which has the following properties: (1) The collection consists of infinitely many distributions, no two of which are identical; (2) For every θ, $P_\theta[X = x] = 0$ except perhaps when $x = 1, 2, 3, \ldots$ [here X is a r.v. with the distribution indexed by θ]; and (3) A nontrivial sufficient statistic exists (that is, $t(X) = X$ is not the only sufficient statistic).

8.8H Let X_1, X_2 be two independent observations, each with the same distribution. Give an example of a distribution (besides the Cauchy covered in Example 8.1.19) where no nontrivial sufficient statistic exists.

8.9H As in Problem 8.8H, but the distribution required to be such that $E_\theta X_1$ and $\mathrm{Var}_\theta(X_1)$ exist and do not depend on θ.

Problems 8.10H and 8.11H present comprehensive studies of estimation in particular contexts, tying together the results of the various sections of Chapters 7 and 8. (Some aspects of these problems have been treated individually in the text.)

8.10H Let $X_1, \ldots, X_n (n \geq 1)$ be independent r.v.'s, each with density

$$f(x|\theta) = \begin{cases} \dfrac{1}{\theta}, & 0 \leq x \leq \theta \\ 0, & \text{otherwise}, \end{cases}$$

where θ is unknown but $\theta \in \Theta = \{z: z > 0\}$.
(a) Find the maximum-likelihood estimator (say $\hat{\theta}_n$) of θ. [This wording does not necessarily imply that $\hat{\theta}_n$ exists or is unique.]
(b) Determine whether or not $\hat{\theta}_n$ is: consistent; unbiased; asymptotically unbiased.
(c) Find the iterated MLE (IMLE) of θ. Find the method of moments estimator of θ.
(d) Let $Y = \hat{\theta}_n$. Find the limiting distribution of $n(Y - \theta)$.
(e) Prove that $Y = \max(X_1, \ldots, X_n)$ is a sufficient statistic for θ, via the Neyman Factorization Theorem. Prove that Y is a minimal sufficient statistic for θ.
(f) Prove that the family of probability density functions

$$f(y|\theta) = \begin{cases} n\dfrac{y^{n-1}}{\theta^n}, & 0 \leq y \leq \theta \\ 0, & \text{otherwise} \end{cases}$$

for $\theta \in \Theta = \{z: z > 0\}$ is complete.
(g) Prove that

$$\frac{2}{n}S_n = \frac{2}{n}(X_1 + \cdots + X_n)$$

is an unbiased estimator of θ, and find $\mathrm{Var}_\theta((2/n)S_n)$. Give an expression for an estimator that has minimum variance among all unbiased estimators of θ.

(h) Suppose you are told that, for any unbiased estimator $\varphi_n = \varphi_n(X_1, \ldots, X_n)$ of θ, we have

$$E_\theta(\varphi_n - \theta)^2 = \text{Var}_\theta(\varphi_n) \geq \frac{\theta^2}{n(n+2)}.$$

Then prove that $[(n+1)/n]\ Y$ is the "unique" MVU estimator of θ. [A reference is Kiefer (1952).]

(i) If the Cramér-Rao lower bound on the variance of unbiased estimators $\varphi_n(X_1, \ldots, X_n)$ of θ held here, it would say that

$$\text{Var}_\theta(\varphi_n) \geq \underline{\hspace{2cm}}.$$

8.11H Let $X_1, \ldots, X_n\ (n \geq 1)$ be independent random variables, each with density

$$f(x|\theta) = \begin{cases} e^{-(x-\theta)}, & x \geq \theta \\ 0, & \text{otherwise,} \end{cases}$$

where $\theta \in \Theta = \mathcal{R}$.

(a) through (i). Precisely as in (a) through (i) of Problem 8.10H, but with: $Y = \min(X_1, \ldots, X_n)$ in parts (d), (e), (h); $S_n/n - 1$ in part (g); $\text{Var}_\theta(\varphi_n) \geq 1/n^2$ in part (h); and part (f) replaced by the corresponding problem for the density of the new Y.

8.12H Let $X_1, \ldots, X_n$ be independent random variables with density $f(x|\theta)$ for $\theta \in \Theta = \{\theta_1, \theta_2\}$.

(a) Prove directly [that is, without using Dynkin's Theorem (Theorem 8.1.25)] that

$$t_n = \frac{\displaystyle\prod_{i=1}^n f(X_i|\theta_2)}{\displaystyle\prod_{i=1}^n f(X_i|\theta_1)}$$

is a sufficient statistic for θ.

(b) Prove that t_n is a minimal sufficient statistic.

8.13H Suppose that, from a population of N items (e.g., automobiles) that contains an unknown number θ of defective items with $\theta \in \Theta = \{0, 1, 2, \ldots, N\}$, a random sample of size $n\ (1 \leq n \leq N)$ is drawn under SRS without replacement. Let

$$X_i = \begin{cases} 1, & \text{if the } i\text{th item drawn is defective} \\ 0, & \text{otherwise} \end{cases}$$

$(i = 1, 2, \ldots, n)$. Show that (based on observations $X_1, \ldots, X_n$) the statistic $t(X_1, \ldots, X_n) = X_1 + \cdots + X_n$ is a sufficient statistic. Is it minimal sufficient? $[X_1 + \cdots + X_n$ is the number of defectives in the sample, and its distribution is hypergeometric with $n, \theta, N]$

8.14H Prove directly that the normal family with μ unknown but σ^2 fixed known is complete.

CHAPTER 9

Tests of Hypotheses

In this chapter we cover the subject of **tests of hypotheses**. This subject is covered in detail in most books on statistics at every level. Often this detail is given at the expense of point estimation, interval estimation, ranking and selection, and decision theory (which are sometimes even omitted). Usually, also, the detail is technical, with insufficient consideration being given to the underlying philosophy and to decision theory (which is treated in detail in general in Chapter 12). We give a balanced view of the subject, giving the motivation as well as the technical detail, and covering the contribution of decision theory to an integrated view of the topic as well as the contribution of the "classical" way of looking at the subject.

9.1. SIMPLE AND COMPOSITE NULL AND ALTERNATIVE HYPOTHESES

A hypothesis-testing problem usually results from questions like: "Does smoking cause cancer?"; "Do seat belts reduce car accident injuries?"; "Do atomic power plants increase radiation levels?"; or "Does adding putative catalyst A to a certain chemical process increase the yield?" **Thus, we have an underlying parameter** θ (in our four examples this might be a cancer rate, an injury rate, a radiation level, or a process yield) **and we wish to determine whether it changes in specified ways** (e.g., "Does it increase?") **when an element of a system is changed** (e.g., smoking is added, seat belts are added, atomic power plants are added, or a putative catalyst is added).

Formally, let us make the following assumption (which represents no restriction, but gives us a precise notation).

Assumption 9.1.1. Suppose that X is a r.v. with d.f. $F(x|\theta)$ where θ is unknown, $\theta \in \Theta$. [Here X and θ may be multivariate.]

Let us now talk in terms of the question "Do atomic power plants increase radiation levels?" Then it may be that a long history of precise study has shown that to date the average level of radiation per year per person is $\theta_0 = 1.2$ units on some standard scale in the area within a 25-mile radius of a proposed model atomic power plant site. In fact, study has shown that the level of radiation per year in this area is random and normally distributed with a mean level of $\theta_0 = 1.2$ and a variance of $\sigma^2 = .09$; thus, a person chosen at random has a level X_1 that is an $N(\theta_0, \sigma^2)$ r.v. If n persons' radiation exposure is measured in this area next year, we will observe independent r.v.'s $X_1, \ldots, X_n$ that are each $N(\theta, \sigma^2)$, *where*: $\theta = \theta_0$ if an atomic power plant *does not* operate in the area; *and θ is unknown, $\theta \in \Theta = \{x: -\infty < x < +\infty\}$, if an atomic power plant does operate in the area.*

The hypothesis that the atomic power plant has no effect (or a null effect) is called the **null hypothesis**, denoted H_0, and is the assertion that $\theta = \theta_0$. The **alternative hypothesis**, denoted H_1, that it has an effect (either of increase *or* of decrease) is the assertion that $\theta \neq \theta_0$. (As noted in Definition 9.1.3, the alternative hypothesis in this problem could well be taken as $\theta > \theta_0$. This would be appropriate *if* we are sure that it could not possibly be true that $\theta < \theta_0$, and, as we see in Example 9.2.2, in that case (of the alternative taken as $\theta > \theta_0$ instead of $\theta \neq \theta_0$) we have greater chance of detecting the fact that $\theta > \theta_0$ when it is true. However, we have little chance of detecting the fact that $\theta < \theta_0$ if it is true and we use such a "one-sided" alternative hypothesis. Although we may believe that $\theta < \theta_0$ is unthinkable, we clearly sacrifice some of our scientific objectivity by not allowing for it, and we obviate the possibility of detecting facts that fly in the face of the prejudices of the time. Clearly, such does not serve the cause of truth well, and for this reason **we believe one-sided alternatives should be used much less widely than they are at present**.)

Note that **each "hypothesis" is a subset of Θ.** It is also useful to distinguish whether, for any specified hypothesis $H \subseteq \Theta$, the distribution of X is completely determined or not.

Definition 9.1.2. Suppose Assumption 9.1.1 holds. Any $H \subseteq \Theta$ is called a **hypothesis**. Often one hypothesis H_0 is called the **null hypothesis**, and another hypothesis H_1 is called the **alternative hypothesis**.

Definition 9.1.3. A hypothesis $H \subseteq \Theta$ is called **simple** if knowing $\theta \in H$ completely specifies $F(x|\theta)$. Otherwise, H is called a **composite** hypothesis.

Thus, in our atomic power plant example, H_0 is a simple null hypothesis, whereas H_1 is a composite alternative hypothesis. [*Note:* **It is not the case that H_0 and H_1 are unique for a particular problem.** Thus, the alternative hypothesis in the atomic power plant example could just as well be taken to be $H_1^* = \{\theta: \theta \in \Theta, \theta > \theta_0\}$. This would be an alternative of increase, whereas H_1 was an alternative of change ($+$ or $-$).]

It is important to note that it is not as simple to "test" a hypothesis as the foregoing simplified discussion might imply. Thus, we talked of sampling n people during a year of atomic power plant operation and comparing their radiation levels to θ_0. Yet the n people we choose will usually only be a sample of the N people living within 25 miles of the atomic power plant. For the N people the level θ may vary not only randomly (being a $N(\theta, \sigma^2)$ r.v.) but also by class of person (e.g., it might be higher for dentists and X-ray technicians; different—higher or lower—for new residents, people who were away part of the year on business or vacation, and babies; lower as distance from the atomic power plant increases; higher downwind from the plant; lower for people who dwell in basement apartments; and so on). It could also vary in general with wind velocities and directions, and with precipitation (e.g., precipitation might tend to take radioactive particles to ground level, whereas wind would tend to take them to certain sections of the area or out of the area). It could also vary with the correlation experienced between peak load periods (when the most radiation might be emitted) and wind velocity. (Other factors that we would like to control include the level of background radiation, which varies as Sun spots vary, and so on.)

These problems of experimental validity also occur in other problem areas. If the question is "Does smoking cause cancer?" and we just compare smokers and nonsmokers, the retort is "Smokers may tend to be people with a predisposition to cancer." If one "smokes up" nonsmokers, the retort is "Those who let you do it are different"; if one "desmokes" smokers, the same retort calls the experimental results' validity into question. (Cigarette companies are experts at such retorts!) (To answer such questions effectively and totally, we really need to find the causal mechanism. Nonetheless, an experiment was performed on dogs that seems to obviate all retorts except "Humans are not dogs."[1] To this we can say "Some are—especially those who, for economic gain, lead others to smoke." However, dogs (as well as guinea pigs, and so on) are customarily used to test drugs, heart disease remedies and theories, and so on, and are felt to be sufficiently comparable to human beings to validate the results. Only in a Hitlerite society could many of the important medical hypotheses be tested on human populations.)

Figuring out how to conduct an experiment so that factors such as those just outlined do not nullify its validity is called **designing an experiment** (or **experimental design**) and is a specialty of statisticians. It is for this reason that a statistician is usually employed on good research projects before any observations are made: in conjunction with experts in the subject matter of the specific area where the question arose, the statistician formulates an experimental design that will yield data valid for the study of the question.

PROBLEMS FOR SECTION 9.1

9.1.1 In the following hypothesis testing problems, $X \sim N(\mu, \sigma^2)$ and σ^2 is unknown. Determine whether each hypothesis is simple or composite.
(a) H: $\mu = \mu_0$, μ_0 a known constant.
(b) H: $\mu > \mu_0$, μ_0 a known constant.

[1]See Hammond, Auerbach, Kirman, and Garfinkel (1970).

(c) H: $\mu \neq \mu_0$, μ_0 a known constant.

(d) H: $\mu \in I$, where I is a specified interval.

9.1.2 Are the following hypotheses simple or composite?

(a) H: X has an exponential p.d.f. with some parameter θ.

(b) H: $F_X(x|\theta) = F_X(x|\theta_0)$, θ_0 a fixed known number.

(c) When $X \sim N(\mu, \sigma^2)$ with μ and σ^2 both unknown, H: $\mu = \mu_0$.

(d) When $X \sim N(\mu, \sigma^2)$ with μ and σ^2 both unknown, H: $\{\mu = \mu_0$ and $\sigma^2 = \sigma_0^2\}$, where μ_0 and σ_0^2 are fixed known numbers.

9.2. TESTS; ERRORS OF TYPE I AND TYPE II; POWER

Suppose Assumption 9.1.1 holds, that is, X is a r.v. with d.f. $F(x|\theta)$, where θ is unknown, $\theta \in \Theta$. Suppose we have a null hypothesis H_0 and an alternative hypothesis H_1. Our inference as to whether H_0 or H_1 contains the true θ will be based on observing X (whose d.f. $F(x|\theta)$ varies as $\theta \in \Theta$ varies). (In terms of the atomic power plant example of Section 9.1, we can think of $\Theta = \mathcal{R}$, $H_0 = \{\theta_0\}$, and $H_1 = \{\theta: \theta \in \Theta, \theta \neq \theta_0\}$. We then wish to decide whether the true $\theta = \theta_0$ or the true $\theta \neq \theta_0$.) So, for some outcomes $X = x$ we will decide $\theta \in H_0$, while for the other outcomes $X = x$ we will decide $\theta \in H_1$. A "test" is a specification of these subsets of the set of possible outcomes $\mathcal{X}$ for some specification of H_0, H_1, Θ, X:

Definition 9.2.1. Suppose that X is a r.v. with d.f. $F(x|\theta)$ where θ is unknown, $\theta \in \Theta$, and that a null hypothesis H_0 and an alternative hypothesis H_1 have been specified. The problem of deciding (after observing X) either that $\theta \in H_0$ (called **accepting the null hypothesis**) or that $\theta \in H_1$ (called **rejecting the null hypothesis**) is called a **hypothesis-testing problem**. H_0 is called **true** if $\theta \in H_0$, and **false** if $\theta \notin H_0$.

If the set of possible outcomes of X is $\mathcal{X}$, then a division of $\mathcal{X}$ into two disjoint and exhaustive subsets A (called the **acceptance region**, or **region of acceptance of** H_0) and R (called the **critical region**, or **region of rejection of** H_0) such that if we find $X \in A$ we accept H_0 and if we find $X \in R$ we reject H_0, is called a (**nonrandomized**) **test of** H_0 **versus** H_1. [See Figure 9.2-1.]

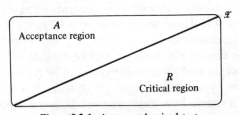

$\mathcal{X}$

A
Acceptance region

R
Critical region

Figure 9.2-1. A nonrandomized test.

Note that if we let $\phi(x)$ denote the probability that we reject H_0 after observing $X = x$, then for a nonrandomized test,

$$\phi(x) = \begin{cases} 1, & \text{if } x \in R \\ 0, & \text{if } x \in A. \end{cases}$$

However, for some points x it may be reasonable to flip a coin with some probability $\phi(x)$ of heads and decide to reject H_0 if heads turns up, otherwise accepting H_0. This is called a **randomized** test:

Definition 9.2.2. A **(randomized) test** for a hypothesis-testing problem is a function (called a **test function**)$\phi(x)$, defined for $x \in \mathscr{X}$, such that $0 \le \phi(x) \le 1$ for all $x \in \mathscr{X}$. If we observe X, we flip a coin with probability $\phi(X)$ of heads and reject (accept) H_0 if heads (tails) occurs. [Note that $\phi(\cdot)$ is also called a **critical function**.]

Such tests are usually needed only if X is a discrete r.v.; this need will be studied in later sections and can be ignored for now. (We will talk in terms of test functions, but these can be considered to take only values 0 or 1.)

Now when we conduct a test in a hypothesis-testing problem, two errors are possible: we can reject H_0 when it is true, and we can accept H_0 when it is false. These errors, and their probabilities of occurrence, are of central importance and hence have special names associated with them:

Definition 9.2.3. In a hypothesis-testing problem, rejecting H_0 when it is true is called an **error of type I**. [The probability of rejecting a true H_0 depends on the test $\phi(\cdot)$ employed and the true $\theta \in H_0$, and is called the **level (of significance)** of the test or the **size of the critical region**.]

Accepting H_0 when it is false is called an **error of type II**. [The probability of rejecting a false H_0 depends on the test $\phi(\cdot)$ employed and the true $\theta \in \Theta \cap \bar{H}_0$, and is called the **power** of the test. Note that power is defined for all θ in Θ that are not in H_0; this is often a larger set than H_1.]

From the definition of the level of a test (i.e., the size of a critical region), it is clear that for each critical region there is a corresponding size of critical region, hence knowing the critical region automatically implies information on the size of the test. Thus these are closely related concepts.

Example 9.2.4. Let us now illustrate these concepts using **the atomic power plant example of Section 9.1**. There we observe $X = (X_1, \ldots, X_n) \in \mathscr{X} = \mathscr{R}^n$ where $X_1, \ldots, X_n$ are independent r.v.'s, each $N(\theta, \sigma^2)$ with θ unknown, $\theta \in \Theta = \mathscr{R}$, and $\sigma^2 = .09$. (The case of unknown σ^2 will be considered later in this chapter, since it is more complicated.) Our null hypothesis is $H_0 = \{\theta_0\}$ where $\theta_0 = 1.2$, and our alternative hypothesis is $H_1 = \{\theta: \theta \in \mathscr{R}, \theta \ne \theta_0\}$. (As we noted in Section 9.1, H_0 is a simple hypothesis whereas H_1 is a composite hypothesis.) In our decision to accept or reject H_0 we will (if we restrict ourselves to nonrandomized tests; in Section 9.3 we will see that this restriction is possible here without loss) need to decide, for each possible value $x = (x_1, \ldots, x_n)$ of $X = (X_1, \ldots, X_n)$, whether $x \in A$ or $x \in R$. A reasonable way to do this would be to base our decision on a sufficient (hopefully, minimal sufficient) statistic for the problem, since it retains all information about θ that is possessed by $X = (X_1, \ldots, X_n)$. From Example 8.1.32 we know that $X_1 + \cdots + X_n$ is such a statistic. But by Example 8.3.10 we know that in this situation $\overline{X} = (X_1 + \cdots + X_n)/n$ is a BUE of θ, so it may make sense to compare $\overline{X}$ with θ_0 in order to make our acceptance or rejection decision.

Suppose we desire to have the level of our test be $\alpha = .05$. Two possible tests are the test that rejects H_0 iff $|\overline{X} - \theta_0| > a$, that is, the test with critical function

$$\phi_1(x) = \begin{cases} 1, & \text{if } |\bar{x} - \theta_0| > a \\ 0, & \text{otherwise;} \end{cases} \tag{9.2.5}$$

and the test that rejects H_0 iff $\overline{X} > \theta_0 + b$, that is, the test with critical function

$$\phi_2(x) = \begin{cases} 1, & \text{if } \bar{x} > \theta_0 + b \\ 0, & \text{otherwise.} \end{cases} \tag{9.2.6}$$

In both cases a and b are to be set to give level $\alpha = .05$. What a and b are these, and how do the tests compare with regard to power?

For the test with critical function $\phi_1(\cdot)$ given in equation (9.2.5), the **level** is

$$P_{\theta_0}\left[|\overline{X} - \theta_0| > a\right]$$

$$= 1 - P_{\theta_0}\left[|\overline{X} - \theta_0| \leq a\right] = 1 - P_{\theta_0}\left[-a \leq \overline{X} - \theta_0 \leq a\right]$$

$$= 1 - P_{\theta_0}\left[-\frac{a}{\sigma/\sqrt{n}} \leq \frac{\overline{X} - \theta_0}{\sigma/\sqrt{n}} \leq \frac{a}{\sigma/\sqrt{n}}\right]$$

$$= 1 - P\left[-a\frac{\sqrt{n}}{\sigma} \leq Y \leq a\frac{\sqrt{n}}{\sigma}\right] \tag{9.2.7}$$

$$= 1 - \left[\Phi\left(a\frac{\sqrt{n}}{\sigma}\right) - \Phi\left(-a\frac{\sqrt{n}}{\sigma}\right)\right]$$

$$= 1 - \left[\Phi\left(a\frac{\sqrt{n}}{\sigma}\right) - \left\{1 - \Phi\left(a\frac{\sqrt{n}}{\sigma}\right)\right\}\right]$$

$$= 2\left[1 - \Phi\left(a\frac{\sqrt{n}}{\sigma}\right)\right],$$

where: Y is a $N(0,1)$ r.v. since (see Example 5.5.29) $\overline{X}$ is $N(\theta_0, \sigma^2/n)$; and $\Phi(z) = P[Y \leq z]$ (e.g., review especially the last paragraph of Example 6.3.5). To obtain level $\alpha = .05$ for our test, we set

$$
\begin{cases}
.05 = 2\left[1 - \Phi\left(a\dfrac{\sqrt{n}}{\sigma}\right)\right], \\[2ex]
.025 = 1 - \Phi\left(a\dfrac{\sqrt{n}}{\sigma}\right), \\[2ex]
\Phi\left(a\dfrac{\sqrt{n}}{\sigma}\right) = .975, \\[2ex]
a\dfrac{\sqrt{n}}{\sigma} = \Phi^{-1}(.975) = 1.96, \\[2ex]
a = 1.96\dfrac{\sigma}{\sqrt{n}} = \dfrac{.588}{\sqrt{n}},
\end{cases}
\qquad (9.2.8)
$$

where $\Phi^{-1}(.975) = 1.96$ (i.e., $\Phi(1.96) = .975$) was determined using Table 11, and we used the fact that $\sigma^2 = .09$ (so $\sigma = .3$) in this example. So if, say, $n = 100$, then $a = .0588$; that is, we reject H_0 iff $|\overline{X} - \theta_0| > .0588$.

The **power** of the test with critical function $\phi_1(\cdot)$ is (for $\theta \in \Theta \cap \overline{H}_0$, i.e., for $\theta \neq \theta_0$) the probability

$$
\begin{aligned}
P_\theta\big[|\overline{X} - \theta_0| > a\big] &= 1 - P_\theta\big[|\overline{X} - \theta_0| \leq a\big] \\[1ex]
&= 1 - P_\theta\big[-a \leq \overline{X} - \theta_0 \leq a\big] \\[1ex]
&= 1 - P_\theta\big[-a + \theta_0 - \theta \leq \overline{X} - \theta \leq a + \theta_0 - \theta\big] \\[1ex]
&= 1 - P_\theta\left[\frac{-a + \theta_0 - \theta}{\sigma/\sqrt{n}} \leq \frac{\overline{X} - \theta}{\sigma/\sqrt{n}} \leq \frac{a + \theta_0 - \theta}{\sigma/\sqrt{n}}\right] \\[1ex]
&= 1 - P_\theta\left[\frac{-a + \theta_0 - \theta}{\sigma/\sqrt{n}} \leq Y \leq \frac{a + \theta_0 - \theta}{\sigma/\sqrt{n}}\right] \\[1ex]
&= 1 - \left[\Phi\left(\frac{a + \theta_0 - \theta}{\sigma/\sqrt{n}}\right) - \Phi\left(\frac{-a + \theta_0 - \theta}{\sigma/\sqrt{n}}\right)\right] \\[1ex]
&= 1 - \left[\Phi\left(1.96 + \frac{\theta_0 - \theta}{\sigma}\sqrt{n}\right) - \Phi\left(-1.96 + \frac{\theta_0 - \theta}{\sigma}\sqrt{n}\right)\right],
\end{aligned}
\qquad (9.2.9)
$$

where Y is a $N(0, 1)$ r.v. and $a = 1.96\sigma/\sqrt{n}$ was substituted. As a function of θ, say $f(\theta)$, the rejection probability (9.2.9) has the properties: $f(\theta_0) = \alpha = .05$; $f(\theta_0 + x) = f(\theta_0 - x)$ for all x; $f(\theta_2) > f(\theta_1)$ for all $\theta_2 > \theta_1 \geq \theta_0$; and $\lim_{\theta \to +\infty} f(\theta) = 1$. (See Problem 9.2.)

Now, **for the test with critical function** $\phi_2(\cdot)$ given in equation (9.2.6) the probability of rejection of H_0 is

$$P_\theta\left[\overline{X} > \theta_0 + b\right] = 1 - P_\theta\left[\overline{X} \leq \theta_0 + b\right]$$

$$= 1 - P_\theta\left[\frac{\overline{X} - \theta}{\sigma/\sqrt{n}} \leq \frac{b + \theta_0 - \theta}{\sigma/\sqrt{n}}\right]$$

$$= 1 - P_\theta\left[Y \leq \frac{b + \theta_0 - \theta}{\sigma/\sqrt{n}}\right] \tag{9.2.10}$$

$$= 1 - \Phi\left(\frac{b + \theta_0 - \theta}{\sigma/\sqrt{n}}\right),$$

where Y is a $N(0, 1)$ r.v. To set the **level** to $\alpha = .05$ requires that

$$\begin{cases} .05 = P_{\theta_0}\left[\overline{X} > \theta_0 + b\right], \\[2mm] .05 = 1 - \Phi\left(\dfrac{b + \theta_0 - \theta_0}{\sigma/\sqrt{n}}\right), \\[2mm] .05 = 1 - \Phi\left(b\dfrac{\sqrt{n}}{\sigma}\right), \\[2mm] \Phi\left(b\dfrac{\sqrt{n}}{\sigma}\right) = .95, \\[2mm] b\dfrac{\sqrt{n}}{\sigma} = 1.64, \\[2mm] b = 1.64\dfrac{\sigma}{\sqrt{n}} = \dfrac{.492}{\sqrt{n}}. \end{cases} \tag{9.2.11}$$

So if, say, $n = 100$, then $b = .0492$; that is, we reject H_0 iff $\overline{X} - \theta_0 > .0492$. As a function of θ, say $g(\theta)$, the rejection probability (9.2.10) has the properties: $g(\theta_0) = .05$; $g(\theta_2) > g(\theta_1)$ for all $\theta_2 > \theta_1$; and $\lim_{\theta \to +\infty} g(\theta) = 1$. (See Problem 9.2.)

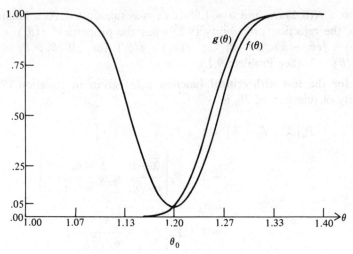

Figure 9.2-2. Rejection probabilities of two tests.

The **rejection probabilities of the tests with critical functions** $\phi_1(\cdot)$ **and** $\phi_2(\cdot)$ are plotted in Figure 9.2-2 for $n = 100$. From this graph we see that: both tests have the same level; and $g(\theta) > f(\theta)$ for $\theta > \theta_0$, while $g(\theta) < f(\theta)$ for $\theta < \theta_0$. Thus, if we are sure that either $\theta = \theta_0$ or $\theta > \theta_0$, then H_1 would be $\theta > \theta_0$ and we should use $\phi_2(\cdot)$ (it yields the same level as $\phi_1(\cdot)$ and more power for all $\theta > \theta_0$); whereas if we a priori think we may encounter $\theta < \theta_0$ also, we should use $\phi_1(\cdot)$ in order to have a suitably high probability of rejection when θ is less than θ_0. The curves in Figure 9.2-2 would be useful in the situation where we could only afford $n = 100$ and wanted to see what power this would yield for the two tests considered. **Often n is set so that the power at a specified θ has at least a certain specified value**; for example, if for the test using $\phi_1(\cdot)$ we wanted to have power $\geq .95$ when $\theta = 1.23$, we would set n as follows:

$$\begin{cases} .95 \leq P_{\theta=1.23}\big[|\overline{X} - \theta_0| > a\big], \\ .95 \leq 1 - \left[\Phi\left(1.96 + \dfrac{1.2 - 1.23}{.3}\sqrt{n}\right) - \Phi\left(-1.96 + \dfrac{1.2 - 1.23}{.3}\sqrt{n}\right)\right], \\ \Phi(1.96 - .1\sqrt{n}) - \Phi(-1.96 - .1\sqrt{n}) \leq .05. \end{cases}$$

$$(9.2.12)$$

Solving (9.2.12) by trial and error (i.e., choose an n, calculate $\Phi(1.96 - .1\sqrt{n}) - \Phi(-1.96 - .1\sqrt{n})$, and so on) we find that the smallest n that will satisfy (9.2.12) is $n = 1296$.

The concepts of probability of type I error (level of significance), probability of type II error, and power of a test were defined in Definition 9.2.3. However, **in**

the case of a composite null hypothesis, Definition 9.2.3 does not specify what the "level of significance" is, since under a composite H_0 a number of different θ's (hence, different distributions of X under which to compute the $P_\theta[\phi(X)$ rejects $H_0]$) are possible. If Θ is the parameter space,

$$H_0: \theta \in \Theta_0,$$

and

$$H_1: \theta \in \Theta_1$$

(with $\overline{\Theta}_0 = \Theta_1$), then **the size of the critical region (or type I error probability) for a composite H_0 is defined as**

$$\alpha \equiv \max_{\theta \in \Theta_0} P_\theta\big[\phi(X) \text{ rejects } H_0\big] = \max_{\theta \in \Theta_0} \alpha(\theta), \qquad (9.2.13)$$

and the power of the test $\phi(\cdot)$ is a function of θ:

$$\mathscr{P}(\theta) \equiv P_\theta\big[\phi(X) \text{ rejects } H_0\big], \qquad \theta \in \Theta_1. \qquad (9.2.14)$$

$\beta(\theta) \equiv 1 - \mathscr{P}(\theta)$, the probability of type II error at $\theta \in \Theta_1$, is also called the value of the operating characteristic at θ, and the curve $\beta(\theta)$ is called the **operating characteristic curve (OC-curve).**

It is clear that an experimenter's goal would ideally be to minimize both the type I and type II error probabilities, since one desires neither to reject H_0 when H_0 is true nor to accept H_0 when H_0 is false (i.e., when H_1 is true). The probabilities of these occurrences are denoted by α and β, respectively, hence the experimenter would like to have both α and β a minimum (ideally both zero). However, if the number n of observations is fixed, then the probabilities α and β cannot be controlled independently (when $\alpha \downarrow$, $\beta \uparrow$). However, the experimenter may minimize one of the probabilities (α, β) while keeping the other no larger than a specified level. Conventionally, we fix the level of significance function (or size of the critical region) to not exceed α_0 and minimize β (i.e., maximize power) subject to the constraint $\alpha \leq \alpha_0$; α_0 is then called **the level of significance.**

What the type I error probability bound α_0 should be fixed at is somewhat arbitrary (though decision theory, studied in Chapter 12, provides a logical way to choose α_0 by relating to the costs of the possible errors). It has become customary to choose α_0 as one of a number of usual values that may be called "the holy numbers": .005, .01, .025, .05, .10, .20. Of these, .05 is in the most common use (is the holiest number), whereas .01 is a distant second in use (with the other choices being rarely used). This has some benefit in that it reduces the quantity of tables needed to carry out various tests. Choosing α as .05, or 1 chance in 20, seems to many to be an intuitively reasonable action. However, when choosing α one also needs to consider the power $1 - \beta$, and, if this is too low, a higher value of α than .05 may be desirable. (For example, if we are testing a new medical treatment and we know in advance that its effect if any will be in a range where an α of .05 will imply a power of at most $1 - \beta = .06$, then it may be sensible to use a higher α than .05, otherwise the experiment may not be worth running unless a larger sample size can be obtained.)

It is desirable to have the power of a test be at least as large as its level of significance (since we should be more likely to reject a false H_0 than a true H_0). A test with this property is called unbiased:

Definition 9.2.15.   A test $\phi(\cdot)$ is said to be **unbiased** if

$$\max_{\theta \in \Theta_0} P_\theta \big[\phi(X) \text{ rejects } H_0 \big] \leq \min_{\theta \in \Theta_1} P_\theta \big[\phi(X) \text{ rejects } H_0 \big].$$

Example 9.2.16.   The test $\phi_1(\cdot)$ in (9.2.5) is unbiased, whereas test $\phi_2(\cdot)$ in (9.2.6) is not unbiased (it is biased); see Figure 9.2-2.

Remark 9.2.17.   Note that earlier we have at times needed to flip a coin with some probability of heads (e.g., just before and in Definition 9.2.2 with a general probability of heads and later at equation (9.3.22) with probability .05 of heads). Where can such coins be obtained? A first answer to this question is that experiments have been done in the past (e.g., rolling dice or drawing from a well-shuffled deck of cards or a well-stirred urn) and tables of the results prepared; since these were prepared with care and extensively tested, their use is usually preferable to performing your own experiment. The first such tables were prepared by Tippett (1927), and the most extensive were prepared by The RAND Corporation (1955). These tables gave **random digits** chosen from 0, 1, 2, 3, 4, 5, 6, 7, 8, 9 rather than numbers on the interval 0 to 1. However, if we wish to flip a coin with probability .95, for example, of heads, choose two digits from the table. If the digits are 01, 02, ..., 95 say heads occurred (whereas if the digits are 96, 97, 98, 99, 00 say tails occurred). Tippett gave 41,600 digits, while The RAND Corporation gave a million. A similar table, with 50 random digits, is given in Table 4.7-1.

Since such tables are often insufficient and/or cumbersome for large sampling experiments, sample surveys, and simulations, procedures for generating numbers with similar properties by numerical methods have been developed and are usually available in a so-called **random number generator** in many digital computer languages and subroutine libraries. For a discussion of one good random number generator, see Example 4.7.3; for a discussion of testing of many generators (and information on which ones were of poor quality) see Dudewicz and Ralley (1981).

PROBLEMS FOR SECTION 9.2

9.2.1 An urn contains 10 balls, of which θ balls are blue (the rest being red and white). We are interested in testing the null hypothesis H_0: $\theta = 3$ versus H_1: $\theta = 4$. Suppose we take a sample of size 3 balls, and reject H_0 if all 3 draws yield blue balls. Compute the error probabilities α and β, assuming
(a) Sampling was done without replacement.
(b) Sampling was done with replacement.

9.2.2 The manufacturer of an imported automobile claims that the average miles per gallon (mpg) of this type of car is at least 30. Suppose that the mpg of a randomly selected car is a normally distributed r.v. with mean μ and variance $\sigma^2 = 25$. To check the claim, we consider the hypothesis-testing problem H_0: $\mu < 30$ versus H_a: $\mu \geq 30$. We take a random sample of 36 cars from this manufacturer's output, find mpg for each of the cars, and then compute $\overline{X}$ of the mpg's of the 36 cars. Suppose it is decided to reject H_0 iff $\overline{X} \geq 32$.
(a) Compute the size of the critical region (i.e., α). (Note that the null hypothesis is composite, so we compute the supremum of a probability as $\mu \to 30$.)
(b) Compute β (and hence power) for all $\mu \geq 30$, and graph the OC-curve. Also draw the power curve.

9.2.3 It is desired to test H_0: $\mu \leq 10$ versus H_1: $\mu > 10$ on the basis of a random sample of size 25 from a normal population with unknown mean μ and variance $\sigma^2 = 4$. If the probability of Type I error is to be $\alpha = .025$ and the test is $\phi(X) = 1$ if $\overline{X} > c$ (and $= 0$ otherwise, where $X = (X_1, \ldots, X_{25})$ denotes the random sample),
(a) Find c (and hence the critical region).
(b) Find β for $\mu = 10, 10.5, 11, 11.5, 12, 12.5, 13, \ldots$ and use the results to sketch the OC-curve on graph paper. Also draw the power curve on the same axes.

9.2.4 (a) Consider testing the simple null hypothesis H_0: $\theta = \theta_0$ versus the simple alternative hypothesis H_1: $\theta = \theta_1$, where θ is the mean of a normal population with known variance σ^2. Suppose we take a random sample of size n (to be determined) and use test $\phi(x) = 1$ if $\overline{x} > c$ (and $= 0$ otherwise). How large an n is needed to obtain probability of Type I error of α and power of $1 - \beta$?
(a) Suppose $\theta_0 = 5$ and $\theta_1 = 8$. If $\sigma^2 = 4$, find the values of c and n such that $\alpha = .05$ and $\beta = .05$.

9.2.5 Consider a Poisson distribution with mean $\lambda \in \{2, 3\}$. Consider testing H_0: $\lambda = 3$ versus H_1: $\lambda = 2$. A random sample of size 5 is taken and the test calls for rejection of H_0 iff $\overline{X} < c$. If α is to be .05 (or the closest number to .05 you can find in the Poisson table), find the critical region to use.

9.2.6 It is desired to test H_0: $\mu = 10$ versus H_1: $\mu \neq 10$, where μ is the population mean of a normal population with standard deviation $\sigma = 3$. A random sample of size $n = 9$ is taken and the test $\phi(x) = 1$ if $|\overline{x} - 10| > c$ (and $= 0$ otherwise) is used.
(a) Find the values of c to use for each of $\alpha = .01, .02, .05, .10$.
(b) Find the power of each of the four tests in part (a) when $\mu = 7(.25)13$, and draw their power curves.

9.2.7 It is desired to test H_0: $p = .2$ versus H_1: $p = .4$ for a binomial distribution with $n = 10$. For the test $\phi(X) = 1$ if $X \leq 3$ (and $= 0$ otherwise), find α and β. Can you find a better test (i.e., with improved, i.e. smaller, Type I and II errors) with the same $n = 10$?

9.2.8 Consider testing H_0: X is exponential with mean 2, versus H_1: X is exponential with mean 3. A random sample of size $n = 3$ is taken, and the test is

$$\phi(x) = 1 \quad \text{if } \frac{\prod_{i=1}^{3} f(x_i|3)}{\prod_{i=1}^{3} f(x_i|2)} \leq 1$$

(and $= 0$ otherwise), where $f(x|\theta)$ is the exponential p.d.f. with mean θ. Find α and β for this test.

9.2.9 Let $\phi(\cdot)$ be a randomized test. Show that $\overline{\phi}(\cdot) = 1 - \phi(\cdot)$ is also a randomized test. Compute the relationship between the power functions of tests $\phi(\cdot)$ and $\overline{\phi}(\cdot)$.

9.2.10 Consider a random sample of size n from a distribution with mean μ and variance σ^2, with n large enough that it is reasonable to assume that $\overline{X}$ has a normal distribution. To test H_0: $\mu = \mu_0$ versus H_1: $\mu \neq \mu_0$, a suggested test is $\phi(X) = 1$ if $|\overline{X} - \mu_0| \geq c$ (and $= 0$ otherwise). Find an approximate α-level critical region for this test if σ^2 is known. Find an expression for its power.

9.2.11 As in Problem 9.2.10, but now with σ^2 unknown.

9.3. THE NEYMAN-PEARSON LEMMA; ITS GENERALIZATIONS AND USES

To this point in this chapter, we have considered both intuitively and precisely null and alternative, simple and composite, hypotheses (Section 9.1) and the hypothesis-testing problem including tests, level, and power with examples (Section 9.2). **In this section we present a general method (the Neyman-Pearson Lemma) of obtaining "best" tests of simple hypotheses versus simple alternatives,** see how the method sometimes provides "best" tests for composite hypotheses, and consider an application to legislative apportionment. Succeeding sections consider a decision-theoretic view of the hypothesis-testing problem, giving a preview of the methods of Chapter 12 for this special case (Section 9.4), and consider specific hypothesis-testing problems that often occur in practice (Sections 9.5ff).

First we formulate a definition of a **"best" (or "most powerful") test of a simple null hypothesis versus a simple alternative hypothesis,** and then state and prove the Neyman-Pearson Lemma.[2]

Definition 9.3.1. In a hypothesis-testing problem where H_0 and H_1 are both simple, a test with critical function $\phi(\cdot)$ is called **most powerful** (or **most powerful**

---

[2] Although we state the Neyman-Pearson Lemma for the absolutely continuous and discrete cases, it holds in general. See, for example, Lehmann (1959), pp. 65–68.

of level α) if it has level α [i.e., P_{θ_0}[Rejecting H_0 using $\phi(\cdot)$] = α] and no other test of level α has a larger power at H_1 [i.e.,

$$P_{\theta_1}\left[\text{Rejecting } H_0 \text{ using } \phi(\cdot)\right] \geq P_{\theta_1}\left[\text{Rejecting } H_0 \text{ using } \psi(\cdot)\right]$$

for all critical functions $\psi(\cdot)$ such that P_{θ_0}[Rejecting H_0 using $\psi(\cdot)$] = α].

[*Note:* P_{θ_0}**[Rejecting H_0 using $\phi(\cdot)$] = $E_{\theta_0}\psi(X)$**. This relationship between rejection probability and expected value of the critical function will be used extensively to obtain a simple notation.]

The crux of the problem of finding a most powerful test of level α is to specify a critical region R such that it has probability α when H_0 is true, and no other region R' (which also has probability α when H_0 is true) can have a larger probability than does R when H_1 is true.

A motivation often given for putting in the critical region R those x such that $f(x|\theta_1)/f(x|\theta_0) > k$ **is the following.** In the discrete case, putting x in R contributes $f(x|\theta_0) = P_{\theta_0}[X = x]$ to level and $f(x|\theta_1) = P_{\theta_1}[X = x]$ to power. Now, subject to a restriction on the level (level = α), we want the most power, so we put in R those x that give us the most power-per-level, that is, those that have the highest values of the power-to-level ratio $f(x|\theta_1)/f(x|\theta_0)$. That is, for some k put in R all x such that $f(x|\theta_1)/f(x|\theta_0) > k$. To see this in an example, suppose there are two possible values of θ (θ_0 and θ_1) and X may have the possible values 0, 1, 2 with probabilities as specified in the following table.

x	0	1	2
$p(x\|\theta_0)$	.05	.05	.90
$p(x\|\theta_1)$	.90	.08	.02

(Note that this example features a subset of the values in Example 7.2.6.) Suppose we choose $\alpha = .05$. Then critical region $R = \{0\}$ has level .05 (since the probability that $X \in R$ is .05 when H_0 is true). The critical region $R' = \{1\}$ also has level .05. Critical region R is preferred to critical region R' since both have the same probability of Type I error (.05), but R has higher probability of rejection when H_1 is true (.90, as opposed to only .08 for R'). Note that the power-per-level ratios are $.90/.05 = 18$ for the point 0, and $.08/.05 = 1.6$ for the point 1, and $.02/.90 = .022$ for the point 2. Thus, we obtain the most powerful test by putting into the critical region points with the highest $p(x|\theta_1)/p(x|\theta_0)$ ratios.

Having motivated the most powerful test's form of critical region, we now state and prove the Neyman-Pearson Lemma, which formalizes these ideas.

Theorem 9.3.2. Neyman-Pearson Lemma. Suppose that X is a r.v. with d.f. $F(x|\theta)$ where θ is unknown, $\theta \in \Theta$ and $x \in \mathcal{X}$. Assume $F(x|\theta)$ is either absolutely continuous [in which case let $f(x|\theta)$ denote its density at x] or discrete [in which case let $f(x|\theta)$ denote $P_\theta[X = x]$]. Suppose that $H_0 = \{\theta_0\}$ and $H_1 = \{\theta_1\}$ [often written as H_0: $\theta = \theta_0$ and H_1: $\theta = \theta_1$ in this case] are simple null and alternative hypotheses, respectively.

For testing H_0 versus H_1 after observing X, if a test with critical function $\phi(\cdot)$ satisfies (for some k)

$$E_{\theta_0}\phi(X) = \alpha \qquad (9.3.3)$$

and

$$\phi(x) = \begin{cases} 1, & \text{when } f(x|\theta_1) > kf(x|\theta_0) \\ 0, & \text{when } f(x|\theta_1) < kf(x|\theta_0), \end{cases} \qquad (9.3.4)$$

then it is most powerful for testing H_0 versus H_1 at level α.

Proof: [We give the proof for the absolutely continuous case, the discrete case being analogous with summations replacing integrals.] We write, for example $\int_{-\infty}^{\infty} g(x)\,dx$ as $\int_{x \in \mathscr{X}} g(x)\,dx$ as a shorthand (since the sets over which we are integrating are notationally complex). For this use, define

$$\begin{cases} c_1 = \{x: f(x|\theta_1) > kf(x|\theta_0)\}, \\ c_2 = \{x: f(x|\theta_1) < kf(x|\theta_0)\}, \\ c_3 = \{x: f(x|\theta_1) = kf(x|\theta_0)\}. \end{cases} \qquad (9.3.5)$$

Suppose $\phi(\cdot)$ satisfies equations (9.3.3) and (9.3.4). Let $\psi(\cdot)$ be the critical function of any other test with level α. Then the difference of the powers of the two tests at H_1 is

$$E_{\theta_1}\phi(X) - E_{\theta_1}\psi(X) = E_{\theta_1}[\phi(X) - \psi(X)]$$

$$= \int_{x \in \mathscr{X}} [\phi(x) - \psi(x)] f(x|\theta_1)\,dx$$

$$= \int_{x \in c_1} [\phi(x) - \psi(x)] f(x|\theta_1)\,dx \qquad (9.3.6)$$

$$+ \int_{x \in c_2} [\phi(x) - \psi(x)] f(x|\theta_1)\,dx$$

$$+ \int_{x \in c_3} [\phi(x) - \psi(x)] f(x|\theta_1)\,dx.$$

Using the definitions of c_1, c_2, and c_3, we know that: $\phi(x) = 1$ for $x \in c_1$; and $\phi(x) = 0$ for $x \in c_2$. Substituting these in equation (9.3.6) and then using the facts $f(x|\theta_1) > kf(x|\theta_0)$ for $x \in c_1$, $f(x|\theta_1) < kf(x|\theta_0)$ for $x \in c_2$, and $f(x|\theta_1) = kf(x|\theta_0)$ for $x \in c_3$, we find

$$E_{\theta_1}\phi(X) - E_{\theta_1}\psi(X) = \int_{x \in c_1} [1 - \psi(x)] f(x|\theta_1)\, dx$$

$$+ \int_{x \in c_2} [-\psi(x)] f(x|\theta_1)\, dx$$

$$+ \int_{x \in c_3} [\phi(x) - \psi(x)] f(x|\theta_1)\, dx$$

$$\geq \int_{x \in c_1} [1 - \psi(x)] kf(x|\theta_0)\, dx$$

$$+ \int_{x \in c_2} [-\psi(x)] kf(x|\theta_0)\, dx$$

$$+ \int_{x \in c_3} [\phi(x) - \psi(x)] kf(x|\theta_0)\, dx \qquad (9.3.7)$$

$$= \int_{x \in c_1} [\phi(x) - \psi(x)] kf(x|\theta_0)\, dx$$

$$+ \int_{x \in c_2} [\phi(x) - \psi(x)] kf(x|\theta_0)\, dx$$

$$+ \int_{x \in c_3} [\phi(x) - \psi(x)] kf(x|\theta_0)\, dx$$

$$= k\int_{x \in \mathscr{X}} [\phi(x) - \psi(x)] f(x|\theta_0)\, dx$$

$$= kE_{\theta_0}[\phi(X) - \psi(X)] = k(\alpha - \alpha) = 0.$$

Hence $E_{\theta_1}\phi(X) \geq E_{\theta_1}(X)$, as was to be shown. ∎

Example 9.3.8. Suppose we have (or wish to find) a critical function that satisfies equation (9.3.4). If $f(x|\theta_1)$ and $f(x|\theta_0)$ are each > 0 for all $x \in \mathscr{X}$, then (9.3.4) can be rewritten as

$$\phi(x) = \begin{cases} 1, & \text{when } \dfrac{f(x|\theta_1)}{f(x|\theta_0)} > k \\[2ex] 0, & \text{when } \dfrac{f(x|\theta_1)}{f(x|\theta_0)} < k. \end{cases} \qquad (9.3.9)$$

Thus, the classification of a point x into the rejection region ($\phi(x) = 1$) or acceptance region ($\phi(x) = 0$) depends "only" on the likelihood-ratio $f(X|\theta_1)/f(X|\theta_0)$, which is (see Example 8.1.29) a minimal sufficient statistic in this case. (We put "only" in quotes since, on the "boundary" $f(X|\theta_1)/f(X|\theta_0) = k$, $\phi(x)$ may be selected in many ways in general. In an absolutely continuous case, usually $P_\theta[f(X|\theta_1)/f(X|\theta_0) = k] = 0$ ($\theta = \theta_0, \theta_1$). In a discrete case this probability may be > 0 and, to make $\phi(\cdot)$ have level α, we may need to use randomization ($0 < \phi(x) < 1$ for some x's).)

Note: The Neyman-Pearson lemma was proven with essentially no "regularity" or other restrictions of any sort. (Many authors write equation (9.3.4) in terms of the ratio $f(x|\theta_1)/f(x|\theta_0)$ as at equation (9.3.9), and must therefore exclude cases where $f(x|\theta_0)$ may be zero. Some of these cases are important. One such case is discussed in Example 9.3.17.)

Example 9.3.10. Suppose we observe $X = (X_1, \ldots, X_n)$ where $X_1, \ldots, X_n$ are independent r.v.'s, each $N(\mu, \sigma^2)$ where μ is unknown ($-\infty < \mu < +\infty$) and $\sigma^2 > 0$ is known. Find a critical function for a most powerful level $\alpha(0 < \alpha < 1)$ test of H_0: $\mu = \mu_0$ versus H_1: $\mu = \mu_1$ where $\mu_1 > \mu_0$.

By the Neyman-Pearson Lemma, we know that if a test satisfies (9.3.4) and (9.3.3) it is most powerful of level α for this hypothesis-testing problem. Now here $f(x|\mu_1)$ and $f(x|\mu_0)$ are each > 0 for all $x \in \mathcal{X} = \mathcal{R}^n$, so we wish to find those $x = (x_1, \ldots, x_n)$ for which $f(x|\mu_1)/f(x|\mu_0) > k$. Using (8.1.33) we find

$$\frac{f(x|\mu_1)}{f(x|\mu_0)} = \frac{\displaystyle\prod_{i=1}^{n} \left\{ \frac{1}{\sqrt{2\pi}\,\sigma} e^{-\frac{1}{2}\left(\frac{x_i - \mu_1}{\sigma}\right)^2} \right\}}{\displaystyle\prod_{i=1}^{n} \left\{ \frac{1}{\sqrt{2\pi}\,\sigma} e^{-\frac{1}{2}\left(\frac{x_i - \mu_0}{\sigma}\right)^2} \right\}}$$

$$= \frac{\left(\dfrac{1}{\sqrt{2\pi}\,\sigma}\right)^n e^{-\frac{1}{2\sigma^2}\sum_{i=1}^{n} x_i^2} \; e^{-\frac{1}{2\sigma^2}\left\{-2\mu_1 \sum_{i=1}^{n} x_i + n\mu_1^2\right\}}}{\left(\dfrac{1}{\sqrt{2\pi}\,\sigma}\right)^n e^{-\frac{1}{2\sigma^2}\sum_{i=1}^{n} x_i^2} \; e^{-\frac{1}{2\sigma^2}\left\{-2\mu_0 \sum_{i=1}^{n} x_i + n\mu_0^2\right\}}} \qquad (9.3.11)$$

$$= e^{\frac{1}{\sigma^2}(\mu_1 - \mu_0)\sum_{i=1}^{n} x_i - \frac{n}{2\sigma^2}(\mu_1^2 - \mu_0^2)}.$$

Since $f(x|\mu_1)/f(x|\mu_0) > 0$ for all $x \in \mathscr{X}$, we may take $k > 0$ (otherwise the rejection region is $\mathscr{X}$ and level = power = 1). Thus, this ratio is $> k$ iff

$$
\begin{cases}
\dfrac{1}{\sigma^2}(\mu_1 - \mu_0) \sum_{i=1}^{n} x_i - \dfrac{n}{2\sigma^2}(\mu_1^2 - \mu_0^2) > \ln k \\[2mm]
\Leftrightarrow 2(\mu_1 - \mu_0) \sum_{i=1}^{n} x_i - n(\mu_1^2 - \mu_0^2) > 2\sigma^2 \ln k \\[2mm]
\Leftrightarrow 2(\mu_1 - \mu_0) \sum_{i=1}^{n} x_i > 2\sigma^2 \ln k + n(\mu_1^2 - \mu_0^2) \qquad (9.3.12) \\[2mm]
\Leftrightarrow \sum_{i=1}^{n} x_i > \dfrac{2\sigma^2 \ln k + n(\mu_1^2 - \mu_0^2)}{2(\mu_1 - \mu_0)} \\[2mm]
\Leftrightarrow \bar{x} > \dfrac{2\sigma^2 \ln k + n(\mu_1^2 - \mu_0^2)}{2n(\mu_1 - \mu_0)},
\end{cases}
$$

where we used the fact that $\mu_1 > \mu_0$, when we divided by $\mu_1 - \mu_0$, to establish that we did not need to reverse the inequality. Now if k, σ^2, μ_1, μ_0, n are fixed, then

$$
k' = \frac{2\sigma^2 \ln k + n(\mu_1^2 - \mu_0^2)}{2n(\mu_1 - \mu_0)} \qquad (9.3.13)
$$

is just another constant and $f(x|\mu_1)/f(x|\mu_0) > k$ iff $\bar{x} > k'$. So if $\phi(\cdot)$ sets $\phi(x) = 1$ iff $\bar{x} > k'$, then $\phi(\cdot)$ satisfies (9.3.4). What value should k' then have if we wish $\phi(\cdot)$ to satisfy (9.3.3)? We find

$$
E_{\mu_0}\phi(X) = P_{\mu_0}[\bar{X} > k'] = P_{\mu_0}\left[\frac{\bar{X} - \mu_0}{\sigma/\sqrt{n}} > \frac{k' - \mu_0}{\sigma/\sqrt{n}} \right]
$$
$$
= 1 - \Phi\left(\frac{k' - \mu_0}{\sigma/\sqrt{n}} \right), \qquad (9.3.14)
$$

which will equal α iff

$$
\begin{cases}
\alpha = 1 - \Phi\left(\dfrac{k' - \mu_0}{\sigma/\sqrt{n}} \right), \\[2mm]
\Phi\left(\dfrac{k' - \mu_0}{\sigma/\sqrt{n}} \right) = 1 - \alpha, \\[2mm]
\dfrac{k' - \mu_0}{\sigma/\sqrt{n}} = \Phi^{-1}(1 - \alpha) \\[2mm]
k' = \mu_0 + \dfrac{\sigma}{\sqrt{n}} \Phi^{-1}(1 - \alpha).
\end{cases} \qquad (9.3.15)
$$

Thus, the test that rejects iff $\overline{X} > \mu_0 + (\sigma/\sqrt{n})\Phi^{-1}(1 - \alpha)$ is most powerful of level α in our case. Note that the test does not depend on μ_1, that is, the *same* test is most powerful for every $\mu_1 > \mu_0$ (although of course the power differs for different μ_1's). Such a test will be called **uniformly most powerful (UMP)** for testing H_0: $\mu = \mu_0$ versus H_1: $\mu > \mu_0$, or UMP one-sided (since it is not UMP for testing H_0: $\mu = \mu_0$ versus H_1: $\mu = \mu^* < \mu_0$). This is the test we were led to in Example 9.2.4 (see $\phi_2(\cdot)$ in that example) by considerations of sufficiency.

Our development in Example 9.3.10 justifies the statement of the first paragraph of Example 9.2.4 that in this situation we could restrict ourselves without loss to nonrandomized tests: a nonrandomized test is most powerful.

We next define precisely the "uniformly most powerful" test concept (which arose in Example 9.3.10) and then consider an example where $f(x|\theta_0)$ may be zero.

Definition 9.3.16. A test $\phi(\cdot)$ is called **uniformly most powerful (UMP) (of level α)** for testing a simple hypothesis H_0 against a composite hypothesis H, if this test is most powerful of level α for testing H_0 versus H_1 for each simple hypothesis $H_1 \in H$.

Example 9.3.17.* (In this example we consider an important case in which $f(x|\theta_0)$ may be zero. We see below that there is not a unique most powerful test in general, and that the way in which we randomize when $f(x|\theta_1) = kf(x|\theta_0)$ can be very important.)

Suppose $X_1, \ldots, X_n$ are independent r.v.'s, each uniform on $(0, \theta)$ where θ is unknown, $\theta \in \Theta = \{z: z > 0\}$. Find a most powerful level $\alpha = .05$ test of H_0: $\theta = 1$ versus H_1: $\theta = 2$ and plot $E_\theta \phi_1(X)$ as a function of θ. Find the most powerful level $\alpha = .05$ test of H_0: $\theta = 1$ versus H_1: $\theta = 2$ based on observing the sufficient (see Example 8.1.4) statistic $Y = \max(X_1, \ldots, X_n)$, and plot $E_\theta \phi_2(X)$ as a function of θ. [We use $\phi_1(\cdot)$ and $\phi_2(\cdot)$ as notation for the critical functions of the two respective tests.]

First, suppose we observe $X = (X_1, \ldots, X_n)$ and want to find a most powerful level $\alpha = .05$ test of H_0: $\theta = 1$ versus H_1: $\theta = 2$. By the Neyman-Pearson Lemma, a $\phi_1(\cdot)$ satisfying (9.3.4) and (9.3.3) will be most powerful. Now (see Example 8.1.4)

$$f(x|\theta = 1) = \begin{cases} 1, & \text{if } 0 \le \min(x_1, \ldots, x_n) \le \max(x_1, \ldots, x_n) \le 1 \\ 0, & \text{otherwise} \end{cases}$$

$$(9.3.18)$$

---

*This example may be omitted at a first reading.

TABLE 9.3-1
$f(x|\theta = 1)$ and $f(x|\theta = 2)$

Case	$f(x\|\theta = 1)$	$f(x\|\theta = 2)$
I. $\min(x_1,\ldots,x_n) < 0$	0	0
II. $\min(x_1,\ldots,x_n) \geq 0$ and $\max(x_1,\ldots,x_n) \leq 1$	1	$\dfrac{1}{2^n}$
III. $\min(x_1,\ldots,x_n) \geq 0$ and $1 < \max(x_1,\ldots,x_n) \leq 2$	0	$\dfrac{1}{2^n}$
IV. $\min(x_1,\ldots,x_n) \geq 0$ and $2 < \max(x_1,\ldots,x_n)$	0	0

and

$$f(x|\theta = 2) = \begin{cases} \dfrac{1}{2^n}, & \text{if } 0 \leq \min(x_1,\ldots,x_n) \leq \max(x_1,\ldots,x_n) \leq 2 \\ 0, & \text{otherwise.} \end{cases}$$

$$(9.3.19)$$

For various conditions on $x = (x_1,\ldots,x_n)$ the values of $f(x|\theta = 1)$ and $f(x|\theta = 2)$ are given in Table 9.3-1.

Now, when is $f(x|\theta = 2) > kf(x|\theta = 1)$, when is $f(x|\theta = 2) < kf(x|\theta = 1)$, and when is $f(x|\theta = 2) = kf(x|\theta = 1)$? It is simple to verify (using Table 9.3-1) that the answer is as given in Table 9.3-2.

Thus, no matter what our choice of k, to satisfy equation (9.3.4), we must set $\phi_1(x) = 1$ when case III occurs; we can set $\phi_1(x)$ as we like when cases I or IV occur; and in case II, we must set $\phi_1(x) = 1$ if we choose $k < 1/2^n$, we can choose $\phi_1(x)$ as we like if we choose $k = 1/2^n$, and we must set $\phi_1(x) = 0$ if we choose $k > 1/2^n$. Now

$$P_{\theta=1}[\text{Case I, or case III, or case IV}] = 0, \qquad (9.3.20)$$

so even if we *always* rejected on observing an x that fell into cases I, III, IV, our level would be zero. So, for level $\alpha = .05$ some rejection in case II must be made

TABLE 9.3-2
$f(x|\theta = 2)$ versus $kf(x|\theta = 1)$

Case	$f(x\|\theta = 2) > kf(x\|\theta = 1)$	$f(x\|\theta = 2) = kf(x\|\theta = 1)$	$f(x\|\theta = 2) < kf(x\|\theta = 1)$
I.	Never	Always	Never
II.	Iff $k < \dfrac{1}{2^n}$	Iff $k = \dfrac{1}{2^n}$	Iff $k > \dfrac{1}{2^n}$
III.	Always	Never	Never
IV.	Never	Always	Never

possible. $k > 1/2^n$ does not allow any, and $k < 1/2^n$ requires always rejecting (which yields level = 1). Hence, we need $k = 1/2^n$ if we are to be able to obtain any $0 < \alpha < 1$ (in particular $\alpha = .05$).

So suppose $k = 1/2^n$ is chosen. Then $\phi_1(x) = 1$ for x in case III satisfies equation (9.3.4), and we can set $\phi_1(x)$ in cases I, II, IV as we like. Since when cases I or IV occur H_0: $\theta = 1$ is clearly false, set $\phi_1(x) = 1$ in those cases. Now let us set $\phi_1(x)$ for case II so as to satisfy (9.3.3): $E_{\theta=1}\phi_1(X) = \alpha$ (in particular, we desire $\alpha = .05$). One way to accomplish this is to set $\phi_1(x) = \gamma$ for all x in case II, γ then being chosen to yield level α:

$$E_{\theta=1}\phi_1(X)$$
$$= \gamma P_{\theta=1}[\text{case II}] + P_{\theta=1}[\text{case I, or case III, or case IV}] \quad (9.3.21)$$
$$= \gamma \cdot 1 + 0 = \gamma.$$

Thus, choose $\gamma = \alpha = .05$.

So a most powerful level $\alpha = .05$ test of H_0: $\theta = 1$ versus H_1: $\theta = 2$ is given by

$$\phi_1(x) = \begin{cases} .05, & \text{if } \min(x_1, \ldots, x_n) \geq 0 \text{ and } \max(x_1, \ldots, x_n) \leq 1 \\ 1, & \text{otherwise.} \end{cases} \quad (9.3.22)$$

The power function of this test is calculated as follows. For $0 < \theta \leq 1$,

$$E_\theta\phi_1(X) = .05P_\theta\big[\min(X_1, \ldots, X_n) \geq 0 \text{ and } \max(X_1, \ldots, X_n) \leq 1\big]$$
$$+ 1 \cdot P_\theta\big[\overline{\min(X_1, \ldots, X_n) \geq 0 \text{ and } \max(X_1, \ldots, X_n) \leq 1}\big]$$
$$= (.05)(1) + (1)(0) = .05. \quad (9.3.23)$$

For $1 < \theta$,

$$E_\theta\phi_1(X) = .05P_\theta\big[\min(X_1, \ldots, X_n) \geq 0 \text{ and } \max(X_1, \ldots, X_n) \leq 1\big]$$
$$+ 1 \cdot P_\theta\big[\overline{\min(X_1, \ldots, X_n) \geq 0 \text{ and } \max(X_1, \ldots, X_n) \leq 1}\big]$$
$$= .05\left(\frac{1}{\theta}\right)^n + 1 \cdot \left(1 - \left(\frac{1}{\theta}\right)^n\right) = 1 - \frac{.95}{\theta^n}. \quad (9.3.24)$$

The resulting curve is plotted as a solid line in Figure 9.3-1. It has

$$E_{\theta=1}\phi_1(X) = .05 \quad \text{and} \quad E_{\theta=2}\phi_1(X) = 1 - \frac{.95}{2^n};$$

the Neyman-Pearson Lemma assures us that any other test $\psi(\cdot)$ with $E_{\theta=1}\psi(X) = .05$ has power $E_{\theta=2}\psi(X) \leq E_{\theta=2}\phi(X)$.

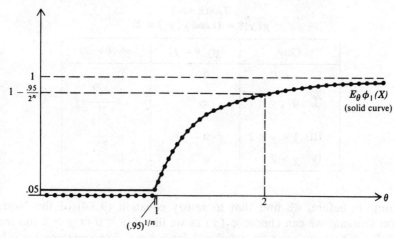

Figure 9.3-1. $E_\theta \phi_1(X)$ and $E_\theta \phi_2(X)$. (The graph has $n = 3$.)

Now, for the **second** part, suppose we observe $Y = \max(X_1, \ldots, X_n)$ and want to find a most powerful level $\alpha = .05$ test of H_0: $\theta = 1$ versus H_1: $\theta = 2$. Again we will use the Neyman-Pearson Lemma. Here

$$P_\theta[Y \le y] = P_\theta[\max(X_1, \ldots, X_n) \le y]$$

$$= P_\theta[X_1 \le y, \ldots, X_n \le y] = (P_\theta[X_1 \le y])^n$$

$$= \begin{cases} 0, & \text{if } y < 0 \\ y^n/\theta^n, & \text{if } 0 \le y \le \theta \\ 1, & \text{if } y > \theta. \end{cases} \tag{9.3.25}$$

Hence, the density involved is

$$g(y|\theta) = \begin{cases} n\dfrac{y^{n-1}}{\theta^n}, & \text{if } 0 \le y \le \theta \\ 0, & \text{otherwise,} \end{cases} \tag{9.3.26}$$

and

$$g(y|\theta = 1) = \begin{cases} ny^{n-1}, & \text{if } 0 \le y \le 1 \\ 0, & \text{otherwise,} \end{cases} \tag{9.3.27}$$

while

$$g(y|\theta = 2) = \begin{cases} n\dfrac{y^{n-1}}{2^n}, & \text{if } 0 \le y \le 2 \\ 0, & \text{otherwise.} \end{cases} \tag{9.3.28}$$

Hence, a table analogous to Table 9.3-1 may be obtained. See Table 9.3-3. Here,

TABLE 9.3-3
$g(y|\theta = 1)$ and $g(y|\theta = 2)$

Case	$g(y|\theta = 1)$	$g(y|\theta = 2)$
I. $y < 0$	0	0
II. $0 \le y \le 1$	ny^{n-1}	$n\dfrac{y^{n-1}}{2^n}$
III. $1 < y \le 2$	0	$n\dfrac{y^{n-1}}{2^n}$
IV. $y > 2$	0	0

analyzing as before, we find that to satisfy equation (9.3.4) of the Neyman-Pearson Lemma: we can choose $\phi_2(y)$ as we like if $y < 0$ or $y > 2$ (no matter what value k has); we must set $\phi_2(y) = 1$ for $1 < y \le 2$ (no matter what value k has); and we set $\phi_2(y) = 1$ when $0 < y < 1$ iff

$$n\frac{y^{n-1}}{2^n} > kny^{n-1} \Leftrightarrow k < \frac{1}{2^n}. \qquad (9.3.29)$$

As before, only $k = 1/2^n$ allows us to have $\alpha = .05$. Now in case II we may feel intuitively that large values of Y are more likely to indicate that $H_1: \theta = 2$ is true than are small values of Y; then instead of choosing $\phi_2(y) = .05$ for y in case II, we will wish to set

$$\phi_2(y) = \begin{cases} 1, & \text{if } y > c \\ 0, & \text{if } y \le c, \end{cases} \qquad (9.3.30)$$

where c is chosen to obtain level $\alpha = .05$:

$$.05 = E_{\theta=1}\phi_2(Y) = P_{\theta=1}[Y > c]$$
$$= 1 - P_{\theta=1}[Y \le c] = 1 - \frac{c^n}{1^n} \qquad (9.3.31)$$

so $c = (.95)^{1/n}$. The function $E_\theta\phi_2(Y)$ is now

$$E_\theta\phi_2(Y) = P_\theta\left[Y > (.95)^{1/n}\right]$$
$$= \begin{cases} 0, & \text{if } \theta \le (.95)^{1/n} \\ 1 - \dfrac{.95}{\theta^n}, & \text{if } \theta > (.95)^{1/n}, \end{cases} \qquad (9.3.32)$$

which is graphed in Figure 9.3-1 as a series of dots.

The tests $\phi_1(X)$ and $\phi_2(Y)$ obtained above are different and (see Figure 9.3-1) have different rejection probability functions. $\phi_1(X)$ is most powerful among tests based on $X = (X_1, \ldots, X_n)$; $\phi_2(Y)$ is most powerful among tests based on $Y = \max(X_1, \ldots, X_n)$. Since Y is a sufficient statistic, we should question why the two tests should be different: wouldn't we expect to obtain the *same* test as best even if we first reduced the data to a sufficient statistic? The answer is yes, we would, and **in the sense of the Neyman-Pearson Lemma they are equivalent since they have the same level (.05) and the same power at H_1: $\theta = 2$ $(1 - .95/2^n)$.** In fact, the same test could have been chosen based on either $X = (X_1, \ldots, X_n)$ or $Y = \max(X_1, \ldots, X_n)$; we chose different ones because when looking at X our intuition led us to randomize over all $(X_1, \ldots, X_n)$ with $\max(X_1, \ldots, X_n) \leq 1$, whereas when looking at Y our intuition led us to set $\phi_2(\cdot)$ to 0 at some such $(X_1, \ldots, X_n)$ and to 1 at others. **Thus, looking at the sufficient statistics for a problem may lead our intuition to choose more appropriately on the "boundary" $f(x|\theta_1) = kf(x|\theta_0)$.**

The considerations of the preceding paragraph are not trivial. *In practice, we often wish to know if θ is "small" or "large"* (these are our intuitive H_0 and H_1), and simple H_0 and H_1 are set up as a way of obtaining a "best" test with, it is hoped, reasonable properties, such as $E_\theta \phi(X) \downarrow$ as $\theta \uparrow$. Thus, in the preceding example we would usually prefer $\phi_2(Y)$ to $\phi_1(X)$, since for the latter $E_\theta \phi_1(X)$ remains constant over $0 < \theta \leq 1$ while $E_\theta \phi_2(Y)$ goes quickly to 0 as $\theta \downarrow$.

Remark 9.3.33. In continuous cases, the "boundary" where $f(x|\theta_1) = kf(x|\theta_0)$ typically has probability zero under both H_0 and H_1, and hence plays no role in choosing k to satisfy (9.3.3) and (9.3.4) in the Neyman-Pearson Lemma.

In discrete cases, typically the boundary has positive probability. **The Neyman-Pearson Lemma does not require that boundary points be treated "equally":** if $f(y|\theta_1) = kf(y|\theta_0)$ and $f(z|\theta_1) = kf(z|\theta_0)$, we can reject at y and accept at z. **Intuitively, however, we may desire to treat such y and z equally. This implies setting**

$$\phi(x) = \begin{cases} 1, & \text{if } f(x|\theta_1) > kf(x|\theta_0) \\ \gamma, & \text{if } f(x|\theta_1) = kf(x|\theta_0) \\ 0, & \text{if } f(x|\theta_1) < kf(x|\theta_0) \end{cases} \quad (9.3.34)$$

and solving for a pair (k, γ) which solves equation (9.3.3), that is, $E_{\theta_0} \phi(X) = \alpha$.

As we noted, if the boundary has probability zero in a particular problem, then the choice of γ in equation (9.3.34) will be irrelevant. However, in many discrete problems one finds the boundary has positive probability. One then finds a value of k such that

$$P_{\theta_0}[f(X|\theta_1) > kf(X|\theta_0)] < \alpha < P_{\theta_0}[f(X|\theta_1) \geq kf(X|\theta_0)]. \quad (9.3.35)$$

Here the left side corresponds to the pair $(k, 0)$ and the right side corresponds to the pair $(k, 1)$. The difference of the sides is the probability of the boundary; putting none of the boundary into the rejection region gives us a level less than the desired α, while putting all of the boundary into the rejection region (this corresponds to the right side of equation (9.3.35)) gives us a level greater than the desired α. **Putting proportion γ of the boundary into the rejection region where**

$$\gamma = \frac{\alpha - P_{\theta_0}[\,f(X|\theta_1) > kf(X|\theta_0)]}{P_{\theta_0}[\,f(X|\theta_1) = kf(X|\theta_0)]} \tag{9.3.36}$$

will then provide a pair (k, γ) that satisfies equation (9.3.3).

Example 9.3.37. It is not necessarily the case that we will be testing hypotheses about the parameters of a given class (or family) of distributions as in Examples 9.3.10 and 9.3.17. Sometimes we desire to test quite different distributions as H_0 or H_1. We now illustrate this case.

Let X be a single observation with a p.d.f. $f(x)$ that is positive only on the interval $[0, 1]$. We desire to test the simple hypotheses H_0 and H_1 given by

$$H_0: X \text{ is uniform on } (0,1) \quad \text{vs.} \quad H_1: X \text{ is beta } B(x|\alpha = 1, \lambda = 0),$$

that is,

$$H_0: f_0(x) = I_{[0,1]}(x) \quad \text{vs.} \quad H_1: f_1(x) = 2xI_{[0,1]}(x).$$

Here we have not yet talked of a θ_0 and θ_1. To do so, we simply set $\Theta = \{\theta_0, \theta_1\}$, $f(x|\theta_0) = f_0(x)$, $f(x|\theta_1) = f_1(x)$, $H_0 = \{\theta_0\}$, and $H_1 = \{\theta_1\}$.

By the Neyman-Pearson Lemma, we know that a test which satisfies (9.3.4) and (9.3.3) is most powerful of level α for this hypothesis-testing problem. Here, for $0 \le x \le 1$,

$$\frac{f(x|\theta_1)}{f(x|\theta_0)} = \frac{f_1(x)}{f_0(x)} = 2x,$$

which is $> k$ iff $2x > k$, so we set

$$\phi(x) = \begin{cases} 1, & \text{if } x > k/2 = k^* \text{ (say)} \\ 0, & \text{if } x < k^*. \end{cases} \tag{9.3.38}$$

[Note that $P_\theta[X = k^*] = 0$ under both $\theta = \theta_0$ and $\theta = \theta_1$, hence we need not worry about what decision to take when we find $X = k^*$; whether we set $\phi(k^*) = 0$ or $\phi(k^*) = 1$, the level and power of the test under H_0 and H_1 will remain the same.] Since (9.3.38) satisfies (9.3.4), we now seek a value of k^* such that (9.3.3) is satisfied, that is, such that this is a level α test; for these computations assume we desire $\alpha = .03$. Now we solve

$$.03 = E_{\theta_0}\phi(X) = 1 \cdot P_{\theta_0}[X > k^*] + 0 \cdot P_{\theta_0}[X < k^*]$$

$$= \int_{k^*}^1 I_{[0,1]}(x)\, dx = 1 - k^*, \tag{9.3.39}$$

hence $k^* = .97$ and

$$\phi(x) = \begin{cases} 1, & \text{if } x > .97 \\ 0, & \text{if } x \leq .97 \end{cases}$$

is a most powerful test of level $\alpha = .03$. Its power is

$$E_{\theta_1}\phi(X) = \int_{.97}^{1} 2x I_{[0,1]}(x)\, dx = 1 - (.97)^2 = .0591,$$

hence its type II error probability is $\beta = 1 - .0591 = .9409$.

Note that for larger α's (probability of type I error) the power is larger and hence the probability of type II error is smaller (e.g., if $\alpha = .05$, power $= .0975$ and $\beta = .9025$). To increase power (i.e., decrease β) while keeping $\alpha = .03$, we need a larger sample size (in this example we had a sample of $n = 1$ observation).

In the next example we illustrate the Neyman-Pearson Lemma and use of (9.3.36) in a discrete case.

Example 9.3.40. Let $X_1, X_2, \ldots, X_{10}$ be a random sample of size 10 from a Bernoulli distribution with unknown probability of success p. Suppose it is desired to test the simple H_0 vs. simple H_1

$$H_0\colon p = 0.5 \quad \text{vs.} \quad H_1\colon p = 0.4,$$

with a most powerful level $\alpha = .05$ test.

Here, let $f(x_1, x_2, \ldots, x_{10}|\theta)$ denote the joint probability function of $X_1, X_2, \ldots, X_{10}$ when the success probability is θ. Then for all possible values of $x_1, x_2, \ldots, x_{10}$ (i.e., each 0 or 1) we have

$$\frac{f(x_1, x_2, \ldots, x_{10}|\theta_1)}{f(x_1, x_2, \ldots, x_{10}|\theta_0)} = \frac{(0.4)^{\sum x_i}(0.6)^{10 - \sum x_i}}{(0.5)^{\sum x_i}(0.5)^{10 - \sum x_i}} > k$$

iff

$$(0.8)^{\sum x_i}\left(\frac{6}{5}\right)^{10 - \sum x_i} > k$$

iff

$$\sum x_i \cdot \ln(0.8) + \left(10 - \sum x_i\right)\ln(6/5) > \ln(k)$$

iff

$$\sum_{i=1}^{10} x_i < \frac{\ln(k) - 10\ln(6/5)}{\ln(6/5) - \ln(0.8)} \equiv k'. \tag{9.3.41}$$

Note that under H_0, $\sum X_i$ is $B(10, 0.5)$, while under H_1, $\sum X_i$ is $B(10, 0.4)$. As discussed in Remark 9.3.33, this is a case where the boundary has positive probability. If we set $k' = 2$ in (9.3.41), hence rejecting H_0 iff $f(X|\theta_1) > 2f(X|\theta_0)$, that is, iff $\sum X_i < 2$, we will have level (using Table 5)

$$P_{\theta_0}\left(\sum X_i < 2\right) = .0108,$$

while $k' = 3$ yields level (again using Table 5)

$$P_{\theta_0}\left(\sum X_i < 3\right) = .0547.$$

Thus there is no k' for which $P_{\theta_0}(\sum X_i < k') = .05$. To obtain a most powerful level $\alpha = .05$ test we need to randomize on the boundary. As at (9.3.35), we find k' such that

$$P_{\theta_0}\left(f(X|\theta_1) > kf(X|\theta_0)\right) < \alpha < P_{\theta_0}\left(f(X|\theta_1) \geq kf(X|\theta_0)\right),$$

that is,

$$P_{\theta_0}\left[\sum X_i < k'\right] < .05 < P_{\theta_0}\left[\sum X_i \leq k'\right],$$

and from our analysis above we know $k' = 2$ has this property, and set boundary randomization as in (9.3.36):

$$\gamma = \frac{.05 - .0108}{.0439} = .8929.$$

Thus, a most powerful level $\alpha = .05$ test is given by

$$\phi(x) = \begin{cases} 1, & \text{if } \sum X_i < 2 \\ .8929, & \text{if } \sum X_i = 2 \\ 0, & \text{if } \sum X_i > 2. \end{cases} \qquad (9.3.42)$$

The power of this test is

$$E_{\theta_1}\phi(X) = 1 \cdot P\left(\sum X_i < 2 | p = 0.4\right) + (.8929)P\left(\sum X_i = 2 | p = 0.4\right)$$

$$= .0463 + (.8929)(.1209) = .1543$$

and $\beta = .8457$.

Although it is tempting to state this is a "bad" test (since its power is rather low—not much above its level), by the Neyman-Pearson Lemma there is no test that will give more power while maintaining level $\alpha = .05$. For better power (while maintaining level .05), we need n larger than 10.

Typically in applications, the alternative hypothesis H_1 is a composite hypothesis. Although the Neyman-Pearson Lemma deals with simple H_0 vs. simple H_1, in many important cases the same test is most powerful for each alternative in H_1. Then that test is (see Definition 9.3.16) called uniformly most powerful (UMP) of level α. We saw an example of this in Example 9.3.10. **We will now give another example where we find a UMP test (and also see how H_0 can sometimes be allowed to be a composite hypothesis), an example where no UMP test exists, and a condition under which UMP tests always exist.**

Example 9.3.43. Let $X_1, X_2, \ldots, X_n$ be independent r.v.'s, each with the exponential p.d.f. with mean θ:

$$f_{X_i}(x_i | \theta) = e^{-x_i/\theta}/\theta \cdot I_{(0,\infty)}(x_i).$$

Consider testing H_0: $\theta = \theta_0$ vs. H_1: $\theta > \theta_0$.

Let θ_1 be an arbitrary point in (θ_0, ∞) and consider testing H_0: $\theta = \theta_0$ vs. H_1^*: $\theta = \theta_1$. By the Neyman-Pearson Lemma, a most powerful test of level α is

$$\phi(x) = \begin{cases} 1, & \text{if } f(x|\theta_1)/f(x|\theta_0) > k \\ 0, & \text{if } f(x|\theta_1)/f(x|\theta_0) < k \end{cases}$$

with $E_{\theta_0}\phi(X) = \alpha$, where $x = (x_1, \ldots, x_n)$ and $X = (X_1, \ldots, X_n)$. Since (for $x_1, x_2, \ldots, x_n > 0$)

$$\frac{f(x|\theta_1)}{f(x|\theta_0)} = \frac{\left(\dfrac{1}{\theta_1}\right)^n e^{-\sum x_i/\theta_1}}{\left(\dfrac{1}{\theta_0}\right)^n e^{-\sum x_i/\theta_0}} > k$$

iff

$$\sum x_i \left(\frac{1}{\theta_0} - \frac{1}{\theta_1}\right) > \ln\left(k\left(\frac{\theta_1}{\theta_0}\right)^n\right)$$

iff

$$\sum_{i=1}^{n} x_i > \frac{\theta_0\theta_1}{\theta_1 - \theta_0} \ln\left(k(\theta_1/\theta_0)^n\right) \equiv k' \text{ (say)},$$

a most powerful level α test is given by

$$\phi(x) = \begin{cases} 1, & \text{if } \sum x_i > k' \\ 0, & \text{if } \sum x_i < k' \end{cases}$$

where k' is to be set so that

$$E_{\theta_0}\phi(X) = \alpha.$$

Now under H_0, $X_1 + \cdots + X_n$ has the gamma distribution $G(x|n-1, \theta_0, 0)$, so for given n, θ_0, and α, we solve

$$\int_{k'}^{\infty} \frac{1}{\theta_0^n \Gamma(n)} e^{-x/\theta_0} x^{n-1} \, dx = \alpha$$

for k'. The critical region consists of all n-tuples $(x_1, x_2, \ldots, x_n)$ such that $x_1 + x_2 + \cdots + x_n > k'$.

For example, if $n = 10$, $\alpha = .05$, and $\theta_0 = 1.5$, then from Table 9 (with $\alpha = n - 1 = 10 - 1 = 9$, $\gamma = 1 - .05 = .95$; note that the row heading α in Table 9 should not be confused with the level of significance in this example—it is the same symbol used for a different quantity, as it is usually used to denote one of the parameters of the gamma distribution)

$$\frac{k'}{\theta_0} = 15.705,$$

hence $k' = 23.5575$. Thus a most powerful test of level .05 rejects H_0: $\theta = 1.5$ iff $X_1 + X_2 + \cdots + X_{10} > 23.5575$, that is, iff $\overline{X} > 2.35575$.

Now looking at the derivation above, we see we will find the same k' regardless of the choice of $\theta_1 \in (\theta_0, \infty)$; hence the same test is most powerful for any value of $\theta_1 \in (\theta_0, \infty)$, that is, we have a UMP level α test.

If our H_0 is also composite, H_0: $\theta \leq \theta_0$, then for any fixed value $\theta_0^* \in (0, \theta_0]$ we can find a uniformly most powerful test of H_0^*: $\theta = \theta_0^*$ vs. H_1: $\theta > \theta_0$. If we determine k' from

$$\alpha = \sup_{\theta_0^* \in (0, \theta_0)} \int_{k'}^{\infty} \frac{e^{-x/\theta_0^*} x^{n-1}}{(\theta_0^*)^n \Gamma(n)} \, dx \qquad (9.3.44)$$

then the probability of type I error at any $\theta_0^* \in (0, \theta_0]$ will be $\leq \alpha$. It is reasonable to call this a level α UMP test for testing composite H_0 vs. composite H_1. Since the supremum is (check this) attained at the boundary, if we wish to test composite H_0: $\theta \leq \theta_0$ vs. H_1: $\theta > \theta_0$ at maximum allowable type I error probability α, it is reasonable to take H_0 as the simple hypothesis $\theta = \theta_0$.

Of course, **there is not a UMP test in every situation, as the following example shows.**

Example 9.3.45. Let $X_1, X_2, \ldots, X_n$ be a random sample from the $N(\mu, \sigma^2)$ distribution with σ^2 known. Consider testing H_0: $\mu = \mu_0$ vs. H_1: $\mu \neq \mu_0$.

Here $\Theta_1 = \mathcal{R} - \{\mu_0\}$. For any $\mu_1 \in \Theta_1$ with $\mu_1 < \mu_0$, the most powerful level α test can be verified to be

$$\phi_1(x) = \begin{cases} 1, & \text{if } \overline{x}_n < k \\ 0, & \text{if } \overline{x}_n > k. \end{cases} \qquad (9.3.46)$$

For any $\mu_1 \in \Theta_1$ with $\mu_1 > \mu_0$, the most powerful level α test is

$$\phi_2(x) = \begin{cases} 1, & \text{if } \bar{x}_n > k \\ 0, & \text{if } \bar{x}_n < k. \end{cases} \tag{9.3.47}$$

Since the most powerful test depends on the choice of $\mu_1 \in H_1$ (for values of μ_1 to the left of μ_0 test $\phi_1(\cdot)$ is most powerful, whereas to the right of μ_0 test $\phi_2(\cdot)$ is most powerful), no UMP test exists.

Note that $\phi_1(\cdot)$ *is* a UMP level α test for testing H_0: $\mu = \mu_0$ vs. H_1: $\mu < \mu_0$, and also $\phi_2(\cdot)$ is a UMP level α test for testing H_0: $\mu = \mu_0$ vs. H_1: $\mu > \mu_0$.

Next we introduce the concept of a monotone likelihood ratio, which is the condition noted before Example 9.3.48 that (when it holds) enables us to determine UMP tests for one-sided alternative hypotheses with ease.

Definition 9.3.48. Suppose that X is a r.v. with d.f. $F(x|\theta)$, where θ is unknown, $\theta \in \Theta \subseteq \mathcal{R}$ [so θ is a one-dimensional parameter]. Assume $F(x|\theta)$ is either absolutely continuous [in which case let $f(x|\theta)$ denote its density at x] or discrete [in which case let $f(x|\theta)$ denote $P_\theta[X = x]$]. Then the d.f. $F(x|\theta)$ of X is said to have a **monotone likelihood ratio in $T(x)$ (MLR)** if, for some statistic $T(X)$,

$$\frac{f(x|\theta_2)}{f(x|\theta_1)} \uparrow \text{ as } T(x) \uparrow \tag{9.3.49}$$

for all $\theta_2 > \theta_1 (\theta_2, \theta_1 \in \Theta)$ and for all $x \in \mathcal{X}$.

Note: Equation (9.3.34) can hold only if $f(x|\theta_2)/f(x|\theta_1)$ is a function of $T(x)$, and the *same* function $T(x)$ must be used for each pair $\theta_2 > \theta_1$. An example will now be given. (For a case where there is no such $T(x)$, take X to have the Cauchy p.d.f. $f(x|\theta) = \pi^{-1} (1 + (x - \theta)^2)^{-1}$.)

Example 9.3.50. Let $X_1, X_2, \ldots, X_n$ be a random sample of size n from a Poisson distribution with unknown parameter λ. Determine whether $X = (X_1, X_2, \ldots, X_n)$ has an MLR.

Here the joint point probability function of $X_1, X_2, \ldots, X_n$ is

$$f(x_1, x_2, \ldots, x_n|\lambda) = \frac{e^{-n\lambda}\lambda^{\sum x_i}}{\prod x_i!} \prod I_{\{0,1,2,\ldots\}}(x_i).$$

Let $\lambda_2 > \lambda_1$ be two values in the parameter space $\Theta = (0, \infty)$. Then (for $x = (x_1, x_2, \ldots, x_n)$ such that $I_{\{0,1,2,\ldots\}}(x_i) > 0$)

$$\frac{f(x_1, x_2, \ldots, x_n|\lambda_2)}{f(x_1, x_2, \ldots, x_n|\lambda_1)} = \left(\frac{\lambda_2}{\lambda_1}\right)^{\sum x_i} e^{-n(\lambda_2 - \lambda_1)}$$

which increases as $T(x) = \Sigma x_i$ increases because $\lambda_2/\lambda_1 > 1$. Hence $(X_1, \ldots, X_n)$ has an MLR in $T(x) = \Sigma x_i$.

The following theorem enables us to use a MLR to find UMP tests for one-sided hypotheses.

Theorem 9.3.51. Suppose that X is a r.v. with d.f. $F(x|\theta)$ where θ is unknown, $\theta \in \Theta$, $x \in \mathcal{X}$. Assume $F(x|\theta)$ has a monotone likelihood ratio in $T(x)$. Suppose that H_0: $\theta = \theta_0$ and H_1: $\theta > \theta_0$ are simple null and composite alternative hypotheses, respectively.

For testing H_0 versus H_1 after observing X, if a test with critical function $\phi(\cdot)$ satisfies (for some C)

$$E_{\theta_0}\phi(X) = \alpha \qquad (9.3.52)$$

and

$$\phi(x) = \begin{cases} 1, & \text{when } T(x) > C \\ 0, & \text{when } T(x) < C, \end{cases} \qquad (9.3.53)$$

then it is UMP of level α for testing H_0 versus H_1.

Proof: Consider the problem of testing H_0: $\theta = \theta_0$ versus H_1^*: $\theta = \theta_1$ for a fixed $\theta_1 > \theta_0$. Then both H_0 and H_1^* are simple, so by the Neyman-Pearson Lemma (Theorem 9.3.2) a test that satisfies (for some k) (9.3.52) and

$$\phi(x) = \begin{cases} 1, & \text{if } f(x|\theta_1) > kf(x|\theta_0) \\ 0, & \text{if } f(x|\theta_1) < kf(x|\theta_0) \end{cases} \qquad (9.3.54)$$

is most powerful for testing H_0 versus H_1^* at level α. Since we assumed $F(x|\theta)$ had a MLR in $T(x)$, (9.3.54) can be rewritten as

$$\phi(x) = \begin{cases} 1, & \text{if } \dfrac{f(x|\theta_1)}{f(x|\theta_0)} > k \\ 0, & \text{if } \dfrac{f(x|\theta_1)}{f(x|\theta_0)} < k \end{cases} \qquad (9.3.55)$$

or, since $f(x|\theta_2)/f(x|\theta_1)\uparrow$ as $T(x)\uparrow$ for all $\theta_2 > \theta_1$, as

$$\phi(x) = \begin{cases} 1, & \text{if } T(x) > C \\ 0, & \text{if } T(x) < C \end{cases} \qquad (9.3.56)$$

for some C. Thus, a test satisfying (9.3.52) and (9.3.53) is most powerful for testing H_0 versus H_1^* at level α. As in Example 9.3.10, we find (see Problem 9.15) that the test is the same regardless of which θ_1 was chosen (as long as $\theta_1 > \theta_0$). Hence, a test satisfying (9.3.52) and (9.3.53) is most powerful for testing

H_0: $\theta = \theta_0$ versus H_1^*: $\theta = \theta_1$ at level α for every $\theta_1 > \theta_0$, that is, is UMP of level α for testing H_0 versus H_1.   ■

Remark 9.3.57. If H_1 in Theorem 5.3.51 is replaced by H_1^*: $\theta_1 < \theta_0$, then a UMP test satisfies (9.3.52) and

$$\phi(x) = \begin{cases} 1, & \text{if } T(x) < C \\ 0, & \text{if } T(x) > C. \end{cases}$$

In Example 9.3.43 we found a UMP test for the exponential distribution from first principles. In the following example, we use MLR considerations in this same case, which simplifies the process considerably.

Example 9.3.58. (In this example we obtain a UMP test via MLR considerations.) Suppose $X_1, \ldots, X_n$ are independent r.v.'s, each with the density of an exponential distribution with mean θ (see Theorem 5.2.5), that is,

$$g(x|\theta) = \begin{cases} \dfrac{1}{\theta} e^{-x/\theta}, & \text{if } x \geq 0 \\ 0, & \text{if } x < 0, \end{cases}$$

where θ is unknown, $\theta \in \Theta = \{y: y > 0\}$. Based on $X = (X_1, \ldots, X_n)$ with $n = 31$, find a UMP level $\alpha = .05$ test of H_0: $\theta = 10$ versus H_1: $\theta > 10$. [In Problem 9.4H we see that this test is also a UMP level $\alpha = .05$ test of H_0: $\theta \leq 10$ versus H_1: $\theta > 10$.]

First, does the d.f. $F(x|\theta)$ of X have a MLR (and, if so, in what)? Here the density of X is

$$f(x|\theta) = g(x_1|\theta) \ldots g(x_n|\theta) = \begin{cases} \dfrac{1}{\theta^n} e^{-(x_1 + \cdots + x_n)/\theta}, & \text{if } x_1, \ldots, x_n \geq 0 \\ 0, & \text{otherwise,} \end{cases}$$

$$(9.3.59)$$

so (for $x \in \mathscr{X}$ and $\theta_1, \theta_2 \in \Theta$)

$$\frac{f(x|\theta_2)}{f(x|\theta_1)} = \left(\frac{\theta_1}{\theta_2}\right)^n e^{-(x_1 + \cdots + x_n)\left(\frac{1}{\theta_2} - \frac{1}{\theta_1}\right)} = \left(\frac{\theta_1}{\theta_2}\right)^n e^{(x_1 + \cdots + x_n)(\theta_2 - \theta_1)/(\theta_1 \theta_2)}$$

$$(9.3.60)$$

which (for all $\theta_2 > \theta_1$; $\theta_2, \theta_1 \in \Theta$) is an increasing function of $T(x) = x_1 + \cdots + x_n$. Thus (by Definition 9.3.48) $F(x|\theta)$ has a MLR in $x_1 + \cdots + x_n$.

Using Theorem 9.3.51, it follows that any test with $E_{\theta_0}\phi(X) = .05$ and (for some C)

$$\phi(x) = \begin{cases} 1, & \text{when } x_1 + \cdots + x_n > C \\ 0, & \text{when } x_1 + \cdots + x_n < C \end{cases} \qquad (9.3.61)$$

is a UMP level .05 test of H_0: $\theta = 10$ versus H_1: $\theta > 10$. Now if $\phi(\cdot)$ satisfies (9.3.61), then

$$E_{\theta_0}\phi(X) = P_{\theta_0}[X_1 + \cdots + X_n > C]. \qquad (9.3.62)$$

Here (by Example 5.5.60, using $n = 31$ and $\theta_0 = 10$) $Y = X_1 + \cdots + X_n$ has the gamma distribution $G(x|n - 1, \theta_0, 0) = G(x|30, 10, 0)$. To set C so that equation (9.3.62) holds is to set C so that $P[Y > C] = .05$, or $P[Y \leq C] = .95$. Using Table 9, we find this requires

$$\frac{C}{\theta_0} = 40.691 \qquad (9.3.63)$$

or

$$C = 406.91. \qquad (9.3.64)$$

Hence, we have found the desired UMP test of H_0: $\theta = 10$ versus H_1: $\theta > 10$, and it rejects H_0 iff $X_1 + \cdots + X_{31} > 406.91$, that is, iff

$$\bar{X} > \frac{406.91}{31} = 13.13. \qquad (9.3.65)$$

Example 9.3.66. Let $X_1, X_2, \ldots, X_n$ be a random sample of size n from a Poisson distribution with unknown parameter λ. Find a UMP level α test for testing H_0: $\lambda = \lambda_0$ vs. H_1: $\lambda < \lambda_0$.

From Example 9.3.50, we know that $(X_1, X_2, \ldots, X_n)$ has a MLR in ΣX_i. Hence by Theorem 9.3.51 and Remark 9.3.57, a UMP level α test has critical function $\phi(x)$ such that

$$E_{\lambda_0}\phi(X) = \alpha$$

with

$$\phi(x) = \begin{cases} 1, & \text{if } \sum x_i < k \\ 0, & \text{if } \sum x_i > k. \end{cases}$$

Suppose $\lambda_0 = 2$, $n = 7$, and $\alpha = .05$. Then in seeking k we find (from Table 7, since under H_0 ΣX_i is Poisson with mean $(2)(7) = 14$)

$$P_{\lambda_0}\left(\sum X_i < 8\right) = .0316 \quad \text{and} \quad P_{\lambda_0}\left(\sum X_i \leq 8\right) = .0620.$$

Hence, in this case randomization on the boundary will play a role and (see Remark 9.3.33) taking $k = 8$,

$$\gamma = \frac{\alpha - P\left(\sum X_i < k | \lambda_0\right)}{P\left(\sum X_i = k | \lambda_0\right)} = \frac{.05 - .0316}{.0620 - .0316} = .61,$$

and the UMP level .05 test for H_0: $\lambda = 2$ vs. H_1: $\lambda < 2$ is

$$\phi(x) = \begin{cases} 1, & \text{if } \sum x_i < 8 \\ .61, & \text{if } \sum x_i = 8 \\ 0, & \text{if } \sum x_i > 8. \end{cases}$$

The power curve of this test can be computed using

$$\mathscr{P}(\lambda) = P\left(\sum X_i < 8 | \lambda\right) + (.61)P\left(\sum X_i = 8 | \lambda\right)$$

where $\sum X_i$ is Poisson with parameter 7λ. For example, if $\lambda = 1.1$ then $\sum X_i$ is Poisson with $\lambda = 7.7$ and

$$\mathscr{P}(\lambda) = .4956 + (.61)(.1388) = .58.$$

The probability of type II error when $\lambda = 1.1$ is therefore $1 - .58 = .42$.

Example 9.3.67. Let $X_1, X_2, \ldots, X_n$ be a random sample from the beta distribution $B(x | \alpha, \lambda)$ with α unknown and λ known, for which the p.d.f. of X_i is

$$f(x_i | \alpha) = \frac{\Gamma(\alpha + \lambda + 2)}{\Gamma(\alpha + 1)\Gamma(\lambda + 1)} x_i^\alpha (1 - x_i)^\lambda I_{[0,1]}(x_i).$$

Consider testing H_0: $\alpha = \alpha_0$ versus H_1: $\alpha > \alpha_0$ at level .05.
    Since for $\alpha_1 < \alpha_2$

$$\frac{f(x | \alpha_2)}{f(x | \alpha_1)} = \left(\frac{\Gamma(\alpha_2 + \lambda + 2)\Gamma(\alpha_1 + 1)}{\Gamma(\alpha_1 + \lambda + 2)\Gamma(\alpha_2 + 1)}\right)^n \left(\prod x_i\right)^{\alpha_2 - \alpha_1} \left(\prod I_{[0,1]}(x_i)\right)$$

which, for fixed $\alpha_2 - \alpha_1 > 0$, increases as $\prod x_i$ increases, $(X_1, X_2, \ldots, X_n)$ has a MLR in $\prod x_i$. Hence a UMP level .05 test has critical function $\phi(x)$ with

$$E_{\alpha_0}\phi(X) = .05 \tag{9.3.68}$$

and

$$\phi(x) = \begin{cases} 1, & \text{if } \prod x_i > k \\ 0, & \text{if } \prod x_i < k. \end{cases}$$

Here k is determined using equation (9.3.68). For example, if $n = 1$, $\alpha_0 = 1$, $\lambda = 1$, then to solve $.05 = E_{\alpha_0}\phi(X) = P(X_1 > k|\alpha = 1, \lambda = 1)$ we use Table 8 (since X_1 is $B(x|1,1)$ and symmetric about $x = .5$) to find $k = 1 - .13535 = .86465$. Hence a UMP level $.05$ test rejects H_0 iff $X_1 > .86465$.

Example 9.3.69. Let $X_1, X_2, \ldots, X_n$ be independent $N(\mu, \sigma^2)$ r.v.'s with σ^2 known. Then the joint p.d.f. of $(X_1, X_2, \ldots, X_n)$ is

$$f(x_1, x_2, \ldots, x_n|\mu) = (\sqrt{2\pi}\,\sigma)^{-n} \exp\left(-\sum(x_i - \mu)^2/(2\sigma^2)\right)$$

$$= (\sqrt{2\pi}\,\sigma)^{-n} \exp\left(\left(-\sum x_i^2 + 2\mu\sum x_i - n\mu^2\right)/(2\sigma^2)\right),$$

hence for $\mu_2 > \mu_1$ we have

$$\frac{f(x_1, x_2, \ldots, x_n|\mu_2)}{f(x_1, x_2, \ldots, x_n|\mu_1)} = \exp\left(\left(2(\mu_2 - \mu_1)\sum x_i - n(\mu_2^2 - \mu_1^2)\right)/(2\sigma^2)\right),$$

which is an increasing function of $\sum x_i$. Hence $(X_1, \ldots, X_n)$ has an MLR in $\sum X_i$.

Binomial, Poisson, normal, one parameter gamma, and one parameter beta r.v.'s **each possess a MLR in some statistic. These each belong to the one-parameter exponential family, and the result is true for that family in some generality:**

Theorem 9.3.70. If $X = (X_1, \ldots, X_n)$ has a distribution in the one-parameter exponential family, that is, has p.d.f.

$$f(x_1, \ldots, x_n|\theta) = e^{T(x_1, \ldots, x_n)c(\theta) + c_0(\theta) + \varphi_0(x_1, \ldots, x_n)}$$

with $c(\cdot)$ a nondecreasing function, then $(X_1, \ldots, X_n)$ has an MLR in $T(X_1, \ldots, X_n)$.

Proof: For $\theta_2 > \theta_1$, $c(\theta_2) > c(\theta_1)$ and hence

$$\frac{f(x_1, \ldots, x_n|\theta_2)}{f(x_1, \ldots, x_n|\theta_1)} = e^{T(x_1, \ldots, x_n)(c(\theta_2) - c(\theta_1)) + (c_0(\theta_2) - c_0(\theta_1))}$$

is nondecreasing in $T(x_1, \ldots, x_n)$ as was to be shown.   ∎

Remark 9.3.71. Not all distributions possess a MLR in some statistic. For example, the Cauchy distribution does not. (We leave verification of this remark as an exercise, which is simplest when the sample is of size 1 and the density has the form of equation (8.1.20).)

We now proceed to the last business of this section, an application of (a slight generalization of) the Neyman-Pearson Lemma to legislative apportionment.[3] The generalization we need (others are given by, e.g., Rao (1965), pp. 375–377,

---

[3] This application is due to Reinhardt (1966).

and are useful in maximization or minimization subject to constraints) is the following:

Theorem 9.3.72. Let $f_1, \ldots, f_n$, $g_1, \ldots, g_n$, A, B be ≥ 0 with $A < B$. If $w_1, \ldots, w_n$ are such that $A \leq w_i \leq B$ $(i = 1, \ldots, n)$ and (for some k) satisfy

$$\sum_{i=1}^{n} g_i w_i = c, \qquad (9.3.73)$$

then by choosing

$$w_i = \begin{cases} B, & \text{if } f_i > kg_i \\ A, & \text{if } f_i < kg_i \end{cases} \qquad (9.3.74)$$

we maximize $\sum_{i=1}^{n} f_i w_i$ subject to the restraint $\sum_{i=1}^{n} g_i w_i = c$.

The proof of Theorem 9.3.72 is essentially that of Theorem 9.3.2 with $\phi(x)$ now restricted to the interval $[A, B]$ rather than the interval $[0, 1]$ and is left as an exercise (Problem 9.6H) while we now proceed to our example.

Example 9.3.75. Legislative Apportionment. Suppose that a state is divided into n voting units called "districts" and that p_i is the proportion of the state's population in district $i (i = 1, \ldots, n)$. If we let $w_i^* = \{$The number of legislators-per-person in district $i\}$ $(i = 1, \ldots, n)$, then the set of numbers $\{w_1^*, \ldots, w_n^*\}$ represents any apportionment. [If we apportioned exactly in proportion to district population, we would have $w_1^* = \ldots = w_n^*$ and Lp_i of the L legislators would be from district $i(1 \leq i \leq n)$.]

Following the Supreme Court's 1962 *Baker vs. Carr* decision that apportionment of state legislatures must be essentially proportional to population, it was suggested that "essentially proportional to population" be taken to mean

$$\frac{\max(w_1^*, \ldots, w_n^*)}{\min(w_1^*, \ldots, w_n^*)} \leq 1 + \varepsilon \qquad (9.3.76)$$

for a specified $\varepsilon > 0$ [since w_i is the number of legislators-per-person in district i, criterion (9.3.76) means the best-represented district is not to be more than 100ε percent better represented than the worst-represented district—where "best" and "worst" apply respectively to w_i^* being "large" or "small," and not to the quality of the legislators], and $\varepsilon = .5$ was spoken for strongly.

Suppose r_i is the fraction of the legislators from district i whom one party (party R, say) can expect to control, whereas $d_i = 1 - r_i$ is the fraction the other party (party D, say) can expect to control $(i = 1, \ldots, n)$. [We assume only two parties.] *We then ask*: "If criterion (9.3.76) is to be satisfied, how effective can partisan choice of $\{w_1^*, \ldots, w_n^*\}$ be?"

A measure of the success of partisan tinkering by a party (let us say party R to be specific) is the fraction of the legislature expected to be controlled by party R,

$$\frac{\sum_{i=1}^{n} w_i^* r_i p_i}{\sum_{i=1}^{n} w_i^* p_i}, \tag{9.3.77}$$

and our question is one of the maxima and minima of (9.3.77) over choices of $\{w_1^*, \ldots, w_n^*\}$ subject to restraint (9.3.76).

In Theorem 9.3.72 by taking $f_i = r_i p_i$, $g_i = p_i$, and $w_i = w_i^*/\min (w_1^*, \ldots, w_n^*)$ $(i = 1, \ldots, n)$, we find $A = 1$ and $B = 1.5$ are our limits on w_i $(i = 1, \ldots, n)$ and the result is: If $w_1^*, \ldots, w_n^*$ are such that $1 \leq w_i^*/\min (w_1^*, \ldots, w_n^*) \leq 1.5$ $(i = 1, \ldots, n)$ and (for some k) satisfy

$$\frac{\sum_{i=1}^{n} w_i^* p_i}{\min (w_1^*, \ldots, w_n^*)} = c, \tag{9.3.78}$$

then by choosing

$$\frac{w_i^*}{\min (w_1^*, \ldots, w_n^*)} = \begin{cases} 1.5, & \text{if } r_i > k \\ 1, & \text{if } r_i < k \end{cases} \tag{9.3.79}$$

we maximize $\sum_{i=1}^{n} w_i^* r_i p_i/\min (w_1^*, \ldots, w_n^*)$ subject to the restraint

$$\sum_{i=1}^{n} w_i^* p_i/\min (w_1^*, \ldots, w_n^*) = c.$$

Since $\{w_1^*, \ldots, w_n^*\}$ that maximize (9.3.77) [subject to (9.3.76) with $\varepsilon = .5$] will satisfy (9.3.78) for *some* c, it follows that choosing $\{w_1^*, \ldots, w_n^*\}$ to satisfy (9.3.79) for *some* k will maximize (9.3.77). (The minimization follows similarly by taking $f_i = p_i$ and $g_i = r_i p_i$, since to maximize $1/x$ is to minimize $x(x > 0)$.)

Although Example 9.3.75 is of interest in states where "districts" (or "counties") are fixed and are assigned a variable number of representatives, in other states "districts" may also be manipulated (gerrymandering). In such cases, a party may be interested in maximizing the proportion of districts that are considered "safe" for it, and other considerations than the Neyman-Pearson Lemma come into play.

PROBLEMS FOR SECTION 9.3

9.3.1 (a) Suppose X has the gamma p.d.f. $f(x|\beta) = \Gamma^{-1}(\alpha)\beta^{-\alpha}e^{-x/\beta}x^{\alpha-1}I_{(0, \infty)}(x)$ with α known. To test $H_0: \beta = 1$ versus $H_1: \beta = 2$, suppose we take a random sample of size n, $X_1, X_2, \ldots, X_n$. Show that the best test (most powerful test of

H_0 against H_1 at any specified level a_0) is based on the sufficient statistic for β (i.e., on $X_1 + X_2 + \cdots + X_n$). Hence, find a level a_0 most powerful test for H_0 against H_1. Is this test unbiased?

(b) Repeat part (a) for H_0: $\beta = \beta_0$ versus H_1: $\beta = \beta_1$, $\beta_1 > \beta_0$, and hence generalize part (a) to find a uniformly most powerful level a_0 test for H_0: $\beta = \beta_0$ versus H_1: $\beta > \beta_0$. Finally, show that the power curve is a nondecreasing function of β.

9.3.2 Let $X_1, X_2, \ldots, X_n$ be a random sample of size n from the unit displaced exponential p.d.f. $f(x|\theta) = e^{-(x-\theta)}I_{(\theta, \infty)}(x)$. Use the Neyman-Pearson Lemma to find an α-level most powerful test for H_0: $\theta = \theta_0$ versus H_1: $\theta = \theta_1$, $\theta_1 > \theta_0$.

9.3.3 (a) Let $X_1, X_2, \ldots, X_5$ be a random sample of size 5 from a Poisson distribution with mean λ. Use the Neyman-Pearson Lemma to find an $\alpha = .05$ level most powerful test for H_0: $\lambda = 1$ versus H_1: $\lambda = 2$. Find the power of this test.

(b) Let $X_1, X_2, \ldots, X_n$ be a random sample of size n from a Poisson distribution with mean λ. Show that any most powerful α-level test for H_0: $\lambda = \lambda_0$ versus H_1: $\lambda = \lambda_1$ $(\lambda_1 > \lambda_0)$ is based on the minimal sufficient statistic for λ. Generalize this test to find a uniformly most powerful test for H_0: $\lambda = \lambda_0$ versus H_1: $\lambda > \lambda_0$; also find an expression for the power and show that the test is unbiased.

9.3.4 (a) In Example 9.3.10 we developed an α-level UMP test for H_0: $\mu = \mu_0$ versus H_1: $\mu > \mu_0$, when $X_1, X_2, \ldots, X_n$ was a random sample of size n from a $N(\mu, \sigma^2)$ distribution with σ known. If H_0 **is also composite**, H_0: $\mu \leq \mu_0$, then for any $\mu_0^* \in (-\infty, \mu_0]$ we can find a UMP test for H_0^*: $\mu = \mu_0^*$ versus H_1: $\mu > \mu_0$. If we determine k' such that

$$\sup_{\mu_0^* \in (-\infty, \mu_0]} P_{\mu_0^*}(\overline{X} > k') = \alpha$$

(as in equation (9.3.15)), then the probability of type I error at any $\mu_0^* \in (-\infty, \mu_0]$ will be $\leq \alpha$. *Show* that the actual supremum is achieved at $\mu_0^* = \mu_0$. (We therefore call this a **UMP level α test for the composite** H_0: $\mu \leq \mu_0$ versus H_1: $\mu > \mu_0$.) Because α (as a function of μ_0^*) is largest at the boundary point μ_0, often one replaces the composite null H_0: $\mu \leq \mu_0$ by the simple H_0: $\mu = \mu_0$.

(b) Repeat part (a) for H_0: $\mu \geq \mu_0$ versus H_1: $\mu < \mu_0$.

9.3.5 Using the Neyman-Pearson Lemma, show that there is no UMP α-level test for testing H_0: $\sigma^2 = \sigma_0^2$ versus H_1: $\sigma^2 \neq \sigma_0^2$, based on a random sample of size n from a $N(\mu, \sigma^2)$ population with μ known. Also show how the power function of the Neyman-Pearson test for H_0: $\sigma^2 = \sigma_0^2$ versus H_1: $\sigma^2 = \sigma_1^2$ $(\sigma_1^2 > \sigma_0^2)$ changes as a function of $c = \sigma_1^2/\sigma_0^2$.

9.3.6 Let X be a sample of size 1 from a discrete distribution $p(x)$. It is desired to test H_0: $p(\cdot) = p_0(\cdot)$ versus H_1: $p(\cdot) = p_1(\cdot)$ where $p_0(x)$ and $p_1(x)$ are given as

					x					
	2	4	6	8	10	12	14	16	18	20
$p_0(x)$	.01	.02	.03	.04	.05	.06	.07	.22	.25	.25
$p_1(x)$	.04	.04	.09	.16	.20	.24	.08	.05	.05	.05

Find all critical regions of size $\alpha = .07$, and from these find the one critical region that has minimum β (maximum power).

9.3.7 Based on a random sample of size n from a normal population with known mean μ and unknown variance σ^2, it is desired to test H_0: $\sigma^2 = \sigma_0^2$ versus H_1: $\sigma^2 > \sigma_0^2$. Use the idea of an MLR to find a UMP α-level test. Find an expression for the OC-curve, and show that the test is unbiased. Can you generalize your results to the case of μ unknown?

9.3.8 **(a)** For each following combination of hypothesis and underlying distribution, find an α-level UMP test (if one exists). Assume a random sample $X_1, X_2, \ldots, X_n$ of size n is available for testing.

(i) H_0: $\theta \le \theta_0$ versus H_1: $\theta > \theta_0$, $f(x|\theta) = \theta x^{-(\theta+1)} I_{[1, \infty)}(x)$.

(ii) H_0: $\theta \ge \theta_0$ versus H_1: $\theta < \theta_0$, $f(x|\theta) = \dfrac{1}{\theta} x^{(1-\theta)/\theta} I_{(0,1)}(x)$.

(b) Find expressions for the power functions in part **(a)**.

9.3.9 Let $X_1, X_2, \ldots, X_n$ be a random sample of size n from a $N(\mu, \sigma^2)$ distribution. For each following pair of hypotheses, show that the power of the α-level UMP test increases as n increases. Also show that each of the tests is unbiased.
(a) H_0: $\mu \le \mu_0$ versus H_1: $\mu > \mu_0$, when σ is known.
(b) H_0: $\mu \ge \mu_0$ versus H_1: $\mu < \mu_0$, when σ is known.
(c) H_0: $\sigma^2 \le \sigma_0^2$ versus H_1: $\sigma^2 > \sigma_0^2$, when μ is known.
(d) H_0: $\sigma^2 \ge \sigma_0^2$ versus H_1: $\sigma^2 < \sigma_0^2$, when μ is known.

9.3.10 Consider Problem 9.3.9 with μ and σ^2 both unknown.

9.3.11 Based on a random sample of size n with p.d.f. $f(\cdot)$, it is desired to test H_0: $f(x) = (2\pi)^{-0.5} e^{-x^2/2}$ $(-\infty < x < \infty)$ versus H_1: $f(x) = \pi^{-1}(1 + x^2)^{-1}$ $(-\infty < x < \infty)$. Use the Neyman-Pearson Lemma to find an α-level most powerful test. For $\alpha = .05$, find the critical region and power of the test you find.

9.3.12 Let $X_1, X_2, \ldots, X_{25}$ be outcomes of 25 independent Bernoulli trials with common probability of success p. It is desired to test H_0: $\{p \le .4$ or $p \ge .6\}$ versus H_1: $p \in (.4, .6)$. A suggested test is

$$\phi(X) = \begin{cases} 1, & \text{if } c_1 < \sum_{i=1}^{25} X_i < c_2 \\[2mm] \gamma_1, & \text{if } \sum_{i=1}^{25} X_i = c_1 \\[2mm] \gamma_2, & \text{if } \sum_{i=1}^{25} X_i = c_2 \\[2mm] 0, & \text{otherwise.} \end{cases}$$

(a) Using the normal approximation to the binomial distribution, find c_1 and c_2 such that $E_{p=.4}\phi(X) = \alpha = E_{p=.6}\phi(X)$, where $\alpha = .05$.
(b) Use the exact (binomial) distribution to find an $\alpha = .05$ level test, and $c_1, c_2, \gamma_1, \gamma_2$ such that $E_{p=.4}\phi(X) = \alpha = E_{p=.6}\phi(X)$.

9.3.13 **(a)** For a Poisson population, it is desired to test H_0: $\lambda = \lambda_0$ versus H_1: $\lambda = \lambda_1$ $(\lambda_1 > \lambda_0)$. How large a sample size is needed to obtain an α-level most powerful test with power $1 - \beta$? (Assume the sample size is large enough to apply the Central Limit Theorem.)

(b) Compute the sample size in part **(a)** if $\lambda_0 = 2$, $\lambda_1 = 1$, $\alpha = .05$, and $1 - \beta = .90$.

9.3.14 In Example 9.3.75, suppose a state has $n = 10$ districts, each with $100p_i = 10\%$ of the population ($i = 1, 2, \ldots, 10$), and a legislature of size $L = 100$. Suppose $r_1 = r_2 = r_3 = r_4 = 1.0$, $r_5 = r_6 = r_7 = r_8 = r_9 = r_{10} = 0.0$.

   (a) Find $w_1^*, \ldots, w_{10}^*$ that maximize (9.3.77) for $\varepsilon = 0.5$. What value does (9.3.77) then have?

   (b) As in part **(a)**, but for minimization.

   (c) In each of parts **(a)** and **(b)**, how many legislators will party R control?

9.4. A DECISION-THEORETIC VIEW OF THE HYPOTHESIS-TESTING PROBLEM

In this section we cover the contribution of decision theory to an integrated view of the hypothesis-testing problem, thus also giving a preview of the methods of Chapter 12 for what amounts to an important special case (the hypothesis-testing problem). The discussion in this section is largely informal.

In a hypothesis-testing problem (see Definition 9.2.1) where $H_0 = \{\theta_0\}$ and $H_1 = \{\theta_1\}$ are both simple, we observe a r.v. X with d.f. $F(x|\theta)$ where θ is unknown, $\theta \in \Theta$. Then any test $\phi(\cdot)$ has two error probabilities associated with it: $\alpha(\phi) = E_{\theta_0}\phi(X)$ (probability of error of Type I, i.e., probability of rejecting a true H_0) and $1 - \beta(\phi) = 1 - E_{\theta_1}\phi(X)$ (probability of error of Type II, i.e., probability of accepting a false H_0).[4] Thus, the point $(\alpha(\phi), 1 - \beta(\phi))$ is a measure of the goodness, or badness, of the test $\phi(\cdot)$: The smaller the coordinates, the better the test. This point

$$r(\phi) = (\alpha(\phi), 1 - \beta(\phi)) \tag{9.4.1}$$

is called the **risk point** of the test $\phi(\cdot)$, and if we plot the risk points $(\alpha(\phi), 1 - \beta(\phi))$ for *every possible* test $\phi(\cdot)$ based on X for the specific hypothesis-testing problem we are considering, we will fill a convex region as in Figure 9.4-1. Recalling that a subset S of $\mathcal{R}^k$ is called **convex** if $x, y \in S$ implies $\lambda x + (1 - \lambda)y \in S$ for all λ ($0 < \lambda < 1$), we see that our claim is that if $r(\phi_1)$ and $r(\phi_2)$ are risk points of tests ϕ_1 and ϕ_2, then $\lambda r(\phi_1) + (1 - \lambda)r(\phi_2) = (\lambda\alpha(\phi_1) + (1 - \lambda)\alpha(\phi_2), \lambda(1 - \beta(\phi_1)) + (1 - \lambda)(1 - \beta(\phi_2)))$ is the risk point of some test ϕ_3 as long as $0 < \lambda < 1$. Formally:

Theorem 9.4.2. For any hypothesis-testing problem where H_0 and H_1 are both simple, the set $R = \{r(\phi): \phi(\cdot) \text{ is a test}\}$ of risk points of all possible tests is a convex subset of the unit square $I_2 = \{(x, y): 0 \le x, y \le 1\}$.[5]

---

[4] Whereas earlier [see equation (9.2.14)] the probability of Type II error was denoted by $\beta(\cdot)$, here we denote it by $1 - \beta(\cdot)$. Both notations are in wide use, and you can assess which notation is in use from the context.

[5] The considerations of this section can be generalized to composite hypotheses, but are no longer as simple (and so are best left as a special case of the full generality in Chapter 12).

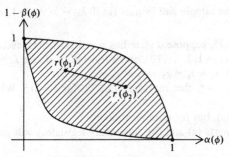

Figure 9.4-1. The set of risk points is convex.

Proof: First, for any test $\phi(\cdot)$, $\alpha(\phi)$ and $1 - \beta(\phi)$ are probabilities. Hence, $0 \le \alpha(\phi) \le 1$ and $0 \le 1 - \beta(\phi) \le 1$. Hence, $r(\phi) \in I_2$ for all $\phi(\cdot)$. Thus, $R \subseteq I_2$.

Next, suppose $r(\phi_1)$ and $r(\phi_2)$ are the risk points of tests $\phi_1(\cdot)$ and $\phi_2(\cdot)$. Then $\phi_3(\cdot) = \lambda\phi_1(\cdot) + (1 - \lambda)\phi_2(\cdot)$ is a test for $0 < \lambda < 1$ (check this claim; i.e., verify that $0 \le \phi_3(x) \le 1$ for all $x \in \mathcal{X}$) and has (check this) risk point

$$r(\phi_3) = \big(\lambda\alpha(\phi_1) + (1 - \lambda)\alpha(\phi_2),$$

$$\lambda\big(1 - \beta(\phi_1)\big) + (1 - \lambda)\big(1 - \beta(\phi_2)\big)\big) \qquad (9.4.3)$$

$$= \lambda r(\phi_1) + (1 - \lambda)r(\phi_2).$$

Hence, R is a convex set.   ∎

Note that the points $(0, 1)$ and $(1, 0)$ are always in the convex set R:

Lemma 9.4.4. For any hypothesis-testing problem where H_0 and H_1 are both simple, the set $R = \{r(\phi): \phi(\cdot) \text{ a test}\}$ includes $(0, 1)$ and $(1, 0)$.

Proof: If $\phi_1(\cdot) \equiv 1$, then $r(\phi_1) = (1, 0)$; whereas if $\phi_2(\cdot) \equiv 0$, then $r(\phi_2) = (0, 1)$.   ∎

Can we, by considering risk points of tests, restrict ourselves to a "few" tests (instead of the tests that lead to the whole convex set of risk points)? Now if the risk point of a test ϕ_1 is such that for some other test ϕ_2 we have $\alpha(\phi_1) > \alpha(\phi_2)$ and $1 - \beta(\phi_1) > 1 - \beta(\phi_2)$, then ϕ_2 has smaller Type I error *and* smaller Type II error. In such a case, we would surely prefer ϕ_2. (See Figure 9.4-2.) Of course, even if $\alpha(\phi_1) \ge \alpha(\phi_2)$ and $1 - \beta(\phi_1) \ge 1 - \beta(\phi_2)$ we have no use for ϕ_1: ϕ_2 is at least as good (and perhaps better) with respect to both types of error. In fact, if $\alpha(\phi_1) = \alpha(\phi_2)$ and $1 - \beta(\phi_1) = 1 - \beta(\phi_2)$, we can dispense with one of ϕ_1, ϕ_2 since they have the same risk point ($r(\phi_1) = r(\phi_2)$). These considerations are formalized as follows.

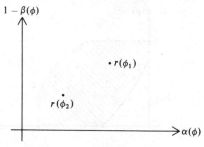

Figure 9.4-2. ϕ_2 preferred to ϕ_1.

Definition 9.4.5. For any hypothesis-testing problem where H_0 and H_1 are simple, test ϕ_2 is said to be **better than** test ϕ_1 (or test ϕ_1 is said to be **worse than** test ϕ_2) if $\alpha(\phi_2) \leq \alpha(\phi_1)$ and $1 - \beta(\phi_2) \leq 1 - \beta(\phi_1)$ with at least one strict inequality ($<$). We say ϕ_1 is **no better than** ϕ_2 if $\alpha(\phi_2) \leq \alpha(\phi_1)$ and $1 - \beta(\phi_2) \leq 1 - \beta(\phi_1)$.

Definition 9.4.6. For any hypothesis-testing problem where H_0 and H_1 are both simple, let $T = \{\phi(\cdot): \phi(\cdot) \text{ is a test}\}$. Any class of tests $C \subseteq T$ is called **complete** (or a **complete class of tests**) if for each test $\phi_1 \notin C$ there is a test $\phi_2 \in C$ such that ϕ_2 is better than ϕ_1. A class C is called **essentially complete** if for each test $\phi_1 \notin C$ there is a test $\phi_2 \in C$ such that ϕ_1 is no better than ϕ_2. A class C is called **minimal complete** if C is complete, but if any $\phi_2 \in C$ is removed from C the resulting class is not complete. A class C is called **minimal essentially complete** if C is essentially complete, but if any $\phi_2 \in C$ is removed from C, the resulting class is not essentially complete.

Thus, by considering risk points of tests we can restrict ourselves to a "few" tests instead of the tests that lead to the whole convex set of risk points, since no "worse" tests (Definition 9.4.5) should be considered and, among equivalent tests, only one need be considered: Those tests whose risk points fall on the lower boundary of the convex set of risk points form a minimal complete class C_1 (see Figure 9.4-3).[6] But this class C_1 may still contain tests ϕ_1 and ϕ_2 such that $r(\phi_1) = r(\phi_2)$. If we then retain only ϕ_1 in each such case (i.e., if a number of tests have the same risk point, eliminate all but one of these tests) we obtain a minimal essentially complete class C_2. Of course, C_2 contains tests that can give us any "desirable" risk point.

Now that we have seen how (by consideration of risk points of tests) we can restrict ourselves to a "few" tests, how do we do this in practice? (That is, how do we obtain a minimal essentially complete class of tests?) By the Neyman-Pearson Lemma (Theorem 9.3.2 and Problem 9.3H) for testing simple H_0 versus simple

---

[6] It is implicitly assumed that the convex set of risk points is closed (i.e., contains its boundary). This is true but difficult to prove. For the mathematical details see Lehmann (1959), p. 67.

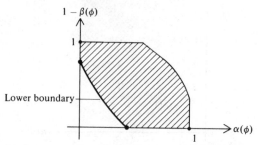

Figure 9.4-3. Risk points of minimal complete class.

H_1 after observing X, a test $\phi(\cdot)$ is most powerful of level α iff it has level α and satisfies (9.3.4) for some k. Thus, we have the following.

Theorem 9.4.7. For testing simple H_0 versus simple H_1 after observing X, the collection of tests $\{\phi_\alpha(\cdot),\ \alpha \le \alpha_0\}$ is minimal essentially complete. Here $\phi_\alpha(\cdot)$ is a test of level α that satisfies (9.3.4), and α_0 is the smallest α for which $1 - \beta(\phi_\alpha) = 0$ [i.e., with regard to Figure 9.4-3, the smallest α at which the convex set of risk points touches the horizontal axis; usually $\alpha_0 = 1$].

Ultimately, the question arises: Once we have obtained the minimal essentially complete class in Theorem 9.4.7 (i.e., a class of tests that yields the lower boundary shown in Figure 9.4-3), how should we select one member out of this class? This is a disputed question, and several general principles have been proposed, each of which will lead to *an* answer; however, the choice may have to be made on pragmatic grounds (since there may be no quantity called *the* answer[7])—it depends on which $(\alpha, 1 - \beta)$ on the lower boundary is suitable for our particular situation.

The several proposed methods of choosing one of the tests of the minimal essentially complete class clarify the problems involved, and we now discuss them. Each method essentially attempts to reduce the risk point $r(\phi) = (\alpha(\phi), 1 - \beta(\phi))$, which is two-dimensional (a point in the plane) to a one-dimensional number $f(r(\phi))$ (a point on a line). If the resulting number $f(r(\phi))$ is such that one can agree to prefer ϕ_2 to ϕ_1 whenever $f(r(\phi_2)) < f(r(\phi_1))$, we are done: We choose that ϕ which minimizes $f(r(\phi))$. [Unfortunately no function $f(\cdot)$ has yet been proposed for which statisticians can agree to prefer ϕ_2 to ϕ_1 whenever $f(r(\phi_2)) < f(r(\phi_1))$ *in every problem*. Probably none exists.] The proposed $f(\cdot)$ are as follows.

---

[7]Of course, proponents of the various methods might like us to think they were "the" (not "an") answer. And if, as some say, "Philosophers come after the scientists have left and make principles," then the debate may grow bitter and the voices strident. A lucid introduction to the lurid debates now raging in some statistical circles was given by a great statistician, J. Wolfowitz (1962), and is recommended reading for those wishing to pursue this avenue.

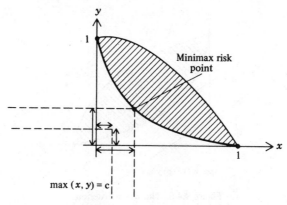

Figure 9.4-4. The minimax criterion.

Definition 9.4.8. When testing simple H_0 versus simple H_1 after observing X, we choose a test from the minimal essentially complete class $C_\alpha = \{\phi_\alpha(\cdot),\ \alpha \le \alpha_0\}$ of Theorem 9.4.7. A test that minimizes (for some p with $0 \le p \le 1$)

$$f(r(\phi)) = p\alpha(\phi) + (1 - p)(1 - \beta(\phi))\qquad(9.4.9)$$

is called **Bayes (with respect to the a priori distribution $(p, 1 - p)$)**, or a **Bayes rule.** A test that minimizes

$$f(r(\phi)) = \max\{\alpha(\phi), 1 - \beta(\phi)\}\qquad(9.4.10)$$

is called **minimax**, or a **minimax (risk) rule.** A test that minimizes

$$f(r(\phi)) = \max\{\alpha(\phi) - \min\{\alpha(\phi)\colon \phi \in C_\alpha\},$$
$$(1 - \beta(\phi)) - \min\{1 - \beta(\phi)\colon \phi \in C_\alpha\}\}\qquad(9.4.11)$$

is called **minimax regret,**[8] or a **minimax regret rule.**

A geometrical interpretation of the minimax rule can be given with respect to the convex set of risk points, as follows. On the dashed lines in Figure 9.4-4, $f(x, y) = \max(x, y)$ is constant, at say value c. As $c\uparrow$, the quantity $f(x, y)\uparrow$. Thus, since we desire to minimize $f(r(\phi)) = \max\{\alpha(\phi), 1 - \beta(\phi)\}$, we choose a test corresponding to the first risk point (of those corresponding to tests in the minimal essentially complete class) touched (by the dashed lines) as $c\uparrow$.

---

[8]If $(\alpha(\phi), 1 - \beta(\phi))$ is the *risk* in terms of errors of Types I and II that we incur by using ϕ, then the *regret* we incur is $(\alpha(\phi) - b_1, (1 - \beta(\phi)) - b_2)$, where b_1 is the smallest $\alpha(\phi)$ could be for any ϕ, and b_2 is the smallest $1 - \beta(\phi)$ could be for any ϕ. If H_0 is true, we must suffer at least b_1 as our Type I error; the increment of $\alpha(\phi) - b_1$ is due to using ϕ, while b_1 is common to all rules (similarly for Type II error).

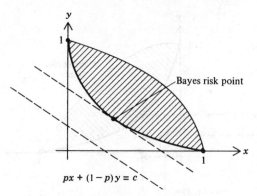

Figure 9.4-5. The Bayes criterion.

The geometrical interpretation of the Bayes rule is similar to that of the minimax rule. The quantity $f(x, y) = px + (1 - p)y$ is constant, say at value c, on the dashed line in Figure 9.4-5. Since we wish to minimize $f(r(\phi)) = p\alpha(\phi) + (1 - p)(1 - \beta(\phi))$, we choose a test corresponding to any risk point (of those corresponding to tests in the minimal essentially complete class) first touched (by the dashed line) as $c \uparrow$.

From Figures 9.4-4 and 9.4-5, it is clear that the minimax rule is a Bayes rule with respect to $(p, 1 - p)$ for some $p(0 \leq p \leq 1)$. [*Note*: It is easy to show that it is not the case that "$p = 0.5$ always." However, it is the case that $\alpha(\phi) = 1 - \beta(\phi)$ for the minimax rule ϕ.] So, finally we ask: **How do we find a Bayes rule?** A rule ϕ is Bayes with respect to $(p, 1 - p)$ (where p is fixed with $0 < p < 1$; if $p = 0$ or $p = 1$ the Bayes rule is obvious) iff it minimizes (9.4.9). But (using the notation of Theorem 9.3.2 and its proof)

$$f(r(\phi)) = p\alpha(\phi) + (1 - p)(1 - \beta(\phi))$$

$$= pE_{\theta_0}\phi(X) + (1 - p)E_{\theta_1}(1 - \phi(X))$$

$$= p\int_{x \in \mathcal{X}} \phi(x)f(x|\theta_0)\,dx + (1 - p)$$

$$\times \int_{x \in \mathcal{X}} (1 - \phi(x))f(x|\theta_1)\,dx$$

$$= \int_{x \in \mathcal{X}} [p\phi(x)f(x|\theta_0) + (1 - p)(1 - \phi(x))f(x|\theta_1)]\,dx.$$

(9.4.12)

However, the quantity being integrated is ≥ 0, so we minimize $f(r(\phi))$ by (if possible) choosing $\phi(x)$ for each x so as to minimize

$$p\phi(x)f(x|\theta_0) + (1 - p)(1 - \phi(x))f(x|\theta_1). \qquad (9.4.13)$$

But for a specified x, either $pf(x|\theta_0) > (1 - p)f(x|\theta_1)$ (in which case $\phi(x) = 0$ minimizes (9.4.13)) or $pf(x|\theta_0) < (1 - p)f(x|\theta_1)$ (in which case $\phi(x) = 1$ minimizes (9.4.13)) or $pf(x|\theta_0) = (1 - p)f(x|\theta_1)$ (in which case $\phi(x)$ can be arbitrary with $0 \le \phi(x) \le 1$), so the Bayes rule sets

$$\phi(x) = \begin{cases} 1, & \text{if } (1 - p)f(x|\theta_1) > pf(x|\theta_0) \\ 0, & \text{if } (1 - p)f(x|\theta_1) < pf(x|\theta_0). \end{cases} \qquad (9.4.14)$$

This is (since $p \ne 1$) essentially the Neyman-Pearson test (see Theorem 9.3.2) with $k = p/(1 - p)$.

Thus, in testing simple H_0 versus simple H_1 after observing X, any rule that satisfies (9.4.14) for all $x \in \mathcal{X}$ is Bayes with respect to $(p, 1 - p)$. This holds for any p with $0 \le p \le 1$. Recall that in Definition 9.4.8 $(p, 1 - p)$ **was called an a priori (or prior) distribution, for reasons we will now make clear**

Suppose we have a hypothesis-testing problem with simple $H_0 = \{\theta_0\}$ and simple $H_1 = \{\theta_1\}$, and observe X. Suppose that, before the experiment, we find out that θ is a r.v. such that $P[\theta = \theta_0] = p$ and $P[\theta = \theta_1] = 1 - p$ [this is the case if, say, a person (usually called "nature") chooses the d.f. $F(x|\theta)$ of X by picking at random from a bin full of d.f.'s $100p$ percent of which are $F(x|\theta_0)$ and $100(1 - p)$ percent of which are $F(x|\theta_1)$]. Then (using the notation of Theorem 9.3.2 in the discrete case)

$$P[X = x] = pf(x|\theta_0) + (1 - p)f(x|\theta_1). \qquad (9.4.15)$$

So, before observing X, we knew $P[\theta = \theta_0] = p$ and $P[\theta = \theta_1] = 1 - p$. After observing X, we can find the a posteriori (or posterior) probability that $\theta = \theta_0$ or $\theta = \theta_1$ (using Bayes' rule (Theorem 2.3.9)) as

$$P[\theta = \theta_0|X = x] = \frac{P[\theta = \theta_0, X = x]}{P[X = x]}$$

$$= \frac{P[X = x|\theta = \theta_0]P[\theta = \theta_0]}{P[X = x|\theta = \theta_0]P[\theta = \theta_0] + P[X = x|\theta = \theta_1]P[\theta = \theta_1]}$$

$$= \frac{pf(x|\theta_0)}{pf(x|\theta_0) + (1 - p)f(x|\theta_1)}, \qquad (9.4.16)$$

$$P[\theta = \theta_1|X = x] = \frac{(1 - p)f(x|\theta_1)}{pf(x|\theta_0) + (1 - p)f(x|\theta_1)}. \qquad (9.4.17)$$

If we then decide θ_0 or θ_1 [i.e., $\phi(x) = 0$ or $\phi(x) = 1$] according, respectively, as (9.4.16) or (9.4.17) is the larger, we are simply stating to be "true" that one of $\{\theta_0, \theta_1\}$ which has the larger posterior probability. This is (see (9.4.14)) *precisely what a Bayes rule with respect to $(p, 1 - p)$ does.*

PROBLEMS FOR SECTION 9.4

9.4.1 (a) Let $X_1, X_2, \ldots, X_n$ be a random sample of size n from a normal population with unknown mean μ and known variance σ^2. Consider the hypothesis-testing problem $H_0: \mu = \mu_0$ versus $H_1: \mu = \mu_1$ with $\mu_0 < \mu_1$. Let $\phi(\cdot)$ be the most powerful test, derived using the Neyman-Pearson Lemma. Plot the collection of all possible risk points $r(\phi) = (\alpha(\phi), 1 - \beta(\phi))$.

(b) As in part (a), for the case $\mu_0 > \mu_1$.

9.4.2 Let $X_1, X_2, \ldots, X_n$ be a random sample of size n from a Poisson distribution with mean λ. Consider the hypothesis-testing problem $H_0: \lambda = \lambda_0$ versus $H_1: \lambda = \lambda_1$ with $\lambda_1 > \lambda_0$.

(a) Find the most powerful test and plot the set of all risk points.

(b) Show that $\alpha(\phi) + (1 - \beta(\phi))$ is minimized when ϕ is given by $\phi(X_1, X_2, \ldots, X_n) = 1$ if $\overline{X} > c$ (and $= 0$ otherwise).

(c) If $\lambda_0 = 1$, $\lambda_1 = 2$, and $n = 10$, find the value of c that minimizes $\alpha(\phi) + (1 - \beta(\phi))$. Also find the minimum value.

9.4.3 Let $X_1, X_2, \ldots, X_n$ be a random sample of size n from a Bernoulli distribution with probability of success p. Consider the hypothesis-testing problem $H_0: p = p_0$ versus $H_1: p = p_1$ with $p_1 < p_0$.

(a) Find a most powerful test for this problem at a given α-level; call this test ϕ_1.

(b) Show that ϕ_1 minimizes $\alpha(\phi) + (1 - \beta(\phi))$ among all ϕ such that $\alpha(\phi) = \alpha$.

(c) If $p_0 = .5$, $p_1 = .4$, and $n = 10$, find the value of $\alpha(\phi_1) + (1 - \beta(\phi_1))$.

9.4.4 If C is a complete class and contains no proper essentially complete subclass, show that C is minimal complete and minimal essentially complete.

9.4.5 In Problem 9.4.2(c), find the Bayes test ϕ_B with respect to prior $(.6, .4)$. What action does it take if $\overline{X} = 1.5$? If $\overline{X} = 2.5$?

9.4.6 In Problem 9.4.2(c), find a minimax test ϕ_M. Show that it is also a minimax regret test ϕ_{MR}. Show the test of Problem 9.4.2(c), ϕ_B of Problem 9.4.5, ϕ_M, and ϕ_{MR} on the diagram of Problem 9.4.2(a).

9.5. TESTING NORMAL MEANS (ONE POPULATION)

One hypothesis-testing problem (see Definition 9.2.1) that occurs frequently in practice has $X = (X_1, \ldots, X_n)$ where $X_1, \ldots, X_n$ are independent r.v.'s, each $N(\mu, \sigma^2)$ where μ is unknown with $\mu \in \Theta = \{x: -\infty < x < +\infty\}$, $\sigma^2 > 0$ is known, $H_0 = \{\mu_0\}$, and H_1 may have several forms. The case where $H_1 = \{\mu_1\}$ with $\mu_1 > \mu_0$ was studied in Example 9.3.10. Using the Neyman-Pearson Lemma, we found that the test which rejects iff

$$\overline{X} > \mu_0 + \frac{\sigma}{\sqrt{n}} \Phi^{-1}(1 - \alpha) \qquad (9.5.1)$$

is most powerful of level α in this case. We also showed that if $H_1 = \{\mu_1: \mu_1 > \mu_0\}$, the same test is UMP one-sided. If $H_1 = \{\mu_1\}$ with $\mu_1 < \mu_0$, or if $H_1 = \{\mu_1: \mu_1 < \mu_0\}$, analogous results are easily shown (Problem 9.26).

Thus, for each of simple and one-sided alternative hypotheses, there is a "best" test available to us. In the case of *two-sided* alternatives (e.g., $H_1 = \{\mu_1:$ $\mu_1 < \mu_0$, or $\mu_1 > \mu_0\}$) we discussed two tests in a special case in Example 9.2.4. For this case there is no "best" (UMP) test (Example 9.3.45), but tests that reject iff

$$\overline{X} - \mu_0 < a \quad \text{or} \quad \overline{X} - \mu_0 > b \qquad (9.5.2)$$

(for some a and b that give the proper level) form an essentially complete class of tests.

Now suppose our hypothesis-testing problem is as above [$X = (X_1, \ldots, X_n)$ where $X_1, \ldots, X_n$ are independent r.v.'s, each $N(\mu, \sigma^2)$ where μ is unknown with $\mu \in \Theta = \{x: -\infty < x < +\infty\}$, $H_0 = \{\mu_1\}$] for one of the possible choices of H_1 studied, **but that (instead of having $\sigma^2 > 0$ known) we have $\sigma^2 > 0$ unknown.** Since even the null hypothesis H_0: $\mu = \mu_0$ is no longer a simple hypothesis. (because the distribution of X will be different for different values of σ^2), the Neyman-Pearson Lemma does not solve this problem by providing a "best" test. However (see Example 8.1.32 and Problem 8.16) for $n \geq 2$

$$\left(\overline{X}, \sum_{i=1}^{n} (X_i - \overline{X})^2 / (n-1) \right) \qquad (9.5.3)$$

is a minimal sufficient statistic for the problem and hence (see Problem 9.13H) a test need be based only on the sufficient statistic (9.5.3) in order to have any "good" properties. Now, **what is a reasonable way to base a test on the sufficient statistic (9.5.3)?** First, let us reexamine the case where σ^2 is known. There, to be specific considering the case $H_1 = \{\mu_1\}$ with $\mu_1 > \mu_0$, the Neyman-Pearson test rejects (see equation (9.5.1)) iff

$$\overline{X} > \mu_0 + \frac{\sigma}{\sqrt{n}} \Phi^{-1}(1 - \alpha)$$

$$\Leftrightarrow \overline{X} - \mu_0 > \frac{\sigma}{\sqrt{n}} \Phi^{-1}(1 - \alpha) \qquad (9.5.4)$$

$$\Leftrightarrow \frac{\overline{X} - \mu_0}{\sigma/\sqrt{n}} > \Phi^{-1}(1 - \alpha).$$

That is, the Neyman-Pearson test rejects iff $\overline{X} - \mu_0$ is "too large." This is intuitively reasonable since when H_0: $\mu = \mu_0$ is true, $\overline{X} - \mu_0$ should be "close" to zero (it is then a $N(0, \sigma^2/n)$ r.v.), whereas when H_1: $\mu = \mu_1$ with $\mu_1 > \mu_0$ is true, $\overline{X} - \mu_0$ should be "far" from zero (it is then a $N(\mu_1 - \mu_0, \sigma^2/n)$ r.v.); hence, it seems reasonable to reject iff

$$\overline{X} - \mu_0 > c \qquad (9.5.5)$$

480 TESTS OF HYPOTHESES

and set c for level α. In setting c in (9.5.5) for level α we desire

$$P_{\mu_0}[\bar{X} - \mu_0 > c] = \alpha, \qquad (9.5.6)$$

and divide by $\sigma/\sqrt{n}$ so that we will be dealing with the $N(0,1)$ distribution (for which tables, for example Table 11, are available):

$$P_{\mu_0}\left[\frac{\bar{X} - \mu_0}{\sigma/\sqrt{n}} > \frac{c}{\sigma/\sqrt{n}}\right] = \alpha. \qquad (9.5.7)$$

Solving equation (9.5.7) for c, we find (essentially as in Example 9.3.10)

$$\begin{cases} 1 - \Phi\left(\dfrac{c}{\sigma/\sqrt{n}}\right) = \alpha, \\[2mm] \Phi\left(\dfrac{c}{\sigma/\sqrt{n}}\right) = 1 - \alpha, \\[2mm] \dfrac{c}{\sigma/\sqrt{n}} = \Phi^{-1}(1 - \alpha), \\[2mm] c = \dfrac{\sigma}{\sqrt{n}}\Phi^{-1}(1 - \alpha). \end{cases} \qquad (9.5.8)$$

Now if it is reasonable (in fact via use of the Neyman-Pearson Lemma we know it is "best") to reject when

$$\frac{\bar{X} - \mu_0}{\sqrt{\sigma^2/n}} \qquad (9.5.9)$$

is "too large" in the case of a known σ^2, perhaps in the case of an unknown σ^2 we should consider doing similarly after replacing σ^2 by a good estimator of σ^2. However (see (7.1.13)) the second component of our sufficient statistic (9.5.3) is a good estimator of σ^2; since it is used often, it is usually denoted by

$$s^2 \equiv \frac{\sum\limits_{i=1}^{n}(X_i - \bar{X})^2}{n - 1}. \qquad (9.5.10)$$

So, for the σ^2 unknown case our intuition leads us (by analogy to the σ^2 known case) to consider the test that rejects when

$$\frac{\bar{X} - \mu_0}{s/\sqrt{n}} \qquad (9.5.11)$$

is "too large." In order to obtain level α for this test we need to set c so that

$$P_{\mu_0}\left[\frac{\bar{X} - \mu_0}{s/\sqrt{n}} > c\right] = \alpha. \qquad (9.5.12)$$

We could do this *if* we knew the probability distribution of (9.5.11) and that distribution was tabled. In Theorem 9.5.13 and Lemma 9.5.15, we find that that distribution is one already studied in Chapter 4.

Theorem 9.5.13. If Y_1 has the $N(0,1)$ distribution [see Definition 4.2.18], if Y_2 has the $\chi_m^2(0)$ distribution [see Definition 4.2.13], and if Y_1 and Y_2 are independent r.v.'s, then

$$Z = \frac{Y_1}{\sqrt{Y_2/m}} \qquad (9.5.14)$$

has the Student's t-distribution with m degrees of freedom [see Definition 4.2.26].

Proof: This follows by using the methods studied in Section 4.6, and is left as a review exercise (Problem 9.27).   ∎

Lemma 9.5.15. If $X_1, \ldots, X_n$ are independent r.v.'s, each $N(\mu_0, \sigma^2)$, then $\overline{X} = (X_1 + \cdots + X_n)/n$ and $s^2 = \sum_{i=1}^{n} (X_i - \overline{X})^2/(n-1)$ are independent r.v.'s. It follows that

$$\frac{\overline{X} - \mu_0}{s/\sqrt{n}} \qquad (9.5.16)$$

has the Student's t-distribution with $m = n - 1$ degrees of freedom.

Proof: Before giving a precise proof, we note the following motivation. Consider $\overline{X}$ and $X_i - \overline{X}$ for any fixed i ($1 \le i \le n$). Now $(\overline{X}, X_i - \overline{X})$ has a bivariate normal distribution [see the footnote to Problem 7.9H] since $(X_1, \ldots, X_n)$ has a multivariate normal distribution (see Problem 9.28). Also, an easy computation yields (see Problem 9.29)

$$\rho(\overline{X}, X_i - \overline{X}) = \frac{\text{Cov}(\overline{X}, X_i - \overline{X})}{\sigma(\overline{X})\sigma(X_i - \overline{X})}$$

$$= \frac{\text{Cov}(\overline{X}, X_i) - \text{Cov}(\overline{X}, \overline{X})}{\sigma(\overline{X})\sigma(X_i - \overline{X})} \qquad (9.5.17)$$

$$= \frac{\text{Cov}((X_1 + \cdots + X_n)/n, X_i) - \text{Var}(\overline{X})}{\sigma(\overline{X})\sigma(X_i - \overline{X})} = 0.$$

Hence, by Theorem 5.3.25 $\overline{X}$ and $X_i - \overline{X}$ are independent. It follows easily (see Problem 9.30) that $\overline{X}$ and $(X_i - \overline{X})^2$ are independent. Since i was arbitrary, $\overline{X}$ is independent of each of $(X_1 - \overline{X})^2, \ldots, (X_n - \overline{X})^2$ (see Problem 9.14H).

*A precise proof proceeds as follows.** Based on the r.v.'s $X_1, \ldots, X_n$ we define n new r.v.'s

$$
\begin{cases}
Y_1 &= \dfrac{1}{\sqrt{n}}(X_1 + X_2 + X_3 + X_4 + \cdots + X_{n-2} + X_{n-1} + X_n), \\[2mm]
Y_2 &= \dfrac{1}{\sqrt{2}}(X_1 - X_2), \\[2mm]
Y_3 &= \dfrac{1}{\sqrt{3}\sqrt{2}}(X_1 + X_2 - 2X_3), \\[2mm]
Y_4 &= \dfrac{1}{\sqrt{4}\sqrt{3}}(X_1 + X_2 + X_3 - 3X_4), \\[2mm]
&\vdots \\[2mm]
Y_{n-1} &= \dfrac{1}{\sqrt{n-1}\sqrt{n-2}}(X_1 + X_2 + X_3 + X_4 + \cdots + X_{n-2} - (n-2)X_{n-1}), \\[2mm]
Y_n &= \dfrac{1}{\sqrt{n}\sqrt{n-1}}(X_1 + X_2 + X_3 + X_4 + \cdots + X_{n-2} + X_{n-1} - (n-1)X_n).
\end{cases}
\tag{9.5.18}
$$

((9.5.18) is called the **Helmert orthogonal transformation**.) Since $(X_1, \ldots, X_n)$ has a multivariate normal distribution, so does $(Y_1, \ldots, Y_n)$. Now a useful general form for $Y_i (2 \le i \le n)$ is

$$
Y_i = \frac{1}{\sqrt{i}\sqrt{i-1}} \left(\sum_{j=1}^{i-1} X_j - (i-1)X_i \right).
\tag{9.5.19}
$$

Then we can find *which* multivariate normal distribution $(Y_1, \ldots, Y_n)$ has by calculating (see Problem 9.31)

$$
\begin{cases}
EY_1 = \sqrt{n}\,\mu_0, \; EY_2 = \cdots = EY_n = 0, \\[2mm]
\mathrm{Var}(Y_1) = \mathrm{Var}(Y_2) = \cdots = \mathrm{Var}(Y_n) = \sigma^2, \\[2mm]
\mathrm{Cov}(Y_1, Y_i) = 0 \quad (2 \le i \le n), \\[2mm]
\mathrm{Cov}(Y_i, Y_j) = 0 \quad (2 \le i < j \le n).
\end{cases}
\tag{9.5.20}
$$

Hence, $Y_1, \ldots, Y_n$ are n independent r.v.'s, so Y_1 is independent of $Y_2, \ldots, Y_n$ and hence (see Problem 9.32) any function of Y_1 is independent of any function

---

*As this was already proven by another method in Theorem 5.5.34, the present method (using the important Helmert transformation) may be skipped if the instructor desires. (The result can also be proven using Basu's Theorem (Theorem 8.2.23); see Problem 8.2.1.)

of $Y_2, \ldots, Y_n$. Since (see Problem 9.33)

$$\begin{cases} Y_1 = \sqrt{n}\,\overline{X}, \\ Y_2^2 + \cdots + Y_n^2 = \displaystyle\sum_{i=1}^{n} (X_i - \overline{X})^2 = (n-1)s^2 \end{cases} \qquad (9.5.21)$$

it follows that $\overline{X}$ is independent of s^2.

To complete the proof, we wish to show that (9.5.16) has a certain Student's t-distribution. Following the hint of Theorem 9.5.13, we write

$$\frac{\overline{X} - \mu_0}{s/\sqrt{n}} = \frac{\dfrac{\sqrt{n}}{\sigma}(\overline{X} - \mu_0)}{s/\sigma}, \qquad (9.5.22)$$

where $(\sqrt{n}/\sigma)(\overline{X} - \mu_0)$ is a $N(0,1)$ r.v. that is independent (by the first part of the present theorem) of s/σ. Thus, if we can show that s/σ is $\sqrt{Y_2/(n-1)}$ where Y_2 is a $\chi^2_{n-1}(0)$ r.v., we are (by use of Theorem 9.5.13) done. Now using (9.5.21)

$$\begin{aligned} \frac{s}{\sigma} &= \sqrt{\frac{s^2}{\sigma^2}} = \sqrt{\frac{Y_2^2 + \cdots + Y_n^2}{(n-1)\sigma^2}} \\ &= \sqrt{\left\{ \left(\frac{Y_2}{\sigma}\right)^2 + \cdots + \left(\frac{Y_n}{\sigma}\right)^2 \right\} \Big/ (n-1)}\,, \end{aligned} \qquad (9.5.23)$$

where $Y_2/\sigma, \ldots, Y_n/\sigma$ are independent $N(0,1)$ r.v.'s. Using Problem 9.34, the proof is complete. [Note that these results also justify the nomenclature "loss of 1 degree of freedom" noted following equation (7.1.13).] ∎

We are now in a position to provide a c that solves equation (9.5.12), since (via Lemma 9.5.15) we know that (9.5.11) has the Student's t-distribution with $n - 1$ degrees of freedom. First we need some notation. [For the $N(0,1)$ distribution we also needed a notation for that number c such that if X is a $N(0,1)$ r.v., then $P[X \le c] = x$; namely $\Phi(c) = x$, or $c = \Phi^{-1}(x)$.]

Definition 9.5.24. If a r.v. X has the Student's t-distribution with m degrees of freedom, we will say X **has the t_m distribution**, and will (for $0 < \alpha < 1$) denote the solution c of the equation

$$P[X \le c] = \alpha \qquad (9.5.25)$$

by writing $t_m(c) = \alpha$, or $c = t_m^{-1}(\alpha)$. Thus, we have the following.

Theorem 9.5.26. For the hypothesis-testing problem with $X = (X_1, \ldots, X_n)$ where $X_1, \ldots, X_n$ are independent r.v.'s, each $N(\mu, \sigma^2)$ where $\mu(-\infty < \mu < +\infty)$

and $\sigma^2(\sigma^2 > 0)$ are both unknown, $H_0 = \{\mu_0\}$, and $H_1 = \{\mu_1\}$ with $\mu_1 > \mu_0$, the test that rejects iff

$$\frac{\overline{X} - \mu_0}{s/\sqrt{n}} > t_n^{-1}(1 - \alpha) \qquad (9.5.27)$$

has level α. Similar tests are easily obtained [see Problem 9.35] for other alternatives H_1.

Although we were not able to use the Neyman-Pearson Lemma to show that this test in Theorem 9.5.26, called the *t-test*, has good properties [we reasoned to the test by using analogy to the $\sigma^2 > 0$ known case and sufficient statistics], in fact it has good properties. Since their development is mathematically intricate we will not discuss them here.

As we gave detailed formulas above in Section 9.5 for the one-sided alternative of increase in the mean (i.e., H_1: $\mu_1 > \mu_0$), and noted (without full details) that "similar tests are easily obtained for other alternatives H_1," for completeness we supply those details in Table 9.5-1.

Example 9.5.28. A light-bulb manufacturer claims that the light bulbs produced by his/her company have an average life of 1200 hours. A consumer protection agency wishes to test this claim, against the alternative of fraudulent advertising (i.e., the alternative that average life span is less than 1200 hours). A random sample of 16 bulbs is chosen from production and tested as to life times. The summary statistics turn out to be $\overline{X} = 1148.5$ hours and $s^2 = 12544.224$. Based on these summary statistics, and at the $\alpha = .05$ level of significance, what conclusions are reached?

In practice, often it can be difficult to choose the null and alternative hypotheses. The null hypothesis can be set up as an equality, for example, H_0: $\mu = \mu_0$, since the Type I error probability achieves its maximum when $\mu = \mu_0$. Thus for a given α, if we take our null hypothesis to be H_0: $\mu = \mu_0$ and a one-sided H_0 (H_0: $\mu < \mu_0$ or H_0: $\mu > \mu_0$) is more appropriate, there is no problem since the latter forms have their largest α at H_0: $\mu = \mu_0$. Setting up the alternative hypothesis (also commonly known as the "researcher's hypothesis") is more complex. To set up H_1, find what statement needs to be established.

Since we have H_0: $\mu \geq 1200$ vs. H_1: $\mu < 1200$ where μ is average life of the light bulbs produced by this manufacturer as our null and alternative hypotheses and $\overline{X}$ and s^2 are already available, we next compute

$$T = \frac{\overline{X} - \mu_0}{s/\sqrt{n}} = \frac{1148.5 - 1200}{\sqrt{12544.224}/\sqrt{16}} = -1.8393.$$

Since $t_{n-1}^{-1}(1 - \alpha) = t_{15}^{-1}(.95) = 1.753$ and $T < -t_{n-1}^{-1}(1 - \alpha)$, there is sufficient evidence against H_0, and we conclude that (at the $\alpha = .05$ level of significance) H_0 should be rejected in favor of the alternative.

Note that when the null hypothesis is rejected at a given level α we know that if, in fact, H_0 is true, then there is at most probability α of observing the data we

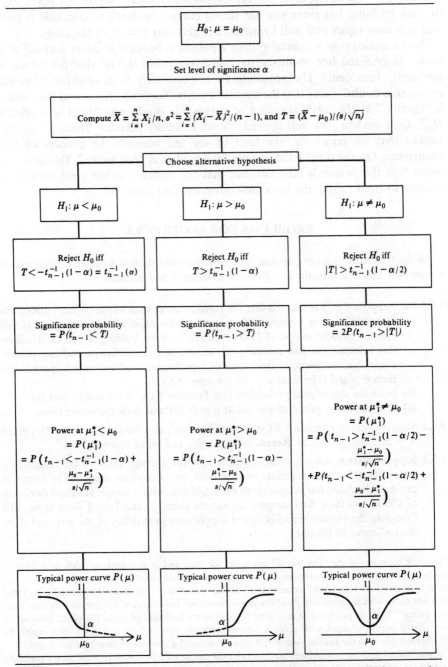

TABLE 9.5-1
Testing normal means, one population, σ^2 unknown: Summary of procedure for 3 alternatives*

$$H_0: \mu = \mu_0$$

Set level of significance α

Compute $\bar{X} = \sum_{i=1}^{n} X_i /n$, $s^2 = \sum_{i=1}^{n} (X_i - \bar{X})^2/(n-1)$, and $T = (\bar{X} - \mu_0)/(s/\sqrt{n})$

Choose alternative hypothesis

| $H_1: \mu < \mu_0$ | $H_1: \mu > \mu_0$ | $H_1: \mu \neq \mu_0$ |

Reject H_0 iff
$T < -t_{n-1}^{-1}(1-\alpha) = t_{n-1}^{-1}(\alpha)$

Reject H_0 iff
$T > t_{n-1}^{-1}(1-\alpha)$

Reject H_0 iff
$|T| > t_{n-1}^{-1}(1-\alpha/2)$

Significance probability
$= P(t_{n-1} < T)$

Significance probability
$= P(t_{n-1} > T)$

Significance probability
$= 2P(t_{n-1} > |T|)$

Power at $\mu_1^* < \mu_0$
$= P(\mu_1^*)$
$= P\left(t_{n-1} < -t_{n-1}^{-1}(1-\alpha) + \dfrac{\mu_0 - \mu_1^*}{s/\sqrt{n}}\right)$

Power at $\mu_1^* > \mu_0$
$= P(\mu_1^*)$
$= P\left(t_{n-1} > t_{n-1}^{-1}(1-\alpha) - \dfrac{\mu_1^* - \mu_0}{s/\sqrt{n}}\right)$

Power at $\mu_1^* \neq \mu_0$
$= P(\mu_1^*)$
$= P\left(t_{n-1} > t_{n-1}^{-1}(1-\alpha/2) - \dfrac{\mu_1^* - \mu_0}{s/\sqrt{n}}\right)$
$+ P\left(t_{n-1} < -t_{n-1}^{-1}(1-\alpha/2) + \dfrac{\mu_0 - \mu_1^*}{s/\sqrt{n}}\right)$

Typical power curve $P(\mu)$

Typical power curve $P(\mu)$

Typical power curve $P(\mu)$

*In this table: T is a random variable whose numerical value is computed from the data; t_{n-1} is a Student's t random variable with $n-1$ degrees of freedom; and $t_{n-1}^{-1}(q)$ is the number such that $P(t_{n-1} \leq t_{n-1}^{-1}(q)) = q$. When significance probability is computed, T is treated as a number (and *not* as a random variable).

have observed. On the other hand, if we do not reject H_0, we casually say that we "accept H_0." However, more correct terminology is that "we do not reject H_0" (it *may* be false, but there was not strong enough evidence to conclude it false *and* still only reject *true* null hypotheses of this sort $100\alpha\%$ of the time).

As an analogy, in a judicial system a person is brought to court accused of a crime. In civilized free countries, the null hypothesis (H_0) is* that the person is not guilty (innocent). The prosecution's responsibility is to establish "beyond reasonable doubt" that (H_1:) the person is guilty. Suppose after a trial the verdict is, "guilty." If the jury's standard of reasonable doubt was "level $\alpha = .05$ for H_0," then such a jury will convict 5% of innocent persons. Thus, a "guilty" verdict may be erroneous; the level of the test controls the chances of this occurrence. On the other hand, suppose the verdict is "not guilty." This does not mean that the person is innocent, but that the evidence is not great enough to convict without raising the innocent-conviction rate above 5%.

PROBLEMS FOR SECTION 9.5

In the following problems, assume that the parent distribution from which the random sample was taken is normally distributed with mean μ and variance σ^2.

9.5.1 **(a)** Suppose that it is claimed that the average career span of professional athletes in a certain sport is 6 years, with a standard deviation of 1.5 years. To test this claim, a random sample of 25 observations is taken, yielding $\overline{X} = 5.75$. Based on this information, and assuming σ^2 known, is there sufficient evidence to conclude that the average career span of a professional athlete in this sport is less than 6 years? (Use level $\alpha = .05$ for your test.)

(b) Find the significance probability (see Problem 9.14) of the test in part (a).

(c) Determine the power of the test at $\mu = 1(.5)5$ and draw the power curve.

9.5.2 Suppose that in Problem 9.5.1 we do not know σ^2, and the sample of size 25 yielded $\overline{X} = 5.75$ and $s^2 = 2.56$. Repeat parts (a), (b), and (c) of Problem 9.5.2.[9]

9.5.3 Suppose that a real-estate agent claims that the average value of the homes in a certain neighborhood is greater than \$60,000, and a random sample of 16 homes in this neighborhood has sample mean value \$65,450. with a sample standard deviation of \$9500. Do these data support the agent's claim? (Take Type I error to be .01.) Compute the (approximate) observed significance probability of the test, and draw the OC-curve of the test.

---

*In some countries of the "free world" this is not the case, and in that instance (such as in France, where the burden is on the defendant to prove innocence) those countries are regarded by us as less than fully civilized. Note that "innocent until proven guilty" does not mean that the judge and jury will not come with the prejudice that "the police would not have charged this person if he/she were not guilty." Thus, in practice one may need to overcome a prejudice of guilt. The point, however, is not that a person charged with a crime who is innocent may sit back and relax (that would be foolhardy), but that the judicial system will give the accused a measure of benefit of the doubt.

[9] If you cannot find the probabilities you need (for the significance probability) in the tables available, use linear interpolation in the available tables. (Another alternative is to use a computer program, such as that given by Dudewicz and Dalal (1972), to calculate the exact values needed.)

9.5.4 A certain clothing manufacturer's pants carry a size label stating "85 cm waist." A random sample of 26 pairs of these pants is measured as to waist size, and we find $\overline{X} = 86$ cm, $s^2 = 4.84$ cm^2. Is there sufficient evidence to conclude (at level $\alpha = .10$) that the average waist size of these pants is significantly different from 85 cm? (Test the hypothesis, compute the significance probability, and draw the power curve.)

9.6. TESTING NORMAL VARIANCES (ONE POPULATION)

The hypothesis-testing problem of concern in this section is the one with $X = (X_1, \ldots, X_n)$ where $X_1, \ldots, X_n$ are independent r.v.'s, each $N(\mu, \sigma^2)$ where μ is known $(-\infty < \mu < +\infty)$, σ^2 is unknown with $\sigma^2 \in \Theta = \{x\colon\ x > 0\}$, $H_0 = \{\sigma_0^2\}$, and H_1 may have several forms. First, we will study the case where $H_1 = \{\sigma_1^2\}$ with $\sigma_1^2 > \sigma_0^2$, and will reason intuitively to a test as follows. For this problem we know that

$$\hat{\sigma}^2 = \frac{\sum\limits_{i=1}^{n} (X_i - \mu)^2}{n} \tag{9.6.1}$$

is a good estimator of σ^2. In fact, $\hat{\sigma}^2$ is a minimal sufficient statistic for σ^2 (Problem 9.38) and is the unique MVU estimator of σ^2 (Problem 9.16H). Thus, it seems intuitively reasonable to reject H_0 iff

$$\hat{\sigma}^2 > k, \tag{9.6.2}$$

where k is a constant chosen (if such a choice is possible) to give level α. Now

$$P_{\sigma_0^2}[\hat{\sigma}^2 > k] = P_{\sigma_0^2}\left[\frac{\sum\limits_{i=1}^{n} (X_i - \mu)^2}{n} > k \right]$$

$$= P_{\sigma_0^2}\left[\sum\limits_{i=1}^{n} \left(\frac{X_i - \mu}{\sigma_0} \right)^2 > \frac{nk}{\sigma_0^2} \right] \tag{9.6.3}$$

and since (by Problem 9.34) $\sum\limits_{i=1}^{n} ((X_i - \mu)/\sigma_0)^2$ has the $\chi_n^2(0)$ distribution, Table 10 can be used to find k. Thus, we have the following:

Theorem 9.6.4.   For the hypothesis-testing problem with $X = (X_1, \ldots, X_n)$ where $X_1, \ldots, X_n$ are independent r.v.'s, each $N(\mu, \sigma^2)$ where μ is known $(-\infty < \mu < +\infty)$, σ^2 is unknown $(\sigma^2 > 0)$, $H_0 = \{\sigma_0^2\}$, and $H_1 = \{\sigma_1^2\}$ with $\sigma_1^2 > \sigma_0^2$, the test that rejects iff

$$\frac{\sum\limits_{i=1}^{n} (X_i - \mu)^2}{n} > k \tag{9.6.5}$$

(where k satisfies $P[Y > nk/\sigma_0^2] = \alpha$ for Y a $\chi_n^2(0)$ r.v.) has level α. Similar tests are easily obtained [as in Problem 9.35] for other alternatives H_1.

In fact, the test of Theorem 9.6.4 is most powerful (see Problem 9.39). **Now if μ $(-\infty < \mu < +\infty)$ is unknown, what do we do?** As in Section 9.5, we cannot use the Neyman-Pearson Lemma (since now not even H_0 is a simple hypothesis), but we do know a minimal sufficient statistic for the problem. Hence, we may consider replacing μ in (9.6.5) by a good estimator based on the minimal sufficient statistic, namely the estimator $\bar{X}$, and rejecting iff

$$\frac{\sum_{i=1}^{n}(X_i - \bar{X})^2}{n} > k'. \tag{9.6.6}$$

Since, in the proof of Lemma 9.5.15, we established that $(n-1)s^2/\sigma^2$ has a $\chi_{n-1}^2(0)$ distribution in this case, we may (by choosing k' to satisfy

$$P\left[Y > \frac{nk'}{\sigma_0^2}\right] = \alpha \tag{9.6.7}$$

for Y a $\chi_{n-1}^2(0)$ r.v.) obtain our level α test. [This again justifies the "loss of 1 degree of freedom" nomenclature noted following equation (7.1.13).]

As we gave detailed formulas above for the one-sided alternative of increase in the variance (i.e., H_1: $\sigma^2 > \sigma_0^2$) and noted that "similar tests are easily obtained for other alternatives H_1," for completeness we supply those details in Table 9.6-1.

Example 9.6.8. The standard deviation of the diameter of parts produced by a certain machine has a specification that it should not be greater than 0.5 millimeters (because these parts are to mesh with others produced elsewhere, and this will not be possible if there is "too much" variability). In such situations, the standard deviation sometimes "shifts" (changes). If the standard deviation is determined to exceed 0.5 millimeters, the production process is stopped and the machine is adjusted. On a given day a random sample of 14 parts is taken from the production of this machine, diameters of these parts are measured, and the mean and standard deviation are computed. Suppose that we find $s = .64$. Should we stop the production process to adjust the machine? (Use $\alpha = .05$.)

Here we have H_0: $\sigma^2 = 0.25$ vs. H_1: $\sigma^2 > 0.25$. To test the hypothesis, we compute

$$\chi^2 = \frac{(n-1)s^2}{\sigma_0^2} = \frac{(13)(.64)^2}{(.5)^2} = 21.2992.$$

With $\alpha = .05$, $\chi_{n-1,1-\alpha}^{2^{-1}}(0) = 22.3621$. Since $\chi^2 = 21.2992$ does not exceed $\chi_{n-1,1-\alpha}^{2^{-1}}(0) = 22.3621$, there is not sufficient evidence to reject H_0, so we do not stop the production process. (That 21.2992 is "close" does not matter: Even

TABLE 9.6-1

Testing normal variances, one population, μ unknown: Summary of procedure for 3 alternatives*

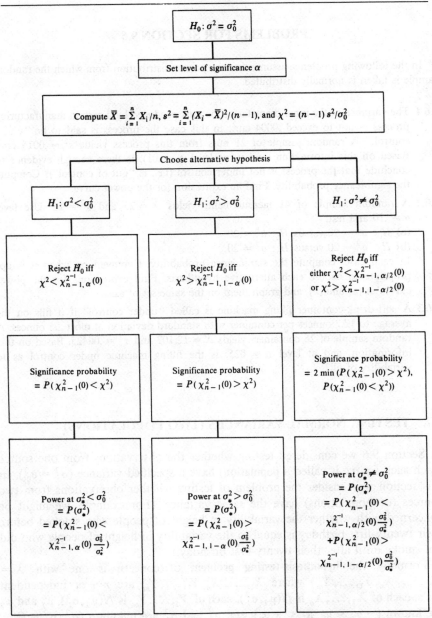

$$H_0: \sigma^2 = \sigma_0^2$$

Set level of significance α

Compute $\overline{X} = \sum_{i=1}^{n} X_i / n,\ s^2 = \sum_{i=1}^{n} (X_i - \overline{X})^2 / (n-1),$ and $\chi^2 = (n-1)\, s^2 / \sigma_0^2$

Choose alternative hypothesis

$H_1: \sigma^2 < \sigma_0^2$	$H_1: \sigma^2 > \sigma_0^2$	$H_1: \sigma^2 \neq \sigma_0^2$
Reject H_0 iff $\chi^2 < \chi_{n-1,\,\alpha}^{2^{-1}}(0)$	Reject H_0 iff $\chi^2 > \chi_{n-1,\,1-\alpha}^{2^{-1}}(0)$	Reject H_0 iff either $\chi^2 < \chi_{n-1,\,\alpha/2}^{2^{-1}}(0)$ or $\chi^2 > \chi_{n-1,\,1-\alpha/2}^{2^{-1}}(0)$
Significance probability $= P(\chi_{n-1}^2(0) < \chi^2)$	Significance probability $= P(\chi_{n-1}^2(0) > \chi^2)$	Significance probability $= 2 \min (P(\chi_{n-1}^2(0) > \chi^2),\ P(\chi_{n-1}^2(0) < \chi^2))$
Power at $\sigma_*^2 < \sigma_0^2$ $= P(\sigma_*^2)$ $= P\left(\chi_{n-1}^2(0) < \chi_{n-1,\,\alpha}^{2^{-1}}(0) \frac{\sigma_0^2}{\sigma_*^2}\right)$	Power at $\sigma_*^2 > \sigma_0^2$ $= P(\sigma_*^2)$ $= P\left(\chi_{n-1}^2(0) > \chi_{n-1,\,1-\alpha}^{2^{-1}}(0) \frac{\sigma_0^2}{\sigma_*^2}\right)$	Power at $\sigma_*^2 \neq \sigma_0^2$ $= P(\sigma_*^2)$ $= P\left(\chi_{n-1}^2(0) < \chi_{n-1,\,\alpha/2}^{2^{-1}}(0) \frac{\sigma_0^2}{\sigma_*^2}\right)$ $+ P\left(\chi_{n-1}^2(0) > \chi_{n-1,\,1-\alpha/2}^{2^{-1}}(0) \frac{\sigma_0^2}{\sigma_*^2}\right)$

Typical power curves are similar in shape to those shown in Table 9.5-1 for testing one normal mean.

---

*In this table, χ^2 is a random variable whose numerical value is computed from the data; $\chi_{n-1}^2(0)$ is a central chi-square r.v. with $n-1$ degrees of freedom; and $\chi_{n-1,\,q}^2(0)$ is the number below which $\chi_{n-1}^2(0)$ lies with probability q. When significance probability is computed, χ^2 is treated as a number (and *not* as a random variable).

waiting for a value of 22.3621 or larger, 5% of the times that the machine is *not* in need of repair we will decide to stop it for repair.)

PROBLEMS FOR SECTION 9.6

In the following problems, assume that the parent distribution from which the random sample is taken is normally distributed.

9.6.1 The variance of the inner diameter of the nuts produced by a certain manufacturing process is not to exceed .0004 cm^2; in this case the process is said to be "under control." A random sample of 21 nuts from this process yields $s^2 = .0015$ cm^2. Based on this information (and using level $\alpha = .01$), is there enough evidence to conclude that the process is not under control (i.e., is "out of control")? Compute the significance probability. Find an expression for the power curve.

9.6.2 A random sample of 41 measurements yields $\overline{X} = 25$ and $s^2 = 16$. Use level $\alpha = .10$ and test:
(a) H_0: $\sigma^2 = 20$ versus H_a: $\sigma^2 < 20$.
(b) H_0: $\sigma^2 = 20$ versus H_a: $\sigma^2 \neq 20$.
In each case, compute the significance probability. Comment on when it is appropriate to choose each alternative hypothesis. Find expressions for the power curves in (a) and (b), and graph them on the same set of axes.

9.6.3 A soft-drink-container filling machine is called "under control" if it fills on the average to 12.2 ounces per container with standard deviation at most .05 ounces. A random sample of 26 containers yields $\overline{X} = 12.102$ and $s^2 = .00425$. Based on this information, and at level $\alpha = .025$, is the filling machine under control as to variability of fill?

9.7. TESTING NORMAL VARIANCES (TWO POPULATIONS)

In Section 9.6 we considered testing whether the observations from one source (each such source is called a **population**) have a specified variance ($\sigma^2 = \sigma_0^2$). In this section we consider the problem of testing whether observations from two sources (or populations) have the same variance. (For example, we might be concerned with whether the variability in height of people who smoked before their twenty-first birthday is equal to the variability in height of people who did not smoke until after their twenty-first birthday.)

Formally the **hypothesis-testing problem** of concern is one with $X = (X_1, \ldots, X_n, Y_1, \ldots, Y_m)$ where $X_1, \ldots, X_n, Y_1, \ldots, Y_m$ are $n + m$ independent r.v.'s, **each of** $X_1, \ldots, X_n$ is $N(\mu_1, \sigma_1^2)$, **each of** $Y_1, \ldots, Y_m$ is $N(\mu_2, \sigma_2^2)$, μ_1 and μ_2 **are known** ($-\infty < \mu_1, \mu_2 < +\infty$), **and** σ_1^2 and σ_2^2 **are unknown** ($\sigma_1^2, \sigma_2^2 \in \Theta = \{(x, y): x > 0, y > 0\}$), $H_0 = \{(\sigma_1^2, \sigma_2^2): \sigma_1^2 = \sigma_2^2 > 0\}$, and H_1 may have several forms. Let us consider first *the case* where $H_1 = \{(\sigma_1^2, \sigma_2^2): \sigma_1^2 > \sigma_2^2\}$. We can reason to a test intuitively as follows. We know (see Section 9.6) that $\hat{\sigma}_i^2$ is a good estimator of σ_i^2 ($i = 1, 2$) where

$$\hat{\sigma}_1^2 = \frac{\sum\limits_{j=1}^{n} (X_j - \mu_1)^2}{n}, \; \hat{\sigma}_2^2 = \frac{\sum\limits_{j=1}^{m} (Y_j - \mu_2)^2}{m}. \tag{9.7.1}$$

So, we can consider rejecting H_0 if $\hat{\sigma}_1^2 / \hat{\sigma}_2^2$ is much larger than 1; that is, reject H_0 iff

$$\frac{\hat{\sigma}_1^2}{\hat{\sigma}_2^2} > k, \tag{9.7.2}$$

where k is a constant chosen (if such a choice is possible) to give level α. Now (using the results of Problems 9.43 and 9.32)

$$P_{\sigma_1^2, \sigma_2^2}\left[\frac{\hat{\sigma}_1^2}{\hat{\sigma}_2^2} > k\right] = P_{\sigma_1^2, \sigma_2^2}\left[\frac{\sum\limits_{j=1}^{n} (X_j - \mu_1)^2 / n}{\sum\limits_{j=1}^{m} (Y_j - \mu_2)^2 / m} > k\right]$$

$$= P_{\sigma_1^2, \sigma_2^2}\left[\frac{\sum\limits_{j=1}^{n} \left(\frac{X_j - \mu_1}{\sigma_1}\right)^2 / n}{\sum\limits_{j=1}^{m} \left(\frac{Y_j - \mu_2}{\sigma_2}\right)^2 / m} > \frac{\sigma_2^2}{\sigma_1^2} k\right] \tag{9.7.3}$$

$$= P\left[Y > \frac{\sigma_2^2}{\sigma_1^2} k\right],$$

where Y has the $F(n, m)$ distribution, so Table 12 can be used to find a k that gives level α. Thus, we have the following:

Theorem 9.7.4. For the hypothesis-testing problem with $X = (X_1, \ldots, X_n, Y_1, \ldots, Y_m)$ where $X_1, \ldots, X_n, Y_1, \ldots, Y_m$ are $n + m$ independent r.v.'s, each of $X_1, \ldots, X_n$ is $N(\mu_1, \sigma_1^2)$, each of $Y_1, \ldots, Y_m$ is $N(\mu_2, \sigma_2^2)$, μ_1 and μ_2 are known ($-\infty < \mu_1, \mu_2 < +\infty$), σ_1^2 and σ_2^2 are unknown ($\sigma_1^2, \sigma_2^2 > 0$), $H_0 = \{\sigma_1^2 = \sigma_2^2\}$, and $H_1 = \{\sigma_1^2 > \sigma_2^2\}$, the test that rejects iff

$$\frac{\sum\limits_{j=1}^{n} (X_j - \mu_1)^2 / n}{\sum\limits_{j=1}^{m} (Y_j - \mu_2)^2 / m} > k \tag{9.7.5}$$

(where k satisfies $P[Y > \sigma_2^2 k / \sigma_1^2] = \alpha$ for Y an $F(n, m)$ r.v.) has level α. Similar tests are easily obtained [as in Problem 9.35] for other alternatives H_1.

Now **if μ_1 and μ_2 are unknown**, we may (see Section 9.6) consider estimating them by $\overline{X}$ and $\overline{Y}$ respectively, then rejecting iff

$$\frac{\sum\limits_{j=1}^{n} (X_j - \overline{X})^2 \Big/ (n-1)}{\sum\limits_{j=1}^{m} (Y_j - \overline{Y})^2 \Big/ (m-1)} > k'. \qquad (9.7.6)$$

Since the left side of equation (9.7.6) has the $F(n-1, m-1)$ distribution when multiplied by σ_2^2 / σ_1^2, we may (by choosing k' to satisfy

$$P\left[Y > \frac{\sigma_2^2 k'}{\sigma_1^2}\right] = \alpha \qquad (9.7.7)$$

for Y an $F(n-1, m-1)$ r.v.) obtain our level α test. [When μ_1 and μ_2 are unknown we must have $n \geq 2$ and $m \geq 2$ (otherwise we do not obtain a proper F-distribution).]

Note: In the case of equation (9.7.3) k [in the case of equation (9.7.7), k'] is chosen so the quantity in question equals α *when H_0 is true*, that is, when $\sigma_1^2 = \sigma_2^2$. Hence, our solution does not involve the (unknown) quantities σ_1^2 and σ_2^2.

As we gave detailed formulas above for the one-sided alternative of larger variance in source 1 (i.e., H_1: $\sigma_1^2 > \sigma_2^2$), and noted that "similar tests are easily obtained for other alternatives H_1," for completeness we supply details in Table 9.7-1.

Example 9.7.8. Two different scales are to be compared as to the variability they have for weights around 5.0 grams. One object is weighed 11 times on scale 1, and the computed standard deviation is 3.4 grams; the object is weighed 21 times on scale 2 and yields a standard deviation of 5.2. Based on this information, can we conclude that the scales have different variabilities of measurement? (Use $\alpha = .10$.)

Here we have H_0: $\sigma_1^2 = \sigma_2^2$ vs. H_1: $\sigma_1^2 \neq \sigma_2^2$, and find $F = s_1^2 / s_2^2 = (3.4)^2 / (5.2)^2 = .427515$ with $n_1 - 1 = 10$ degrees of freedom in the numerator and $n_2 - 1 = 20$ in the denominator. At $\alpha = .10$ $F_{10, 20, .95}^{-1} = 2.35$, and (note that $F_{n_1-1, n_2-1, \alpha}^{-1} = 1/F_{n_2-1, n_1-1, 1-\alpha}$) $F_{10, 20, .05}^{-1} = 1/F_{20, 10, .95}^{-1} = 1/2.77 = .36011$. Since $F = .43$ is neither smaller than $F_{n_1-1, n_2-1, \alpha/2}^{-1} = .36$ nor larger than $F_{n_1-1, n_2-1, 1-\alpha/2}^{-1} = 2.35$, we do not reject the contention that the observed

TABLE 9.7-1

Testing normal variances, two populations, means unknown: Summary of procedure for 3 alternatives*

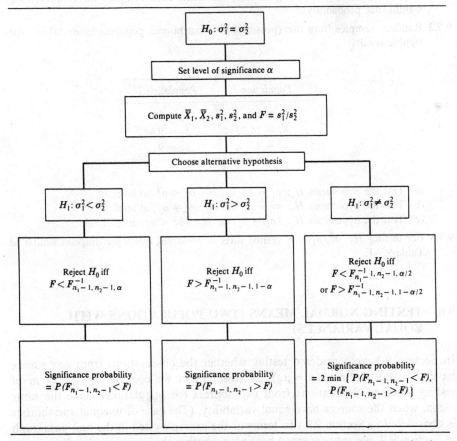

$H_0 : \sigma_1^2 = \sigma_2^2$

Set level of significance α

Compute $\bar{X}_1, \bar{X}_2, s_1^2, s_2^2$, and $F = s_1^2/s_2^2$

Choose alternative hypothesis

$H_1 : \sigma_1^2 < \sigma_2^2$	$H_1 : \sigma_1^2 > \sigma_2^2$	$H_1 : \sigma_1^2 \neq \sigma_2^2$
Reject H_0 iff $F < F_{n_1 - 1, n_2 - 1, \alpha}^{-1}$	Reject H_0 iff $F > F_{n_1 - 1, n_2 - 1, 1 - \alpha}^{-1}$	Reject H_0 iff $F < F_{n_1 - 1, n_2 - 1, \alpha/2}^{-1}$ or $F > F_{n_1 - 1, n_2 - 1, 1 - \alpha/2}^{-1}$
Significance probability $= P(F_{n_1 - 1, n_2 - 1} < F)$	Significance probability $= P(F_{n_1 - 1, n_2 - 1} > F)$	Significance probability $= 2 \min \{ P(F_{n_1 - 1, n_2 - 1} < F), P(F_{n_1 - 1, n_2 - 1} > F) \}$

*In this table, F is a random variable whose numerical value is computed from the data; $F_{n_1 - 1, n_2 - 1}$ is an r.v. with the F-distribution with $n_1 - 1$ and $n_2 - 1$ degrees of freedom; and $F_{n_1 - 1, n_2 - 1, q}^{-1}$ is the number below which $F_{n_1 - 1, n_2 - 1}$ lies with probability q. When significance probability is computed, F is treated as a number (and *not* as a random variable).

difference in the computed standard deviations is due solely to chance: There is thus not sufficient evidence to reject H_0.

PROBLEMS FOR SECTION 9.7

In the following problems, assume that each parent distribution from which a random sample is taken is normally distributed.

9.7.1 In a study of gas mileage (miles per gallon, mpg) of compact cars, a random sample of 41 domestic cars on a test course of 200 miles gave $\bar{X}_1 = 28.6$, $s_1^2 = 4.84$. A random sample of 31 imported cars on the same test course gave $\bar{X}_2 = 27.8$, $s_2^2 = 10.89$. At level $\alpha = .10$, do these data indicate that the variances of domestic versus imported cars are significantly different? Also compute the (approximate) significance probability.

9.7.2 Random samples from two (possibly) different normal populations are taken, with sample results:

Population 1	Population 2
$n_1 = 11$	$n_2 = 16$
$\bar{X}_1 = 14.23$	$\bar{X}_2 = 9.68$
$s_1^2 = 4$	$s_2^2 = 9$

(a) Test the hypothesis H_0: $\sigma_1^2 = \sigma_2^2$ vs. H_1: $\sigma_1^2 < \sigma_2^2$, at level .05.

(b) Test the hypothesis H_0: $\sigma_1^2 = \sigma_2^2$ vs. H_1: $\sigma_1^2 \neq \sigma_2^2$, at level .05.

(c) Test the hypothesis H_0: $2\sigma_1^2 = \sigma_2^2$ vs. H_1: $2\sigma_1^2 < \sigma_2^2$, at level .05.

9.7.3 For testing H_0: $\sigma_1^2/\sigma_2^2 = k$ against three alternatives, develop a diagram similar to Table 9.7-1.

9.8. TESTING NORMAL MEANS (TWO POPULATIONS WITH EQUAL VARIANCES)

In Section 9.5 we considered testing whether the observations from one source have a specified mean ($\mu = \mu_0$). In this section we consider the problem of testing whether observations from two sources (or populations) have the same mean, when the sources have equal variability. (The case of unequal variabilities is considered in Section 9.9.) In terms of the example cited in the first paragraph of Section 9.7, we are concerned here with whether the "early smokers" have the same mean height as the "late and nonsmokers," and are assuming the variabilities of the heights to be equal.

Formally, the **hypothesis-testing problem** of concern is one with $X = (X_1, \ldots, X_n, Y_1, \ldots, Y_m)$ where $X_1, \ldots, X_n, Y_1, \ldots, Y_m$ are $n + m$ **independent** r.v.'s, each of $X_1, \ldots, X_n$ is $N(\mu_1, \sigma^2)$, each of $Y_1, \ldots, Y_m$ is $N(\mu_2, \sigma^2)$, μ_1 and μ_2 **are unknown** ($-\infty < \mu_1, \mu_2 < +\infty$), σ^2 **is known** ($\sigma^2 > 0$), $H_0 = \{\mu_1 = \mu_2\}$, and H_1 may have several forms. Let us consider first the case where $H_1 = \{\mu_1 > \mu_2\}$. We can reason to a test intuitively as follows. We know that $\bar{X}$ and $\bar{Y}$ are respectively good estimators of μ_1 and μ_2. So consider rejecting H_0 if $\bar{X}$ is much larger than $\bar{Y}$; that is, reject H_0 iff

$$\bar{X} - \bar{Y} > c, \qquad (9.8.1)$$

where c is a constant to be chosen (if such a choice is possible) to give level α.

Now (by work paralleling that following equation (9.5.5)) we solve for c:

$$
\begin{cases}
P_{\mu_1 = \mu_2}[\,\overline{X} - \overline{Y} > c\,] = \alpha, \\[2ex]
P_{\mu_1 = \mu_2}\left[\dfrac{\overline{X} - \overline{Y}}{\sqrt{\sigma^2\left(\dfrac{1}{n} + \dfrac{1}{m}\right)}} > \dfrac{c}{\sqrt{\sigma^2\left(\dfrac{1}{n} + \dfrac{1}{m}\right)}}\right] = \alpha, \\[4ex]
1 - \Phi\left(\dfrac{c}{\sigma\sqrt{\dfrac{1}{n} + \dfrac{1}{m}}}\right) = \alpha, \\[4ex]
c = \sigma\sqrt{\dfrac{1}{n} + \dfrac{1}{m}}\;\Phi^{-1}(1 - \alpha).
\end{cases}
\tag{9.8.2}
$$

So c can be found as desired. Similar tests are easily obtained for *other* alternatives H_1. Note that we can rewrite our test (using equations (9.8.1) and (9.8.2)) as one that rejects iff

$$
\frac{\overline{X} - \overline{Y}}{\sqrt{\sigma^2\left(\dfrac{1}{n} + \dfrac{1}{m}\right)}} > \Phi^{-1}(1 - \alpha).
\tag{9.8.3}
$$

(This will help us in the case of unknown σ^2.)

Now **if σ^2 is unknown**, we would consider estimating it and rejecting iff the left side of equation (9.8.3) [with σ^2 replaced by an appropriate estimator] exceeds some constant [which can hopefully be set to obtain level α]. Now we could estimate σ^2 by

$$
s_1^2 = \frac{\displaystyle\sum_{j=1}^{n}\left(X_j - \overline{X}\right)^2}{n - 1}
\tag{9.8.4}
$$

or by

$$
s_2^2 = \frac{\displaystyle\sum_{j=1}^{m}\left(Y_j - \overline{Y}\right)^2}{m - 1},
\tag{9.8.5}
$$

and our estimators would have reasonable properties. However, s_1^2 and s_2^2 are (since $X_1, \ldots, X_n$ are independent of $Y_1, \ldots, Y_m$) independent r.v.'s, so we might ask: Can we somehow combine s_1^2 and s_2^2 to obtain an even better estimator of σ^2? If we combine them according to their respective d.f. of $n-1$ and $m-1$ into a weighted average, we obtain a third estimator

$$s_P^2 = \frac{\sum\limits_{j=1}^{n} \left(X_j - \bar{X} \right)^2 + \sum\limits_{j=1}^{m} \left(Y_j - \bar{Y} \right)^2}{n + m - 2}. \tag{9.8.6}$$

So, what about the test that rejects iff

$$\frac{\bar{X} - \bar{Y}}{\sqrt{\dfrac{\sum\limits_{j=1}^{n} \left(X_j - \bar{X} \right)^2 + \sum\limits_{j=1}^{m} \left(Y_j - \bar{Y} \right)^2}{n + m - 2} \left(\dfrac{1}{n} + \dfrac{1}{m} \right)}} > k'? \tag{9.8.7}$$

From the results of Section 9.5 it follows that when H_0 is true, the left side of equation (9.8.7) has Student's t-distribution with $n + m - 2$ d.f. [this is because the left side is the ratio of the $N(0,1)$ r.v.

$$\frac{\bar{X} - \bar{Y}}{\sigma \sqrt{\dfrac{1}{n} + \dfrac{1}{m}}} \tag{9.8.8}$$

and the square root of the χ_{n+m-2}^2 r.v.

$$\sum_{j=1}^{n} \left(\frac{X_j - \bar{X}}{\sigma} \right)^2 + \sum_{j=1}^{m} \left(\frac{Y_j - \bar{Y}}{\sigma} \right)^2 \tag{9.8.9}$$

divided by its d.f., and these two r.v.'s are independent]. Hence, a proper choice for k' is

$$k' = t_{n+m-2}^{-1}(1 - \alpha). \tag{9.8.10}$$

Similar tests are easily obtained (see Problem 9.35) for *other alternatives* H_1.

As we gave detailed formulas above for the one-sided alternative of larger mean in source 1 (i.e., $\mu_1 > \mu_2$), and noted that "similar tests are easily obtained for other alternatives H_1," for completeness we supply details in Table 9.8-1.

Example 9.8.11. Consider Example 9.7.8. Since it was established that H_0: $\sigma_1^2 = \sigma_2^2$ is not rejected, let us assume that $\sigma_1^2 = \sigma_2^2$ and test the hypothesis that the scales give the same mean weight. Suppose in the sample of size 11 we found $\bar{X}_1 = 4.82$ grams, and in the sample of size 21 we found $\bar{X}_2 = 5.81$ grams. Are the scales reporting the same mean weight on the average?

TABLE 9.8-1

Testing normal means, two populations, same unknown variance: Summary of procedure for 3 alternatives*

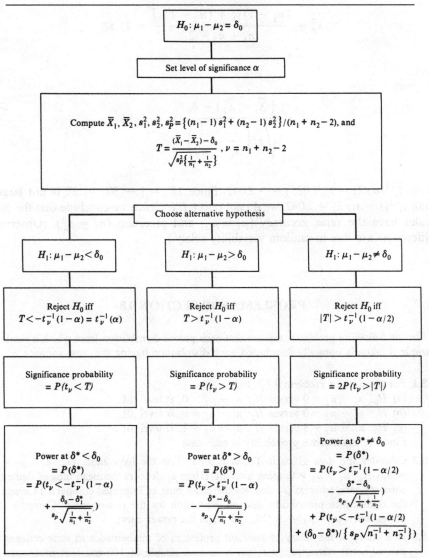

$$H_0: \mu_1 - \mu_2 = \delta_0$$

Set level of significance α

Compute $\overline{X}_1, \overline{X}_2, s_1^2, s_2^2, s_P^2 = \{(n_1 - 1) s_1^2 + (n_2 - 1) s_2^2\}/(n_1 + n_2 - 2)$, and

$$T = \frac{(\overline{X}_1 - \overline{X}_2) - \delta_0}{\sqrt{s_P^2\{\frac{1}{n_1} + \frac{1}{n_2}\}}}, \quad \nu = n_1 + n_2 - 2$$

Choose alternative hypothesis

$H_1: \mu_1 - \mu_2 < \delta_0$	$H_1: \mu_1 - \mu_2 > \delta_0$	$H_1: \mu_1 - \mu_2 \neq \delta_0$
Reject H_0 iff $T < -t_\nu^{-1}(1-\alpha) = t_\nu^{-1}(\alpha)$	Reject H_0 iff $T > t_\nu^{-1}(1-\alpha)$	Reject H_0 iff $|T| > t_\nu^{-1}(1-\alpha/2)$
Significance probability $= P(t_\nu < T)$	Significance probability $= P(t_\nu > T)$	Significance probability $= 2P(t_\nu > |T|)$
Power at $\delta^* < \delta_0$ $= P(\delta^*)$ $= P(t_\nu < -t_\nu^{-1}(1-\alpha)$ $+ \frac{\delta_0 - \delta_1^*}{s_P\sqrt{\frac{1}{n_1} + \frac{1}{n_2}}})$	Power at $\delta^* > \delta_0$ $= P(\delta^*)$ $= P(t_\nu > t_\nu^{-1}(1-\alpha)$ $- \frac{\delta^* - \delta_0}{s_P\sqrt{\frac{1}{n_1} + \frac{1}{n_2}}})$	Power at $\delta^* \neq \delta_0$ $= P(\delta^*)$ $= P(t_\nu > t_\nu^{-1}(1-\alpha/2)$ $- \frac{\delta^* - \delta_0}{s_P\sqrt{\frac{1}{n_1} + \frac{1}{n_2}}})$ $+ P(t_\nu < -t_\nu^{-1}(1-\alpha/2)$ $+ (\delta_0 - \delta^*)/\{s_P\sqrt{n_1^{-1} + n_2^{-1}}\})$

Typical power curves are similar in shape to those shown in Table 9.5-1 for testing one normal mean.

*In this table, T is a random variable whose numerical value is computed from the data; t_ν is a Student's t random variable with ν degrees of freedom; and $t_\nu^{-1}(q)$ is the number such that $P(t_\nu \leq t_\nu^{-1}(q)) = q$. When significance probability is computed, T is treated as a number (and *not* as a random variable).

Here we have $H_0: \mu_1 - \mu_2 \equiv \delta = 0$ vs. $H_1: \mu_1 - \mu_2 \neq 0$, and let us choose $\alpha = .05$. We find

$$s_P^2 = \frac{(n_1 - 1)s_1^2 + (n_2 - 1)s_2^2}{n_1 + n_2 - 2} = 21.88$$

and

$$T = \frac{(\overline{X}_1 - \overline{X}_2) - \delta_0}{\sqrt{s_P^2 \left(\dfrac{1}{n_1} + \dfrac{1}{n_2} \right)}} = -.5686.$$

Now $t_\nu^{-1}(\alpha/2) = t_{30}^{-1}(.025) = -2.042$. Since $|T| = |-.57| = .57$ is not larger than $t_\nu^{-1}(1 - \alpha/2) = 2.042$, we do not reject H_0. Hence we conclude that the two scales have the same accuracy ($\mu_1 = \mu_2$) and precision ($\sigma_1^2 = \sigma_2^2$). (Observed differences are due to random variability solely.)

PROBLEMS FOR SECTION 9.8

In the following problems, assume that each parent distribution from which a random sample is taken is normally distributed, each distribution having the same variance σ^2.

9.8.1 For the data in Problem 9.7.2, test
   (a) $H_0: \mu_1 - \mu_2 = 0$ versus $H_1: \mu_1 - \mu_2 > 0$, at level .01.
   (b) $H_0: \mu_1 - \mu_2 = 0$ versus $H_1: \mu_1 - \mu_2 \neq 0$, at level .01.
   (c) $H_0: \mu_1 - \mu_2 = 3$ versus $H_1: \mu_1 - \mu_2 \neq 3$, at level .01.
   Find the significance probability in each case.

9.8.2 Consider the data given in Problem 9.7.1. Test the hypothesis $H_0: \mu_1 - \mu_2 = 0$ versus $H_1: \mu_1 - \mu_2 \neq 0$, using level .01. (Here μ_1 denotes the mean mpg of domestic compact cars, whereas μ_2 denotes the mean mpg of imported compacts.) Compute the significance probability, and an expression for the power curve. Compute the power when $\mu_1 - \mu_2 = .5(.5)4$, and graph the power curve.

9.8.3 In a study of the salary of assistant professors of mathematics in state colleges in two adjacent states, suppose that a random sample of 100 assistant professors in each of the two states yields: $\overline{X}_1 = 29,600$ and $s_1 = 1100$ in state 1, $\overline{X}_2 = 30,800$ and $s_2 = 1000$ in state 2. Based on this data, is there any reason to believe that state 2 offers a more attractive salary than state 1, at level .02? Compute the significance probability.

9.8.4 Show algebraically that if $n_1 = n_2$, then $s_P^2 = (s_1^2 + s_2^2)/2$.

9.8.5 Suppose times taken by two ambulance companies (from time the message is received, to the time when the patient is brought into the hospital emergency room) are

	Time (minutes)					
Company 1	10.3	8.5	9.8	10.8	9.3	$\overline{X}_1 = 9.74,\ s_1^2 = .793$
Company 2	8.2	16.4	9.7	13.2	9.4	$\overline{X}_2 = 11.00,\ s_2^2 = 5.154$

Test the hypothesis that company 1 is faster. (Use level .05.)

9.8.6 The following data (*source: Sports Illustrated*, September 1, 1983, issue) gives rushing yards per game for the 1982 season for each of the 28 teams in the (American) National Football League (NFL), by conference (14 teams being in each of the American Football Conference (AFC) and the National Football Conference (NFC). Based on this data, at level .05 is there enough evidence to conclude that the AFC and NFC groups differ in mean on rushing yards per game? (Treat the data as two random samples of size 14.)

AFC Team	Yards	NFC Team	Yards
Bills	152	Cowboys	146
Patriots	150	Saints	140
Dolphins	149	Cardinals	134
Jets	146	Falcons	131
Steelers	132	Redskins	127
Chargers	125	Packers	120
Raiders	120	Rams	114
Colts	116	Lions	114
Broncos	113	Bears	110
Bengals	105	Bucs	106
Chiefs	105	Vikings	101
Browns	97	Giants	94
Oilers	89	Eagles	92
Seahawks	88	49ers	82

9.9. TESTING NORMAL MEANS (TWO POPULATIONS WITH UNEQUAL VARIANCES: THE BEHRENS-FISHER PROBLEM)

In Section 9.8 we considered hypothesis-testing problems involving the means of two populations that have the same variance (which may be known or unknown). In this section we consider such problems when we cannot assume the variabilities of the two populations (e.g., "early smokers" and "late smokers and nonsmokers") to be the same.

Formally, the **hypothesis-testing problem** of concern is one with $X = (X_1, \ldots, X_n, Y_1, \ldots, Y_m)$ where $X_1, \ldots, X_n, Y_1, \ldots, Y_m$ are $n + m$ independent r.v.'s, each of $X_1, \ldots, X_n$ is $N(\mu_1, \sigma_1^2)$, each of $Y_1, \ldots, Y_m$ is $N(\mu_2, \sigma_2^2)$, μ_1 and μ_2 are **unknown** $(-\infty < \mu_1, \mu_2 < +\infty)$, σ_1^2 and σ_2^2 are **known** $(\sigma_1^2, \sigma_2^2 > 0$ but $\sigma_1^2 \neq \sigma_2^2)$, $H_0 = \{\mu_1 = \mu_2\}$, and H_1 may have several forms. Let us consider first *the case* where $H_1 = \{\mu_1 > \mu_2\}$. As in the development leading to (9.8.1) in Section 9.8, we consider rejecting H_0 iff

$$\bar{X} - \bar{Y} > c, \tag{9.9.1}$$

where c is a constant to be chosen (if such a choice is possible) to give level α. Now as at equation (9.8.2) we can find such a c:

$$
\left\{
\begin{array}{c}
P_{\mu_1 = \mu_2}[\bar{X} - \bar{Y} > c] = \alpha, \\[2em]
P_{\mu_1 = \mu_2}\left[\dfrac{\bar{X} - \bar{Y}}{\sqrt{\dfrac{\sigma_1^2}{n} + \dfrac{\sigma_2^2}{m}}} > \dfrac{c}{\sqrt{\dfrac{\sigma_1^2}{n} + \dfrac{\sigma_2^2}{m}}}\right] = \alpha, \\[3em]
1 - \Phi\left[\dfrac{c}{\sqrt{\dfrac{\sigma_1^2}{n} + \dfrac{\sigma_2^2}{m}}}\right] = \alpha, \\[3em]
c = \sqrt{\dfrac{\sigma_1^2}{n} + \dfrac{\sigma_2^2}{m}}\ \Phi^{-1}(1 - \alpha).
\end{array}
\right.
\tag{9.9.2}
$$

Similar tests are easily obtained for *other alternatives* H_1. Since in previous sections we have given detailed tables (Tables 9.5-1, 9.6-1, 9.7-1, and 9.8-1) of the details for the other alternatives H_1, here we leave it as an exercise to provide the details for H_1: $\mu_1 < \mu_2$ and H_1: $\mu_1 \neq \mu_2$.

Now if σ_1^2 and σ_2^2 are **unknown** we would consider estimating them by s_1^2 (see equation (9.8.4)) and s_2^2 (see equation (9.8.5)) respectively, and rejecting iff

$$\frac{\bar{X} - \bar{Y}}{\sqrt{\dfrac{s_1^2}{n} + \dfrac{s_2^2}{m}}} > k'. \tag{9.9.3}$$

However (see Problem 9.47), the distribution of the left side of (9.9.3) is not Student's t-distribution when H_0 is true; in fact, the distribution of the left side depends on n, m, and σ_1^2/σ_2^2. Hence, it is not possible to choose a k' such that the test given by (9.9.3) has level α (since the probability of rejection varies as

σ_1^2/σ_2^2 varies, instead of remaining constant at α). *The distribution of the quantity*

$$\frac{\overline{X} - \overline{Y}}{\sqrt{\dfrac{s_1^2}{n} + \dfrac{s_2^2}{m}}} \tag{9.9.4}$$

(*when H_0 is true*) *is called the* **Behrens-Fisher distribution** *with parameters n, m,* σ_1^2/σ_2^2. *The hypothesis-testing problem we are considering* (*with σ_1^2 and σ_2^2 unknown*) *is called the* **Behrens-Fisher problem**, and represents (in Sections 9.5–9.9) the first time we have encountered a situation where we could not obtain a level α test by "substituting a good estimator of an unknown parameter in the procedure used when that parameter is known."

One proposed solution to the Behrens-Fisher problem, which we will call the **Neyman-Bartlett solution**, *proceeds as follows.* Either $n < m$ or $n \geq m$, so let us suppose without any loss of generality that $n \geq m$. Define new r.v.'s $Z_1, \ldots, Z_m$ by

$$Z_i = X_i - Y_i \ (i = 1, \ldots, m). \tag{9.9.5}$$

Then $Z_1, \ldots, Z_m$ are independent $N(\mu_1 - \mu_2, \sigma_1^2 + \sigma_2^2)$ r.v.'s, and we can solve the problem of testing H_0: $\mu_1 - \mu_2 = 0$ versus H_1: $\mu_1 - \mu_2 > 0$ by (see Theorem 9.5.26) rejecting H_0 iff

$$\frac{\overline{Z} - 0}{\sqrt{\dfrac{\displaystyle\sum_{i=1}^{m} (Z_i - \overline{Z})^2}{(m-1)m}}} > t_m^{-1}(1 - \alpha), \tag{9.9.6}$$

that is, iff [letting $\overline{X}(m) = (X_1 + \cdots + X_m)/m$, which is to be distinguished from $\overline{X} = (X_1 + \cdots + X_m + X_{m+1} + \cdots + X_n)/n$]

$$\frac{\overline{X}(m) - \overline{Y}}{\sqrt{\dfrac{\displaystyle\sum_{i=1}^{m} ((X_i - Y_i) - (\overline{X}(m) - \overline{Y}))^2}{(m-1)m}}} > t_{m-1}^{-1}(1 - \alpha). \tag{9.9.7}$$

As Scheffé has pointed out,[10] the Neyman-Bartlett solution essentially has two drawbacks. First, it throws away the $n - m$ observations $X_{m+1}, \ldots, X_n$ com-

---

[10] See Scheffé (1943). References to the Neyman-Bartlett solution are given on p. 35.

pletely. Second, the outcome of the test depends on the order of the observations in the samples. *Scheffé has proposed another solution (which we will call the* **Scheffé solution** *as follows*: Reject H_0 iff

$$\frac{\bar{X} - \bar{Y}}{\sqrt{\dfrac{\displaystyle\sum_{i=1}^{m} \left(\left(X_i - \sqrt{\dfrac{m}{n}}\, Y_i \right) - \left(\bar{X}(m) - \sqrt{\dfrac{m}{n}}\, \bar{Y} \right) \right)^2}{(m-1)m}}} > t_{m-1}^{-1}(1 - \alpha). \quad (9.9.8)$$

When H_0 is true, the left side of (9.9.8) has (Problem 9.20H) Student's t-distribution with $m - 1$ d.f., so the test is of level α. Note that this test uses $\bar{X}$ (not $\bar{X}(m)$) in the numerator and hence does not suffer from one of the maladies of the Neyman-Bartlett solution. However, the order of the observations still affects the outcome of the test. Scheffé has shown[11] that, in a certain framework, this dependence on order cannot be eliminated and has recommended that because of this dependence his solution should *not* be used.[12]

A third solution is to return to the Behrens-Fisher statistic (9.9.4) *and attempt to use it as in* (9.9.3) *for some* k'. What we will call the **Hsu solution** *takes* $k' = t_{f_0-1}^{-1}(1 - \alpha)$ *where* $f_0 = min\,(m, n)$, *and has*[13] *level* $\leq \alpha$. Other authors have suggested replacing $f_0 - 1$ with other (larger) quantities in order to obtain higher power (and also, of course, higher level hopefully $\approx \alpha$ and hopefully never $\gg \alpha$). For example, **Welch suggested**

$$\mathscr{F} = \frac{\left(\dfrac{s_1^2}{n} + \dfrac{s_2^2}{m} \right)^2}{\dfrac{\left(s_1^2/n \right)^2}{n-1} + \dfrac{\left(s_2^2/m \right)^2}{m-1}}, \quad (9.9.9)$$

and we can (Problem 9.49) show that

$$f_0 - 1 = min\,(n - 1, m - 1) \leq \mathscr{F} \leq (n - 1) + (m - 1). \quad (9.9.10)$$

Such tests do not guarantee the stated level of test α, and for reasonably large $f_0 - 1$ (e.g., 10 or more) do not reduce the $t_f^{-1}(1 - \alpha)$ value appreciably (and hence do not greatly affect the probabilities of acceptance and rejection). Hence, we would usually choose $f = f_0 - 1$ rather than $f = \mathscr{F}$ or some other quantity.

In summary, in the context of this section (where the experimenter has fixed sample sizes n and m and cannot, for example, decide to take more data) **we recommend the Hsu solution be used in practice.** It is simple to use and

---

[11] See Scheffé (1944).
[12] See p. 1503 of Scheffé (1970).
[13] See p. 1502 of Scheffé (1970).

understand, has control of the level of significance, and (unless n and m are very small) has good power properties in comparison with its competitors. (Cases where n and m are able to be changed are discussed in Section 9.10; there, substantial gains are possible by taking advantage of the control over n and m.)

PROBLEMS FOR SECTION 9.9

In the following problems, assume that each parent distribution from which a random sample is taken is normally distributed.

9.9.1 Consider the data of Problem 9.8.6. Test H_0: $\mu_1 - \mu_2 = 0$ versus H_1: $\mu_1 - \mu_2 \neq 0$, at level .05, using
(a) The Neyman-Bartlett test.
(b) The Scheffé solution.
(c) Welch's solution.
(d) Hsu's solution.
[*Note*: For the Neyman-Bartlett and Scheffé solutions, the order of the data is important, and different solutions are obtained by taking different orderings of the original data. The data are *not* to be put in ranked order for these solutions, so take the order to be alphabetical by team. Also note that the sample sizes of the two samples are equal in this problem.] Compare the results with those found in Problem 9.8.6 (where techniques of Section 9.8 were used); are the results contradictory?

9.9.2 Consider the data given in Problem 9.8.5. Test H_0: $\mu_1 - \mu_2 = 0$ versus H_1: $\mu_1 - \mu_2 < 0$, at level .05, using
(a) The Neyman-Bartlett test.
(b) The Scheffé solution.
(c) Welch's solution.
(d) Hsu's solution.

9.10. TESTING NORMAL MEANS: EXACT SOLUTION OF THE BEHRENS-FISHER PROBLEM

In Sections 9.5, 9.8, and 9.9, we have been dealing with cases where there is one source of normal observations (Section 9.5) and where there are two sources of normal observations—with possibly different means (Section 9.8 for the case of equal variances, Section 9.9 for the case of unequal variances). In each case, the tests given are optimal when the variance(s) are known, but do not have all the properties we would like (such as exact level .05 or power .99 at a specified alternative) when the variance(s) are unknown. **In this section, we will see that these problems are essentially unavoidable if the number of observations is preset** and we cannot (after doing some statistical analysis) decide to take a few more observations, **but that if we have the option of taking additional data then these problems (such as the Behrens-Fisher problem) can be solved.** The methods used are the simplest possible case of what is (in generality) called **sequential statistical**

analysis (for full details, see Govindarajulu (1981); for a brief introduction, see Section 9.11).

First, let us demonstrate that there is a need for a new type of statistical procedure different from those that we have studied so far. To do this, we will show a result that was first given by Dantzig in 1940 (with a much simpler proof due to Stein in 1945; Dantzig later went on to develop linear programming, and his proof involved many pages of involved geometrical arguments, whereas Stein's uses the Neyman-Pearson Lemma):

Theorem 9.10.1. Let $X_1, X_2, \ldots, X_n$ be independent $N(\mu, \sigma^2)$ r.v.'s with both μ and σ^2 unknown. Consider testing H_0: $\mu = \mu_0$ vs. H_1: $\mu = \mu_1$ (with $\mu_1 > \mu_0$) at level α. Then no single-stage test[14] with level α can have power $> \alpha$.

Proof: Consider any test ϕ. The power of ϕ cannot exceed the power of the Neyman-Pearson test when the value of the variance is σ^2, hence the power of ϕ is (see (9.5.1) for the Neyman-Pearson test)

$$\leq 1 - \Phi\left(\Phi^{-1}(1 - \alpha) - \frac{\mu_1 - \mu_0}{\sigma/\sqrt{n}} \right).$$

Since this is true for all $\sigma^2 > 0$, the power of ϕ cannot exceed

$$\min_{\sigma} \left\{ 1 - \Phi\left(\Phi^{-1}(1 - \alpha) - \frac{\mu_1 - \mu_0}{\sigma/\sqrt{n}} \right) \right\}$$

$$= \alpha,$$

which proves the theorem.   ∎

The following rule for taking observations (called a **sampling rule**) looks at a first set of data, then decides how much additional data is needed, then analyzes all of the data and reaches a decision. Since there are two stages at which data is collected, this is called a **two-stage rule** (or a **two-stage procedure**), which is the simplest kind of sequential procedure. This is the procedure on which the solutions of this section will be based, and after stating the procedure we will show that it leads to a statistic with Student's t-distribution.

Two-Stage Sampling Rule 9.10.2. Fix $n_0 \geq 2$ and $w > 0$. Take an initial sample of size n_0, say $X_1, X_2, \ldots, X_{n_0}$. Calculate

$$\overline{X}(n_0) = \sum_{j=1}^{n_0} X_i/n_0, \quad s^2 = \sum_{j=1}^{n_0} \left(X_j - \overline{X}(n_0) \right)^2 \big/ (n_0 - 1),$$

$$n = \max \left\{ n_0 + 1, \left[(ws)^2 \right] \right\}.$$

---

[14] That is, a test that analyzes the data and reaches a conclusion (hence excluding tests that might ask for more data before making a conclusion to accept or reject).

where $[y]$ denotes the smallest integer $\geq y$. Take $n - n_0$ additional observations $X_{n_0+1}, \ldots, X_n$. Calculate

$$\overline{Y}(n - n_0) = \sum_{j=n_0+1}^{n} X_j \big/ (n - n_0), \ \tilde{\overline{X}} = b\overline{X}(n_0) + (1 - b)\overline{Y}(n - n_0) \quad (9.10.3)$$

where

$$b = \frac{n_0}{n}\left(1 + \sqrt{1 - \frac{n}{n_0}\left(1 - \frac{n - n_0}{(ws)^2}\right)}\right). \quad (9.10.4)$$

Theorem 9.10.5. If $X_1, X_2, \ldots$ are independent $N(\mu, \sigma^2)$ r.v.'s, then

$$\frac{\tilde{\overline{X}} - \mu}{1/w} \quad (9.10.6)$$

has Student's t-distribution with $n_0 - 1$ degrees of freedom.

Proof: Consider the more general statistic

$$U = \frac{\sum_{i=1}^{n} a_i X_i - \mu}{\sqrt{z}} \quad (9.10.7)$$

where $a_1, \ldots, a_{n_0}, \ldots, a_n$ are chosen such that

$$a_1 + \cdots + a_n = 1, \ a_1 = \cdots = a_{n_0}, \ s^2(a_1^2 + \cdots + a_n^2) = z. \quad (9.10.8)$$

Then the d.f. of U is

$$F_U(u) = P(U \leq u) = P\left(\frac{\sum_{i=1}^{n} a_i X_i - \mu}{\sqrt{z}} \leq u\right)$$

$$= P\left(\frac{\sum_{i=1}^{n} a_i X_i - \mu}{s\sqrt{a_1^2 + \cdots + a_n^2}} \leq u\right), \quad \text{since } s^2(a_1^2 + \cdots + a_n^2) = z$$

$$= \int_0^{\infty} P\left(\frac{\sum_{i=1}^{n} a_i X_i - \mu}{s\sqrt{a_1^2 + \cdots + a_n^2}} \leq u \,\middle|\, s^2 = \gamma\sigma^2/(n_0 - 1)\right) f_{\frac{s^2}{\sigma^2}(n_0-1)}(\gamma)\, d\gamma,$$

where we integrate a conditional probability, essentially using Theorem 5.3.28,

$$= \int_0^\infty P\left(\left.\frac{\sum\limits_{i=1}^{n(\gamma)} a_i X_i - \mu}{\sqrt{\gamma}\,\sigma\sqrt{a_1^2 + \cdots + a_{n(\gamma)}^2}}\sqrt{n_0 - 1} \le u\,\right|\,s^2 = \gamma\sigma^2/(n_0 - 1)\right)$$

$$\times f_{\chi^2_{n_0-1}}(\gamma)\,d\gamma,$$

where we use Theorem 5.5.34 for the chi-square distribution and $n(\gamma)$ denotes $\max\{n_0 + 1, [\gamma\sigma^2/((n_0 - 1)z)]\}$,

$$= \int_0^\infty P\left(\frac{\sum\limits_{i=1}^{n(\gamma)} a_i X_i - \mu}{\sqrt{\gamma}\,\sigma\sqrt{a_1^2 + \cdots + a_{n(\gamma)}^2}}\sqrt{n_0 - 1} \le u\right) f_{\chi^2_{n_0-1}}(\gamma)\,d\gamma,$$

where (since $a_1 = \cdots = a_{n_0}$) $\sum\limits_{i=1}^{n(\gamma)} a_i X_i = a_1 n_0 \overline{X}(n_0) + \sum\limits_{i=n_0+1}^{n(\gamma)} a_i X_i$ is independent of s^2 (which is—see Rule 9.10.2—based on $X_1, \ldots, X_{n_0}$) since we have normal observations and Theorem 5.5.34, hence we could drop the conditional part of the probability (as we then have $P(A|B)$ with A and B independent events),

$$= \int_0^\infty P\left(\frac{\sum\limits_{i=1}^{n(\gamma)} a_i X_i - \mu}{\sigma\sqrt{a_1^2 + \cdots + a_{n(\gamma)}^2}} \le \frac{u\sqrt{\gamma}}{\sqrt{n_0 - 1}}\right) f_{\chi^2_{n_0-1}}(\gamma)\,d\gamma$$

$$= \int_0^\infty \Phi\left(\frac{u\sqrt{\gamma}}{\sqrt{n_0 - 1}}\right) f_{\chi^2_{n_0-1}}(\gamma)\,d\gamma,$$

since $\sum\limits_{i=1}^{n(\gamma)} a_i X_i$ is a normal r.v. (since $n(\gamma)$ is a fixed number and not a r.v.) with mean $(a_1 + \cdots + a_{n(\gamma)})\mu = 1 \cdot \mu = \mu$ (since $a_1 + \cdots + a_n = 1$) and variance $\sigma^2(a_1^2 + \cdots + a_{n(\gamma)}^2)$,

$$= \int_0^\infty \Phi\left(\frac{u\sqrt{\gamma}}{\sqrt{n_0 - 1}}\right) \frac{1}{2^{\frac{n_0-1}{2}}\,\Gamma\left(\frac{n_0 - 1}{2}\right)} \gamma^{\frac{n_0-1}{2} - 1} e^{-\gamma/2}\,d\gamma,$$

by Definition 4.2.13.

Differentiating, we then find the p.d.f. of U is

$$f_U(u) = \frac{d}{du} F_U(u)$$

$$= \int_0^\infty \sqrt{\frac{\gamma}{n_0 - 1}} \, \phi\left(\frac{u\sqrt{\gamma}}{\sqrt{n_0 - 1}}\right) \frac{1}{2^{\frac{n_0-1}{2}} \Gamma\left(\frac{n_0 - 1}{2}\right)} \gamma^{\frac{n_0-1}{2} - 1} e^{-\gamma/2} \, d\gamma$$

$$= \int_0^\infty \frac{1}{\sqrt{n_0 - 1}} \frac{1}{\sqrt{2\pi}} e^{-\frac{1}{2}u^2 \frac{\gamma}{n_0-1}} \frac{1}{2^{\frac{n_0-1}{2}} \Gamma\left(\frac{n_0 - 1}{2}\right)} \gamma^{\frac{n_0}{2} - 1} e^{-\gamma/2} \, d\gamma$$

$$= \frac{1}{\sqrt{\pi(n_0 - 1)} \, \Gamma\left(\frac{n_0 - 1}{2}\right)} \int_0^\infty \frac{1}{2^{n_0/2}} \gamma^{\frac{n_0}{2} - 1} e^{-\frac{1}{2}\gamma\left(1 + \frac{u^2}{n_0 - 1}\right)} \, d\gamma$$

$$= \frac{1}{\sqrt{(n_0 - 1)\pi} \, \Gamma\left(\frac{n_0 - 1}{2}\right)} \int_0^\infty \frac{y^{\frac{n_0}{2} - 1} e^{-y}}{\left(1 + \frac{u^2}{n_0 - 1}\right)^{n_0/2}} \, dy,$$

using the change of variables

$$y = \frac{\gamma}{2}(1 + u^2/(n_0 - 1))$$

$$= \frac{\Gamma\left(\frac{n_0}{2}\right)}{\sqrt{(n_0 - 1)\pi} \, \Gamma\left(\frac{n_0 - 1}{2}\right)} \frac{1}{\left(1 + \frac{u^2}{n_0 - 1}\right)^{n_0/2}}, \quad -\infty < u < \infty,$$

which is (see Definition 4.2.26) the p.d.f. of a Student's-t r.v. with $n_0 - 1$ degrees of freedom. Thus, we have shown that the statistic U of equation (9.10.7) has a Student's t-distribution with $n_0 - 1$ degrees of freedom. Since $\tilde{X}$ is the special case that occurs when we require $a_{n_0+1} = \cdots = a_n$, the theorem follows (i.e., (9.10.6) has a Student's t-distribution with $n_0 - 1$ degrees of freedom). ∎

To summarize our results to this point: Let $X_1, X_2, \ldots$ be independent $N(\mu, \sigma^2)$ r.v.'s with both μ and σ^2 unknown. Testing $H_0 \colon \mu = \mu_0$ vs. $H_1 \colon \mu = \mu_1$ (with $\mu_1 > \mu_0$) at level α cannot be solved with a single-stage procedure (this is Theorem 9.10.1). If we first take $n_0 \geq 2$ observations, then compute how many more observations to take from

$$n = \max\left\{n_0 + 1, \left[(ws)^2\right]\right\}$$

where n is the total number of observations we will take (so we take $n - n_0$ more after the first stage) and s^2 is calculated from the first n_0 observations (this is Sampling Rule 9.10.2), then the statistic

$$\frac{\tilde{\tilde{X}} - \mu}{1/w}$$

has Student's t-distribution with $n_0 - 1$ degrees of freedom where $\tilde{\tilde{X}}$ is defined in (9.10.3) (this is Theorem 9.10.5). **All this is true for any $w > 0$.**

   Let us now choose w so that we test H_0 vs. H_1 with level α and power β. Since $\tilde{\tilde{X}}$ is an estimator of μ, let us choose to reject H_0 iff $\tilde{\tilde{X}} > c$. Now level α requires $P_{H_0}(\tilde{\tilde{X}} > c) = \alpha$. However,

$$P_{H_0}(\tilde{\tilde{X}} > c) = P_{\mu_0}\left(\frac{\tilde{\tilde{X}} - \mu_0}{1/w} > \frac{c - \mu_0}{1/w}\right) = P\left(t_{n_0-1} > \frac{c - \mu_0}{1/w}\right),$$

which will equal α if we set

$$\frac{c - \mu_0}{1/w} = t_{n_0-1}^{-1}(1 - \alpha),$$

that is,

$$c = \mu_0 + \frac{1}{w}t_{n_0-1}^{-1}(1 - \alpha). \qquad (9.10.9)$$

For power β we need $P_{H_1}(\tilde{\tilde{X}} > c) = \beta$. However,

$$P_{H_1}(\tilde{\tilde{X}} > c) = P_{\mu_1}\left(\tilde{\tilde{X}} > \mu_0 + \frac{1}{w}t_{n_0-1}^{-1}(1 - \alpha)\right)$$

$$= P_{\mu_1}\left(\frac{\tilde{\tilde{X}} - \mu_1}{1/w} > \frac{\mu_0 - \mu_1}{1/w} + t_{n_0-1}^{-1}(1 - \alpha)\right)$$

$$= P_{\mu_1}\left(-\frac{\tilde{\tilde{X}} - \mu_1}{1/w} \le \frac{\mu_1 - \mu_0}{1/w} - t_{n_0-1}^{-1}(1 - \alpha)\right)$$

$$= P\left(t_{n_0-1} \le \frac{\mu_1 - \mu_0}{1/w} - t_{n_0-1}^{-1}(1 - \alpha)\right)$$

(since the t-distribution of $(\tilde{\tilde{X}} - \mu_1)/(1/w)$ is symmetric about 0, $-(\tilde{\tilde{X}} - \mu_1)/(1/w)$ has the same distribution), which will equal β if we set

$$\frac{\mu_1 - \mu_0}{1/w} - t_{n_0-1}^{-1}(1 - \alpha) = t_{n_0-1}^{-1}(\beta),$$

that is,

$$w = \frac{t_{n_0-1}^{-1}(1 - \alpha) + t_{n_0-1}^{-1}(\beta)}{\mu_1 - \mu_0}. \tag{9.10.10}$$

Thus, we have shown

Theorem 9.10.11. Let $X_1, X_2, \ldots$ be independent $N(\mu, \sigma^2)$ r.v.'s with μ and σ^2 both unknown. For testing H_0: $\mu = \mu_0$ vs. H_1: $\mu = \mu_1$ (with $\mu_1 \geq \mu_0$), if we use Sampling Rule 9.10.2 with w as given in (9.10.10) and reject iff $\tilde{X} > c$ (with c as given in (9.10.9)) our test will have level α and power β.

Example 9.10.12. Suppose that it is desired to test whether a proposed "improvement" will increase the yield of a certain process, the chances of accepting a useless "improvement" to be 5% and the chances of accepting an improvement of 1 unit to be 90%. Suppose we choose $n_0 = 11$ in Sampling Rule 9.10.2. Then the level $\alpha = .05$ test of H_0: $\mu = 0$ against the alternative H_1: $\mu > 0$ with power $\beta = .90$ when $\mu = 1$, rejects H_0 iff

$$\tilde{X} > 0 + \frac{1.812}{\dfrac{1.812 + 1.372}{1 - 0}} = 0.569.$$

If our first sample has the 11 values (differences from the old process mean yield) of 2.2, 1.8, -1.1, 2.1, 1.3, 1.1, -0.4, -1.4, 1.7, 0.8, 0.7, we would find $\overline{X}(n_0) = 0.80$, $s^2 = 1.57$, and

$$n = \max\left\{12, \left[(3.184s)^2\right]\right\} = \max\{12, [15.916]\} = 16.$$

Hence $n - n_0 = 16 - 11 = 5$ additional observations are needed. Suppose these are 3.2, -0.6, 1.2, 0.1, -0.7. Then $\overline{Y}(5) = 0.64$, $b = 0.721$, and $\tilde{X} = 0.755$. Since $\tilde{X}$ exceeds 0.569, we reject H_0 (i.e., we decide the improvement will increase process yield).

Choice of n_0. Note that a reasonable way to choose n_0 may be obtained as follows. The procedure of Theorem 9.10.11 has the same level and power for *all* n_0 that are at least 2. What differs with the choice of n_0 is the total sample size n required, namely, the larger of $n_0 + 1$ and $[(ws)^2]$ where w is given in equation (9.10.10). To keep $n_0 + 1$ small (thus minimizing sampling costs), we wish to keep n_0 as small as possible. However, $[(ws)^2]$ is approximately w^2s^2 (except for rounding up to the next integer if this quantity is not an integer), and s^2 is approximately σ^2, while w compensates for the need to estimate σ^2 by s^2. As s^2 is a better estimator of σ^2 for large n_0, w decreases as n_0 increases, as can be seen from Table 13 of the t-distribution and the fact that

$$w = \frac{t_{n_0-1}^{-1}(1 - \alpha) + t_{n_0-1}^{-1}(\beta)}{\mu_1 - \mu_0}.$$

If we have level .05 and power .90 as in Example 9.10.12, then (with $\mu_1 - \mu_0 = 1$) we find the following values of w for various choices of n_0:

n_0	2	6	11	15	20	25	30	∞
w	9.392	3.491	3.184	3.106	3.057	3.029	3.010	2.927

Thus, if we choose n_0 very small we will find w large due to the fact that n_0 was small (and that then s^2 is a very variable estimator). However, if we choose n_0 of 11 or more, then w will be within 9% of the limiting value as $n_0 \to \infty$ (which is the case where σ^2 is essentially known). Hence, **we recommend in practice that n_0 be set at 11 or more** (in order to optimize—i.e., to minimize—the total sample size n), **and any n_0 of 11 or more should be a satisfactory choice in terms of keeping n as small as possible** (of course, the smallest possible would be the sample size needed for the desired level and power at the specified alternative when the variance is known).

Note: With the methods of this section we are able to control *both* the level of the test *and* its power at a specified alternative of interest. This is greatly desirable in practice, and is unattainable with the more widely known methods discussed in earlier sections.

When we have two sources of normal observations with different means and possibly different variances, the testing problem regarding the means is known as the **Behrens-Fisher problem** and was discussed using single-stage procedures in Section 9.9. We saw there that Hsu's method was recommended for use in practice—though no single-stage method can allow us to control both the level and the power (this follows from Theorem 9.10.1), and in fact it is widely believed that "no exact solution of the Behrens-Fisher problem exists"—by which is meant that one cannot exactly control the level of the test. However, **the methods of this section allow us to give a test for the Behrens-Fisher problem that has both the desired level and the desired power.** We proceed as follows. Suppose that $X_1, X_2, \ldots$ are independent $N(\mu_1, \sigma_1^2)$ r.v.'s, while $Y_1, Y_2, \ldots$ are independent $N(\mu_2, \sigma_2^2)$ r.v.'s with all of $\mu_1, \mu_2, \sigma_1^2, \sigma_2^2$ unknown. For testing H_0: $\mu_1 = \mu_2$ vs. H_1: $\mu_1 \neq \mu_2$ at level α, with power β when $|\mu_1 - \mu_2| = d > 0$, choose $n_0 \geq 2$ and sample each population independently using Sampling Rule 9.10.2. We then find $\tilde{\overline{X}}$ and $\tilde{\overline{Y}}$, and it is reasonable (since these respectively estimate μ_1 and μ_2) to reject H_0 iff $|\tilde{\overline{X}} - \tilde{\overline{Y}}| > c$. Thus, the level of this test is

$$P_{H_0}\left(|\tilde{\overline{X}} - \tilde{\overline{Y}}| > c\right) = P_{\mu_1 = \mu_2}\left(\left|\frac{\tilde{\overline{X}} - \mu_1}{1/w} - \frac{\tilde{\overline{Y}} - \mu_2}{1/w}\right| > \frac{c}{1/w}\right)$$

$$= P\left(|t_1 + t_2| > wc\right)$$

TABLE 9.10-1

Value $c_{1-\gamma}(n_0)$ such that $P(t_1 + t_2 \le c_{1-\gamma}(n_0)) = 1 - \gamma$, where t_1 and t_2 are independent Student's t r.v.'s with $n_0 - 1$ d.f. each

$1 - \gamma$ \\ n_0	2	3	4	5	6	7	8	9	10	15	20	25	30
.75	2.00	1.37	1.21	1.14	1.10	1.07	1.05	1.04	1.03	1.00	0.99	0.98	0.98
.80	2.75	1.76	1.54	1.44	1.38	1.35	1.32	1.30	1.29	1.25	1.24	1.23	1.22
.85	3.93	2.27	1.94	1.80	1.72	1.68	1.64	1.62	1.60	1.55	1.53	1.51	1.51
.90	6.16	3.04	2.50	2.29	2.18	2.11	2.06	2.02	2.00	1.93	1.90	1.88	1.87
.95	12.63	4.57	3.50	3.11	2.91	2.79	2.71	2.66	2.61	2.50	2.45	2.42	2.41
.975	25.42	6.54	4.59	3.94	3.63	3.45	3.33	3.24	3.18	3.02	2.95	2.91	2.88
.99	63.7	10.28	6.31	5.14	4.60	4.30	4.11	3.98	3.89	3.64	3.54	3.48	3.45

Source: Dudewicz, Ramberg, and Chen (1975), p. 17.

where (by Theorem 9.10.5) t_1 and t_2 are independent Student's t r.v.'s with $n_0 - 1$ degrees of freedom each (and we have used the fact that $-t_2$ and t_2 have the same distribution since the t-distribution is symmetric about zero). Thus, if we choose

$$c = \frac{c_{1-\alpha/2}(n_0)}{w} \qquad (9.10.13)$$

where $c_{1-\gamma}(n_0)$ is the point below which the r.v. $t_1 + t_2$ has probability $1 - \gamma$, then our test will have level α. $c_{1-\gamma}(n_0)$ is tabled in Table 9.10-1. It can be shown that the power of this test is

$$F_{n_0}\left(-c_{1-\alpha/2}(n_0) - dw\right) + F_{n_0}\left(-c_{1-\alpha/2}(n_0) + dw\right) \qquad (9.10.14)$$

where $F_{n_0}(\cdot)$ is the distribution function of $t_1 + t_2$, and is tabled in Table 9.10-2. If we evaluate (9.10.14) at various w's until a w where the power is at least β is found, then we will have the desired test.

Example 9.10.15. Suppose we choose $n_0 = 10$. Then the level $\alpha = .20$ test of H_0: $\mu_1 = \mu_2$ against the alternative H_1: $\mu_1 \ne \mu_2$ with power $\beta = .70$ when $d = 1$ rejects H_0 iff

$$|\tilde{\tilde{X}} - \tilde{\tilde{Y}}| > \frac{2.00}{w}.$$

Here w is determined (since $F_{10}(-2 - w) = 1 - F_{10}(2 + w)$) by

$$1 - F_{10}(2 + w) + F_{10}(-2 - w) = .70,$$

TABLE 9.10-2

$F_{n_0}(t)$, the distribution function of $t_1 + t_2$ where t_1 and t_2 are independent Student's t r.v.'s with $n_0 - 1$ degrees of freedom each

t \ n_0	2	3	4	5	6	7	8	9	10	11	12	13	14	15	20	25	30
0.0	.4999	.4999	.4999	.4999	.4999	.4999	.4999	.4999	.4999	.4999	.4999	.4999	.4999	.4999	.4999	.4999	.4999
0.1	.5158	.5208	.5229	.5241	.5248	.5254	.5257	.5260	.5262	.5264	.5266	.5267	.5268	.5269	.5272	.5274	.5275
0.2	.5317	.5415	.5457	.5481	.5496	.5506	.5514	.5520	.5524	.5528	.5531	.5533	.5535	.5537	.5544	.5547	.5550
0.3	.5473	.5620	.5684	.5719	.5742	.5757	.5768	.5777	.5783	.5789	.5793	.5797	.5800	.5803	.5812	.5818	.5822
0.4	.5628	.5822	.5907	.5954	.5984	.6004	.6019	.6030	.6039	.6046	.6052	.6057	.6061	.6065	.6077	.6085	.6089
0.5	.5779	.6021	.6126	.6184	.6221	.6246	.6265	.6279	.6290	.6299	.6306	.6312	.6317	.6322	.6337	.6346	.6352
0.6	.5927	.6215	.6340	.6410	.6453	.6483	.6505	.6521	.6534	.6545	.6554	.6561	.6567	.6572	.6591	.6601	.6608
0.7	.6071	.6404	.6549	.6629	.6679	.6713	.6738	.6757	.6772	.6785	.6794	.6803	.6810	.6816	.6837	.6849	.6857
0.8	.6211	.6588	.6751	.6841	.6897	.6936	.6964	.6986	.7003	.7016	.7027	.7037	.7045	.7051	.7075	.7089	.7098
0.9	.6345	.6765	.6946	.7046	.7108	.7151	.7182	.7206	.7224	.7239	.7252	.7262	.7271	.7278	.7304	.7319	.7329
1.0	.6475	.6935	.7134	.7242	.7311	.7357	.7391	.7417	.7437	.7453	.7466	.7478	.7487	.7495	.7523	.7539	.7550
1.1	.6600	.7099	.7313	.7431	.7504	.7554	.7591	.7618	.7640	.7657	.7671	.7683	.7693	.7702	.7732	.7749	.7761
1.2	.6720	.7255	.7485	.7610	.7688	.7742	.7780	.7810	.7833	.7851	.7866	.7879	.7889	.7899	.7930	.7948	.7961
1.3	.6834	.7405	.7648	.7781	.7863	.7919	.7960	.7991	.8015	.8034	.8050	.8063	.8075	.8084	.8117	.8136	.8149
1.4	.6943	.7547	.7803	.7942	.8029	.8087	.8130	.8162	.8187	.8207	.8223	.8237	.8249	.8259	.8293	.8313	.8326
1.5	.7048	.7681	.7950	.8094	.8184	.8245	.8289	.8322	.8348	.8369	.8386	.8400	.8412	.8422	.8457	.8478	.8491
1.6	.7147	.7809	.8088	.8238	.8331	.8393	.8439	.8473	.8499	.8520	.8538	.8552	.8564	.8575	.8611	.8631	.8645
1.7	.7242	.7930	.8218	.8372	.8467	.8532	.8578	.8613	.8639	.8661	.8679	.8693	.8706	.8716	.8753	.8774	.8788
1.8	.7332	.8044	.8340	.8498	.8595	.8660	.8707	.8742	.8770	.8792	.8809	.8824	.8837	.8847	.8884	.8905	.8919
1.9	.7418	.8151	.8454	.8615	.8714	.8780	.8827	.8863	.8890	.8912	.8930	.8945	.8957	.8968	.9004	.9025	.9039
2.0	.7499	.8252	.8561	.8725	.8824	.8891	.8938	.8974	.9001	.9023	.9041	.9056	.9068	.9079	.9115	.9136	.9149
2.1	.7577	.8347	.8661	.8826	.8926	.8993	.9040	.9075	.9103	.9124	.9142	.9157	.9169	.9180	.9215	.9236	.9249
2.2	.7651	.8436	.8754	.8920	.9020	.9087	.9134	.9169	.9196	.9217	.9235	.9249	.9261	.9272	.9307	.9327	.9340
2.3	.7721	.8520	.8841	.9007	.9107	.9173	.9220	.9254	.9281	.9302	.9319	.9333	.9345	.9355	.9389	.9409	.9421
2.4	.7788	.8599	.8922	.9087	.9187	.9252	.9298	.9332	.9358	.9379	.9395	.9409	.9421	.9430	.9464	.9482	.9495
2.5	.7852	.8673	.8996	.9162	.9260	.9324	.9369	.9402	.9428	.9448	.9464	.9478	.9489	.9498	.9530	.9548	.9560

n_0 / t	2	3	4	5	6	7	8	9	10	11	12	13	14	15	20	25	30
2.6	.7912	.8742	.9066	.9230	.9327	.9390	.9434	.9466	.9491	.9511	.9526	.9539	.9550	.9559	.9590	.9607	.9618
2.7	.7970	.8807	.9130	.9293	.9388	.9450	.9493	.9524	.9548	.9567	.9582	.9594	.9605	.9614	.9643	.9659	.9670
2.8	.8025	.8868	.9190	.9350	.9444	.9504	.9546	.9576	.9599	.9617	.9632	.9644	.9654	.9662	.9690	.9706	.9716
2.9	.8078	.8925	.9245	.9403	.9495	.9553	.9594	.9623	.9645	.9663	.9676	.9688	.9697	.9705	.9732	.9746	.9756
3.0	.8128	.8979	.9297	.9452	.9541	.9598	.9637	.9665	.9686	.9703	.9716	.9727	.9736	.9743	.9768	.9782	.9791
3.1	.8176	.9029	.9344	.9497	.9583	.9638	.9676	.9703	.9723	.9739	.9751	.9761	.9770	.9777	.9800	.9813	.9821
3.2	.8221	.9076	.9388	.9537	.9622	.9675	.9711	.9736	.9756	.9771	.9782	.9792	.9800	.9807	.9828	.9841	.9848
3.3	.8265	.9121	.9429	.9575	.9657	.9708	.9742	.9766	.9785	.9799	.9810	.9819	.9826	.9833	.9853	.9864	.9871
3.4	.8307	.9162	.9466	.9609	.9688	.9737	.9770	.9793	.9811	.9824	.9834	.9843	.9850	.9855	.9874	.9885	.9891
3.5	.8347	.9201	.9501	.9640	.9717	.9764	.9795	.9817	.9833	.9846	.9856	.9864	.9870	.9875	.9893	.9902	.9908
3.6	.8385	.9238	.9533	.9669	.9743	.9788	.9817	.9838	.9854	.9865	.9874	.9882	.9888	.9893	.9909	.9917	.9923
3.7	.8422	.9273	.9563	.9695	.9766	.9809	.9837	.9857	.9871	.9882	.9891	.9898	.9903	.9908	.9923	.9930	.9935
3.8	.8457	.9305	.9591	.9719	.9788	.9829	.9855	.9874	.9887	.9897	.9905	.9912	.9917	.9921	.9934	.9941	.9946
3.9	.8491	.9336	.9617	.9741	.9807	.9846	.9871	.9889	.9901	.9911	.9918	.9924	.9928	.9932	.9944	.9951	.9955
4.0	.8524	.9365	.9640	.9761	.9824	.9861	.9885	.9902	.9913	.9922	.9929	.9934	.9938	.9942	.9953	.9959	.9962
4.1	.8555	.9392	.9662	.9779	.9840	.9875	.9898	.9913	.9924	.9932	.9938	.9943	.9947	.9950	.9960	.9966	.9969
4.2	.8585	.9417	.9683	.9796	.9854	.9888	.9909	.9923	.9933	.9941	.9947	.9951	.9955	.9958	.9967	.9971	.9974
4.3	.8614	.9442	.9702	.9812	.9867	.9899	.9919	.9932	.9942	.9949	.9954	.9958	.9961	.9964	.9972	.9976	.9979
4.4	.8641	.9464	.9720	.9826	.9879	.9909	.9928	.9940	.9949	.9955	.9960	.9964	.9967	.9969	.9976	.9980	.9982
4.5	.8668	.9486	.9736	.9839	.9890	.9918	.9936	.9947	.9955	.9961	.9966	.9969	.9972	.9974	.9980	.9983	.9985
4.6	.8694	.9506	.9751	.9851	.9899	.9926	.9943	.9953	.9961	.9966	.9970	.9973	.9976	.9978	.9983	.9986	.9988
4.7	.8719	.9526	.9765	.9862	.9908	.9933	.9949	.9959	.9966	.9971	.9974	.9977	.9979	.9981	.9986	.9989	.9990
4.8	.8743	.9544	.9779	.9872	.9916	.9940	.9954	.9964	.9970	.9974	.9978	.9980	.9982	.9984	.9988	.9991	.9992
4.9	.8766	.9561	.9791	.9881	.9923	.9946	.9959	.9968	.9974	.9978	.9981	.9983	.9985	.9986	.9990	.9992	.9993
5.0	.8788	.9578	.9803	.9889	.9930	.9951	.9964	.9972	.9977	.9981	.9983	.9985	.9987	.9988	.9992	.9993	.9994
5.1	.8810	.9593	.9813	.9897	.9935	.9956	.9967	.9975	.9980	.9983	.9986	.9987	.9989	.9990	.9993	.9995	.9995

Source: Dudewicz and Dalal (1975), p. 52.

and from the tables we find $w = 3.0$. Thus, we will reject H_0 if the estimates of the means differ by $2.00/3.0 = .67$ or more.

PROBLEMS FOR SECTION 9.10

In the following problem, assume that each parent distribution from which a random sample is taken is normally distributed.

9.10.1 For the first $n_0 = 4$ data points as given in the data of Problem 9.8.5, to test H_0: $\mu_1 - \mu_2 = 0$ versus $H_1: |\mu_1 - \mu_2| = 2$
   (a) What additional sample sizes do we need from each of the populations if we desire level .05 and power .95?
   (b) If we desire level .05 and can take 1 additional data point from each population, what power will result?
   (c) Carry out the test in part (b), using the first 5 data points of the data of Problem 9.8.5.

9.11. THE LIKELIHOOD-RATIO TEST & SEQUENTIAL LR TEST (SPRT)

In Section 9.3 we discussed best tests and uniformly most powerful tests. Since most real-world alternatives are composite, UMP tests are usually desirable. (Unfortunately, as we have shown, a UMP test does not always exist.) In Theorem 9.3.51 we saw how to find a UMP test using the MLR property. In this section we generalize this to a general method of finding a possibly-good test in any testing problem. Under certain "regularity" conditions on the distribution of the data, the "large sample size" (i.e., limiting as $n \to \infty$) distribution of the test statistic turns out to be chi-square. Hence even if the exact tables needed are not available, if n is "large" the test may still be used in practice. The procedure given is general, and in many cases yields the only known test.

The discussion of the LR test is followed by an introduction to sequential analysis through the sequential LR test (which is usually called the Sequential Probability Ratio Test or SPRT, and was first formulated by Abraham Wald).

Definition 9.11.1. Let X be a r.v. with d.f. $F(x|\theta)$ where θ is unknown, $\theta \in \Theta \subseteq \mathcal{R}^k$. Assume $F(x|\theta)$ is either absolutely continuous (in which case let $f(x|\theta)$ denote its density at x) or discrete (in which case let $f(x|\theta)$ denote $P_\theta[X = x]$). Consider the hypothesis testing problem $H_0: \theta \in \Theta_0$ vs. $H_1: \theta \in \Theta_1$. Let $X = (X_1, \ldots, X_n)$ be a random sample of size n, and define

$$\lambda(\mathbf{x}) = \frac{\max_{\theta \in \Theta_0} f(\mathbf{x}|\theta)}{\max_{\theta \in \Theta} f(\mathbf{x}|\theta)}.$$

Then a level α **likelihood-ratio test** for H_0 vs. H_1 is given by critical function

$$\phi(\mathbf{x}) = \begin{cases} 1, & \text{if } \lambda(\mathbf{x}) < c \\ 0, & \text{if } \lambda(\mathbf{x}) \geq c \end{cases} \qquad (9.11.2)$$

where c is determined by the equation $\max\limits_{\theta \in \Theta_0} E_\theta(\phi(X)) = \alpha$.

Note that **(9.11.2) is a generalization of the Neyman-Pearson test** of (9.3.4). For simple H_0 and simple H_1, (9.11.2) reduces to the test of the Neyman-Pearson Lemma. (This is true *if* a likelihood-ratio test of level α exists. This may not be the case for all α, even in continuous cases, as shown in Solomon (1975). Also see Problem 9.11.1.) Also note that $0 \leq \lambda(\mathbf{x}) \leq 1$ since the numerator is the maximum with respect to θ over a smaller subset of Θ than is the denominator (which is over all of Θ). Thus if H_0 is true we expect $\lambda(\mathbf{x})$ "close" to 1, whereas when H_0 is false we expect a denominator larger than the numerator (hence $\lambda(\mathbf{x})$ "close" to zero).

We now give several examples and a major theorem regarding the likelihood-ratio test.

Example 9.11.3. Let $X = (X_1, X_2, \ldots, X_n)$ be independent r.v.'s, each $N(\mu, \sigma^2)$, where μ and σ^2 are both unknown. Consider testing H_0: $\mu = \mu_0$ versus H_1: $\mu \neq \mu_0$. Here $\Theta = \{\theta = (\mu, \sigma^2): -\infty < \mu < \infty, \sigma^2 > 0\}$ and $\Theta_0 = \{\theta = (\mu, \sigma^2): \mu = \mu_0, \sigma^2 > 0\}$, and X has p.d.f. $f(\mathbf{x}|\theta) = (\sqrt{2\pi}\sigma)^{-n} \exp\left(-\sum\limits_{i=1}^{n}(x_i - \mu)^2/(2\sigma^2)\right)$. Since, viewed as a function of θ, $f(\mathbf{x}|\theta)$ is simply the likelihood function, finding its maximum under H_0 (i.e., over Θ_0) is simply finding the value of $f(\mathbf{x}|\theta)$ when $\theta = \hat{\theta} = (\hat{\mu}, \hat{\sigma}^2)$, that is, at the MLE of (μ, σ^2). Under H_0, this maximum occurs at $\mu = \mu_0$ and $\sigma^2 = \sum\limits_{i=1}^{n}(X_i - \mu_0)^2/n$ (see Example 7.2.13), while the maximum of $f(\mathbf{x}|\theta)$ over Θ is (see Example 7.2.17) achieved at $\hat{\mu} = \overline{X}$ and $\hat{\sigma}^2 = \sum\limits_{i=1}^{n}(X_i - \overline{X})^2/n$. Thus

$$\lambda(\mathbf{x}) = \frac{\max\limits_{\Theta_0} f(\mathbf{x}|\theta)}{\max\limits_{\Theta} f(\mathbf{x}|\theta)} = \left(\frac{\sum(X_i - \overline{X})^2}{\sum(X_i - \mu_0)^2}\right)^{\frac{n}{2}} \frac{e^{-\frac{n}{2}\frac{\Sigma(X_i - \mu_0)^2}{\Sigma(X_i - \mu_0)^2}}}{e^{-\frac{n}{2}\frac{\Sigma(X_i - \overline{X})^2}{\Sigma(X_i - \overline{X})^2}}}$$

$$= \left(\frac{\sum(X_i - \overline{X})^2}{\sum(X_i - \mu_0)^2}\right)^{\frac{n}{2}} = \left(\frac{\sum(X_i - \overline{X})^2}{\sum(X_i - \overline{X} + \overline{X} - \mu_0)^2}\right)^{\frac{n}{2}}$$

$$= \left(\frac{\sum(X_i - \overline{X})^2}{\sum(X_i - \overline{X})^2 + n(\overline{X} - \mu_0)^2 + 2\sum(X_i - \overline{X})(\overline{X} - \mu_0)}\right)^{\frac{n}{2}}$$

and

$$\left(\lambda(\mathbf{x})\right)^{\frac{2}{n}} = \frac{\sum(X_i - \overline{X})^2}{\sum(X_i - \overline{X})^2 + n(\overline{X} - \mu_0)^2} = \frac{1}{1 + \dfrac{n(\overline{X} - \mu_0)^2}{\sum(X_i - \overline{X})^2}}$$

since

$$\sum_{i=1}^{n}(X_i - \overline{X})(\overline{X} - \mu) = (\overline{X} - \mu)\sum_{i=1}^{n}(X_i - \overline{X}) = 0.$$

Since $0 \le \lambda(\mathbf{x}) \le 1$,

$$\lambda(\mathbf{x}) < c \text{ iff } (\lambda(\mathbf{x}))^{\frac{2}{n}} < c_1$$

$$\text{iff } \frac{1}{1 + \dfrac{n(\overline{X} - \mu_0)^2}{\sum(X_i - \overline{X})^2}} < c_1$$

$$\text{iff } \frac{n(\overline{X} - \mu_0)^2}{\sum(X_i - \overline{X})^2} > \frac{1 - c_1}{c_1}$$

$$\text{iff } \frac{n(\overline{X} - \mu_0)^2}{\dfrac{\sum(X_i - \overline{X})^2}{n - 1}} > \frac{1 - c_1}{c_1/(n - 1)}$$

$$\text{iff } \frac{n(\overline{X} - \mu_0)^2}{s^2} > K$$

where $K = (1 - c_1)(n - 1)/c_1$. Since $n(\overline{X} - \mu_0)^2/\sigma^2$ is $\chi_1^2(0)$, $(n - 1)s^2/\sigma^2$ is $\chi_{n-1}^2(0)$, and $\overline{X}$ is independent of s^2, it follows that

$$\frac{n(\overline{X} - \mu_0)^2}{s^2} = \frac{\dfrac{n(\overline{X} - \mu_0)^2}{\sigma^2}}{(n - 1)\dfrac{s^2}{\sigma^2}\bigg/(n - 1)} \text{ is } F_{1, n-1}.$$

Therefore, at level α we reject H_0 iff

$$\frac{n(\overline{X} - \mu_0)^2}{s^2} > F^{-1}_{1, n-1, 1-\alpha}$$

or equivalently

$$\phi(X) = \begin{cases} 1, & \text{if } n(\overline{X} - \mu_0)^2/s^2 > F^{-1}_{1, n-1, 1-\alpha} \\ 0, & \text{otherwise} \end{cases} \tag{9.11.4}$$

is the level α likelihood-ratio test for H_0 vs. H_1.

Remark 9.11.5. If a r.v. T has Student's t-distribution with m degrees of freedom, then T can be represented as the ratio

$$T = \frac{Z}{\sqrt{\dfrac{\chi_m^2(0)}{m}}}$$

where Z is $N(0,1)$, $\chi_m^2(0)$ is central chi-square with m degrees of freedom, and Z, $\chi_m^2(0)$ are independent r.v.'s. But then we also have

$$T^2 = \frac{Z^2}{\dfrac{\chi_m^2(0)}{m}} = \frac{\chi_1^2(0)/1}{\chi_m^2(0)/m} = F_{1, m}. \tag{9.11.6}$$

Thus using (9.11.6) test (9.11.4) can be rewritten as

$$\phi^*(X) = \begin{cases} 1, & \text{if } |T| = |\sqrt{n}\,(\overline{X} - \mu_0)/s| > t^{-1}_{n-1}(1 - \alpha/2) \\ 0, & \text{otherwise.} \end{cases} \tag{9.11.7}$$

Hence a level α test for the hypothesis H_0: $\mu = \mu_0$ versus H_1: $\mu \neq \mu_0$ is to reject H_0 if

$$|T| = |\sqrt{n}\,(\overline{X} - \mu_0)/s| > t^{-1}_{n-1}(1 - \alpha/2),$$

which is the test obtained in Section 9.5.

Example 9.11.8. Let $X_1, X_2, \ldots, X_n$ be independent r.v.'s, each with the exponential p.d.f.

$$f(x|\alpha, \lambda) = \frac{1}{\lambda} e^{-(x-\alpha)/\lambda} I_{[\alpha, \infty)}(x),$$

TESTS OF HYPOTHESES

λ known. Suppose it is desired to test H_0: $\alpha = \alpha_0$ vs. H_1: $\alpha > \alpha_0$. Find the likelihood-ratio test.

Here the parameter spaces are

$$\Theta = \{\alpha: \alpha > \alpha_0, \alpha \in R\}, \qquad \Theta_0 = \{\alpha_0\},$$

and the p.d.f. of $(X_1, \ldots, X_n)$ is

$$f(x_1, x_2, \ldots, x_n | \alpha) = \frac{1}{\lambda^n} e^{-\sum_{i=1}^{n}(x_i - \alpha)/\lambda} I_{[\alpha, \infty)}(y_1)$$

where $y_1 = \min(x_1, x_2, \ldots, x_n)$. Under H_0,

$$\max_{\Theta_0} f(x_1, x_2, \ldots, x_n | \alpha) = \frac{1}{\lambda^n} e^{-\sum_{i=1}^{n}(x_i - \alpha_0)/\lambda} I_{[\alpha_0, \infty)}(y_1),$$

while under Θ,

$$\max_{\Theta} f(x_1, x_2, \ldots, x_n | \alpha) = \frac{1}{\lambda^n} e^{-\sum(x_i - \hat{\alpha})/\lambda} I_{[\hat{\alpha}, \infty)}(y_1)$$

with $\hat{\alpha} = y_1 = \min(x_1, x_2, \ldots, x_n)$. Thus

$$\lambda(\mathbf{x}) = \frac{\max_{\Theta_0} f(x_1, x_2, \ldots, x_n | \alpha)}{\max_{\Theta} f(x_1, x_2, \ldots, x_n | \alpha)}$$

$$= e^{-\sum_{i=1}^{n}(x_i - \alpha_0)/\lambda + \sum_{i=1}^{n}(x_i - \hat{\alpha})/\lambda} \frac{I_{[\alpha_0, \infty)}(y_1)}{I_{[\hat{\alpha}, \infty)}(y_1)}$$

$$= e^{n(\alpha_0 - \hat{\alpha})/\lambda} I_{[\alpha_0, \infty)}(y_1) / I_{[\hat{\alpha}, \infty)}(y_1)$$

$$= e^{n(\alpha_0 - \hat{\alpha})/\lambda} I_{[\alpha_0, \infty)}(y_1)$$

since $I_{[\hat{\alpha}, \infty)}(y_1) = 1$. Thus the likelihood-ratio test for H_0: $\alpha = \alpha_0$ vs. $\alpha > \alpha_0$ is

$$\phi(x) = \begin{cases} 1, & \text{if } e^{n(\alpha_0 - \hat{\alpha})/\lambda} I_{[\alpha_0, \infty)}(y_1) < c \\ 0, & \text{otherwise} \end{cases}$$

$$= \begin{cases} 1, & \text{if } \hat{\alpha} < \alpha_0, \text{ or } \alpha_0 \leq \hat{\alpha} \text{ and } \hat{\alpha} > k = \alpha_0 - \dfrac{\lambda}{n}\ln(c) \\ 0, & \text{otherwise.} \end{cases}$$

To determine k, note that for a level α^* test

$$
\begin{aligned}
\alpha^* &= P_0(\hat{\alpha} > \max(\alpha_0, k)) + P_0(\hat{\alpha} < \alpha_0) \\
&= P_0(Y_1 > \max(\alpha_0, k)) + P_0(Y_1 < \alpha_0) \\
&= P_0(X_1 > \max(\alpha_0, k), X_2 > \max(\alpha_0, k), \ldots, X_n > \max(\alpha_0, k)) \\
&\quad + P_0(Y_1 < \alpha_0) \\
&= \left(P_0(X_1 > \max(\alpha_0, k))\right)^n + \left(1 - P_0(Y_1 > \alpha_0)\right) \\
&= \left(\int_{\max(\alpha_0, k)}^{\infty} \frac{1}{\lambda} e^{-(x-\alpha_0)/\lambda} \, dx\right)^n + 1 - \left(\int_{\alpha_0}^{\infty} \frac{1}{\lambda} e^{-(x-\alpha_0)/\lambda} \, dx\right)^n \\
&= \left(e^{\min\left(0, \frac{\alpha_0 - k}{\lambda}\right)}\right)^n + 1 - (1)^n
\end{aligned}
$$

or

$$
k = \alpha_0 - \frac{\lambda}{n} \ln(\alpha^*).
$$

Thus for a given level of significance α^* (we are denoting the level of significance by α^* since the usual symbol has been used for the parameter of displacement in the distribution), we reject H_0 iff

$$
Y_1 = \min(X_1, X_2, \ldots, X_n) > \alpha_0 - \frac{\lambda}{n} \ln(\alpha^*).
$$

Example 9.11.9. The Likelihood-Ratio Test in a Discrete Case. Consider the lion's appetite problem of Example 7.2.6, where the distributions are

i	0	1	2	3	4
$p(i\|\theta_1)$	.00	.05	.05	.80	.10
$p(i\|\theta_2)$	.05	.05	.80	.10	.00
$p(i\|\theta_3)$	.90	.08	.02	.00	.00

Here a single r.v. $X = x_0$ is observed, and it is desired to test H_0: $\theta = \theta_3$ vs. H_1: $\theta \in \{\theta_1, \theta_2\}$, so $\Theta = \{\theta_1, \theta_2, \theta_3\}$ and $\Theta_0 = \{\theta_3\}$. Now

$$
\lambda(i) = \frac{\max_{\theta \in \Theta_0} p(i|\theta)}{\max_{\theta \in \Theta} p(i|\theta)}
$$

can be tabulated as

i	0	1	2	3	4
$\lambda(i)$	1	1	.025	.00	.00

If we choose level of significance $\alpha = .02$, then the likelihood-ratio test rejects iff $\lambda(i) < c$, where c is determined so that

$$\alpha = P_{\theta_3}(\lambda(i) < c).$$

Now under H_0 the distribution of $\lambda(i)$ is $P(\lambda(i) = 1) = .98$, $P(\lambda(i) = .025) = .02$, $P(\lambda(i) = .00) = .00$. Hence the likelihood-ratio test calls for rejection of H_0 iff $\lambda(i) < 1$, and hence rejects H_0 iff $X = 2, 3,$ or 4 is observed.

The null distribution of $\lambda(X)$ is not always as easy to find as in the preceding examples, and is most often tedious and difficult to find. For this reason, we give a general result on the distribution of $\lambda(X)$ for large sample size n.

Theorem 9.11.10. If the r.v. X satisfies certain regularity conditions, then $-2\ln(\lambda(X))$ is asymptotically $\chi_\nu^2(0)$ where

$$\nu = (\text{Number of independent parameters under } \Theta)$$

$$- (\text{Number of independent parameters under } \Theta_0).$$

For a proof, and details of the conditions, see Wilks (1962), pp. 419–420.

As the final topic of this section, we briefly introduce sequential analysis. When data come to us one (or a few) piece(s) at a time, a decision may become clear early if effects are consistent and strong and if we analyze the data as they arrive (rather than waiting until they are all in). Methods for analyzing data in two steps (called stages) were covered in Section 9.10. For analyzing piece by piece as each new data item arrives, tests are generally based on the likelihood-ratio of Definition 9.11.1. However, now the critical point in equation (9.11.2) can be allowed to depend on how many pieces of data we have in hand: After m observations we can reject H_0 if $\lambda(x) \leq c_m^*$, accept H_0 if $\lambda(x) \geq d_m^*$, and continue sampling if $c_m^* < \lambda(x) < d_m^*$. If we have simple H_0 vs. simple H_1, then

$$\lambda(x_1, x_2, \ldots, x_m) = \frac{f(x_1, x_2, \ldots, x_m | \theta_0)}{\max\left[f(x_1, x_2, \ldots, x_m | \theta_0), f(x_1, x_2, \ldots, x_m | \theta_1)\right]}$$

$$= \frac{1}{1 + \dfrac{f(x_1, x_2, \ldots, x_m | \theta_1)}{f(x_1, x_2, \ldots, x_m | \theta_0)}}.$$

As this is a decreasing function of $f(x_1, x_2, \ldots, x_m | \theta_1)/f(x_1, x_2, \ldots, x_m | \theta_0)$, we can equivalently examine the likelihood ratio and reject for large values (which correspond to small values of λ):

$$\text{Reject } H_0 \text{ if } \frac{f(x_1, x_2, \ldots, x_m | \theta_1)}{f(x_1, x_2, \ldots, x_m | \theta_0)} \geq d_m$$

$$\text{Accept } H_0 \text{ if } \frac{f(x_1, x_2, \ldots, x_m | \theta_1)}{f(x_1, x_2, \ldots, x_m | \theta_0)} \leq c_m$$

Observe X_{m+1} if the ratio is between c_m and d_m.

Therefore, this test could also be called a sequential Neyman-Pearson test. Since when the variables are discrete the likelihood ratio is a ratio of probabilities, the test is sometimes called **a sequential probability ratio test.** The first such test was given by Abraham Wald in the late 1940s, and took $c_1 = c_2 = \cdots = c$ and $d_1 = d_2 = \cdots = d$ (with $c \leq d$); it is called **Wald's SPRT.** Tests with boundaries c_m and d_m that change as m changes were first proposed and investigated by Lionel Weiss in the 1950s and by Weiss and Jack Kiefer in the 1960s. These tests have some optimal properties in terms of the average number of observations needed to reach a decision; details are beyond the scope of this text, and for them see Govindarajulu (1981).

We will now summarize (without proof) some of the major results on the Wald SPRT. Since the exact analysis of sequential rules is complicated, a number of approximations (which have been studied extensively and are known to be of high accuracy) are used in these results and their applications.

Theorem 9.11.11. Let $X_1, X_2, \ldots$ be independent r.v.'s, each with the same p.d.f. (or point probability function) $f(x)$. It is desired to test H_0: $f = f_0$ vs. H_1: $f = f_1$ at level α and type II error β (hence power $1 - \beta$). Set

$$c_m = \frac{\beta}{1 - \alpha} < \frac{1 - \beta}{\alpha} = d_m, \quad R_m(X_1, \ldots, X_m) = \frac{f_1(X_1) \cdots f_1(X_m)}{f_0(X_1) \cdots f_0(X_m)}$$

$$(m = 1, 2, \ldots)$$

and proceed as follows (where $c = c_1 = c_2 = \ldots, d = d_1 = d_2 = \ldots$):

Step 1: Observe X_1. If $R_1 \geq d$, reject H_0. If $R_1 \leq c$, accept H_0. Otherwise go to step 2.

Step 2: Observe X_2. If $R_2 \geq d$, reject H_0. If $R_2 \leq c$, accept H_0. Otherwise go to step 3.

Step i: Observe X_i. If $R_i \geq d$, reject H_0. If $R_i \leq c$, accept H_0. Otherwise go to step $i + 1$.

The resulting test has level $\alpha' \simeq \alpha$ and type II error $\beta' \simeq \beta$.

One could conceive of the Wald SPRT of Theorem 9.11.11 going on forever observing more data (i.e., having R_i in the "continuation region" where we are told to observe another random variable ($i = 1, 2, 3, \ldots$)). In fact, this cannot happen, no matter what distribution the X_i's have:

Theorem 9.11.12. Let N denote the (random) number of observations taken by the Wald SPRT of Theorem 9.11.11. Let $F(x)$ denote the c.d.f. of the r.v.'s X_i ($i = 1, 2, \ldots$). Then $P_F(N < \infty) = 1$, and $E_F N < \infty$, no matter what F is.

One of the reasons we gave for going to a sequential analysis of the data was that we could (we hoped) reach decisions sooner, that is, with less data. Thus, we will desire to know $E_F N$:

Theorem 9.11.13. Let $Z_i = \ln(f_1(X_i)/f_0(X_i))$, $i = 1, 2, \ldots$. Then

$$E_F(N) = \begin{cases} \dfrac{E_F(Z_1 + \cdots + Z_N)}{E_F Z_1} \\[2ex] \approx \dfrac{\left(\ln\left(\dfrac{\beta}{1-\alpha}\right)\right)P_F(D_0) + \left(\ln\left(\dfrac{1-\beta}{\alpha}\right)\right)P_F(D_1)}{E_F Z_1}, & \text{if } E_F Z_1 \neq 0 \\[3ex] \dfrac{E_F(Z_1 + \cdots + Z_N)^2}{E_F Z_1^2} \\[2ex] \approx \dfrac{\left(\ln\left(\dfrac{\beta}{1-\alpha}\right)\right)^2 P_F(D_0) + \left(\ln\left(\dfrac{1-\beta}{\alpha}\right)\right)^2 P_F(D_1)}{E_F Z_1^2}, & \text{if } E_F Z_1 = 0, \end{cases}$$

for any c.d.f. F, where D_0 denotes that the Wald SPRT decides to accept H_0, and D_1 denotes that the Wald SPRT decides to reject H_0.

Example 9.11.14. A large quantity of electronic chips (for computerized equipment) have been ordered, and the contract has specified that at least 90% of them are to be able to pass certain critical tests and that the shipment would be subject to sampling inspection on arrival. The test is to be conducted in such a way that if 85% or fewer are satisfactory then the chances of accepting the lot will be at most 1%, whereas if 95% or more are satisfactory then the chances of accepting the lot will be at least 99%. Find a fixed sample test, and a Wald SPRT, and compare them.

Let p denote the proportion of the lot that is able to pass the critical tests; of course p is unknown with $0 \leq p \leq 1$ and will be estimated by sampling from the lot at random without replacement. We can regard the problem as one of hypothesis testing with respect to p, with H_0: $p \geq .90$ vs. H_1: $p < .90$, and the requirements

$$P_p(\text{Accept } H_0) \leq .01 \quad \text{if } p \leq .85$$

$$P_p(\text{Accept } H_0) \geq .99 \quad \text{if } p \geq .95.$$

We will replace this composite versus composite hypothesis-testing problem with the simple versus simple hypothesis-testing problem H_0': $p = .95$ vs. H_1': $p = .85$, using level .01 and type II error .01 (which will satisfy the requirements at the points $p = .95$ and $p = .85$, respectively). For this problem, both the fixed-sample Neyman-Pearson test and the Wald SPRT look at the ratio

$$\frac{f(x_1,\ldots,x_m|p = .95)}{f(x_1,\ldots,x_m|p = .85)} = \frac{(.95)^{\sum x_i}(.05)^{m-\sum x_i}}{(.85)^{\sum x_i}(.15)^{m-\sum x_i}} = (3.3529)^{\sum x_i}/3^m$$

where $f(x_1,\ldots,x_m|p)$ denotes the joint probability function of $X_1,\ldots,X_m$ when the success probability (for satisfying the requirements) is p, and X_i is either 1 (the ith item sampled meets the requirements) or 0 (the ith item sampled fails).

Taking logarithms as in Example 9.3.40, we see that **the Neyman-Pearson test will reject** H_0' if $\overline{X} < k$ (otherwise accepting H_0'), where k and the number of observations n are set to meet the level and power requirements. Since we expect n to be large, the exact tables of the binomial will not include the cases we need, and we use the fact that (for large n) $\overline{X}$ is approximately $N(p, p(1-p)/n)$ to find

$$P_p(\overline{X} < k) = P_p\left(\frac{\sqrt{n}(\overline{X}-p)}{\sqrt{p(1-p)}} < \frac{\sqrt{n}(k-p)}{\sqrt{p(1-p)}}\right) \approx \Phi\left(\frac{\sqrt{n}(k-p)}{\sqrt{p(1-p)}}\right). \quad (9.11.15)$$

As our requirements are

$$P_{p=.95}(\overline{X} < k) = .01, \qquad P_{p=.85}(\overline{X} < k) = .99,$$

using equation (9.11.15) we find the simultaneous equations

$$\Phi\left(\frac{\sqrt{n}(k - .95)}{\sqrt{(.95)(.05)}}\right) = .01, \qquad \Phi\left(\frac{\sqrt{n}(k - .85)}{\sqrt{(.85)(.15)}}\right) = .99,$$

or (using the tables of the standard normal distribution)

$$\frac{\sqrt{n}(k - .95)}{\sqrt{(.95)(.05)}} = -2.33, \qquad \frac{\sqrt{n}(k - .85)}{\sqrt{(.85)(.15)}} = 2.33. \quad (9.11.16)$$

Taking the ratio of the two equations in (9.11.16) yields a linear equation in k, which we solve for k, finding

$$k = \frac{.95 + (.85)\sqrt{\dfrac{(.95)(.05)}{(.85)(.15)}}}{1 + \sqrt{\dfrac{(.95)(.05)}{(.85)(.15)}}} = .9121. \quad (9.11.17)$$

Using $k = .9121$ in either equation in (9.11.16), we find $n = 179.5$, hence (since sample sizes must be integers) **the Neyman-Pearson test will require a sample of $n = 180$ items from the lot.** This is the fixed sample size test asked for in the statement of this problem. It samples 180 items, finds the proportion of acceptable items $\overline{X}$ in those 180 items, and accepts the lot if $\overline{X} \geq .9121$ (otherwise it rejects the lot).

The Wald SPRT has (see Theorem 9.11.11)

$$c_m = \frac{.01}{1 - .01} = \frac{1}{99} < \frac{1 - .01}{.01} = 99 = d_m, \qquad (9.11.18)$$

and continues sampling when (after observing m observations)

$$\frac{1}{99} < \frac{3^m}{(3.3529)^{x_1 + \cdots + x_m}} < 99 \qquad (9.11.19)$$

(while rejecting the lot if the ratio is ≥ 99, accepting if $\leq .0101$). Taking logarithms in (9.11.19), we find that an equivalent statement is

$$-\ln(99) < m \ln(3) - (X_1 + \cdots + X_m) \ln(3.3529) < \ln(99)$$

or

$$-\frac{\ln(99)}{m} < \ln(3) - \ln(3.3529)\overline{X} < \frac{\ln(99)}{m}$$

or

$$\frac{\ln(3)}{\ln(3.3529)} - \frac{1}{m}\frac{\ln(99)}{\ln(3.3529)} < \overline{X} < \frac{\ln(3)}{\ln(3.3529)} + \frac{1}{m}\frac{\ln(99)}{\ln(3.3529)}$$

or

$$.9081 - \frac{3.7982}{m} < \overline{X} < .9081 + \frac{3.7982}{m}. \qquad (9.11.20)$$

Thus, the Wald SPRT samples until the first time that $\overline{X}$ falls outside the bounds given in equation (9.11.20); if it falls out below, the lot is rejected (whereas if it falls out above, the lot is accepted). (Although at equation (9.11.19) we had been rejecting the lot if we fell out above, in the derivation of equation (9.11.20) note that the upper limit on the ratio transformed into the lower limit on $\overline{X}$.) In Figure 9.11-1 we show a graphical interpretation of the Wald SPRT in this example (which is typical of its behavior in general). When the point $(m, \overline{X})$ observed falls between the two curves [whose equations are the limits in equation (9.11.20)], another observation is taken; when $(m, \overline{X})$ falls above the top curve,

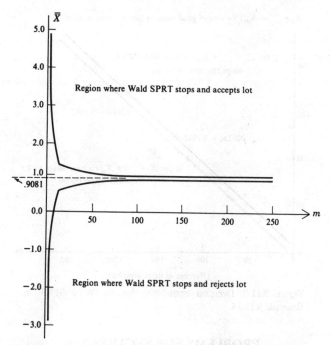

Figure 9.11-1. Decision boundaries for the Wald SPRT in Example 9.11.14.

we stop and accept the lot; and, when $(m, \overline{X})$ falls below the bottom curve, we stop and reject the lot. Note that the curves are asymptotic to .9081. Also note that we cannot fall outside a curve until that curve is within $(0, 1)$; hence, we cannot reject the lot until $m = 5$ observations have been made (and we then reject the lot if $\overline{X}$ is less than .15; that is, we reject the lot if the first 5 observations are all failures). Similarly, we cannot accept the lot until $m = 42$ observations have been taken (and we then accept the lot if $\overline{X}$ is at least .9985, i.e., we accept the lot if the first 42 items tested are all good). For very good (or very bad) lots this is much faster acceptance/rejection than the Neyman-Pearson test, which requires a sample of 180 items in all cases. (Since that test will use as its critical number of good items $(.9121)(180) = 164.178$, we could stop that test as soon as 165 good items are found, or, as soon as 16 bad items are found, and accept/reject the lot, respectively—since at either of those points the remaining observations could not possibly change whether the ultimate $\overline{X}$ based on all 180 items would be above or below .9121.) (It is more usual to multiply equation (9.11.20) by m and then make a graphical interpretation, since that graph can also easily be used in practice to keep track of the progress of the test; see Figure 9.11-2. We have given Figure 9.11-1 since it is very intuitively easy to see from it that the test will always stop with probability 1, whereas from Figure 9.11-2 one might think the test could stay in the continuation region forever.)

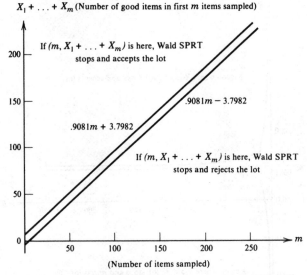

Figure 9.11-2. Decision boundaries for the Wald SPRT in Example 9.11.14.

PROBLEMS FOR SECTION 9.11

9.11.1 Let X be a $N(\theta, 1)$ r.v. where θ is unknown, $\theta \in \Theta = \{\theta_0, \theta_1\}$ with $\theta_0 = 0$ and $\theta_1 = 1$. Consider testing H_0: $\theta = \theta_0$ versus H_1: $\theta = \theta_1$.

  (a) Find the Neyman-Pearson test of level $\alpha = .50$, and find its power. [*Hint*: This test will reject iff $X > 0$.]

  (b) Find the likelihood-ratio $\lambda(x)$ of Definition 9.11.1, and graph it as a function of x. Let c vary in (9.11.2) to find all levels for which there is a likelihood-ratio test. [*Hint*: Only for $\alpha \le .309$ and $\alpha = 1$.]

  (c) Generalize (9.11.2) to allow for randomization when $\lambda(x) = c$. Then, find a randomized likelihood-ratio test of level $\alpha = .50$, and find its power.

  (d) Is the test of part **(c)** the same as the test of part **(a)**? Use your result to comment on the assertion "Although the likelihood-ratio test may not exist for all levels α, by allowing randomization on the boundary one can find such a test." (In particular, note whether the test thus obtained has the same power as the Neyman-Pearson test; if different, which is preferred?)

9.11.2 Let $X_{i1}, X_{i2}, \ldots, X_{in_i}$ $(i = 1, 2)$ be random samples from two independent populations with respective distributions $N(\mu_1, \sigma^2)$, $N(\mu_2, \sigma^2)$. Derive the likelihood-ratio test for H_0: $\mu_1 = \mu_2$ versus H_1: $\mu_1 \ne \mu_2$ at level α. Compare this test with the "2-sample t-test" of Section 9.8, and show that the two tests are equivalent. (Recall that $T_{n-1}^2 = F_{1, n-1}$.)

9.11.3 Let $X_1, \ldots, X_n$ be a random sample of size n from a $N(\mu, \sigma^2)$ distribution, where μ and σ^2 are both unknown. Derive an α-level likelihood-ratio test for H_0: $\sigma^2 = \sigma_0^2$ versus H_1: $\sigma^2 \ne \sigma_0^2$.

9.11.4 Consider the setting of Problem 9.11.2 with $\mu_1, \mu_2, \sigma_1^2, \sigma_2^2$ all unknown. Derive the likelihood-ratio test for H_0: $\sigma_1^2 = \sigma_2^2$ versus H_1: $\sigma_1^2 \ne \sigma_2^2$.

9.11.5 Let $X_1, X_2, \ldots, X_n$ be independent Bernoulli r.v.'s with the same unknown probability of success p. Find the likelihood-ratio test for H_0: $p = p_0$ versus H_1: $p \neq p_0$.

9.11.6 Consider a random sample of size 1 from p.d.f. $f(x|\theta) = 2\theta^{-2}(\theta - x)I_{(0,\theta)}(x)$. Derive the likelihood-ratio test for H_0: $\theta = \theta_0$ versus H_1: $\theta \neq \theta_0$.

9.11.7 **(a)** In Problem 9.11.5, if $p_0 = 1/2$, level is chosen as .05, and type II error is to be .01 when $|p - p_0| = .10$, what n will be needed? (Use the normal approximation to the binomial.)

(b) Show the test of part **(a)** and the WSPRT on a figure like Figure 9.11-1. Compare the continuation and stopping regions.

(b) Show the test of part **(a)** and the WSPRT on a figure like Figure 9.11-2. Compare the continuation and stopping regions.

(d) Take a coin and flip it repeatedly to obtain your data for this part. Apply the test of part **(a)** and also the WSPRT to test fairness of the coin. Which test stops sooner for you?

9.12. THE CHI-SQUARE TEST OF GOODNESS-OF-FIT

Two important problems are addressed in Sections 9.12 and 9.13. In Section 9.12 the problem is that of "goodness-of-fit." This problem arises when we try to justify an assumption such as that of normality (exponentiality, etc.) of the data set. The chi-square test allows us to assess the validity of such an assumption. (Of course, conclusions of any procedure will be correct only if its assumptions are satisfied, hence assessment of such assumptions is an important problem in statistics.) **The problem discussed in Section 9.13 is that of "independence."** This problem arises when we sample from a population based on two classification variables; for example, in human populations, classification variables may be the sex of the person and his/her amount of smoking. The question we then wish to answer is whether the sex of the person is independent of the amount of smoking. Similar problems include testing whether the political affiliation of a person is independent of the region where that person resides.

Definition 9.12.1. Suppose we have available $s(\geq 1)$ sets of observations, and that set i consists of $n_i > 0$ observations ($i = 1, 2, \ldots, s$). Suppose each observation in set i is classified into one of k_i mutually exclusive and exhaustive categories ($1 \leq i \leq s$). Let

$$\Pi_{ij} = P\,[\text{An observation in set } i \text{ falls into category } j] \qquad (9.12.2)$$

(so, of course, $\Pi_{i1} + \cdots + \Pi_{ik_i} = 1$ for $1 \leq i \leq s$), and assume $\Pi_{ij} > 0$ for all i, j. Let

$$f_{ij} = \left(\begin{array}{l} \text{The proportion of the observations} \\ \text{in set } i \text{ that fall into category } j \end{array} \right). \qquad (9.12.3)$$

Now, in general, the Π_{ij}'s will be functions of some unknown parameter $\theta \in \Theta \subseteq \mathcal{R}^r$. A statistic $t = (t_1, \ldots, t_r)$ is called a **minimum chi-square (MCS) estimator** of $\theta = (\theta_1, \ldots, \theta_r)$ if it minimizes

$$
\chi^2(\theta) = \sum_{i=1}^{s} \frac{1}{n_i} \sum_{j=1}^{k_i} \frac{(f_{ij} - \Pi_{ij})^2}{\Pi_{ij}}
$$
$$
= \sum_{i=1}^{s} \frac{1}{n_i} \left(\sum_{j=1}^{k_i} \frac{f_{ij}^2}{\Pi_{ij}} - 1 \right).
$$

(9.12.4)

Note that the statistic (9.12.4), $\chi^2(\theta)$, which is to be minimized, is a weighted sum of deviations of f_{ij}'s from Π_{ij}'s. The MCS method, as we have given it, applies only in the cases of (1) a discrete distribution, or (2) a continuous distribution where the observations are categorized.

Definition 9.12.5. Assume the set-up of Definition 9.12.1. A statistic $t = (t_1, \ldots, t_r)$ is called a **modified MCS (MMCS) estimator** of $\theta = (\theta_1, \ldots, \theta_r)$ if it minimizes

$$
(\chi'(\theta))^2 = \sum_{i=1}^{s} \frac{1}{n_i} \sum_{j=1}^{k_i} \frac{(f_{ij} - \Pi_{ij})^2}{f_{ij}}
$$
$$
= \sum_{i=1}^{s} \frac{1}{n_i} \left(\sum_{j=1}^{k_i} \frac{\Pi_{ij}^2}{f_{ij}} - 1 \right).
$$

(9.12.6)

[While the MCS method needs all $\Pi_{ij} > 0$, the MMCS method needs all $f_{ij} > 0$.]

Example 9.12.7. Suppose $X_1, \ldots, X_n$ are independent r.v.'s, each Poisson with parameter $\lambda > 0$ unknown. Find the MMCS estimator of λ.

Here we have $s = 1$ sample and $r = 1$ parameter. If we take our $k_i = k$ categories as category i meaning a value of $i - 1$ ($i = 1, \ldots, k - 1$) and category k meaning a value $\geq k - 1$, then

$$
\begin{cases}
\Pi_{1j} = e^{-\lambda} \dfrac{\lambda^{j-1}}{(j-1)!} & (j = 1, \ldots, k-1) \\
\Pi_{1k} = \displaystyle\sum_{z=k-1}^{\infty} e^{-\lambda} \dfrac{\lambda^z}{z!}.
\end{cases}
$$

(9.12.8)

Denote $f_{11}, \ldots, f_{1k}$ simply by $f_1, \ldots, f_k$. We now seek to choose λ to minimize

$$
(\chi'(\theta))^2 = \sum_{i=1}^{s} \frac{1}{n_i} \sum_{j=1}^{k_i} \frac{(f_{ij} - \Pi_{ij})^2}{f_{ij}}
$$
$$
= \frac{1}{n} \left(\sum_{j=1}^{k} \frac{\Pi_{1j}^2}{f_j} - 1 \right).
$$

(9.12.9)

To minimize (9.12.9) we need only minimize

$$\sum_{j=1}^{k} \frac{\Pi_{1j}^2}{f_j} = \sum_{j=1}^{k-1} \frac{1}{f_j} \left(e^{-\lambda} \frac{\lambda^{j-1}}{(j-1)!} \right)^2 + \frac{1}{f_k} \left(\sum_{z=k-1}^{\infty} e^{-\lambda} \frac{\lambda^z}{z!} \right)^2. \quad (9.12.10)$$

At this point, derivatives and numerical work come into play. Usually results are harder to obtain than (but comparable to) MLE's.

We proved in Chapter 5 that the sum of n independent chi-square r.v.'s with 1 degree of freedom each is a chi-square r.v. with n degrees of freedom. Also recall that the square of a standard normal random variable is a chi-square r.v. with 1 degree of freedom. These two facts together yield procedures that are extremely useful in applications.

The general technique of **the chi-square test for goodness-of-fit** proceeds as follows. Suppose we are sampling from a d.f. $F(x)$ (which may depend on parameter(s) θ). Divide the range of the distribution into k mutually exclusive and exhaustive intervals, say $I_1, I_2, \ldots, I_k$. Each interval has a probability of containing an r.v. with d.f. $F(x)$, $P(X \in I_i) = \pi_i$, $i = 1, 2, \ldots, k$. Each sample value falls into exactly one of the intervals. Let $O_1, O_2, \ldots, O_k$ be the respective observed numbers of the observations $X_1, \ldots, X_n$ in the intervals $I_1, I_2, \ldots, I_k$. Then the vector $\mathbf{O} = (O_1, O_2, \ldots, O_k)$ has a multinomial distribution

$$P(O_1 = o_1, O_2 = o_2, \ldots, O_k = o_k) = \frac{n!}{\displaystyle\prod_{i=1}^{k} o_i!} \prod_{i=1}^{k} \pi_i^{o_i}$$

with $\sum_{i=1}^{n} o_i = n$ and $\sum_{i=1}^{n} \pi_i = 1$, and

$$E(O_i) = n\pi_i \equiv e_i, \quad \mathrm{Var}(O_i) = n\pi_i(1 - \pi_i) \quad (i = 1, 2, \ldots, k).$$

If $k = 2$, then

$$\frac{X_1 - n\pi_1}{\sqrt{n\pi_1(1 - \pi_1)}} \xrightarrow{d} N(0, 1),$$

hence

$$\frac{(O_1 - n\pi_1)^2}{n\pi_1(1 - \pi_1)} \xrightarrow{d} \chi_1^2(0).$$

But using the fact that $O_2 = n - O_1$, we algebraically find that

$$\frac{(O_1 - n\pi_1)^2}{n\pi_1} + \frac{(O_2 - n\pi_2)^2}{n\pi_2} = \frac{(O_1 - n\pi_1)^2}{n\pi_1(1 - \pi_1)}$$

hence the above convergence means that

$$\sum_{i=1}^{2} \frac{(O_i - n\pi_i)^2}{n\pi_i} \xrightarrow{d} \chi_1^2(0).$$

For a general k, the quantity

$$T = \sum_{i=1}^{k} \frac{(O_i - n\pi_i)^2}{n\pi_i} = \sum_{i=1}^{k} \frac{(O_i - e_i)^2}{e_i} \qquad (9.12.11)$$

has a complicated exact distribution. However T **is asymptotically** $\chi_{k-1}^2(0)$. Note that for $k = 2$ we showed that the asymptotic distribution of T is chi-square with $k - 1 = 1$ degrees of freedom; the asymptotic distribution for general k follows this same rule of having $k - 1$ degrees of freedom. [For details of the proof, see, e.g., Kendall and Stuart (1967), p. 421.] Now, **we want to test the hypothesis** H_0: $F(x) = F_0(x)$ where any parameters in $F_0(x)$ are completely specified. **First compute** π_i, $i = 1, 2, \ldots, k$ (these π_i may depend on the unknown parameters of $F(x)$), next compute $\hat{\pi}_i$ (the MLE of π_i) and $\hat{e}_i \equiv n\hat{\pi}_i$. If H_0 is true, then intuitively we expect $O_i \simeq e_i$ (and hence $O_i \simeq \hat{e}_i$), in which case $(O_i - e_i)^2/e_i$ is small and thus T is small. (Note that $T = 0$ iff $O_i = e_i$ for $i = 1, 2, \ldots, k$. Thus T further away from zero indicates data less compatible with the claimed null distribution.) **Hence for large n a level α test is given by**

$$\phi(\mathbf{O}) = \begin{cases} 1, & \text{if } T > \chi_{k-1, 1-\alpha}^{2^{-1}}(0) \\ 0, & \text{otherwise.} \end{cases} \qquad (9.12.12)$$

If we do not reject H_0, then we have enough agreement between the theoretical frequencies and observed frequencies that the data could well have come from $F_0(x)$. Of course, there are many theoretical distributions $G_0(x)$ with the same theoretical frequencies in the respective intervals as $F_0(x)$, hence yielding the same value of T. Any of those $G_0(x)$ would also not be rejected. Thus, failure to reject H_0 does not necessarily mean H_0 is true. In statistical practice, however, one proceeds assuming that the data comes from $F_0(x)$ when H_0 is not rejected.

For theoretical reasons, the distribution of T for large n is better approximated by a $\chi_{k-1}^2(0)$ r.v. if $e_i \geq 5$. If some of the e_i's do not satisfy this "rule of thumb," in practice we combine smaller classes and adjust the statistic T accordingly. (Otherwise, the approximation can be very poor and invalidate the conclusions.)

Example 9.12.13. [This example is based on Gibbons (1985), p. 79.] The works known to have been written by a certain author have been analyzed as to sentence length, and a full enumeration of the results has given the distribution of length of sentences in this author's works. A newly found manuscript is claimed to have been written by the same author. Below are data on sentence length taken from a sample of 2000 sentences from the newly found manuscript.

Use these data to make a judgment as to whether the new manuscript is by the same author.

	Proportion of Sentences	
Number of Words	Known Author (π_i)	New Manuscript ($\hat{p}_i$)
3 or fewer	.010	.007
4–5	.030	.024
6–8	.041	.031
9–12	.102	.034
13–16	.263	.250
17–20	.279	.203
21–24	.118	.198
25–27	.105	.156
28–29	.042	.081
30 or more	.010	.016

Using (9.12.11), in a computationally simpler form

$$T = \sum_{i=1}^{k} \frac{(O_i - e_i)^2}{e_i} = \sum_{i=1}^{k} \frac{O_i^2}{e_i} - \sum_{i=1}^{k} 2O_i + \sum_{i=1}^{k} e_i$$

$$= \sum_{i=1}^{k} \frac{O_i^2}{e_i} - n,$$

(9.12.14)

$n = 2000$ since the observed frequency of the new manuscript is based on 2000 sentences. Calling these frequencies $\hat{p}_i$, (9.12.14) reduces to

$$T = \sum_{i=1}^{k} \frac{(n\hat{p}_i)^2}{n\pi_i} - n = n\left(\sum_{i=1}^{k} \frac{\hat{p}_i^2}{\pi_i} - 1 \right).$$

(9.12.15)

Using (9.12.15), we compute $T = 380.0808$. Hence at the $\alpha = .001$ level of significance, we find the computed value T is larger than $\chi_{9,.999}^{2-1}(0) = 27.877$, so there is sufficient evidence to conclude that there is not agreement between the sentence-length distributions of the known author and the author of the new manuscript.

Note that **similar methods** as in Example 9.12.13 **can be used to classify newly found musical compositions, newly found sculptures** from (e.g.) ancient Greece, **newly found artifacts and the like**. In each instance, we need to have a characteristic to compare on (sentence length for the manuscript, note frequency for the musical composition, etc.).

PROBLEMS FOR SECTION 9.12

9.12.1 To test whether people have any inclination other than random choice of an integer number between 1 and 10, 500 people are selected at random and asked "Choose a number between 1 and 10." Suppose the observed frequency of choices is

Number chosen	1	2	3	4	5	6	7	8	9	10
Observed frequency	63	54	30	31	52	49	46	57	58	60

Based on this data, at level .01, is there sufficient evidence to conclude that people are not choosing randomly?

9.12.2 On a certain intelligence test, scores are supposed to follow a normal distribution, with mean $\mu = 100$ and variance $\sigma^2 = 225$. Suppose a random sample of 1000 people yields scores classified into six classes as follows:

Class	[0, 70)	[70, 85)	[85, 100)	[100, 115)	[115, 130)	[130, ∞)
Number	34	114	360	344	120	28

Based on this data, test the distributional claim at the .05 level of significance.

9.12.3 From an automobile assembly line, a sample of 100 automobiles is taken on each of the 5 weekdays, and the brakes are inspected. Suppose the number of cars with defective brakes on each weekday is:

Day	1	2	3	4	5
Number defective	4	8	3	2	5

Based on this data, at the level .05, is there sufficient evidence to claim the proportion of defectives is not constant from day to day? [*Hint*: Although you need to estimate the hypothesized common probability p from the data as $\hat{p} = 22/500$ = .044, you may be tempted to then just proceed as in the case when 500 cars have been sampled and we wish to test the hypothesis that they have equal probabilities of falling into the various days. However, that is clearly incorrect, as then the observed numbers add to 500, and in our problem they add to only 22. Our present problem is called one of $k = 5$ **independent samples**, and it is correctly treated by calculating $T/(1 - \hat{p})$, where T is as in equation (9.12.11), which is compared to $\chi^2_{k-1,1-\alpha}(0)$ as before. This formula follows from our work in Section 9.13 which follows. It is noted here since *commonly the results of the present section are mistakenly applied to problems of this sort*. The rule to use is: If you need to estimate the probabilities of the categories, then the results of this section do not apply, and also if the observed counts do not add to the number of observations then the methods of this section do not apply.]

9.13. $r \times c$ CONTINGENCY TABLES

Sometimes the data in a statistical experiment is **categorical** rather than numerical (e.g., race, sex, and hair color are categorical; height, age, and weight are numerical). In this section we study the **multinomial** experiment in which data is classified with respect to two categorical variables. For example, a sociologist may be concerned with whether there is a tendency for sons to choose the same occupation or profession as their fathers; or, if smoking habits are independent of the sex of the person. A psychologist may want to know whether the nature of a person's occupation has any relationship to the drinking habits of the person, etc.

Suppose a random sample of size n is taken in one of these cases. Then (e.g., in the first case) the people will be classified with respect to the nature of the father's employment and the son's occupation. This data can be summarized in a two-way table, called an $r \times c$ **contingency table** (r for number of rows, and c for number of columns). **The null hypothesis is (usually) that the row categories are independent of the column categories** as opposed to the alternative hypothesis that there is some dependence between the row and column categories. Testing this hypothesis is the objective of this section.

With the data classified in r-rows and c-columns, the observed frequencies based on this two-way classification are noted. Any person falls into exactly one of the $r \cdot c$ cells with some (unknown) probability π_{ij} for cell (i, j), $i = 1, 2, \ldots, r$; $j = 1, 2, \ldots, c$. Let O_{ij} be the observed frequency of cell (i, j). Let $\pi_{i\cdot} = \sum_{j=1}^{c} \pi_{ij}$, $i = 1, 2, \ldots, r$, and $\pi_{\cdot j} = \sum_{i=1}^{r} \pi_{ij}$, $j = 1, 2, \ldots, c$ denote the respective marginal row and marginal column probabilities. The hypotheses of interest are

$$\begin{cases} H_0 \colon \text{Row and column categories are independent} \\ H_1 \colon \text{Row and column categories are dependent.} \end{cases} \tag{9.13.1}$$

Since under H_0 row and column categories are independent, therefore under H_0

$$\pi_{ij} = \pi_{i\cdot} \times \pi_{\cdot j}, \text{ for every pair } (i, j),$$

and the expected frequency of occurrence of cell (i, j) is $E_{ij} \equiv n\pi_{ij}$. Now $(O_{11}, O_{12}, \ldots, O_{rc})$ has a multinomial distribution with cell probabilities $(\pi_{11}, \pi_{12}, \ldots, \pi_{rc})$, with $\sum_{i, j} \pi_{ij} = 1$, hence (9.12.11) here is

$$T = \sum_{j=1}^{c} \sum_{i=1}^{r} \frac{(O_{ij} - E_{ij})^2}{E_{ij}}$$

and has an asymptotic chi-square distribution. However, the E_{ij}'s are unknown, so **we find maximum likelihood estimates, and substitute them in** T. Since, under

TABLE 9.13-1
The notation π_{ij}, $\pi_{i\cdot}$, and $\pi_{\cdot j}$.

		Column Categories				Row marginal probabilities
		1	2	3	c	
Row	1	π_{11}	π_{12}	π_{13}	$\cdots$ π_{1c}	$\pi_{1\cdot}$
Categories	2	π_{21}	π_{22}	π_{23}	$\cdots$ π_{2c}	$\pi_{2\cdot}$
	3	π_{31}	π_{32}	π_{33}	$\cdots$ π_{3c}	$\pi_{3\cdot}$
	$\vdots$					
	r	π_{r1}	π_{r2}	π_{r3}	$\cdots$ π_{rc}	$\pi_{r\cdot}$
Column marginal probabilities		$\pi_{\cdot 1}$	$\pi_{\cdot 2}$	$\pi_{\cdot 3}$	$\pi_{\cdot c}$	

H_0, row and column categories are independent, $E_{ij} = n\pi_{ij} = n\pi_{i\cdot}\pi_{\cdot j}$, and the estimates of the E_{ij}'s can be obtained by finding the estimates of the $\pi_{i\cdot}$'s and $\pi_{\cdot j}$'s. To do this, let $R_i = \sum_i O_{ij}$ and $C_j = \sum_j O_{ij}$; then the MLE of $\pi_{i\cdot}$ is $\hat{\pi}_{i\cdot} = R_i/n$, and that of $\pi_{\cdot j}$ is C_j/n. Since $\sum_i \pi_{i\cdot} = 1 = \sum_j \pi_{\cdot j}$, we estimate $r - 1$ $\pi_{i\cdot}$'s and $c - 1$ $\pi_{\cdot j}$'s, and $\hat{E}_{ij} = R_i C_j/n$. Therefore (for large n)

$$T = \sum_{j=1}^{c} \sum_{i=1}^{r} \frac{\left(O_{ij} - \hat{E}_{ij}\right)^2}{\hat{E}_{ij}} \qquad (9.13.2)$$

has a chi-square distribution. The degrees of freedom for the chi-square are computed as follows: Overall there are $rc - 1$ parameters (because $\sum_j \sum_i \pi_{ij} = 1$); under H_0 we estimated $(r - 1) + (c - 1)$ parameters; therefore the degrees of freedom for the chi-square statistic are $(rc - 1) - ((r - 1) + (c - 1)) = (r - 1)(c - 1)$. Hence to test (9.13.1) we first calculate T, and reject H_0 iff $T > \chi^{2^{-1}}_{(r-1)(c-1), 1-\alpha}(0)$.

In summary, for large n a level α test for hypothesis (9.13.1) is given by

$$\phi(\mathbf{O}) = \begin{cases} 1, & \text{if } T > \chi^{2^{-1}}_{(r-1)(c-1), 1-\alpha}(0) \\ 0, & \text{otherwise.} \end{cases} \qquad (9.13.3)$$

Example 9.13.4. A sociologist wants to know if there is an association between a person's income and the person's political affiliation. The sociologist randomly samples 300 registered voters and determines the political affiliation and income of each. The data is summarized in the table below in a two-way classification. Based on this data, can we conclude there is an association between the income and political affiliation? (Use the .05 level of significance.)

		Annual Income $30,000. or more		≥ $20,000. but < $30,000.		≥ $12,000. but < $20,000.		< $12,000.		Row Total
P o l i t i c a l	A f f i l i a t i o n	Republican		25		15		10		110
		60								
		36.67	14.84	25.67	0.02	25.66	4.43	22	6.55	
		Democrat		40		45		45		160
		30								
		53.33	10.21	37.33	0.19	37.34	1.57	32	5.28	
		Other		5		10		5		30
		10								
		10	0.00	7	0.57	7	1.29	6	0.17	
		Column Total								
		100		70		70		60		$n = 300$

This problem is one of testing hypotheses as at (9.13.1). We now proceed to compute the test statistic. The **small box at the lower left of each cell** is the computed estimate of E_{ij} for that cell, and we find

$$T = \sum_{j=1}^{c} \sum_{i=1}^{r} \frac{\left(O_{ij} - \hat{E}_{ij}\right)^2}{\hat{E}_{ij}} = \sum_{j=1}^{c} \sum_{i=1}^{r} \frac{O_{ij}^2}{\hat{E}_{ij}} - n = 45.10782. \qquad (9.13.5)$$

Since $\chi^2_{(3-1)(4-1),.95}(0) = 12.5916$, our test rejects H_0: Based on the given data we conclude that there is an association between political affiliation and income of a person. Looking at the contributions to T of each cell (i, j), one can seek to find where the association is strongest; these contributions are shown (to two decimal places) in the **small box at the lower right of each cell**. We see that the **predominant effect** is that more persons with incomes above $30,000 have affiliated with the Republicans (and fewer with the Democrats), than would be the case if affiliation and income were independent. With this effect removed, T would reduce to $45.11 - 14.84 - 10.21 = 20.06$, which is still significant at the .05 level (since it is greater than 12.59). Thus, a **significant secondary effect** is that of the next highest cells' T contribution: Of persons with incomes below $12,000, more have affiliated with the Democrats (and fewer with the Republicans) than would be the case if affiliation and income were independent. If this effect is removed, then T reduces further, now to $20.06 - 6.55 - 5.28 = 8.43$, which is not significant by itself; thus, it may well be that **there are no other significant effects shown in the data.**

Example 9.13.6. Applications in Employment Discrimination Cases. Statistical evidence is often of vital importance in litigation involving employment discrimination, and often the statistical issues lend themselves to contingency table analysis. Often an **"affected class"** (such as blacks, females, employees over age

40) is defined in the lawsuit and this class is compared to all other employees in the defendant employer's work force. The subject matter of the comparison is the **proportion of employees receiving some benefit of employment over a stated period of time (e.g., promotion,** transfer). Thus, we have an $r \times c$ contingency table with $r = 2$ and $c = 2$, or a **2 × 2 contingency table.** The **null hypothesis H_0** to be tested is independence of the row and column classifications, that is, **equality of the two employee classes in** the probability of a randomly chosen member of the class **receiving the particular benefit of employment.** When H_0 is rejected, unlawful discrimination is a permissible inference. (If we find that we reject H_0 and the affected class has received a high proportion of benefit, the possibility of "reverse discrimination" is suggested.) In a particular case, the plaintiff alleged discrimination in promotions during a particular year. Among 3909 employees in the defendant-employer's work force at the beginning of that year, the plaintiff class consisted of 461 employees, 125 of whom received a promotion, compared to 1099 in the residual class. Test for discrimination.

From the data given, we construct the following 2 × 2 contingency table (where the computed estimate of E_{ij} is given in the small box at the lower left of each cell and the contribution of that cell to T is given in the small box at the lower right of each cell):

	Affected Class		All Other		Total
Promoted	125		1099		1224
	144.34	2.59	1079.65	.35	
Not Promoted	336		2349		2685
	316.65	1.18	2368.35	.16	
Total	461		3448		3909

(For example, $1224/3909 = .31$ and $461/3909 = .12$. Hence under independence of rows and columns we expect $(3909)(.31)(.12) = 144.34$ in the "Promoted, Affected Class" category.) Hence we find that

$$T = \sum_{j=1}^{2} \sum_{i=1}^{2} \frac{\left(O_{ij} - \hat{E}_{ij}\right)^2}{\hat{E}_{ij}} = 2.59 + 1.18 + .35 + .16 = 4.28.$$

Since $\chi^2_{(2-1)(2-1),.95}(0) = \chi^2_{1,.95}(0) = 3.84$, we reject H_0, and conclude that there is not independence in the receipt of the promotion benefits over the two classes. The highest contributions to the chi-square statistic come from the Affected Class having fewer than expected promotions, hence discrimination against this class in promotion is a permissible inference.

In countering the foregoing argument, the defendant-employer noted that there were a number of different occupations and grades within the work force and that the different occupations were governed by different promotion criteria (as were the grades within an occupation). Therefore, the defendant-employer argued for computation of a separate chi-square for each 2×2 table (for each occupation and grade in its work force), and when this was done it was found that the chi-square combining all the classes was not significant. [The details of combining the chi-squares of the tables are straightforward; if one adds independent chi-squares, the degrees of freedom add. However, other factors must also be considered, such as whether the affected class might be concentrated in the lower-paying jobs, which would raise a new issue of discrimination in classification or assignment. For further discussion of such issues, see Dawson, Hankey, and Myers (1982).]

PROBLEMS FOR SECTION 9.13

9.13.1 A large college offers a word-processing course to its students on a free "workshop" basis. The course consists of five lectures, and is offered at three different times of the day: 8–9 A.M., 11–12 A.M., and 3–4 P.M. A random sample of 250 enrolled students is taken and number of lecture days missed is recorded. Suppose the data is:

		Number of Lectures Missed					
		0	1	2	3	4	5
Time	8 A.M.	34	7	9	12	5	6
of	11 A.M.	27	14	12	9	8	11
Day	3 P.M.	48	13	14	5	5	11

Based on this data, at level .10, is there any evidence that there is an association between the number of lectures missed and the time of the day the course is taken? Compute the significance probability.

9.13.2 Four-hundred students are taking introductory English and introductory Mathematics courses simultaneously. Suppose their course grades are:

		Mathematics Grade			
		A	B	C	D or F
English	A	48	23	28	7
Grade	B	28	29	29	13
	C	13	43	35	30
	D or F	12	14	16	32

At level .10, are the grades in Mathematics and English related? If so, use the technique of boxed chi-square contributions to identify those categories that caused the rejection, and the technique of comparing the estimates to the observations in those categories to determine the pattern of departure from independence that we have observed. Compute the significance probability.

9.13.3 Of 400 winning tickets in a raffle, 180 were found to be even-numbered, and 220 were odd-numbered, tickets. Based on this information, test the hypothesis that there was a 50/50 split between odd- and even-numbered tickets at level .05.

9.13.4 Show that in the case $r = 2$, T of equation (9.13.2) reduces to the expression noted in the hint to Problem 9.12.3.

PROBLEMS FOR CHAPTER 9

9.1 For the question "Do seat belts reduce accident injuries?" noted in Section 9.1, specify several sources of variability that, if not controlled through careful experimental design, could vitiate any study's results.

9.2 In Example 9.2.4, prove that the two rejection probabilities considered [following equation (9.2.9) and following display (9.2.11)] have the respective properties: $f(\theta_0) = \alpha = .05$, $f(\theta_0 + x) = f(\theta_0 - x)$ for all x, $f(\theta_2) > f(\theta_1)$ for all $\theta_2 > \theta_1 \geq \theta_0$, and $\lim_{\theta \to \infty} f(\theta) = 1$; and $g(\theta_0) = .05$, $g(\theta_2) > g(\theta_1)$ for all $\theta_2 > \theta_1$, and $\lim_{\theta \to \infty} g(\theta) = 1$.

9.3 In Example 9.2.4, if we desire the test using critical function $\phi_2(\cdot)$ to have level $\alpha = .05$ and power $\geq .95$ when $\theta = 1.23$, what is the smallest n that we can use?

9.4 For the hypothesis-testing problem discussed in Example 9.2.4, a third test sets $\phi_3(x) = .05$ for all $x \in \mathscr{X}$. (Thus, if this test is to be used, then we can just as well take no observations since this test ignores them and simply flips a coin with probability .05 of heads.) Show that this test has level $\alpha = .05$.

Thus, **obtaining a test with level α is trivial in general.** Much more important is obtaining a test of level α that has "good" properties with regard to power; this is often overlooked in cookbook statistics courses and texts. Graph the power of the test using $\phi_3(\cdot)$ as a function of θ, say $h(\theta)$. Compare it with $f(\theta)$ and $g(\theta)$ as shown in Figure 9.2-2.

9.5 For the hypothesis-testing problem discussed in Example 9.2.4, a fourth test sets

$$\phi_4(x) = \begin{cases} 1, & \text{if } |\bar{x} - \theta_0| \leq c \\ 0, & \text{otherwise.} \end{cases}$$

What value of c should be used to obtain level $\alpha = .05$ using this test? Graph the power of the test using $\phi_4(\cdot)$ as a function of θ, say $i(\theta)$. Compare it with $f(\theta)$, $g(\theta)$, and $h(\theta)$ (see Figure 9.2-2 and Problem 9.4). Does this show that we can, with a little ingenuity, construct a test that is worse than the one based only on flipping a coin? Explain.

9.6 Suppose that $X_1, \ldots, X_n$ are independent r.v.'s, each $N(\mu, 1)$. If we desire to test H_0: $\mu = 0$ versus H_1: $\mu \neq 0$ at level $\alpha = .05$, using the test that rejects when $|\bar{X}| > c$ [where c is set to obtain level .05], then what is the smallest value of n that will guarantee power $\geq .95$ when $|\mu| = 1$?

9.7 For the hypothesis-testing problem considered in Theorem 9.3.2, suppose $f(x|\theta_1)$ and $f(x|\theta_0)$ are each > 0 for all $x \in \mathscr{X}$. Show that if t is a sufficient statistic for the problem, then in order to satisfy (9.3.4) a test need be based only on t.

9.8 Suppose we observe $X = (X_1, \ldots, X_n)$ where $X_1, \ldots, X_n$ are independent r.v.'s, each $N(\mu, \sigma^2)$ where μ is unknown $(-\infty < \mu < +\infty)$ and $\sigma^2 = 1$ is known. For the problem of testing H_0: $\mu = 0$ versus H_1: $\mu = 1$ at level $\alpha = .05$ using a most powerful test, find the smallest value of n that will guarantee power $\geq .90$. Using this n, graph the power curve. (Calculate the power at least for $\mu = \pm.5, \pm 1, \pm 1.5$, ± 2 for your graph. Also consider $\mu = 0$.)

9.9 Suppose we observe $X = (X_1, \ldots, X_n)$ where $X_1, \ldots, X_n$ are independent r.v.'s, each $N(\mu, \sigma^2)$ where μ is unknown $(-\infty < \mu < +\infty)$ and σ^2 is known $(\sigma^2 > 0)$. For the problem of testing H_0: $\mu = \mu_0$ versus H_1: $\mu = \mu_1(> \mu_0)$ at level α $(0 < \alpha < 1)$ using a most powerful test, show that using (for $0 < \gamma < 1$)

$$n \geq \left[\frac{\Phi^{-1}(1 - \gamma) - \Phi^{-1}(1 - \alpha)}{\mu_0 - \mu_1} \sigma \right]^2$$

will yield level $\leq \alpha$ and power $\geq \gamma$.

9.10 In Example 9.3.10 the test that rejects H_0 when $\overline{X} > \mu_0 + (\sigma/\sqrt{n})\Phi^{-1}(1 - \alpha)$ has level α $(0 < \alpha < 1)$. If this test has power γ at H_1: $\mu = \mu_1(> \mu_0)$, then at what value of μ does this test have power $1 - \gamma$?

9.11 Show that in the statement of the Neyman-Pearson Lemma we may assume without loss that $k \geq 0$. [*Hint*: If $k < 0$, what is the value of $E_{\theta_0}\phi(X)$?] Can $k = 0$ also be excluded?

9.12 Suppose that, in Example 9.3.17, we choose to set $\phi(x)$ to 0 in Case I and Case IV. The resulting test is (say)

$$\phi_3(x) = \begin{cases} .05, & \text{if } \min(x_1, \ldots, x_n) \geq 0 \text{ and } \max(x_1, \ldots, x_n) \leq 1 \\ 1, & \text{if } \min(x_1, \ldots, x_n) \geq 0 \text{ and } 1 < \max(x_1, \ldots, x_n) \leq 2 \\ 0, & \text{otherwise.} \end{cases}$$

Is $\phi_3(\cdot)$ a most powerful level $\alpha = .05$ test of H_0: $\theta = 1$ versus H_1: $\theta = 2$? Find and graph $E_\theta \phi_3(X)$ on a facsimile of Figure 9.3-1.

9.13 Suppose that we observe X and wish to test H_0 versus H_1 (where H_0 and/or H_1 may be composite hypotheses). The **likelihood-ratio test**[15] can be defined as: Reject H_0 iff (at the observed value of X)

$$\frac{\displaystyle\sup_{\theta \in H_1} L(\theta)}{\displaystyle\sup_{\theta \in H_0} L(\theta)} > k, \qquad\qquad (*)$$

where $L(\theta)$ is the likelihood function of equation (7.2.2) and k is arbitrary. Show that if H_0 and H_1 are simple hypotheses, then the likelihood-ratio test is most powerful. [*Hint*: Use the Neyman-Pearson Lemma.] How should $(*)$ be restated if we wish to allow cases where $L(\theta)$ may be 0 to be considered?

9.14 Suppose we are to observe X and have a hypothesis-testing problem of H_0 versus H_1, where H_0 and/or H_1 may be composite. Suppose we have a test of level α for each α $(0 \leq \alpha \leq 1)$, say $\phi_\alpha(X)$. Our intention is to use test $\phi_{\alpha^*}(X)$ if we decide to test the hypothesis at level $\alpha = \alpha^*$. If we observe $X = x$, then the **significance probability** of x, say $\alpha_{SP}(x, \phi_\alpha)$, is defined as the smallest α for which $\phi_\alpha(x) = 1$ [the smallest α for which we would surely reject if we observed $X = x$]. Often an experimenter will report $\alpha_{SP}(x, \phi_\alpha)$ in his work. Then an experimenter with a possibly different desired level, say α', will *often* know: that he would also decide to reject if the reported $\alpha_{SP}(x, \phi_\alpha) \leq \alpha'$; and that he would not decide to reject if the reported $\alpha_{SP}(x, \phi_\alpha) > \alpha'$. (We say *often*, not always, because the assumption that the tests $\phi_\alpha(X)$ have the property

$$\phi_{\alpha_1}(x) = 1 \Rightarrow \phi_{\alpha_2}(x) = 1, \quad \text{for all } \alpha_2 > \alpha_1, \quad \text{for all } x \qquad (*)$$

is needed and is not always satisfied.)

[15] Note that this differs from Definition 9.11.1, but is also widely used as a definition of "the" likelihood-ratio test. Show that the two definitions lead to the same test.

In Example 9.3.10 a test of level α, say $\phi_\alpha(X)$, was given for each $\alpha(0 < \alpha < 1)$. [$\alpha = 0$ can be obtained by never rejecting, and $\alpha = 1$ can be obtained by always rejecting.] Suppose there that $\sigma^2 = 100$, $\mu_0 = 0$, $\mu_1 = 1$, $\mu = 100$, and $\overline{X} = 2.68$ is found. What is $\alpha_{\text{SP}}(2.68, \phi_\alpha)$? Does it change if we change μ_1 to 3? What if $\sigma^2 = 10$? What if $\sigma^2 = 1$?

9.15 In the proof of Theorem 9.3.51 (UMP tests for MLR cases) we stated that the given test was the same regardless of which θ_1 was chosen (as long as $\theta_1 > \theta_0$). Prove this; that is, show that $\phi(x)$ does not depend on the particular $\theta_1 > \theta_0$ chosen.

9.16 Show that if the density of $X = (X_1, \ldots, X_n)$ is a member of the one-parameter exponential family (see Definition 8.2.12), then the d.f. $F(x|\theta)$ of X has a MLR [in which $T(x)$?] iff $c_1(\theta)$ is a nondecreasing function of θ (i.e., iff $c_1(\theta_2) - c_1(\theta_1) \geq 0$ for all $\theta_2 > \theta_1$]. Show that X in Example 9.3.58 is a member of the one-parameter exponential family, and conclude immediately that $F(x|\theta)$ has a MLR in $x_1 + \cdots + x_n$.

9.17 Prove that for any hypothesis-testing problem where H_0 and H_1 are both simple, if the set $R = \{r(\phi): \phi(\cdot) \text{ a test}\}$ includes the point $(\alpha, 1 - \beta)$, then it also includes the point $(1 - \alpha, \beta)$. [A special case was covered in Lemma 9.4.4.]

9.18 Prove that the class of all tests is a complete class of tests.

9.19 Prove that any complete class of tests is also an essentially complete class of tests.

9.20 How does the figure below indicate that, if we specify interest in a Bayes rule with respect to $(p, 1 - p)$, there may be several risk points that qualify?

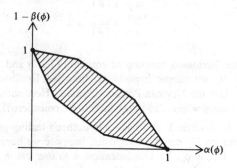

9.21 Show that the quantities (9.4.10) and (9.4.11) are equal. Deduce that the minimax risk and minimax regret rules are the same. [This is not so in general decision theory problems.]

9.22 Prove that the slope of the line $px + (1 - p)y = c$, used in our explanation of the Bayes criterion (see Figure 9.4-5), is negative when $0 < p < 1$.

9.23 If $p = 0$, which tests ϕ are Bayes (i.e., what restrictions on $\phi(x)$ besides $0 \leq \phi(x) \leq 1$ must a test satisfy to be Bayes)? Similarly for $p = 1$. [*Hint*: See the discussion preceding (9.4.14).]

9.24 In Example 9.3.58 we considered observing $X = (X_1, \ldots, X_{31})$ where $X_1, \ldots, X_{31}$ are independent r.v.'s, each exponential with unknown mean $\theta > 0$. Then (for any $\theta_1 > 10$) a most powerful level $\alpha = .05$ test of H_0: $\theta = 10$ versus H_1: $\theta = \theta_1$ rejects H_0 iff $\overline{X} > 13.13$.

Fix $p(0 < p < 1)$. When does a Bayes rule with respect to $(p, 1 - p)$ reject H_0? Does the Bayes rule with respect to $(p, 1 - p)$ depend on θ_1? For what value(s) of p does the Bayes rule have level $\alpha = .05$? For what value of θ_1 does the level $\alpha = .05$ Bayes rule reject iff $\overline{X} > 13.13$?

9.25 Consider the case of Problem 9.24. When does the minimax rule reject H_0? What is the level of the minimax rule? For what value(s) of θ_1 is this level .05? For what value(s) of θ_1 does the minimax rule reject iff $\overline{X} > 13.13$? What is the level of the minimax rule that rejects iff $\overline{X} > 13.13$?

9.26 In Example 9.3.10 we found a most powerful test in a hypothesis-testing problem with $H_1 = \{\mu_1\}(\mu_1 > \mu_0)$, and we showed that this test is UMP for $H_1 = \{\mu_1: \mu_1 > \mu_0\}$. Find a UMP test of level α in the same hypothesis-testing problem but with $H_1 = \{\mu_1: \mu_1 < \mu_0\}$.

9.27 Prove Theorem 9.5.13.

9.28 Verify that, in the terms of Definition 4.5.4, the r.v. $(X_1, \ldots, X_n)$ in Lemma 9.5.15 actually does have a multivariate normal distribution.

9.29 Verify (see (9.5.17)) that in the proof of Lemma 9.5.15 we have

$$\text{Cov}\left(\frac{X_1 + \cdots + X_n}{n}, X_i\right) - \text{Var}(\overline{X}) = 0.$$

9.30 Prove that if two r.v.'s X_1 and X_2 are independent, then $g_1(X_1)$ and $g_2(X_2)$ are also independent (for any fixed functions $g_1(\cdot)$ and $g_2(\cdot)$) [*Hint*: See Theorems 5.3.16 and 5.3.20.]

9.31 Verify that (9.5.20) is true.

9.32 Prove that if $X_1, \ldots, X_n$ are independent r.v.'s, then $g_1(X_1)$ and $g_2(X_2, \ldots, X_n)$ are also independent. (This generalizes Problem 9.30.)

9.33 Verify that (9.5.21) is true.

9.34 Let $X_1, \ldots, X_n$ be independent $N(0,1)$ r.v.'s. Prove that $X_1^2 + \cdots + X_n^2$ has the $\chi_n^2(0)$ distribution. [*Hint*: Prove the result for $n = 1$ and then use part (iv) of Theorem 5.5.64. A laborious application of the methods of Section 4.6 would also work. Or, use m.g.f.'s.]

9.35 Fix $p(0 < p < 1)$. For the hypothesis-testing problem of Theorem 9.5.26 with H_1: $\mu = \mu_1(> \mu_0)$ replaced by H_1: $\mu \neq \mu_0$, show that the test which rejects iff

$$\frac{\overline{X} - \mu_0}{s/\sqrt{n}} < t_{n-1}^{-1}(\alpha p) \quad \text{or} \quad \frac{\overline{X} - \mu_0}{s/\sqrt{n}} > -t_{n-1}^{-1}(\alpha(1 - p)) \quad (*)$$

has level α. (A similar class of tests is noted in Problem 9.12H.)

9.36 The test stated in Theorem 9.5.26 [i.e., reject iff (9.5.27) occurs] has level α no matter what our alternative H_1: The reason we changed to another rejection region when we changed H_1 [see Problem 9.35] was to obtain "good" power against "far" points in the new alternative. Actually, a graph of the power of each test would be similar to Figure 9.2-2. Evaluating the power explicitly involves using tables of what is called the **noncentral t-distribution** (with $n - 1$ degrees of freedom); these tables are like Table 13 (for the t-distribution), but involve one such table for *every noncentrality value we need* (hence, for a large number of values if the tables are to be useful); hence, they are voluminous and are not given here. However, if $g(\mu)$ denotes the probability that (9.5.27) holds, and if $f(\mu)$ denotes the probability that $(*)$ of

Problem 9.35 holds, prove that

$$\begin{cases} f(\mu_0) = g(\mu_0) = \alpha; \\ g(\mu) > f(\mu) \text{ for } \mu > \mu_0, \ g(\mu) < f(\mu) \text{ for } \mu < \mu_0, \\ \quad \text{if } p = 1/2 \text{ and } \alpha < 1/2; \\ f(\mu_0 + x) = f(\mu_0 - x) \text{ for all } x, \text{ if } p = 1/2; \\ f(\mu_2) > f(\mu_1) \text{ for all } \mu_2 > \mu_1 \geq \mu_0, \text{ if } p = 1/2: \\ g(\mu_2) > g(\mu_1) \text{ for all } \mu_2 > \mu_1; \text{ and} \\ \lim_{\mu \to \infty} f(\mu) = \lim_{\mu \to \infty} g(\mu) = 1. \end{cases}$$

This shows that our picture here is indeed similar to that of Figure 9.2-2.

9.37 If Y_1 has the $N(\delta, 1)$ distribution, if Y_2 has the $\chi_m^2(0)$ distribution, and if Y_1 and Y_2 are independent r.v.'s, then

$$Y = \frac{Y_1}{\sqrt{Y_2/m}}$$

is said to have the **noncentral t-distribution** with m degrees of freedom and **noncentrality δ**. Show that, in the context of Theorem 9.5.26,

$$\frac{\overline{X} - \mu_0}{s/\sqrt{n}}$$

has a noncentral t-distribution when H_0 is false. (Find δ and m.)

9.38 Let $X_1, \ldots, X_n$ be independent r.v.'s, each $N(\mu, \sigma^2)$ where μ is known ($-\infty < \mu < +\infty$) and σ^2 is unknown ($\sigma^2 > 0$). Prove that $\hat{\sigma}^2$ given in equation (9.6.1) is a minimal sufficient statistic.

9.39 Use the Neyman-Pearson Lemma to show that the test of Theorem 9.6.4 is most powerful. If we take H_1 to be $\{\sigma^2: \sigma^2 > \sigma_0^2\}$, do we find that the test of Theorem 9.6.4 is UMP one-sided?

9.40 Show that if Y has the $\chi_n^2(0)$ distribution, then $EY = n$ [*Hint*: Write Y as $X_1^2 + \cdots + X_n^2$, where $X_1, \ldots, X_n$ are independent $N(0,1)$ r.v.'s.]

9.41 Show that the power, when $\sigma^2 = \sigma_1^2$, of the level α test specified in Theorem 9.6.4 can be written as

$$g(\sigma_1^2) = P\left[Y > \frac{\sigma_0^2}{\sigma_1^2} L_{1-\alpha}^{-1} \right],$$

where Y is a $\chi_n^2(0)$ r.v. and $L_{1-\alpha}^{-1}$ is the number such that

$$P\left[Y < L_{1-\alpha}^{-1} \right] = 1 - \alpha.$$

Prove that $g(\sigma_1^2) > g(\sigma_2^2)$ for $\sigma_1^2 > \sigma_2^2$, that $\lim_{\sigma_1 \to 0} g(\sigma_1^2) = 0$, and that

$$\lim_{\sigma_1 \to \infty} g(\sigma_1^2) = 1.$$

9.42 Show that the power at each specified σ_1^2, of the level α test specified in Theorem 9.6.4, increases if n is increased.

9.43 Show that if Y_1 has the $\chi_n^2(0)$ distribution, Y_2 has the $\chi_m^2(0)$ distribution, and Y_1 and Y_2 are independent r.v.'s (with $n \geq 2, m \geq 2$), then

$$Y = \frac{Y_1/n}{Y_2/m}$$

has the F-distribution $F(n, m)$.

9.44 Consider the hypothesis-testing problem of Theorem 9.7.4 with H_0 and H_1 replaced respectively by $H_0 = \{\sigma_1^2 = c\sigma_2^2\}$ and $H_1 = \{\sigma_1^2 > c\sigma_2^2\}$ where $c > 0$ is a specified number. Obtain an explicit formula [comparable to (9.7.5)] for a level α test in this case, and show how to choose any constants that you use. If $n = 10$, $m = 20$, $c = 16$, and $\alpha = .05$, when will your test reject H_0?

9.45 Let $X_1, \ldots, X_n, Y_1, \ldots, Y_m$ be $n + m$ independent r.v.'s. Suppose that $X_1, \ldots, X_n$ are each $N(\mu_1, \sigma^2)$; $Y_1, \ldots, Y_m$ are each $N(\mu_2, \sigma^2)$; μ_1 and μ_2 are unknown $(-\infty < \mu_1, \mu_2 < +\infty)$; and $\sigma^2 > 0$ is known. Find a complete minimal sufficient statistic for (μ_1, μ_2). Find the unique MVU estimator of μ_1; of μ_2. (This justifies the reasoning that led to test (9.8.1) in Section 9.8.)

9.46 Let ϕ_P denote the test specified by (9.8.7) and (9.8.10). Derive similar tests ϕ_1 and ϕ_2 based respectively on the left side of equation (9.8.3) with σ^2 replaced by s_1^2 and s_2^2. (Be sure to give the k_1' and k_2' for these tests.) Study whether: ϕ_P is uniformly more powerful than either of ϕ_1 and ϕ_2; ϕ_1 is uniformly more powerful than ϕ_2 if $n > m$; ϕ_1 has the same power as ϕ_2 if $n = m$; and ϕ_2 is uniformly more powerful than ϕ_1 if $n < m$.

9.47 Show that (when H_0 is true) (9.9.4), called the **Behrens-Fisher statistic**, has the same distribution as (for some a and b) does

$$\frac{Y}{\sqrt{aC_1 + bC_2}}$$

where Y is a $N(0,1)$ r.v., C_1 is a χ_{n-1}^2 r.v., C_2 is a χ_{m-1}^2 r.v., and Y, C_1, C_2 are independent. For what values of a and b is the preceding true?

Prove that $aC_1 + bC_2$ (where C_1 is a χ_{n-1}^2 r.v., C_2 is a χ_{m-1}^2 r.v., and C_1 and C_2 are independent) has the chi-square distribution iff $a = b = 1$. Deduce when (9.9.4) has a Student's t-distribution.

9.48 Consider the two hypothesis-testing problems of Section 9.8 (i.e., σ^2 known and σ^2 unknown) with H_0 and H_1 replaced by $H_0 = \{\mu_1 = \mu_2 + c\}$ and $H_1 = \{\mu_1 > \mu_2 + c\}$, where $c > 0$ is a specified number. Obtain an explicit formula for a level α test in each case, and show how to choose any constants that you use.

9.49 Prove that equation (9.9.10) is true.

9.50 In this chapter we have seen that in cases of two-sided alternatives we usually obtain a class of tests rather than one "best" test. (For example, see Problem 9.12H.) That one of these tests which devotes $\alpha/2$ of α as a probability of rejecting due to "large" values of the test statistic (and $\alpha/2$ as a probability of rejecting due to "small" values of the test statistic) when H_0 is true, is called a **two-sided equal-tail test**. [For example, $\phi_\alpha^{(p)}(\cdot)$ in Problem 9.12H with $p = \frac{1}{2}$.]

Let $X = (X_1, \ldots, X_n)$, where $X_1, \ldots, X_n$ are independent $N(\mu, \sigma^2)$ r.v.'s and μ is known. For $n = 10$ and $\alpha = .10$, compute the power curve of the two-sided equal-tail test of H_0: $\sigma^2 = 1$ versus H_1: $\sigma^2 \neq 1$. For $n = 10$ and $\alpha = .10$, compute the power curve of the one-sided test of H_0: $\sigma^2 = 1$ versus H_1: $\sigma^2 > 1$. Plot the two power curves on the same graph.

9.51 Man A (a track star) has run the mile twice in competitions, with times of 3.8, 3.4. Man B (another track star) has run the mile thrice in competitions, with times of 3.7, 3.6, 4.1. Assume that man A and man B ran independently of each other, and that each one's times are independent observations of his running ability. Let $\mu_A(\mu_B)$ denote the average time it takes man $A(B)$ to run the mile in competitions. Similarly, let his variance be $\sigma_A^2(\sigma_B^2)$.

    (a) Based on these results, perform a two-sided equal-tail (see Problem 9.50) test of $\mu_A = \mu_B$ at level $\alpha = .05$. Assume $\sigma_A^2 = \sigma_B^2 = .04$. State precisely the statistical assumptions that you are making.

    (b) As in part (a), but with $\sigma_A^2 = .04$, $\sigma_B^2 = .09$.

    (c) As in part (a), but with $\sigma_A^2 = \sigma_B^2$ unknown.

    (d) For the problem as in part (a), but with σ_A^2 and σ_B^2 both unknown, what can be said?

9.52 In Problem 7.6 and Example 7.4.23 we considered the seasonal snowfall in Rochester, New York, for the last 97 years in the context of point estimation. Now it turns out that the snowfalls for 1939–40 and prior years were measured at the Federal Building at Church and North Fitzhugh Streets in downtown Rochester, but that from 1940–41 onward the snowfalls have been measured by the National Weather Service at the Rochester-Monroe County airport. This poses an interesting question: "Should snowfalls from 1939–40 and previous years be considered in a statement about 'average Rochester snowfall'?"

    If $X_1, \ldots, X_{97}$ are independent $N(\mu, \sigma^2)$ r.v.'s, the answer is (based on our estimation work in Chapter 7) clearly "Yes," for our estimator will be more concentrated about μ if it is based on 97 observations than if it is based on only 41 observations. Yet if $X_1, \ldots, X_{97}$ are independent r.v.'s, but $X_1, \ldots, X_{56}$ are $N(\mu_1, \sigma^2)$ while $X_{57}, \ldots, X_{97}$ are $N(\mu_2, \sigma^2)$ where $\mu_1 \neq \mu_2$, then the observations would be measuring different phenomena and should probably not be combined. Thus, test (at level $\alpha = .05$) $H_0: \mu_1 = \mu_2$ versus $H_1: \mu_1 \neq \mu_2$, assuming σ^2 is unknown. What is the significance probability of the data (see Problem 9.14)? [Use a two-sided equal-tail test (see Problem 9.50).]

    Now a skeptical person (e.g., a scientist) mist question the assumption of equal variances. If $X_1, \ldots, X_{56}$ are $N(\mu_1, \sigma_1^2)$ while $X_{57}, \ldots, X_{97}$ are $N(\mu_2, \sigma_2^2)$, test (via a two-sided equal-tail test) $H_0: \sigma_1^2 = \sigma_2^2$ versus $H_1: \sigma_1^2 \neq \sigma_2^2$. Use level $\alpha = .05$. Find the significance probability of the data.

    Now, what is your estimate of the average seasonal snowfall in Rochester, and why have you chosen a particular estimator?

    [Reference: *The Times-Union*, Rochester, New York, March 10, 1972, p. 1B.]

HONORS PROBLEMS FOR CHAPTER 9

9.1H In Definition 9.3.1 we stated that in a hypothesis-testing problem where H_0 and H_1 are both simple, a test with critical function $\phi(\cdot)$ is called *most powerful of level* α if $E_{\theta_0}\phi(X) = \alpha$ and, for all critical functions $\psi(\cdot)$ such that $E_{\theta_0}\psi(X) = \alpha$, $E_{\theta_1}\phi(X) \geq E_{\theta_1}\psi(X)$. Then in the Neyman-Pearson Lemma we proved that if $\phi(\cdot)$ has level α and satisfies (9.3.4), then $\phi(\cdot)$ is most powerful of level α.

    We will now call a test with critical function $\phi(\cdot)$ **most powerful of level** $\leq \alpha$ if $E_{\theta_0}\phi(X) \leq \alpha$ and, for all critical functions $\psi(\cdot)$ such that $E_{\theta_0}\psi(X) \leq \alpha$, $E_{\theta_1}\phi(X) \geq E_{\theta_1}\psi(X)$.

Prove that if $\phi(\cdot)$ satisfies (9.3.3) and (9.3.4), then it is most powerful of level $\leq \alpha$. (This is a slight extension of the Neyman-Pearson Lemma.) [*Hint*: A slight modification of the proof of Theorem 9.3.2 will suffice to prove the desired result.]

9.2H Prove that for testing simple H_0 versus simple H_1 after observing X (the context of the Neyman-Pearson Lemma) there exists a critical function $\phi(\cdot)$ and a constant k such that (9.3.3) and (9.3.4) hold (i.e., you can obtain a level α test if you choose $\phi(\cdot)$ according to (9.3.4) as long as you choose k properly).

9.3H Prove that for testing simple H_0 versus simple H_1 after observing X (the context of the Neyman-Pearson Lemma) if $\phi(\cdot)$ is most powerful of level α, then it satisfies (9.3.4) for some k.

Also prove that if $\phi(\cdot)$ is most powerful of level $\leq \alpha$ (see Problem 9.1H), then it satisfies (9.3.3) (i.e., has level α) unless there exists a test of level $< \alpha$ that has power 1.

9.4H In Definition 9.3.16 we defined a UMP test of level α for simple H_0 versus composite H_1, and in Theorem 9.3.51 we showed how to obtain UMP tests of H_0: $\theta = \theta_0$ versus H_1: $\theta > \theta_0$ in MLR cases. Thus, this work, as well as our definition of a most powerful test (Definition 9.3.1), is specifically for the case of simple H_0. For composite H_0, we call a test **most powerful of level** α if Definition 9.3.1 is satisfied, with "level α" replaced by

$$\sup_{\theta \in H_0} P_\theta \left[\text{Rejecting } H_0 \text{ using } \phi(\cdot) \right] = \alpha. \qquad (*)$$

Suppose that in Theorem 9.5.51 we replace H_0: $\theta = \theta_0$ by H_0^*: $\theta \leq \theta_0$; and equation (9.3.52) by $(*)$, that is, by

$$\sup_{\theta \in H_0} E_\theta \phi(X) = \alpha.$$

Then show that the theorem remains true (and hence shows us how to obtain UMP level α tests of H_0^*: $\theta \leq \theta_0$ versus H_1: $\theta > \theta_0$ in MLR cases; in fact, the UMP level α test of H_0: $\theta = \theta_0$ versus H_1: $\theta > \theta_0$ is the UMP level α test of H_0^*: $\theta \leq \theta_0$ versus H_1: $\theta > \theta_0$).

9.5H Let A represent the collection of all one-parameter exponential families, and let B represent the collection of all MLR families. Then in Example 9.3.58 (see also Problem 9.16) we showed that $X = (X_1, \ldots, X_n)$ where $X_1, \ldots, X_n$ are independent r.v.'s with the same exponential distribution density with mean θ is in $A \cap B$. Give examples of X in $\overline{A} \cap B$, and in $A \cap \overline{B}$.

9.6H Prove Theorem 9.3.72.

9.7H In connection with Example 9.3.75, Reinhardt (in the article referenced in footnote 3) states that the choice of the r_i's is crucial since for party R in the Montana legislature he found minima and maxima of quantity (9.3.77) of .50 and .68 for one "reasonable" set of r_i's, and .23 and .40 for another "reasonable" set. However, since the respective spreads of quantity (9.3.77) indicated as possible are then .18 and .17, the approach does seem to show how much can be gained by the party in power apportioning (and it is substantial!).

Work out the minimum and maximum for some state other than Montana. How sensitive is the solution to $r_1, \ldots, r_n$? Since infinitely many values of k are possible in (9.3.79), how can we ever compute the answer? [*Hint*: If $r_{[1]} \leq \cdots \leq r_{[n]}$, denote $r_1, \ldots, r_n$ in numerical order, then as we lower k no change is noted in (9.3.79) except when k "crosses" an r_i.]

9.8H Prove that the maximum of (9.3.77) referred to in Example 9.3.75 is the value k for which (9.3.79) yields the maximum.

9.9H Specify a hypothesis-testing problem where we find a convex set of risk points similar to the one displayed in Problem 9.20. [*Hint*: Consider a case where X takes on only finitely many values.]

9.10H Repeated Tests of Significance. In some hypothesis-testing problems (especially in complex ones) there may be several tests we would consider using, and whose relationship to each other is not clear. (Even in simple problems, the Bayes rule with respect to $(p, 1 - p)$, the minimax rule, and the most powerful level α test may not bear a clear relation to one another until some effort is invested; see Problems 9.24 and 9.25.) Suppose we observe X and have available tests $\phi_1, \phi_2, \ldots, \phi_n$, each with level α; that is,

$$\alpha = E_{\theta_0}\phi_1(X) = E_{\theta_0}\phi_2(X) = \cdots = E_{\theta_0}\phi_n(X).$$

Then we sometimes say that we want to be "extra sure" H_0 is not false, and reject if *any one* of $\phi_1, \ldots, \phi_n$ calls for rejection (e.g., see Cramér (1946), pp. 422–423). What relation does the level of this combined test, say ϕ with

$$\phi(x) = 1 - (1 - \phi_1(x)) \cdots (1 - \phi_n(x)),$$

bear to α? [*Hint*: Show that

$$\alpha \leq E_{\theta_0}\phi(X) \leq \min(n\alpha, 1),$$

and that $E_{\theta_0}\phi(X) = \alpha$ and $E_{\theta_0}\phi(X) = \min(n\alpha, 1)$ can occur. Hence, if we use even $n = 2$, the true (but unknown) level may be unacceptably large if we really desire level α.]

9.11H Data Snooping. Suppose we observe X and run a level α test $\phi(X)$ of some simple hypothesis H_0. Then even if H_0 is true, we have probability α of rejecting H_0. If we observe $X_1, \ldots, X_n$ (independent r.v.'s, each with the same distribution as X, for which H_0 is true) and test H_0 independently n times, the number Z of sets of data in which H_0 is rejected in a binomial r.v. with n trials and $p = \alpha$, and has expected value $EZ = np = n\alpha$. (For example, if $n = 1000$ and $\alpha = .01$, we expect to declare H_0 false in 10 of the 1000 data sets just due to the random nature of the data.) Hence, if we were to use the test to find which of $X_1, \ldots, X_n$ seem "odd" and then "test" the "odd" ones with the same test, all would be rejected *and the test would not be of level* α; its level would instead be 1!

Does the above apply to the situation in which a person, looking through an almanac or other source of data, is struck by some data given (thinks it "odd") and then tests it? Explain. (For example, we may be struck,[16] on reading a list of how many games were played in each World Series, by the fact that more than half of the series played since World War II's end have lasted a full 7 games...$15/27 = .555$ in 1945–1971. If we then test the hypothesis that nothing "unusual" is going on, we will reject it...since we formulated the hypothesis precisely because it looked as though something odd was happening. Thus, although it may well be that we have discovered something profound while reading the almanac, we have no

---

[16] W Simon ["'Back-to-the-wall' effect?," *Science*, Vol. 174 (1971), pp. 774–775] was so struck. Although he admits that "There are...difficulties associated with statistical interpretation of rare events defined after the fact...," he goes on to gainsay the difficulties. Many others do not even realize that difficulties exist! [Even excellent books sometimes run afoul of this difficulty; for example, see Cramér (1946), pp. 457ff.]

statistical backing unless we gather future data to test the hypothesis suggested by the past data.)

9.12H In Definition 9.4.6 we considered complete classes for testing simple H_0 versus simple H_1. For any hypothesis-testing problem where H_0 is simple (but H_1 may be composite) call a test ϕ_2 **better than** a test ϕ_1 if $\alpha_{\theta_0}(\phi_2) \leq \alpha_{\theta_0}(\phi_1)$ and $1 - \beta_\theta(\phi_2) \leq 1 - \beta_\theta(\phi_1)$ for all $\theta \in H_1$ with at least one strict inequality ($<$). Extend the rest of Definitions 9.4.5 and 9.4.6, to simple H_0 versus composite H_1.

Suppose we observe $X = (X_1, \ldots, X_n)$ where $X_1, \ldots, X_n$ are independent r.v.'s, each $N(\mu, \sigma^2)$ where μ is unknown ($-\infty < \mu < +\infty$) and $\sigma^2 > 0$ is known. Suppose it is desired to test H_0: $\mu = \mu_0$ at level α ($0 < \alpha < 1$). In Example 9.2.4 we considered $\phi_1(\cdot)$ (reject iff $|\overline{X} - \mu_0| > a$) and $\phi_2(\cdot)$ (reject iff $\overline{X} - \mu_0 > b$), showing how to choose a and b to obtain level α in each case. In Example 9.3.10 we saw $\phi_2(\cdot)$ is UMP for H_0: $\mu = \mu_0$ versus H_1: $\mu > \mu_0$.

Prove that there is no UMP test for testing H_0: $\mu = \mu_0$ versus H_1: $\mu \neq \mu_0$. [*Hint*: Compare any such supposed UMP test with the Neyman-Pearson test of H_0: $\mu = \mu_0$ versus H_1: $\mu = \mu_1$ ($\mu_1 > \mu_0$), which is unique.]

Consider the class of tests $C = \{ \phi_\alpha^{(p)}(\cdot), 0 \leq p \leq 1, 0 \leq \alpha \leq 1 \}$ where

$$\phi_\alpha^{(p)}(x) = \begin{cases} 1, & \text{if } \overline{x} - \mu_0 \leq a(p) \\ 1, & \text{if } \overline{x} - \mu_0 > b(p) \\ 0, & \text{otherwise;} \end{cases}$$

here $a(p)$ and $b(p)$ are chosen to satisfy

$$P_{\mu_0}\left[\overline{X} - \mu_0 < a(p) \right] = \alpha p,$$

$$P_{\mu_0}\left[\overline{X} - \mu_0 > b(p) \right] = \alpha(1 - p).$$

Find $a(p)$ and $b(p)$ explicitly. Prove that $\phi_\alpha^{(p)}(\cdot)$ has level α. Is C an essentially complete class of tests? (Figure 9.2-2 plotted the rejection probabilities for $\phi_\alpha^{(p)}(\cdot)$ when $\alpha = .05$ for $p = .00$ and for $p = .50$.) If C is essentially complete, then in this testing problem we must simply decide what proportion of level should go toward protecting against $\mu_1 < \mu_0$ (the rest going toward protecting against $\mu_1 > \mu_0$).

9.13H Generalizing Problem 9.7 (which treated the case of simple null and alternative hypotheses), show that for a general hypothesis-testing problem the class C of all tests based on a sufficient statistic t is (see Problem 9.12H) essentially complete. [*Hint*: See Problem 12 of Lehmann (1986), p. 64, and the references given there.]

9.14H The motivation given at the beginning of the proof of Lemma 9.5.15 would, in fact, yield a precise proof that $\overline{X}$ and s^2 are independent r.v.'s *if* the result "If (for $1 \leq i \leq n$) Y and W_i are independent, then Y and $W_1 + \cdots + W_n$ are independent" were true. Either prove this or give a counterexample.

9.15H Let $X_1, \ldots, X_n$ be independent $N(\mu, \sigma^2)$ r.v.'s. While proving Lemma 9.5.15 we showed that $\sum_{i=1}^{n} (X_i - \overline{X})^2 / \sigma^2$ has the $\chi_{n-1}^2(0)$ distribution. (Verify this.)

P. Nemenyi ("A handy set of $n - 1$ contrasts...," *Research Report No. 1*, Department of Statistics, Virginia State College, Petersburg, Virginia) has suggested that instead of the Helmert orthogonal transformation (9.5.18) we use the transformation

$$Y_j = \left(X_j - \overline{X} \right) + A\left(X_n - \overline{X} \right) \quad (1 \leq j \leq n - 1)$$

with A equal to a real root (does one exist?) of

$$(n-1)A^2 - 2A = 1.$$

Show that $Y_1, \ldots, Y_{n-1}$ are then independent $N(0, \sigma^2)$ r.v.'s, and that $Y_1^2 + \cdots + Y_{n-1}^2 = \sum_{i=1}^{n} (X_i - \overline{X})^2$. Deduce that $\sum_{i=1}^{n} (X_i - \overline{X})^2/\sigma^2$ has the $\chi_{n-1}^2(0)$ distribution.

If we also define $Y_n = (X_1 + \cdots + X_n)$, can we use Nemenyi's transformation to prove that $\overline{X}$ and s^2 are independent r.v.'s? If so, is Nemenyi's transformation a simpler way to prove Lemma 9.5.15 than is Helmert's transformation? [*Hint:* Review Problem 9.33.]

9.16H Let $X_1, \ldots, X_n$ be independent r.v.'s, each $N(\mu, \sigma^2)$ where μ is known ($-\infty < \mu < +\infty$) and σ^2 is unknown ($\sigma^2 > 0$). Prove that $\hat{\sigma}^2$ given in equation (9.6.1) is the unique MVU estimator of σ^2. [*Hint:* Use Theorem 8.3.8.]

9.17H Despite the results of Problems 9.38 and 9.16H, $\hat{\sigma}^2$ is not perfect as an estimator of σ^2 in the μ known context, as the following considerations demonstrate. Suppose we wish to consider a class of estimators defined by

$$\hat{\sigma}^2(c) = c\hat{\sigma}^2 = c \sum_{i=1}^{n} \frac{(X_i - \mu)^2}{n}.$$

Show that

$$E_{\sigma^2}\left(\hat{\sigma}^2(c) - \sigma^2\right)^2 = \left(c^2 \frac{n+2}{n} - 2c + 1\right)\sigma^4,$$

which is minimized by choosing $c = n/(n+2)$, not by choosing $c = 1$. Hence, if the average squared error [which was considered in another estimation context at Definition 7.1.23ff] is our criterion of goodness of an estimator, $\hat{\sigma}^2$ is beaten by $\hat{\sigma}^2(n/(n+2))$ for every value of σ^2 (i.e., uniformly in σ^2).

9.18H Let $X_1, X_2, \ldots$ be a sequence of r.v.'s. Suppose that X_n has Student's t-distribution with n d.f. Show (first by characteristic function methods, and then directly) that the limiting distribution of X_n is $N(0,1)$; that is, for every x (see Definition 6.2.4)

$$\lim_{n \to \infty} P[X_n \leq x] = \Phi(x).$$

9.19H Use Slutsky's Theorem (see Theorem 6.3.12) to prove the result of Problem 9.18H. [*Hint:* Use Slutsky's theorem to show that

$$\sqrt{n}\frac{\overline{X}-\mu}{\sqrt{\dfrac{\sum_{i=1}^{n}(X_i-\overline{X})^2}{n-1}}} - \sqrt{n}\frac{\overline{X}-\mu}{\sigma} \xrightarrow{P} 0$$

and (see Definition 6.3.2) immediately deduce the desired result.]

9.20H Prove that when H_0 is true, the left side of equation (9.9.8) has Student's t-distribution with $m-1$ d.f.

9.21H Compare the power of the Neyman-Bartlett and Scheffé solutions to the Behrens-Fisher problem. In particular, prove the Scheffé solution is more powerful.

CHAPTER 10

Interval Estimation

In Chapters 7 and 8 we considered how to estimate an unknown parameter (e.g., θ) by a point (e.g., $\hat{\theta}$) in such a way that $\hat{\theta}$ is "close" to θ (e.g., $E\hat{\theta} \equiv \theta$, $\text{Var}(\hat{\theta})$ small, and so on). In this chapter we consider **interval estimation**; that is, how to estimate θ by an interval of values $\{x: \hat{\theta}_L < x < \hat{\theta}_U\}$ (abbreviated $(\hat{\theta}_L, \hat{\theta}_U)$) that has high probability of including θ but that also has, say, small average length $E(\hat{\theta}_U - \hat{\theta}_L)$. This subject is intimately related to tests of hypotheses (Chapter 9), and is grasped most easily in the context of general confidence sets (which may, but need not, be intervals) (Section 10.1). Some applications to various important cases are given (Sections 10.2ff), while others are treated in the problems, and still others can be constructed from the related tests by using the techniques of Section 10.1.

10.1. CONFIDENCE SETS AND TESTS OF HYPOTHESES

Some situations in which hypothesis-testing problems arise were described in Section 9.1. Generally, these were of the type "*Does* making a certain modification to some system or process change a particular parameter θ?" or "*Is* my parameter θ equal to θ_0?" In interval estimation we are concerned with the same situations, but instead ask "*How much* does making a certain modification to some system or process change a particular parameter θ?" or "*How large* is my parameter θ?" (Another approach to these latter questions is that of point estimation.)

Before introducing confidence sets in full generality, let us consider a special case; the results here will be helpful to our intuition. Suppose X is a univariate r.v. with d.f. $F(x|\theta)$ where θ is an unknown univariate parameter, $\theta \in \Theta$. Suppose we have available a test of the simple hypothesis H_0: $\theta = \theta_0$ *versus* the composite alternative H_1: $\theta \neq \theta_0$, and that test rejects iff $X < a$ or $X > b$, where a and b are specified numbers such that

$$P_{\theta_0}[X < a, \text{ or } X > b] = \alpha; \tag{10.1.1}$$

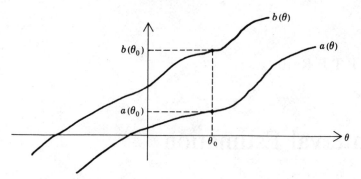

Figure 10.1-1. The function $a(\cdot)$ and $b(\cdot)$.

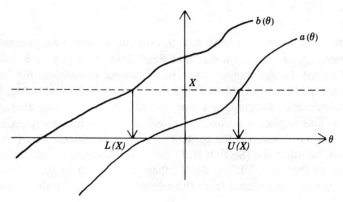

Figure 10.1-2. Construction of the interval $(L(\overline{X}), U(\overline{X}))$.

that is, such that the test has level α. Then usually a and b will be functions of θ_0, say $a = a(\theta_0)$ and $b = b(\theta_0)$. Consider plotting $a(\cdot)$ and $b(\cdot)$, as in Figure 10.1-1, for every θ. Then for a specified $\theta = \theta_0$, we have heights $a(\theta_0) < b(\theta_0)$, and (by (10.1.1))

$$P_{\theta_0}\big[a(\theta_0) \le X \le b(\theta_0)\big] = 1 - \alpha. \qquad (10.1.2)$$

Now (see Figure 10.1-2) plot the r.v. X on the vertical axis and draw a horizontal dashed line through it. Let $L(X)$ denote the value of θ at the intersection of the dashed line with the graph of $b(\theta)$, and $U(X)$ the value of θ at the intersection with the graph of $a(\theta)$. (We assume for now that $a(\theta)$ and $b(\theta)$ are such that there is, for each possible value of X, exactly one intersection of each type. More general cases will be considered in the context of confidence sets.) Then we claim that

$$P_{\theta}\big[L(X) \le \theta \le U(X)\big] \overset{\theta}{=} 1 - \alpha; \qquad (10.1.3)$$

that is, θ has probability $1 - \alpha$ (for example, .95 if $\alpha = .05$) of lying between

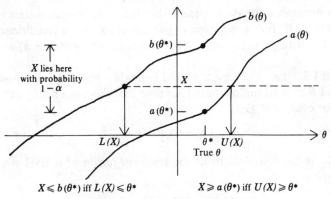

$X \leq b(\theta^*)$ iff $L(X) \leq \theta^*$ $X \geq a(\theta^*)$ iff $U(X) \geq \theta^*$

Figure 10.1-3. Proof of equation (10.1.3).

$L(X)$ and $U(X)$. The proof is as follows: If θ^* is the true value of θ, then by (10.1.2), $P_{\theta^*}[a(\theta^*) \leq X \leq b(\theta^*)] = 1 - \alpha$. But $a(\theta^*) \leq X \leq b(\theta^*)$ iff $L(X) \leq \theta^* \leq U(X)$ (see Figure 10.1-3), which proves the result.

The interval $(L(X), U(X))$ is then called a "confidence interval" for θ with "confidence coefficient" $1 - \alpha$. The concept extends to the multivariate case:

Definition 10.1.4. Let X be a r.v. with d.f. $F(x|\theta)$ where θ is unknown, $\theta \in \Theta$. [Here X and θ may be multivariate.] If (10.1.3) holds, then the interval $(L(X), U(X))$ is called a **confidence interval** for θ with **confidence coefficient** $1 - \alpha$.

If we have a multivariate, for example two-dimensional, parameter $\theta = (\theta_1, \theta_2)$, then "$\theta \in (L(X), U(X))$" means "$L_1(X) \leq \theta_1 \leq U_1(X)$ and $L_2(X) \leq \theta_2 \leq U_2(X)$," which is a rectangle (see Figure 10.1-4). But why shouldn't other shapes (e.g., the dashed figure in Figure 10.1-4) be allowed; perhaps they will have an even higher confidence coefficient. Thus, we are led to consider general confidence sets, which are subsets of Θ in which we have (hopefully high) confidence θ lies.

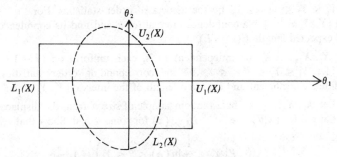

Figure 10.1-4. Confidence sets in two dimensions.

We now generalize the development that led, from a univariate r.v. X and a test (see (10.1.1)) for a univariate parameter θ, to a confidence interval $(L(X), U(X))$ with property (10.1.3) (confidence coefficient $1 - \alpha$) as follows.

Theorem 10.1.5. Let X be a r.v. with d.f. $F(x|\theta)$ where θ is unknown, $\theta \in \Theta$. [Here X and θ may be multivariate.] Suppose that there is a set C_θ of values of X such that for every $\theta \in \Theta$

$$P_\theta[X \in C_\theta] = 1 - \alpha. \tag{10.1.6}$$

[That is, C_{θ_0} is the complement of the rejection region of a level α test of H_0: $\theta = \theta_0$.] *Define*

$$S(X) = \{\theta^*: X \in C_{\theta^*}\}. \tag{10.1.7}$$

[That is, $S(X)$ is the collection of all θ^*'s for which observing X does not lead to rejection of H_0: $\theta = \theta^*$.] *Then*

$$P_\theta[\theta \in S(X)] \overset{\theta}{\equiv} 1 - \alpha. \tag{10.1.8}$$

Proof: We easily find, using (10.1.7) and (10.1.6), that

$$P_\theta[\theta \in S(X)] \overset{\theta}{\equiv} P_\theta[\theta \in \{\theta^*: X \in C_{\theta^*}\}]$$

$$\overset{\theta}{\equiv} P_\theta[X \in C_\theta] \overset{\theta}{\equiv} 1 - \alpha. \qquad \blacksquare \tag{10.1.9}$$

Definition 10.1.10. Let X be a r.v. with d.f. $F(x|\theta)$ where θ is unknown, $\theta \in \Theta$. [Here X and θ may be multivariate.] If (10.1.8) holds, then the set $S(X)$ is called a **confidence set** for θ with **confidence coefficient** $1 - \alpha$.

This definition is to confidence sets as Definition 10.1.4 is to confidence intervals.

PROBLEMS FOR SECTION 10.1

10.1.1 Let $X_1, X_2, \ldots, X_n$ be a random sample from a uniform distribution on $(0, \theta)$, and let $Y_1 \leq Y_2 \leq \cdots \leq Y_n$ be the associated order statistics. For "a" fixed, show that $[Y_n, Y_n a^{-1/n}]$ is a confidence interval for θ and find its confidence coefficient and expected length $E(U - L)$.

10.1.2 Let $X_1, X_2, \ldots, X_n$ be independent r.v.'s, each uniform on $(\theta - 1/2, \theta + 1/4)$, and let $Y_1 \leq Y_2 \leq \cdots \leq Y_n$ be the corresponding order statistics. Find the confidence coefficient and expected length of the interval (Y_1, Y_n) for θ.

10.1.3 (a) Let $X_1, X_2, \ldots, X_n$ be a random sample of size n from the displaced exponential p.d.f. $f(x|\theta) = e^{-(x-\theta)}I_{(\theta, \infty)}(x)$ for some $\theta > 0$. Show that

$$P\left(Y_1 + \frac{1}{n}\ln(\alpha) \leq \theta \leq Y_1\right) = 1 - \alpha,$$

where $Y_1 \leq Y_2 \leq \cdots \leq Y_n$ are the corresponding order statistics. Note that the expected length of this interval is $(\ln(\alpha))/n$.

(b) Suppose we consider (Y_1, Y_n) as a confidence interval for θ. Find the confidence coefficient of this interval, and also its expected length.

10.1.4 Let X_1, X_2 be independent exponential r.v.'s with respective means θ_1, θ_2. Show that $S(X_1, X_2) = \{(\theta_1, \theta_2): \theta_1 X_1 + \theta_2 X_2 \leq a\}$ is a $100(1 - (1 + a)e^{-a})\%$ confidence set for the joint parameter (θ_1, θ_2). Find the "a" needed for a 95% confidence set. Find the 95% confidence set when $X_1 = 3$, $X_2 = 1.5$.

10.2. CONFIDENCE INTERVALS FOR ONE NORMAL MEAN

In this section we consider confidence intervals (and make some remarks about confidence sets) for one normal mean, first in the case where σ^2 is known, and then in the case where σ^2 is unknown.

Example 10.2.1. Let $X_1, \ldots, X_n$ be independent $N(\mu, \sigma^2)$ r.v.'s where μ is unknown with $\mu \in \Theta = \{x: -\infty < x < +\infty\}$ and $\sigma^2 > 0$ is known. Find a confidence interval for μ with confidence coefficient $1 - \alpha = .95$.

Here $\bar{X} = (X_1 + \cdots + X_n)/n$ is a minimal sufficient statistic, and hence we should let our confidence interval for μ depend on $X_1, \ldots, X_n$ solely through $\bar{X}$. In this case, good tests[1] of the hypothesis H_0: $\mu = \mu_0$ were studied in Section 9.5 and (see (9.5.2)) a typical member of a reasonable class rejects H_0: $\mu = \mu_0$ iff

$$\bar{X} - \mu_0 < \frac{\sigma}{\sqrt{n}} \Phi^{-1}(\alpha p) \quad \text{or} \quad \bar{X} - \mu_0 > \frac{\sigma}{\sqrt{n}} \Phi^{-1}(1 - \alpha(1 - p)), \quad (10.2.2)$$

where p $(0 \leq p \leq 1)$ is fixed but arbitrary. (Note that p is usually taken to be either 0, or 1, or 0.5; these correspond to one-sided $(0, 1)$ and two-sided equal-tail (0.5) tests, respectively. Although these three special values are used almost exclusively in practice, and the possibility of allowing greater protection against one of the deviations $\mu < \mu_0$ or $\mu > \mu_0$ than against the other is not felt to be of importance in most practice, the fact that all three tests are members of a larger class allows for a unified theory and ease of understanding.)

Since when H_0 is true (10.2.2) occurs with probability α, its complement occurs with probability $1 - \alpha$:

$$P_{\mu_0}\left[\mu_0 + \frac{\sigma}{\sqrt{n}} \Phi^{-1}(\alpha p) \leq \bar{X} \leq \mu_0 + \frac{\sigma}{\sqrt{n}} \Phi^{-1}(1 - \alpha(1 - p))\right] = 1 - \alpha.$$

$$(10.2.3)$$

---

[1] *Any* level α test of H_0: $\mu = \mu_0$ (defined for all possibilities μ_0) can be used to obtain a confidence set for μ with confidence coefficient $1 - \alpha$. However (see Problem 10.1H) "good" confidence sets come from "good" tests. Thus, "good" tests are the tests of interest to us.

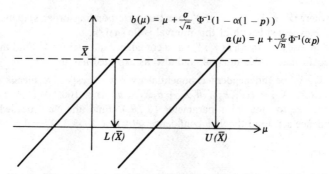

Figure 10.2-1. Constuction of $(L(X), U(X))$.

Thus (see (10.1.2)) here our functions $a(\mu)$ and $b(\mu)$ are

$$
\begin{cases}
a(\mu) = \mu + \dfrac{\sigma}{\sqrt{n}} \Phi^{-1}(\alpha p), \\[2ex]
b(\mu) = \mu + \dfrac{\sigma}{\sqrt{n}} \Phi^{-1}(1 - \alpha(1 - p)).
\end{cases}
\tag{10.2.4}
$$

To construct our confidence interval $(L(\overline{X}), U(\overline{X}))$, we proceed as in Figure 10.1-2 (see Figure 10.2-1), finally obtaining the solution via solving $\overline{X} = b(\mu)$ for $L(\overline{X})$ and $\overline{X} = a(\mu)$ for $U(\overline{X})$:

$$
\begin{cases}
L(\overline{X}) = \overline{X} - \dfrac{\sigma}{\sqrt{n}} \Phi^{-1}(1 - \alpha(1 - p)), \\[2ex]
U(\overline{X}) = \overline{X} - \dfrac{\sigma}{\sqrt{n}} \Phi^{-1}(\alpha p).
\end{cases}
\tag{10.2.5}
$$

Thus,

$$
P_\mu \left[\overline{X} - \frac{\sigma}{\sqrt{n}} \Phi^{-1}(1 - \alpha(1 - p)) \le \mu \le \overline{X} - \frac{\sigma}{\sqrt{n}} \Phi^{-1}(\alpha p) \right] \overset{\mu}{=} 1 - \alpha. \tag{10.2.6}
$$

In the desired case of $1 - \alpha = .95$, if we choose $p = .5$ [one of many possible choices] and use Table 11, we find (see Problem 10.2) our interval is

$$
\left(\overline{X} - 1.96 \frac{\sigma}{\sqrt{n}},\ \overline{X} + 1.96 \frac{\sigma}{\sqrt{n}} \right). \tag{10.2.7}
$$

In fact, $p = .5$ is a reasonable choice since of all p $(0 \le p \le 1)$ it yields (see Problem 10.3) the one with the smallest length, namely length equal to

$$
\frac{\sigma}{\sqrt{n}} \left\{ \Phi^{-1}\left(1 - \frac{\alpha}{2}\right) - \Phi^{-1}\left(\frac{\alpha}{2}\right) \right\} = 2 \frac{\sigma}{\sqrt{n}} \Phi^{-1}\left(1 - \frac{\alpha}{2}\right). \tag{10.2.8}
$$

Note: If we were concerned with a confidence interval that would put an *upper* *bound* on μ, we could choose $p = 1$ in (10.2.5) and obtain the interval

$$\left(-\infty, \ \overline{X} + \frac{\sigma}{\sqrt{n}} \Phi^{-1}(1 - \alpha)\right). \tag{10.2.9}$$

We can (see Problem 10.6) similarly obtain a *lower bound* on μ.

Also note that we obtained parallel lines $a(\mu)$ and $b(\mu)$ in Figure 10.2-1 as a result of our holding p fixed independent of μ. If we chose different p's for various μ values we would obtain other curves.

We next consider the case where σ^2 is unknown.

Example 10.2.10. Let $X_1, \ldots, X_n$ be independent $N(\mu, \sigma^2)$ r.v.'s where μ is unknown ($-\infty < \mu < +\infty$) and σ^2 is unknown ($\sigma^2 > 0$). Find a confidence interval for μ with confidence coefficient $1 - \alpha = .95$.

In this case, good tests of the hypothesis H_0: $\mu = \mu_0$ were obtained in Theorem 9.5.26 and (see Problem 9.35) a typical test rejects H_0: $\mu = \mu_0$ iff

$$\overline{X} - \mu_0 < \frac{s}{\sqrt{n}} t_{n-1}^{-1}(\alpha p) \quad \text{or} \quad \overline{X} - \mu_0 > \frac{s}{\sqrt{n}} t_{n-1}^{-1}(1 - \alpha(1 - p)), \tag{10.2.11}$$

where p ($0 \le p \le 1$) is fixed but arbitrary. By a development similar to that following (10.2.2) we find (see Problem 10.8)

$$\begin{cases} L = \overline{X} - \dfrac{s}{\sqrt{n}} t_{n-1}^{-1}(1 - \alpha(1 - p)), \\[2mm] U = \overline{X} - \dfrac{s}{\sqrt{n}} t_{n-1}^{-1}(\alpha p). \end{cases} \tag{10.2.12}$$

In the desired case of $1 - \alpha = .95$, if we choose $p = .5$ [one of many possible choices] and use Table 13, we find (see Problem 10.9) our interval is

$$\left(\overline{X} - 2.57 \frac{s}{\sqrt{6}}, \ \overline{X} + 2.57 \frac{s}{\sqrt{6}}\right) \quad \text{if } n = 6. \tag{10.2.13}$$

Here we needed to assume a value of n (we took $n = 6$ for purposes of illustration) since the quantity $t_{n-1}^{-1}(\cdot)$ is a function of n. [At (10.2.5) we had $\Phi^{-1}(\cdot)$, which was not a function of n, in the case of known $\sigma^2 > 0$.]

In fact, $p = .5$ is a reasonable choice here also since, as was the case in the instance of a known $\sigma^2 > 0$, it yields (see Problem 10.10) the shortest length

$$2 \frac{s}{\sqrt{n}} t_{n-1}^{-1}\left(1 - \frac{\alpha}{2}\right). \tag{10.2.14}$$

Note: In the case of known σ^2 the intervals had fixed length, so by an appropriate choice of n we could specify the length of the interval on μ. (For example, if we have $p = .5$, we simply take n to be the smallest integer greater than or equal to the solution x of the equation

$$2\frac{\sigma}{\sqrt{x}}\Phi^{-1}\left(1 - \frac{\alpha}{2}\right) = L_0$$

and obtain an interval of length L_0 [or slightly less].) In this case the length is a random variable (e.g., see (10.2.14) for the length in the case $p = .5$) since s is a r.v. and hence cannot be specified in advance of the experiment unless we have some idea of how large s will be (which we might if we had an idea of the size of σ^2).

Example 10.2.15. The average high-school grade point average (GPA) of the entering freshman class at a certain college is desired to be estimated. (For example, we may do this if we desire to know the GPA and the college will not release this information.) Based on a random sample of 25 freshmen, the sample mean and sample variance are $\overline{X} = 2.93$ and $s^2 = 0.519841$. Find a 95% confidence interval for the true average high-school GPA of the entering class.

Let μ denote the true high-school GPA. Then the confidence interval for μ, based on formula (10.2.12), is

$$\left(\overline{X} - \frac{s}{\sqrt{n}}t_{n-1}^{-1}(1 - \alpha/2),\ \overline{X} + \frac{s}{\sqrt{n}}t_{n-1}^{-1}(1 - \alpha/2)\right),$$

where we took $p = 0.5$. Now $n = 25$, and because the confidence coefficient is $.95 = 1 - \alpha$, we have $t_{n-1}^{-1}(1 - \alpha/2) = 2.064$. Therefore the confidence interval for μ is $(2.6324, 3.2276)$.

In each of Examples 10.2.1 and 10.2.10, and in Section 10.1, **we have obtained confidence intervals from tests of hypotheses. However, another method of obtaining confidence intervals** (which is not always feasible, but when it is often yields answers quickly and neatly) **is available** and will now be explained. (Since the result is closely related to Theorem 10.1.5, we could call it a corollary. However, it makes no use of hypothesis-testing ideas.) We call this the **"pivotal quantity" method**.

Lemma 10.2.16. Let X be a r.v. with d.f. $F(x|\theta)$ where θ is unknown, $\theta \in \Theta$. [Here X and θ may be multivariate.] Suppose there is a function $g(X, \theta)$ whose distribution is known and does not depend on θ. Then it is easy to find sets S of possible values of $g(X, \theta)$ such that

$$P[g(X, \theta) \in S] \equiv 1 - \alpha. \qquad (10.2.17)$$

However, each such set S yields us a confidence set for θ since

$$P_\theta[\theta \in \{\theta: g(X, \theta) \in S\}] \overset{\theta}{=} 1 - \alpha. \qquad (10.2.18)$$

Remark 10.2.19. The function $g(X, \theta)$ is called a **pivotal quantity** for determining a confidence interval for θ. The most important objective with this method is to find the distribution of this pivotal quantity and the percentile points of its distribution. Often the distribution is well-known. We will now demonstrate the use of this new method of finding confidence intervals below and in subsequent sections.

Example 10.2.20. As in Example 10.2.1, let $X_1, \ldots, X_n$ be independent $N(\mu, \sigma^2)$ r.v.'s with μ unknown and σ^2 known. Then

$$g(X_1, \ldots, X_n, \mu) = \frac{\overline{X} - \mu}{\sigma/\sqrt{n}} \qquad (10.2.21)$$

has the $N(0, 1)$ distribution, which does not depend on μ. One possible choice of S, $S = \{x: -1.96 \le x \le 1.96\}$, yields

$$P\big[g(X_1, \ldots, X_n, \mu) \in S\big] = .95$$

$$= P\left[-1.96 \le \frac{\overline{X} - \mu}{\sigma/\sqrt{n}} \le 1.96\right]$$

$$= P\left[-1.96 \frac{\sigma}{\sqrt{n}} \le \overline{X} - \mu \le 1.96 \frac{\sigma}{\sqrt{n}}\right] \qquad (10.2.22)$$

$$= P\left[\overline{X} - 1.96 \frac{\sigma}{\sqrt{n}} \le \mu \le \overline{X} + 1.96 \frac{\sigma}{\sqrt{n}}\right].$$

This is the same interval as at (10.2.7).

PROBLEMS FOR SECTION 10.2

10.2.1 Let $X_1, X_2, \ldots, X_n$ (n to be determined) be a random sample of size n from a $N(\mu, \sigma^2)$ distribution with σ^2 known. Let $(L(X_1, X_2, \ldots, X_n), U(X_1, X_2, \ldots, X_n))$ be the $100(1 - \alpha)\%$ confidence interval for μ given by (10.2.5). Show that in order to estimate μ to within ε with $100(1 - \alpha)\%$ confidence we need a sample of size $n = [(\Phi^{-1}(1 - \alpha))^2 \sigma^2/\varepsilon^2]$. (Here, $[x]$ denotes the smallest integer greater than or equal to x; e.g. $[24.81] = 25$.)

10.2.2 Let $X_1, X_2, \ldots, X_n$ be a random sample of size n from a $N(\mu, \mu^2)$ distribution. Find
(a) A $100(1 - \alpha)\%$ confidence interval for μ.
(b) A $100(1 - \alpha)\%$ confidence interval for μ^2.

10.2.3 Let $X_1, X_2, \ldots, X_n$ (n large enough to justify applying the Central Limit Theorem) be independent r.v.'s, each Poisson with mean λ. Find an (approximate) $100(1 - \alpha)\%$ confidence interval for λ.

10.2.4 Let $X_1, X_2, \ldots, X_n$ be a random sample of size n from the p.d.f. $f(x|\beta) = \Gamma^{-1}(\alpha)\beta^{-\alpha}e^{-x/\beta}x^{\alpha-1}I_{[0,\infty)}(x)$ with α known. Use the Central Limit Theorem to construct a pivotal quantity, and then find an (approximate) $100(1 - \alpha)\%$ confidence interval for β.

10.2.5 Using the data of Problem 9.5.1, construct a confidence interval for μ with confidence coefficient **(a)** .99; **(b)** .95; **(c)** .90; **(d)** .80. Does the length of the intervals increase or decrease as the confidence coefficient decreases?

10.2.6 For a given confidence coefficient, a confidence interval (for a parameter θ) is "better" if it has shorter length. Consider the confidence intervals (10.2.12) for μ when σ^2 is unknown (in the normal distribution case).
(a) Find the expected length of the confidence interval.
(b) Show that the expected length decreases as n increases.
(c) Show that as the confidence coefficient decreases, the expected length also decreases.

10.2.7 Let $X_1, X_2, \ldots, X_n$ be a random sample of size n from some p.d.f. (not necessarily normal) with mean μ and variance σ^2 (both finite, with σ^2 known). Use the pivotal quantity method and the Central Limit Theorem to construct a $100(1 - \alpha)\%$ confidence interval for μ.

10.2.8 Let $X_1, X_2, \ldots, X_n$ be a random sample of size n from the p.d.f. $f(x|\beta) = \Gamma(\beta + 3)2^{-1}\Gamma^{-1}(\beta)x^2(1 - x)^{\beta-1}I_{(0,1)}(x)$. Use the pivotal quantity method to construct a $100(1 - \alpha)\%$ confidence interval for β.

10.2.9 In Problem 9.5.1, construct a 95% confidence interval for μ. If the sample size were 100, what confidence interval would be obtained? If the sample size were 225? 400?

10.2.10 Using the data in Problem 9.5.4, construct a confidence interval for μ with confidence coefficient **(a)** .80; **(b)** .90; **(c)** .95; **(d)** .98; **(e)** .99.

10.2.11 Let $X_1, X_2, \ldots, X_n$ be a random sample from an exponential distribution with p.d.f. $f(x|\lambda) = \lambda e^{-\lambda x}I_{(0,\infty)}(x)$. Recall that the MLE of λ is $1/\overline{X}$, and converges in distribution (law) to $N(\lambda, \lambda^2/n)$. Use this information and the pivotal quantity method to construct an (approximate) $100(1 - \alpha)\%$ confidence interval for λ.

10.3. CONFIDENCE INTERVALS FOR ONE NORMAL VARIANCE

In this section we consider confidence intervals for one normal variance in the case where μ is known. The case where μ is unknown is handled by a simple modification. The technique used in both of these cases is based on Lemma 10.2.15.

Let $X_1, X_2, \ldots, X_n$ be independent $N(\mu, \sigma^2)$ r.v.'s where μ may be known or unknown. We wish to find a confidence interval for σ^2 with confidence coefficient $1 - \alpha$.

Case I: Confidence Interval for σ^2 when μ is known.   Since $\sum\limits_{i=1}^{n}(X_i - \mu)^2/\sigma^2$ is $\chi_n^2(0)$,

$$P\left(\chi_{n,\alpha/2}^{2^{-1}}(0) \le \frac{\sum\limits_{i=1}^{n}(X_i - \mu)^2}{\sigma^2} \le \chi_{n,1-\alpha/2}^{2^{-1}}(0)\right) = 1 - \alpha,$$

and hence a confidence interval for σ^2 with confidence coefficient $1 - \alpha$ is

$$
\left(\frac{\sum_{i=1}^{n} (X_i - \mu)^2}{\chi_{n,1-\alpha/2}^{2^{-1}}(0)} , \frac{\sum_{i=1}^{n} (X_i - \mu)^2}{\chi_{n,\alpha/2}^{2^{-1}}(0)} \right). \tag{10.3.1}
$$

Case II: **Confidence Interval for σ^2 when μ is unknown.** Since $(n - 1)s^2/\sigma^2$ $= \sum_{i=1}^{n} (X_i - \overline{X})^2/\sigma^2$ is $\chi_{n-1}^2(0)$, as in case I a $1 - \alpha$ confidence interval for σ^2 is

$$
\left(\frac{\sum_{i=1}^{n} (X_i - \overline{X})^2}{\chi_{n-1,1-\alpha/2}^{2^{-1}}(0)} , \frac{\sum_{i=1}^{n} (X_i - \overline{X})^2}{\chi_{n-1,\alpha/2}^{2^{-1}}(0)} \right). \tag{10.3.2}
$$

Example 10.3.3. Based on a random sample of size 23 from a normal distribution, suppose $s^2 = 12.68$. Find a 90% confidence interval for σ^2.

Here μ is unknown and $1 - \alpha = .90$, hence $\chi_{n-1,1-\alpha/2}^{2^{-1}}(0) = \chi_{22,.95}^{2^{-1}}(0) = 33.9244$ and $\chi_{n-1,\alpha/2}^{2^{-1}}(0) = \chi_{22,.05}^{2^{-1}}(0) = 12.338$. Hence the desired 90% confidence interval is $(8.223, 22.61)$.

Sometimes experimenters wish to find **a confidence interval for σ** (rather than for σ^2), and it is easy to obtain this from the interval on σ^2:

$$
1 - \alpha = P\left(\chi_{n-1,\alpha/2}^{2^{-1}}(0) \le \frac{\sum (X_i - \overline{X})^2}{\sigma^2} \le \chi_{n-1,1-\alpha/2}^{2^{-1}}(0) \right) \tag{10.3.4}
$$

$$
= P\left(\sqrt{\chi_{n-1,\alpha/2}^{2^{-1}}(0)} \le \sqrt{\frac{\sum (X_i - \overline{X})^2}{\sigma^2}} \le \sqrt{\chi_{n-1,1-\alpha/2}^{2^{-1}}(0)} \right)
$$

because both the values and the random variable are positive. Thus a $1 - \alpha$ confidence interval for σ is

$$
\left(\frac{\sqrt{\sum (X_i - \overline{X})^2}}{\sqrt{\chi_{n-1,1-\alpha/2}^{2^{-1}}(0)}} , \frac{\sqrt{\sum (X_i - \overline{X})^2}}{\sqrt{\chi_{n-1,\alpha/2}^{2^{-1}}(0)}} \right). \tag{10.3.5}
$$

For example, a 90% confidence interval for σ in Example 10.3.3 is $(2.868, 4.755)$.

To complete the discussion of confidence intervals for σ^2 (or for σ), we now discuss **large sample intervals.** Note that most tables of the chi-square distribution only go up to 100 degrees of freedom. The following method allows us to deal with large n **using the limiting distribution.** Recall (see Example 6.3.16) that

$$
\sqrt{n}\,(s - \sigma) \xrightarrow{d} N(0, \sigma^2/2),
$$

that is,

$$\frac{\sqrt{n}\,(s - \sigma)}{\sigma/\sqrt{2}} \stackrel{d}{\to} N(0, 1).$$

Therefore

$$P\left(\Phi^{-1}(\alpha/2) \leq \sqrt{2n}\,\frac{(s - \sigma)}{\sigma} \leq \Phi^{-1}(1 - \alpha/2) \right) \simeq 1 - \alpha, \quad (10.3.6)$$

hence a $1 - \alpha$ confidence interval for σ based on a large sample is (since $\Phi^{-1}(1 - \alpha/2) = -\Phi^{-1}(\alpha/2)$)

$$\left(\frac{s}{1 + \dfrac{\Phi^{-1}(1 - \alpha/2)}{\sqrt{2n}}}, \frac{s}{1 - \dfrac{\Phi^{-1}(1 - \alpha/2)}{\sqrt{2n}}} \right). \quad (10.3.7)$$

An interval for σ^2 is obtained by simply squaring the limits in (10.3.7).

In the case of unknown μ, interval (10.3.2) requires $n \geq 2$ in order to yield a confidence interval. However, even in the case of $n = 1$ an interval for σ that has probability at least $1 - \alpha$ of including σ can be obtained, as we will now see. (This result was originated by Rosenblatt (1966).)

Example 10.3.8. Let X be a $N(\mu, \sigma^2)$ r.v. with μ $(-\infty < \mu < +\infty)$ and $\sigma^2 > 0$ both unknown. Let $c > 0$ be chosen to satisfy

$$\Phi\left(\frac{1}{c} \right) - \Phi\left(-\frac{1}{c} \right) = \alpha. \quad (10.3.6)$$

Then

$$
\begin{aligned}
P[\sigma \in (0, c|X|)] &= P\left[\frac{\sigma}{c} \leq |X| \right] = 1 - P\left[\frac{\sigma}{c} > |X| \right] \\
&= 1 - P\left[-\frac{\sigma}{c} < X < \frac{\sigma}{c} \right] \\
&= 1 - P\left[-\frac{1}{c} - \frac{\mu}{\sigma} < \frac{X - \mu}{\sigma} < \frac{1}{c} - \frac{\mu}{\sigma} \right] \\
&= 1 - \left\{ \Phi\left(\frac{1}{c} - \frac{\mu}{\sigma} \right) - \Phi\left(-\frac{1}{c} - \frac{\mu}{\sigma} \right) \right\}.
\end{aligned}
\quad (10.3.7)
$$

Since $\Phi(a - b) - \Phi(-a - b)$ is largest when $b = 0$ (see Problem 10.16), using (10.3.6) we find

$$P[\sigma \in (0, c|X|)] \geq 1 - \left\{ \Phi\left(\frac{1}{c} \right) - \Phi\left(-\frac{1}{c} \right) \right\} = 1 - \alpha. \quad (10.3.8)$$

Hence, the interval $(0, c|X|)$ has probability at least $1 - \alpha$ of covering σ.

PROBLEMS FOR SECTION 10.3

10.3.1 Consider the data given in Problem 9.6.2.
   (a) Construct a 90% confidence interval for σ^2.
   (b) Construct a 90% confidence interval for σ.
   (c) Construct a 90% large sample confidence interval for σ (developed in this section at (10.3.7)).
   (d) Compute the length of the intervals in parts (b) and (c), and comment on why one is shorter.

10.3.2 Consider the data given in Problem 9.6.3. Construct a 95% confidence interval for σ^2.

10.3.3 Let $X_1, X_2, \ldots, X_n$ be a random sample of size n from a normal distribution with known mean μ and unknown variance σ^2. Construct a $100(1 - \alpha)\%$ confidence interval for σ^2. Compute the expected length of this interval, say $E_{\sigma^2}(n, \alpha)$. Find $\lim_{n \to \infty} E_{\sigma^2}(n, \alpha)$ when α is fixed, and $\lim_{\sigma \to 0} E_{\sigma^2}(n, \alpha)$ when n is fixed.

10.3.4 As in Problem 10.3.3, but now with μ also unknown.

10.3.5 Let $X_1, X_2, \ldots, X_n$ be a random sample of size n from a $N(\mu, \sigma^2)$ distribution with μ and σ^2 both unknown. Consider the parameter of interest to be the coefficient of variation σ/μ; note that the MLE of σ/μ is $s_n/\overline{X}_n$. It was shown in Example 6.3.18 that $\sqrt{n}((s_n/\overline{X}_n) - (\sigma/\mu))$ converges in distribution to the $N(O, V(\mu, \sigma^2))$ with $V(\mu, \sigma^2) = (\sigma^2/(2\mu^2)) + (\sigma^4/\mu^4)$. Construct an (appropriate) asymptotic pivotal quantity, and use it to construct an (approximate) $100(1 - \alpha)\%$ confidence interval for
   (a) The coefficient of variation σ/μ.
   (b) The signal-to-noise ratio μ/σ.

10.4. CONFIDENCE INTERVALS FOR A SUCCESS PROBABILITY

Let $X_1, \ldots, X_n$ be independent r.v.'s, each Bernoulli with unknown probability of success $p (0 \le p \le 1)$. In this section we study confidence intervals for p.

Here (by an easy modification of Problem 8.17) $\overline{X} = (X_1 + \cdots + X_n)/n$ is a minimal sufficient statistic, so we would expect to be able to base a good test on $\overline{X}$ alone. For testing H_0: $p = p_0$, it is clear intuitively that a good test will reject iff

$$\overline{X} < c_1, \quad \text{or} \quad \overline{X} > c_2, \tag{10.4.1}$$

where c_1 and c_2 are chosen (if possible) to give level α. (See Problem 10.17.)

When we try to use Theorem 10.1.5 (see also Figure 10.1-2) to construct our confidence interval, we encounter a problem studied in Problem 10.17 and alluded to in Problem 10.3H: since $\overline{X}$ is a discrete r.v. (its possible values are $0, 1/n, 2/n, \ldots, 1$), the level α test of H_0: $p = p_0$ with rejection region (10.4.1) is usually randomized. Hence, for "most" values of p $(0 \le p \le 1)$ there do not exist $a(p)$ and $b(p)$ (see (10.1.2)) such that

$$P_p[a(p) \le \overline{X} \le b(p)] = 1 - \alpha. \tag{10.4.2}$$

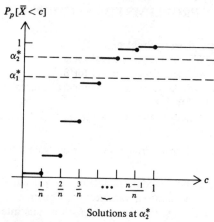

Solutions at α_2^*

Figure 10.4-1. Solutions c of $P_p|\overline{X} < c| = \alpha/2$. [Graph for $n = 7$, $p = .40$, $\alpha = .05$.]

Suppose we desire an equal-tail (see Problem 10.15) interval. Then we would like to solve

$$P_p\left[\overline{X} < a(p)\right] = \frac{\alpha}{2} \tag{10.4.3}$$

and

$$P_p\left[\overline{X} > b(p)\right] = \frac{\alpha}{2} \tag{10.4.4}$$

for $a(p)$ and $b(p)$ (respectively) for each p ($0 \le p \le 1$). To see that this is not possible consider, say, equation (10.4.3). For a fixed p, $P_p[\overline{X} < c]$ jumps each time c passes one of the points $0, 1/n, 2/n, \ldots, 1$ and remains constant between (see Figure 10.4-1). Hence, for most $\alpha/2$ (e.g., $\alpha/2 = \alpha_1^*$ in Figure 10.4-1) there is no solution $a(p)$ to equation (10.4.3), though for different $\alpha/2$ (e.g., $\alpha/2 = \alpha_2^*$ in Figure 10.4-1) there are many solutions.*

However, for each a ($0 < a \le 1$) there is a unique p for which equation (10.4.3) is solved, and for each b ($0 \le b < 1$) there is a unique p for which equation (10.4.4) is solved. The points (p, b) are plotted in Figure 10.4-2, and should be compared with the curve $b(\theta)$ in Figure 10.1-1 to see graphically the nature of our present difficulties.

Now suppose we graph the points (p, b) for $b = 0, 1/n, \ldots, (n-1)/n$ (the dots in Figure 10.4-2) as well as the points (p, a) for $a = 1/n, 2/n, \ldots, 1$. (See Figure 10.4-3.) Then for any observed value of $\overline{X}$ except 0 or 1 (i.e., for $\overline{X} = 1/n, \ldots, (n-1)/n$) an interval is determined. This interval does not {contain the true p with probability $\ge 1 - \alpha$}; the proof is as follows. Suppose that p_0 is the true value of p. Then [talking in terms of Figure 10.4-3 for the case

*At this point, at a first reading, skip the next two paragraphs of this section.

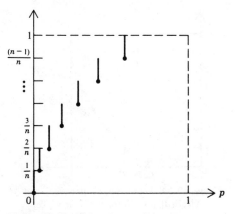

Figure 10.4-2. The points (p, b). [Graph for $n = 7$, $\alpha = .05$.]

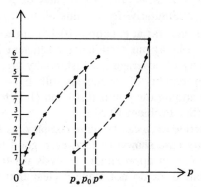

Figure 10.4-3. Points (p, a) and (p, b). [Graph for $n = 7$, $\alpha = .05$.]

$n = 7$, without loss of generality since the same argument works for any n] the interval generated by the procedure specified fails to cover p_0 iff $\overline{X} \geq 6/7$ or $\overline{X} \leq 1/7$. Since at p_* $P[\overline{X} \geq 6/7] = \alpha/2$, at p_0 $P[\overline{X} \geq 6/7] > \alpha/2$ (since $p_0 > p_*$). Similarly, since at p^* $P[\overline{X} \leq 1/7] = \alpha/2$, at p_0 $P[\overline{X} \leq 1/7] > \alpha/2$ (since $p_0 < p^*$). (See Problem 10.19.) Hence,

$$P_{p_0}\left[2/7 \leq \overline{X} \leq 5/7\right] = 1 - P_{p_0}\left[\overline{X} \geq 6/7\right] - P_{p_0}\left[\overline{X} \leq 1/7\right]$$

$$< 1 - P_{p_*}\left[\overline{X} \geq 6/7\right] - P_{p^*}\left[\overline{X} \leq 1/7\right] \quad (10.4.5)$$

$$\leq 1 - \alpha.$$

However, if we expand the intervals produced by our procedure by moving all b points up by $1/n$ (and all a points down by $1/n$), resulting in Figure 10.4-4, the proposed procedure will yield an interval with probability $\geq 1 - \alpha$ of containing the true value p_0. For *now* the interval generated by the procedure specified fails

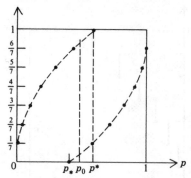

Figure 10.4-4. Points (p, a) [lowered] and (p, b) [raised]. [Graph for $n = 7$, $\alpha = .05$.]

to cover p_0 iff $\overline{X} \geq 1.0$ or $\overline{X} \leq .0$. Since for a value of $p^* > p_0$ $P_{p^*}[\overline{X} \geq 1.0] = \alpha/2$, $P_{p_0}[\overline{X} \geq 1.0] < \alpha/2$. Similarly, for a value of $p_* < p_0$ $P_{p_*}[\overline{X} \leq .0] = \alpha/2$, so $P_{p_0}[\overline{X} \leq .0] < \alpha/2$. Hence (as at equation (10.4.5) but with new points p_* and p^* as shown in Figure 10.4-4) our confidence coefficient is $\geq 1 - \alpha$. (In fact, sometimes the probability of coverage is substantially greater than $1 - \alpha$.) It is easy to show that the probability of coverage is still $\geq 1 - \alpha$ if we complete the proposed procedure by adding the points $(0,0)$ and $(1,1)$ to the upper and lower "curves," respectively. (See Problem 10.20.)

Thus, the case of discrete r.v.'s can be quite complex, as the preceding analysis of the success probability case shows. In fact, even good texts often either skip these cases entirely, or use an approximate analysis via treating $\overline{X}$ as approximately normally distributed, or do not make it clear that the confidence is not $= 1 - \alpha$ but rather $\geq 1 - \alpha$ with $\gg 1 - \alpha$ being a not uncommon occurrence.

Excellent charts for $1 - \alpha = .95$ and .99 for $n = 8, 10, 12, 16, 20, 24, 30, 40, 60, 100, 200, 400, 1000$ are given on pp. 228–229 of Pearson and Hartley (1970). There it was possible (due to the result shown in Problem 10.18) to use only the "bottom half" of graphs like that in Figure 10.4-4 and still have the complete situation covered. **One of these charts (the one for $1 - \alpha = .95$) is reproduced in Figure 10.4-5.** This chart is used as follows: If we observe $c = 26$ successes in $n = 100$ trials (so $c/n = .26$), an (at least) 95% confidence interval for p is $.18 \leq p \leq .36$ (this is read along the left and bottom axes); whereas if we observe $c = 88$ successes in $n = 100$ trials (so $c/n = .88$), an (at least) 95% confidence interval for p is $.80 \leq p \leq .93$ (this is read along the right and top axes).

It is common in practice to have a large sample size beyond the scope of the tables and charts. In such cases, note that $(\hat{p} - p)/\sqrt{pq/n}$ is approximately standard normal and thus is a pivotal quantity. Hence **a confidence interval with approximate confidence coefficient $1 - \alpha$ is**

$$\left(\hat{p} - \sqrt{\frac{\hat{p}\hat{q}}{n}}\ \Phi^{-1}(1 - \alpha/2),\ \hat{p} + \sqrt{\frac{\hat{p}\hat{q}}{n}}\ \Phi^{-1}(1 - \alpha/2) \right). \quad (10.4.6)$$

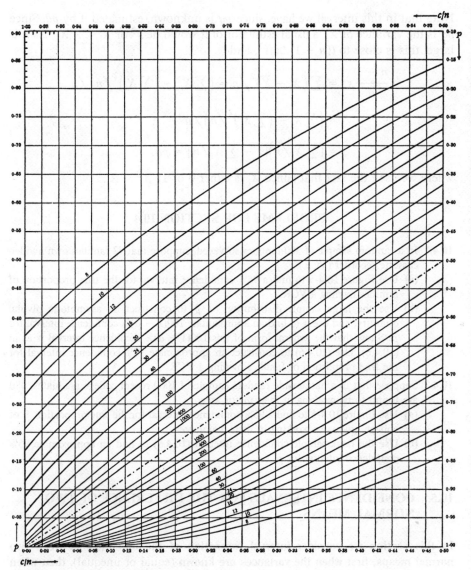

Figure 10.4-5. Chart providing confidence limits for a success probability p. c represents the observed number of successes in n trials. The numbers printed along the curves indicate the sample size n. (From E. S. Pearson and H. O. Hartley (eds.), *Biometrika Tables for Statisticians, Volume I* (3 ed. reprinted with additions), Cambridge University Press, London, 1970, pp. 228–229. Reprinted by the kind permission of the Biometrika Trustees.)

Note that in this interval we have, since pq is unknown, estimated it by $\hat{p}\hat{q}$. Since pq is the variance of X_i, a usual estimator of it would be s^2 of $X_1, \ldots, X_n$. As n is large, this is close to $((n-1)/n)s^2$, and

$$\frac{n-1}{n}s^2 = \sum (X_i - \bar{X})^2/n = \left(\sum X_i^2 - \left(\sum X_i \right)^2/n \right)/n$$

$$= \left(\sum X_i - \left(\sum X_i \right)^2/n \right)/n$$

$$= \left(\sum X_i/n \right)\left(1 - \sum X_i/n \right) = \hat{p}\hat{q},$$

where we used the fact that (since X_i is either 0 or 1) $X_i^2 = X_i$.

PROBLEMS FOR SECTION 10.4

10.4.1 In a random sample of 300 families surveyed, suppose that 72 families own a video cassette recorder (VCR).

(a) Use Figure 10.4-5 to find a 95% confidence interval for the true proportion of families owning a VCR.

(b) Use the large sample distribution of $\hat{p}$ to construct an asymptotic pivotal quantity, and use it to find an approximate $100(1 - \alpha)\%$ confidence interval for p. Show that the general form of this $100(1 - \alpha)\%$ confidence interval is as in (10.4.6). Use (10.4.6) to construct an approximate 95% confidence interval for the true proportion of families owning a VCR.

10.4.2 Suppose that in a nationwide random sample of 1000 recent college graduates, 480 are found to be working in their major area.

(a) Use Figure 10.4-5 to find a 95% confidence interval for the true proportion p of college graduates working in their major area.

(b) Use the large sample confidence interval (10.4.6) to find an approximate 95% confidence interval for p.

10.5. CONFIDENCE INTERVALS FOR THE DIFFERENCE OF TWO NORMAL MEANS

In this section we consider interval estimation of the difference between two normal means, first when the variances are known (equal or unequal), then when the variances are unknown and equal, and finally when the variances are unknown and may be unequal.

Let $X_{i1}, X_{i2}, \ldots, X_{in_i}$ be independent normal r.v.'s with mean μ_i and variance σ_i^2 $(i = 1, 2)$.

Case I: σ_1^2 **and** σ_2^2 **are known.** Recall that

$$\frac{(\bar{X}_1 - \bar{X}_2) - (\mu_1 - \mu_2)}{\sqrt{\dfrac{\sigma_1^2}{n_1} + \dfrac{\sigma_2^2}{n_2}}} \text{ is } N(0, 1)$$

where $\bar{X}_i = (X_{i1} + X_{i2} + \cdots + X_{in_i})/n_i$ $(i = 1, 2)$, and hence is a pivotal quantity. We have

$$P\left(\Phi^{-1}(\alpha/2) \le \frac{(\bar{X}_1 - \bar{X}_2) - (\mu_1 - \mu_2)}{\sqrt{\dfrac{\sigma_1^2}{n_1} + \dfrac{\sigma_2^2}{n_2}}} \le \Phi^{-1}(1 - \alpha/2)\right) = 1 - \alpha,$$

and therefore a $100(1 - \alpha)\%$ confidence interval for $\mu_1 - \mu_2$ is

$$\left((\bar{X}_1 - \bar{X}_2) - \Phi^{-1}(1 - \alpha/2)\sqrt{\frac{\sigma_1^2}{n_1} + \frac{\sigma_2^2}{n_2}},\right.$$

$$\left.(\bar{X}_1 - \bar{X}_2) + \Phi^{-1}(1 - \alpha/2)\sqrt{\frac{\sigma_1^2}{n_1} + \frac{\sigma_2^2}{n_2}}\right). \tag{10.5.1}$$

Case II: σ_1^2 **and** σ_2^2 **are unknown but equal.** Here calculate $\bar{X}_i = \sum_{j=1}^{n_i} X_{ij}/n_i$ and $s_i^2 = \sum_{j=1}^{n_i} (X_{ij} - \bar{X}_i)^2/(n_i - 1)$ $(i = 1, 2)$, and $s_P^2 = ((n_1 - 1)s_1^2 + (n_2 - 1)s_2^2)/(n_1 + n_2 - 2)$. Then the pivotal quantity

$$\frac{(\bar{X}_1 - \bar{X}_2) - (\mu_1 - \mu_2)}{\sqrt{s_P^2\left(\dfrac{1}{n_1} + \dfrac{1}{n_2}\right)}} \text{ is } t_{n_1 + n_2 - 2},$$

hence a $100(1 - \alpha)\%$ confidence interval for $\mu_1 - \mu_2$ is

$$\left((\bar{X}_1 - \bar{X}_2) - t_{n_1 + n_2 - 2}^{-1}(1 - \alpha/2)\sqrt{s_P^2\left(\frac{1}{n_1} + \frac{1}{n_2}\right)},\right.$$

$$\left.(\bar{X}_1 - \bar{X}_2) + t_{n_1 + n_2 - 2}^{-1}(1 - \alpha/2)\sqrt{s_P^2\left(\frac{1}{n_1} + \frac{1}{n_2}\right)}\right). \tag{10.5.2}$$

Case III: σ_1^2 **and** σ_2^2 **totally unknown.** Using two-stage sampling rule 9.10.2 for both populations,

$$\frac{\left(\tilde{\bar{X}}_1 - \tilde{\bar{X}}_2\right) - (\mu_1 - \mu_2)}{1/w}$$

is a pivotal quantity whose distribution is that of $Y - Z$ where Y and Z are independent $t_{n_0 - 1}$ r.v.'s. This distribution is tabled in Tables 9.10-1 and 9.10-2, hence confidence intervals can easily be obtained. In particular, since in Table 9.10-1 we denote by $c_{1-\gamma}(n_0)$ a quantity such that $P(Y - Z \le c_{1-\gamma}(n_0)) = 1 - \gamma$, a $100(1 - \alpha)\%$ confidence interval for $\mu_1 - \mu_2$ is

$$\left(\left(\tilde{\bar{X}}_1 - \tilde{\bar{X}}_2 \right) - \frac{c_{1-\alpha/2}(n_0)}{w}, \ \left(\tilde{\bar{X}}_1 - \tilde{\bar{X}}_2 \right) + \frac{c_{1-\alpha/2}(n_0)}{w} \right). \quad (10.5.3)$$

Example 10.5.4. Consider estimating the difference between the mean relief times for headache remedies A and B. A random sample of 10 patients using drug A yields sample mean $\bar{X}_1 = 12.3$ minutes and $s_1^2 = 6.5$, while a random sample of 10 patients using drug B gives sample mean $\bar{X}_2 = 10.1$ minutes and $s_2^2 = 4.1$ min^2. Construct a 95% confidence interval for the true difference in the mean relief times μ_1 and μ_2.

Assuming that mean relief times are normally distributed and that the variances of the two populations although unknown are equal (we could test the hypothesis H_0: $\sigma_1^2 = \sigma_2^2$ as in Chapter 9 first, and go to Case III's procedure and (10.5.3) if we rejected, but see the discussion at the end of Example 10.6.3 on desirability of going to a two-stage procedure, if possible, even without testing variance equality), we have $n_1 = n_2$, $s_p^2 = (s_1^2 + s_2^2)/2 = (6.5 + 4.1)/2 = 5.3$, and $t_{n_1+n_2-2}^{-1}(1 - \alpha/2) = t_{18}^{-1}(.975) = 2.101$. Hence the 95% confidence interval on $\mu_1 - \mu_2$ based on (10.5.2) is $(.0369, 4.3631)$.

PROBLEMS FOR SECTION 10.5

10.5.1 (a) Consider the data given in Problem 9.8.3. Since sample sizes are large ($n_1 = n_2 = 100$), assume the sample values of the standard deviations equal the true population values. Construct a 95% confidence interval for the true difference between the mean salaries of assistant professors of mathematics in the two states, $\mu_1 - \mu_2$.

(b) Consider the same data as in part (a). Now assume that variances of the two populations are unknown but equal. Construct a 90% confidence interval for $\mu_1 - \mu_2$. Compare the length of this confidence interval with the length of the interval found in part (a).

(c) If σ_1^2, σ_2^2 are unknown and (possibly) unequal, use (10.5.3) to find a 90% confidence interval for $\mu_1 - \mu_2$ that pins down $\mu_1 - \mu_2$ within $500. (Assume that, after the second stage of observations, $\tilde{\bar{X}}_1 = \bar{X}_1$ and $\tilde{\bar{X}}_2 = \bar{X}_2$.)

10.5.2 Let $X_1, X_2, \ldots, X_{n_1}$ be a random sample from a $N(\mu_1, \sigma_1^2)$ distribution, and independently let $Y_1, Y_2, \ldots, Y_{n_2}$ be a random sample from a $N(\mu_2, \sigma_2^2)$ distribution. Construct a $100(1 - \alpha)\%$ confidence interval for the true difference $\mu_1 - \mu_2$ if $\sigma_1^2/\sigma_2^2 = \delta$, a known value, with σ_1^2 and σ_2^2 unknown.

10.5.3 Recall the "overlapping coefficient," the common overlapped area between two distributions (see Problem 7.2.3): If X is $N(\mu_1, \sigma^2)$ and Y is $N(\mu_2, \sigma^2)$, then the overlapping coefficient Δ is defined by $\Delta = 2\Phi(-|\mu_1 - \mu_2|/(2\sigma))$. If $\mu_1 < \mu_2$, then $\Delta = 2\Phi((\mu_1 - \mu_2)/(2\sigma))$. A point estimate of Δ can be obtained by substituting point estimates of parameters based on a random sample of size m from

$N(\mu_1, \sigma^2)$ and an independent random sample of size n from $N(\mu_2, \sigma^2)$: $\hat{\Delta} = 2\Phi((\bar{X} - \bar{Y})/(2s_P))$, where $s_P^2 = ((m-1)s_x^2 + (n-1)s_y^2)/(m+n-2)$.

(a) Prove that, when $\min(m, n) \to \infty$,

$$
Z_{m,n} = \frac{2\left(\Phi^{-1}\left(\dfrac{\hat{\Delta}}{2}\right) - \Phi^{-1}\left(\dfrac{\Delta}{2}\right)\right)}{\sqrt{\left(\dfrac{1}{m} + \dfrac{1}{n}\right)\left(1 + \dfrac{2r}{(1+r)^2}\left(\Phi^{-1}\left(\dfrac{\Delta}{2}\right)\right)^2\right)}},
$$

where $r = \min(m, n)/\max(m, n)$, has a standard normal limiting distribution. Therefore, $Z_{m,n}$ is an asymptotic pivotal quantity. Based on this, construct a $100(1 - \alpha)\%$ confidence interval for Δ.

(b) Construct a 90% confidence interval for the overlapped area between the distributions of salaries of assistant professors in Problem 9.8.3.

10.6.   CONFIDENCE INTERVAL FOR THE RATIO OF TWO NORMAL VARIANCES

This section is to confidence intervals what Section 9.7 is to testing. A pivotal quantity is used again. The assumptions on the distributions and independence are as in Section 10.5.

In order to construct the confidence interval for σ_1^2/σ_2^2 with confidence coefficient $1 - \alpha$, recall that

$$
\left(\frac{(n_1 - 1)s_1^2}{\sigma_1^2} \bigg/ (n_1 - 1)\right) \bigg/ \left(\frac{(n_2 - 1)s_2^2}{\sigma_2^2}\bigg/(n_2 - 1)\right) \text{ is } F_{n_1 - 1, n_2 - 1},
$$

which is independent of σ_1^2 and σ_2^2, hence

$$
P\left(F_{n_1 - 1, n_2 - 1}^{-1}(\alpha/2) \leq \frac{s_1^2}{s_2^2}\frac{\sigma_2^2}{\sigma_1^2} \leq F_{n_1 - 1, n_2 - 1}^{-1}(1 - \alpha/2)\right) = 1 - \alpha
$$

(where we have kept probability $\alpha/2$ in each end of the distribution to avoid complexity). Therefore **a $100(1 - \alpha)\%$ confidence interval for σ_1^2 / σ_2^2** is

$$
\left(\frac{s_1^2}{s_2^2}\frac{1}{F_{n_1-1,n_2-1}^{-1}(1 - \alpha/2)}, \frac{s_1^2}{s_2^2}\frac{1}{F_{n_1-1,n_2-1}^{-1}(\alpha/2)}\right). \tag{10.6.1}
$$

Since $F_{n_1 - 1, n_2 - 1}^{-1}(\alpha/2) = 1/F_{n_2 - 1, n_1 - 1}^{-1}(1 - \alpha/2)$, the confidence interval for σ_1^2/σ_2^2 can be written as

$$
\left(\frac{s_1^2}{s_2^2}\frac{1}{F_{n_1-1,n_2-1}^{-1}(1 - \alpha/2)}, \frac{s_1^2}{s_2^2}F_{n_2-1,n_1-1}^{-1}(1 - \alpha/2)\right). \tag{10.6.2}
$$

Example 10.6.3. Find a 90% confidence interval for σ_1^2/σ_2^2 in the context of Example 10.5.4.

Here $n_1 = n_2 = 10$, hence $F_{9,9}^{-1}(.95) = 3.18$. With $s_1^2 = 6.5$ and $s_2^2 = 4.1$, we find the 90% confidence interval for σ_1^2/σ_2^2 is (.4985, 5.0415). (Wide intervals on variances are the rule, as variance estimates are highly variable. As a result of this, the two-stage procedure is recommended whenever feasible when the interest is in the means rather than (as in Section 10.5) first testing equality of variances: the test has low power and so is unlikely to detect even substantial variance differences.)

PROBLEMS FOR SECTION 10.6

10.6.1 Construct a 95% confidence interval for the ratio of the variances σ_1^2/σ_2^2, for the data given in
   (a) Problem 9.7.1.
   (b) Problem 9.7.2.
   (c) Problem 9.8.3.
   (d) Problem 9.8.5.
   (e) Problem 9.8.6.

10.6.2 **(a)** Let $X_1, X_2, \ldots, X_m$ be a random sample of size m from a $N(\mu_1, \sigma^2)$ distribution, and independently let $Y_1, Y_2, \ldots, Y_n$ be a random sample of size n from a $N(\mu_2, \sigma^2)$ distribution. Use the pooled variance estimate to construct a $100(1 - \alpha)\%$ confidence interval for σ^2.
   (b) If $m = 13$, $n = 12$, $s_1^2 = 14.2$, $s_2^2 = 10.6$, construct a 90% confidence interval for σ^2.
   (c) In part **(b)**, find a 90% confidence interval for σ_1^2/σ_2^2 if $\sigma_1^2 = \text{Var}(X_i)$ and $\sigma_2^2 = \text{Var}(Y_j)$ may be different.

10.7. LARGE SAMPLE CONFIDENCE INTERVAL FOR DIFFERENCE OF TWO PROBABILITIES OF SUCCESS

Let $X_1, X_2, \ldots, X_{n_1}$ be a sequence of Bernoulli trials with success probability p_1, and $Y_1, Y_2, \ldots, Y_{n_2}$ be a second sequence of Bernoulli trials with success probability p_2. We now find a **confidence interval for $p_1 - p_2$ based on large samples** (i.e., $n_1 > 30$ and $n_2 > 30$), with approximate confidence coefficient $1 - \alpha$.

Since $\hat{p}_1 = \sum_{i=1}^{n_1} X_i/n_1 \overset{p}{\to} p_1$, $\hat{p}_2 = \sum_{i=1}^{n_2} Y_i/n_2 \overset{p}{\to} p_2$, and (denoting $q_1 = 1 - p_1$, $q_2 = 1 - p_2$)

$$\frac{(\hat{p}_1 - \hat{p}_2) - (p_1 - p_2)}{\sqrt{\dfrac{p_1 q_1}{n_1} + \dfrac{p_2 q_2}{n_2}}} \overset{d}{\to} N(0, 1)$$

independent of p_1 and p_2, we have

$$P\left(\Phi^{-1}(\alpha/2) \leq \frac{(\hat{p}_1 - \hat{p}_2) - (p_1 - p_2)}{\sqrt{\dfrac{p_1 q_1}{n_1} + \dfrac{p_2 q_2}{n_2}}} \leq \Phi^{-1}(1 - \alpha/2) \right) \simeq 1 - \alpha. \quad (10.7.1)$$

If we estimate the denominator by a consistent estimator and solve the inequality, we find **an approximate $100(1 - \alpha)\%$ confidence interval for $p_1 - p_2$** is

$$\left((\hat{p}_1 - \hat{p}_2) - \Phi^{-1}(1 - \alpha/2)\sqrt{\frac{\hat{p}_1 \hat{q}_1}{n_1} + \frac{\hat{p}_2 \hat{q}_2}{n_2}}, \right.$$

$$(10.7.2)$$

$$\left. (\hat{p}_1 - \hat{p}_2) + \Phi^{-1}(1 - \alpha/2)\sqrt{\frac{\hat{p}_1 \hat{q}_1}{n_1} + \frac{\hat{p}_2 \hat{q}_2}{n_2}} \right).$$

(Here, $p_1 q_1$ and $p_2 q_2$ have been estimated; see the note following (10.4.6).)

Example 10.7.3. Based on a random sample of size 300 Alabamians it was found that 180 of 300 households have an automatic dishwasher, while a random sample of size 200 in Mississippi found 140 households with an automatic dishwasher. Construct a 98% confidence interval for the true difference in the proportions of households having dishwashers in these two adjacent states.

Here $\hat{p}_1 = 180/300 = .60$, $\hat{q}_1 = .40$, $n_1 = 300$; $\hat{p}_2 = 140/200 = .70$, $\hat{q}_2 = .30$, $n_2 = 200$, and $\Phi^{-1}(1 - \alpha/2) = \Phi^{-1}(.99) = 2.33$. Hence a 98% approximate confidence interval based on (10.7.2) is given by

$$\left((.60 - .70) - (2.33)\sqrt{\frac{(.60)(.40)}{300} + \frac{(.70)(.30)}{200}}, \right.$$

$$\left. (.60 - .70) + (2.33)\sqrt{\frac{(.6)(.4)}{300} + \frac{(.7)(.3)}{200}} \right)$$

$$= (-.2002171, .0002171).$$

Note, in particular, that based on these samples it is not possible (at the 98% level of confidence, i.e., with a 2% null hypothesis error rate) to reject the assertion that H_0: $p_1 = p_2$. However, if p_1 exceeds p_2, it is by at most .0002, whereas p_1 may be smaller than p_2 by up to .2002. Hence for all practical purposes the interval establishes that $p_1 \leq p_2$. (We assume here that a difference of .001 or less is of no practical significance in this problem.)

PROBLEMS FOR SECTION 10.7

10.7.1 Cloud-seeding is sometimes used in an attempt to cause rain. Suppose there are two cloud-seeding methods, and both methods are tried on different occasions to determine if one method is superior to the other. Suppose that in a random sample of 60 attempts with the first method, 24 successes were observed; whereas an independent random sample of 50 attempts with the second method led to 16 successes, with the same criterion of "success" of cloud-seeding.

Let p_1 and p_2 be the true success rates for the first and second methods, respectively. Based on the above data, find a 90% large sample confidence interval for $p_1 - p_2$. Based on this confidence interval, is one method superior to the other?

10.7.2 To estimate the true difference between the proportions of defective merchandise of two electronic manufacturing companies, a 90% confidence interval is to be constructed. Suppose a random sample of 500 units from company 1 yields 15 defectives, while an independent random sample of 400 units from company 2 yields 16 defectives. Construct the confidence interval, and use it to assess whether one company has a statistically significant higher rate of defectives. Also use the interval to assess whether the companies have practically significantly different rates of defectives (with the criterion being the rates are different enough to make a difference in practice if they differ by .02 or more).

10.8. CONFIDENCE INTERVALS VS. HYPOTHESIS TESTING: A DUALITY

In this section we first briefly discuss **lower and upper confidence bounds (denoted by LCB and UCB) for a real-valued parameter θ**, and then discuss **the relationship between confidence intervals** (confidence bounds) **and two-sided hypothesis tests** (one-sided hypothesis tests).

Definition 10.8.1. Let $X_1, X_2, \ldots, X_n$ be independent and identically distributed r.v.'s, each with distribution function $F_X(\cdot | \theta)$. Then $U(X_1, X_2, \ldots, X_n)$ is called a **100(1 − α)% upper confidence bound (UCB)** for a function $h(\theta)$ if, for every θ,

$$P_\theta\big(h(\theta) \le U(X_1, X_2, \ldots, X_n)\big) \ge 1 - \alpha; \qquad (10.8.2)$$

and $(-\infty, U(X_1, X_2, \ldots, X_n)]$ is called a 100(1 − α)% upper confidence interval for $h(\theta)$. Similarly $L(X_1, X_2, \ldots, X_n)$ is called a **100(1 − α)% lower confidence bound (LCB)** for a function $h(\theta)$ if, for every θ,

$$P_\theta\big(L(X_1, X_2, \ldots, X_n) \le h(\theta)\big) \ge 1 - \alpha; \qquad (10.8.3)$$

and $[L(X_1, X_2, \ldots, X_n), +\infty)$ is called a 100(1 − α)% lower confidence interval for $h(\theta)$. If $P(U \ge 0) \equiv 1$, then $-\infty$ can be replaced by zero.

Remark 10.8.4. If $U(X_1, X_2, \ldots, X_n)$ and $L(X_1, X_2, \ldots, X_n)$ are $100(1 - \alpha/2)\%$ UCB and LCB respectively, then

$$\left(L(X_1, X_2, \ldots, X_n), U(X_1, X_2, \ldots, X_n) \right)$$

is an (at least) $100(1 - \alpha)\%$ confidence interval.

Example 10.8.5. (In many cases one can use a pivotal quantity to obtain UCB's and LCB's.) Consider a random sample of size n from a normal population with mean μ and variance σ^2 both unknown. Construct upper and lower confidence bounds for σ^2.

Since $(n - 1)s^2/\sigma^2$ is $\chi^2_{n-1}(0)$, for every σ^2

$$1 - \alpha = P\left((n - 1)\frac{s^2}{\sigma^2} \le \chi^{2^{-1}}_{n-1, 1-\alpha}(0) \right)$$

$$= P\left((n - 1)\frac{s^2}{\chi^{2^{-1}}_{n-1, 1-\alpha}(0)} \le \sigma^2 \right). \tag{10.8.6}$$

Hence $(n - 1)s^2/\chi^{2^{-1}}_{n-1, 1-\alpha}(0)$ is a $100(1 - \alpha)\%$ LCB for σ^2, and

$$\left[\frac{(n - 1)s^2}{\chi^{2^{-1}}_{n-1, 1-\alpha}(0)}, +\infty \right)$$

is a lower $100(1 - \alpha)\%$ confidence interval for σ^2. Also for every σ^2

$$1 - \alpha = P\left((n - 1)\frac{s^2}{\sigma^2} \ge \chi^{2^{-1}}_{n-1, \alpha}(0) \right) = P\left(\sigma^2 \le \frac{(n - 1)s^2}{\chi^{2^{-1}}_{n-1, \alpha}(0)} \right), \tag{10.8.7}$$

hence $(n - 1)s^2/\chi^{2^{-1}}_{n-1, \alpha}(0)$ is a UCB for σ^2, and $(0, (n - 1)s^2/\chi^{2^{-1}}_{n-1, \alpha}(0)]$ is an upper confidence interval for σ^2. Also, $[(n - 1)s^2/\chi^{2^{-1}}_{n-1, 1-\alpha}(0), (n - 1)s^2/\chi^{2^{-1}}_{n-1, \alpha}(0)]$ is a $100(1 - 2\alpha)\%$ confidence interval for σ^2.

Example 10.8.8. In Example 10.8.5 a $100(1 - \alpha)\%$ UCB for μ is $\bar{X} + t^{-1}_{n-1}(1 - \alpha)s/\sqrt{n}$, while a $100(1 - \alpha)\%$ LCB for μ is $\bar{X} - t^{-1}_{n-1}(1 - \alpha)s/\sqrt{n}$. Therefore

$$\left[\bar{X} - t^{-1}_{n-1}(1 - \alpha)\frac{s}{\sqrt{n}}, \ \bar{X} + t^{-1}_{n-1}(1 - \alpha)\frac{s}{\sqrt{n}} \right]$$

is a $100(1 - 2\alpha)\%$ confidence interval for μ.

Discussion 10.8.9. Duality between Hypothesis Testing and Confidence Intervals.
In Section 10.1 we defined and constructed a $100(1 - \alpha)\%$ confidence interval using a level α test of hypothesis for (e.g.) a normal mean, when the alternative hypothesis on μ is two-sided. We can similarly obtain one-sided confidence intervals (or confidence bounds) via a one-sided alternative hypothesis. In this discussion, however, our goal is **to obtain a level α test of H_0:** $\mu = \mu_0$ vs. H_1:

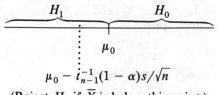

$$\mu_0 - t_{n-1}^{-1}(1 - \alpha)s/\sqrt{n}$$
(Reject H_0 if $\overline{X}$ is below this point.)

Figure 10.8-1. Rejection region is $\overline{X}$ below LCB.

$\mu \neq \mu_0$ (or H_0: $\mu \geq \mu_0$ vs. H_1: $\mu < \mu_0$, or H_0: $\mu \leq \mu_0$ vs. H_1: $\mu > \mu_0$) **via a 100$(1 - \alpha)$% confidence interval** (or $100(1 - \alpha)$% confidence bounds) **for** μ.

Consider testing H_0: $\mu = \mu_0$ vs. H_1: $\mu \neq \mu_0$ at level α, and also a $100(1 - \alpha)$% interval for μ denoted $CI(\mu) = (L(X_1, X_2, \ldots, X_n), U(X_1, X_2, \ldots, X_n))$. **We can base a level α test for H_0 vs. H_1 on confidence interval $CI(\mu)$, as follows.** Let

$$\phi(X_1, \ldots, X_n) = \begin{cases} 1, & \text{if } \mu_0 \notin CI(\mu) \\ 0, & \text{if } \mu_0 \in CI(\mu). \end{cases}$$

Then $E_{\mu_0}\phi(X_1, \ldots, X_n) = P_{\mu_0}[\mu_0 \notin CI(\mu)] = 1 - \alpha$, as in Section 10.1. In other words, the test rejects H_0 iff $\mu_0 \notin CI(\mu)$, and does not reject H_0 (accepts H_0) iff $\mu_0 \in CI(\mu)$.

For the one-sided test case, consider H_0: $\mu \geq \mu_0$ vs. H_1: $\mu < \mu_0$ (the treatment of H_0: $\mu \leq \mu_0$ vs. H_1: $\mu > \mu_0$ is similar) at level of significance α. Consider the UCB for μ, $\overline{X} + t_{n-1}^{-1}(1 - \alpha)s/\sqrt{n} = $ UCB. Then reject H_0 iff $\mu_0 \geq \overline{X} + t_{n-1}^{-1}(1 - \alpha)s/\sqrt{n}$, and do not reject (accept) H_0 iff $\mu_0 < \overline{X} + t_{n-1}^{-1}(1 - \alpha)s/\sqrt{n}$. This test is

$$\phi(X) = \begin{cases} 1, & \text{if } \mu_0 \geq \overline{X} + t_{n-1}^{-1}(1 - \alpha)s/\sqrt{n} \Leftrightarrow \overline{X} \leq \mu_0 - t_{n-1}^{-1}(1 - \alpha)s/\sqrt{n} \\ 0, & \text{if } \mu_0 < \overline{X} + t_{n-1}^{-1}(1 - \alpha)s/\sqrt{n} \end{cases}$$

(see Figure 10.8-1 for a graphical interpretation of the test) and has level α: $E_{\mu_0}\phi(X) = \alpha$.

Thus hypothesis testing and confidence intervals are dual concepts to each other: one can be obtained from the other. However, it is often difficult to specify μ_0 for testing, while on the other hand an interval gives us an immediate assessment of the possible values of μ. For this reason, confidence intervals are often preferred to hypothesis testing in modern statistical practice.

PROBLEMS FOR SECTION 10.8

10.8.1 Modify Discussion 10.8.9 for the following pairs of hypotheses (use level of significance α).

(a) H_0: $\sigma_1^2 = \sigma_0^2$ versus H_1: $\sigma_1^2 \neq \sigma_0^2$.

(b) H_0: $\sigma_1^2 \geq \sigma_0^2$ versus H_1: $\sigma_1^2 < \sigma_0^2$.

(c) H_0: $\sigma_1^2/\sigma_2^2 \geq \delta$ versus H_1: $\sigma_1^2/\sigma_2^2 < \delta$.

(d) H_0: $\sigma_1^2/\sigma_2^2 = \delta$ versus H_1: $\sigma_1^2/\sigma_2^2 \neq \delta$.

(e) H_0: $\mu_1 - \mu_2 = d_0$ versus H_1: $\mu_1 - \mu_2 \neq d_0$.

(f) H_0: $\mu_1 - \mu_2 \leq d_0$ versus H_1: $\mu_1 - \mu_2 > d_0$.

10.8.2 (a) Recall that we constructed a 95% confidence interval for the ratio of variances in Problem 10.6.1. In each case, use the interval to test H_0: $\sigma_1^2 = \sigma_2^2$ against H_1: $\sigma_1^2 \neq \sigma_2^2$ at level $\alpha = .05$.

(b) For each of the five cases, find a 95% lower confidence bound for σ_1^2/σ_2^2.

(c) Based on the 95% lower confidence bounds in part (b), solve part (a) (against H_1': $\sigma_1^2 > \sigma_2^2$).

10.8.3 In Problem 10.2.10: (a) Find a 95% upper confidence bound for μ. (b) Find a 90% lower confidence bound for μ.

10.8.4 If $X_1, X_2, \ldots, X_n$ is a random sample of size n from the p.d.f. $f(x|\beta) = 2\beta^{-2}(\beta - x)I_{(0,\beta)}(x)$, show that $Z_i = (\beta - X_i)/\beta$ has a distribution that is independent of the parameter β. Let $Y_1 \leq Y_2 \leq \cdots \leq Y_n$ be the order statistics corresponding to $Z_1, Z_2, \ldots, Z_n$. Note that the MLE of β is $X_{(n)} = \max(X_1, \ldots, X_n)$. Use this information to find an (approximate) $100(1 - \alpha)\%$ lower confidence bound for β.

10.8.5 In Problem 10.3.1:

(a) Construct a 90% upper confidence bound for σ^2.

(b) Construct a 90% upper confidence bound for σ.

(c) Based on the limiting distribution, construct a 90% upper confidence bound for σ.

10.8.6 In Problem 10.3.2:

(a) Construct a 95% upper confidence bound for σ^2.

(b) Construct a 95% upper confidence bound for σ.

(c) Construct a large sample 95% upper confidence bound for σ.

10.8.7 In Problem 10.4.2:

(a) Use large sample properties of $\hat{p}$ to find an approximate 95% upper confidence bound for p.

(b) Use large sample properties of $\hat{p}$ to find an approximate 95% lower confidence bound for p.

10.8.8 In Problem 10.6.2(b), find a 99% upper confidence bound for σ^2.

10.8.9 In Problem 10.7.1, find an approximate 95% upper confidence bound for $p_1 - p_2$.

PROBLEMS FOR CHAPTER 10

10.1 Verify that in (10.2.4) we have $a(\mu) \leq b(\mu)$ for all α, p.

10.2 Verify that when $1 - \alpha = .95$ and $p = .5$

$$\begin{cases} \overline{X} - \dfrac{\sigma}{\sqrt{n}}\Phi^{-1}(1 - \alpha(1 - p)) = \overline{X} - 1.96\dfrac{\sigma}{\sqrt{n}}, \\[2mm] \overline{X} - \dfrac{\sigma}{\sqrt{n}}\Phi^{-1}(\alpha p) = \overline{X} + 1.96\dfrac{\sigma}{\sqrt{n}}. \end{cases}$$

10.3 Prove that of all intervals (10.2.5), the one with $p = .5$ has the smallest length. [Related considerations were contained in Problem 6.13.]

10.4 Prove the equality in (10.2.8).

10.5 Verify that if $p = 1$ in (10.2.5), the interval becomes (10.2.9).

10.6 Obtain a lower bound on μ analogous to upper bound (10.2.9).

10.7 Suppose that in Example 10.2.1 we choose $a(\mu)$ and $b(\mu)$ as at (10.2.4), but with

$$p = p(\mu) = \begin{cases} 1, & \text{if } \mu \geq 0 \\ 0, & \text{if } \mu < 0. \end{cases}$$

Construct the graph that now replaces Figure 10.2-1. For the case $1 - \alpha = .95$, what confidence interval do we now obtain (i.e., the new $(L(\overline{X}), U(\overline{X}))$ that replaces (10.2.7))? Be explicit. Why might we (or why might we not) want to use such an interval? (Speak in terms of real-world problems.)

10.8 Derive (10.2.12) in full detail.

10.9 Verify that when $1 - \alpha = .95$, $p = .5$, and $n = 6$,

$$\begin{cases} \overline{X} - \dfrac{s}{\sqrt{n}} t_{n-1}^{-1}(1 - \alpha(1 - p)) = \overline{X} - 2.57 \dfrac{s}{\sqrt{6}}, \\[2mm] \overline{X} - \dfrac{s}{\sqrt{n}} t_{n-1}^{-1}(\alpha p) = \overline{X} - 2.57 \dfrac{s}{\sqrt{6}}. \end{cases}$$

10.10 Prove that of all intervals (10.2.12), the one with $p = .5$ has the smallest length. Show that this length is given by (10.2.14).

10.11 Example 10.2.20 used the method of Lemma 10.2.16 of finding confidence intervals, for the problem previously studied in Example 10.2.1. Do the same for the problem of Example 10.2.10.

10.12 In the example of seasonal snowfall in Rochester, New York (see Problem 9.52), what confidence interval on μ do we obtain if we assume that:
  (a) $X_1, \ldots, X_{97}$ are independent $N(\mu, \sigma^2)$ r.v.'s with μ and σ^2 unknown.
  (b) $X_1, \ldots, X_{56}$ are independent $N(\mu_1, \sigma^2)$ r.v.'s, $X_{57}, \ldots, X_{97}$ are independent $N(\mu, \sigma^2)$ r.v.'s, and μ_1, μ, σ^2 are unknown.
  (c) $X_1, \ldots, X_{56}$ are independent $N(\mu_1, \sigma_1^2)$ r.v.'s, $X_{57}, \ldots, X_{97}$ are independent $N(\mu, \sigma_2^2)$ r.v.'s, and $\mu_1, \mu, \sigma_1^2, \sigma_2^2$ are unknown.
  [*Hint:* Your interval in (b) should be "better" than your interval in (c) since in (b) more is known about σ^2.] Based on Problem 9.52, which interval do you recommend should be used to guide the Highway Department in its purchases of road salt for the next season?

10.13 In Example 10.3.3 we found an interval for σ^2 when μ was unknown. Find upper and lower bounds (see (10.2.9)ff) on σ^2 for the case of unknown μ.

10.14 Derive confidence intervals for σ^2 in the contexts of (a) μ known and (b) μ unknown, as was done in Section 10.3, but using the tests for corresponding problems obtained in Section 9.6 (and not using Lemma 10.2.16).

10.15 Man A (a track star) has run the mile twice in competitions, with times of 3.8, 3.4. Man B (another track star) has run the mile thrice in competitions, with times of 3.7, 3.6, 4.1. Assume that man A and man B ran independently of each other, and that each one's times are independent observations of his running ability. Let $\mu_A(\mu_B)$ denote the average time it takes man $A(B)$ to run the mile in competitions. Similarly, let his variance be $\sigma_A^2(\sigma_B^2)$.

Assuming all observations are normally distributed, give a two-sided equal-tail confidence interval for $\mu_B - \mu_A$ (with confidence coefficient .95) if:

(a) $\sigma_A^2 = \sigma_B^2 = .04$.

(b) $\sigma_A^2 = .04$, $\sigma_B^2 = .09$.

(c) $\sigma_A^2 = \sigma_B^2$ but the common value is unknown.

(d) What can be said if σ_A^2, σ_B^2 are both unknown?

Note by "equal-tail" (see Problem 9.50 for a similar concept in hypothesis testing) we mean the interval comes from "cutting off" two tails of a distribution with equal probability in each tail. For example, in (10.3.2) we put probability .025 in each tail of a $\chi_n^2(0)$ distribution.

[*Hint*: Corresponding tests were studied in Sections 9.8 and 9.9. Also see Problem 9.51.]

10.16 Prove that for any fixed $a > 0$, $\Phi(a - b) - \Phi(-a - b)$ is largest when $b = 0$.

10.17 Let $X_1, \ldots, X_n$ be independent r.v.'s, each Bernoulli with unknown probability of success p ($0 \le p \le 1$). Find a most powerful level $\alpha = .05$ test of H_0: $p = p_0$ versus H_1: $p = p_1$ where $1 \ge p_1 > p_0 \ge 0$. Is this test UMP for testing H_0: $p = p_0$ versus H_1: $p > p_0$? Note that the test is randomized (due to the r.v.'s being discrete) for all but a few of the possible values of α (which ones?).

10.18 In Figure 10.4-2 a relation between the points (p, a) and (p, b) can be given as follows. Prove that if (for some l with $1 \le l \le n - 1$) p_1 is such that $P_{p_1}[\overline{X} < l/n] = \alpha/2$ and p_2 is such that $P_{p_2}[\overline{X} > (n - l)/n] = \alpha/2$, then $p_2 = 1 - p_1$.

10.19 If $X_1, \ldots, X_n$ are independent Bernoulli r.v.'s with parameter p ($0 \le p \le 1$), prove that $P_p[\overline{X} \ge c]$ increases as p increases, while $P_p[\overline{X} \le c]$ decreases as p increases.

10.20 Prove that the confidence interval procedure for a success probability proposed in Section 10.4 still has probability of coverage $\ge 1 - \alpha$ when the points $(0, 0)$ and $(1, 1)$ are added as noted following Figure 10.4-4.

HONORS PROBLEMS FOR CHAPTER 10

10.1H In Theorem 10.1.5 we saw how to construct a confidence set $S(X)$ for a parameter θ based on a r.v. X by using any level α test of the hypothesis H_0: $\theta = \theta_0$ (the test being defined for all possibilities θ_0), the confidence coefficient being $1 - \alpha$. We now wish to justify the notion that "good" tests yield "good" confidence sets.

One good property we could look for in a confidence set with confidence coefficient $1 - \alpha$ would be that

$$P_\theta[\theta^* \in S(X)] \qquad (*)$$

be small for $\theta^* \ne \theta$ (small probability of including false values). Prove that: If a test ϕ of level α of H_0: $\theta = \theta_0$ is UMP [see Definition 9.3.16] against the alternative $H(\theta_0)$, then (among all confidence sets for θ with confidence coefficient $1 - \alpha$) its related confidence set $S_\phi(X)$ minimizes $(*)$ for all $\theta \in H(\theta^*)$.

10.2H Since the test corresponding to the upper-bound interval (10.2.9) in Example 10.2.1 has a "good" property (it is UMP one-sided), by Problem 10.1H interval (10.2.9) has a good property. State that property precisely and explicitly.

10.3H Suppose that the tests used to obtain (10.1.6) in Theorem 10.1.5 are randomized. Can we then obtain different confidence sets $S(x)$ from independent experiments that yield the same value $X = x$? [In such cases, which arise in the case of discrete r.v.'s, for example, we would often change α slightly in order to eliminate the need for randomization.]

10.4H In Example 10.2.10 $X_1, \ldots, X_n$ were independent $N(\mu, \sigma^2)$ r.v.'s with both $\mu(-\infty < \mu < +\infty)$ and σ^2 ($\sigma^2 > 0$) unknown, and we desired a confidence interval for μ with confidence coefficient $1 - \alpha = .95$. Such an interval was obtained [in fact, a whole class of such intervals was obtained] (see (10.2.12)) but had the undesirable property that its length was a r.v. [except in the cases $p = 0$ and $p = 1$, where the length was infinite]. We now show that this is unavoidable.

(a) For the case of known σ^2, use a sufficiency argument and Problem 10.3 to show that of all fixed-length confidence intervals with confidence coefficient $1 - \alpha$, (10.2.5) with $p = .5$ has the smallest length, namely,

$$d(\sigma) = 2\Phi^{-1}\left(1 - \frac{\alpha}{2}\right)\frac{\sigma}{\sqrt{n}}.$$

Using Lebesgue measure as the "length" of a set, extend this result to confidence sets.

(b) For the case of unknown σ^2, show there is no fixed-length confidence interval with confidence coefficient $1 - \alpha$. [*Hint*: Suppose there is such an interval, with length l (say). For each known σ we must have $l \geq d(\sigma)$.] Extend this result to confidence sets.

[Note that when we say random length of the confidence interval with confidence coefficient $1 - \alpha$ is "unavoidable," we mean unavoidable (as proven in (b)) if a sample size n is fixed before any experimentation. If, instead, we take a preliminary sample of n_0 observations (essentially for purposes of estimating σ^2) followed by a second sample of a random number of observations (the larger σ^2 appears to be based on the first n_0 observations, the more observations we take in this second stage) a fixed-length interval with confidence coefficient $1 - \alpha$ *can* be obtained. See Stein (1945) and Section 10.5].

10.5H At the end of Problem 10.12 we asked "...which interval...should be used to guide the Highway Department in its purchases of road salt for the next season?" However, the intervals under consideration were all intervals on μ, the average seasonal snowfall. For the purpose of a purchase for the next season it is more appropriate to base our decision on an interval on X, the next seasonal snowfall. Such an interval with the property

$$P[\,g(X_1, \ldots, X_n) \leq X \leq h(X_1, \ldots, X_n)\,] \equiv 1 - \alpha$$

is called a **prediction interval** for X based on $X_1, \ldots, X_n$. Find such intervals in the context of Problem 10.12. [*Hint*: See Hahn (1970).]

10.6H Let $X_1, \ldots, X_n$ be independent Poisson r.v.'s with unknown parameter $\mu \geq 0$. Based on the equal-tail test that rejects H_0: $\mu = \mu_0$ iff $\overline{X} < c_1$ or $\overline{X} > c_2$, find an equal-tail confidence interval for μ with confidence coefficient $\geq 1 - \alpha$. [*Hint*: This study will parallel that of Section 10.4 (for a success probability) to a large degree. A reference is pp. 80–83, 227 of Pearson and Hartley (1970).]

CHAPTER 11

Ranking and Selection Procedures

In this chapter we cover the subject of **ranking and selection procedures**. This subject has been developed so recently (its start is usually traced to a 1954 paper by R. E. Bechhofer) that it is as yet not covered in any but a few books on statistics (and then often only very briefly) even though its practical applicability is such that it has immediate and important applications to almost every field. (In many cases, problems that are not actually problems of hypothesis-testing were forced into that framework due to a lack of ranking and selection procedures before 1954. Since a proper treatment can now be given to such problems, it seems especially important to cover this material in courses at every level.) The ranking and selection problem formulation is very suggestive of decision theory (to be covered in Chapter 12), whose formulation by Abraham Wald in the 1940s stimulated statistics to move more fully into its present role as "the science of decision making."[1]

11.1. THE GENERAL RANKING PROBLEM

A ranking and selection problem usually results from questions like: "Which brand of cigarettes is least likely to cause cancer?"; "Which type of seat belt reduces car accident injuries the most?"; "Which type of atomic power plant increases radiation levels the least?"; or "Which type of catalyst increases a certain chemical process yield the most?" (Compare these with the corresponding questions, given in the first paragraph of Section 9.1, which led to hypothesis-testing problems.) Other questions leading to ranking and selection problems include "Which television shows captured the highest proportions of the prime audience last night, and in what order?"; and "How do the candidates for President of the United States rank at present in popularity?".

Thus, we have several alternatives (in our first four examples these might be: brands of cigarettes; types of seat belts; types of atomic power plants; or types of

---

[1] For historical notes and references, see pp. 28–31 of Wald (1950).

catalysts), each of which has an underlying parameter θ (in our first four examples this might be: a cancer rate; an injury rate; a radiation level; or a process yield) and we wish to determine which alternative has the "best" (e.g., largest or smallest in many cases) θ. This is a problem of **selection**. In our last two examples, on the other hand, we wish to order the alternatives (television shows or political candidates) based on their θ-values. This is a problem of **ranking**. [Thus, "selection" refers to choosing the best (e.g., in baseball this is the goal since there is only a first prize) whereas "ranking" refers to one of the many other possible goals (e.g., in the Olympic Games the goal may be to select the best three in order since there are three medals: gold, silver, and bronze).]

A general formulation that we will use is as follows. We have k (≥ 2) sources of observations (each such source is called a **population**) denoted by $\pi_1, \pi_2, \ldots, \pi_k$. From source i we may obtain independent and identically distributed observations $X_{i1}, X_{i2}, X_{i3}, X_{i4}, \ldots$ whose distribution involves an unknown parameter θ_i ($1 \leq i \leq k$); except for the value of θ_i the distribution is assumed not to differ from population to population. Our **goal** is to select that population which has the largest parameter $\max(\theta_1, \theta_2, \ldots, \theta_k)$.[2] We are to perform the selection in such a way that the probability $P(\text{CS})$ of selecting the correct population is at least P^* (where P^* is a specified number between $1/k$ and 1; see Problem 11.1) whenever the largest and next largest of $\theta_1, \theta_2, \ldots, \theta_k$ are "sufficiently far" apart [it being usually impossible to satisfy $P(\text{CS}) \geq P^*$ for all $\theta_1, \theta_2, \ldots, \theta_k$, since the θ's could then be arbitrarily close together]; the demand that any proposed procedure satisfy this criterion is called the **probability requirement**. [Without the probability requirement the situation would be as trivial as a level α test with no power requirement (see Problem 9.4), where a simple flip of a coin suffices.] More general formulations can be considered (and will sometimes be noted in what follows), but this one (with minor variations such as a goal of selecting that population which has the smallest parameter $\min(\theta_1, \theta_2, \ldots, \theta_k)$) accounts for more than 75% of the work in this area to date.

Let us now illustrate this general formulation in terms of a specific question that arises in poultry science:[3] "Which stock of chickens lays the most eggs?" (New chicken stocks are under constant development, and the question of selecting the best is considered at agricultural experiment stations year after year. Similar applications arise in other fields.) So, suppose it is desired to select that one of $k = 10$ stocks of chickens which has the highest mean egg production. As would be expected, we take chickens of each type (n of each type, say), observe the egg laying of the $kn = 10n$ chickens for a period of time [this happens to be 500 days; at that age a pullet is eliminated] in a controlled environment, and select a stock (population) based on the observations obtained. If (as is often

---

[2] If several populations have the parameter $\max(\theta_1, \theta_2, \ldots, \theta_k)$, selection of any one of these is regarded as satisfying the goal.

[3] See Becker (1961). Also see Dudewicz (1969b).

assumed) the observations from π_i ($X_{i1}, X_{i2}, \ldots, X_{in}$) are each $N(\mu_i, \sigma^2)$ r.v.'s with $\sigma = 72$, we select that stock (population) with the highest average (over its n pullets) of eggs-per-500-days in the trial. If we desire $P(\text{CS}) \geq P^* = .90$, say, whenever the best-laying stock out-lays the next-best-laying stock by 10 or more eggs per chicken in 500 days on the average [i.e., whenever

$$\mu_{[10]} - \mu_{[9]} \geq \delta^* = 10 \qquad (11.1.1)$$

where $\mu_{[1]} \leq \cdots \leq \mu_{[9]} \leq \mu_{[10]}$ denote $\mu_1, \ldots, \mu_{10}$ in numerical order], it can be shown [and will be in Section 11.2] that $n = 462$ pullets of each type will be required.

PROBLEMS FOR SECTION 11.1

11.1.1 An agricultural research station wishes to evaluate five new varieties of strawberry plants that, through genetic engineering, are cold-resistant down to 25°F. They wish to find the variety with the largest mean yield per plant. Suppose the yield of variety i, in quarts per season, is an $N(\mu_i, \sigma^2)$ r.v. ($i = 1, 2, 3, 4, 5$). If they take independent random samples of size n from each variety, they could then
(i) Test H_0: $\mu_1 = \mu_2 = \cdots = \mu_5$ (this uses a test developed in Chapter 14); or
(ii) Seek to select the variety whose mean yield is $\max(\mu_1, \mu_2, \ldots, \mu_5)$.
(a) If they use option (i), what variety will they choose if H_0 is rejected? What guarantees, if any, will they have on the probability ($P(\text{CS})$) that that variety is the best?
(b) If they use option (ii), what $P(\text{CS})$ guarantees will they have?

11.1.2 In Problem 11.1.1, if option (i) of testing H_0 is taken, often a selection is made even if H_0 is not rejected (e.g., because one of the five varieties must be marketed). Comment on whether this has implications for the choice between options (i) and (ii).

11.2. SELECTION OF THE BEST (LARGEST MEAN) NORMAL POPULATION

One selection problem (see Section 11.1) that occurs frequently in practice is that in which the $k \geq 2$ **populations** $\pi_1, \ldots, \pi_k$ (sources of observations) are such that if $X_{i1}, X_{i2}, \ldots$ are n independent **observations** from π_i, then each X_{ij} is $N(\mu_i, \sigma^2)$ where μ_i is unknown and σ^2 is known ($1 \leq i \leq k$). Let

$$\mu_{[1]} \leq \cdots \leq \mu_{[k]} \qquad (11.2.1)$$

denote the ordered values of $\mu_1, \ldots, \mu_k$. Our **goal** is to select a population with mean $\mu_{[k]}$. If we formulate a procedure for selecting one of the k populations and declaring the selected population to be "best," we would like a reasonable probability of having it be, in fact, best.

One intuitively reasonable procedure is to proceed as follows. Take independent samples of n independent observations from each of the k populations, use the observations from π_i to estimate μ_i, say by $\hat{\mu}_i$ $(1 \leq i \leq k)$, and select the[4] population π_l for which

$$\hat{\mu}_l = \max(\hat{\mu}_1, \ldots, \hat{\mu}_k). \tag{11.2.2}$$

Since (see Example 8.1.32)

$$\bar{X}_i = \frac{X_{i1} + \cdots + X_{in}}{n} \tag{11.2.3}$$

is a sufficient statistic for μ_i, it seems reasonable (see Problem 11.1H) to let

$$\hat{\mu}_i = \bar{X}_i \ (1 \leq i \leq k). \tag{11.2.4}$$

Thus, our **procedure** (called the **means procedure**) is to take k independent sets of n independent observations each (n observations per population), compute the sample means, and select (as being best) that population which yielded the largest sample mean.

We now wish to choose n (the sample size per population) in a rational way. One such way is to choose the smallest n that satisfies a **probability requirement** such as

$$P(\text{CS}) \geq P^* \quad \text{whenever } \mu_{[k]} - \mu_{[k-1]} \geq \delta^* \tag{11.2.5}$$

where "CS" (for correct selection) denotes the final selection of a population with population mean $\mu_{[k]}$, and P^* $(1/k < P^* < 1$; see Problem 11.1) and δ^* $(\delta^* > 0)$ are specified by the experimenter. With probability requirement (11.2.5) we will be at least $100P^*\%$ sure (95% sure when $P^* = .95$) of selecting the best population whenever the best mean $\mu_{[k]}$ is at least δ^* better than the second best mean $\mu_{[k-1]}$.

To solve for the smallest n that satisfies (11.2.5), as we do in Theorem 11.2.11, it will be convenient to make the following:

Definition 11.2.6. $\bar{X}_{(i)}$ is the sample mean obtained from the population that has population mean $\mu_{[i]}$ $(1 \leq i \leq k)$, while $\bar{X}_{[1]} \leq \cdots \leq \bar{X}_{[k]}$ denote the sample means $\bar{X}_1, \ldots, \bar{X}_k$ in numerical order.

Theorem 11.2.7. The $P(\text{CS})$ of the means procedure equals

$$\int_{-\infty}^{\infty} \Phi\left(y + \frac{\mu_{[k]} - \mu_{[1]}}{\sigma/\sqrt{n}}\right) \cdots \Phi\left(y + \frac{\mu_{[k]} - \mu_{[k-1]}}{\sigma/\sqrt{n}}\right) \phi(y) \, dy. \tag{11.2.8}$$

---

[4]In general, this could fail to be unique, although we will see that in this section it is unique with probability 1 (see Problem 11.2).

Proof: The $P(\text{CS})$ is the probability that the sample mean $(\overline{X}_{(k)})$ from the population with the largest mean $\mu_{[k]}$ is the largest sample mean $(\overline{X}_{[k]})$:

$$
\begin{aligned}
P(\text{CS}) &= P\left[\overline{X}_{(k)} = \overline{X}_{[k]}\right] \\[4pt]
&= P\left[\overline{X}_{(k)} = \max\left(\overline{X}_{(1)}, \ldots, \overline{X}_{(k)}\right)\right] \\[4pt]
&= P\left[\overline{X}_{(1)} < \overline{X}_{(k)}, \ldots, \overline{X}_{(k-1)} < \overline{X}_{(k)}\right] \\[4pt]
&= P\left[\overline{X}_{(i)} < \overline{X}_{(k)}, \quad i = 1, \ldots, k-1\right] \\[4pt]
&= P\left[\frac{\overline{X}_{(i)} - \mu_{[i]}}{\sigma/\sqrt{n}} < \frac{\overline{X}_{(k)} - \mu_{[k]}}{\sigma/\sqrt{n}} + \frac{\mu_{[k]} - \mu_{[i]}}{\sigma/\sqrt{n}}, \right. \qquad (11.2.9)\\[4pt]
&\left. \qquad\qquad\qquad\qquad\qquad\qquad i = 1, \ldots, k-1\right] \\[4pt]
&= P\left[Y_i < Y_k + \frac{\mu_{[k]} - \mu_{[i]}}{\sigma/\sqrt{n}}, \quad i = 1, \ldots, k-1\right],
\end{aligned}
$$

where $Y_1, \ldots, Y_k$ are independent $N(0,1)$ r.v.'s. [Here we used Problem 7.15 or Theorem 5.5.64 to show $\overline{X}_{(i)}$ is $N(\mu_{[i]}, \sigma^2/n)$. The $Y_1, \ldots, Y_k$ are independent since the $\overline{X}_{(1)}, \ldots, \overline{X}_{(k)}$ are.] Thus (since Y_k is a $N(0,1)$ r.v. and $Y_1, \ldots, Y_{k-1}, Y_k$ are independent r.v.'s and $\phi(y) = (\sqrt{2\pi})^{-1} \exp(-.5 y^2)$)

$$
\begin{aligned}
P(\text{CS}) &= \int_{-\infty}^{\infty} P\left[Y_i < y + \frac{\mu_{[k]} - \mu_{[i]}}{\sigma/\sqrt{n}}, \quad i = 1, \ldots, k-1\right]\phi(y)\,dy \\[4pt]
&= \int_{-\infty}^{\infty} P\left[Y_1 < y + \frac{\mu_{[k]} - \mu_{[1]}}{\sigma/\sqrt{n}}\right] \cdots \\[4pt]
&\qquad\qquad \times P\left[Y_{k-1} < y + \frac{\mu_{[k]} - \mu_{[k-1]}}{\sigma/\sqrt{n}}\right]\phi(y)\,dy \qquad (11.2.10)\\[4pt]
&= \int_{-\infty}^{\infty} \Phi\left(y + \frac{\mu_{[k]} - \mu_{[1]}}{\sigma/\sqrt{n}}\right) \cdots \Phi\left(y + \frac{\mu_{[k]} - \mu_{[k-1]}}{\sigma/\sqrt{n}}\right)\phi(y)\,dy. \quad \blacksquare
\end{aligned}
$$

Theorem 11.2.11. The $P(\text{CS})$ of the means procedure is (among all sets of possible population means $\mu_1, \ldots, \mu_k$ that satisfy $\mu_{[k]} - \mu_{[k-1]} \geq \delta^*$) minimized when

$$
\mu_{[1]} = \cdots = \mu_{[k-1]} = \mu_{[k]} - \delta^* \qquad (11.2.12)
$$

[this is called the **least favorable configuration (LFC)** of the population means]. In the LFC, the P(CS), say P_{LFC}(CS), is given by

$$P_{\text{LFC}}(\text{CS}) = \int_{-\infty}^{\infty} \Phi^{k-1}\left(x + \frac{\delta^* \sqrt{n}}{\sigma}\right) \phi(x)\, dx. \qquad (11.2.13)$$

This P_{LFC}(CS) is an increasing function of n and $\rightarrow 1$ as $n \rightarrow \infty$. Hence, there is a unique smallest sample size n per population for which probability requirement (11.2.5) is satisfied:

$$n = \left\{ \text{The smallest integer} \geq \frac{h_k^2(P^*)\sigma^2}{(\delta^*)^2} \right\}, \qquad (11.2.14)$$

where $h_k(P^*)$ is the solution h of the equation

$$\int_{-\infty}^{\infty} \Phi^{k-1}(x + h)\phi(x)\, dx = P^*. \qquad (11.2.15)$$

Proof: Since $\Phi(z)$ is an increasing function of z, by expression (11.2.8) for the P(CS) it follows that the P(CS) $\downarrow$ as $\mu_{[k]} - \mu_{[i]} \downarrow$, for each of $i = 1, \ldots, k - 1$. Subject to the restriction $\mu_{[k]} - \mu_{[k-1]} \geq \delta^*$, we make $\mu_{[k]} - \mu_{[i]}$ smallest when we set

$$\mu_{[1]} = \cdots = \mu_{[k-1]} = \mu_{[k]} - \delta^*.$$

Hence, the P(CS) is minimized (subject to $\mu_{[k]} - \mu_{[k-1]} \geq \delta^*$) when (11.2.12) holds. But when (11.2.12) holds, the P(CS) given by (11.2.8) reduces simply to

$$f(n) = \int_{-\infty}^{\infty} \Phi^{k-1}\left(x + \frac{\delta^* \sqrt{n}}{\sigma}\right) \phi(x)\, dx. \qquad (11.2.16)$$

This is clearly an increasing function of n with $f(0) = 1/k$ (see Problem 11.3) and $f(n) \rightarrow 1$ as $n \rightarrow \infty$. In order to make the P(CS) $\geq P^*$ whenever $\mu_{[k]} - \mu_{[k-1]} \geq \delta^*$, we can proceed as follows. Find the smallest P(CS) can be when $\mu_{[k]} - \mu_{[k-1]} \geq \delta^*$ [this is given by (11.2.16)] and make n large enough that this minimum is $\geq P^*$. Thus, we set

$$\int_{-\infty}^{\infty} \Phi^{k-1}(x + h)\phi(x)\, dx = P^*, \qquad (11.2.17)$$

solve for h, and then (since $\delta^* \sqrt{n}/\sigma$ is h) solve for n. However, n must be an integer (whereas $h^2\sigma^2/(\delta^*)^2$ need not be) so we may need to round up the quantity $h^2\sigma^2/(\delta^*)^2$ [e.g., 5.46 becomes 6]. ∎

Remark 11.2.18. Tables of the solution $h_k(P^*)$ of equation (11.2.15) (for various k and P^* values) were given by R. E. Bechhofer (1954) in his pioneering paper "A single-sample multiple decision procedure for ranking means of normal populations with known variances." [In fact, that paper also discussed, and gave

TABLE 11.2-1

Solutions h of $\int_{-\infty}^{\infty} \Phi^{k-1}(x+h)\phi(x)\,dx = P^*$

P^* \ k	2	3	4	5	6	7	8	9	10
.9995	4.6535	4.9163	5.0639	5.1661	5.2439	5.3066	5.3590	5.4039	5.4432
.9990	4.3703	4.6450	4.7987	4.9049	4.9856	5.0505	5.1047	5.1511	5.1917
.9950	3.6428	3.9517	4.1224	4.2394	4.3280	4.3989	4.4579	4.5083	4.5523
.99	3.2900	3.6173	3.7970	3.9196	4.0121	4.0861	4.1475	4.1999	4.2456
.98	2.9045	3.2533	3.4432	3.5722	3.6692	3.7466	3.8107	3.8653	3.9128
.97	2.6598	3.0232	3.2198	3.3529	3.4528	3.5324	3.5982	3.6543	3.7030
.96	2.4759	2.8504	3.0522	3.1885	3.2906	3.3719	3.4390	3.4961	3.5457
.95	2.3262	2.7101	2.9162	3.0552	3.1591	3.2417	3.3099	3.3679	3.4182
.94	2.1988	2.5909	2.8007	2.9419	3.0474	3.1311	3.2002	3.2590	3.3099
.93	2.0871	2.4865	2.6996	2.8428	2.9496	3.0344	3.1043	3.1637	3.2152
.92	1.9871	2.3931	2.6092	2.7542	2.8623	2.9479	3.0186	3.0785	3.1305
.91	1.8961	2.3082	2.5271	2.6737	2.7829	2.8694	2.9407	3.0012	3.0536
.90	1.8124	2.2302	2.4516	2.5997	2.7100	2.7972	2.8691	2.9301	2.9829
.88	1.6617	2.0899	2.3159	2.4668	2.5789	2.6676	2.7406	2.8024	2.8560
.86	1.5278	1.9655	2.1956	2.3489	2.4627	2.5527	2.6266	2.6893	2.7434
.84	1.4064	1.8527	2.0867	2.2423	2.3576	2.4486	2.5235	2.5868	2.6416
.82	1.2945	1.7490	1.9865	2.1441	2.2609	2.3530	2.4286	2.4926	2.5479
.80	1.1902	1.6524	1.8932	2.0528	2.1709	2.2639	2.3403	2.4049	2.4608
.75	.9539	1.4338	1.6822	1.8463	1.9674	2.0626	2.1407	2.2067	2.2637
.70	.7416	1.2380	1.4933	1.6614	1.7852	1.8824	1.9621	2.0293	2.0873
.65	.5449	1.0568	1.3186	1.4905	1.6168	1.7159	1.7970	1.8653	1.9242
.60	.3583	.8852	1.1532	1.3287	1.4575	1.5583	1.6407	1.7102	1.7700
.55	.1777	.7194	.9936	1.1726	1.3037	1.4062	1.4899	1.5604	1.6210
.50	—	.5565	.8368	1.0193	1.1526	1.2568	1.3418	1.4133	1.4748
.45	—	.3939	.6803	.8662	1.0019	1.1078	1.1941	1.2666	1.3289
.40	—	.2289	.5215	.7111	.8491	.9567	1.0443	1.1178	1.1810
.35	—	.0585	.3578	.5510	.6915	.8008	.8897	.9643	1.0284
.30	—	—	.1855	.3827	.5257	.6369	.7272	.8030	.8679
.25	—	—	—	.2014	.3472	.4604	.5523	.6292	.6951
.20	—	—	—	—	.1489	.2643	.3579	.4361	.5032
.15	—	—	—	—	—	.0364	.1319	.2117	.2800

Reprinted with the permission of the Institute of Mathematical Statistics

tables for, much more general goals than simply selecting the best population. An indication of such other goals was given in Section 11.1 above.] These tables cover $k = 2(1)10$ and are given in Table 11.2-1 above. (For $k > 10$ see Problem 11.5 and Remark 11.2.19.)

Remark 11.2.19. An approximation to the solution $h_k(P^*)$ of equation (11.2.15) is of interest because: (1) sometimes the k and P^* of interest to us will not be ones for which $h_k(P^*)$ is tabled;[5] (2) the tables may not be readily available when needed; and (3) in some circumstances a quick method of approximation will be desired. A number of approximations have been given in the literature. One which has been found[6] to be among the better ones is

$$h_k(P^*) \approx 2\sqrt{-\ln(1 - P^*)} \qquad (11.2.20)$$

or (since $\delta^*\sqrt{n}/\sigma$ is h)

$$n \approx n_1 = \frac{-4\sigma^2 \ln(1 - P^*)}{(\delta^*)^2}. \qquad (11.2.21)$$

This approximation n_1 has the property that as $P^* \to 1$, $n_1/n \to 1$.[7] Note that this approximation can be applied with the aid of only a pocket calculator, and allows us to readily assess approximately the effects (on the sample size n required per population) of changes in δ^*, σ^2, and P^*.

We next give a numerical example of the use of the selection procedure just developed.

Example 11.2.22. An automobile *s*afety *r*estraint *s*ystem (SRS) is a system designed to reduce injuries to passengers during crashes. Suppose that when such a system is built and tested, sensors in the test car (e.g., in a mannequin) measure an index of cranial injury (e.g., due to force applied to the skull and duration of the force) and that this measurement is subject to chance (random) variation that makes it a $N(\mu, \sigma^2)$ r.v.; here μ is unknown and varies from one SRS to another, while $\sigma^2 = 5$ is known and does not vary from one SRS to another (e.g., it may depend primarily on the measuring process). If we have $k = 5$ SRS's and wish to select the best (here the one with the smallest index of cranial injury, $\mu_{[1]}$) with probability at least $P^* = .90$ whenever $\mu_{[2]} - \mu_{[1]} \geq \delta^* = 1.0$, how many observations [here test crashes under some standard conditions of speed, attitude, and so on] per population do we need? If our budget restricts us to $n = 25$ observations per population (since this is a very costly experiment) is the experiment worth conducting at all? [Or should we perhaps arbitrarily select a few of the $k = 5$ alternatives and test them more extensively, perhaps retaining the deleted alternatives for testing in the future as funds become available?]

First, it is simple to show (by replacing each observation X by $-X$) that this problem is equivalent to selecting the population with the largest mean (largest of $-\mu_1, \ldots, -\mu_k$) (see Problem 11.7). Thus, from Table 11.2-1 we find our $h_k(P^*)$

---

[5]In addition to the tables noted in Remark 11.2.18 and Problem 11.5, others have been given by S. S. Gupta for $k = 2(1)51$ and $P^* = .75, .90, .95, .975, .99$ [see p. 810 of Gupta (1963); note that on p. 810 his n is our $k - 1$, his α is our $1 - P^*$, and his tabled value is $h_k(P^*)/\sqrt{2}$]. Also, D. Teichroew tabled P^* as a function of h for $k = 2(1)10$ and $h/\sqrt{2} = .00(.01)6.09$ [Teichroew (1955); note that his tables with his $r = 1$ are the ones appropriate here.]
[6]See Dudewicz and Zaino (1971).
[7]See Dudewicz (1969).

is $h_5(.90) = 2.60$; hence, n must be the smallest integer greater than or equal to

$$\frac{h^2\sigma^2}{(\delta^*)^2} = \frac{(2.60)^2(5)}{(1.0)^2} = 33.80, \qquad (11.2.23)$$

namely $n = 34$.

If we restricted to $n = 25$, we will have an $h_5(P^*)$ equal to

$$\frac{\delta^*\sqrt{n}}{\sigma} = \frac{(1.0)(5)}{\sqrt{5}} = \sqrt{5} = 2.24. \qquad (11.2.24)$$

From Table 11.2-1 we see that with $k = 5$ and $h = 2.24$ we have a P^* of about .84. Hence, the experiment would seem to be worth conducting (since $P^* = .84$ is much better than random choice, which yields $P^* = .20$ in the case $k = 5$).

We might also ask "What is the smallest δ^* for which $n = 25$ will guarantee probability $P^* = .90$?" This is the δ^* for which

$$\frac{\delta^*\sqrt{n}}{\sigma} = 2.60, \qquad (11.2.25)$$

namely $\delta^* = (2.60)(\sqrt{5})/5 = 1.16$, and does not differ greatly from 1.0.

So far in this section, we have considered selection of the best (largest mean) normal population when the variances of populations are equal and known. In practice, variances are rarely known, and often are not even known to be equal. Thus, **we will now examine procedures for cases in which the goal is as at (11.2.5), but X_{ij} is $N(\mu_i, \sigma_i^2)$ with μ_i and σ_i^2 both unknown $(1 \le i \le k)$.**

In a similar setting in Chapter 9 (see Theorem 9.10.1), we saw that no single-stage test could solve a testing problem. Here it is also true that no single-stage selection procedure can solve the selection problem (for details, see Dudewicz (1971)). A solution of the problem was first given by Dudewicz and Dalal (1975), who proved the

Theorem 11.2.26. Let X_{ij} be $N(\mu_i, \sigma_i^2)$ $(i = 1, 2, \ldots, k; \ j = 1, 2, \ldots)$ and independent. Consider the goal of selecting a population with mean $\mu_{[k]}$ so that $P(CS) \ge P^*$ whenever $\mu_{[k]} - \mu_{[k-1]} \ge \delta^*(1/k < P^* < 1, \ \delta^* > 0)$. This is guaranteed by the procedure that samples according to Two-Stage Sampling Rule 9.10.2 with $w = h/\delta^*$ where h (which depends on n_0, k, and P^*) solves the equation

$$\int_{-\infty}^{\infty} \left(F_{n_0}(z + h) \right)^{k-1} f_{n_0}(z) \, dz = P^*, \qquad (11.2.27)$$

where F_{n_0} and f_{n_0} are, respectively, the c.d.f. and p.d.f. of a Student's t r.v. with $n_0 - 1$ degrees of freedom.

Remark 11.2.28. Tables of the quantity $h_{n_0}(k, P^*)$ needed in Theorem 11.2.26 have been provided in a convenient form by Dudewicz, Ramberg, and Chen (1975). The table for $k = 2$ was given in Table 9.10-1 (since it was used in the

TABLE 11.2-2
Solution $h_{n_0}(k, P^*)$ of Equation (11.2.27)

$k = 3$

P^* \ n_0	2	3	4	5	6	7	8	9	10	15	20	25	30
.75	3.52	2.15	1.86	1.74	1.67	1.63	1.60	1.57	1.56	1.51	1.49	1.48	1.47
.80	4.59	2.59	2.20	2.04	1.95	1.89	1.85	1.83	1.80	1.75	1.72	1.71	1.70
.85	6.31	3.17	2.62	2.40	2.28	2.21	2.16	2.13	2.10	2.03	1.99	1.98	1.96
.90	9.64	4.05	3.22	2.90	2.73	2.63	2.57	2.52	2.48	2.39	2.34	2.32	2.30
.95	19.40	5.86	4.29	3.75	3.48	3.32	3.21	3.14	3.08	2.94	2.87	2.84	2.81
.975	38.7	8.25	5.50	4.63	4.22	3.98	3.82	3.72	3.64	3.43	3.35	3.30	3.27
.99	96.2	12.83	7.44	5.91	5.23	4.86	4.62	4.46	4.34	4.04	3.92	3.85	3.81

$k = 4$

P^* \ n_0	2	3	4	5	6	7	8	9	10	15	20	25	30
.75	4.77	2.66	2.25	2.08	1.99	1.93	1.89	1.86	1.84	1.78	1.75	1.74	1.73
.80	6.16	3.13	2.59	2.38	2.26	2.19	2.14	2.11	2.08	2.01	1.98	1.96	1.95
.85	8.41	3.77	3.03	2.75	2.60	2.51	2.45	2.41	2.37	2.28	2.24	2.22	2.21
.90	12.80	4.75	3.66	3.26	3.06	2.93	2.85	2.80	2.75	2.63	2.58	2.55	2.54
.95	25.76	6.80	4.80	4.14	3.81	3.62	3.50	3.41	3.34	3.17	3.10	3.06	3.03
.975	51.4	9.53	6.10	5.05	4.57	4.29	4.11	3.99	3.90	3.67	3.57	3.51	3.48
.99	128	14.79	8.21	6.40	5.62	5.19	4.92	4.74	4.60	4.27	4.13	4.05	4.01

$k = 5$

P^* \ n_0	2	3	4	5	6	7	8	9	10	15	20	25	30
.75	5.95	3.05	2.53	2.32	2.21	2.14	2.09	2.06	2.03	1.96	1.93	1.91	1.90
.80	7.65	3.56	2.89	2.63	2.49	2.40	2.35	2.30	2.27	2.19	2.15	2.13	2.12
.85	10.43	4.25	3.34	3.00	2.83	2.72	2.65	2.60	2.56	2.46	2.41	2.39	2.37
.90	15.90	5.32	4.00	3.53	3.29	3.15	3.05	2.99	2.94	2.81	2.75	2.72	2.69
.95	32.04	7.58	5.20	4.42	4.05	3.84	3.70	3.60	3.53	3.34	3.26	3.21	3.18
.975	64.1	10.61	6.58	5.37	4.83	4.52	4.32	4.18	4.08	3.83	3.72	3.66	3.62
.99	160	16.47	8.82	6.78	5.90	5.43	5.13	4.93	4.79	4.43	4.28	4.20	4.14

$k = 6$

P^* \ n_0	2	3	4	5	6	7	8	9	10	15	20	25	30
.75	7.10	3.39	2.76	2.52	2.38	2.30	2.25	2.21	2.18	2.10	2.06	2.04	2.03
.80	9.12	3.93	3.13	2.82	2.66	2.57	2.50	2.45	2.42	2.32	2.28	2.26	2.24
.85	12.43	4.66	3.60	3.21	3.01	2.89	2.81	2.75	2.70	2.59	2.54	2.51	2.49
.90	18.96	5.82	4.28	3.74	3.47	3.31	3.21	3.13	3.08	2.93	2.87	2.84	2.81
.95	38.29	8.26	5.53	4.66	4.25	4.01	3.86	3.75	3.67	3.46	3.38	3.33	3.30
.975	76.7	11.56	6.97	5.64	5.03	4.69	4.48	4.33	4.22	3.95	3.83	3.77	3.73
.99	192	17.97	9.34	7.09	6.13	5.62	5.30	5.09	4.93	4.55	4.39	4.30	4.25

TABLE 11.2-2
Solution $h_{n_0}(k, P^*)$ of Equation (11.2.27) (continued)

$k = 7$

P^* \ n_0	2	3	4	5	6	7	8	9	10	15	20	25	30
.75	8.23	3.68	2.96	2.67	2.53	2.44	2.37	2.33	2.30	2.21	2.17	2.14	2.13
.80	10.58	4.25	3.33	2.99	2.81	2.70	2.63	2.58	2.54	2.43	2.38	2.36	2.34
.85	14.42	5.03	3.81	3.37	3.15	3.02	2.93	2.87	2.82	2.70	2.64	2.61	2.59
.90	22.01	6.27	4.51	3.92	3.62	3.45	3.33	3.25	3.19	3.04	2.97	2.93	2.91
.95	44.53	8.88	5.81	4.85	4.41	4.15	3.98	3.87	3.79	3.57	3.47	3.42	3.39
.975	89.3	12.43	7.32	5.86	5.20	4.84	4.61	4.45	4.34	4.05	3.93	3.86	3.82
.99	223	19.34	9.79	7.35	6.32	5.78	5.44	5.21	5.05	4.64	4.48	4.39	4.33

$k = 8$

P^* \ n_0	2	3	4	5	6	7	8	9	10	15	20	25	30
.75	9.36	3.95	3.13	2.81	2.65	2.55	2.48	2.43	2.40	2.30	2.25	2.23	2.21
.80	12.02	4.55	3.51	3.13	2.93	2.81	2.73	2.68	2.63	2.52	2.47	2.44	2.42
.85	16.40	5.37	4.01	3.52	3.28	3.13	3.04	2.97	2.92	2.78	2.72	2.69	2.67
.90	25.05	6.68	4.72	4.07	3.75	3.56	3.44	3.35	3.29	3.12	3.05	3.01	2.98
.95	50.76	9.45	6.06	5.03	4.54	4.27	4.09	3.97	3.88	3.65	3.55	3.50	3.46
.975	101.9	13.24	7.63	6.05	5.35	4.97	4.72	4.56	4.44	4.13	4.00	3.93	3.89
.99	256	20.62	10.20	7.58	6.49	5.91	5.56	5.32	5.15	4.73	4.55	4.46	4.40

$k = 9$

P^* \ n_0	2	3	4	5	6	7	8	9	10	15	20	25	30
.75	10.49	4.20	3.28	2.93	2.75	2.64	2.57	2.52	2.48	2.37	2.33	2.30	2.28
.80	13.47	4.82	3.67	3.25	3.04	2.91	2.82	2.76	2.72	2.60	2.54	2.51	2.49
.85	18.37	5.68	4.18	3.65	3.39	3.23	3.13	3.06	3.00	2.86	2.80	2.76	2.74
.90	28.08	7.06	4.91	4.21	3.86	3.66	3.53	3.44	3.37	3.20	3.12	3.08	3.05
.95	57.0	9.99	6.29	5.18	4.66	4.37	4.19	4.06	3.96	3.72	3.62	3.56	3.53
.975	114.5	13.99	7.91	6.22	5.48	5.08	4.82	4.65	4.52	4.20	4.07	4.00	3.95
.99	287	21.8	10.58	7.79	6.64	6.03	5.66	5.41	5.23	4.80	4.62	4.53	4.46

$k = 10$

P^* \ n_0	2	3	4	5	6	7	8	9	10	15	20	25	30
.75	11.60	4.43	3.42	3.04	2.85	2.73	2.65	2.60	2.55	2.44	2.39	2.36	2.35
.80	14.90	5.08	3.82	3.36	3.13	3.00	2.90	2.84	2.79	2.66	2.60	2.57	2.55
.85	20.34	5.98	4.33	3.77	3.48	3.32	3.21	3.13	3.08	2.92	2.86	2.82	2.80
.90	31.12	7.41	5.09	4.33	3.96	3.75	3.62	3.52	3.45	3.26	3.18	3.14	3.11
.95	63.2	10.49	6.50	5.32	4.77	4.47	4.27	4.14	4.04	3.79	3.68	3.62	3.18
.975	127.1	14.70	8.17	6.38	5.60	5.17	4.91	4.73	4.60	4.26	4.13	4.05	4.01
.99	318	22.9	10.92	7.98	6.77	6.14	5.75	5.49	5.31	4.86	4.68	4.58	4.51

TABLE 11.2-2
Solution $h_{n_0}(k, P^*)$ of Equation (11.2.27) (continued)

$k = 11$

P^*＼n_0	2	3	4	5	6	7	8	9	10	15	20	25	30
.75	12.72	4.64	3.54	3.14	2.93	2.81	2.72	2.66	2.62	2.50	2.45	2.42	2.40
.80	16.34	5.32	3.95	3.46	3.22	3.07	2.98	2.91	2.86	2.72	2.66	2.63	2.61
.85	22.31	6.25	4.48	3.87	3.57	3.40	3.28	3.20	3.14	2.98	2.91	2.87	2.85
.90	34.15	7.75	5.25	4.44	4.06	3.83	3.69	3.59	3.51	3.32	3.24	3.19	3.16
.95	69.4	10.97	6.70	5.44	4.87	4.55	4.35	4.21	4.10	3.84	3.73	3.67	3.63
.975	139.7	15.38	8.41	6.52	5.71	5.26	4.99	4.80	4.66	4.32	4.18	4.10	4.05
.99	350	24.0	11.25	8.16	6.90	6.24	5.84	5.57	5.38	4.91	4.73	4.62	4.56

$k = 12$

P^*＼n_0	2	3	4	5	6	7	8	9	10	15	20	25	30
.75	13.84	4.85	3.66	3.23	3.01	2.88	2.79	2.73	2.68	2.55	2.50	2.47	2.45
.80	17.77	5.54	4.07	3.56	3.30	3.14	3.04	2.97	2.92	2.77	2.71	2.68	2.66
.85	24.27	6.52	4.61	3.97	3.65	3.47	3.35	3.26	3.20	3.03	2.96	2.92	2.90
.90	37.17	8.07	5.40	4.54	4.14	3.91	3.76	3.65	3.57	3.37	3.28	3.24	3.21
.95	75.6	11.42	6.88	5.56	4.96	4.63	4.42	4.27	4.16	3.89	3.78	3.72	3.68
.975	152.3	16.02	8.63	6.66	5.81	5.34	5.06	4.86	4.72	4.37	4.23	4.15	4.10
.99	382	25.0	11.55	8.32	7.01	6.32	5.91	5.64	5.44	4.96	4.77	4.67	4.60

$k = 13$

P^*＼n_0	2	3	4	5	6	7	8	9	10	15	20	25	30
.75	14.95	5.04	3.77	3.31	3.08	2.94	2.85	2.78	2.73	2.60	2.54	2.51	2.49
.80	19.21	5.76	4.19	3.64	3.37	3.21	3.10	3.03	2.97	2.82	2.76	2.72	2.70
.85	26.24	6.77	4.74	4.06	4.73	3.53	3.41	3.32	3.25	3.08	3.01	2.97	2.94
.90	40.20	8.38	5.54	4.64	4.22	3.97	3.82	3.71	3.63	3.42	3.33	3.28	3.25
.95	81.8	11.86	7.05	5.67	5.05	4.70	4.48	4.33	4.22	3.94	3.82	3.76	3.72
.975	164.8	16.64	8.85	6.78	5.90	5.42	5.12	4.92	4.78	4.42	4.27	4.19	4.14
.99	413	26.0	11.84	8.47	7.11	6.41	5.98	5.70	5.50	5.01	4.81	4.71	4.64

$k = 14$

P^*＼n_0	2	3	4	5	6	7	8	9	10	15	20	25	30
.75	16.06	5.23	3.87	3.39	3.15	3.00	2.90	2.83	2.78	2.65	2.59	2.55	2.53
.80	20.64	5.97	4.30	3.72	3.44	3.27	3.16	3.08	3.02	2.86	2.80	2.76	2.74
.85	28.20	7.01	4.86	4.14	3.80	3.60	3.46	3.37	3.30	3.12	3.05	3.01	2.98
.90	43.23	8.67	5.67	4.73	4.29	4.04	3.87	3.76	3.68	3.46	3.37	3.32	3.29
.95	88.1	12.27	7.22	5.77	5.12	4.76	4.54	4.38	4.27	3.98	3.86	3.80	3.75
.975	177.4	17.24	9.05	6.90	5.98	5.49	5.18	4.98	4.83	4.46	4.31	4.22	4.17
.99	445	27.0	12.11	8.61	7.21	6.48	6.05	5.76	5.55	5.05	4.85	4.74	4.68

TABLE 11.2-2
Solution $h_{n_0}(k, P^*)$ of Equation (11.2.27) (continued)

$k = 15$

n_0 / P^*	2	3	4	5	6	7	8	9	10	15	20	25	30
.75	17.17	5.41	3.97	3.46	3.21	3.05	2.95	2.88	2.83	2.69	2.63	2.59	2.57
.80	22.07	6.17	4.40	3.80	3.50	3.32	3.21	3.13	3.07	2.91	2.84	2.80	2.77
.85	30.17	7.24	4.97	4.22	3.86	3.65	3.52	3.42	3.35	3.16	3.09	3.01	3.01
.90	46.25	8.96	5.80	4.82	4.36	4.09	3.93	3.81	3.72	3.50	3.41	3.35	3.32
.95	94.3	12.68	7.37	5.87	5.20	4.83	4.59	4.43	4.32	4.02	3.90	3.83	3.79
.975	190.0	17.81	9.24	7.01	6.06	5.55	5.24	5.03	4.88	4.50	4.34	4.26	4.20
.99	476	27.9	12.37	8.75	7.30	6.55	6.11	5.81	5.60	5.09	4.88	4.78	4.71

$k = 16$

n_0 / P^*	2	3	4	5	6	7	8	9	10	15	20	25	30
.75	18.28	5.58	4.06	3.53	3.26	3.11	3.00	2.93	2.87	2.72	2.66	2.63	2.60
.80	23.50	6.36	4.50	3.87	3.56	3.37	3.26	3.17	3.11	2.94	2.87	2.83	2.81
.85	32.13	7.46	5.07	4.29	3.92	3.70	3.56	3.47	3.39	3.20	3.12	3.07	3.05
.90	49.28	9.23	5.92	4.90	4.42	4.15	3.97	3.85	3.77	3.54	3.44	3.39	3.35
.95	100.5	13.07	7.52	5.96	5.27	4.88	4.64	4.48	4.36	4.06	3.93	3.86	3.82
.975	202.6	18.37	9.42	7.11	6.14	5.62	5.29	5.08	4.92	4.53	4.38	4.29	4.24
.99	508	28.8	12.62	8.88	7.39	6.62	6.16	5.86	5.65	5.12	4.92	4.81	4.74

$k = 17$

n_0 / P^*	2	3	4	5	6	7	8	9	10	15	20	25	30
.75	19.40	5.74	4.15	3.59	3.32	3.15	3.05	2.97	2.91	2.76	2.69	2.66	2.63
.80	24.93	6.55	4.59	3.94	3.61	3.42	3.30	3.21	3.15	2.98	2.90	2.86	2.84
.85	34.09	7.68	5.17	4.37	3.98	3.75	3.61	3.51	3.43	3.24	3.15	3.11	3.08
.90	52.30	9.50	6.03	4.97	4.48	4.20	4.02	3.90	3.81	3.57	3.47	3.42	3.38
.95	106.7	13.45	7.66	6.04	5.33	4.94	4.69	4.52	4.40	4.09	3.96	3.89	3.85
.975	215.3	18.90	9.60	7.21	6.21	5.67	5.34	5.12	4.96	4.57	4.41	4.32	4.27
.99	542	29.6	12.86	9.00	7.47	6.68	6.22	5.91	5.69	5.16	4.95	4.84	4.76

$k = 18$

n_0 / P^*	2	3	4	5	6	7	8	9	10	15	20	25	30
.75	20.51	5.90	4.23	3.66	3.37	3.20	3.09	3.01	2.95	2.79	2.72	2.69	2.66
.80	26.36	6.73	4.68	4.00	3.67	3.47	3.34	3.25	3.19	3.01	2.93	2.89	2.87
.85	36.05	7.89	5.27	4.43	4.03	3.80	3.65	3.55	3.47	3.27	3.18	3.14	3.10
.90	55.3	9.76	6.14	5.04	4.54	4.25	4.06	3.94	3.84	3.60	3.50	3.45	3.41
.95	112.9	13.81	7.80	6.13	5.39	4.99	4.73	4.56	4.44	4.12	3.99	3.92	3.87
.975	227.7	19.43	9.77	7.31	6.28	5.73	5.39	5.16	5.00	4.60	4.43	4.35	4.29
.99	571	30.5	13.09	9.12	7.55	6.74	6.27	5.95	5.73	5.19	4.98	4.86	4.79

TABLE 11.2-2
Solution $h_{n_0}(k, P^*)$ of Equation (11.2.27) (continued)

$k = 19$

P^* \ n_0	2	3	4	5	6	7	8	9	10	15	20	25	30
.75	21.61	6.06	4.32	3.71	3.42	3.24	3.13	3.04	2.98	2.82	2.75	2.71	2.69
.80	27.79	6.91	4.77	4.06	3.72	3.51	3.38	3.29	3.22	3.04	2.96	2.92	2.89
.85	38.01	8.09	5.37	4.50	4.08	3.85	3.69	3.59	3.51	3.30	3.21	3.16	3.13
.90	58.4	10.01	6.25	5.11	4.59	4.29	4.10	3.97	3.88	3.63	3.53	3.47	3.44
.95	119.1	14.17	7.93	6.20	5.45	5.04	4.78	4.60	4.47	4.15	4.02	3.95	3.90
.975	240.2	19.94	9.93	7.40	6.34	5.78	5.43	5.20	5.04	4.63	4.46	4.37	4.32
.99	604	31.3	13.31	9.23	7.62	6.80	6.31	5.99	5.77	5.22	5.00	4.89	4.81

$k = 20$

P^* \ n_0	2	3	4	5	6	7	8	9	10	15	20	25	30
.75	22.72	6.21	4.39	3.77	3.46	3.28	3.16	3.08	3.02	2.85	2.78	2.74	2.72
.80	29.22	7.08	4.85	4.12	3.76	3.56	3.42	3.32	3.26	3.07	2.99	2.95	2.92
.85	39.98	8.29	5.46	4.56	4.13	3.89	3.73	3.62	3.54	3.33	3.24	3.19	3.16
.90	61.4	10.25	6.35	5.18	4.64	4.34	4.14	4.01	3.91	3.66	3.56	3.50	3.46
.95	125.3	14.52	8.05	6.28	5.51	5.08	4.82	4.64	4.51	4.18	4.04	3.97	3.92
.975	252.9	20.43	10.09	7.49	6.40	5.83	5.48	5.24	5.07	4.66	4.49	4.40	4.34
.99	635	32.1	13.52	9.34	7.69	6.86	6.36	6.03	5.80	5.25	5.03	4.91	4.84

$k = 21$

P^* \ n_0	2	3	4	5	6	7	8	9	10	15	20	25	30
.75	23.83	6.36	4.47	3.82	3.51	3.32	3.20	3.11	3.05	2.88	2.81	2.77	2.74
.80	30.65	7.24	4.93	4.17	3.81	3.59	3.45	3.36	3.29	3.10	3.02	2.97	2.94
.95	41.94	8.48	5.54	4.62	4.18	3.93	3.77	3.65	3.57	3.35	3.26	3.21	3.18
.90	64.4	10.49	6.44	5.24	4.69	4.38	4.18	4.04	3.94	3.69	3.58	3.52	4.48
.95	131.5	14.86	8.17	6.35	5.56	5.13	4.86	4.67	4.54	4.21	4.07	3.99	3.95
.975	265.7	20.92	10.24	7.57	6.46	5.88	5.52	5.28	5.11	4.68	4.51	4.42	4.36
.99	667	32.8	13.72	9.44	7.76	6.91	6.40	6.07	5.84	5.27	5.05	4.93	4.86

$k = 22$

P^* \ n_0	2	3	4	5	6	7	8	9	10	15	20	25	30
.75	24.94	6.50	4.54	3.88	3.55	3.36	3.23	3.15	3.08	2.91	2.83	2.79	2.76
.80	32.08	7.40	5.01	4.23	3.85	3.63	3.49	3.39	3.32	3.12	3.04	2.99	2.96
.85	43.90	8.67	5.63	4.67	4.22	3.97	3.80	3.69	3.60	3.38	3.29	3.24	3.20
.90	67.4	10.72	6.54	5.30	4.74	4.42	4.22	4.08	3.98	3.71	3.60	3.54	3.51
.95	137.7	15.19	8.29	6.42	5.61	5.17	4.89	4.71	4.57	4.23	4.09	4.02	3.97
.975	278	21.39	10.39	7.65	6.52	5.92	5.56	5.31	5.14	4.71	4.53	4.44	4.38
.99	700	33.6	13.93	9.54	7.83	6.96	6.44	6.11	5.87	5.30	5.07	4.95	4.88

TABLE 11.2-2

Solution $h_{n_0}(k, P^*)$ of Equation (11.2.27) (continued)

$k = 23$

P^* \ n_0	2	3	4	5	6	7	8	9	10	15	20	25	30
.75	26.05	6.64	4.61	3.92	3.59	3.39	3.27	3.18	3.11	2.93	2.85	2.81	2.78
.80	33.51	7.56	5.08	4.28	3.89	3.67	3.52	3.42	3.34	3.15	3.06	3.02	2.99
.85	45.86	8.85	5.71	4.73	4.27	4.00	3.83	3.72	3.63	3.41	3.31	3.26	3.22
.90	70.4	10.95	6.63	5.36	4.78	4.46	4.25	4.11	4.00	3.74	3.63	3.57	3.53
.95	143.9	15.51	8.40	6.49	5.66	5.21	4.93	4.74	4.60	4.26	4.11	4.04	3.99
.975	291	21.85	10.53	7.73	6.57	5.96	5.59	5.35	5.17	4.73	4.56	4.46	4.40
.99	730	34.3	14.12	9.63	7.89	7.01	6.48	6.14	5.90	5.32	5.10	4.97	4.90

$k = 24$

P^* \ n_0	2	3	4	5	6	7	8	9	10	15	20	25	30
.75	27.16	6.78	4.68	3.97	3.63	3.43	3.30	3.20	3.14	2.95	2.88	2.83	2.81
.80	34.93	7.72	5.15	4.33	3.93	3.70	3.55	3.45	3.37	3.17	3.08	3.04	3.01
.85	47.82	9.03	5.78	4.78	4.31	4.04	3.87	3.75	3.66	3.43	3.33	3.28	3.24
.90	73.5	11.17	6.72	5.42	4.82	4.49	4.28	4.14	4.03	3.76	3.65	3.59	3.55
.95	150.1	15.83	8.51	6.55	5.71	5.25	4.96	4.77	4.63	4.28	4.14	4.06	4.01
.975	303	22.30	10.67	7.80	6.63	5.63	5.63	5.38	5.20	4.76	4.58	4.48	4.42
.99	762	35.1	14.31	9.73	7.95	7.05	6.52	6.18	5.93	5.37	5.12	4.99	4.92

$k = 25$

P^* \ n_0	2	3	4	5	6	7	8	9	10	15	20	25	30
.75	28.27	6.91	4.74	4.02	3.67	3.46	3.33	3.23	3.16	2.98	2.90	2.85	2.83
.80	36.36	7.87	5.22	4.38	3.97	3.74	3.58	3.48	3.40	3.19	3.11	3.06	3.03
.85	49.78	9.21	5.86	4.83	4.35	4.07	3.90	3.77	3.68	3.45	3.35	3.30	3.26
.90	76.5	11.38	6.80	5.47	4.87	4.53	4.31	4.17	4.06	3.78	3.67	3.61	3.57
.95	156.3	16.14	8.62	6.62	5.75	5.28	4.99	3.80	4.66	4.30	4.16	4.08	4.03
.975	316	22.74	10.80	7.88	6.68	6.05	5.66	5.41	5.23	4.78	4.60	4.50	4.44
.99	794	35.8	14.49	9.82	8.01	7.10	6.56	6.21	5.96	5.37	5.14	5.01	4.94

solution of the Behrens-Fisher problem given in Section 9.10). Tables for $k = 3(1)25$ are given in Table 11.2-2.

PROBLEMS FOR SECTION 11.2

11.2.1 (a) An experiment is to be conducted to find the best available pain reliever, based on time to relief of pain. Suppose there are 10 pain relievers available. It is desired to select the best one with probability at least .95, when the best beats

the next best by at least 5 minutes. It is assumed that the variance of time to pain relief is equal to 16 for each pain reliever, and that the times are normally distributed. Find the minimum sample size n needed for this experiment using
(i) Formula (11.2.17) due to Bechhofer.
(ii) Approximation (11.2.21) due to Dudewicz.
Compare the answers in parts (i) and (ii).
(b) What happens to the sample size n needed when P^* decreases to .90? When δ^* increases to 10? When σ^2 decreases to 9?

11.2.2 In Problem 11.2.1, what is the smallest δ^* for which $n = 15$ will guarantee probability .95? [Using formulas (11.2.17) and (11.2.21) to obtain exact and approximate values of δ^*.]

11.2.3 In Problem 11.2.1, what is the guaranteed probability P^* if we take a random sample of size 10 from each of the populations? [Use formulas (11.2.17) and (11.2.21).]

11.2.4 Often the choice of sample size is not under the statistician's control, but the data has already been collected when the client comes to the statistician. The statistician then elicits the experiment and the goal from the client, and the statistician's job is data analysis and interpretation.

For example, suppose a fast-food chain would like to run that one of four possible advertising campaigns for which the average weekly gross sales increase will be the highest. To ascertain this, they test each strategy in eight different locations for a week, with the following results (in 1000's of dollars):

Free Trip Giveaway	Lottery	Free Drink	Celebrity Endorsement
23.8	18.6	23.4	16.4
18.6	17.8	18.8	18.6
25.3	16.5	25.5	25.9
20.3	22.8	21.3	21.3
21.6	23.6	22.6	20.6
17.4	19.8	18.9	18.3
19.9	14.3	20.9	17.5
20.5	18.8	22.2	20.9

Assuming the average weekly sales increases for each strategy are normally distributed with the same variance $\sigma^2 = 4$:
(a) Select a strategy that you will claim has the highest weekly sales increase.
(b) Find the minimum probability that the selected strategy is in fact the strategy with the largest weekly sales increase when the probability must be guaranteed up to sales differences as small as $\delta^* = 1.5$ among the strategies.

11.2.5 In Problem 11.2.4, suppose the variances of the four populations are unequal and unknown. Consider $n_0 = 8$ observations from each of the four populations as initial samples to estimate the variances.
(a) Find the total final sample sizes needed by the Dudewicz-Dalal procedure. (Suppose we still desire $\delta^* = 1.5$ and $P^* = .95$.) How many more samples do we need from each of the four populations respectively to attain the goal?
(b) If we cannot take more data, suppose we set $n_0 = 7$, and set $P^* = .95$. For which choice of δ^* will we have $n_1 = n_2 = n_3 = n_4 = 8$?
(c) Choose δ^* as in part (b), compute $\tilde{X}_i$ ($i = 1, 2, 3, 4$), and make a selection.

11.3. SELECTION OF THE BEST (SMALLEST VARIANCE) NORMAL POPULATION

In Section 11.2 we studied one selection problem that occurs frequently in practice, selection of the population with the largest mean. **In this section we study the selection of the population with the least variability (as measured by variance).** For example, if we have available several measuring instruments such as scales, the most precise one is that with the least variance. As a second example, if several sources of supply are available for parts with the same mean, the source with the least variability will be the most desirable one (since its parts will meet the specifications the largest percentage of the time). As a third example, if light bulbs produced by several processes have approximately the same average life, the process that produces bulbs with the least variability (variance) of life may be the most desirable in terms of customer satisfaction with the product.

We assume here that the $k \geq 2$ **populations** $\pi_1, \ldots, \pi_k$ (sources of observations) are such that if $X_{i1}, X_{i2}, \ldots$ are n independent **observations** from π_i, then each X_{ij} is $N(\mu_i, \sigma_i^2)$ where μ_i is unknown and σ_i^2 is unknown $(1 \leq i \leq k)$. Let

$$\sigma_{[1]}^2 \leq \cdots \leq \sigma_{[k]}^2 \tag{11.3.1}$$

denote the ordered values of $\sigma_1^2, \ldots, \sigma_k^2$. Our **goal** is to select a population with variance $\sigma_{[1]}^2$. If we formulate a procedure for selecting one of the k populations and declaring the selected population to be "best," we would (as in Section 11.2 in a different context) like a reasonable probability of having it be, in fact, best.

One intuitively reasonable procedure is to proceed as follows. Take independent samples of n independent observations from each of the k populations, use the observations from π_i to estimate σ_i^2, say by $\hat{\sigma}_i^2$ $(1 \leq i \leq k)$, and select the[8] population π_l for which

$$\hat{\sigma}_l^2 = \min\left(\hat{\sigma}_1^2, \ldots, \hat{\sigma}_k^2\right). \tag{11.3.2}$$

Since, for $n \geq 2$,

$$s_i^2 = \frac{\sum_{j=1}^{n} \left(X_{ij} - \overline{X}_i\right)^2}{n-1} \quad \text{with} \quad \overline{X}_i = \frac{X_{i1} + \cdots + X_{in}}{n} \tag{11.3.3}$$

is a "good" unbiased estimator of σ_i^2 based on a minimal sufficient statistic for (μ_i, σ_i^2), it seems reasonable (see Problem 11.4H) to let

$$\hat{\sigma}_i^2 = s_i^2 \ (1 \leq i \leq k). \tag{11.3.4}$$

Thus, our **procedure** is to take k independent sets of n independent observations each ($n \geq 2$ observations per population), compute s_i^2 $(1 \leq i \leq k)$, and select (as being best) that population which yielded the smallest of $s_1^2, \ldots, s_k^2$.

---

[8] In general, this could fail to be unique, although we will see that in this section it is unique with probability 1 (see Problem 11.9).

We now wish to choose n (the sample size per population) in a rational way. One such way is to choose the smallest n that satisfies a **probability requirement** such as

$$P(\text{CS}) \geq P^* \quad \text{whenever} \quad \sigma_{[2]}^2 \geq \theta^* \sigma_{[1]}^2, \tag{11.3.5}$$

where **CS** (for correct selection) denotes the final selection of a population with population variance $\sigma_{[1]}^2$, and P^* $(1/k < P^* < 1$; see Problem 11.10) and θ^* $(\theta^* > 1)$ are specified by the experimenter. With probability requirement (11.3.5) we will be at least $100P^*$ percent sure (90% sure when $P^* = .90$) of selecting the best population whenever the best variance $\sigma_{[1]}^2$ is exceeded by the second best variance $\sigma_{[2]}^2$ by at least $100(\theta^* - 1)$ percent.

To solve for the smallest n that satisfies (11.3.5), as we do in Theorem 11.3.11, it will be convenient to make the following definition.

Definition 11.3.6. $s_{(i)}^2$ is that one of $s_1^2, \ldots, s_k^2$ obtained from the population with population variance $\sigma_{[i]}^2$ $(1 \leq i \leq k)$, while $s_{[1]}^2 \leq \cdots \leq s_{[k]}^2$ denote $s_1^2, \ldots, s_k^2$ in numerical order.

Theorem 11.3.7. The $P(\text{CS})$ of the selection procedure equals

$$\int_0^\infty \left[1 - G_{n-1}\left(y \frac{\sigma_{[1]}^2}{\sigma_{[2]}^2} \right) \right] \cdots \left[1 - G_{n-1}\left(y \frac{\sigma_{[1]}^2}{\sigma_{[k]}^2} \right) \right] g_{n-1}(y) \, dy, \tag{11.3.8}$$

where $G_{n-1}(\cdot)$ and $g_{n-1}(\cdot)$ are the d.f. and p.d.f. of a $\chi_{n-1}^2(0)$ r.v., respectively.

Proof: The $P(\text{CS})$ is the probability that the one of $s_1^2, \ldots, s_k^2$ (namely, $s_{(1)}^2$) from the population with the smallest variance $\sigma_{[1]}^2$ is the smallest of $s_1^2, \ldots, s_k^2$ (namely $s_{[1]}^2$):

$$P(\text{CS}) = P\left[s_{(1)}^2 = s_{[1]}^2 \right]$$

$$= P\left[s_{(1)}^2 = \min\left(s_{(1)}^2, \ldots, s_{(k)}^2 \right) \right]$$

$$= P\left[s_{(1)}^2 < s_{(2)}^2, \ldots, s_{(1)}^2 < s_{(k)}^2 \right]$$

$$= P\left[s_{(i)}^2 > s_{(1)}^2, i = 2, \ldots, k \right] \tag{11.3.9}$$

$$= P\left[\frac{s_{(i)}^2}{\sigma_{[i]}^2} \geq \frac{s_{(1)}^2}{\sigma_{[1]}^2} \frac{\sigma_{[1]}^2}{\sigma_{[i]}^2}, i = 2, \ldots, k \right]$$

$$= P\left[Y_i > Y_1 \frac{\sigma_{[1]}^2}{\sigma_{[i]}^2}, i = 2, \ldots, k \right],$$

where $Y_1, \ldots, Y_k$ are independent $\chi_{n-1}^2(0)$ r.v.'s. [Here we used the proof of

Lemma 9.5.15 to show $(n-1)s_{(i)}^2/\sigma_{[i]}^2$ is $\chi_{n-1}^2(0)$. The $Y_1, \ldots, Y_k$ are independent since the $s_{(1)}^2, \ldots, s_{(k)}^2$ are.] Thus,

$$P(CS) = \int_{-\infty}^{\infty} P\left[Y_i > y\frac{\sigma_{[1]}^2}{\sigma_{[i]}^2}, i = 2, \ldots, k\right]g_{n-1}(y)\,dy$$

$$= \int_0^{\infty} P\left[Y_2 > y\frac{\sigma_{[1]}^2}{\sigma_{[2]}^2}\right] \cdots P\left[Y_k > y\frac{\sigma_{[1]}^2}{\sigma_{[k]}^2}\right]g_{n-1}(y)\,dy \qquad (11.3.10)$$

$$= \int_0^{\infty}\left[1 - G_{n-1}\left(y\frac{\sigma_{[1]}^2}{\sigma_{[2]}^2}\right)\right] \cdots \left[1 - G_{n-1}\left(y\frac{\sigma_{[1]}^2}{\sigma_{[k]}^2}\right)\right]g_{n-1}(y)\,dy. \quad \blacksquare$$

Theorem 11.3.11. The $P(CS)$ of the selection procedure is (among all sets of possible population variances $\sigma_1^2, \ldots, \sigma_k^2$ that satisfy $\sigma_{[2]}^2 \geq \theta^*\sigma_{[1]}^2$) minimized when

$$\theta^*\sigma_{[1]}^2 = \sigma_{[2]}^2 = \cdots = \sigma_{[k]}^2 \qquad (11.3.12)$$

[this is called the **least favorable configuration** (LFC) of the population variances]. In the LFC, the $P(CS)$, say $P_{LFC}(CS)$, is given by

$$P_{LFC}(CS) = \int_0^{\infty}\left[1 - G_{n-1}\left(\frac{y}{\theta^*}\right)\right]^{k-1}g_{n-1}(y)\,dy. \qquad (11.3.13)$$

Proof: Since $G_{n-1}(z)$ is an increasing function of z, by expression (11.3.8) for the $P(CS)$ it follows that the $P(CS)\downarrow$ as $\sigma_{[1]}^2/\sigma_{[i]}^2\uparrow$, for each $i = 2, \ldots, k$. Subject to the restriction $\sigma_{[2]}^2 \geq \theta^*\sigma_{[1]}^2$, we make $\sigma_{[1]}^2/\sigma_{[i]}^2$ largest when we set

$$\theta^*\sigma_{[1]}^2 = \sigma_{[2]}^2 = \cdots = \sigma_{[k]}^2.$$

Hence, the $P(CS)$ is minimized (subject to $\sigma_{[2]}^2 \geq \theta^*\sigma_{[1]}^2$) when (11.3.12) holds. But when (11.3.12) holds, the $P(CS)$ given by (11.3.8) reduces simply to (11.3.13). $\blacksquare$

Remark 11.3.14. Limited tables of the $P_{LFC}(CS)$ of equation (11.3.13) were given by Bechhofer and Sobel (1954). Those tables cover the cases $n - 1 = 1(1)20$ and $\theta^* = 1.2(.2)2.2$ for $k = 2, 3, 4$. An approximation is suggested for other cases. Although details of the derivation of this approximation will not be covered here, we note that the approximation uses sample size

$$n_V = \frac{2h_k^2(P^*)}{(\ln(\theta^*))^2} = 2(\ln(k-1)) + 1. \qquad (11.3.15)$$

(Here, $h_k(P^*)$ comes from Table 11.2-1 for the normal means selection problem.)

PROBLEMS FOR SECTION 11.3

11.3.1 Consider equation (11.3.13). Show that
(a) As $\theta^* \to 1$ with n fixed, $P_{LFC}(CS) \to 1/k$.
(b) As $n \to \infty$ with θ^* fixed, $P_{LFC}(CS) \to 1$.
(c) As k increases, $P_{LFC}(CS)$ decreases.

11.3.2 In Problem 11.2.4 with $k = 4$ and $n = 8$, select the strategy with the smallest variance, using $P^* = .95$. What is the smallest θ^* you can use?

11.3.3 Along the lines of Section 11.3, develop a procedure for selection of the normal population with the largest variance, when
(a) The means are unknown.
(b) The means are known.

11.4. EXTENSIONS AND GENERALIZATIONS; SUBSET SELECTION

In Section 11.1 we discussed what the concept of a ranking problem is, and in Sections 11.2 and 11.3 we discussed two important such problems (selection of the largest mean normal population and selection of the smallest variance normal population, respectively). Our discussion, although probably by far the most extensive yet available in any textbook, is necessarily only an introduction to what is by now a vast area in which important new results are appearing each year.[9] **In this section we note very briefly (and with appropriate references) some ways in which the results of Sections 11.2 and 11.3 have been and are being extended and generalized.** Some references to published accounts of applications in various fields are given throughout the chapter, and you should be able to find additional applications in most fields of application.

The **essential problem formulation** given in Section 11.1 is that we have **populations** (sources of observations) $\pi_1, \ldots, \pi_k$ ($k \geq 2$). From source i we obtain observations $X_{i1}, X_{i2}, \ldots$ which are independent and identically distributed r.v.'s, but whose d.f. contains an unknown parameter θ_i ($1 \leq i \leq k$). We have a **goal** (e.g., select the population associated with $\theta_{[k]} = \max(\theta_1, \ldots, \theta_k)$) and **probability requirement** (e.g., $P(CS) \geq P^*$ whenever $\theta_{[k]} - \theta_{[k-1]} \geq \delta^*$, where $1/k < P^* < 1$ and $\delta^* > 0$), and desire a **procedure** that satisfies the probability requirement (e.g., select the population yielding $\overline{X}_{[k]} = \max(\overline{X}_1, \ldots, \overline{X}_k)$, the largest of the sample means based on n observations). Then:

1. Section 11.2 discussed the case where for $i = 1, \ldots, k$ the observations from π_i are $N(\mu_i, \sigma^2)$ with σ^2 known (e.g., $\sigma = 72$ eggs in 500 days) and $\theta_i = \mu_i$. In practice, often σ^2 is not known exactly. In that case, a procedure is available[10] which proceeds in two stages; first it takes a few (n_0, say)

---

[9] For extensive references, see Dudewicz and Koo (1982). For recent results, see Dudewicz (1985) and Rizvi (1985).

[10] See Bechhofer, Dunnett, and Sobel (1954).

observations from each of $\pi_1, \ldots, \pi_k$ and uses them to estimate σ^2, then it uses this estimate of σ^2 in order to determine how many additional observations to take from each population.

2. In Sections 11.2 and 11.3 it was assumed that the number of observations available from each of the k populations $\pi_1, \ldots, \pi_k$ would be the same; that is, if n_i denotes the number of observations to be taken from π_i ($1 \le i \le k$), it was assumed we would take $n_1 = n_2 = \cdots = n_k = n$ (say). Indeed, in light of Problem 11.1H it seems reasonable to take the same sample size n from each population. However, sometimes, either because past observations are available for some of the populations or because of the loss of some observations (e.g., in the example of Section 11.1, some of the pullets may die before termination at 500 days), we will in fact have unequal sample sizes from the populations. This difficult problem has received little attention even in the basic cases of Sections 11.2 and 11.3 (see Problems 11.6H and 11.7H). Our intuitive feeling, that "acting as if we actually have the same sample size $n = \min(n_1, \ldots, n_k)$ from each population should underestimate the true $P(CS)$," may not be true in all cases. Even if this feeling is proven correct in some cases, however, we would still like to make use of the additional $n_1 - n, \ldots, n_k - n$ observations from $\pi_1, \ldots, \pi_k$ to make a stronger statement about the $P(CS)$ than the statement that uses $n = \min(n_1, \ldots, n_k)$ only (as well as basing the decision on all available observations). Recently these problems have been receiving increasing attention.[11]

3. A variant of the problem of Section 11.2 is that in which we assume that the variance of observations from π_i is σ_i^2 ($1 \le i \le k$) with the σ_i^2's *known* but *unequal*. We than ask: "If I have a total sample size n at my disposal, how should I allocate it among the k populations so as to do "best" in my $P(CS)$?" This has been studied recently (see Problems 11.13 and 11.15) but is far from solved.

4. Another variant of the problem of Section 11.2 is that in which we assume that the variance of observations from π_i is σ_i^2 ($1 \le i \le k$) with the σ_i^2's *unknown* as well as *unequal*. It is known that no procedure which requires only a single stage of observations can satisfy the probability requirement in this case. A two-stage procedure was given in Section 11.2, and also holds for the subset selection formulations of the problem studied below in this section.

5. Other problems involve such considerations as the following: In what sense(s) might our selection procedures be optimal? If our observations are obtained sequentially (one at a time, rather than all at once) it may become clear soon which one is best, or it may become clear that several are not best; how can we stop early or stop taking observations on inferior populations (respectively) and still guarantee a reasonable probability requirement? If we do not know the distribution of our observations, how can

[11]See Sitek (1972) and Dudewicz (1974).

we proceed? The literature of the area is large, and the foregoing are only a few of the more important of many important results obtained that make substantial contributions to the solution of meaningful and substantive problems.

The approach to the selection problem taken in Sections 11.2 and 11.3 is called the "**indifference zone**" **approach** (because we specify we must have $P(CS) \geq P^*$ whenever $\mu_{[k]} - \mu_{[k-1]} \geq \delta^*$, but are apparently "indifferent" when $\mu_{[k]} - \mu_{[k-1]} < \delta^*$). This approach is relatively reasonable for small to moderate k (say $k \leq 15$). For moderate to large k (say $k \geq 100$), it requires more observations than we can afford, many of these observations being on inferior populations. (For example, if we have $k = 10{,}000$ possible cancer drugs, we may wish simply to select the few best for further extensive testing.) For such problems Gupta (1956) pioneered an approach called **subset selection**. Here we desire to select a subset S of $\Pi = \{\pi_1, \ldots, \pi_k\}$ such that the probability that the best population (the one with mean $\mu_{[k]}$ in Section 11.2; the one with variance $\sigma_{[1]}^2$ in Section 11.3) is in S in $\geq P^*$. The subset size and composition are random, and we desire a rule that makes the number of populations in $S[\#(S)]$ "small" (e.g., $E(\#(S)) \leq 1 + \varepsilon$ for some $\varepsilon > 0$ under some restrictions on $\mu_1, \ldots, \mu_k$). We will give a two-stage solution to this problem in the setting of Section 11.2 (selection of best means).

The setting now is that we have $k \geq 2$ **populations** $\pi_1, \ldots, \pi_k$ such that the observations $X_{i1}, X_{i2}, \ldots$ from π_i are each $N(\mu_i, \sigma_i^2)$ where μ_i and σ_i^2 are unknown ($1 \leq i \leq k$) and all observations are independent. The **goal** is to select a subset S of $\{\pi_1, \ldots, \pi_k\}$ in such a way that we satisfy the **probability requirement**

$$P(CS) \equiv P\big(\text{At least one population with mean } \mu_{[k]} \text{ is in } S\big) \geq P^*$$

$$\text{for all } \mu_1, \ldots, \mu_k, \sigma_1^2, \ldots, \sigma_k^2, \quad (11.4.1)$$

where P^* ($1/k < P^* < 1$) is specified in advance by the experimenter. This formulation of the problem was first given by Gupta (1956), who solved the problem when $\sigma_1^2 = \sigma_2^2 = \cdots = \sigma_k^2 = \sigma^2$ with σ^2 known and also with σ^2 unknown. The case where the variances are all unknown (and are not known to be equal) was first solved by Dudewicz and Dalal (1975), who provided the following procedure:

Theorem 11.4.2. Let X_{ij} be $N(\mu_i, \sigma_i^2)$ ($i = 1, \ldots, 2, \ldots, k;\ j = 1, 2, \ldots$) and independent. For the goal of selecting a subset S of $\{\pi_1, \ldots, \pi_k\}$ that includes at least one population with mean $\mu_{[k]}$ in such a way that (11.4.1) is satisfied, sample according to Two-Stage Sampling Rule 9.10.2 with $w = h/d$ where h solves (11.2.27). Include in S all populations π_i for which

$$\bar{\bar{X}}_i \geq \bar{\bar{X}}_{[k]} - d. \quad (11.4.3)$$

Note that the "yardstick" of comparison among the resulting estimates $\tilde{X}_1, \tilde{X}_2, \ldots, \tilde{X}_k$ of $\mu_1, \mu_2, \ldots, \mu_k$ is $d > 0$, which is under the control of the experimenter. Thus, the experimenter may set d, and if a population yields an estimated mean that is farther than d from the largest estimate $\tilde{X}_{[k]}$, he/she can be sure that population will be "rejected" (not included in the selected subset S). This is similar to a power requirement in hypothesis-testing; instead of asking for power at least .99 (e.g.) when means differ by δ^*, the experimenter is asking that populations that are below the best-estimated mean by d or more be able to be rejected.

Example 11.4.4. We have $k = 23$ methods of making paint that is supposed to be able to preserve metal from rusting in outdoor conditions of salt spray. The time it takes a test piece of metal painted with paint prepared with method i to rust is a normal r.v.; the means and variances are unknown, and the observations are independent. In the past we have always used $n_0 = 20$ test plates per paint. Now we wish to select a subset containing the best, and want to be able to exclude from the selected subset any treatment whose estimated mean time-to-rust is lower than that of the best paint in the sample by $d = 0.5$ years. How should we proceed?

From Theorem 11.4.2 we know that use of Two-Stage Sampling Rule 9.10.2 with $w = h/d = 2h$ will suffice. Here $k = 23$, $n_0 = 20$, and suppose the experimenter wants to be 99% sure the best paint is in the selected subset. Then h is chosen to solve (11.2.27) by use of Table 11.2-2, which yields $h = 5.10$. Hence the experimenter will use $n_i = \max\{n_0 + 1, [(ws_i)^2]\} = \max\{21, [(10.2s_i)^2]\}$ observations from π_i. If the $\tilde{X}_i$ turn out to be (for populations $\pi_1, \ldots, \pi_{23}$), after putting them in increasing order,

$$0.3, 0.4, 1.1, 1.2, 1.4, 1.4, 1.4, 1.6, 1.9, 2.1, 2.1,$$

$$2.5, 2.7, 2.9, 3.1, 3.3, 3.5, 3.8, 3.9, 3.9, 4.0, 4.1, 4.2$$

then all populations with estimates of $4.2 - 0.5 = 3.7$ years or more will be selected. Thus, the selected subset will contain the top six paints tested. A consumer-testing service might at this point recommend these six paints as the best, and perhaps (since differences among them cannot be judged significant) call the least expensive of them a "best buy." A paint company wishing to market the best paint might enter these six into another test designed (by the methods of Section 11.2) to select the best of the six.

PROBLEMS FOR SECTION 11.4

11.4.1 In Problem 11.2.4, use the procedure of Theorem 11.4.2 to select a subset containing the best strategy, with $P^* = .95$, $k = 4$, $n_0 = 7$. (Use the smallest d for which $n_1 = n_2 = n_3 = n_4 = 8$ in this case, as no more samples are available.) What S is selected?

11.4.2 In Problem 11.4.1, suppose additional observations are available and we desire $d = .5$ (a yardstick of $500.). What n_1, n_2, n_3, n_4 are needed?

11.4.3 A manufacturer is considering which of five different suppliers of O-rings to use. The problem is to determine which suppliers should not be considered because their O-rings fail at cold temperatures. Samples of 25 O-rings are taken from each supplier and tested at colder and colder temperatures until they fail. Suppose the actual mean temperatures at failure are

Supplier j	1	2	3	4	5
$\overline{X}_j$	14.4	12.3	9.1	8.6	9.2

Assuming that the actual temperatures for each supplier's O-rings are normally distributed with common variance $\sigma^2 = 5$, what suppliers should be eliminated from consideration since they are not in the subset containing the best (smallest mean) O-ring population? [*Hint*: Since the variances are known and equal, and in this setting the experimenter does not wish to control the yardstick, Gupta's original procedure may be used. It selects in S all populations with $\overline{X}_i$ within $h_k(P^*)\sigma/\sqrt{n}$ of the smallest of $\overline{X}_1, \overline{X}_2, \ldots, \overline{X}_k$ when the goal is selection of a subset containing the population with the smallest mean.]

PROBLEMS FOR CHAPTER 11

11.1 In the "probability requirement" $P(CS) \geq P^*$ discussed in Section 11.1, we required that $1/k < P^* < 1$. Show that such a requirement with $0 \leq P^* \leq 1/k$ is trivial (i.e., can be achieved without taking any observations).

11.2 In footnote 4 we claimed that, if we choose $\hat{\mu}_i$ as in equation (11.2.4), then $\max(\hat{\mu}_1, \ldots, \hat{\mu}_k)$ is unique with probability 1. Prove this result.

11.3 Prove that $f(0) = 1/k$, where $f(n)$ is specified by equation (11.2.16). [Of course, if $n = 0$, there is no sampling. If we then choose a population as "best" at random, our $P(CS)$ will be $1/k$. The derivation of equation (11.2.16) assumed $n \geq 1$, but we thus see it has a simple interpretation even if $n = 0$.]

11.4 Show that, in the special case of just $k = 2$ populations, the $P(CS)$ of the means procedure discussed in Section 11.2 is given by

$$\Phi\left(\frac{\mu_{[2]} - \mu_{[1]}}{\sqrt{2}\,\sigma/\sqrt{n}}\right).$$

11.5 Milton (1963) in his Table II tabulated

$$\int_{-\infty}^{\infty} \Phi^{k-1}\left(\frac{x\sqrt{\rho} + H}{\sqrt{1-\rho}}\right)\phi(x)\,dx$$

for $H = .00(.05)5.15$, $k = 3(1)10(5)25$, $\rho = .00(.05)1.00$. How could we use these tables to find the h that solves equation (11.2.15)? (We might wish to do so for $k > 10$, since Bechhofer's tables, noted in Remark 11.2.18, only extend to $k = 10$ for the problem of selecting the best.)

11.6 Man A and man B (track stars) have run the mile in competitions a number of times each. Assume that man A and man B ran independently of each other, and that each one's times are independent observations of his running ability. Let $\mu_A(\mu_B)$ denote the average time it takes man $A(B)$ to run the mile in competitions. Similarly, let his variance be $\sigma_A^2(\sigma_B^2)$. We have available n_1 observations of A and n_2 observations of B, and know that $\sigma_A^2 = .04$, $\sigma_B^2 = .09$, and the observations are normally distributed. We wish to select the man (of A, B) who on the average has the lowest time for running the mile in competitions.

(a) If we select A when $\overline{X}_A < \overline{X}_B$ (and select B otherwise, where $\overline{X}_A$ is the average of the n_1 observations on A and $\overline{X}_B$ is the average of the n_2 observations on B), give an exact expression for the probability of a correct selection, $P(\text{CS})$, as a function of $\delta = \mu_{[2]} - \mu_{[1]} \geq 0$. [Of course, $\mu_{[2]} = \max(\mu_A, \mu_B)$, and $\mu_{[1]} = \min(\mu_A, \mu_B)$.] Table the $P(\text{CS})$ for $\delta = 0, .1, .2, .3, .4, .5$ if $n_1 = 2$, $n_2 = 3$ (still with $\sigma_A^2 = .04$, $\sigma_B^2 = .09$).

(b) If we have $n_1 = 2$ and $n_2 = 3$ (still with $\sigma_A^2 = .04$, $\sigma_B^2 = .09$), what is the largest P^* such that $P(\text{CS}) \geq P^*$ whenever $\delta \geq .3$? If our observations are 3.8, 3.4 and 3.7, 3.6, 4.1 on A and B (respectively), do we select A or B?

Note: Compare this problem with Problems 9.51 and 10.15, where hypothesis-testing and interval estimation were discussed for this same situation.

11.7 Show in detail that (as was stated in Example 11.2.22) the problem of selecting the population with the smallest mean $\mu_{[1]}$ easily reduces to a problem of selecting a population with a largest mean, and that no new complexities are thus introduced.

11.8 In Example 11.2.22, suppose we are convinced (by previous experience in the field) that 2 of the $k = 5$ SRS's will be greatly inferior to the best. Use (11.2.8) to show we may then set n as for a problem with $k' = 5 - 2 = 3$ populations and still have a guarantee of approximately P^*. What n will now be required in Example 11.2.22?

11.9 In footnote 8, we claimed that if we choose $\hat{\sigma}_i^2$ as in equation (11.3.4), then $\min(\hat{\sigma}_1^2, \dots, \hat{\sigma}_k^2)$ is unique with probability 1. Prove this result. (See Problem 11.2.)

11.10 In the "probability requirement" $P(\text{CS}) \geq P^*$ discussed in Section 11.3, we required that $1/k < P^* < 1$. Show that (as in Problem 11.1) such a requirement with $0 \leq P^* \leq 1/k$ is trivial.

11.11 Show that the $P_{\text{LFC}}(\text{CS})$ of equation (11.3.13) is an increasing function of n and $\rightarrow 1$ as $n \rightarrow \infty$. [Hence, there is a unique smallest sample size n per population for which probability requirement (11.3.5) is satisfied.]

11.12 In Section 11.1 we discussed an example from poultry science and stated that (for specific values of certain parameters) $n = 462$ pullets of each type would be required. Use the results of Section 11.2 to show that $n = 462$ is the required sample size per type.

11.13 An experimenter has been presented with $k = 10$ varieties of rice developed by researchers. They seem promising, and he wishes to run an experiment in order to select that variety which has the highest mean yield per acre. He plans to plant n acres with each variety (so nk total acres will be planted), the acres for any particular variety being selected at random from the nk acres available. (This is called a *Completely Randomized Design* of the experiment. The purpose of the randomization is to ensure that if the acres are not uniform in their effects on rice production, each variety will have an equal chance at both good and bad acreage; if one variety were to obtain all the "good" acres, the results of the experiment could be very misleading.) All nk observations of yield, in tons/acre, will be assumed independent.

The experimenter assumes that the yield of an acre planted with variety i is a $N(\mu_i, \sigma_i^2)$ r.v. $(1 \le i \le k)$ where $\mu_1, \ldots, \mu_k$ are unknown and that $\sigma_1^2 = \cdots = \sigma_k^2 = \sigma^2 = 1$. Intuitively, he decides to base his decision on sample means of yields and will select that variety which yields the largest sample mean yield. If he requires that he have probability at least $P^* = .90$ of selecting the variety that has the highest mean yield whenever $\mu_{[k]} - \mu_{[k-1]} \ge \delta^* = .1$ (here $\mu_{[1]} \le \cdots \le \mu_{[k]}$ denote the ranked values of $\mu_1, \ldots, \mu_k$), what is the smallest sample size n that he can use?

11.14 Suppose an experimenter has k populations $\pi_1, \ldots, \pi_k$ and wishes to run an experiment in order to select that one which has the largest mean. Observations from π_i are $N(\mu_i, \sigma_i^2)$ $(1 \le i \le k)$ where $\mu_1, \ldots, \mu_k$ are unknown and $\sigma_1^2, \ldots, \sigma_k^2$ are known (but not necessarily equal). He requires that he have probability $\ge P^*$ $(1/k < P^* < 1)$ of selecting the population that has the largest mean whenever $\mu_{[k]} - \mu_{[k-1]} \ge \delta^*$ ($\delta^* > 0$). (See Problem "3" of Section 11.4 and Section 11.2.)

(a) Show that if we set the number n_i of observations from π_i $(1 \le i \le k)$ so that

$$\frac{\sigma_1^2}{n_1} = \cdots = \frac{\sigma_k^2}{n_k} \qquad (*)$$

then the tables of Bechhofer (see Remark 11.2.18) of solutions of equation (11.2.15) may be used to set $n_1, \ldots, n_k$ so as to guarantee the probability requirement. If $k = 3$, $\sigma_1^2 = \sigma_2^2 = 1$, $\sigma_3^2 = 9$, $P^* = .90$, and $\delta^* = .1$, what number of observations should we take on the populations if we adopt this method?

(b) Bechhofer[12] notes that his suggestion of a solution, for the case of $\sigma_1^2, \ldots, \sigma_k^2$ known but unequal, via $(*)$ is not optimal. For the case $k = 2$, find the optimal allocation. [*Hint*: First find an exact expression for the $P(\text{CS})$ if n_1 observations are taken from π_1 and n_2 observations are taken from π_2. Show that subject to the restraint $n_1 + n_2 = n$ (n a positive integer) the $P(\text{CS})$ is uniformly maximized over all configurations where $\mu_1 \ne \mu_2$ by choosing n_1 and n_2 so that

$$\frac{\sigma_1}{n_1} = \frac{\sigma_2}{n_2}.] \qquad (**)$$

(c) In part (b), if the pair (n_1, n_2) that $(**)$ and $n_1 + n_2 = n$ specify is not a pair of integers, then we must know how to move to the optimal pair of *integers* (n_1^*, n_2^*). (Sample sizes must be integers.) Let $[x]$ denote the largest integer $\le x$. Show that the optimal pair (n_1^*, n_2^*) is either $([n_1] + 1, [n_2])$ or $([n_1], [n_2] + 1)$[13] [here (n_1, n_2) is the solution of $(**)$ and $n_1 + n_2 = n$], and that $(n_1^*, n_2^*) = ([n_1], [n_2] + 1)$ iff

$$\frac{\sigma_1^2}{\sigma_2^2} \le \frac{[n_1]([n_1] + 1)}{(n - [n_1])(n - ([n_1] + 1))}.$$

[12] See p. 24 of his paper referenced in Remark 11.2.18.
[13] This, and other parts of this problem, were discussed by Dudewicz and Dalal (1975).

(d) Ignoring the fact that sample sizes must be integers, compare allocation of a sample size n via ($*$) with allocation via ($**$) in the case $k = 2$, as follows. Let n_U be the sample size needed for an allocation via ($*$) to achieve a $P_{\text{LFC}}(\text{CS}) = P^*$ and let n_0 be the sample size needed for an allocation via ($**$) to achieve a $P_{\text{LFC}}(\text{CS}) = P^*$. Show that

$$\frac{n_U}{n_0} = 2\frac{1 + a}{(1 + \sqrt{a})^2},$$

where $a = \sigma_2^2/\sigma_1^2$. Compute the ratio for $a = 1(1)10$. [This gives us an idea of how much we lose by using allocation via ($*$), instead of the optimal allocation ($**$), in the case $k = 2$. The optimal allocation in the case $k > 2$ is not known. The comparison for the case $k = 2$ may give us a hint as to how much we lose by not knowing it.]

(e) Show by example that allocation via ($*$) is not optimal for $k > 2$.

11.15 Consider the problem described in the introduction to Problem 11.14. There both proposed methods (($*$) and ($**$)) of assigning sample sizes to populations require (in general) different numbers of observations per population. However, there are cases (e.g., when a statistician is consulted after an experiment has been run, or in special applications where the main cost of sampling from π_i is due to taking any observations at all from π_i with additional observations costing little ($1 \le i \le k$)) where we have $n_1 = \cdots = n_k = n$ (say), where n_i denotes the number of observations from π_i ($1 \le i \le k$).

(a) The problem of finding the minimum of the $P(\text{CS})$ for $\mu_{[k]} - \mu_{[k-1]} \ge \delta^*$ in this case appears at least as complex as the problem of optimal allocation for $k > 2$ discussed in Problem 11.14. Thus, in practice we might be tempted to evaluate the $P(\text{CS})$, acting as if all of $\pi_1, \ldots, \pi_k$ had variance equal to $\max(\sigma_1^2, \ldots, \sigma_k^2)$, and to assume that this furnishes a lower bound on the $P(\text{CS})$. Show that

$$P(\text{CS}) = \int_{-\infty}^{\infty} \left\{ \prod_{i=1}^{k-1} \Phi\left(\frac{\sigma_{(k)}}{\sigma_{(i)}} x + \frac{\mu_{[k]} - \mu_{[i]}}{\sigma_{(i)}}\sqrt{n} \right) \right\} \phi(x)\, dx.$$

(Here $\sigma_{(i)}^2$ is the variance of the population with mean $\mu_{[i]}$, $1 \le i \le k$.) Show that $dP(\text{CS})/d(\sigma_{(k)}) > 0$ in a neighborhood of $\mu_{[1]} = \cdots = \mu_{[k]}$. Deduce that if we have $\sigma_1^2 = \cdots = \sigma_{k-1}^2 = 1$ and $\sigma_k^2 = .5$ and [hoping to lower bound the $P(\text{CS})$] act as if $\sigma_k^2 = 1$, we could overestimate the $P(\text{CS})$.

(b) If we have $\sigma_1^2 = \cdots = \sigma_{k-1}^2 = .5$ and $\sigma_k^2 = 1$, can we upper bound the $P(\text{CS})$ by acting as if $\sigma_k^2 = .5$?

HONORS PROBLEMS FOR CHAPTER 11

11.1H In section 11.2, at (11.2.4) we invoked sufficiency in order to justify basing our decision on the sample means $\overline{X}_1, \ldots, \overline{X}_k$. It was shown by Hall (1959) that **the resulting procedure is most-economical.** *No other procedure that takes a specified number (m, say) of observations per population can have both* **(1)** *$m < n$ where n is the means procedure sample size studied in Section 11.2, and* **(2)** *satisfy probability requirement (11.2.5).*

Assume the results just stated. Let $\mathscr{P}_M(n_1, \ldots, n_k)$ denote a procedure based on sample means of n_1 observations from $\pi_1, \ldots, n_k$ observations from π_k; thus, the most-economical procedure is $\mathscr{P}_M(n, \ldots, n)$ and it takes nk total observations in order to satisfy probability requirement (11.2.5). Let $\mathscr{P}(n_1, \ldots, n_k)$ denote any procedure based on n_1 observations from $\pi_1, \ldots, n_k$ observations from π_k. **(a)** Show that $\mathscr{P}_M(n, \ldots, n)$ is "better" (in some reasonable sense) than $\mathscr{P}_M(n_1, \ldots, n_k)$ when $n_1 + \cdots + n_k = nk$ (i.e., the "best" allocation of nk observations for the means procedure is the allocation of the same number of observations to each population). **(b)** Show that $\mathscr{P}_M(n, \ldots, n)$ is "better" than any $\mathscr{P}(n_1, \ldots, n_k)$ with $n_1 + \cdots + n_k \leq nk$.

11.2H The procedure of Section 11.2 chooses the common sample size per population n in such a way that (under certain conditions of independence, normality, and so on, stated in Section 11.2) probability requirement (11.2.5) is satisfied: $P(CS) \geq P^*$ whenever $\mu_{[k]} - \mu_{[k-1]} \geq \delta^*$. Thus, with sample size n per population we are assured probability at least P^* of actually selecting the best population, as long as the best is at least δ^* better than the second best. However, even if the best is not δ^* better than the second best, it may be much more than δ^* better than the third best. Does the procedure of Section 11.2 offer any guarantee, in such situations, of obtaining one of the "few best"? Strengthening probability requirement (11.2.5), show that the procedure considered actually guarantees

$$P\Big[\text{Selecting a population } \pi_l \text{ with } \mu_{[k]} - \mu_l < \delta^* \Big] \geq P^*.$$

[Related considerations in a more complex situation were studied by Sievers (1971).]

11.3H Show that the $P(CS)$ of the means procedure of Section 11.2 (which was expressed as a single integral in Theorem 11.2.7) is equal to

$$P\left[Y_i < \frac{\mu_{[k]} - \mu_{[i]}}{\sqrt{2}\,\sigma/\sqrt{n}}, \quad i = 1, \ldots, k-1 \right], \qquad (*)$$

where Y_i is a $N(0,1)$ r.v. $(1 \leq i \leq k-1)$ and $\mathrm{Cov}(Y_i, Y_j) = .5$ $(i \neq j)$. Does $(Y_1, \ldots, Y_{k-1})$ have the multivariate normal distribution discussed in Section 4.5? (If, so, what are μ and Σ here? Using $(*)$, find the minimum (among all sets of possible means $\mu_1, \ldots, \mu_k$ that satisfy $\mu_{[k]} - \mu_{[k-1]} \geq \delta^*$) of the $P(CS)$. (Compare your result with that of Theorem 11.2.11.)

11.4H In Section 11.3, at (11.3.4) we invoked sufficiency in order to justify basing our decision on $s_1^2, \ldots, s_k^2$. Develop considerations like those of Problem 11.1H to justify basing our decision on $s_1^2, \ldots, s_k^2$.

11.5H Show that the $P(CS)$ of the procedure of Section 11.3 (which was expressed as a single integral in Theorem 11.3.7) is equal to

$$P\left[Y_i \geq \sigma_{[1]}^2/\sigma_{[i+1]}^2, \quad i = 1, \ldots, k-1 \right]$$

where Y_i is a r.v. with the F-distribution $F(n-1, n-1)$ and the joint density of $Y_1, \ldots, Y_{k-1}$ is that studied in Example 4.6.21, with n replaced by $n-1$. [*Hint*: See Problem 9.43.]

Compare your results with those of Problem 11.3H. Can you define a "multivariate F-distribution" by analogy?

11.6H On p. 276 of their paper (see Remark 11.3.14), Bechhofer and Sobel mention the case where one has n_1 observations from $\pi_1, \ldots, n_k$ observations from π_k. They also give an expression for the $P(\text{CS})$ in that case [their Equation (11) with $t = 1$ and $n_{(i)}$ the number of observations from the population with population variance $\sigma^2_{[i]}$], say

$$f_{k, \theta*}(n_{(1)}, \ldots, n_{(k)}). \qquad (*)$$

Can $(*)$ actually be evaluated? [*Hint*: If you are told $k = 3$, $\theta^* = 2.0$, $n_1 = 2$, $n_2 = 4$, $n_3 = 6$, do you know $n_{(1)}, n_{(2)}, n_{(3)}$?] Does $(*)$ increase as $n_{(i)}$ increases $(1 \leq i \leq k)$? [If so, we would be able to lower bound $(*)$ by $f_{k, \theta*}(m, \ldots, m)$ where $m = \min(n_{(1)}, \ldots, n_{(k)}) = \min(n_1, \ldots, n_k)$; this lower bound can be calculated.]

11.7H In the context of Section 11.2, if we actually have $n_1, \ldots, n_k$ observations from $\pi_1, \ldots, \pi_k$ (respectively), and base our decision on the sample means $\overline{X}_1, \ldots, \overline{X}_k$ that use all observations, is our $P(\text{CS})$ always greater than or equal to the $P(\text{CS})$ calculated assuming $n = \min(n_1, \ldots, n_k)$ observations from each of the populations?

11.8H Suppose we have experimented as specified in Section 11.2, but now wish to estimate $\mu_{[k]}$ (the largest population mean) rather than select the population associated with $\mu_{[k]}$. Is $\overline{X}_{[k]}$ a good estimator of $\mu_{[k]}$? [*Hint*: Find sup $E\overline{X}_{[k]}$ and inf $E\overline{X}_{[k]}$, where we are maximizing and minimizing over the set of all possible $(\mu_1, \ldots, \mu_k)$.][14]

11.9H Consider the situation of Problem 11.13, but now the experimenter avows that although it is well-known that $\sigma_1^2 = \cdots = \sigma_k^2 = \sigma^2$, the common value σ^2 is unknown. The experiment can, however, be performed in two stages since at the test site climate is such that two crops can be grown in 1 year. Suppose that the two-stage procedure referenced in problem "1" of Section 11.4 is used, and that in the first stage $n_0 = 2$ observations are taken on each variety. What number n_1 of observations on each variety should be taken in the second stage? (n_1 will depend on the results of the first stage. Plot a graph of n_1 as a function of the results of the first stage.) [*Notes*: For solution of this problem you will probably have to use approximations to the multivariate t-distribution. For example, see Dunnett and Sobel (1954); Dunnett and Sobel (1955); and Armitage and Krishnaiah (1966). For the goal of a complete ranking of $k = 3$, 4, or 5 populations, tables and an interesting application to ranking of competing consumer or producer goods were given by Freeman, Kuzmack, and Maurice (1967) in a study supported by Consumers Union, Mount Vernon, New York.]

11.10H The problems of: (1) selecting that one of k television programs (available to a television audience in a given area) which can claim the largest proportion of the total audience; (2) selecting that one of the 36 "bettable" numbers on an unbalanced roulette wheel which has the largest probability associated with it; (3) selecting that one of the 6 faces of a loaded die that has the largest probability of landing face up; and (4) selecting that one of k Presidential candidates who has

---

[14] This problem can arise when, for example, we wish to decide whether or not to continue research on the set of populations $\{\pi_1, \ldots, \pi_k\}$. See Dudewicz (1973). Also see Blumenthal and Cohen (1968) for additional applications and results on the case $k = 2$.

the highest proportion of voters in favor of his election in a given state; are **selection problems involving a multinomial distribution.** (See Example 3.5.3.)

This problem was discussed by Bechhofer, Elmaghraby, and Morse (1959), who considered one's observation to be $\mathbf{X} = (X_1, \ldots, X_k)$ with the multinomial distribution of Definition 3.5.1. [Thus, we sample n people, each of whom has probability p_i of belonging to category i and let X_i be the number observed to belong to category i out of the n $(1 \le i \le k)$. Then $0 \le p_1 \le 1, \ldots, 0 \le p_k \le 1$, and $p_1 + \cdots + p_k = 1$.] They let $p_{[1]} \le \cdots \le p_{[k]}$ denote $p_1, \ldots, p_k$ in numerical order, let $X_{[k]}$ denote $\max(X_1, \ldots, X_k)$, and propose to select that component (television show, roulette number, die face, or presidential candidate, for example) which[15] yielded $X_{[k]}$ as being associated with $p_{[k]}$. If we desire $P(CS) \ge P^*$ whenever $p_{[k]} \ge \theta^* p_{[k-1]}$ (where $1/k < P^* < 1$ and $\theta^* > 1$ are set by the experimenter), the necessary number of people to be sampled, n, has been tabulated and an approximation given.

(a) In many cases of elections, $k = 2$ and pollsters use $n = 2000$.[16] With $\theta^* = 1.1$ roughly what P^* does this guarantee? If we have $k = 3$ "serious" candidates (i.e., candidates whose $p > .01$), what P^* does $n = 2000$ give us?

(b) How good are television ratings? [*Hint*: With $k = 6$, $n = 2000$, $\theta^* = 1.1$, roughly what P^* do we obtain? Now that is for simply selecting the best. How should the complete ranking case compare?]

11.11H Consider the problem discussed in Problems 9.51 and 10.15, from the ranking and selection point of view. [A special case was studied in Problem 11.6.]

---

[15] This may not be unique. In case of ties, one of the tied categories is selected at random.

[16] Pollsters use (or are presumed to use) the sophisticated statistical sampling methods described in, for example, Raj (1968), which have been developed over the last 50 years. This should increase their P^* with a fixed n, but how much it does has apparently not yet been studied.

CHAPTER 12

Decision Theory

One of the definitions of "statistics" (as it exists at present) calls it "the science of decision making." We largely agree with this definition. This chapter has as its goal the elucidation and explication of the aims, axioms, terminology, and results (and how these can be seen as unifying concepts, bringing together, say, point estimation, statistical inference principles, hypothesis-testing, interval estimation, ranking and selection procedures, and so on under one roof) of what is called **statistical decision theory** (or sometimes simply **decision theory**).

In Section 12.1 we cover the general formulation and principles of decision theory. The following three sections cover several special cases, studied already in detail in previous chapters, from the decision-theoretic viewpoint (hypothesis-testing in Section 12.2, interval estimation in Section 12.3, and ranking and selection in Section 12.4). Section 12.5 presents some general results of decision theory, while Section 12.6 introduces an overview of the area of statistics (and of the terminology of some of its subfields) through a discussion of a specific example.

12.1. THE GENERAL PROBLEM OF STATISTICS

In the "decision theory" view of the "general problem of statistics," two main components of the problem are: observations (data) with a usually not fully known distribution (e.g., the distribution of the data may contain an unknown parameter θ that lies in some known set Θ); and possible numerical losses/gains due to choosing one of a number of possible decisions. The expected loss (gains are negative losses) is a primary consideration in evaluating decisions. [For example, in Section 9.4 we saw that for the problem of testing a simple hypothesis H_0 ($\theta = \theta_0$) against a simple alternative H_1 ($\theta = \theta_1$), where θ was unknown, we could decide either "H_0 is true" or "H_1 is true." Letting our loss be the "number of incorrect decisions" (which is either 0 or 1), the expected loss involved the error probabilities of Types I and II.]

In the general formulation of decision theory, we observe a r.v. X (which may be multivariate) with d.f. $F(x|\theta)$ where $\theta \in \Theta$ is unknown, and if we choose decision d from the set of all possible decisions $\mathscr{D}$, then we suffer a loss $l(\theta, d)$. A "decision rule" is a method of choosing d from $\mathscr{D}$ after observing $x \in \mathscr{X}$, that is, a function $s(x) = d$. Our average loss (called **risk**) $E_\theta l(\theta, s(X))$ is a function of both θ and the decision rule $s(\cdot)$, called the risk function $r_\theta(s)$, and is *the* criterion by which rules are compared. The problem is then to study general properties of "good" rules, and to find them in specific cases. **We now define precisely the major quantities just introduced.**

Definition 12.1.1. A general **statistical decision problem** is a triplet $(\Theta, \mathscr{D}, l)$ and a r.v. X. The r.v. X (called the **data**) has a d.f. $F(x|\theta)$ where θ is unknown but it is known that $\theta \in \Theta$. [A problem with no such r.v. X is called a **no-data decision problem**.] The set of possible values of the r.v. X will be denoted by $\mathscr{X}$.

θ is called the **state of nature**, while the nonempty set Θ is called the **parameter space**. The nonempty set $\mathscr{D}$ is called the **decision space** or **action space**.

Finally, l is called the **loss function** and to each $\theta \in \Theta$ and $d \in \mathscr{D}$ it assigns a real number $l(\theta, d)$.

Definition 12.1.2. For a statistical decision problem $(\Theta, \mathscr{D}, l)$, X, a **(nonrandomized) decision rule** is a function $s(\cdot)$ that to each $x \in \mathscr{X}$ assigns a member d of $\mathscr{D}$: $s(x) = d$.

A **randomized decision rule** is a function $s(\cdot)$ that for each $x \in \mathscr{X}$ specifies a probability distribution according to which a member d of $\mathscr{D}$ is to be chosen. This probability distribution will be denoted by $s(x)$.

Definition 12.1.3. The **risk function** $r_\theta(s)$ of a decision rule $s(X)$ for a statistical decision problem $(\Theta, \mathscr{D}, l)$, X (the **expected loss** or **average loss** when θ is the true state of nature and a decision is chosen by rule $s(\cdot)$) is

$$r_\theta(s) = E_\theta l(\theta, s(X)). \tag{12.1.4}$$

In Section 9.4 our decision rules were tests, which were also either randomized or nonrandomized (although this was not stressed). A fundamental precept of decision theory is that all of our losses (or gains) should be incorporated into the loss function $l(\cdot, \cdot)$ for the problem, so that then it is reasonable to consider *only* the risk function (average loss (12.1.4)) in seeking a "good" decision rule. As in Section 9.4 (see the paragraph preceding Definition 9.4.5 through Definition 9.4.6) **we can use the risk function to restrict ourselves to a "few" decision rules (instead of all decision rules) as follows.** Suppose $s_1(\cdot)$ and $s_2(\cdot)$ are decision rules for some statistical decision problem $(\Theta, \mathscr{D}, l)$, X. If

$$r_\theta(s_1) > r_\theta(s_2), \quad \text{all } \theta \in \Theta, \tag{12.1.5}$$

then $s_2(\cdot)$ has a smaller average loss no matter what the state of nature θ, and we will surely prefer $s_2(\cdot)$. (See Figure 9.4-2 for an illustration for the case where Θ contains only two points, in the hypothesis-testing case.) Even if

$$r_\theta(s_1) \geq r_\theta(s_2), \quad \text{all } \theta \in \Theta, \tag{12.1.6}$$

we have no use for $s_1(\cdot)$: $s_2(\cdot)$ is at least as good for all states of nature θ. Using this analysis as motivation, we now make the following definitions.

Definition 12.1.7. For any statistical decision problem $(\Theta, \mathcal{D}, l)$, X, decision rule $s_2(\cdot)$ is said to be **better than** decision rule $s_1(\cdot)$ (or decision rule $s_1(\cdot)$ is said to be **worse than** decision rule $s_2(\cdot)$) if

$$\begin{cases} r_\theta(s_2) \leq r_\theta(s_1), & \text{all } \theta \in \Theta \\ r_{\theta^*}(s_2) < r_{\theta^*}(s_1), & \text{at least one } \theta^* \in \Theta. \end{cases} \tag{12.1.8}$$

We say $s_1(\cdot)$ is **no better than** $s_2(\cdot)$ if

$$r_\theta(s_2) \leq r_\theta(s_1), \quad \text{all } \theta \in \Theta. \tag{12.1.9}$$

Definition 12.1.10. For any statistical decision problem $(\Theta, \mathcal{D}, l)$, X, let $D = \{s(\cdot): s(\cdot) \text{ is a decision rule}\}$. Any class of decision rules $C \subseteq D$ is called **complete** (or a **complete class (of decision rules)**) if for each $s_1 \notin C$, there is an $s_2 \in C$ such that s_2 is better than s_1. A class C is called **essentially complete** if for each $s_1 \notin C$, there is an $s_2 \in C$ such that s_1 is no better than s_2. A class C is called **minimal complete** if C is complete but if any $s_2 \in C$ is removed from C, the resulting class is not complete. A class C is called **minimal essentially complete** if C is essentially complete but if any $s_2 \in C$ is removed from C, the resulting class is not essentially complete.

The above notions (see Definition 12.1.7) of possible comparisons of two decision rules s_1 and s_2 allow us to *sometimes* state each of the following: "s_2 is better than s_1," (written $s_2 \succ s_1$), "s_1 is better than s_2" (written $s_1 \succ s_2$), and "s_2 and s_1 are equivalent" (written $s_2 \sim s_1$) (i.e., "s_2 is at least as good as $s_1(s_2 \succsim s_1)$," and s_1 is at least as good as $s_2(s_1 \succsim s_2)$"). *However*, it is also possible that we

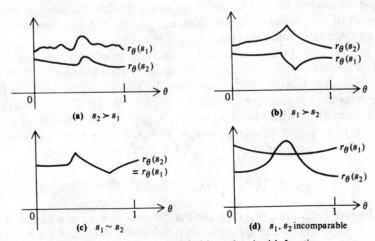

Figure 12.1-1. Comparisons of decision rules via risk functions.

may have "s_1 and s_2 are incomparable," that is, $r_\theta(s_1) < r_\theta(s_2)$ for at least one $\theta \in \Theta$, and $r_\theta(s_1) > r_\theta(s_2)$ for at least one $\theta \in \Theta$. For example, in Figure 12.1-1 we sketch risk functions leading to each of the above conclusions. (Here $\Theta = \{x: 0 \le x \le 1\}$.) Since the possibility of our not being able to prefer s_1 or s_2 (simultaneously for all θ) exists (they may be incomparable), our ordering of decision rules is called a partial ordering (see Problem 12.1).

In Section 9.4 we were able to find a minimal essentially complete class of decision rules very easily, by use of the Neyman-Pearson Lemma (see Theorem 9.4.7), and then proceeded to the question of how to select one member out of that minimal essentially complete class. In the general case, things are not so simple. Before studying this question further, we will first give an example that illustrates the concepts introduced so far and will motivate those still to come.

Example 12.1.11. Suppose we have two possible states of nature (e.g., a "bull" market and a "bear" market); that is, $\Theta = \{\theta_1, \theta_2\}$ with $\theta_1 \ne \theta_2$, and six possible decisions (e.g., six possible investment strategies), that is $\mathcal{D} = \{d_1, d_2, d_3, d_4, d_5, d_6\}$, and that our loss function $l(\theta, d)$ is as given in the following table [e.g., if we take decision d_5 (investment strategy 5) when $\theta = \theta_2$ (in a "bear" market), we suffer a loss of $l(\theta_2, d_5) = 8$].

$l(\theta, d)$						
θ \ d	d_1	d_2	d_3	d_4	d_5	d_6
θ_1	17	19	14	10	9	9
θ_2	14	4	4	6	8	16

Suppose we observe no r.v. X, that is, we have a no-data decision problem. Find the set D of all possible decision rules and graph their risk functions. Find a minimal essentially complete class of decision rules.

In general (see Definition 12.1.2), a decision rule $s(x)$ specifies, for each $x \in \mathcal{X}$, a probability distribution according to which a member d of $\mathcal{D}$ is to be chosen. Since no X is observed in this example, a decision rule s for this problem simply specifies a probability distribution on $\mathcal{D}$, so the set D of all decision rules s is the set of all $s_\mathbf{p}$ where $\mathbf{p} = (p_1, p_2, p_3, p_4, p_5, p_6)$ with $p_1 \ge 0$, $p_2 \ge 0$, $p_3 \ge 0$, $p_4 \ge 0$, $p_5 \ge 0$, $p_6 \ge 0$, and $p_1 + p_2 + p_3 + p_4 + p_5 + p_6 = 1$. (Rule $s_\mathbf{p}$ takes decision d_i with probability p_i ($i = 1, 2, 3, 4, 5, 6$).) Simply stated,

$$D = \{ s_\mathbf{p} : \mathbf{p} = (p_1, \ldots, p_6) \text{ is a probability distribution} \}. \quad (12.1.12)$$

Now the risk function $r_\theta(s_\mathbf{p})$ of a general decision rule $s_\mathbf{p}$ is a pair of numbers $(r_{\theta_1}(s_\mathbf{p}), r_{\theta_2}(s_\mathbf{p}))$ since there are only two possible θ's in Θ, and the risk function can thus be represented as a point in the plane (and is therefore often called a

risk point). But

$$r_{\theta_1}(s_{\mathbf{p}}) = E_{\theta_1} l(\theta_1, s_{\mathbf{p}})$$

$$= \sum_{i=1}^{6} l(\theta_1, d_i) P_{\theta_1}[s_{\mathbf{p}} \text{ selects } d_i] = \sum_{i=1}^{6} l(\theta_1, d_i) p_i \quad (12.1.13)$$

$$= 17p_1 + 19p_2 + 14p_3 + 10p_4 + 9p_5 + 9p_6.$$

Similarly,

$$r_{\theta_2}(s_{\mathbf{p}}) = 14p_1 + 4p_2 + 4p_3 + 6p_4 + 8p_5 + 16p_6, \quad (12.1.14)$$

so

$$\left(r_{\theta_1}(s_{\mathbf{p}}), r_{\theta_2}(s_{\mathbf{p}})\right) = (17p_1 + 19p_2 + 14p_3 + 10p_4 + 9p_5 + 9p_6,$$
$$\qquad\qquad (12.1.15)$$
$$14p_1 + 4p_2 + 4p_3 + 6p_4 + 8p_5 + 16p_6).$$

The nonrandomized decision rules are six in number: the one with $p_i = 1$, say s_i, always takes decision d_i $(1 \le i \le 6)$. Their risk points are easy to find and are plotted in Figure 12.1-2. (Note that although each of the six points is labeled s_i, it is actually $(r_{\theta_1}(s_i), r_{\theta_2}(s_i))$ that is plotted. The dashed lines are solely to aid in finding coordinates of the points plotted and have no other significance.) To plot the risk points of the randomized decision rules we need first to review some old material and introduce some new material. We will return to this problem in Example 12.1.18.

The material needed to finish Example 12.1.11 is connected with that dealing with convex sets, which we will now discuss.

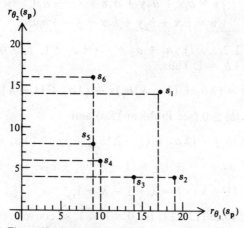

Figure 12.1-2. Nonrandomized risk points for example 12.1.11.

Recall that a point in the plane (x_1, x_2) can be represented as a **vector**

$$\mathbf{x} = \begin{pmatrix} x_1 \\ x_2 \end{pmatrix},$$

and that a point in $\mathscr{R}^k$ can be represented as a vector

$$\mathbf{x} = \begin{pmatrix} x_1 \\ x_2 \\ \vdots \\ x_k \end{pmatrix}.$$

A subset S of $\mathscr{R}^k$ is called **convex** if $\mathbf{x}, \mathbf{y} \in S$ implies $\lambda\mathbf{x} + (1 - \lambda)\mathbf{y} \in S$ for all λ with $0 < \lambda < 1$; that is, S is convex if all of the line segment joining two points of S, is itself in S. If we have a finite number of vectors $\mathbf{x}, \mathbf{y}, \mathbf{z}, \ldots, \mathbf{u}$, we will be interested in the smallest convex set that contains all of them, called **the convex set generated by $\mathbf{x}, \mathbf{y}, \mathbf{z}, \ldots, \mathbf{u}$**. A representation for this set (which is also called the **convex hull of $\mathbf{x}, \mathbf{y}, \mathbf{z}, \ldots, \mathbf{u}$**) is given in our next theorem.

Theorem 12.1.16. The convex hull of the points $\mathbf{x}, \mathbf{y}, \mathbf{z}, \ldots, \mathbf{u}$ is the set of all points

$$\alpha\mathbf{x} + \beta\mathbf{y} + \gamma\mathbf{z} + \cdots + \omega\mathbf{u}, \qquad (12.1.17)$$

with $\alpha \geq 0, \beta \geq 0, \ldots, \omega \geq 0$, and $\alpha + \beta + \gamma + \cdots + \omega = 1$. [Each point of the form (12.1.17) is called a **convex combination of the points $\mathbf{x}, \mathbf{y}, \mathbf{z}, \ldots, \mathbf{u}$**.]

Proof: First, the set of all points of form (12.1.17) is a convex set. To show this, we must show that if $\mathbf{v}$ and $\mathbf{w}$ are two such points, then so is $\lambda\mathbf{v} + (1 - \lambda)\mathbf{w}$ as long as $0 < \lambda < 1$. Since $\mathbf{v}$ and $\mathbf{w}$ are such points, we can (if there are l vectors $\mathbf{x}, \mathbf{y}, \mathbf{z}, \ldots, \mathbf{u}$) write

$$\begin{cases} \mathbf{v} = a_1\mathbf{x} + a_2\mathbf{y} + a_3\mathbf{z} + \cdots + a_l\mathbf{u}, \\ \mathbf{w} = b_1\mathbf{x} + b_2\mathbf{y} + b_3\mathbf{z} + \cdots + b_l\mathbf{u}, \end{cases}$$

where $a_i \geq 0$ $(i = 1, 2, \ldots, l)$, $a_1 + a_2 + \cdots + a_l = 1$, $b_i \geq 0$ $(i = 1, 2, \ldots, l)$, and $b_1 + b_2 + \cdots + b_l = 1$. Thus,

$$\lambda\mathbf{v} + (1 - \lambda)\mathbf{w} = (\lambda a_1 + (1 - \lambda)b_1)\mathbf{x} + (\lambda a_2 + (1 - \lambda)b_2)\mathbf{y} + \cdots.$$

Since $\lambda a_i + (1 - \lambda)b_i \geq 0$ (see Problem 12.4) and

$$\big(\lambda a_1 + (1 - \lambda)b_1\big) + \big(\lambda a_2 + (1 - \lambda)b_2\big) + \cdots + \big(\lambda a_l + (1 - \lambda)b_l\big)$$

$$= \lambda(a_1 + a_2 + \cdots + a_l) + (1 - \lambda)(b_1 + b_2 + \cdots + b_l)$$

$$= \lambda \cdot 1 + (1 - \lambda) \cdot 1 = \lambda + 1 - \lambda = 1,$$

$\lambda\mathbf{v} + (1 - \lambda)\mathbf{w}$ is of form (12.1.17) for $0 < \lambda < 1$, so convexity is proven.

Second, we must show that no smaller convex set can contain the points $\mathbf{x}, \mathbf{y}, \mathbf{z}, \ldots, \mathbf{u}$. This follows if we show that a convex set H containing $\mathbf{x}, \mathbf{y}, \mathbf{z}, \ldots, \mathbf{u}$

must contain

$$\alpha x + \beta y + \gamma z + \cdots + \omega u$$

whenever $\alpha \geq 0$, $\beta \geq 0$, $\gamma \geq 0, \ldots, \omega \geq 0$, and $\alpha + \beta + \gamma + \cdots + \omega = 1$, which we will now do. First, since H is convex and contains x and y, H contains

$$q = \frac{\alpha}{\alpha + \beta}x + \frac{\beta}{\alpha + \beta}y.$$

Next, since H is convex and contains q and z, H must contain

$$\frac{\alpha + \beta}{\alpha + \beta + \gamma}q + \frac{\gamma}{\alpha + \beta + \gamma}z = \frac{\alpha}{\alpha + \beta + \gamma}x + \frac{\beta}{\alpha + \beta + \gamma}y + \frac{\gamma}{\alpha + \beta + \gamma}z.$$

Finally, we find by induction (see Problem 12.5) that H must contain

$$\frac{\alpha}{\alpha + \beta + \gamma + \cdots + \omega}x + \cdots + \frac{\omega}{\alpha + \beta + \gamma + \cdots + \omega}u$$

$$= \alpha x + \beta y + \cdots + \omega u. \quad \blacksquare$$

Example 12.1.18.   Continuation of Example 12.1.11. Continuing Example 12.1.11, we now wish to plot the risk points of the randomized decision rules. (Those of the nonrandomized rules were plotted in Figure 12.1-2.) For any such rule s_p, the risk point is (see (12.1.15)) the vector

$$\begin{pmatrix} r_{\theta_1}(s_p) \\ r_{\theta_2}(s_p) \end{pmatrix} = \begin{pmatrix} 17p_1 + 19p_2 + 14p_3 + 10p_4 + 9p_5 + 9p_6 \\ 14p_1 + 4p_2 + 4p_3 + 6p_4 + 8p_5 + 16p_6 \end{pmatrix}$$

$$= p_1\begin{pmatrix} 17 \\ 14 \end{pmatrix} + p_2\begin{pmatrix} 19 \\ 4 \end{pmatrix} + p_3\begin{pmatrix} 14 \\ 4 \end{pmatrix} \quad (12.1.19)$$

$$+ p_4\begin{pmatrix} 10 \\ 6 \end{pmatrix} + p_5\begin{pmatrix} 9 \\ 8 \end{pmatrix} + p_6\begin{pmatrix} 9 \\ 16 \end{pmatrix}.$$

However, this is just a point in the convex hull of the risk points of the nonrandomized decision rules, and as p varies over all probability distributions (i.e., as we consider all decision rules) we generate (by Theorem 12.1.16) the convex hull of the six nonrandomized decision rules' risk points

$$\begin{pmatrix} 17 \\ 14 \end{pmatrix}, \begin{pmatrix} 19 \\ 4 \end{pmatrix}, \begin{pmatrix} 14 \\ 4 \end{pmatrix}, \begin{pmatrix} 10 \\ 6 \end{pmatrix}, \begin{pmatrix} 9 \\ 8 \end{pmatrix}, \text{ and } \begin{pmatrix} 9 \\ 16 \end{pmatrix}.$$

Thus, the set of all risk points is convex and closed, and is plotted in Figure 12.1-3. It is easy to see that the rules leading to the hatched (//////) part of the boundary of the set of risk points (in Figure 12.1-3) form a minimal essentially complete class: any other rule s either yields a risk point on this hatched part of the boundary (in which case it is no better) or yields a risk point elsewhere in the

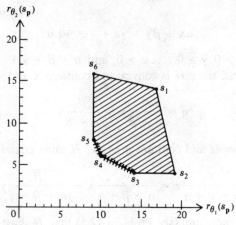

Figure 12.1-3. Closed convex set of risk points for Example 12.1.11.

set, in which case some decision rule t with a risk point on the hatched part of the boundary has $r_{\theta_1}(t) \leq r_{\theta_1}(s)$ and $r_{\theta_2}(t) \leq r_{\theta_2}(s)$ with at least one strict inequality $(<)$. (To see this, just note that if $(r_{\theta_1}(t), r_{\theta_2}(t))$ is the risk point of a decision rule t, then any rule s with a risk point $(r_{\theta_1}(s), r_{\theta_2}(s))$ in the shaded region in Figure 12.1-4 is inferior to t.) The rules forming this minimal essentially complete class are those with $(p_1, p_2, p_3, p_4, p_5, p_6)$ with

$$\begin{cases} (1) & p_1 = p_2 = p_3 = p_6 = 0, \ p_4 \geq 0, \ p_5 = 1 - p_4 \geq 0; \\ (2) & p_1 = p_2 = p_5 = p_6 = 0, \ p_3 \geq 0, \ p_4 = 1 - p_3 \geq 0; \end{cases} \quad (12.1.20)$$

that is, (1) those that randomize between d_4 and d_5; and (2) those that randomize between d_3 and d_4.

Returning to the problem stated immediately preceding Example 12.1.11, how do we find a minimal complete (or better essentially complete) class of decision

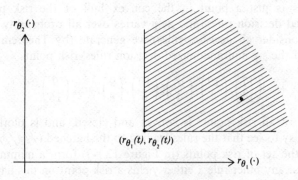

Figure 12.1-4. Rules worse than t.

rules in the general decision problem $(\Theta, \mathscr{D}, l)$, X? (Here in the general case, we have no simple solution like use of the Neyman-Pearson Lemma in Section 9.4.) A helpful notion here is that of "admissibility." Recall (see (12.1.5), (12.1.6), Figure 12.1-1, and Figure 12.1-4) that many decision rules are "beaten" by other decision rules. Could the set of those rules that are not so "beaten" (called "**admissible**" rules) be a minimal complete class? We will now investigate this question, first defining "admissibility" precisely and then proving some complete class results.

Definition 12.1.21. For any statistical decision problem $(\Theta, \mathscr{D}, l)$, X, decision rule $s(\cdot)$ is said to be **admissible** if there is no decision rule $t(\cdot)$ that is better than $s(\cdot)$. A rule is said to be **inadmissible** if it is not admissible.

Lemma 12.1.22. If $s_1(\cdot)$ and $s_2(\cdot)$ are two admissible decision rules for the same statistical decision problem $(\Theta, \mathscr{D}, l)$, X, then either $s_1 \sim s_2$ or s_1 and s_2 are incomparable.

Proof: See Problem 12.7.   ∎

Theorem 12.1.23. For a statistical decision problem $(\Theta, \mathscr{D}, l)$, X, if a minimal complete class C exists, then $C = A$ where A is the set of all admissible rules.

Proof: It is easy to show that A is a subset of every complete class (Problem 12.8); hence, $A \subseteq C$. It remains to show that $C \subseteq A$.

For suppose it is *not* the case that $C \subseteq A$. Then there is a rule s_0 such that $s_0 \in C$ and $s_0 \notin A$.

Since s_0 is inadmissible, there is a rule $s \succsim s_0$. If $s \in C$, let $s_1 = s$. If $s \notin C$, there is (since C is complete) an $s_1 \in C$ such that $s_1 \succ s$ (hence, $s_1 \succ s_0$). Thus, there is a rule $s_1 \in C$ such that $s_1 \succ s_0$.

Now let C_1 be C with s_0 removed. We claim C_1 is then complete (which contradicts the assumption that C is minimal complete, and thereby shows that the assertion upon which the contradiction was based ("it is *not* the case that $C \subseteq A$") is false; i.e., it shows that $C \subseteq A$).

For suppose $t \notin C_1$. If $t = s_0$, then $s_1 \in C_1$ and $s_1 \succ s_0$. If $t \neq s_0$, there must be a rule $t' \in C$ such that $t' \succ t$. If $t' = s_0$, then $s_1 \succ t$ and $s_1 \in C_1$. If $t' \neq s_0$, then $t' \in C_1$ and $t' \succ t$. Thus, there is always a rule in C_1 that is better than such a rule t, so C_1 is complete, the contradiction which completes the proof.   ∎

Thus, **for problems where a minimal complete class C exists (these comprise most of the problems of interest to us) the problem of finding that class C is equivalent to finding the set A of all admissible rules. The problem of finding the admissible rules** (it suffices to find only one rule for each risk point, for if several rules are admissible and have the same risk point, then all but one of the rules can be deleted from A, forming A', and A' will be an essentially complete class; in fact, A' will be minimal essentially complete (see Problem 12.10)) **is intimately connected with the notions of Bayes (and to some extent of minimax) rules,** which we will discuss after giving an example.

Example 12.1.24. In Example 12.1.18 the admissible rules are those corresponding to the hatched boundary of the set of risk points in Figure 12.1-3. It was
shown there that there is exactly one rule corresponding to each such point
(although other risk points may correspond to several rules (see Problem 12.11)),
and that their class was minimal essentially complete.

We will now give the general definition of a Bayes decision rule.

Definition 12.1.25. Let $(\Theta, \mathscr{D}, l)$, X be a statistical decision problem. Let $B(\theta)$
be a distribution function on Θ. The quantity

$$R_{B(\theta)}(s) = Er_\theta(s) \qquad (12.1.26)$$

is called the **Bayes risk of $s(\cdot)$ with respect to the a priori distribution $B(\theta)$.** [It is
calculated as if θ were a r.v. with d.f. $B(\theta)$.] A decision rule $t(\cdot)$ is called **Bayes
(with respect to the a priori distribution $B(\theta)$)** if $t(\cdot)$ has the smallest[1] Bayes risk:

$$R_{B(\theta)}(t) = \inf_{s \in D} R_{B(\theta)}(s). \qquad (12.1.27)$$

Recall (see the discussion following Theorem 9.4.7) that once we have a class
C (perhaps minimal essentially complete) of decision rules from which we desire
to choose *one* rule, the risk function $r_\theta(s)$ is generally of little help since rules in
C are incomparable (see Figure 12.1-1). Thus, **what is really needed is a way to
assign a number to each decision rule, with the desirability of a decision rule
increasing as this number decreases. The Bayes risk is one proposal for such a
number, and a Bayes rule is best when this method of assigning numbers is used.**

We can interpret the Bayes risk (12.1.26) of $s(\cdot)$ as the average risk when in
fact θ is a r.v. with d.f. $B(\theta)$. If this approach is taken, then $B(\theta)$ is usually said
to involve **subjective (or personal) probability:** it incorporates our "feelings"
about what θ may actually occur. The suggestion that we ought to attempt to
formulate our "feelings" about θ in such a $B(\theta)$ and use the resulting Bayes rule
has been responsible for insane debates and ill will in statistics (one reason being
the insistence of some proponents of this method that it is the only method any
sensible person ought to use), and we will leave that subject to those who have
nothing better to do with their time. We should **note that there are several cases
in which the proper approach may be to use a Bayes rule for a specified $B(\theta)$.**
First, θ may actually be a r.v. and if the same situation has been faced many
times before, we may have a good knowledge of $B(\theta)$. [For example, the severity
of fires at alarms on Saturday nights in July is a random phenomenon θ, and past
experience gives us a good idea of the distribution $B(\theta)$ over severities. It is
reasonable to use a Bayes rule with respect to $B(\theta)$ in allocating fire-fighting
apparatus and personnel to such alarms.] **Second,** there may be partial knowledge
about θ that can be well-incorporated into such a $B(\theta)$. [For example, a business
executive may have insight into a real-world system that can be expressed in

[1] It may be helpful to review Note 6.2.15 (on "sup" and "inf") at this point.

terms of θ being a r.v. with a $B(\theta)$ in a certain class of possible distributions. It is then reasonable for him or her to give special consideration to the set of Bayes rules for such $B(\theta)$'s.] **Third**, it has been shown[2] that, if our preferences for combinations of θ's and decisions d satisfy certain axioms, then the decision we will make will be that which we would take if θ were known to be a r.v. with a certain $B(\theta)$. [The weakness of this third case is that the axioms involved are very strong. For example, if we prefer a prospect (future possible occurrence) P_1 to P_2, and prefer P_2 to P_3, then we are required to prefer P_1 to P_3. But if we are, say, choosing to bet on a certain player in a sports event, we could prefer P_1 to P_2, P_2 to P_3, yet P_3 to P_1 (since situations are well-known where P_1 usually beats P_2, P_2 usually beats P_3, yet P_3 usually bests P_1). Also, in subjects of scientific inference we may validly state we have no preference between whether a hypothesis is true or not, but that we simply wish to determine the truth of the matter. The third case then falls apart at the outset.]

Of course, in some situations it may be the case that no Bayes rule exists (e.g., see Problem 12.13). For this reason we define "ε-Bayes" rules (rules that come within ε of the inf of $R_{B(\theta)}(s)$):

Definition 12.1.28. Let $(\Theta, \mathscr{D}, l)$, X be a statistical decision problem. Let $B(\theta)$ be a d.f. on Θ, and let ε be > 0. A decision rule $t(\cdot)$ is called **ε-Bayes (with respect to $B(\theta)$)** if

$$R_{B(\theta)}(t) \le \inf_{s \in D} R_{B(\theta)}(s) + \varepsilon. \tag{12.1.29}$$

[However, even ε-Bayes rules may fail to exist.]

We now give the genral definition of a minimax decision rule (and, for reasons similar to those leading to the introduction of the ε-Bayes rules, of the ε-minimax decision rules).

Definition 12.1.30. Let $(\Theta, \mathscr{D}, l)$, X be a statistical decision problem. Let ε be > 0. A decision rule $t(\cdot)$ is called **minimax** if

$$\sup_{\theta \in \Theta} r_\theta(t) = \inf_{s \in D} \sup_{\theta \in \Theta} r_\theta(s), \tag{12.1.31}$$

and **ε-minimax** if

$$\sup_{\theta \in \Theta} r_\theta(t) \le \inf_{s \in D} \sup_{\theta \in \Theta} r_\theta(s) + \varepsilon. \tag{12.1.32}$$

Before continuing on to study the relationships between Bayes rules, admissible rules, and (minimal essentially) complete classes, **we will now give an example (which provides some insight into Bayes rules).**

[2] See Ferguson (1967), pp. 17–19, for an introduction to this topic.

Example 12.1.33. Continuing Examples 12.1.11, 12.1.18, and 12.1.24, find a Bayes rule with respect to the a priori distribution $B(\theta)$ that assigns probability w to θ_1 and $1 - w$ to θ_2 (where $0 \le w \le 1$).

This no-data decision problem has two possible states of nature (θ_1, θ_2) and six possible decisions $(d_1, d_2, d_3, d_4, d_5, d_6)$, and a general decision rule $s_{\mathbf{p}}$ (see (12.1.12)) takes decision d_i with probability p_i $(1 \le i \le 6)$ where $\mathbf{p} = (p_1, p_2, p_3, p_4, p_5, p_6)$ is a probability distribution. Since (see (12.1.15))

$$\begin{pmatrix} r_{\theta_1}(s_{\mathbf{p}}) \\ r_{\theta_2}(s_{\mathbf{p}}) \end{pmatrix} = \begin{pmatrix} 17p_1 + 19p_2 + 14p_3 + 10p_4 + 9p_5 + 9p_6 \\ 14p_1 + 4p_2 + 4p_3 + 6p_4 + 8p_5 + 16p_6 \end{pmatrix}, \quad (12.1.34)$$

$$R_{B(\theta)}(s_{\mathbf{p}}) = Er_\theta(s_{\mathbf{p}}) = wr_{\theta_1}(s_{\mathbf{p}}) + (1 - w)r_{\theta_2}(s_{\mathbf{p}})$$

$$= w(17p_1 + 19p_2 + 14p_3 + 10p_4 + 9p_5 + 9p_6)$$

$$+ (1 - w)(14p_1 + 4p_2 + 4p_3 + 6p_4 + 8p_5 + 16p_6) \quad (12.1.35)$$

$$= p_1(14 + 3w) + p_2(4 + 15w) + p_3(4 + 10w)$$

$$+ p_4(6 + 4w) + p_5(8 + w) + p_6(16 - 7w).$$

However, this is minimized by choosing $p_i = 1$ (where p_i is that one of $p_1, p_2, p_3, p_4, p_5, p_6$ with the smallest coefficient) and the other p_i's = 0. If we graph the coefficients as functions of w (see Figure 12.1-5) we find that a Bayes rule is to choose $p_3 = 1$ when $0 < w \le \frac{1}{3}$, $p_4 = 1$ when $\frac{1}{3} \le w \le \frac{2}{3}$, and $p_5 = 1$ when $\frac{2}{3} \le w < 1$ (since, e.g., $4 + 10w$ is the smallest multiplier of a p_i when $0 \le w < \frac{1}{3}$, and it multiplies p_3). At the "boundary" w's ($w = \frac{1}{3}, \frac{2}{3}$) we can also randomize since more than one multiplier has the same minimum value (e.g., at

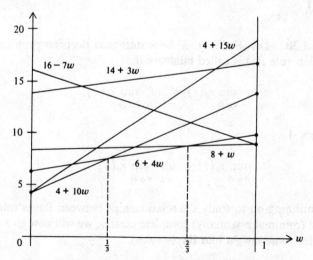

Figure 12.1-5. Components of Bayes risk in Example 12.1.33.

$w = \frac{1}{3}$ both $4 + 10w$ and $6 + 4w$, which multiply p_3 and p_4 respectively, have the same minimum value $7\frac{1}{3}$; hence, any rule with $p_3 + p_4 = 1$ is then Bayes). The points $\frac{1}{3}, \frac{2}{3}$ were determined graphically; for example, the lower point is the intersection of the lines $4 + 10w$ and $6 + 4w$:

$$\begin{cases} 4 + 10w = 6 + 4w, \\ \quad\quad 6w = 2, \\ \quad\quad\quad w = \frac{1}{3}. \end{cases} \tag{12.1.36}$$

So by varying $0 < w < 1$ (i.e., the a priori distribution $B(\theta)$) we find that the set of all **positive-Bayes rules** (i.e., rules each of which is Bayes with respect to some $B(\theta)$ that sets neither w nor $1 - w$ to 0) consists of s_3, s_4, s_5, rules that randomize between d_3 and d_4, and rules that randomize between d_4 and d_5. These rules' risk points generate precisely the hatched portion of the boundary of the convex set of risk points (see Figure 12.1-3). The set of *all* Bayes rules consists of those rules plus the rules that are Bayes for $w = 0$ (s_2, s_3, and rules that randomize between d_2 and d_3) and for $w = 1$ (s_5, s_6, and rules that randomize between d_5 and d_6).

When Θ consists of only two points (here θ_1 and θ_2) the Bayes rule may be found geometrically as follows. We want a rule whose risk point minimizes (see (12.1.35))

$$w r_{\theta_1}(s_{\mathbf{p}}) + (1 - w) r_{\theta_2}(s_{\mathbf{p}}). \tag{12.1.37}$$

But this quantity is constant at value k on the line

$$w r_{\theta_1}(s_{\mathbf{p}}) + (1 - w) r_{\theta_2}(s_{\mathbf{p}}) = k. \tag{12.1.38}$$

If $w = 1$, this is the line

$$r_{\theta_1}(s_{\mathbf{p}}) = k \tag{12.1.39}$$

($x = b$ is the x-y plane); otherwise ($0 \le w < 1$) it is the line (in standard $y = mx + b$ form)

$$r_{\theta_2}(s_{\mathbf{p}}) = \frac{-w}{1 - w} r_{\theta_1}(s_{\mathbf{p}}) + \frac{k}{1 - w}, \tag{12.1.40}$$

with intercept $k/(1 - w)$ and negative (unless $w = 0$) slope $-w/(1 - w)$. All rules whose risk points lie on this line will have Bayes risk k, but if k is "too small" there are no such rules. However, if we increase k until the line "just touches" the convex set of risk points, we will find the Bayes rules' risk point (and hence the Bayes rules) for the given a priori distribution. See Figure 12.1-6 for a typical case. (Also see Figure 9.4-5 for a similar construction in the case of hypothesis testing.) Note that what we called "positive-Bayes" rules are precisely the admissible rules in this example.

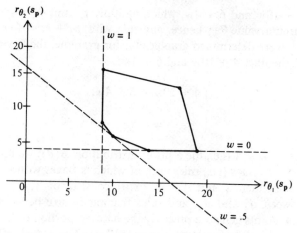

Figure 12.1-6. Graphical interpretation of Bayes rules.

We continue now to the relationships between Bayes rules, admissible rules, and (minimal essentially) complete classes. Most of our work will now deal with the case where Θ is finite (although the results are true in considerably more generality, their proofs and statements in that generality are beyond the scope of this book). **We will first prove a lemma that will be used in proving that all admissible rules are Bayes rules.**

Lemma 12.1.41. Let $(\Theta, \mathscr{D}, l)$, X be a statistical decision problem with Θ finite (i.e., $\Theta = \{\theta_1, \ldots, \theta_k\}$). Then the set S of all risk points [see (12.1.13)] of decision rules s,

$$S = \left\{ (y_1, \ldots, y_k) : y_1 = r_{\theta_1}(s), \ldots, y_k = r_{\theta_k}(s) \text{ for some decision rule } s \right\},$$

$$(12.1.42)$$

is a convex subset of $\mathscr{R}^k$.

Proof: Let $u = (u_1, \ldots, u_k)$ and $v = (v_1, \ldots, v_k)$ be in S. Then by the definition of S, there are decision rules $s(\cdot)$ and $t(\cdot)$ such that

$$u_j = r_{\theta_j}(s), \, v_j = r_{\theta_j}(t) \qquad (1 \le j \le k). \qquad (12.1.43)$$

Let λ be fixed ($0 < \lambda < 1$). Let $\alpha(\cdot)$ be a decision rule that with probability λ takes the same decision as rule $s(\cdot)$ (and with probability $1 - \lambda$ takes the same decision as rule $t(\cdot)$). Then (for $j = 1, \ldots, k$)

$$r_{\theta_j}(\alpha) = \lambda r_{\theta_j}(s) + (1 - \lambda) r_{\theta_j}(t), \qquad (12.1.44)$$

so $\lambda u + (1 - \lambda)v$ is in S. Hence, S is convex. ∎

A partial converse of Lemma 12.1.41 states that any convex subset S of $\mathscr{R}^k$ is the set of risk points of at least one decision problem $(\Theta, \mathscr{D}, l)$, X. (See Problem 12.18.) Hence, counterexamples constructed using such sets are valid in general (e.g., see Problem 12.6).

Theorem 12.1.45. Let $(\Theta, \mathscr{D}, l)$, X be a statistical decision problem with Θ finite (i.e., $\Theta = \{\theta_1, \ldots, \theta_k\}$). Then every admissible rule $t(\cdot)$ is also a Bayes rule with respect to some a priori distribution $B(\theta)$.

Proof: Let $S \subseteq \mathscr{R}^k$ be the set of all risk points of decision rules $s(\cdot)$. Let

$$\mathbf{x}' = \left(r_{\theta_1}(t), \ldots, r_{\theta_k}(t) \right) \tag{12.1.46}$$

$$Q(\mathbf{x}) = \left\{ \mathbf{y}: \mathbf{y} \in \mathscr{R}^k, \, y_1 \leq x_1, \ldots, y_k \leq x_k \right\}. \tag{12.1.47}$$

Then $Q(\mathbf{x}) \cap S = \{\mathbf{x}\}$ since $t(\cdot)$ is by assumption an admissible rule (for if any point $\mathbf{z}$ other than $\mathbf{x}$ were in the intersection, there would be a rule with that as its risk point, hence, there would be a better rule than $t(\cdot)$, which would render $t(\cdot)$ inadmissible, a contradiction). Hence, $S_1 = S$ and $S_2 = \{\mathbf{y}: \mathbf{y} \in Q(\mathbf{x}), \mathbf{y} \neq \mathbf{x}\} = Q(\mathbf{x}) - \{\mathbf{x}\}$ are disjoint convex sets, so by the Separating Hyperplane Theorem 12.1.62 there is a vector $\mathbf{p} \neq \mathbf{0}$ such that

$$\mathbf{p}'\mathbf{y} \leq \mathbf{p}'\mathbf{z} \quad (\text{all } \mathbf{y} \in Q(\mathbf{x}) - \{\mathbf{x}\}, \mathbf{z} \in S). \tag{12.1.48}$$

Now $p_1 \geq 0, \ldots, p_k \geq 0$. For if at least one of $p_1, \ldots, p_k$ were negative, say $p_j < 0$, then by taking $\mathbf{y}$ such that y_j is a large (negative) number we could make

$$\mathbf{p}'\mathbf{y} = \sum_{i=1}^{k} p_i y_i > \sum_{i=1}^{k} p_i z_i = \mathbf{p}'\mathbf{z},$$

a contradiction. Now let

$$q_i = \frac{p_i}{p_1 + \cdots + p_k}. \tag{12.1.49}$$

Then $q_1 \geq 0, \ldots, q_k \geq 0, q_1 + \cdots + q_k = 1$ (so $\mathbf{q}$ is a probability distribution on Θ) and

$$\mathbf{q}'\mathbf{y} \leq \mathbf{q}'\mathbf{z} \quad (\text{all } \mathbf{y} \in Q(\mathbf{x}) - \{\mathbf{x}\}, \mathbf{z} \in S); \tag{12.1.50}$$

that is (letting $\mathbf{y} \in Q(\mathbf{x}) - \{\mathbf{x}\} \rightarrow \mathbf{x}$)

$$\sum_{j=1}^{k} q_j r_{\theta_j}(t) \leq \sum_{j=1}^{k} q_j r_{\theta_j}(s) \tag{12.1.51}$$

for any rule $s(\cdot)$ (since any such rule $s(\cdot)$ has a risk point $\mathbf{z} \in S$). Hence, $t(\cdot)$ is a Bayes rule with respect to the a priori distribution $\mathbf{q}$ on Θ. ∎

We will now prove a partial converse to Theorem 12.1.45, after first making precise the notion of a "positive-Bayes" rule (see (12.1.36)ff in Example 12.1.33).

Definition 12.1.52. Let $(\Theta, \mathscr{D}, l)$, X be a statistical decision problem with Θ finite (i.e., $\Theta = \{\theta_1, \ldots, \theta_k\}$). A decision rule $s(\cdot)$ is called **positive-Bayes** (**+ -Bayes**) if it is Bayes with respect to some a priori distribution $B(\theta)$ that assigns positive probability to each θ_j ($j = 1, \ldots, k$).

Theorem 12.1.53. Let $(\Theta, \mathscr{D}, l)$, X be a statistical decision problem with Θ finite (i.e., $\Theta = \{\theta_1, \ldots, \theta_k\}$). Then every + -Bayes rule $t(\cdot)$ is admissible.

Proof: Suppose that $t(\cdot)$ is + -Bayes for $B(\theta)$ which assigns probability p_j to θ_j ($j = 1, \ldots, k$). If $t(\cdot)$ were inadmissible, then for some $s(\cdot)$,

$$\begin{cases} r_{\theta_j}(s) \le r_{\theta_j}(t) & (j = 1, \ldots, k) \\ r_{\theta_i}(s) < r_{\theta_i}(t) & (\text{at least one } i). \end{cases} \tag{12.1.54}$$

Since $p_1 > 0, \ldots, p_k > 0$, this would imply

$$\sum_{j=1}^{k} p_j r_{\theta_j}(s) < \sum_{j=1}^{k} p_j r_{\theta_j}(t), \tag{12.1.55}$$

so that $t(\cdot)$ could not be Bayes with respect to $B(\theta)$, a contradiction. ∎

The complete class theorem will now follow easily from Theorem 12.1.45, Problem 12.3H, and Problem 12.10.

Theorem 12.1.56. Complete Class Theorem. Let $(\Theta, \mathscr{D}, l)$, X be a statistical decision problem with Θ finite (i.e., $\Theta = \{\theta_1, \ldots, \theta_k\}$). If the set S of risk points is closed[3] and bounded[3] then: **(i)** the set of all Bayes rules is a complete class; **(ii)** the set of admissible Bayes rules is a minimal complete class; and **(iii)** the set of admissible Bayes rules with duplication of risk points eliminated is a minimal essentially complete class.

Other important theorems are available that consider Bayes and admissible rules, but the Complete Class Theorem (Theorem 12.1.56) is the major such theorem and should provoke great interest in specification of the class of Bayes rules. (Further detail on computation of Bayes rules will be given in Section 12.5.) For completeness we state two additional results, without proof. (The proof of Theorem 12.1.57 is simple; see Problem 12.19.)

Theorem 12.1.57. Let $(\Theta, \mathscr{D}, l)$, X be a statistical decision problem. If every Bayes rule with respect to a priori distribution $B(\theta)$ has the same risk point, then each such rule is admissible.

---

[3] This hypothesis can be weakened; see Problem 12.3H.

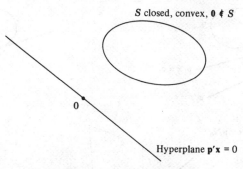

12.1-7. Illustration of Lemma 12.1.59.

Theorem 12.1.58. Let $(\Theta, \mathcal{D}, l)$, X be a statistical decision problem with Θ finite (i.e., $\Theta = \{\theta_1, \ldots, \theta_k\}$). Assume the set S of risk points is bounded[4] and closed.[4] Then all possible $+$-Bayes rules exist (i.e., for every a priori distribution $B(\theta)$ which assigns positive probability p_j to θ_j, $j = 1, \ldots, k$, a Bayes rule exists).

At this point we will prove the **Separating Hyperplane Theorem**, which was needed in the proof of Theorem 12.1.45 (and will be referred to later in this chapter also).*

The Separating Hyperplane Theorem essentially says that two disjoint convex subsets of $\mathcal{R}^k$ may be separated by a plane (in $\mathcal{R}^k$ a "plane" is usually called a hyperplane; in $\mathcal{R}^2$ it is called a line, while in $\mathcal{R}^3$ it is called a plane). We need one other result in order to prove the Separating Hyperplane Theorem, and several related ones (especially the Supporting Hyperplane Theorem) will be useful later in this chapter. These others will simply be stated; for detailed proofs, see, for example, Ferguson (1967), pp. 70–73.

Lemma 12.1.59. If $S \subseteq \mathcal{R}^k$ is closed and convex, and if $0 \notin S$, then there is a $\mathbf{p} \in \mathcal{R}^k$ such that (see Figure 12.1-7)

$$\mathbf{p}'\mathbf{x} > 0 \quad (\text{all } \mathbf{x} \in S).$$

Note that the origin $\mathbf{0}$ lies in every **hyperplane**[5] $\mathbf{p}'\mathbf{x} = 0$; by Lemma 12.1.59 we can choose a $\mathbf{p}$ so that $\mathbf{p}'\mathbf{x} > 0$ for all $\mathbf{x} \in S$. Since (by definition and by analogy with $\mathcal{R}$, $\mathcal{R}^2$, and $\mathcal{R}^3$) $\{\mathbf{x}: \mathbf{p}'\mathbf{x} > 0\}$ and $\{\mathbf{x}: \mathbf{p}'\mathbf{x} < 0\}$ are called the **two sides of**

---

[4] This hypothesis can be weakened, as in Theorem 12.1.56.
*The material in *the remainder of this section may be omitted at a first reading.*
[5] Formally, a **hyperplane** consists of all $\mathbf{x}$ such that $\mathbf{p}'\mathbf{x} = c$, where $\mathbf{p} \neq \mathbf{0}$ and c are constants.

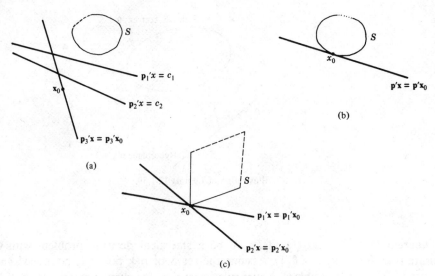

Figure 12.1-8. Illustration of Theorem 12.1.61.

the hyperplane $\mathbf{p}'\mathbf{x} = \mathbf{0}$, this result says we can choose a hyperplane $\mathbf{p}'\mathbf{x} = 0$ so that S is kept on one side of the hyperplane (i.e., the hyperplane does not intersect S).

Lemma 12.1.60. If $S \subseteq \mathscr{R}^k$ is convex, and if $A \subseteq \mathscr{R}^k$ is open, and if $A \subseteq cl(S)$ = closure of S, then $A \subseteq S$.

Lemma 12.1.60 means essentially that any open set contained in the closure of a convex set, is already contained in the convex set which (as can be seen by deleting the boundary) need not be closed itself.

Theorem 12.1.61. If $S \subseteq \mathscr{R}^k$ is convex and if $\mathbf{x}_0$ is either $\notin S$ or is a boundary point of S, then there is a $\mathbf{p} \in \mathscr{R}^k$ such that

$$\mathbf{p} \neq \mathbf{0}, \quad \mathbf{p}'\mathbf{x} \geq \mathbf{p}'\mathbf{x}_0 \quad (\text{all } \mathbf{x} \in S).$$

The situation described is depicted in Figure 12.1-8, where in case **(a)** $\mathbf{x}_0 \notin S$ and in cases **(b)** and **(c)** $\mathbf{x}_0$ is a boundary point of S. Note that $\mathbf{p}$ is not always unique. The part of Theorem 12.1.61 relating to $\mathbf{x}_0$ in the boundary of S is called the **Supporting Hyperplane Theorem** because the hyperplane $\mathbf{p}'\mathbf{x} = \mathbf{p}'\mathbf{x}_0$ is tangent to S and keeps S on one side [essentially by the definition of *sides* of the hyperplane, as noted after Figure 12.1-7]. As we saw in Figure 12.1-8, there may be infinitely many supporting hyperplanes at $\mathbf{x}_0$.

Theorem 12.1.62. Separating Hyperplane Theorem. If S_1 and S_2 are disjoint, convex subsets of $\mathcal{R}^k$, then there is a vector $\mathbf{p} \neq \mathbf{0}$ such that

$$\mathbf{p}'\mathbf{y} \leq \mathbf{p}'\mathbf{x} \quad (\text{all } \mathbf{x} \in S_1, \mathbf{y} \in S_2).$$

Proof: We will proceed by defining a new set

$$S = \{\mathbf{z}: \mathbf{z} = \mathbf{x} - \mathbf{y} \text{ for some } \mathbf{x} \in S_1 \text{ and } \mathbf{y} \in S_2\}.$$

Then $\mathbf{0} \notin S$, for if $\mathbf{0}$ were in S, there would be an $\mathbf{x}$ in S_1 and a $\mathbf{y}$ in S_2 such that $\mathbf{x} - \mathbf{y} = \mathbf{0}$. It would follow that $\mathbf{x} = \mathbf{y}$ with $\mathbf{x} \in S_1$, and $\mathbf{y} \in S_2$, which would be a contradiction since S_1 and S_2 are disjoint. (This proof of $\mathbf{0} \notin S$ fails only if at least one of S_1, S_2 is empty; but in that case $S = \varnothing$, and the theorem is obvious anyway. Hence, we may assume $S_1 \neq \varnothing$, $S_2 \neq \varnothing$.)

Secondly, S is a convex set. For suppose $\mathbf{z}_1$ and $\mathbf{z}_2$ are in S; then (for some $\mathbf{x}_1, \mathbf{x}_2 \in S_1$ and $\mathbf{y}_1, \mathbf{y}_2 \in S_2$) $\mathbf{z}_1 = \mathbf{x}_1 - \mathbf{y}_1$ and $\mathbf{z}_2 = \mathbf{x}_2 - \mathbf{y}_2$. Hence,

$$\beta\mathbf{z}_1 + (1 - \beta)\mathbf{z}_2 = \beta(\mathbf{x}_1 - \mathbf{y}_1) + (1 - \beta)(\mathbf{x}_2 - \mathbf{y}_2)$$

$$= \{\beta\mathbf{x}_1 + (1 - \beta)\mathbf{x}_2\} - \{\beta\mathbf{y}_1 + (1 - \beta)\mathbf{y}_2\},$$

which (for $0 < \beta < 1$) is in S since (for $0 < \beta < 1$) $\beta\mathbf{x}_1 + (1 - \beta)\mathbf{x}_2 \in S_1$ and $\beta\mathbf{y}_1 + (1 - \beta)\mathbf{y}_2 \in S_2$. Hence S is a convex set.

Finally, let us apply Theorem 12.1.61 to the convex subset S of $\mathcal{R}^k$ and $\mathbf{x}_0 = \mathbf{0} \notin S$. This assures us there is a $\mathbf{p} \in \mathcal{R}^k$ $(\mathbf{p} \neq \mathbf{0})$ such that

$$\mathbf{p}'\mathbf{z} \geq \mathbf{p}'\mathbf{0} = 0 \quad (\text{all } \mathbf{z} \in S);$$

hence,

$$\mathbf{p}'\mathbf{x} \geq \mathbf{p}'\mathbf{y} \quad (\text{all } \mathbf{x} \in S_1, \mathbf{y} \in S_2).$$

(See Figure 12.1-9.) ∎

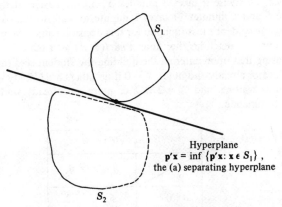

Figure 12.1-9. Illustration of Theorem 12.1.62.

PROBLEMS FOR SECTION 12.1

12.1.1 Find and sketch the convex hull of the four points $\begin{pmatrix} 3 \\ 4 \end{pmatrix}, \begin{pmatrix} 4 \\ 3 \end{pmatrix}, \begin{pmatrix} 3 \\ 3 \end{pmatrix}, \begin{pmatrix} 4 \\ 4 \end{pmatrix}$.

12.1.2 For a certain statistical decision problem $(\Theta, \mathscr{D}, l)$, X, suppose that $\Theta = \{\theta_1, \theta_2, \theta_3\}$, $\mathscr{D} = \{d_1, d_2, d_3\}$, $l(\theta, d)$ is given by

$l(\theta, d)$			
θ \ d	d_1	d_2	d_3
θ_1	0	4	5
θ_2	2	3	0
θ_3	6	0	6

and the probability function of X is

$p_X(x\|\theta) = P_\theta(X = x)$			
x \ θ	θ_1	θ_2	θ_3
x_1	.3	.5	.2
x_2	.7	.5	.8

Compute $(r_{\theta_1}(s_\mathbf{p}), r_{\theta_2}(s_\mathbf{p}), r_{\theta_3}(s_\mathbf{p}))$.

12.1.3 Upon entering a certain dormitory building, a student whose room is on a high floor can either wait for the elevator (d_1), or walk down one flight of stairs to the basement and take the elevator from there (d_2). (These are the only choices this student considers.) The elevator is either in heavy use (θ_1), or not (θ_2). If it is in heavy use, it will take the student 10 minutes to reach his/her room from the entry floor; otherwise it takes 3 minutes. From the basement the corresponding times are 5 and 1 minutes. It takes 1 minute to walk to the basement location. Assuming the student's loss function for this decision equals the time it takes from building entry to reach his/her floor, **find** $l(\theta, d)$ as a table for all θ and all d.

Supposing that upon entering the building the student sees the people waiting for the elevator already and notes $X = 0$ if no others are already waiting, $X = 1$ if one other is waiting, and $X = 2$ if 2 or more are already waiting, let X have probability function

$p_X(x\|\theta)$		
x \ θ	θ_1	θ_2
0	.6	.2
1	.2	.4
2	.2	.4

List all possible nonrandomized decision rules and compute the associated risk points. Similarly for all decision rules. Show the risk points graphically. On the basis of risk, find a minimal complete class of decision rules.

12.1.4 In the setting of Problem 12.1.2, find the Bayes risk of a general (randomized) decision rule, and find a Bayes rule with respect to
(a) A uniform prior, that is, $P(\theta = \theta_i) = 1/3$ for $i = 1, 2, 3$.
(b) The prior $P(\theta = \theta_1) = 1/6$, $P(\theta = \theta_2) = 1/3$, $P(\theta = \theta_3) = 1/2$.

12.1.5 In Problem 12.1.3, find the Bayes risk of a general (randomized) decision rule, with respect to the prior $P(\theta = \theta_1) = p = 1 - P(\theta = \theta_2)$, when
(a) $p = .5$. (b) $p = .3$.

12.1.6 In Problem 12.1.2, find a minimax decision rule.

12.1.7 In Problem 12.1.3, find a minimax decision rule.

12.1.8 Let $\mathbf{p} \in \mathscr{R}^k$ and $c \in \mathscr{R}$ be fixed. Then, by definition, $\{\mathbf{x}: \mathbf{p}'\mathbf{x} = c, \mathbf{x} \in \mathscr{R}^k\}$ is a **hyperplane** in $\mathscr{R}^k$. Define

$$S_1 = \{\mathbf{x}: \mathbf{p}'\mathbf{x} > c\},$$

$$S_2 = \{\mathbf{x}: \mathbf{p}'\mathbf{x} < c\}$$

(these are the two sides of the hyperplane $\mathbf{p}'\mathbf{x} = c$; see the discussion following Figure 12.1-8).
(a) Prove that S_1 and S_2 are each convex sets in $\mathscr{R}^k$.
(b) Prove that S_1 and S_2 are disjoint (i.e., $S_1 \cap S_2 = \varnothing$).
(c) Prove that the hyperplane $\mathbf{p}'\mathbf{x} = c$ divides $\mathscr{R}^k$ into two disjoint parts, in one of which $\mathbf{p}'\mathbf{x} > c$ and in the other of which $\mathbf{p}'\mathbf{x} < c$. Note that both parts are nonempty iff $\mathbf{p} \neq \mathbf{0}$.
(d) What is the conclusion of the Separating Hyperplane Theorem (Theorem 12.1.62) for the disjoint convex sets S_1 and S_2? Are all the allowable $\mathbf{p}_1$'s in the conclusion of that theorem precisely $\mathbf{p}_1 = k\mathbf{p}$ (k any constant > 0)? (Prove or give a counterexample.)
(e) Illustrate the results of parts (a) through (d) by a *carefully* drawn graph of the case $k = 2$, $\mathbf{p}' = (-1,1)$, $c = 1$. (Be sure to prove what the sets S_1 and S_2 are in this case.)

12.1.9 By definition (see Definition 6.1.8) a set $S \subseteq \mathscr{R}^k$ is *convex* if (for all $\mathbf{x}, \mathbf{y} \in S$)

$$\beta\mathbf{x} + (1 - \beta)\mathbf{y} \in S \qquad (\text{all } \beta, 0 < \beta < 1).$$

Prove that if S is convex, $\mathbf{x}_1, \ldots, \mathbf{x}_n \in S$, and $q_1 + \cdots + q_n = 1$ ($q_1 \geq 0, \ldots, q_n \geq 0$), then

$$q_1\mathbf{x}_1 + \cdots + q_n\mathbf{x}_n \in S.$$

[*Hint*: Do the trivial proofs for $n = 1, 2$ and then proceed by induction.]

12.1.10 Let S be any convex subset of $\mathscr{R}$. Prove that $f_1(x) = x^2$, $f_2(x) = |x|$, and $f_3(x) = e^x$ are each convex functions on S.

12.1.11 Let $p \in \mathcal{R}^k$, $c \in \mathcal{R}$. Let $S = \{x: p'x > c\}$. (In Problem 12.1.8 we proved S is convex in $\mathcal{R}^k$.) Prove that the function $f(x)$, defined on this $S \subseteq \mathcal{R}^k$ by $f(x) = p'x$, is convex. For the case $k = 1$, graph S, $f(x)$, and the set

$$S_1 = \{(z_1, z_2)': \text{For some } x \in S, x = z_1 \text{ and } f(x) \le z_2\}.$$

Is S_1 a convex subset of $\mathcal{R}^2$?

12.1.12 Suppose $f(x)$ is a convex function on $S \subseteq \mathcal{R}^k$. Let $S_1 = \{(z_1, \ldots, z_k, z_{k+1})': \text{For some } x \in S, x' = (z_1, \ldots, z_k) \text{ and } f(x) \le z_{k+1}\}$. Prove that S_1 is a convex set in $\mathcal{R}^{k+1}$. [This fact gives $f(x)$ the name *convex* function; for a special case, see Problem 12.1.11.]

12.1.13 Geometric and Arithmetic Means. Let $x_1, \ldots, x_n$ be any n real numbers. If $x_1 \ge 0, \ldots, x_n \ge 0$, then it is well-known that

$$(x_1 \cdots x_n)^{1/n} \le \frac{x_1 + \cdots + x_n}{n} \qquad (*)$$

(the geometric mean is less than or equal to the arithmetic mean). Prove $(*)$ using Jensen's Inequality (Theorem 6.1.10). [*Hint*: Let a r.v. Z be $\ln x_i$ w.p. $1/n$, and let $f(x) = e^x$.]

12.1.14 Assuming that $EZ \in S$, prove Jensen's Inequality (Theorem 6.1.10) for the case $k = 1$. [*Hint*: Since the point $(EZ, f(EZ))$ is on the boundary of the convex set S_1 of Problem 12.1.12, there is (by Theorem 12.1.61) a supporting hyperplane at $(EZ, f(EZ))$; call it $y = mx + b$. Since $(EZ, f(EZ))$ is on this hyperplane, the latter must be $y = f(EZ) + m(x - EZ)$. Compare this line with the curve $y = f(x)$, replace x by a random point Z, and take expected values to complete the proof.] A formal proof for any k is given in, for example, Ferguson (1967), pp. 76–77.

12.1.15 Use Jensen's Inequality for the function $f(x) = e^x$ which is (Problem 12.1.10) convex on $\mathcal{R}^1$, and for a r.v. U for which EU exists and $P(U \in \mathcal{R}) = 1$, to conclude that $EU \in \mathcal{R}$ and $e^{EU} \le Ee^U$ (or $EU \le \ln(Ee^U)$). In fact, show that $EU < \ln(Ee^U)$ if U is *not* {constant w.p. 1}. Prove that $e^{EU} = Ee^U$ iff U is {constant w.p. 1}.

12.1.16 Prove that it is not true that equality holds in Jensen's Inequality (6.1.10) iff Z is {constant w.p. 1}. Compare your result with that of Problem 12.1.15, where (in a special case) we showed equality does hold iff Z is {constant w.p. 1}. How do these results differ? [*Hint*: If the requirement that $f(x)$ be convex is strengthened to require that $f(x)$ be **strictly convex** in the sense that $x, y \in S$ and $0 < \beta < 1$ implies

$$f(\beta x + (1 - \beta)y) < \beta f(x) + (1 - \beta)f(y),$$

then equality will hold in Jensen's Inequality iff Z is {constant w.p. 1}. Prove this result.]

12.2. HYPOTHESIS TESTING

In this section we begin our consideration of the relationships of decision theory with "conventional" (non decision-theoretic) statistical theory. The decision-theoretic view of the hypothesis-testing problem (especially the problem where H_0 and H_1 are both simple hypotheses, the case of composite hypotheses being noted in Problems 9.12H and 9.13H) has already been covered in Section 9.4 (it is helpful to review that section at this point), and the tie-in with the general results of Section 12.1 is clear: a hypothesis-testing problem where $H_0 = \{\theta_0\}$ and $H_1 = \{\theta_1\}$ are both simple and we observe a r.v. X with d.f. $F(x|\theta)$ where θ is unknown ($\theta \in \Theta$), can be regarded as a decision problem $(\Theta, \mathcal{D}, l)$, X where $\Theta = \{\theta_0, \theta_1\}$, X is unaltered, $\mathcal{D} = \{d_0, d_1\}$ where d_0 is the decision to accept H_0 and d_1 is the decision to reject H_0, and where $l(\theta_0, d_0) = l(\theta_1, d_1) = 0$ and $l(\theta_0, d_1) = l(\theta_1, d_0) = 1$. A general randomized decision rule $s(X)$ specifies (see Definition 12.1.2) for each $x \in \mathcal{X}$ a probability distribution $s(x)$ according to which a member d of $\mathcal{D}$ is to be chosen. Thus, $s(X)$ is precisely a general randomized test, and the risk point of $s(X)$ (as at (9.4.1)) is simply a point in $\mathcal{R}^2$ giving the probabilities of Type I and Type II errors of $s(X)$. It then follows easily that the considerations of the rest of Section 9.4 were those of Section 12.1 for the (simple versus simple) hypothesis-testing case.

In Section 12.1 we used a no-data decision problem to illustrate and motivate the concepts of that section (see Examples 12.1.11, 12.1.18, 12.1.24, and 12.1.33). Now, in order to illustrate the gains possible due to having data, we will consider a hypothesis-testing problem with data.

Example 12.2.1. Consider the statistical decision problem $(\Theta, \mathcal{D}, l)$, X where $\Theta = \{\theta_0, \theta_1\}$ with $\theta_0 = 0$ and $\theta_1 = 2$, $\mathcal{D} = \{d_0, d_1\}$ with $d_0 \neq d_1$, $l(\theta_0, d_0) = l(\theta_1, d_1) = 0$, $l(\theta_0, d_1) = l(\theta_1, d_0) = 1$, and X has a normal distribution with unknown mean $\theta \in \Theta$ and known variance $\sigma^2 = 4$. (Thus, we have a hypothesis-testing problem.) Find a minimal essentially complete class of decision rules (tests) and graph their risk points. How would the graph change if we had no data X?

By Theorem 9.4.7, $\{\phi_\alpha(\cdot): \alpha \leq \alpha_0\}$ is a minimal essentially complete class of tests (decision rules) where α_0 is the smallest α for which $1 - \beta(\phi_\alpha) = 0$, where $\phi_\alpha(\cdot)$ is the (level α) Neyman-Pearson test that satisfies

$$E_{\theta_0}\phi(X) = \alpha \tag{12.2.2}$$

and

$$\phi(x) = \begin{cases} 1, & \text{when } f(x|\theta_1) > kf(x|\theta_0) \\ 0, & \text{when } f(x|\theta_1) < kf(x|\theta_0). \end{cases} \tag{12.2.3}$$

In our case (X a $N(\theta, 4)$ r.v.) $f(x|\theta_1)$ and $f(x|\theta_0)$ are each > 0 for all x, so let us consider the case $k > 0$ [$k \leq 0$ yields $\phi(x) \equiv 1$, which gives a (Type I error, Type II error) or risk point of $(1, 0)$]. Now (using the facts $\theta_0 = 0$, $\theta_1 = 2$, and

$\sigma^2 = 4$)

$$f(x|\theta_1) > kf(x|\theta_0)$$

$$\Leftrightarrow \quad \frac{1}{\sqrt{2\pi}\,\sigma}e^{-\frac{1}{2}\left(\frac{x-\theta_1}{\sigma}\right)^2} > k\frac{1}{\sqrt{2\pi}\,\sigma}e^{-\frac{1}{2}\left(\frac{x-\theta_0}{\sigma}\right)^2}$$

$$\Leftrightarrow \quad -\frac{1}{2}\left(\frac{x-\theta_1}{\sigma}\right)^2 > -\frac{1}{2}\left(\frac{x-\theta_0}{\sigma}\right)^2 + \ln k$$

$$\Leftrightarrow \quad -(x-\theta_1)^2 > -(x-\theta_0)^2 + 2\sigma^2 \ln k \qquad (12.2.4)$$

$$\Leftrightarrow \quad 2x(\theta_1 - \theta_0) > (\theta_1^2 - \theta_0^2) + 2\sigma^2 \ln k$$

$$\Leftrightarrow \quad 4x > 4 + 8\ln k$$

$$\Leftrightarrow \quad x > 1 + 2\ln k$$

and the test with critical function (12.2.3) then has

$$E_{\theta_0}\phi(X) = P_{\theta_0}[X > 1 + 2\ln k]$$

$$= 1 - \Phi\left(\frac{1 + 2\ln k - 0}{2}\right) \qquad (12.2.5)$$

$$= 1 - \Phi\left(\frac{1 + 2\ln k}{2}\right),$$

which will equal α iff

$$1 + 2\ln k = 2\Phi^{-1}(1 - \alpha). \qquad (12.2.6)$$

It follows that $\alpha_0 = 1$ (since no test $\phi(\cdot)$ with $k > 0$ has $1 - \beta(\phi) = 0$). Hence, the test $\phi_\alpha(\cdot)$ that rejects iff $X > 2\Phi^{-1}(1 - \alpha)$ has level α and $\{\phi_\alpha(\cdot): \alpha \le 1\}$ is a minimal essentially complete class of tests. To plot the graph we also need

$$1 - \beta(\phi_\alpha) = P_{\theta_1}[X < 2\Phi^{-1}(1 - \alpha)]$$

$$= \Phi\left(\frac{2\Phi^{-1}(1 - \alpha) - 2}{2}\right) \qquad (12.2.7)$$

$$= \Phi(\Phi^{-1}(1 - \alpha) - 1).$$

Hence, the plot consists of $(\alpha, \Phi(\Phi^{-1}(1 - \alpha) - 1))$ for $0 \le \alpha \le 1$ as in Figure 12.2-1. Without data, as in Example 12.1.18 we find the set of risk points is as in Figure 12.2-2, and the rise in $1 - \beta(\phi_\alpha)$ for a given level α is clear.

In hypothesis-testing problems, we can take a *more general loss function* than $l(\theta_0, d_0) = l(\theta_1, d_1) = 0$, $l(\theta_0, d_1) = l(\theta_1, d_0) = 1$. (For example, we might take $l(\theta_0, d_0) = l(\theta_1, d_1) = 0$ and $l(\theta_0, d_1) = 1$ but $l(\theta_1, d_0) = cl(\theta_0, d_1)$ with a $c > 1$.

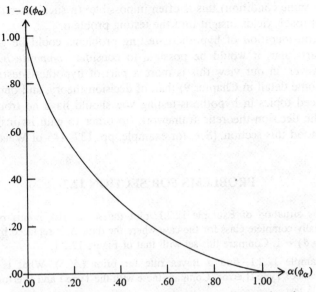

Figure 12.2-1. Risk points of the minimal essentially complete class with data in Example 12.2.1.

This would count Type II error as "worse" than Type I error; for example, if $c = 2$, it is "twice as bad.") This is rarely done, since it yields nothing new (it simply shifts the convex set of risk points by multiplying each y-coordinate by a constant c, while the minimal essentially complete class of tests remains a minimal essentially complete class of tests). We could also attempt to assess *monetary gains and losses* in constructing $l(\theta, d)$. However, in problems of scientific inference (e.g., in the testing of whether a new drug is better than an old

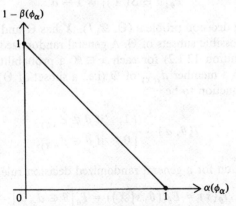

Figure 12.2-2. No-data risk points for Example 12.2.1.

drug for the same condition) this is often impossible. In such cases the decision-theoretic approach yields insight into the testing problem.

Further consideration of hypothesis-testing problems could be given at this point (in particular, it would be possible to consider *composite hypotheses* in detail). However, in our view this is more a part of hypothesis-testing (already covered in some detail in Chapter 9) than of decision theory, and once you learn more advanced topics in hypothesis-testing you should have no trouble putting them into the decision-theoretic framework (in order to gain its insight) if you have understood this section. [See, for example, pp. 137–145 of Weiss (1961).]

PROBLEMS FOR SECTION 12.2

12.2.1 For the situation of Example 12.2.1, plot the set of risk points of a minimal essentially complete class for the case where the data X is replaced by Z that has $P(Z = \theta) = 1$. Compare this set with that of Figure 12.2-1.

12.2.2 In Example 12.2.1, find a Bayes rule for prior $(.5, .5)$. What is its level of significance? Type II error? Compare these with the Type I and II errors of the best level .05 test.

12.3. INTERVAL ESTIMATION

In this section we continue our consideration of the relationships of decision theory with "conventional" (non decision-theoretic) statistical theory, showing how the problem of interval estimation fits into the decision-theoretic framework.

Recall (see Definition 10.1.10) that if X is a r.v. with d.f. $F(x|\theta)$ where θ is unknown and $\theta \in \Theta$ (here X and θ may be multivariate), then the set $S(X)$ is called a *confidence set* for θ with *confidence coefficient* $1 - \alpha$ if

$$P_\theta[\theta \in S(X)] \stackrel{\theta}{=} 1 - \alpha. \qquad (12.3.1)$$

The corresponding decision problem $(\Theta, \mathscr{D}, l)$, X has Θ and X unaltered, while $\mathscr{D}$ consists of all possible subsets of Θ. A general randomized decision rule $s(X)$ specifies (see Definition 12.1.2) for each $x \in \mathscr{X}$ a probability distribution $s(x)$ according to which a member $d_{s(X)}$ of $\mathscr{D}$ (i.e., a subset of Θ) is to be chosen. If we take our loss function to be

$$l(\theta, d) = \begin{cases} 1, & \text{if } \theta \notin d_{s(X)} \\ 0, & \text{if } \theta \in d_{s(X)}, \end{cases} \qquad (12.3.2)$$

then our risk function for a general randomized decision rule $s(X)$ is

$$r_\theta(s) = E_\theta l(\theta, s(X)) = P_\theta[\theta \notin d_{s(X)}]. \qquad (12.3.3)$$

Hence, a confidence set with confidence coefficient $1 - \alpha$ corresponds to a decision rule $s(X)$ with risk function $r_\theta(x) \overset{\theta}{\equiv} \alpha$.

Once the above correspondence has been made, the problem of interval estimation emerges as just a special problem of decision theory, which may hence be treated by the general methods of decision theory. Generalizations of loss function (12.3.2) are possible, but we will not go into those here. As in the case of hypothesis-testing (see Section 12.2), the main value of the decision-theoretic approach may be the insight it yields into the interval-estimation problem and the unity it gives to statistics (since statistical problems can be viewed as decision problems, whether they are problems of hypothesis-testing, interval estimation, or other areas of statistics).

PROBLEMS FOR SECTION 12.3

12.3.1 A confidence interval was given in (10.2.12). Formulate the problem as a decision-theoretic problem, that is, specify $(\Theta, \mathscr{D}, l)$, X. Show what decision rule $s(X)$ the interval (10.2.12) corresponds to.

12.4. RANKING AND SELECTION

In this section we conclude our formal consideration of the relationships of decision theory with "conventional" statistical theory, showing how the problems of ranking and selection fit into the decision-theoretic framework. (An informal discussion of point estimation and decision theory will be given in Section 12.5, essentially through an example.)

To simplify the discussion, we will consider only the problem of selection of the best (largest mean) normal population of Section 11.2. (The results carry over without any difficulty to general problems of ranking and selection.) Recall that we have $k \geq 2$ populations $\pi_1, \dots, \pi_k$ such that if $X_{i1}, X_{i2}, \dots$ are n independent observations from π_i, then each X_{ij} is $N(\mu_i, \sigma^2)$ where μ_i is unknown and σ^2 is known $(1 \leq i \leq k)$. The goal is to select that population with the largest mean $\mu_{[k]} = \max(\mu_1, \dots, \mu_k)$, in such a way that

$$P(\text{CS}) \geq P^* \quad \text{whenever} \quad \mu_{[k]} - \mu_{[k-1]} \geq \delta^* \qquad (12.4.1)$$

(see (11.2.5)). The corresponding decision problem $(\Theta, \mathscr{D}, l)$, X has $\Theta = \mathscr{R}^k$ (the set of all possible $(\mu_1, \dots, \mu_k)$), $X = (X_{11}, \dots, X_{1n}; \dots; X_{k1}, \dots, X_{kn})$, and $\mathscr{D} = \{d_1, \dots, d_k\}$, where d_i denotes the decision that π_i is best $(1 \leq i \leq k)$. If we take our loss function to be

$$l((\mu_1, \dots, \mu_k), d_i) = \begin{cases} 1, & \text{if } \mu_i \neq \max(\mu_1, \dots, \mu_k) \\ 0, & \text{if } \mu_i = \max(\mu_1, \dots, \mu_k), \end{cases} \qquad (12.4.2)$$

then our risk function for a general randomized decision rule $s(X)$ is

$$r_\theta(s) = E_\theta l(\theta, s(X)) = 1 - P_\theta(\text{CS using } s(X)), \qquad (12.4.3)$$

the probability of an incorrect decision when $\theta = (\mu_1, \ldots, \mu_k)$ is true and we use decision rule $s(X)$. Hence, a selection procedure with $P(\text{CS}) \geq P^*$ whenever $\mu_{[k]} - \mu_{[k-1]} \geq \delta^*$ corresponds to a decision rule $s(X)$ whose risk function satisfies

$$r_\theta(s) \leq 1 - P^* \quad \text{for all } \theta \text{ such that} \quad \mu_{[k]} - \mu_{[k-1]} \geq \delta^*. \qquad (12.4.4)$$

With the above correspondence made, the problem of selection fits very neatly into the decision-theoretic framework (of which it was, as we noted at the beginning of Chapter 11, very suggestive). Such problems are sometimes called *multiple-decision* problems, and a number of papers have appeared that consider Bayes and minimax solutions for such problems. (The solutions presented in Chapter 11 generally are these rules for many loss functions.) For example, see Eaton (1967), and the references given there. Important Bayesian decision procedures for selection problems were discussed by Dunnett (1960) (also see the discussion on pp. 31–40 following Dunnett's article).

PROBLEMS FOR SECTION 12.4

12.4.1 For the case of selection discussed as a statistical decision problem, compare the risk of the means procedure (see Section 11.2) with that of the rule which chooses the population that produces the largest first observation.

12.5. GENERAL DECISION THEORY

In this section we continue the discussion of Section 12.1, discussing some aspects of general decision theory (as contrasted with the considerations of Sections 12.2, 12.3, and 12.4, which were concerned with relations of general decision theory with "conventional" statistical theory).

Our first concern in this section is to discuss in more detail the construction (or computation) of Bayes rules. (This was promised in Section 12.1 just before Theorem 12.1.57, and is important because, as was seen in Section 12.1, Bayes rules are important; hence, we need to know how to find them.)

Recall (see Definition 12.1.25) that a Bayes rule for a statistical decision problem $(\Theta, \mathcal{D}, l)$, X and a given a priori distribution $B(\theta)$ on Θ is a decision rule $s(X)$ that has the smallest Bayes risk:

$$R_{B(\theta)}(s) \leq R_{B(\theta)}(t) \qquad (12.5.1)$$

for all decision rules $t(X)$. Now the Bayes risk of a decision rule $s(X)$ is

$$R_{B(\theta)}(s) = E_\theta r_\theta(s)$$
$$= E_\theta E_X l(\theta, s(X)), \quad (12.5.2)$$

where the subscript on the expectation sign denotes the quantity with respect to which the expectation is being performed. Now suppose Θ is finite ($\Theta = \{\theta_1, \ldots, \theta_k\}$), $\mathscr{D}$ is finite ($\mathscr{D} = \{d_1, \ldots, d_m\}$), and X is discrete. Let $b(\theta)$ denote the probability assigned to θ by $B(\theta)$, and let $f(x|\theta)$ denote $P_\theta[X = x]$. Then the Bayes risk (12.5.2) of a rule $s(X)$ can be written as

$$R_{B(\theta)}(s) = \sum_{\theta \in \Theta} \sum_{x \in \mathscr{X}} \sum_{d \in \mathscr{D}} l(\theta, d) s_d(x) f(x|\theta) b(\theta), \quad (12.5.3)$$

where $s_d(x)$ denotes the probability that after observing $X = x$, decision rule $s(X)$ takes decision d. (Recall that a decision rule is a function $s(\cdot)$ which for each $x \in \mathscr{X}$ specifies a probability distribution, denoted by $s(x)$, according to which a member d of $\mathscr{D}$ is to be chosen.) We can now interchange summations in equation (12.5.3) and write

$$R_{B(\theta)}(s) = \sum_{x \in \mathscr{X}} \sum_{d \in \mathscr{D}} s_d(x) \left[\sum_{\theta \in \Theta} l(\theta, d) f(x|\theta) b(\theta) \right]$$
$$= \sum_{x \in \mathscr{X}} \sum_{d \in \mathscr{D}} s_d(x) K(d; x), \quad (12.5.4)$$

where we have defined

$$K(d; x) = \sum_{\theta \in \Theta} l(\theta, d) f(x|\theta) b(\theta). \quad (12.5.5)$$

Now since our aim is to choose $s(\cdot)$ so as to minimize (12.5.4), that is, to choose the probability distribution $s(x)$ for each x in such a way that (12.5.4) is minimized, it is clear we should proceed as follows: For each $x \in \mathscr{X}$, let

$$s_{d_i}(x) = 0, \quad \text{if } K(d_i; x) > \min(K(d_1; x), \ldots, K(d_m; x)). \quad (12.5.6)$$

Then all weight of the probability distribution $s(x)$ will be put on decisions d_j that minimize $K(d; x)$. (If there are several such decisions, the Bayes rule is not unique.) Thus, we have the following.

Theorem 12.5.7. Let $(\Theta, \mathscr{D}, l)$, X be a statistical decision problem. Suppose Θ and $\mathscr{D}$ are finite and X is discrete. Then a rule $s(X)$ is a Bayes rule [with respect to a priori distribution $B(\theta)$ which assigns probability $b(\theta)$ to θ] iff, for all $x \in \mathscr{X}$, $s_{d_i}(x) = 0$ for all d_i for which

$$K(d_i; x) > \min(K(d_1; x), \ldots, K(d_m; x)), \quad (12.5.8)$$

where

$$K(d; x) = \sum_{\theta \in \Theta} l(\theta, d) f(x|\theta) b(\theta). \qquad (12.5.9)$$

This theorem also holds in the general case where Θ and $\mathscr{D}$ need not be finite and X need not be discrete (sums often being replaced by integrals and probabilities often being replaced by density functions in the obvious way) as long as a Bayes rule with respect to $B(\theta)$ exists for the given problem. Note that in any problem, if all we want to know is which action to take (after observing $X = x$), we need not compute the whole rule, but rather only the $K(d; x)$ for $d \in \mathscr{D}$ for the given x. Note also that a Bayes rule need never randomize; we can decide (for each $x \in \mathscr{X}$) to set $s_d(x) = 1$ for some one of the (in general several) d_i's that minimize $K(d; x)$.

Our second concern in this section is to note briefly other important aspects of decision theory. One such aspect is a consideration of facts about minimax decision rules. Since these have already been covered, we will just note that Problems 12.24 and 12.25 are relevant here, and that Problem 12.25 gives a widely used method of finding such rules. A second aspect is a consideration of loss versus regret (see Definition 9.4.8 for a definition of regret, in the special case of hypothesis-testing). Essentially, the question is whether it might be appropriate to replace the loss function $l(\theta, d)$ by a new loss function

$$\text{reg}(\theta, d) = l(\theta, d) - l(\theta) \qquad (12.5.10)$$

(called regret) where $l(\theta)$ is the smallest $l(\theta, d)$ can be for any d (with θ fixed). Indeed, the loss functions used with "conventional" statistical theory (see Sections 12.2, 12.3, and 12.4) are usually already regret functions. Appealing as the idea may seem to some, replacement of loss functions by regret functions (in cases where the loss functions are not already regret functions at the outset) has not gained wide popularity. One reason is that in a practical problem we will suffer losses (not regrets!) after the decision is taken, and decision theory is attempting to take proper account of those losses. Another reason is that (see Problem 12.27) whether we use losses or regrets, we obtain the same Bayes rule for a given a priori distribution $B(\theta)$. A third aspect involves the uses of sufficient statistics. Here it can be shown in great generality that if $(\Theta, \mathscr{D}, l)$, X is a statistical decision problem and $t(X)$ is a sufficient statistic, then: The set of all decision rules for the new statistical decision problem $(\Theta, \mathscr{D}, l)$, $t(X)$ is an essentially complete class of decision rules for the original decision problem $(\Theta, \mathscr{D}, l)$, X. Hence, we can reduce (by sufficiency) the data as much as possible (i.e., use a minimal sufficient statistic if one exists) without "losing any information about θ" as far as the decision problem is concerned. (For example, the $N(\theta, 4)$ r.v. X in Example 12.2.1 would often be the average of several other independent normal r.v.'s.) For the proof (which is not hard, but which we omit) see, for example, p. 120 of Ferguson (1967). (For a related example, see Arnold (1972). The problem of whether we may omit randomization has light shed on it by an example in Section 2 of that paper.) **A fourth (and final) aspect of our discussion is the relation between "point estimation" and decision theory.** Problems of point estimation are essentially decision-theory problems with $\mathcal{D} = \Theta$ (i.e., we wish to "estimate θ"). One example of this sort is given in Problem 12.26, and we will now give another (more theoretical) one.

Example 12.5.11. Let $(\Theta, \mathcal{D}, l)$, X be a decision problem with $\Theta = \mathcal{D} = \mathcal{R}$ (i.e., a problem of point estimation of a real-valued parameter). Suppose that

$$\begin{cases} l(\theta, d) = g(|\theta - d|) \\ g(x) < g(y), \quad \text{whenever } x < y \end{cases} \tag{12.5.12}$$

[i.e., the loss is an increasing function of the absolute deviation of d from θ]. Suppose that X has a density function $f(\cdot)$ such that

$$\begin{cases} f(x) > 0, & (-\infty < x < +\infty) \\ f(\theta + x) = f(\theta - x), & (-\infty < x < +\infty) \\ f(\theta + c_1) > f(\theta + c_2), & \text{whenever } 0 \le c_1 < c_2 \end{cases} \tag{12.5.13}$$

[i.e., X has a positive density, symmetric about θ, with a unique maximum at θ]. Show that, among all nonrandomized decision rules $s(X)$ that satisfy the invariance condition $s(X + c) = s(X) + c$ for all c, $s(X) = X$ has the uniformly smallest risk $r_\theta(s) = El(\theta, s(X))$.

Since $s(\cdot)$ must increase its estimate of θ by c if X increases by c (i.e., since $s(X + c) = s(X) + c$) we have $s(0) = s(X + (-X)) = s(X) + (-X)$ so $s(X) = X + s(0)$. Thus, the most general such rule estimates θ as $X + s$ for some constant s, and for any such nonrandomized rule $s(X)$,

$$r_\theta(s) = El(\theta, s(X))$$

$$= \int_{-\infty}^{\infty} g(|s(x) - \theta|)f(x)\, dx \tag{12.5.14}$$

$$= \int_{-\infty}^{\infty} g(|x + s - \theta|)f(x)\, dx.$$

If we can show that $s = 0$ minimizes (12.5.14), we will have shown that $s(X) = X$ has uniformly smallest risk for all θ among the *translation invariant estimators*; that is, we wish to show that

$$\int_{-\infty}^{\infty} g(|x + s - \theta|)f(x)\, dx \ge \int_{-\infty}^{\infty} g(|x - \theta|)f(x)\, dx. \tag{12.5.15}$$

Now (using the transformation $y = x - \theta$ in the third step)

$$\int_{-\infty}^{\infty} g(|x + s - \theta|) f(x)\, dx - \int_{-\infty}^{\infty} g(|x - \theta|) f(x)\, dx$$

$$= \int_{-\infty}^{\infty} \{ g(|x + s - \theta|) - g(|x - \theta|) \} f(x)\, dx$$

$$= \int_{-\infty}^{\infty} \{ g(|y + s|) - g(|y|) \} f(y + \theta)\, dy \qquad (12.5.16)$$

$$= \int_{-\infty}^{-s/2} \{ g(|y + s|) - g(|y|) \} f(y + \theta)\, dy$$

$$\quad + \int_{-s/2}^{\infty} \{ g(|y + s|) - g(|y|) \} f(y + \theta)\, dy.$$

We now assume without loss that $s \geq 0$ (see Problem 12.28). Then (making the transformation $z = -y - s$ in the second integral in the last expression of (12.5.16)) we find

$$\int_{-\infty}^{\infty} g(|x + s - \theta|) f(x)\, dx - \int_{-\infty}^{\infty} g(|x - \theta|) f(x)\, dx$$

$$= \int_{-\infty}^{-s/2} \{ g(|y + s|) - g(|y|) \} f(y + \theta)\, dy$$

$$\quad + \int_{-\infty}^{-s/2} \{ g(| - z|) - g(| - z - s|) \} f(-z - s + \theta)\, dz$$

$$\qquad (12.5.17)$$

$$= -\int_{-\infty}^{-s/2} \{ g(|y|) - g(|y + s|) \} f(y + \theta)\, dy$$

$$\quad + \int_{-\infty}^{-s/2} \{ g(|z|) - g(|z + s|) \} f(z + s + \theta)\, dz$$

$$= \int_{-\infty}^{-s/2} [g(|y|) - g(|y + s|)] [f(y + s + \theta) - f(y + \theta)]\, dy.$$

But $y + s + \theta \geq y + \theta$ (since $s \geq 0$); and $\theta \geq y + s + \theta \geq y + \theta$ if $y \leq -s$ (hence, for $y \leq -s$ we have $f(y + s + \theta) \geq f(y + \theta)$) while for $-s < y \leq -s/2$ we have $y + s + \theta \geq \theta \geq y + \theta$ with $y + s + \theta$ closer to θ than is $y + \theta$ (hence, for $-s < y \leq -s/2$ we have $f(y + s + \theta) \geq f(y + \theta)$). Thus, for all possible values of y in (12.5.17),

$$f(y + s + \theta) - f(y + \theta) \geq 0. \qquad (12.5.18)$$

Also, for all possible y in (12.5.17),

$$g(|y|) - g(|y + s|) \geq 0. \qquad (12.5.19)$$

Hence, (12.5.17) (and thus (12.5.16)) is ≥ 0, so (12.5.15) holds, proving the desired result. *This result can be stated as follows*: "For fairly general loss functions [those that are increasing functions of the absolute error], the uniformly minimum risk translation invariant decision rule sets $s(X) = X$ if X has a symmetric unimodal positive density with median θ."

PROBLEMS FOR SECTION 12.5

12.5.1 Consider a statistical decision problem where $\Theta = \mathscr{D} = \{0, 1, 2, \ldots, 100\}$, and X is binomial with θ trials and probability of success .05. The loss function is $l(\theta, d) = |\theta - d|$. For the prior distribution which assigns probability $1/101$ to each $\theta \in \Theta$, what action is taken if $X = 0$? If $X = 1$? ... If $X = 100$?

12.5.2 Use the result of Problem 12.25 to seek a minimax rule in Problem 12.5.1.

12.5.3 In Problem 12.1.2, give the regret table.

12.6. AN OVERVIEW

Our purpose in this section is, through a discussion of a specific example, to give an overview of the field of statistics (and of its classification into subfields). Two of these subfields (nonparametric methods and regression analysis) are discussed in Chapters 13 and 14; our main purpose here is to provide further integration of statistics into a coherent whole in the reader's mind. A secondary purpose is to note the terminology commonly used in referring to the various subfields so that a person wishing to pursue specific aspects in greater detail will know what key words to find in surveying books and journal articles. (Of course, not all areas are mentioned—statistics is too large for that—but enough are that the discussion should be enlightening.)

The example to be discussed deals with various aspects of the successful operation of a chain of pizza parlors. If the opening of a new establishment in a particular city (say Mobile, Alabama, to be specific) is under consideration, we are then faced with a problem of making a decision to open or not to open such a facility, with concomitant monetary gains or losses depending on the success of the establishment if opened (a problem of **decision theory**).

In order to assess the situation sufficiently precisely (i.e., to make our risk function small) we will need data X appropriate to our situation. One part of such data might consist of a **sample survey** of a number of people in the Mobile area, asking each questions designed to allow us to gauge their expected consumption of our pizzas if we open the parlor. Some problems here are those of obtaining a representative sample large enough to yield estimates of small variance on expected consumption, those of how to proceed if a person we decide to include in the sample does not respond, and those of how to verify whether the questions are perceived by the respondents as asking what we desire to ask (and whether the respondents are answering truthfully).

Other data obtained might include observations on the consumption of pizzas experienced at the existing pizza-purveying establishments in the area. Such data are random variables, and one question (that of **distribution theory**) is what probability distribution we should assume such data follow. If we have a specific distribution in mind, we may wish to test the hypothesis that it is the true distribution (**goodness-of-fit tests**). Alternatively, we may wish to only make some weak assumptions on the distribution involved (such as its being a member of a unimodal location parameter family as in Example 12.5.11) and attempt to draw inferences hence not dependent on strong distributional assumptions (**nonparametric methods**). If the number of observations is large, we may be able to use **asymptotic theory** to assess the distribution, for example via the empirical d.f. A question that could then arise would be the **efficiency (exact and asymptotic)** of this asymptotic theory with respect to exact theory based on the distribution we think may underlie the data.

If the data obtained with respect to existing establishments span a long time period, we might suspect trends or other changes due to time (since over a long time consumption is probably not a sequence of independent and identically distributed r.v.'s). In order to find and adjust for any time trends, periodicities in the data (e.g., more pizzas sold in winter than in spring), and so on, the techniques of **statistical analysis of stochastic processes (or time series)** are needed.

Once the data has been adequately assessed and a decision taken, if that decision is to open the new parlor in Mobile, new questions arise. One of these is the **estimation** of the demand to be experienced so that the facility may be of adequate size (yet not of excess size). This may also involve predicting not only the initial demand, but also the growth in demand to be expected over the near future. This prediction involves such items as population growth and income levels in the area, and trends in transportation, competition, and so on, and would use the methods of **linear statistical inference and regression analysis**. Since these data are comprised of several interrelated components, the techniques would involve **multivariate analysis**.

In operating the establishment the satisfaction of the customers will be of great importance, and methods of **quality control** will be needed to assure that we act as soon as possible when the production process starts to increase its defective (poor-tasting, burned, and so on) pizzas. It may also be necessary to assess the effects of the establishment's heat and waste on the surrounding environment, and the effects of our "special secret ingredients" on our customers' health (**biometrics**).

In operating the chain of establishments it will be necessary to buy large quantities of apparatus such as ovens, and their expected lifetimes (assessed by **life-testing) and reliability** will have to be studied quantitatively. We may even wish to oversee the design and manufacture of the items using **engineering statistics**.

At some time we will undoubtedly face the question of whether to change the recipe for the pizza or the sequence in which it is produced (what goes on first, for example), which will involve us in the **design and analysis of experiments**, for we will then wish to perform a taste-testing experiment to assess the desirability of the various alternatives.

Other problems to be faced will involve **ranking and selection** of vendors of goods; **testing of hypotheses** about the superiority of goods that are more expensive (e.g., a special cheese); analysis of the sequence of daily sales (involving **sequential methods**); design of our facility to keep waiting time reasonable (**queueing theory and congestion**) and to keep an adequate inventory of supplies without having them kept so long as to spoil (**inventory and storage theory**); and **simulation** of proposed changes in our methods of operation of the chain of pizza parlors in order to pretest our decisions in a less costly environment than the real world.

PROBLEMS FOR SECTION 12.6

12.6.1 Detail at least five statistical aspects of the problem of evaluating a proposed new treatment for cancer.

PROBLEMS FOR CHAPTER 12

12.1 Given a set S, a relation ρ between pairs of members of S is said to be: **reflexive** if $x\rho x$ for all $x \in S$; **antisymmetric** if $x\rho y$ and $y\rho x \Rightarrow x$ and y denote the same element of S; and **transitive** if $x\rho y$ and $y\rho z \Rightarrow x\rho z$. If a relation ρ on a set S is reflexive, antisymmetric, and transitive, it is called a **partial order** and S is said to be **partially ordered** by ρ.

Show that (if we consider two decision rules to be the same if they have the same risk function) the "at least as good as" relation $\succeq$ (see the paragraph following Definition 12.1.10) partially orders the set D of all decision rules.

12.2 Sketch the convex hull of the three vectors $\begin{pmatrix} 1 \\ 0 \end{pmatrix}, \begin{pmatrix} 0 \\ 1 \end{pmatrix}, \begin{pmatrix} 5 \\ 6 \end{pmatrix}$.

12.3 In Example 12.1.18, is a rule that randomizes between d_3 and d_5 a member of the minimal essentially complete class?

12.4 Prove that if $a \geq 0$ and $b \geq 0$, then $\lambda a + (1 - \lambda)b \geq 0$ when $0 \leq \lambda \leq 1$. (Is this true for $\lambda < 0$? For $\lambda > 1$?)

12.5 Show in detail the induction referred to in the proof of Theorem 12.1.16.

12.6 For each of the following figures, suppose that the shaded area is the set of risk points corresponding to all decision rules for some decision problem $(\Theta, \mathscr{D}, l)$, X. Find a subset R_C of this set of risk points such that: if C is a set of decision rules which (for every $r \in R_C$) contains exactly one decision rule with risk point r, then C is a minimal essentially complete class.

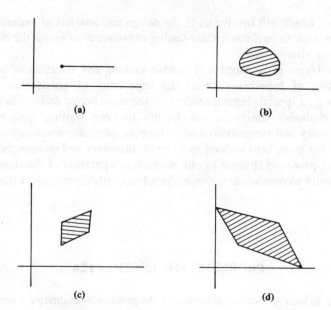

(a)

(b)

(c)

(d)

12.7 Prove Lemma 12.1.22. [*Hint*: See the discussion preceding Figure 12.1-1.]

12.8 For a statistical decision problem $(\Theta, \mathcal{D}, l)$, X, let C be a complete class of decision rules and let A be the set of all admissible decision rules. Prove that $A \subseteq C$.

12.9 For a statistical decision problem $(\Theta, \mathcal{D}, l)$, X, let C be an essentially complete class of decision rules. Prove that if $s_1(\cdot)$ is an admissible decision rule and $s_1 \notin C$, then there is an $s_2(\cdot) \in C$ such that $s_1 \sim s_2$.

12.10 For a statistical decision problem $(\Theta, \mathcal{D}, l)$, X, suppose that the set A of all admissible rules is minimal complete. Let A' be A except that whenever several rules in A have the same risk point, all but one of these rules are deleted. Show that A' is an essentially complete class. Show that A' is a minimal essentially complete class.

12.11 In Example 12.1.18, a risk point (i.e., a point in Figure 12.1-3 that is the risk point of at least one decision rule) may correspond to more than one rule. Find all rules that have risk point $\begin{pmatrix} 15 \\ 10 \end{pmatrix}$. [*Hint*: Since here a general decision rule is $s_\mathbf{p} = (p_1, \ldots, p_6)$ a probability distribution, we must find all $\mathbf{p}$ such that

$$\begin{pmatrix} r_{\theta_1}(s_\mathbf{p}) \\ r_{\theta_2}(s_\mathbf{p}) \end{pmatrix} = \begin{pmatrix} 15 \\ 10 \end{pmatrix},$$

that is, all probability distributions $\mathbf{p}$ such that

$$\begin{pmatrix} 17p_1 + 19p_2 + 14p_3 + 10p_4 + 9p_5 + 9p_6 \\ 14p_1 + 4p_2 + 4p_3 + 6p_4 + 8p_5 + 16p_6 \end{pmatrix} = \begin{pmatrix} 15 \\ 10 \end{pmatrix},$$

that is, all solutions $(p_1, \ldots, p_6)$ of the system of equations

$$\begin{cases} 17p_1 + 19p_2 + 14p_3 + 10p_4 + 9p_5 + 9p_6 = 15, \\ 14p_1 + 4p_2 + 4p_3 + 6p_4 + 8p_5 + 16p_6 = 10, \\ p_1 + p_2 + p_3 + p_4 + p_5 + p_6 = 1, \\ p_1 \geq 0, p_2 \geq 0, p_3 \geq 0, p_4 \geq 0, p_5 \geq 0, p_6 \geq 0. \end{cases}$$

To solve such a system, solve the first equation for p_1 in terms of p_2, p_3, p_4, p_5, p_6. Plug this into the second equation and solve for p_2 in terms of p_3, p_4, p_5, p_6. Use these to solve the third equation for p_3 in terms of p_4, p_5, p_6. Now express p_1 and p_2 in terms of p_4, p_5, p_6 alone (p_3 is already so expressed). Then the inequalities $p_1 \geq 0, p_2 \geq 0, p_3 \geq 0, p_4 \geq 0, p_5 \geq 0, p_6 \geq 0$ restrict the available set of p_4, p_5, p_6 to (say) $F \subseteq \mathcal{R}^3$. Having found F, a general solution consists of picking a point p_4, p_5, p_6 from F and finding the corresponding p_1, p_2, p_3.]

12.12 As in Problem 12.11, but for risk point $\begin{pmatrix} 10 \\ 6 \end{pmatrix}$. What happens if you try the point $\begin{pmatrix} 5 \\ 5 \end{pmatrix}$ (which is not a risk point)?

12.13 Consider the no-data decision problem $(\Theta, \mathcal{D}, l)$ with $\Theta = \mathcal{D} = \mathcal{R}$ and $l(\theta, d) = (\theta - d)^3$. Show that no matter what $B(\theta)$ is used, among the nonrandomized decision rules there is no Bayes rule. [*Hint*: In the plane, plot graphs similar to those in Figure 12.1-1 for a few decision rules. Show that, no matter how small a rule s_1 may make the Bayes risk, it is easy to find another rule s_2 with a smaller risk. Since this risk can be made $< k$ for any specified number k ($-\infty < k < +\infty$), conclude that among all decision rules there is no Bayes rule.]

12.14 In the context of Problem 12.13, show that no ε-Bayes rules exist.

12.15 In the context of Example 12.1.33, find the minimax rule and give a graphical interpretation (see Figure 9.4-4).

12.16 A **least-favorable a priori distribution** $B(\theta)$ *is one that makes the minimum Bayes risk as large as possible.* Deduce from Figure 12.1-5 that in Example 12.1.33 that distribution is $B(\theta)$ with $w = 1$. Show that the minimax rule is a rule that is Bayes for the least-favorable a priori distribution in this example.

12.17 On a graph similar to that in Figure 12.1-6, mark the risk points of all ε-Bayes decision rules, with $\varepsilon = 1$. Similarly for all ε-minimax decision rules, with $\varepsilon = 1$.

12.18 Let S be a nonempty convex subset of $\mathcal{R}^k$. Consider the no-data decision problem $(\Theta, \mathcal{D}, l)$ with $\Theta = \{\theta_1, \ldots, \theta_k\}$, $\mathcal{D} = S$, and $l(\theta_j, d) = d_j$ [the jth component of the decision

$$d = (d_1, \ldots, d_{j-1}, d_j, d_{j+1}, \ldots, d_k)].$$

Show that the set of all risk points of decision rules is S.

Deduce that any convex subset of $\mathcal{R}^k$ is the set of risk points of at least one decision problem $(\Theta, \mathcal{D}, l)$, X (irrespective of whether S is closed and bounded or not). Contrast this with the situation that prevailed in Section 9.4 (see Theorem 9.4.2 and footnote 6 of Chapter 9), where S was closed and bounded as well as convex.

12.19 Prove Theorem 12.1.57. [*Hint*: Assume the contrary and obtain a contradiction.]

12.20 Use the results of Problem 12.18 to show that Theorem 12.1.56 (the Complete Class Theorem) would sometimes be false if S were not required to be closed and bounded.

12.21 For the situation of Example 12.2.1, plot the set of risk points of a minimal essentially complete class for the case where the data X is replaced by $Y = (X_1, X_2, X_3, X_4)$ where X_1, X_2, X_3, X_4 are independent $N(\theta, \sigma^2)$ r.v.'s with $\sigma^2 = 4$. Compare this set with that of Figure 12.2-1; what gain arises from the three additional observations? [*Hint:* The calculations of Example 9.3.10 may be of use to you.]

12.22 Show that the usual loss functions for the hypothesis-testing problem's decision-theoretic statement,

$$\begin{cases} l(\theta_0, d_0) = l(\theta_1, d_1) = 0, \\ l(\theta_0, d_1) = 1, \quad l(\theta_1, d_0) = c > 1, \end{cases}$$

are already regret functions. [*Hint:* See footnote 8 in Chapter 9.]

12.23 Suppose that in a (simple versus simple) hypothesis-testing problem with loss function

$$\begin{cases} l(\theta_0, d_0) = l(\theta_1, d_1) = 0, \\ l(\theta_0, d_1) = 1, \quad l(\theta_1, d_0) = 1, \end{cases}$$

the minimax test has level α and Type II error $1 - \beta$. Show that if the loss function is altered by making

$$l(\theta_1, d_0) = c > 1,$$

then the minimax test for this new problem will have level $\alpha^* > \alpha$ and Type II error $1 - \beta^* < 1 - \beta$. Give a graphical interpretation involving a convex set of risk points.

12.24 Let $(\Theta, \mathcal{D}, l)$, X be a statistical decision problem. Prove that if every minimax rule has the same risk point, then each such rule is admissible. [*Hint:* This result is similar to that of Theorem 12.1.57, which dealt with Bayes rules.] [*Note:* Such a minimax rule is often called **unique**.]

12.25 Let $(\Theta, \mathcal{D}, l)$, X be a statistical decision problem. Prove that: *If a decision rule $s(\cdot)$ has constant risk (i.e., if $r_\theta(s)$ is the same for all θ in Θ) and is a Bayes rule, then it is a minimax rule.* (Hence, if we can "guess" an a priori distribution $B(\theta)$ for which the corresponding Bayes rule has constant risk, we can find a minimax rule.)

12.26 In reliability (life-testing), it is sometimes assumed that the lifetime of an item is a r.v. which is $\geq x$ with probability

$$e^{-(x/\theta)^m}$$

($x \geq 0$) where $m > 0$ is known and $\theta > 0$ is unknown. Suppose n such items are tested and yield independent r.v.'s $X_1, \ldots, X_n$ as their times of "death" (or "failure").

(a) Find an unbiased estimator of θ. Find the MLE of θ based on $X_1, \ldots, X_n$.

(b) Consider the statistical decision problem $(\Theta, \mathcal{D}, l)$, X with $\Theta = \{\theta: \theta > 0\}$, $\mathcal{D} = \Theta$, $X = (X_1, \ldots, X_n)$, and

$$l(\theta, d) = \left(\frac{d - \theta}{\theta}\right)^2.$$

Show that any decision rule that sets

$$d = a\left(X_1^m + \cdots + X_n^m\right)^{1/m}$$

(for some fixed $a > 0$) has constant risk. Is the decision rule that always sets d equal to the MLE admissible? Is the decision rule that always sets d equal to the unbiased estimator found in part **(a)** admissible? Find a minimax decision rule.

12.27 Show that: *Any rule is Bayes with respect to an a priori distribution $B(\theta)$ when we use the loss function, iff that same rule is Bayes when we use the regret function (12.5.10).* Show by example that minimax rules do not have the corresponding property. (Hence, Bayes rules are invariant under the change of a loss function to a regret function, but minimax rules are usually not.)

12.28 In Example 12.5.11, show that

$$\int_{-\infty}^{\infty} \{g(|z - s|) - g(|z|)\} f(z + \theta) \, dz = \int_{-\infty}^{\infty} \{g(|y + s|) - g(|y|)\} f(y + \theta) \, dy.$$

Explain how this justifies the statement following equation (12.5.16) that we can "assume without loss that $s \geq 0$."

12.29 Let $(\Theta, \mathcal{D}, l)$, X, be a statistical decision problem with $\Theta = \mathcal{D} = \mathcal{R}$, $l(\theta, d) = (\theta - d)^2$, and X a $N(\theta, 1)$ r.v. Among all decision rules $s(X)$ such that $s(X + c) = s(X) + c$ for all c, there is one that minimizes $r_\theta(s)$ for all θ. Find it.

12.30 Let $(\Theta, \mathcal{D}, l)$, X be a statistical decision problem with $\Theta = \{-2, 3\}$, $\mathcal{D} = \{d_0, d_1\}$, $l(-2, d_0) = l(3, d_1) = 0$, $l(-2, d_1) = 6$, $l(3, d_0) = 4$, and $X = (X_1, X_2, X_3, X_4)$ where X_1, X_2, X_3, X_4 are independent $N(\theta, 4)$ r.v.'s. For the a priori distribution that assigns probability w to $\theta = -2$ and probability $1 - w$ to $\theta = 3$ ($0 \leq w \leq 1$), find a Bayes rule $s_w(X)$. Plot the risk points $(r_{-2}(s_w), r_3(s_w))$ for $0 \leq w \leq 1$. [*Hint*: Use sufficiency to reduce $X = (X_1, X_2, X_3, X_4)$ to $\bar{X}$ in order to simplify your calculations.] On the same diagram, plot the risk points of the Bayes rules in the no-data decision problem $(\Theta, \mathcal{D}, l)$.

12.31 Let $(\Theta, \mathcal{D}, l)$, X be a statistical decision problem with $\Theta = \mathcal{D} = \{x: 0 \leq x \leq 1\}$, $l(\theta, d) = (d - \theta)^2$, and $X = (X_1, \ldots, X_n)$ where $X_1, \ldots, X_n$ are independent r.v.'s with $P_\theta[X_i = 0] = 1 - \theta$ and $P_\theta[X_i = 1] = \theta$ ($1 \leq i \leq n$). For the a priori distribution that puts a density function $b(\theta) = 2\theta$ for $0 \leq \theta \leq 1$ (and zero otherwise) on θ, find a Bayes decision rule $s(X)$. Compute $r_\theta(s)$. [*Hint*: Use sufficiency to reduce $X = (X_1, \ldots, X_n)$ to a binomial r.v.] Compare $s(\cdot)$ with the decision rule $t(X)$ that sets $t(X) = (X_1 + \cdots + X_n)/n$ (the observed proportion of successes in the sample). How is $r_\theta(s)$ related to $r_\theta(t)$ as $n \to \infty$? What is the Bayes rule for the no-data decision problem $(\Theta, \mathcal{D}, l)$?

12.32 For the decision problem $(\Theta, \mathcal{D}, l)$, X of Problem 12.30, find a minimax decision rule. [*Hint*: See Problem 12.25.]

12.33 An oil slick has spread from 0 (where it occurred) out to a radius $\theta > 0$. The slick is always spread uniformly over the area it covers. The slick is hard to spot from the air unless sea gulls are stuck in it, and luckily (!) three are, at distances X_1, X_2, X_3 from the origin 0. We are thus motivated to consider the following estimation problem in decision-theoretic formulation: $\Theta = \mathscr{D} = \{x: 0 < x < \infty\}$, $l(\theta, d) = ((d/\theta) - 1)^2$, and $X = (X_1, X_2, X_3)$ where X_1, X_2, X_3 are independent r.v.'s, each with a uniform distribution on $(0, \theta)$. For the a priori distribution that puts a density function $b(\theta) = \theta^5 e^{-\theta}/5!$ for $\theta > 0$ (and zero otherwise) on θ, find a Bayes decision rule $s(X)$.

12.34 For the no-data decision problem $(\Theta, \mathscr{D}, l)$ with $\Theta = \{\theta_1, \theta_2, \theta_3, \theta_4\}$, $\mathscr{D} = \{d_1, d_2, d_3, d_4, d_5, d_6, d_7, d_8, d_9\}$, and $l(\theta, d)$ as specified in the following table

	$l(\theta, d)$								
θ \ d	d_1	d_2	d_3	d_4	d_5	d_6	d_7	d_8	d_9
θ_1	80	25	40	89	23	53	74	5	71
θ_2	6	86	79	62	75	83	6	8	44
θ_3	63	86	75	75	87	73	3	12	42
θ_4	9	54	52	67	18	70	47	72	61

find (among all nonrandomized decision rules) the minimax rule.

12.35 Give example(s) to show that it may be the case that
  (a) A Bayes rule is not admissible.
  (b) A minimax rule is not $+$-Bayes.
  (c) An admissible rule is not $+$-Bayes.
  [*Hint*: Take $\Theta = \{\theta_1, \theta_2\}$ and, with Problem 12.18 as justification, plot appropriate sets of risk points in $\mathscr{R}^2$.]

12.36 Each time a tornado alert is given, a certain community has a choice of three possible actions: d_1 (no mobilization), d_2 (partial mobilization), d_3 (full mobilization). Tornado severity is measured on a scale θ with three possible values: $0, .5, 1$. The alert specifies a predicted severity X that is a r.v. for which $P_\theta[X = 0] = 1 - \theta$, $P_\theta[X = .5] = \theta/2 = P_\theta[X = 1]$. It is known that in this area tornadoes of severity 0 occur 50% of the time, with tornadoes of severity .5 and 1 occurring 25% of the time each. The loss incurred by the community by choosing decision d when θ is true is as given in the following table:

	$l(\theta, d)$		
θ \ d	d_1	d_2	d_3
$\theta = 0$	0	-10	-20
$\theta = .5$	50	0	-10
$\theta = 1$	60	50	0

Formulate the problem of deciding on an action as a statistical decision problem $(\Theta, \mathscr{D}, l)$, X with an a priori distribution on θ. (Specify each of $\Theta, \mathscr{D}, l, X, B(\theta)$ carefully and precisely.) What is the Bayes decision rule's action if we observe $X = 0$?

12.37 Suppose for a certain statistical decision problem with $\Theta = \{\theta_1, \theta_2\}$ the set of all risk points is as drawn below. Indicate clearly all risk points corresponding to admissible decision rules.

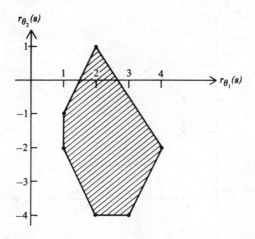

12.38 Suppose that, in a certain statistical decision problem with $\Theta = \{\theta: 0 < \theta\}$, three decision rules s_1, s_2, s_3 have risk functions as plotted below. Assuming no relation not indicated on the graph occurs outside the range of the graph, which decision rules (if any) can be definitely said to be inadmissible? admissible? minimax? Bayes? better than s_1? better than s_2? better than s_3?

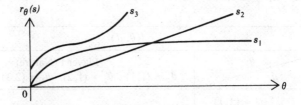

12.39 If we seek to minimize our maximum loss, we desire to use a minimax decision rule, that is, a rule $s(X)$ that achieves the[6]

$$\min_s \max_\theta r_\theta(s).$$

However, if one were a spy for a foreign power, one might seek to make the government worked on follow a policy (decision rule) $t(X)$ that would maximize its minimum loss, that is a rule $t(X)$ that achieves the[6]

$$\max_t \min_\theta r_\theta(t).$$

Call such a rule an **NG strategy**. Suppose we have a decision problem $(\Theta, \mathcal{D}, l)$, X where $\Theta = \{\theta_1, \theta_2\}$ and the set of all risk points is as plotted below. Indicate

---

[6] More precisely we should write "inf" and "sup" for "min" and "max," respectively, as in Definition 12.1.30.

clearly which risk point(s) correspond to *NG* strategies, and specify your method for finding those points.

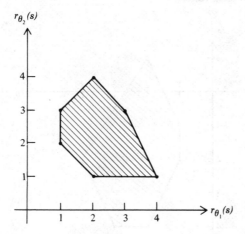

12.40 "**Two-finger Morra**" is a game that has been played in Italy since classical antiquity. The game is played by two people. Each person shows either one or two fingers and, at the same time, calls a guess as to the number of fingers his opponent will show. If exactly one player has a correct guess, he wins a number of dollars equal to the sum of the number of fingers shown (by himself and his opponent). In all other cases there is no gain or loss. If we let, say, (2,1) denote the decision by a player to show two fingers while guessing one, fill in the following loss table.

		$l(\theta, d)$			
	θ	Player I (Nature)			
d		$\theta_1 = (1,1)$	$\theta_2 = (1,2)$	$\theta_3 = (2,1)$	$\theta_4 = (2,2)$
Player II	$d_1 = (1,1)$				
	$d_2 = (1,2)$				
	$d_3 = (2,1)$				
	$d_4 = (2,2)$				

[*Hint*: Recall that this is a loss table for Player II, and that gains are negative losses.]

12.41 A certain organization (e.g., a store, charitable agency, or nonprofit organization) is trying to decide whether or not to make a mailing to a certain group of 1000 people. They assume that, if a person responds, the yield to them from his response is $5. As a first approximation, assume that $10J$ percent will respond, where J is unknown ($J = 0, 1, 2, \ldots, 10$). If expenses connected with the mailing are $1 per person if it is made (e.g., cost of procuring names, printing, postage and so on), complete the following loss table.

$l(J, d)$											
d ╲ J	0	1	2	3	4	5	6	7	8	9	10
d_1 (mail) d_2 (do not mail)											

12.42 Two companies (each with unlimited capital) are to competitively bid for a contract that, if it could be obtained at no cost, would have an economic value of $\$C$ ($C > 0$). The bidding process works as follows. Each company enters a sealed bid of $\$i$ for $i = 0, 1, 2, \ldots$ (of course, with i allowed to be different for each company). The higher bid wins the contract, but as compensation the high bidder must pay the amount of the bid to the low bidder (the other company, whose workers will now be unemployed). If the bids are equal, the contract is assigned by tossing a fair coin and no money changes hands. Complete the following loss table.

$l(\theta, d)$	
d ╲ θ	States of Nature (Company I's bid) 0 1 2 3 4 $\cdots$
Company II's bid 0 1 2 3 4 ⋮	

12.43 Suppose that you are an experimental scientist trying to estimate a new unknown physical constant θ. You are greeted by a Bayesian who tells you of the "personal probability approach." What criticism can you make of this approach as far as your case is concerned?

12.44 Suppose that in a certain decision problem there are five states of nature ($\Theta = \{\theta_1, \theta_2, \theta_3, \theta_4, \theta_5\}$) and that, relative to the a priori distribution $B(\theta)$ that assigns probability $b(i)$ to θ_i ($1 \le i \le 5$) rule $s(\cdot)$ is Bayes. Show that for the situation shown below $s(\cdot)$ is a minimax rule.

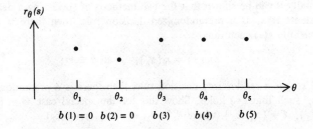

Generalizing this result show that: *for a decision problem with finite* Θ ($\Theta = \{\theta_1, \ldots, \theta_k\}$) *if* $s(\cdot)$ *is a Bayes rule with respect to the a priori distribution that assigns probability* $b(\theta)$ *to* θ ($\theta \in \Theta$), *and if*

$$r_\theta(s) = \max_\theta r_\theta(s)$$

for every θ_i *for which* $b(\theta_i) > 0$, *then* $s(\cdot)$ *is a minimax rule.* (This generalizes Problem 12.25.)

12.45 Let $X(t)$ denote the number of people who have arrived at a certain queue (waiting line) from time 0 to time t ($t > 0$). If arrivals occur in accord with what is called a Poisson process with parameter $\theta > 0$, then we know that

$$P[X(t) = k] = \frac{e^{-\theta t}(\theta t)^k}{k!} \quad (k = 0, 1, 2, \ldots).$$

For the decision problem of estimating θ on the basis of one observation of $X(t)$ for a fixed $t > 0$ (i.e., we observe the number of arrivals from time 0 to fixed time t) with $l(\theta, d) = (d - \theta)^2$, what is the Bayes rule's estimate if the a priori distribution used has a density function $b(\theta) = e^{-\theta}$ for $\theta > 0$ (and zero otherwise)? Find $r_\theta(s)$ for this Bayes rule $s(\cdot)$. Discuss the problem of selecting t. (What is your basis for determining t? What is the ideal theoretical t? What difference would it make if you knew $0 < \theta \le \theta_0$?)

12.46 Consider the decision problem $(\Theta, \mathscr{D}, l)$, X with $\Theta = \mathscr{D} = \{x: 0 < x \le 1\}$, $l(\theta, d) = (d - \theta)^3$, and X a uniform r.v. on $(0, \theta)$. Find a Bayes rule with respect to a uniform a priori distribution on $(0, 1)$ (if one exists; otherwise find an ε-Bayes rule for $\varepsilon = .01$).

HONORS PROBLEMS FOR CHAPTER 12

12.1H Our "**randomized decision rule**" for a statistical decision problem $(\Theta, \mathscr{D}, l)$, X (see Definition 12.1.2) is sometimes called a **behavioral decision rule** [e.g., see Ferguson (1967), p. 25]. Recall that such a rule $s(\cdot)$ specifies, for each possible value $x \in \mathscr{X}$ of X, a probability distribution $s(x)$ on $\mathscr{D}$ according to which a decision $d \in \mathscr{D}$ is selected.

Another method of specifying a decision rule is as follows, which we will call a **prerandomized decision rule**: s_p specifies a probability distribution on the collection of all nonrandomized decision rules. [Thus, the randomization can be performed before we observe X. The resulting nonrandomized rule specifies a unique decision to be taken after observing $X = x$.]

Usually it can be shown that the two methods of specifying a decision rule are equivalent: If s_p is a prerandomized decision rule, then there is a randomized decision rule $s(\cdot)$ such that

$$r_\theta(s) = r_\theta(s_p), \quad \text{all } \theta \in \Theta; \tag{*}$$

and if $s(\cdot)$ is a randomized decision rule, then there is a prerandomized decision rule s_p such that (*) holds. Show this for the special case $\Theta = \{\theta_1, \theta_2\}$, $\mathscr{D} = \{d_1, d_2\}$, $\mathscr{X} = \{x_1, x_2\}$ (where $\theta_1 \ne \theta_2$, $d_1 \ne d_2$, $x_1 \ne x_2$).

12.2H Investigate the conditions under which "randomized decision rules" and "pre-randomized decision rules" (see Problem 12.1H) are equivalent.

12.3H Let $(\Theta, \mathcal{D}, l)$, X be a statistical decision problem with Θ finite (i.e., $\Theta = \{\theta_1, \ldots, \theta_k\}$). Show that if the set S of risk points is bounded from below[7] and closed from below,[8] then the set of all decision rules $s(\cdot)$ such that

$$\left(r_{\theta_1}(s), \ldots, r_{\theta_k}(s)\right) \in \lambda(S)$$

is a minimal complete class. Hence, use Theorem 12.1.23 to deduce that this set of rules consists of precisely the admissible rules. Thus, justify the statement, provoked by Figure 9.4-3, that "admissible rules yield the 'lower boundary' of S."

12.4H A lot of $n = 1000$ items is received in a manufacturing facility. Out of the n items, an unknown number θ are defective and the other $n - \theta$ are good. A sample of size $c = 10$ is drawn at random without replacement, the number X of defectives in this sample is observed, and the lot is then either accepted (d_1) or rejected (d_2).

Defectives in the sample are returned for full credit, and good units in the sample are used in production. Unsampled defectives in an accepted lot cause a loss of $c_1 = 3$ each, and sampling costs $c_2 = 1$ per unit sampled. Hence, the loss due to accepting a lot is

$$c_1(\theta - X) + c_2 c.$$

Each good item returned costs a penalty of $c_3 = 2$ per unit. If a lot is rejected, good items in the sample are kept, only $1000 - (c - X)$ items being returned. Hence, the loss due to rejecting a lot is

$$c_3(1000 - (c - X) - \theta) + c_2 c.$$

(a) If the number of defectives θ in the lot has an a priori distribution that assigns probability

$$g(\theta) = \binom{n}{\theta}(.05)^{\theta}(.95)^{n-\theta}$$

to θ ($\theta = 0, 1, \ldots, 1000$), find the Bayes decision rule.

(b) If the number of defectives θ in the lot has an a priori distribution that assigns probability $g(\theta) = (1001)^{-1}$ to θ ($\theta = 0, 1, \ldots, 1000$), find the Bayes decision rule.

(c) Suppose that a decision rule is to specify both c (the size of the sample) and the decision to be made if a sample of size c is used and X defectives are found in that sample. Find the Bayes rule under the assumption of part **(a)**. Find the Bayes rule under the assumption of part **(b)**.

12.5H In one conventional formulation of statistical decision theory (that used in this chapter, which we will now call **formulation** $\mathcal{F}_1$) we observe $X = x$ and then

[7] $A \subseteq \mathcal{R}^k$ is **bounded from below** if there is a number M such that for every $y \in A$, $y_1 \geq M, \ldots, y_k \geq M$.

[8] A convex set $A \subseteq \mathcal{R}^k$ is **closed from below** if $\lambda(A) \subseteq A$, where $\lambda(A)$ consists of all x such that x is a limit point of A and

$$x = Q(x) \cap cl(A) = \{y : y \in \mathcal{R}^k, y_1 \leq x_1, \ldots, y_k \leq x_k\} \cap cl(A).$$

choose decision d with probability $s_d(x)$. The loss incurred is then some $W(\theta; d; x)$ [this generalizes Chapter 12 slightly; there it was assumed that $W(\theta; d; x) = l(\theta, d)$ was not a function of x]. If $f(x|\theta)$ denotes the $P_\theta[X = x]$ when X is discrete (and the corresponding density function when X is absolutely continuous) where θ is the true value of the unknown parameter, then the risk function of rule $s(\cdot)$ is

$$r_\theta(s) = \sum_x \sum_d W(\theta; d; x) f(x|\theta) s_d(x) \qquad (*)$$

(or a corresponding form with integrals).

In one nonconventional formulation of statistical decision theory (call it **formulation** $\mathscr{F}_2$) we observe $X = x$ and then choose decision d with probability $s_d(x)$, and we later observe that a further r.v. $Y = y$. The loss incurred is then some $W(y; d; x)$. If $f(x, y|\theta)$ denotes the $P_\theta[X = x, Y = y]$ when (X, Y) is a discrete r.v. (and the corresponding joint density function when (X, Y) is absolutely continuous) where θ is the true value of the unknown parameter, then the risk function of rule $s(\cdot)$ is

$$r_\theta(s) = \sum_x \sum_y \sum_d W(y; d; x) f(x, y|\theta) s_d(x) \qquad (**)$$

(or a corresponding form with integrals).

(a) A decision problem of type $\mathscr{F}_1$ is clearly also a decision problem of type $\mathscr{F}_2$ (simply take y to be θ). Prove that: *A decision problem of type $\mathscr{F}_2$ is also a decision problem of type $\mathscr{F}_1$* (i.e., given a decision problem stated in the terms of $\mathscr{F}_2$, show how to choose a loss function in $\mathscr{F}_1$ such that $r_\theta(s)$ will not depend on the formulation used: $(*) = (**)$).

(b) Suppose we have a decision problem of type $\mathscr{F}_1$ with $\Theta = \mathscr{D} = \{\mu: 0 \le \mu < +\infty\}$, X a $N(\theta, 1)$ r.v., and $W(\theta; d; x) = -(\theta - d)^3$. What is the best decision d? (There is a uniquely best decision in this problem.)

(c) Consider the following decision problem (which is stated in form $\mathscr{F}_2$). An automobile whose replacement cost is $20000 can be insured against theft for 1 year for $400. There are two possible decisions: to insure or not to insure. The unknown probability of the automobile being stolen during the year is denoted by θ. Before deciding on insurance, the number of automobiles that were stolen out of 5 automobiles, each with the same probability θ of being stolen, will be observed. If 1 of the 5 were stolen, which decision would be chosen by the Bayes decision rule with respect to a priori distribution $B(\theta)$ which sets $P[\theta \le x] = 1 - (1 - x)^3$ for $0 \le x \le 1$? [*Hint*:

$$\int_0^1 x^a (1 - x)^b \, dx = \frac{a! b!}{(a + b + 1)!}$$

for all positive integers a and b.]

(d) Express the decision problem of part (c) in formulation $\mathscr{F}_1$ (in particular, finding the appropriate loss function $W(\theta; d; x)$).

CHAPTER 13

Nonparametric Statistical Inference

Nonparametric statistics is the subfield of statistics that provides statistical inference procedures which rely on weaker assumptions about the underlying distribution(s) of the population(s) than do the ordinary (e.g., normal distribution) procedures for the same problems. Since such nonparametric procedures assume less about the underlying distribution(s), errors in correct assessment of the nature of the underlying distribution(s) will usually have less effect on nonparametric procedures than on parametric procedures (since the latter usually rely more heavily on the correct assessment of the nature of the underlying distribution(s)). However, the more information we have (and use well) about the underlying distribution(s), the better our statistical inference procedures will be; thus, for a given situation, a nonparametric procedure will usually be the one with greater variance (in point estimation), with less power (in hypothesis-testing), with wider intervals (in confidence interval estimation), with lower probability of correct selection (in ranking and selection), and with higher risk (in decision theory), when compared with a corresponding parametric procedure whose assumptions are not violated. Hence, it is usually advisable to use procedures that eliminate assumptions about the underlying distribution(s) only in so far as those assumptions are seriously doubtful in their validity. In this way, we capture the greatest gain from both the parametric and nonparametric approaches to a problem.

In previous chapters we have studied general methods that turn out to be useful in providing nonparametric inference procedures (such as order statistics or quantiles in Section 7.4) and will soon study others (such as the probability-integral transformation in Problem 13.1). Using these methods we can then study various sorts of decision problems (estimation, hypothesis-testing, confidence intervals, selection procedures, and so on) in more detail. This avoids the "bag of tricks" approach to nonparametric statistics, which leads to an unordered view of the subject.

13.1. NONPARAMETRIC CONFIDENCE INTERVALS

In Section 10.2 we found that if $X_1, \ldots, X_n$ are independent $N(\mu, \sigma^2)$ r.v.'s where μ is unknown with $\mu \in \Theta = \{x \colon -\infty < x < +\infty\}$, then a confidence interval for μ with confidence coefficient $1 - \alpha$ is

$$\left(\overline{X} - \frac{\sigma}{\sqrt{n}} \Phi^{-1}\left(1 - \frac{\alpha}{2}\right), \quad \overline{X} + \frac{\sigma}{\sqrt{n}} \Phi^{-1}\left(1 - \frac{\alpha}{2}\right) \right) \qquad (13.1.1)$$

if $\sigma^2 > 0$ is known, and

$$\left(\overline{X} - \frac{s}{\sqrt{n}} t_{n-1}^{-1}\left(1 - \frac{\alpha}{2}\right), \quad \overline{X} + \frac{s}{\sqrt{n}} t_{n-1}^{-1}\left(1 - \frac{\alpha}{2}\right) \right) \qquad (13.1.2)$$

if $\sigma^2 > 0$ is unknown. As we discussed in Example 7.4.22, while for the normal distribution the mean μ and the population median $\xi_{.5}$ coincide (i.e., $\mu = \xi_{.5}$), in general this is not the case and (in many instances) we then want a confidence interval on $\xi_{.5}$ (the point that "splits the population in half"; i.e., an observation is equally likely to fall above or below $\xi_{.5}$ if we are dealing with a continuous r.v.). **We will now develop a nonparametric interval for ξ_p $(0 < p < 1)$, and then** specialize to the case $p = .5$ in order to compare the nonparametric interval with the parametric ones, (13.1.1) and (13.1.2).

As in Definition 5.6.1, **for n r.v.'s $X_1, \ldots, X_n$ let $Y_1, \ldots, Y_n$ denote the ordered X_i's (i.e., the X_i's ordered so that $Y_1 \leq \cdots \leq Y_n$;** if several X_i's are equal, we can choose one at random for a place Y_i). Then **the sample quantile of order p $(0 < p < 1)$ is**

$$Z_p = Y_{[np]+1}, \qquad (13.1.3)$$

where $[np]$ denotes the largest integer $< np$. We now wish to determine the probability that ξ_p lies between Y_i and Y_j (with $1 \leq i < j \leq n$); if we can control this probability without knowing the distribution of the r.v.'s $X_1, \ldots, X_n$, then we may wish (Y_i, Y_j) (for some i, j) to be our confidence interval on ξ_p.

Theorem 13.1.4. Fix p $(0 < p < 1)$. Let $X_1, \ldots, X_n$ be independent r.v.'s with a continuous d.f. $F(x)$. Then for all i and j $(1 \leq i < j \leq n)$

$$P\left[Y_i \leq \xi_p \leq Y_j \right] = Q(i, j; p, n), \qquad (13.1.5)$$

where

$$Q(i, j; p, n) = \int_p^1 \int_0^p \frac{n!}{(i-1)!(j-i-1)!(n-j)!} \qquad (13.1.6)$$

$$\cdot s^{i-1}(t-s)^{j-i-1}(1-t)^{n-j} \, ds \, dt.$$

Proof: We have (for $1 \le i < j \le n$)

$$P\left[Y_i \le \xi_p \le Y_j\right] = P\left[F(Y_i) \le F(\xi_p) \le F(Y_j)\right]$$
$$= P\left[F(Y_i) \le p \le F(Y_j)\right] = P[S < p < T], \qquad (13.1.7)$$

where we have let $S \equiv F(Y_i)$ and $T \equiv F(Y_j)$. However, it can be shown (see Problem 13.1H) that the joint density function of S and T is

$$f_{S,T}(s, t) = \begin{cases} \dfrac{n!}{(i-1)!(j-i-1)!(n-j)!} \cdot \\ \qquad s^{i-1}(t-s)^{j-i-1}(1-t)^{n-j}, & \text{if } 0 \le s < t \le 1 \\ 0, & \text{otherwise.} \end{cases} \qquad (13.1.8)$$

Hence,

$$P[S < p < T] = \int_p^1 \int_0^p f_{S,T}(s, t)\, ds\, dt = Q(i, j; p, n) \qquad (13.1.9)$$

and the theorem follows. ∎

From Theorem 13.1.4 we immediately obtain the following.

Corollary 13.1.10. Fix p $(0 < p < 1)$. Let $X_1, \ldots, X_n$ be independent r.v.'s with an unknown, but continuous, d.f. Then (Y_i, Y_j) is a confidence interval for ξ_p with confidence coefficient $Q(i, j; p, n)$.

In fact, Corollary 13.1.10 holds even if the common d.f. of $X_1, \ldots, X_n$ is not continuous; however, in this case the confidence coefficient is $\ge Q(i, j; p, n)$ (see Problem 13.4H).

Corollary 13.1.11. Fix p $(0 < p < 1)$. Let $X_1, \ldots, X_n$ be independent r.v.'s with an unknown d.f. Then (Y_i, Y_j) is a confidence interval for ξ_p with confidence coefficient $\ge Q(i, j; p, n)$.

Rather than computing $Q(i, j; p, n)$ from (13.1.6), it is simpler to use the following expression.

Theorem 13.1.12. For $1 \le i < j \le n$ and $0 < p < 1$,

$$Q(i, j; p, n) = \sum_{k=i}^{j-1} \binom{n}{k} p^k (1-p)^{n-k}. \qquad (13.1.13)$$

Proof: By Problem 13.2,

$$Q(i, j; p, n) = P\left[U_i \le p \le U_j\right], \qquad (13.1.14)$$

where $U_1, \ldots, U_n$ are the order statistics in a sample of size n from a uniform distribution on $(0, 1)$. However (see Problem 13.3),

$$P[U_i \leq p \leq U_j] = 1 - P[U_i > p] - P[U_j < p]. \qquad (13.1.15)$$

Since for all l $(1 \leq l \leq n)$

$$P[U_l \leq p] = \sum_{k=l}^{n} \binom{n}{k} p^k (1 - p)^{n-k} \qquad (13.1.16)$$

(the event $\{U_l \leq p\}$ occurs iff at least l of the basic uniform r.v.'s on $(0, 1)$ are $\leq p$), the theorem follows on using (13.1.16) in (13.1.15). ∎

Example 13.1.17. If $p = .5$ and $n = 16$, then (using Table 5 to evaluate $Q(i, j; p, n)$ since Theorem 13.1.12 allows us to write $Q(i, j; p, n)$ as a sum of binomial probabilities) we find that

$$\begin{cases} P[Y_5 \leq \xi_{.5} \leq Y_{12}] = .9234, \\ P[Y_4 \leq \xi_{.5} \leq Y_{12}] = .9512, \\ P[Y_5 \leq \xi_{.5} \leq Y_{13}] = .9512; \end{cases} \qquad (13.1.18)$$

hence, if we desired a 95% confidence interval via a nonparametric method, we would use either (Y_4, Y_{12}) or (Y_5, Y_{13}), each of which has approximately 95% confidence (actually 95.12%). If we chose (Y_4, Y_{12}), our interval would have length

$$Y_{12} - Y_4, \qquad (13.1.19)$$

a r.v. If we instead used interval (13.1.1), we would have nonrandom length

$$.98\sigma, \qquad (13.1.20)$$

while interval (13.1.2) would have random length

$$1.07s. \qquad (13.1.21)$$

It would be of interest to compare the average lengths (13.1.19), (13.1.20), and (13.1.21) (Problem 13.5H); such a comparison shows that **we obtain longer intervals on the average with the nonparametric interval; as a compensation, we are protected against nonnormality of** $X_1, \ldots, X_n$. Thus, **the nonparametric interval should be used if (and only if) normality is subject to serious question in our experiment** (and we do not know what other distribution governs $X_1, \ldots, X_n$).

Example 13.1.22. In Problem 7.6 we gave $X_1, \ldots, X_{88}$, the first $n = 88$ seasonal snowfalls observed at Rochester, New York, since the 1884–85 winter. Find a nonparametric 95% confidence interval on the median snowfall. [*Note*: A similar question was considered in Problem 10.12(a) under the assumption of a normal distribution for amount of snowfall.]

Since ξ_p with $p = .5$ and $n = 88$ is of interest here, we wish to choose (Y_i, Y_j) to be our interval where

$$P\left[Y_i \le \xi_{.5} \le Y_j\right] = .95. \tag{13.1.23}$$

Since by Theorem 13.1.4 and Theorem 13.1.12

$$P\left[Y_i \le \xi_{.5} \le Y_j\right] = \sum_{k=i}^{j-1} \binom{n}{k} p^k (1-p)^{n-k}, \tag{13.1.24}$$

we may (in order to obtain (13.1.23)) try to set i and j so that

$$\begin{cases} P[\xi_{.5} > Y_j] = \sum_{k=j}^{n} \binom{n}{k} p^k (1-p)^{n-k} = .025 \\ P[\xi_{.5} < Y_i] = \sum_{k=0}^{i-1} \binom{n}{k} p^k (1-p)^{n-k} = .025; \end{cases} \tag{13.1.25}$$

that is, set i and j so that

$$\begin{cases} \sum_{k=j}^{88} \binom{88}{k} 2^{-88} = .025 \\ \sum_{k=0}^{i-1} \binom{88}{k} 2^{-88} = .025. \end{cases} \tag{13.1.26}$$

Although Table 5 does not go beyond $n = 20$ (and in fact most tables a student will find do not go beyond $n = 50$), extensive tables are available [*Tables of the Cumulative Binomial Probability Distribution*, Harvard University Press, Cambridge, Mass. (1955), where $n = 88$ occurs on p. 432] and yield

$$\begin{cases} \sum_{k=54}^{88} \binom{88}{k} 2^{-88} = .02111, \quad \sum_{k=53}^{88} \binom{88}{k} 2^{-88} = .03467 \\ \sum_{k=0}^{34} \binom{88}{k} 2^{-88} = .02111, \quad \sum_{k=0}^{35} \binom{88}{k} 2^{-88} = .03467. \end{cases} \tag{13.1.27}$$

Hence

$$P[Y_{35} \le \xi_{.5} \le Y_{54}] = .95778. \tag{13.1.28}$$

By reference to the data $X_1, \ldots, X_{88}$ in Problem 7.6, we find $Y_{35} = 69.2$ and $Y_{54} = 79.3$, whence with 95.8% confidence we state that the median snowfall in Rochester, New York, is between 69.2 inches and 79.3 inches.

Remark 13.1.29. Note that if the binomial distribution tables needed in Example 13.1.22 had not been available, we would have used a normal approximation.

We leave it as an exercise for you to do so in Example 13.1.22 and compare the results with the exact ones given in that example.

Example 13.1.30. A problem often solved by Monte Carlo methods (discussed briefly in Section 4.7) is **estimation of a percentile point** ξ_p **of a r.v.** Z for some p ($0 < p < 1$). If Z has a continuous d.f. $F(z)$, then (see Definition 7.4.19) ξ_p is a point such that $F(\xi_p) = P(Z \le \xi_p) = p$. If $Z_1, \ldots, Z_N$ is a random sample from $F(z)$ and $Z_{(1)}, \ldots, Z_{(N)}$ denote the order statistics in increasing order, then (see Corollary 13.1.10) (for any integers $1 \le r < s \le N$) we find that

$$P\left[Z_{(r)} < \xi_p < Z_{(s)}\right] = \sum_{k=r}^{s-1} \binom{N}{k} p^k (1-p)^{N-k}$$

$$\approx P[V \le s - 1 + 0.5] - P[V \le r - 0.5] \quad (13.1.31)$$

$$= \Phi\left(\frac{s - 1 + 0.5 - Np}{\sqrt{Np(1-p)}}\right) - \Phi\left(\frac{r - 0.5 - Np}{\sqrt{Np(1-p)}}\right),$$

where: V is a normal random variable with mean Np and variance $Np(1 - p)$; Φ denotes the standard normal distribution function; and we have used a normal approximation (with continuity correction) to the binomial sum. To make this probability .95 (and hence find a 95% confidence interval for ξ_p), one may set the last two terms on the right side equal to .975 and .025, respectively, which implies

$$\begin{cases} s - 1 + 0.5 = 1.96\sqrt{Np(1-p)} + Np \\ r - 0.5 = -1.96\sqrt{Np(1-p)} + Np. \end{cases} \quad (13.1.32)$$

Here, r and s need not be integers, and if we simply replace them by $[r]$ and $[s]$, respectively (where $[x]$ denotes the largest integer $\le x$), then the confidence coefficient of our interval on ξ_p may drop below .95. Hence we set

$$\hat{s} = [s] + 1 = \left[1.96\sqrt{Np(1-p)} + Np + 1 + 0.5\right]$$

$$\hat{r} = [r] = \left[-1.96\sqrt{Np(1-p)} + Np + 0.5\right]$$

and (up to the normal approximation adequacy) obtain

$$P\left[Z_{(\hat{r})} < \xi_p < Z_{(\hat{s})}\right] = \sum_{k=r}^{\hat{s}-1} \binom{N}{k} p^k (1-p)^{N-k} \ge .95.$$

Thus, after observing $Z_1, \ldots, Z_N$ we estimate their distribution's pth quantile ξ_p by $Z_{([Np])}$ and assess the precision of the Monte Carlo estimate by giving the interval $(Z_{(\hat{r})}, Z_{(\hat{s})})$ as an (at least) 95% confidence interval on ξ_p.

In Monte Carlo studies, one wishes to use random numbers $X_1, \ldots, X_n$. **A test for the hypothesis of randomness** of $X_1, \ldots, X_n$ was studied by Dudewicz and van der Meulen (1981): Given a random sample $X_1, \ldots, X_n$ ($n \geq 3$) from an absolutely continuous density $f(\cdot)$, let $Y_1 \leq Y_2 \leq \cdots \leq Y_n$ denote the order statistics and define $Y_i = Y_1$ if $i < 1$, $Y_i = Y_n$ if $i > n$. Their test statistic was

$$H(m, n) = \frac{1}{n} \sum_{i=1}^{n} \left\{ \log \frac{n}{2m} (Y_{i+m} - Y_{i-m}) \right\}, \qquad (13.1.33)$$

where m is any positive integer smaller than $n/2$. Their test rejects the hypothesis of uniformity on $(0, 1)$ if $H(m, n)$ is small:

$$\text{Reject if } H(m, n) \leq H^*(m, n) \qquad (13.1.34)$$

where $H^*(m, n)$ is to be chosen so that the test has level of significance p.

Since the exact distribution of test statistic (13.1.33) is very complex even under the null hypothesis (of uniformity on $(0, 1)$), a Monte Carlo study was run. For example, consider the case $n = 10$ (i.e., where we will be testing whether 10 values $X_1, \ldots, X_{10}$ are uniform on $(0, 1)$). Dudewicz and van der Meulen generated $N = 10,000$ samples of $n = 10$ random numbers each, and for each such sample calculated the test statistic with $m = 4$. Then to estimate the $H^*(4, 10)$ needed for a level p test of uniformity, one should take $Z_{(j)}$ with $j = 10000p$; for example, for a level .05 test we estimate that $H^*(4, 10) = Z_{(500)} = -.773908$ (by reference to the original paper, we find that the 500th-from-smallest value of the test statistics that were generated in their study was $-.773908$ in order to find this result). We use equations (13.1.32) and (13.1.31) to find a 95% confidence interval for $H^*(4, 10)$ as $(Z_{(457)}, Z_{(544)})$; from the reference we have this interval $= (-.786353, -.761449)$. Thus, the critical point to use is (with an error of $\pm .01$) $H^*(4, 10) = -.77$.

Example 13.1.35. In Theorem 13.1.14, we gave a confidence interval for the pth quantile ξ_p of a continuous d.f. based on a random sample $X_1, \ldots, X_n$; the confidence $Q(i, j; p, n)$ of the interval was evaluated in Theorem 13.1.12. Such intervals are also of interest **when sampling from a finite population. Suppose we have a sample of size n taken at random without replacement** from a finite population of N items, each item having a distinct value of the characteristic of interest. Let $X_1, X_2, \ldots, X_n$ denote the sample values, and $Y_1 < Y_2 < \cdots < Y_n$ their ordered values; note that $Y_i \neq Y_j$ for all $i \neq j$ since there are n distinct values in the population and sampling is without replacement.

Denote the N distinct values in the population by

$$x_{01} < x_{02} < x_{03} < \cdots < x_{0N}. \qquad (13.1.36)$$

Then the probability function of Y_k, the kth order statistic, is

$$P(Y_k = x_{0t}) = \frac{\binom{t-1}{k-1}\binom{N-t}{n-k}}{\binom{N}{n}} \qquad \text{for } t = k, k+1, \ldots, N-n+k.$$

$$(13.1.37)$$

This is so since the denominator is the number of ways to select n items from N without replacement; the numerator is the number of ways to end up with a sample in which x_{0t} is the kth order statistic (i.e., the number of ways to draw a sample with $k - 1$ items from the $t - 1$ that are smaller than x_{0t}, draw x_{0t}, and draw $n - k$ items from the $N - t$ that are larger than x_{0t}; and t must be between k and $N - n + k$ since when drawing n items the kth ranking must be at least as large as the kth in the whole population, and cannot be larger than the $N - n + k$th in the population (since we know there are $n - k$ larger than it in the sample). Note that (3.1.37) is a hypergeometric distribution (see Definition 3.2.7), and (from Section 3.3) we know that the hypergeometric approaches the binomial.

Therefore, one might think that (Y_i, Y_j) would furnish a confidence interval for $x_{0, Np}$ with confidence close to $Q(i, j; p, n)$, and it can be shown that this is true for large N in the sense that

$$\lim_{N \to \infty} P(Y_i < x_{0, Np} < Y_j) = Q(i, j; p, n). \tag{13.1.38}$$

This allows us to obtain (approximate) confidence intervals for the pth quantile of a finite population.

For example, using the calculations in Example 13.1.22, if we have a finite population of N items and take a sample of $n = 88$ without replacement at random, then (Y_{35}, Y_{54}) will be approximately a 95% confidence interval for the median value in the population.

PROBLEMS FOR SECTION 13.1

13.1.1 (a) Let $X_1, X_2, \ldots, X_{10}$ be a random sample of size 10 from an exponential distribution with mean λ. Give a 90% confidence interval for the 40th percentile, $\xi_{.40}$. [*Hint:* See Corollary 13.1.10.]

(b) If, in fact, the sample observed in part (a) is as listed below, compute the 90% confidence interval for $\xi_{.40}$.

$$1, 1.2, 3.6, 4.8, 2.3, 1.9, 6.1, 3.2, 3.1, 1.3.$$

13.1.2 (a) Suppose a student takes a nationally administered examination and the student's grade is reported as a percentile, for example the 90th percentile, but the actual numerical score $\xi_{.90}$ is not given. If the student obtains 20 random scores of persons who took the examination, based on this information how can the student find a 95% confidence interval for $\xi_{.90}$?

(b) If, in fact, 200 scores (instead of 20) are collected randomly, describe the procedure for computing a 95% confidence interval for $\xi_{.90}$.

13.1.3 (a) Along the lines of Section 13.1, develop a one-sided $100(1 - \alpha)\%$ upper confidence limit for ξ_p, $0 < p < 1$, where ξ_p is the $100p$th percentile point of a continuous distribution from which we have a random sample of size n.

(b) Similarly for a lower confidence limit.

13.2. NONPARAMETRIC TESTING OF QUANTILES ξ_p

In this chapter we have found it convenient to alter our usual order of presentation (point estimation; hypothesis-testing; confidence intervals; ranking and selection; decision theory) slightly. **nonparametric point estimation** was already covered through a discussion of the properties of a nonparametric estimator of $\xi_{.50}$ in Chapter 7 (Example 7.4.22); this is indicative, and nonparametric point estimation will not be discussed further here. We have considered **nonparametric confidence intervals** already (Section 13.1) and will now consider **nonparametric hypothesis-testing**, which divides into problems of two types (for numerical and ordinal data, respectively, in Sections 13.2 and 13.3). (**Nonparametric ranking and selection** was covered briefly in Section 11.4, part 5; see the references for details. **Nonparametric decision theory** has received a great impetus in recent years through work such as that of T. S. Ferguson [e.g., see Ferguson (1973)], but that work is beyond the scope of this book.)

Since (see Corollary 13.1.10) (Y_i, Y_j) is a confidence interval for ξ_p with confidence coefficient $Q(i, j; p, n)$, by the relation given in Chapter 10 between tests of hypotheses and confidence intervals (see Theorem 10.1.5), it follows (see problem 13.5) that **to test the hypothesis H_0 that ξ_p equals a specified value ξ_p^0 at level $1 - Q(i, j; p, n)$ we simply accept H_0 if $Y_i \leq \xi_p^0 \leq Y_j$ and reject H_0 otherwise.**

Example 13.2.1. Since (see Example 13.1.17) in a sample of size $n = 16$ the interval (Y_4, Y_{12}) is a 95.12% confidence interval for $\xi_{.5}$, we can obtain a level $.0488 \approx .05$ test of the hypothesis that $\xi_{.5} = 24.62$ (or any other number of interest) as follows: Form the confidence interval (Y_4, Y_{12}) on $\xi_{.5}$ and

$$\begin{cases} \text{Accept the hypothesis } \xi_{.5} = 24.62, & \text{if } Y_4 \leq 24.62 \leq Y_{12} \\ \text{Reject the hypothesis } \xi_{.5} = 24.62, & \text{otherwise.} \end{cases} \quad (13.2.2)$$

PROBLEMS FOR SECTION 13.2

13.2.1 Based on the data given in Problem 13.1.1, at level of significance .10 test the hypothesis H_0: $\xi_{.40} = 2.0$ versus H_1: $\xi_{.40} \neq 2.0$.

13.2.2 Suppose a random sample of 12 basketball players yields weights: 178, 165, 186, 174, 190, 188, 205, 210, 181, 189, 178, 180. At level of significance .05, test H_0: $\xi_{.5} = 185$ versus H_1: $\xi_{.5} < 185$.

13.2.3 In Problem 13.2.2, test the hypothesis H_0: $\xi_{.75} = 200$ versus H_1: $\xi_{.75} > 200$, at level .10.

13.2.4 In the setting of Problem 13.2.2, construct an 85% upper confidence bound for $\xi_{.5}$. In the same setting, construct an 80% lower confidence bound for $\xi_{.25}$.

13.3. NONPARAMETRIC TESTS FOR ORDINAL DATA

Many of the situations we have dealt with thus far have been ones in which the r.v.'s of interest are observed directly, and hence situations that lend themselves to parametric analysis (if we are able to specify the underlying distribution as a member of a certain family of distributions characterized by one or more parameters; e.g., the normal distributions $N(\mu, \sigma^2)$ characterized by the mean μ and variance σ^2). However, **situations also arise where the basic r.v.'s are not able to be observed directly, but rather, we can only obtain information about their order among a certain set of r.v.'s.** This is the situation of *ordinal* (as opposed to *numerical*) data, and lends itself very naturally to a nonparametric analysis. (In a sense, we could say that the natural parametric analysis is nonparametric!) **Since we can always replace numerical data by their ranks, the following treatment can be used for numerical data as well** (and this may be appropriate in some situations where little is known about the distribution of the data).

Although there are many ways in which ordinal data can arise, we will cover just one (the one that leads to the **sign test**); once the principles that govern this are understood, the multiplicity of tests available for different ways in which ordinal data can arise are easily accessible. Finally, we will cover tests that require that numerical data be ordinalized before it is analyzed (this results in a need for fewer distributional assumptions on the underlying distribution(s)), and will illustrate this class of tests with the **Mann-Whitney-Wilcoxon test**.

Consider the situation where two objects A and B are presented to a judge selected at random from a pool of possible judges, who states his preference according to certain well-defined criteria. [For example, in a marketing test of a new product, or an old product being marketed in a new way or in a new area, the brand of interest (say brand A) is often presented to a consumer along with a competitor (say brand B); the consumer then states which brand he prefers.] Thus, we can regard the situation as one where the basic data is **ordinal**: the judge simply orders the two alternatives (e.g., says "I prefer A to B" in the marketing example). If we define a r.v. X_1 to be 0 if A is preferred to B and 1 if B is preferred to A, then X_1 is a binomial r.v. (see Definition 3.2.3) with $n = 1$ and p equal to the probability that B is preferred to A. If we wish to test the composite null hypothesis that $p \le .1$ against the composite alternative that $p > .1$ (the alternative says brand B is preferred by more than 10% of the population of interest), we could ask n judges independently, thus obtaining $X_1, \ldots, X_n$, and reject H_0 if $\overline{X}$ is "large." More precisely,

Theorem 13.3.1. For the hypothesis-testing problem with $X = (X_1, \ldots, X_n)$ where $X_1, \ldots, X_n$ are independent r.v.'s, each binomial with one trial and success probability p where p $(0 \le p \le 1)$ is unknown, $H_0 = \{ p: p \le p_0 \}$, and $H_1 = \{ p: p > p_0 \}$ with p_0 fixed $(0 < p_0 < 1)$, the test that rejects iff

$$X_1 + \cdots + X_n \ge j \qquad (13.3.2)$$

has level

$$\sum_{k=j}^{n} \binom{n}{k}(p_0)^k (1 - p_0)^{n-k}. \tag{13.3.3}$$

Proof: The probability that the given test rejects H_0 is

$$P_p[X_1 + \cdots + X_n \geq j] = \sum_{k=j}^{n} \binom{n}{k} p^k (1 - p)^{n-k}. \tag{13.3.4}$$

For all $p \leq p_0$, (13.3.4) is largest when $p = p_0$ (see Problem 10.19), and the result follows by the definition of level of significance in the case of a composite null hypothesis (see Problem 9.4H): the largest of the levels attained for any simple $H_0' \in H_0$. ∎

It is clear that we can specify the n needed for a specified level and power in Theorem 13.3.1; see Problem 13.6, for example. **The situation studied in Theorem 13.3.1 can also arise as follows.** Suppose n individuals each test two treatments (A, B) and return respective numerical values on them of V_i and W_i ($i = 1, \ldots, n$). If we let $D_i = W_i - V_i$ ($i = 1, \ldots, n$) and finally set

$$X_i = \begin{cases} 1, & \text{if } D_i \geq 0 \\ 0, & \text{if } D_i < 0 \end{cases} \tag{13.3.5}$$

($i = 1, \ldots, n$), then Theorem 13.3.1 can be used to test hypotheses about $p = P[X_i = 1] = P[D_i \geq 0] = P[W_i - V_i \geq 0] = P[W_i \geq V_i]$, namely about the probability that W_i exceeds V_i (if the "individuals" are agricultural plots and the "treatments" are two wheat varieties, we are dealing with hypotheses on the probability that variety B will have a higher yield than variety A). **Since in this type of example we simply see whether $W_i - V_i$ is positive $(+)$ or negative $(-)$ in each individual, the test of Theorem 13.3.1 has come to be called the *sign test*.** If we have only ordinal data, this is the natural parametric test. If, in fact, we observe W_i, V_i and only look at whether $W_i \geq V_i$, we have discarded some information in order to dispense with the need to know the distributions of W_i and V_i. This is often appropriate. On the other hand, if we know the distributions to be, say, normal and follow such a procedure, then our efficiency (in terms of the ratio n_1/n_2 of the respective sample sizes n_1 and n_2 needed for a specified level and power of the t-test and of the sign test) will be approximately 95% if $n = 4$, 5, or 6 and decreases as n increases (e.g., it is approximately 75% for $n = 13$).[1]

Now we wish to consider, as a final topic in this section, cases in which numerical data are ordinalized, our illustration being what is called the Mann-Whitney-Wilcoxon test. Suppose that we have available some number N of subjects, of whom s will be selected at random to receive a new treatment while

[1] See Walsh (1946) for details of the comparison.

the other $t = N - s$ receive a standard treatment (e.g., for a type of heart disease). (Although much data may be available on patients on whom the "standard" treatment was used in the past, results often differ substantially from one population of patients to another and over time, and the "standard" treatment may not be the same today as it was a year ago. Hence, if we wish to make sure we are comparing results of the "new" and "standard" treatments, and not time- or population-dependent changes, it will usually be necessary to have some number $N - s$ of the patients receive the "standard" treatment while the other s receive the "new" treatment. This is called **controlled experimentation**, and the $N - s$ patients are called the **control group**.) If the responses of the s "new" treatment patients are $Y_1, \ldots, Y_s$ while the responses of the t "standard" treatment patients are $X_1, \ldots, X_t$, we will want to know whether the "new" treatment has changed the response (e.g., the X_i's and Y_j's could be survival times of patients after treatment). Although it may be a tenable assumption that $X_1, \ldots, X_t, Y_1, \ldots, Y_s$ are independent r.v.'s, they are probably not known to have a normal (or other specified) distribution; hence, a method of testing the null hypothesis that the X_i's and Y_j's have the same d.f. is desired that does not assume a specific (say, normal) distribution for $X_1, \ldots, X_t, Y_1, \ldots, Y_s$. Such a method can be given as follows. Consider all $N = s + t$ observations ordered in increasing numerical order. Replace the smallest by the value 1, the next to smallest by $2, \ldots$, the largest by $s + t$. Let the value by which X_i or Y_j is replaced be denoted by $R(X_i)$ or $R(Y_s)$, respectively. Let

$$W_X = R(X_1) + \cdots + R(X_t), \quad W_Y = R(Y_1) + \cdots + R(Y_s). \quad (13.3.6)$$

[*Note*: $W_X + W_Y = 1 + 2 + \cdots + N = N(N + 1)/2$.] Then W_Y will tend to be "large" if the new treatment has increased survival times. Hence, we may decide to reject the null hypothesis iff

$$W_Y \geq c. \quad (13.3.7)$$

In order to set c so that we have a level α test, we will need to know the distribution of W_Y when in fact (H_0) the standard and new treatments lead to the same survival time distribution. However, in that case all $s + t$ observations are equally likely to have any specified rank in the pooled observations; hence, since there are $\binom{N}{s}$ equally likely ways to assign ranks to the Y_j's, the $P_{H_0}[W_Y \geq c]$ equals the number of such ways that lead to a rank sum of at least c, divided by the total number of ways to assign ranks to the Y_j's:

$$P_{H_0}[W_Y \geq c] = \frac{\#(W_Y \geq c)}{\binom{N}{s}}. \quad (13.3.8)$$

Example 13.3.9. A new treatment for increasing egg production has been proposed by a poultry scientist. To test this treatment, it is applied to 7 hens while 7 others receive a similar-looking placebo. (In fact, the experiment is run double-blind.) After a period of time, the following egg yields are observed to have occurred:

i	1	2	3	4	5	6	7
Treatment Y_i	260	248	240	245	255	258	220
Control X_i	230	227	242	244	261	250	265

Does a Mann-Whitney-Wilcoxon test at level .05 accept or reject the hypothesis that the treatment has no beneficial effect?

Here the ranked data are in the order of

Observations	$Y_7 < X_2 < X_1 < Y_3 < X_3 < X_4 < Y_4 < Y_2 < X_6 < Y_5 < Y_6 < Y_1 < X_5 < X_7$
Ranks	$1 \quad 2 \quad 3 \quad 4 \quad 5 \quad 6 \quad 7 \quad 8 \quad 9 \quad 10 \quad 11 \quad 12 \quad 13 \quad 14$

where we have italicized (in boldface) the ranks of the Y_j's. Hence, $W_Y = 67$ (and $W_X = 38$, $W_X + W_Y = 105 = 1 + 2 + \cdots + 14 = 14(15)/2$). Here, we can show (Problem 13.7) that

$$P_{H_0}(W_Y \geq 65) = .064, \quad P_{H_0}(W_Y \geq 66) = .049. \quad (13.3.10)$$

Hence, at level .05 (which is not exactly, but only approximately, attainable) the Mann-Whitney-Wilcoxon test rejects the hypothesis that the treatment has no beneficial effect.

Extensive tables of the critical values and related probabilities of the Mann-Whitney-Wilcoxon test are available [e.g., see the reference cited in Problem 13.9H, pp. 272–282, or Gibbons (1985), pp. 421–428.] However, such tables typically do not allow for cases other than small s and t (such as $s \leq 10$ and $t \leq 10$). A good approximation can, however, be obtained by using a normal approximation to the standardized W_Y, using the fact that when the null hypothesis is true

$$E(W_Y) = s(N + 1)/2, \quad \text{Var}(W_Y) = st(N + 1)/12.$$

Unlike the situation with parametric tests (but rather typical of the situation with nonparametric tests), **the power of the test is hard to get at**: under what alternative are we to calculate this power? Comparisons of power as well as of level can be done under specific parametric alternative hypotheses. There computations show that the efficiency of the Mann-Whitney-Wilcoxon test relative to the t-test for normal alternatives is asymptotically (as $\min(s, t) \to \infty$) $3/\pi \approx .96$, and for all shift alternatives is $\geq .864$. Thus, in the normal case (where we should use the t-test) we are essentially discarding 4% ($= 100 - 96$) of our sample by using the Mann-Whitney-Wilcoxon test; and for some nonnormal alternatives we can be essentially discarding 14% ($= 100 - 86$) of our sample by using the Mann-Whitney-Wilcoxon test instead of the t-test. However, for other types of alternatives the Mann-Whitney-Wilcoxon test can be substantially better than the t-test. Thus, our recommendation is still as before: **If you know you have a normal (or some other specific parametric) distribution for your data, use a parametric procedure; in cases of severe doubt, consider nonparametric procedures.** (The borderline between these two cases is ill-defined, in fact a matter of dispute, and we will not attempt to define it here.)

Historical Note. The origin of the word "non-parametric" (now usually not hyphenated) is attributed to Jacob Wolfowitz in a paper in the 1942 volume of the *Annals of Mathematical Statistics* (now called the *Annals of Statistics*), with an explanation that **parametric** procedures signify those where one makes the assumption that distributions have known form (with a finite number of unknown parameters), whereas **nonparametric** procedures are those that do not require such assumptions. In the 1940s, nonparametric often meant "shortcuts for well-established parametric methods" to many, whereas in the 1950s, it was taken to mean "quick and inefficient methods that are wasteful of information." In the 1960s, the area outgrew its early confines and seemed to be hardly differentiable from parametric statistics at all; by the 1970s, it was recognized (as noted in the introduction to this chapter) as the science of providing statistical inference procedures that rely on weaker assumptions about underlying distributions than do the "more traditional (e.g., normal distribution)" procedures for the same problem. Whereas much of the early work was involved with testing of hypotheses (even to the point of obsession), today the field has expanded into all areas of statistics. Current work is heavily involved with such areas as robustness (see Chapter 15), as well as with all other areas of statistics.

The best **current definition of nonparametric statistics** seems to be that of Gibbons (1985), p. 23, that a statistical technique is called nonparametric if it satisfies at least one of the following five criteria:

1. The data are **count data** of number of observations in each category (or cross-category) [e.g., numbers of successes in treating 20 cancer patients with each of $k = 6$ therapies].
2. The data are **nominal scale** data [e.g., hair color].
3. The data are **ordinal scale** data [e.g., taste desirability of a product noted as 1, 2, 3, 4, or 5].
4. The **inference does not concern a parameter** [e.g., an inference about whether a set of numbers are random on $(0, 1)$].
5. The **assumptions are general** rather than specific [e.g., the assumption of a continuous population distribution].

We would call categories 1, 2, 3, and 4 **naturally nonparametric**, whereas category 5 is **arbitrarily nonparametric** (or artificially nonparametric), since "generality" of assumptions is a matter on which statisticians will disagree (since this is a matter of judgment for which precise criteria are not established). Even for categories such as category 1 (count data), the relatively recent development of log-linear models (where asymptotics are used to justify a normality assumption) may blur the distraction as **parametric procedures are now being developed for naturally nonparametric problems.**

PROBLEMS FOR SECTION 13.3

13.3.1 The sign test can be used to test hypotheses about percentile points of a distribution, for example, H_0: $\xi_p = \xi_0$.

Let $X_1, X_2, \ldots, X_n$ be a random sample of size n from a continuous distribution function $F(x)$ with $100p$th percentile point ξ_p. Test the hypothesis as follows: Define $\psi(x) = 1$ if $x \leq 0$ (and $= 0$ otherwise), and let $Z_i = \psi(X_i - \xi_p)$, $i = 1, 2, \ldots, n$, and $T = Z_1 + Z_2 + \cdots + Z_n$. Note that, under H_0, T is a binomial r.v. with parameters n and p. Use this information to test H_0: $\xi_p = \xi_0$ versus H_1: $\xi_p > \xi_0$ at level .05.

13.3.2 Suppose 8 pairs of twins are randomly chosen. At age 6, one child from each pair is chosen at random and sent to public school, whereas the other twin is sent to a private school. A year later, all the children are given the same test of academic skills supposed to be learned in the school. Suppose the scores are:

Twin Pair Number	1	2	3	4	5	6	7	8
Private	65	69	85	95	96	78	82	76
Public	68	58	84	98	90	75	86	78

Let $p = P\ [X > Y]$ where (X, Y) is the score pair for a set of twins. Test the hypothesis that the $p = .50$ at level .05. [*Hint*: Use the sign test.]

13.3.3 Suppose measurements of blood cholesterol level are taken in randomly chosen children of age 10 in two countries (A and B, say), and yield the data

A	140	180	155	170	210	208	150	195
B	190	180	175	185	200	250	205	

Based on this data, at level .05, is there enough evidence to reject the hypothesis that country A and country B have the same distribution for cholesterol level among their 10-year-old children? [*Hint*: Use the Mann-Whitney-Wilcoxon test.]

13.4. TESTS FOR DISTRIBUTION FUNCTIONS; TESTS OF NORMALITY

The empiric distribution function estimates the underlying true distribution function, and in Chapter 6 we saw that the empiric distribution function converges to the true d.f. In this section we develop techniques for **deciding if a**

random sample is from a prespecified d.f.; in particular, whether a random sample is from a **normal distribution** is a case of great practical importance.

We also develop a procedure for testing **whether two separate sets of data have the same d.f.** [Kolmogorov and Smirnov originally developed these statistical procedures using the maximum vertical distance between the d.f.'s (either one empiric and one theoretical, or both empiric) as a measure of "distance" between the d.f.'s.]

Kolmogorov-Smirnov Test: One Sample Case.   Let $X_1, X_2, \ldots, X_n$ be a random sample of size n from a population with unknown d.f. $F(x)$. Let $F_0(x)$ be a completely specified d.f. Our goal is to test

$$H_0: F(x) = F_0(x) \quad \text{for all } x, \text{ vs. } H_1: F(x) \not\equiv F_0(x).$$

Kolmogorov and Smirnov suggested computing the empiric d.f. $F_n(x)$ based on the data $X_1, X_2, \ldots, X_n$, and then considering the statistic

$$D_n = \sup_x |F_n(x) - F_0(x)| \tag{13.4.1}$$

as a measure of agreement between the empiric and theorized d.f.'s. Note that D_n **is the maximum vertical distance between the empiric d.f.** $F_n(x)$ **and the hypothesized d.f.** $F_0(x)$, and [since $F_n(x)$ is a step function] **occurs at or just before a jump point of** $F_n(x)$ (which greatly simplifies the computation of D_n).

We have shown earlier that $F_n(x) \xrightarrow{P} F_0(x)$ for every x, and, moreover, the Glivenko-Cantelli Theorem shows that $F_n(x)$ converges strongly to $F_0(x)$. Thus, under H_0, D_n is expected to be small (as $n \to \infty$, $D_n \to 0$), and $F_n(x)$ resembles $F_0(x)$ more and more with increasing n. It can be shown that

Theorem 13.4.2.   Under H_0, for $t > 0$,

$$\lim_{n \to \infty} P\left(\sqrt{n}\, D_n \le t\right) = 1 - 2\sum_{i=1}^{\infty} (-1)^{i-1} e^{-2i^2 t^2}. \tag{13.4.3}$$

The **Kolmogorov-Smirnov test then rejects H_0 at level α if $D_n > d_{n,\alpha}$**, where $d_{n,\alpha}$ is such that

$$P_{H_0}(D_n > d_{n,\alpha}) = \alpha. \tag{13.4.4}$$

Use of Theorem 13.4.2 yields the asymptotic critical points

α	.01	.05	.10
$d_{n;\alpha}$	$1.63/\sqrt{n}$	$1.36/\sqrt{n}$	$1.22/\sqrt{n}$

$(13.4.5)$

[Exact values of $d_{n,\alpha}$ are available, for $n \le 40$, in Gibbons (1985), p. 400. The exact values differ little from the asymptotic values unless n is very small.]

Note that this procedure can be used to test $H_0: \{F(x) \text{ is } N(\mu, \sigma^2)\}$ where μ and σ^2 are **known**. In particular, we can thus test for a $N(0,1)$ distribution. **In**

practice, μ and σ^2 are usually not known. A modified Kolmogorov-Smirnov procedure for this case, developed by Lilliefors (1967), will be discussed next.

Lilliefors Test for Normality. Let $X_1, X_2, \ldots, X_n$ be a random sample of size n from a population with unknown d.f. $F(x)$. Our goal is to test whether $F(\cdot)$ is $N(\mu, \sigma^2)$ for any μ and σ^2, that is,

$$H_0: F(x) = \Phi\left(\frac{x - \mu}{\sigma}\right) \text{ vs. } H_1: F(x) \neq \Phi\left(\frac{x - \mu}{\sigma}\right), \qquad (13.4.6)$$

where $\Phi(\cdot)$ is the standard normal d.f. **The Lilliefors test** "standardizes" the data set using estimates of μ and σ, forming $Z_1, Z_2, \ldots, Z_n$ with $Z_i = (X_i - \bar{X})/s$ where $\bar{X} = (X_1 + X_2 + \cdots + X_n)/n$ and $s^2 = \sum_{i=1}^{n} (X_i - \bar{X})^2/(n - 1)$. Let $F_n(z)$ be the empiric d.f. of the $Z_1, Z_2, \ldots, Z_n$. Lilliefors' **test statistic** is

$$D_n^* = \sup_z |F_n(z) - \Phi(z)|. \qquad (13.4.7)$$

To test H_0 vs. H_1 of (13.4.6) at level α, reject H_0 if $D_n^* > d_{n,\alpha}^*$, where $d_{n,\alpha}^*$ is such that

$$P_{H_0}(D_n^* > d_{n,\alpha}^*) = \alpha. \qquad (13.4.8)$$

The asymptotic critical points are

α	.01	.05	.10
$d_{n,\alpha}^*$	$1.031/\sqrt{n}$	$.886/\sqrt{n}$	$.805/\sqrt{n}$

$\qquad (13.4.9)$

[The exact $d_{n,\alpha}^*$, for various n and α, is tabulated in Lilliefors (1967). The exact values differ little from the asymptotic unless n is very small.]

Example 13.4.10. Suppose the number of accidents in a certain area of a city is recorded for 8 weeks as 2, 0, 1, 0, 3, 4, 3, 2. Test H_0: $F(x)$ is Poisson with mean 1.5, versus H_1: $F(x)$ is not Poisson with mean 1.5, where $F(\cdot)$ is the true d.f. of the data. (Use level of significance .05.)

Here, since $F_0(x)$ is specified fully, the **Kolmogorov-Smirnov test** is appropriate. The empiric d.f. is

$$F_n(x) = \begin{cases} .0, & x < 0 \\ .25, & 0 \leq x < 1 \\ .375, & 1 \leq x < 2 \\ .625, & 2 \leq x < 3 \\ .875, & 3 \leq x < 4 \\ 1.0, & 4 \leq x \end{cases}$$

and (see Table 7) a Poisson r.v. with mean 1.5 has d.f.

$$
F_0(x) = \begin{cases}
.0, & x < 0 \\
.2231, & 0 \le x < 1 \\
.5578, & 1 \le x < 2 \\
.8088, & 2 \le x < 3 \\
.9343, & 3 \le x < 4 \\
.9814, & 4 \le x < 5 \\
.9955, & 5 \le x < 6 \\
.9990, & 6 \le x < 7 \\
.9998, & 7 \le x < 8 \\
.9999, & 8 \le x < 9 \\
\vdots &
\end{cases}
$$

Hence we have differences as tabled below:

Range of x	$F_n(x)$	$F_0(x)$	$\lvert F_n(x) - F_0(x) \rvert$
$(-\infty, 0)$	.0	.0	.0000
$[0, 1)$	.25	.2231	.0269
$[1, 2)$	.375	.5578	.1828
$[2, 3)$	.625	.8088	.1838
$[3, 4)$	.875	.9343	.0593
$[4, 5)$	1.0	.9814	.0186
$[5, 6)$	1.0	.9955	.0045
$[6, \infty)$	1.0	$\ge .9990$	$\le .0010$

The largest difference (which is underscored in the table for ease of reference) is .1838. Thus, $D_n = \sup_x |F_n(x) - F_0(x)| = .1838$. Based on a sample of size $n = 8$, the asymptotic critical point at level .05 is [see (13.4.5)] $d_{8,.05} = .481$ [from Gibbons (1985) the exact value is .454]. Hence $D_8 = .1838 < .481 = d_{8,.05}$ and we do not reject H_0. If the distribution of the number of weekly accidents is Poisson with mean 1.5, a D_8 of .481 or less will occur 95% of the time, hence the observed value of .1838 is not "unusual" (is not in the tail that would occur with probability at most .05), which is the reasoning leading us to not reject H_0.

Example 13.4.11. Suppose a random sample of size 10, taken from a population with unknown d.f. $F(x)$, is $(X_1, X_2, \ldots, X_{10}) = (-5.641, 4.297, -4.861, -7.780, 7.580, 12.234, 10.780, -0.201, -10.813, -5.593)$. Test, at level .05, the hypothesis that $F(\cdot)$ is normal with some mean and some variance.

Here, since the mean and variance are not known, we use the **Lilliefors test**. We find that $\overline{X} = 0.00$, $s^2 = 67.33571$, $s = 8.205834$. Transforming X_i to $Z_i = (X_i - \overline{X})/s$ yields $(Z_1, Z_2, \ldots, Z_{10}) = (-.6874, .5237, -.5924, -.9481, .9237, 1.4909, 1.3137, -.0245, -1.3177, -.6816)$.

Since $\Phi(z)$ is increasing while $F_n(z)$ is a step function, the supremum of the difference occurs at or just before a jump point of $F_n(z)$. The table needed to find the supremum is

i	$Z_{(i)}$	$\Phi(Z_{(i)})$	$F_n(Z_{(i)})$	$F_n(Z_{(i)}^-)$	$\left\|F_n(Z_{(i)}) - \Phi(Z_{(i)})\right\|$	$\left\|F_n(Z_{(i)}^-) - \Phi(Z_{(i)}^-)\right\|$
1	-1.3177	.0932	.1	.0	.0068	.0932
2	$-\ .9481$	.1711	.2	.1	.0289	.0711
3	$-\ .6874$	.2451	.3	.2	.0549	.0451
4	$-\ .6816$	.2483	.4	.3	.1517	.0517
5	$-\ .5924$	.2776	.5	.4	$\underline{.2224}$	.1224
6	.0245	.4900	.6	.5	.1100	.0100
7	.5237	.6985	.7	.6	.0015	.0985
8	.9237	.8212	.8	.7	.0212	.1212
9	1.3137	.9049	.9	.8	.0049	.1049
10	1.4909	.9319	1.0	.9	.0681	.0319

where $F_n(Z_{(i)}) = i/n$ and $F_n(Z_{(i)}^-) = (i - 1)/n$, since $Z_{(i)} \leq \ldots \leq Z_{(n)}$. Hence $D_n^* = \sup_z |F_n(z) - \Phi(z)| = \max(.2224, .1224) = .2224$. At level $\alpha = .05$ and for $n = 10$, $d_{8,.05}^* = .280$ (the exact from Lilliefors (1967) is .258). Since $D_n^* < d_n^*$, we do not reject H_0: there is not sufficient evidence to reject the hypothesis that the sample came from a normally distributed population. (In practice, one then acts as if the sample was taken from a normal population with some mean μ and some variance σ^2.)

Kolmogorov-Smirnov Test: Two Sample Case. Let $X_1, X_2, \ldots, X_m$ be a random sample from a population with d.f. $F(x)$, and let $Y_1, Y_2, \ldots, Y_n$ be an independent random sample from a population with d.f. $G(x)$ (where $F(\cdot)$ and $G(\cdot)$ are unknown, but are continuous). To test

$$H_0: F(x) = G(x) \quad \text{for all } x, \quad \text{versus } H_1: F(x) \neq G(x),$$

compute the empiric d.f.'s $F_m(x)$ and $G_n(x)$, and compute

$$D_{m,n} = \sup_x |F_m(x) - G_n(x)|. \tag{13.4.12}$$

Since under H_0 $F(x) = G(x)$, if H_0 is true we expect $D_{m,n}$ to be "small," and the test rejects H_0 at level α if $D_{m,n} > d_{m,n,\alpha}$.

Asymptotic critical points are

α	.01	.05	.10	
$d_{m,n,\alpha}$	$1.63\sqrt{\dfrac{m+n}{mn}}$	$1.36\sqrt{\dfrac{m+n}{mn}}$	$1.22\sqrt{\dfrac{m+n}{mn}}$.	(13.4.13)

(Exact values of $d_{m,n,\alpha}$ are available in Gibbons (1985), pp. 401–403.)

PROBLEMS FOR SECTION 13.4

13.4.1 For the data of Problem 13.3.3, let $F_A(x)$ be the d.f. of cholesterol of 10-year-olds in country A, and $F_B(x)$ in country B. Use the Kolmogorov-Smirnov two-sample test to test H_0: $F_A(x) = F_B(x)$ for all x, versus H_1: $F_A(x) \neq F_B(x)$, at level .05.

13.4.2 Suppose 10 guinea pigs are injected with a compound that causes brain tumors. After the animals contract the disease, they are treated with an antitumor drug. Suppose their survival times (in days) are 15, 10, 25, 19, 26, 14, 16, 20, 11, 18. Transforming this data (using an appropriate transformation), then use Lilliefors' test to test the hypothesis that the data comes from a lognormal distribution. (Use level of significance .05.)

13.4.3 Suppose the time to burnout of an electronic component is recorded (in hundreds of hours) as 8.64, 6.35, 2.85, 4.48, 10.28, 9.75, 7.76, 10.02. At level .05, test the hypothesis that the data is from an exponential distribution with mean 7.5.

PROBLEMS FOR CHAPTER 13

13.1 The Probability-Integral Transformation. Let X be a r.v. with a continuous monotone-increasing d.f. $F(x)$. Show that the r.v. $Y = F(X)$ has a uniform distribution over the interval $(0,1)$. [*Hint*: $P[Y \leq y] = P[F(X) \leq y] = P[X \leq F^{-1}(y)] = F(F^{-1}(y))$, where $F^{-1}(\cdot)$ is the inverse function of $F(\cdot)$ (i.e., $F^{-1}(y)$ is the value x such that $F(x) = y$) which exists since $F(x)$ is continuous and monotone-increasing.] Note that this result holds even if $F(x)$ is merely continuous; see Problem 13.2H.

13.2 Let $X_1, \ldots, X_n$ be independent r.v.'s with a continuous d.f. $F(x)$. Show that $F(Y_1), \ldots, F(Y_n)$ have the same joint distribution as the order statistics $U_1, \ldots, U_n$ in a sample of size n from a uniform distribution on $(0,1)$. Show that (for $1 \leq i < j \leq n$ and $0 < p < 1$)

$$P\left[U_i \leq p \leq U_j\right] = Q(i,:j;p,n).$$

13.3 Verify that equation (13.1.15) holds.

13.4 Show that $Q(1, n; p, n) = 1 - p^n - (1 - p)^n$ and find its limit as $n \to \infty$. What does this say about the confidence coefficient of the interval (Y_1, Y_n) for ξ_p for large n?

13.5 Show in full detail how Theorem 10.1.5 is used (see Section 13.2) to derive a test of level $\alpha = 1 - Q(i, j; p, n)$, for the hypothesis that $\xi_p = \xi_p^0$, from the confidence interval (Y_i, Y_j) on ξ_p.

13.6 Two tennis players (A and B, say) are to play n matches. Assume the matches are independent and that $P(B$ wins match $i) = p$ for $j = 1, \ldots, n$ for some p with $0 < p < 1$. Player A avows that he is at least as good as player B, that is, A states that $p \leq .5$. Using Theorem 13.3.1 we can test this hypothesis at level

$$\alpha = \sum_{k=j}^{n} \binom{n}{k} \bigg/ 2^n$$

by rejecting iff $X_1 + \cdots + X_n \geq j$ (i.e., reject if B wins j or more matches). What j and n should we choose for level $\alpha \approx .05$ and power (probability of rejecting H_0) $\approx .90$ when in fact $p = .6$?

13.7 Show that (13.3.10) holds via **(a)** direct calculation and **(b)** use of standard tables.

13.8 Suppose that Glopco (the General Glop Company), which manufactures breakfast cereals, is going to issue a new superfortified cereal called WheatBombs; this cereal is superficially indistinguishable from their popular cereal WheatBoobs, but will retail for twice the price. These cereals appeal to students' parents.

In order to try to prove WheatBombs' superiority to WheatBoobs (so WheatBoob users can be convinced to switch to the higher-priced WheatBombs), the following experiment is run. Thirty pairs of identical twins are chosen, and one twin eats WheatBoobs for a year whereas the other twin eats WheatBombs for a year. (The packages are coded so they do not know which cereal they are receiving.) At the end of the year, the grade-point average (GPA) for that year of the WheatBoob and WheatBomb eater are compared in each pair. Let B denote the number of the 30 pairs in which the WheatBomb eater had a higher GPA than the WheatBoob eater. Supposing independence of the 30 pairs, we wish to test whether the hypothesis H: "WheatBombs are better than WheatBoobs" ["better" means induce a higher GPA] is true. If we perform a test that decides H is true if $B \geq 22$, what will our significance level be? [The null hypothesis is that the cereals are equivalent with regard to GPA.] Does this test accept H if we observe $B = 20$? What is the significance probability of the result $B = 20$?

If, in fact, the null hypothesis is true, and if 100 independent such experiments are run, which each have significance level .05, what is the expected value of the number of experiments which will reject the null hypothesis?

HONORS PROBLEMS FOR CHAPTER 13

13.1H Prove that the joint density of $S \equiv F(Y_i)$ and $T \equiv F(Y_j)$ $(1 \leq i < j \leq n)$ in Theorem 13.1.4 is given by (13.1.8). [*Hint*: See equation (5.6.5).]

13.2H Let $F(x)$ be a continuous d.f. Define a function $G(y)$ as

$$G(y) = \begin{cases} F^{-1}(y), & \text{if } 0 < y < 1 \text{ and } F^{-1}(y) \text{ exists} \\ F^*(y), & \text{if } 0 < y < 1 \text{ and } F^{-1}(y) \text{ does not exist,} \end{cases}$$

where $F^*(y)$ is the smallest x such that $F(x) = y$. (Note that $G(y) = F^{-1}(y)$ for all y if $F(\cdot)$ is monotone-increasing.) Use $G(\cdot)$ instead of $F^{-1}(\cdot)$, to show that (see Problem 13.1) $Y = F(X)$ has a uniform distribution on the interval $(0, 1)$ even if $F(\cdot)$ is merely continuous (and not necessarily monotone-increasing).

13.3H Let $F(x)$ be an arbitrary d.f. Show how to define a nondecreasing function $G(\cdot)$ such that, if U is a uniform r.v. on $(0, 1)$, then $G(U)$ has d.f. $F(\cdot)$. [*Hint*: Let $G(\cdot)$ be as in Problem 13.2H, but also allow for jump points of $F(\cdot)$.]

13.4H Let $U_1, \ldots, U_n$ be the order statistics in a sample of size n from a uniform distribution on $(0, 1)$. Prove that (for $0 < p < 1$)

$$\{ U_i \leq p \leq U_j \} \Rightarrow \{ G(U_i) \leq G(p) \leq G(U_j) \},$$

where $G(\cdot)$ is the function defined in Problem 13.3H. Hence, conclude that

$$P\big[U_i \le p \le U_j\big] \le P\big[G(U_i) \le G(p) \le G(U_j)\big].$$

Use this result and Problem 13.2 to prove Corollary 13.1.11.

13.5H Compare the averages of the lengths (13.1.19), (13.1.20), and (13.1.21) numerically. (First, "wash out" σ by considering $X_1/\sigma, \ldots, X_n/\sigma$ as the basic r.v.'s in the experiment; justify this step.) [*Hint*: See Harter (1961) for tables from which we can calculate $E(Y_j - Y_i)$.]

13.6H Numerically compare the power curve of the test in Example 13.2.1 with that of the usual test that is used when the observations are normally distributed. How much do we lose by using the nonparametric procedure?

13.7H As in Problem 13.6H, but assume the observations have a uniform density on $\xi_{.5} \pm 1$.

13.8H Using the results of Problems 13.6H and 13.7H, are we better off (when our observations follow a uniform density on $\xi_{.5} \pm 1$) using normal theory or nonparametric theory?

13.9H Suppose that each of n judges (see Section 13.3) now inspects k candidates where $k > 2$. Then each judge specifies some permutation of $(1, 2, \ldots, k - 1, k)$ as his ranking of the k candidates. In this case, we can consider generalizing the sign test to a test of the hypothesis that all candidates are equally likely to receive each rank (i.e., are "equally qualified" to be selected) [e.g., see Chapter 7, pp. 138–184, of Hollander and Wolfe (1973)]; however, in many cases (e.g., sports) it will be more appropriate to attempt to select the "best" candidate.[2] How can we define the "best" candidate? (For example, let $\mathbf{R}_i = (R_{i1}, \ldots, R_{ik})$ denote the random vector of ranks that arises when judge i orders the candidates. Then we might define

$$p_l = P[R_{il} = k]$$

$(1 \le l \le k)$ and define the "best" candidate to be the one who has the largest of $p_1, \ldots, p_k$. Will the same one still be best if we delete one or more other candidates? Not necessarily, and please explain why and give an example.)

[2] Such problems have been touched on in Chapter 11. For more details, see Lee and Dudewicz (1974).

Regression and Linear Statistical Inference; Analysis of Variance

In the preceding chapters, we occasionally assumed that we had available independent random variables $Y_1, \ldots, Y_n$ whose common distribution was known (e.g., each of $Y_1, \ldots, Y_n$ might be a $N(\mu, \sigma^2)$ r.v. with μ and σ^2 both unknown, as in Example 10.2.10), and then we studied methods for making inferences based on the variables $Y_1, \ldots, Y_n$ (e.g., to find a 95% confidence interval for μ, in Example 10.2.10; or to predict a future value Y from the same distribution, as in Problem 10.5H). **In this chapter, we study similar inference problems for the case where each Y_i is related to some variable X_i ($i = 1, \ldots, n$)** that can be observed or controlled [e.g., it might be that $Y = f(X)$ for some known or conjectured function $f(\cdot)$]; in that case, we use the information about $X_1, \ldots, X_n$ in our inference procedure.

Some considerations of the question of relationships between two r.v.'s X and Y were given in Section 5.3 (e.g., independence, covariance, correlation, and conditional expectation): it may be helpful to review them when starting this chapter. **The regression problem** we will study in detail is that involving two variables X and Y and a linear relationship $Y = \alpha + \beta X$. Our aim is to illustrate the main ideas with this study, without the obscuring complexities of the cases with more than two variables (e.g., $Y = \alpha + \beta X + \gamma Z$) or with a nonlinear relationship (e.g., $Y = \alpha + \beta X + \beta^2 Z^2$ or $Y = \alpha + \alpha\beta \sin(X)$) or both (e.g., $Y = \alpha + \beta X + \gamma X^2 + \delta Z + \delta^2 XZ$). (Once the main ideas are understood, the details of formulas and computations for such multivariate and/or nonlinear cases can be referenced in a number of sources; we cover the essentials of the multivariate case in the optional Section 14.5.)

Our study of the relationship $Y = \alpha + \beta X$ encompasses the questions of **estimating the unknown constants α and β** (Section 14.1, which uses material from Chapter 7); **testing hypotheses about α and β** (Section 14.2, which uses material from Chapter 9); **giving confidence intervals for α and β and prediction intervals for a new observation Y** that is governed by the same relationship as are $Y_1, \ldots, Y_n$ (Section 14.3, which uses material from Chapter 10); and **selecting the best of several regressions** and associated experimental design questions (Section

14.4, which uses material from Chapter 11). The case of **multiple regression**, which (like Section 4.5) requires vector and matrix algebra and is optional, is dealt with in Section 14.5.

The second important topic covered in this chapter is **analysis of variance**, a statistical technique for analyzing experiments with several populations and where the results may depend on several effects operating simultaneously. Together with regression analysis, analysis of variance constitutes a major technique of researchers in many fields of endeavor. In earlier chapters (e.g., Section 9.9) we discussed testing the hypothesis H_0: $\mu_1 = \mu_2$ based on independent random samples from two populations. A generalization to testing H_0: $\mu_1 = \mu_2 = \cdots = \mu_k$ in the case of $k \geq 2$ populations is called the **one-way analysis of variance** (Section 14.6). **Two-way analysis of variance** (Section 14.7) deals with similar cases where the observations may be affected by another source of variability (such as: The k populations represent different fertilizers, and they are being used on different varieties of grass).

14.1. ESTIMATION OF REGRESSION PARAMETERS; LINEAR MODELS

In general, suppose that (X, Y) is a random variable with a bivariate distribution function $F_{X,Y}(x, y)$. If we can observe X, then it makes sense (if we are interested in predicting the value of Y) to **predict Y by some function $f(X)$**, since X and Y are related variables. We will now find the "best" such function $f(X)$, after first (in Definition 14.1.1) giving it the special name "regression curve of Y on X."

Definition 14.1.1. The function $f(X)$ for which

$$E(Y - f(X))^2 \tag{14.1.2}$$

is minimized is called the **regression curve of Y on X.**

Theorem 14.1.3. Let (X, Y) have a bivariate d.f. such that $\text{Var}(X)$ and $\text{Var}(Y)$ both exist. Then the regression curve of Y on X is given (for all x) by

$$f(x) = E(Y|X = x). \tag{14.1.4}$$

Proof: Let $f(x)$ denote the conditional expectation $E(Y|X = x)$ (see Definition 5.3.27), and let $\varphi(x)$ be a general function. Then

$$E(Y - \varphi(X))^2 = E((Y - f(X)) + (f(X) - \varphi(X)))^2$$

$$= E(Y - f(X))^2 + E(f(X) - \varphi(X))^2 \tag{14.1.5}$$

$$+ 2E(Y - f(X))(f(X) - \varphi(X)).$$

However (see Theorem 5.3.28 and the discussion following it) $E(\varphi(X)Y) = E(\varphi(X)E(Y|X)) = E(\varphi(X)f(X))$; hence,

$$E(Y - f(X))\varphi(X) = 0 \qquad (14.1.6)$$

and (taking $\varphi(\cdot)$ to be $f(\cdot)$ in (14.1.6))

$$E(Y - f(X))f(X) = 0. \qquad (14.1.7)$$

From (14.1.6) and (14.1.7) we find that the last term in (14.1.5) is zero; hence,

$$E(Y - \varphi(X))^2 = E(Y - f(X))^2 + E(f(X) - \varphi(X))^2, \qquad (14.1.8)$$

which is clearly minimized (as a function of $\varphi(\cdot)$) by taking $\varphi(x) = f(x)$ for all x.   ∎

Sometimes (e.g., because the regression curve $E(Y|X = x)$ of Y on X may be very complex or hard to find, or because we expect an approximately linear relationship to hold between Y and X) we will wish to find the **"best" linear function of X for predicting Y**; we will now (in analogy to Definition 14.1.1 and Theorem 14.1.3) develop this notion.

Definition 14.1.9. The α and β for which $\alpha + \beta X$ causes

$$E(Y - (\alpha + \beta X))^2 \qquad (14.1.10)$$

to be minimized are called the **regression intercept** and **regression slope** (of Y on X), respectively. The line $y = \alpha + \beta x$ is called the **regression line of Y on X**.

Theorem 14.1.11. The regression line of Y on X is given by $y = \alpha + \beta x$ with α and β such that

$$\alpha = E(Y) - \rho(X,Y)\frac{\sigma(Y)}{\sigma(X)}E(X), \qquad (14.1.12)$$

$$\beta = \rho(X,Y)\frac{\sigma(Y)}{\sigma(X)}. \qquad (14.1.13)$$

With this α and β, we find that the **regression line of Y on X** is

$$y = E(Y) - \rho(X,Y)\frac{\sigma(Y)}{\sigma(X)}E(X) + \rho(X,Y)\frac{\sigma(Y)}{\sigma(X)}x \qquad (14.1.14)$$

or

$$\frac{y - E(Y)}{\sigma(Y)} = \rho(X,Y)\frac{x - E(X)}{\sigma(X)}, \qquad (14.1.15)$$

which has mean squared prediction error

$$E(Y - (\alpha + \beta X))^2 = (1 - \rho^2(X, Y))\sigma^2(Y). \qquad (14.1.16)$$

Proof: For a general α and β,

$$\begin{aligned}
E(Y - (\alpha + \beta X))^2 &= E((Y - E(Y)) - \beta(X - E(X)) \\
&\quad - (\alpha - E(Y) + \beta E(X)))^2 \\
&= E(Y - E(Y))^2 + \beta^2 E(X - E(X))^2 \\
&\quad + (\alpha - E(Y) + \beta E(X))^2 \\
&\quad - 2\beta E(Y - E(Y))(X - E(X)) \qquad (14.1.17) \\
&\quad - 2(\alpha - E(Y) + \beta E(X))E(Y - E(Y)) \\
&\quad + 2\beta(\alpha - E(Y) + \beta E(X))E(X - E(X)) \\
&= \sigma^2(Y) + \beta^2 \sigma^2(X) + (\alpha - E(Y) + \beta E(X))^2 \\
&\quad - 2\beta E(Y - E(Y))(X - E(X)) - 0 + 0.
\end{aligned}$$

Now (looking at the last equation in (14.1.17)) we see that α only enters through the term $(\alpha - E(Y) + \beta E(X))^2$, so (for any β) the best α is $E(Y) - \beta E(X)$. With that choice of α (call it α^*) we then find

$$\begin{aligned}
E(Y &- (\alpha^* + \beta X))^2 \\
&= \sigma^2(Y) + \beta^2 \sigma^2(X) - 2\beta E(Y - E(Y))(X - E(X)) \\
&= \sigma^2(Y) + \beta^2 \sigma^2(X) - 2\beta \sigma(X)\sigma(Y)\rho(X, Y) \qquad (14.1.18) \\
&= (\beta\sigma(X) - \rho(X, Y)\sigma(Y))^2 + (1 - \rho^2(X, Y))\sigma^2(Y),
\end{aligned}$$

which is minimized by setting β as in (14.1.13) whence (using this β in α^*) we find α should be set as in (14.1.12). The mean squared prediction error follows easily from (14.1.18) where (with the best β) the first term is zero. ∎

Example 14.1.19. Suppose that (X, Y) has a bivariate d.f. with $\sigma^2(Y) = 10$, $\rho(X, Y) = .5$. Then if we ignore X and predict Y as simply $E(Y)$, we will have a mean squared error of prediction equal to the variance of Y, namely 10. If we use the regression line of Y on X to predict Y, the mean squared error of prediction will (see (14.1.16)) be cut to

$$(1 - \rho^2(X, Y))\sigma^2(Y) = (1 - .25)(10) = \frac{(3)(10)}{4} = 7.5, \quad (14.1.20)$$

which is a 25% reduction. For this reason, it is often said that "the square of the correlation coefficient is the proportion of the variance (of Y) accounted for by linear regression on X," and (14.1.16) is called the residual variance (after linear regression on X).

The regression curve of Y on X (determined in Theorem 14.1.3) and the regression line of Y and X (determined in Theorem 14.1.11) are both theoretical, and complete knowledge about the bivariate d.f. of (X, Y) is needed to calculate them. Although in some situations (such as repetitive sampling from the same bivariate distribution with the X immediately available but the Y unavailable for a long period and in need of prediction; for example, X could be a high-school grade-point average whereas Y could be a corresponding college grade-point average at a certain school) we know this d.f. and can calculate these regressions, often we have available only n independent pairs of observations (X_1, Y_1), $\ldots, (X_n, Y_n)$ and need to estimate the regressions. We will consider this problem now for the linear regression case.

One method of estimating the regression line, called the method of least squares, is to estimate α and β by the $\hat{\alpha}$ and $\hat{\beta}$ (say) that minimize the sums of the squares of the errors in predicting Y_i by $\alpha + \beta X_i$ ($i = 1, \ldots, n$), that is, which minimize

$$S(\alpha, \beta) = \sum_{i=1}^{n} (Y_i - (\alpha + \beta X_i))^2. \tag{14.1.21}$$

We will now derive the $\hat{\alpha}$ and $\hat{\beta}$ that the method of least squares suggests we use; further justification for these estimators will be given later in this section (the Gauss-Markov theorem).

Theorem 14.1.22. Let $(X_1, Y_1), \ldots, (X_n, Y_n)$ be n independent observations from a bivariate d.f. Then the method of least squares estimates the regression line of Y on X [where (X, Y) is an observation from this same bivariate d.f.] by $y = \hat{\alpha} + \hat{\beta} x$ where

$$\hat{\alpha} = \overline{Y} - r_{XY} \frac{s_Y}{s_X} \overline{X}, \tag{14.1.23}$$

$$\hat{\beta} = r_{XY} \frac{s_Y}{s_X}, \tag{14.1.24}$$

$$r_{XY} = \frac{n \sum_{i=1}^{n} X_i Y_i - \sum_{i=1}^{n} X_i \sum_{i=1}^{n} Y_i}{\sqrt{n \sum_{i=1}^{n} X_i^2 - \left(\sum_{i=1}^{n} X_i\right)^2} \sqrt{n \sum_{i=1}^{n} Y_i^2 - \left(\sum_{i=1}^{n} Y_i\right)^2}}, \tag{14.1.25}$$

and

$$
\begin{cases}
s_X^2 = \dfrac{n\sum\limits_{i=1}^{n} X_i^2 - \left(\sum\limits_{i=1}^{n} X_i\right)^2}{n^2}, & s_Y^2 = \dfrac{n\sum\limits_{i=1}^{n} Y_i^2 - \left(\sum\limits_{i=1}^{n} Y_i\right)^2}{n^2}, \\[3em]
\overline{X} = \dfrac{X_1 + \cdots + X_n}{n}, & \overline{Y} = \dfrac{Y_1 + \cdots + Y_n}{n}.
\end{cases}
\tag{14.1.26}
$$

Proof: By definition of the method of least squares, we are to choose α and β as the $\hat{\alpha}$ and $\hat{\beta}$ that minimize (14.1.21):

$$
S(\alpha, \beta) = \sum_{i=1}^{n} \left(Y_i - (\alpha + \beta X_i)\right)^2.
\tag{14.1.27}
$$

If we take the partial derivatives of (14.1.27) with respect to α and β, set them to zero, and solve, we then (see Problem 14.1H) find $\hat{\alpha}$ and $\hat{\beta}$:

$$
\begin{cases}
\dfrac{\partial S(\alpha, \beta)}{\partial \alpha} = \sum\limits_{i=1}^{n} (-2)\left(Y_i - (\alpha + \beta X_i)\right) = 0, \\[2em]
\dfrac{\partial S(\alpha, \beta)}{\partial \beta} = \sum\limits_{i=1}^{n} (-2X_i)\left(Y_i - (\alpha + \beta X_i)\right) = 0,
\end{cases}
\tag{14.1.28}
$$

that is,

$$
\begin{cases}
\sum\limits_{i=1}^{n} Y_i - n\alpha - \beta \sum\limits_{i=1}^{n} X_i = 0, \\[2em]
\sum\limits_{i=1}^{n} X_i Y_i - \alpha \sum\limits_{i=1}^{n} X_i - \beta \sum\limits_{i=1}^{n} X_i^2 = 0,
\end{cases}
\tag{14.1.29}
$$

and (via elementary algebraic manipulations; see Problem 14.6) we find (14.1.23) and (14.1.24). The system of equations (14.1.28) is called the **normal equations**.   ∎

So far in this section, we have been considering our observations $(X_1, Y_1), \ldots, (X_n, Y_n)$ to have been drawn independently from a bivariate population, and this is appropriate in many situations. However, in many other situations (such as in physical science) $X_1, \ldots, X_n$ are not r.v.'s (e.g., they may be amounts of a catalyst provided by an experimenter or amounts of fertilizer). In this case an additional theoretical justification of the least-squares estimators of α and β (note that those estimators in no way made use of the assumption that $X_1, \ldots, X_n$ were r.v.'s, and hence the same estimators apply to the nonrandom $X_1, \ldots, X_n$ case) can be given. The general result that provides this justification is called the **Gauss-Markov theorem**. Stated somewhat informally [for a general statement see Scheffé (1959), p. 14] this theorem says that the best (i.e., minimum variance) unbiased estimators of α and of β, among all estimators that are linear functions of $Y_1, \ldots, Y_n$ when $x_1, \ldots, x_n$ are fixed values, are those obtained by the method of least squares. We will now prove this result for the case of α and β.

Theorem 14.1.30. Let $Y_1, \ldots, Y_n$ be independent observations (taken at respective fixed levels $x_1, \ldots, x_n$ of some independent variable) such that $E(Y_i) = \alpha + \beta x_i$ and $\mathrm{Var}(Y_i) = \sigma^2$ ($i = 1, \ldots, n$). Then, of all estimators of α and β that are linear functions of $Y_1, \ldots, Y_n$ and that are unbiased, the $\hat{\alpha}$ and $\hat{\beta}$ of Theorem 14.1.22 have the smallest respective variances.

Proof: Consider a general linear estimator of α, say $t = u_1 Y_1 + \cdots + u_n Y_n$. (Note that this is the most general linear combination of $Y_1, \ldots, Y_n$.) Now t will be an unbiased estimator of α if $E(t) \equiv \alpha$; that is,

$$
\alpha \equiv E(t) = E\left(\sum_{i=1}^{n} u_i Y_i \right) = \sum_{i=1}^{n} u_i E(Y_i)
$$

$$
= \sum_{i=1}^{n} u_i(\alpha + \beta x_i) = \alpha \sum_{i=1}^{n} u_i + \beta \sum_{i=1}^{n} u_i x_i.
$$

(14.1.31)

Since (14.1.31) must hold for all α, we find we must have

$$
\sum_{i=1}^{n} u_i = 1, \qquad \sum_{i=1}^{n} u_i x_i = 0.
$$

(14.1.32)

The variance of t, which is to be minimized subject to (14.1.32), is

$$
\mathrm{Var}(t) = \mathrm{Var}\left(\sum_{i=1}^{n} u_i Y_i \right) = \left(\sum_{i=1}^{n} u_i^2 \right) \sigma^2;
$$

(14.1.33)

hence, it suffices to minimize $u_1^2 + \cdots + u_n^2$ subject to $u_1 + \cdots + u_n = 1$ and $u_1 x_1 + \cdots + u_n x_n = 0$. Let (for $i = 1, \ldots, n$)

$$
v_i = \frac{\displaystyle\sum_{i=1}^{n} x_i^2 - \left(\sum_{i=1}^{n} x_i \right) x_i}{\displaystyle n \sum_{i=1}^{n} x_i^2 - \left(\sum_{i=1}^{n} x_i \right)^2}.
$$

(14.1.34)

Then we can express u_i as

$$
u_i = v_i + \Delta_i \qquad (i = 1, \ldots, n)
$$

(14.1.35)

for some Δ_i. From (14.1.32), it follows that we must have

$$
\sum_{i=1}^{n} v_i + \sum_{i=1}^{n} \Delta_i = 1, \qquad \sum_{i=1}^{n} v_i x_i + \sum_{i=1}^{n} \Delta_i x_i = 0,
$$

but (as can be easily verified; see Problem 14.9) $\sum_{i=1}^{n} v_i = 1$ and $\sum_{i=1}^{n} v_i x_i = 0$; hence, we must have

$$\sum_{i=1}^{n} \Delta_i = 0, \qquad \sum_{i=1}^{n} \Delta_i x_i = 0.$$

Now using (14.1.35),

$$\sum_{i=1}^{n} u_i^2 = \sum_{i=1}^{n} (v_i + \Delta_i)^2 = \sum_{i=1}^{n} v_i^2 + \sum_{i=1}^{n} \Delta_i^2 + 2 \sum_{i=1}^{n} v_i \Delta_i$$

$$= \sum_{i=1}^{n} v_i^2 + \sum_{i=1}^{n} \Delta_i^2 + 0 \geq \sum_{i=1}^{n} v_i^2$$

(14.1.36)

and the theorem follows.   ∎

The considerations of this section and chapter deal with the area of statistics known as linear models, which deals with statistical inference problems that arise when we assume that a r.v. Y can be expressed as

$$Y = \beta_0 x_0 + \beta_1 x_1 + \cdots + \beta_m x_m + \varepsilon, \qquad (14.1.37)$$

where: $x_0, x_1, \ldots, x_m$, and m are known constants; $\beta_0, \beta_1, \ldots, \beta_m$ are unknown constants; and ε is a r.v. with $E(\varepsilon) = 0$ whose distribution does not vary as the parameters $\beta_0, \beta_1, \ldots, \beta_m$ vary. (If we assume $m = 2$, $x_0 = 1$, $\beta_0 = \alpha$, $x_1 = x$, and $\beta_1 = \beta$, then (14.1.37) becomes the model $Y = \alpha + \beta x + \varepsilon$ studied above.) The general results, of which the results in this section are indicative, are given in sketch in Section 14.5; for detailed consideration, see (e.g.) Graybill (1961).

PROBLEMS FOR SECTION 14.1

14.1.1 Suppose a random sample of 5 observations on the bivariate r.v. (X, Y) yields the values: $(3, 4), (4, 4.8), (0, .5), (5, 6.1), (2, 2)$. Use the method of least squares to estimate the regression line of Y on X.

14.1.2 Let (X, Y) be a trinomial r.v. with probability function $P(X = x, Y = y) = (n!/(x!y!(n - x - y)!))p_1^x p_2^y (1 - p_1 - p_2)^{n-x-y}$ if $0 \leq x + y \leq n$ and $x, y = 0, 1, 2, \ldots, n$ (and $= 0$ otherwise).

  (a) Show that the regression curve of Y on X is the straight line

$$E(Y \mid X = x) = \frac{(n - x)p_2}{1 - p_1} = \frac{np_2}{1 - p_1} - \frac{p_2}{1 - p_1} x.$$

  (b) Based on a random sample of size m, find the least-squares estimator of $p_2/(1 - p_1)$.

  (c) Find the MLE of $p_2/(1 - p_1)$, and compare it with the least-squares estimator found in part (b).

14.1.3 Suppose that the following (X, Y) pairs are the college GPA's Y and high school GPA's X of 8 students: (3.40, 2.95), (3.85, 3.95), (4.00, 4.00), (2.65, 3.10), (3.20, 2.90), (3.50, 3.45), (2.10, 2.85), (3.70, 2.90). For the bivariate r.v. (X, Y), use the method of least squares to estimate the regression line of Y on X.

14.2. TESTING HYPOTHESES ABOUT REGRESSION PARAMETERS

In Section 14.1 we considered the problem of estimating α and β given n independent r.v.'s $Y_1, \ldots, Y_n$ (taken at respective fixed levels $x_1, \ldots, x_n$ of some independent variable) such that $E(Y_i) = \alpha + \beta x_i$ and $\text{Var}(Y_i) = \sigma^2$ ($i = 1, \ldots, n$); for example (see Theorem 14.1.30) the estimators $\hat{\alpha}$ and $\hat{\beta}$ of equations (14.1.23) and (14.1.24) are unbiased and have the smallest variance of all unbiased linear estimators. **In order to test hypotheses about α and/or β, it will be necessary to make some assumptions about the distribution of Y_i ($i = 1, \ldots, n$)** (up to this point we only talked of the mean and variance of Y_i ($i = 1, \ldots, n$)). If we assume that each Y_i has a normal distribution, then (see Problem 14.15) it turns out that $\hat{\alpha}$ and $\hat{\beta}$ are the respective MLE's of α and of β, and that we can find an MLE for σ^2:

Theorem 14.2.1. Let $Y_1, \ldots, Y_n$ be independent r.v.'s where Y_i is $N(\alpha + \beta x_i, \sigma^2)$, where x_i is known and α, β, σ^2 are unknown ($1 \le i \le n$). Then $\hat{\alpha}$ of equation (14.1.23) is the MLE of α, $\hat{\beta}$ of equation (14.1.24) is the MLE of β, and the MLE of σ^2 is

$$\hat{\sigma}^2 = \frac{\sum_{i=1}^{n} \left(Y_i - \hat{\alpha} - \hat{\beta} x_i \right)^2}{n}. \tag{14.2.2}$$

If we examine formulas (14.1.23) and (14.1.24) carefully (Problem 14.16), we find that $\hat{\alpha}$ and $\hat{\beta}$ can be expressed simply as

$$\begin{cases} \hat{\alpha} = \overline{Y} - \dfrac{n \sum_{i=1}^{n} x_i Y_i - \sum_{i=1}^{n} x_i \sum_{i=1}^{n} Y_i}{n \sum_{i=1}^{n} x_i^2 - \left(\sum_{i=1}^{n} x_i \right)^2} \overline{x}, \\[20pt] \hat{\beta} = \dfrac{n \sum_{i=1}^{n} x_i Y_i - \sum_{i=1}^{n} x_i \sum_{i=1}^{n} Y_i}{n \sum_{i=1}^{n} x_i^2 - \left(\sum_{i=1}^{n} x_i \right)^2} \end{cases} \tag{14.2.3}$$

However, we note that each of $\hat{\alpha}$ and $\hat{\beta}$ is a linear combination of $Y_1, \ldots, Y_n$ and hence (see footnote 7 in Chapter 7) the r.v. $(\hat{\alpha}, \hat{\beta})$ has a bivariate normal distribution. We already know the means of this distribution [since we already showed that $E(\hat{\alpha}) = \alpha$ and $E(\hat{\beta}) = \beta$ in Theorem 14.1.30], and it is easy to show (Problem 14.17) that the variances are

$$
\begin{cases}
\operatorname{Var}(\hat{\alpha}) = \dfrac{\sum\limits_{i=1}^{n} x_i^2}{n \sum\limits_{i=1}^{n} x_i^2 - \left(\sum\limits_{i=1}^{n} x_i \right)^2} \sigma^2, \\[4ex]
\operatorname{Var}(\hat{\beta}) = \dfrac{n}{n \sum\limits_{i=1}^{n} x_i^2 - \left(\sum\limits_{i=1}^{n} x_i \right)^2} \sigma^2.
\end{cases}
\tag{14.2.4}
$$

Thus, we have proven the theorem:

Theorem 14.2.5.   Let $Y_1, \ldots, Y_n$ be independent r.v.'s where Y_i is $N(\alpha + \beta x_i, \sigma^2)$ $(1 \le i \le n)$. Then $(\hat{\alpha}, \hat{\beta})$ has a bivariate normal distribution with means (α, β) and variances given by (14.2.4).

Now it can be shown (Problem 14.7H) that $n\hat{\sigma}^2/\sigma^2$ is a $\chi^2_{n-2}(0)$ r.v. and (Problem 14.8H) that it is independent of each of $\hat{\alpha}$ and $\hat{\beta}$. **Hence, as in Section 9.6 in a simpler case, we may easily test the hypothesis $H_0 = \{\sigma_0^2\}$ about σ^2 at level α:** reject iff

$$
\hat{\sigma}^2 > k'',
\tag{14.2.6}
$$

where k'' satisfies $P[Y > nk''/\sigma_0^2] = \alpha$ for Y a $\chi^2_{n-2}(0)$ r.v.

Similarly, we can obtain tests of hypotheses like $H_0 = \{\alpha_0\}$ since (under the null hypothesis)

$$
\frac{\hat{\alpha} - \alpha_0}{\sqrt{\dfrac{\sum\limits_{i=1}^{n} x_i^2}{n \sum\limits_{i=1}^{n} x_i^2 - \left(\sum\limits_{i=1}^{n} x_i \right)^2} \dfrac{n\hat{\sigma}^2}{n-2}}}
\tag{14.2.7}
$$

has the t_{n-2} distribution (see Definition 9.5.24). The test is entirely analogous to that of Theorem 9.5.26: reject iff (14.2.7) exceeds $t_{n-2}^{-1}(1 - \alpha)$. **Similar tests are easily obtained for other alternatives, and for β** (see Problem 14.19).

PROBLEMS FOR SECTION 14.2

14.2.1 Suppose the following table shows the GPA's x of 10 high-school graduates, and also their respective scores Y on an IQ test:

x	2.2	2.4	2.8	2.6	3.2	3.8	3.0	4.0	2.0	2.3
Y	108	112	115	118	121	125	122	130	96	113

Assume the Y_i's are independent r.v.'s with $Y_i \sim N(\alpha + \beta x_i, \sigma^2)$, the x_i's being fixed numbers.

(a) Find least-squares estimators of α, β, and σ^2, and the equation of the estimated least-squares line $\hat{E}(Y_i | x_i) = \hat{\alpha} + \hat{\beta} x_i$.

(b) Plot the points (x_i, Y_i), and the line obtained in part (a), on the same graph.

(c) Test H_0: $\alpha = 0$ versus H_1: $\alpha > 0$ at level of significance .05.

(d) Construct a 95% confidence interval for α, and also a 95% lower confidence bound for α.

(e) Test H_0: $\beta = 0$ versus H_1: $\beta \neq 0$ at level of significance .01.

(f) Construct a 95% confidence interval for β, and also a 95% upper confidence bound for β.

14.2.2 Suppose we observe (x_i, Y_i), $i = 1, 2, \ldots, n$, where the x_i's are fixed numbers and Y_i has a Poisson distribution with mean λx_i. Consider the regression line $E(Y|x) = \lambda x$.

(a) Use the method of least squares to find an estimator of λ.

(b) Use the method of maximum likelihood to find an estimator of λ.

(c) Use the MLE of λ and the Central Limit Theorem to construct an approximate level α test for H_0: $\lambda = \lambda_0$ versus H_1: $\lambda \neq \lambda_0$.

(d) Construct an approximate $100(1 - \alpha)\%$ confidence interval for λ.

14.2.3 Let (x_i, Y_i), $i = 1, 2, \ldots, n$, be a random sample of size n. Suppose that Y (at a given x) has a lognormal distribution with $E(Y | X = x) = \gamma e^{\beta x}$. Find least-squares estimators of the parameters, and a procedure to test each of the hypotheses H_0: $\beta = \beta_0$ and H_0: $\gamma = \gamma_0 > 0$, at level α; construct a $100(1 - \alpha)\%$ confidence interval for each of γ and β.

14.2.4 In the linear regression model $E(Y | x) = \alpha + \beta x$ with Y (at a given x) being $N(\alpha + \beta x, \sigma^2)$, show that the least-squares estimator of β (based on independent r.v.'s $Y_1, Y_2, \ldots, Y_n$ taken at respective x-values of $x_1, x_2, \ldots, x_n$) and $\overline{Y}$ are uncorrelated r.v.'s.

14.3. PREDICTION AND CONFIDENCE INTERVALS IN REGRESSION; COMPUTER PACKAGES FOR REGRESSION

To summarize some results from previous sections, if $Y_1, \ldots, Y_n$ are independent r.v.'s where Y_i is $N(\alpha + \beta x_i, \sigma^2)$ $(1 \leq i \leq n)$, then $(\hat{\alpha}, \hat{\beta})$ given at (14.2.3) has a bivariate normal distribution with mean vector (α, β) and variances as given by

(14.2.4), and σ^2 may be estimated by $\hat{\sigma}^2$ given by (14.2.2), which is stochastically independent of $\hat{\alpha}$ and of $\hat{\beta}$ and $n\hat{\sigma}^2/\sigma^2$ is a $\chi^2_{n-2}(0)$ r.v. **In light of these facts, confidence intervals for σ^2 are obtained easily essentially as in Section 10.3 in a simpler case, and confidence intervals for α and for β follow as in Section 10.2;** for example, a confidence interval for α with confidence coefficient $1 - \gamma$ is given by (L, U) where

$$L = \hat{\alpha} - \sqrt{\frac{\sum\limits_{i=1}^{n} x_i^2}{n \sum\limits_{i=1}^{n} x_i^2 - \left(\sum\limits_{i=1}^{n} x_i\right)^2} \frac{n\hat{\sigma}^2}{n - 2}} \, t_{n-2}^{-1}\left(1 - \frac{\gamma}{2}\right) \qquad (14.3.1)$$

and

$$U = \hat{\alpha} + \sqrt{\frac{\sum\limits_{i=1}^{n} x_i^2}{n \sum\limits_{i=1}^{n} x_i^2 - \left(\sum\limits_{i=1}^{n} x_i\right)^2} \frac{n\hat{\sigma}^2}{n - 2}} \, t_{n-2}^{-1}\left(1 - \frac{\gamma}{2}\right). \qquad (14.3.2)$$

Often we will not be interested in inference (e.g., tests of hypotheses or confidence intervals) about α and β directly, but rather in using the observations $Y_1, \ldots, Y_n$ (taken at respective values $x_1, \ldots, x_n$ of the independent variable) to predict the value of Y we might obtain in the future if the independent variable is set to value x^*. An unbiased estimator of $E(Y) = \alpha + \beta x^*$ is, of course, $\hat{\alpha} + \hat{\beta} x^*$. This $\hat{\alpha} + \hat{\beta} x^*$ is actually an unbiased estimator of two quantities: first, of $\alpha + \beta x^*$; second, of $E(Y)$, the mean of a future observation taken at x^*. The difference between these two quantities becomes clear when we seek confidence intervals about the point estimate $\hat{\alpha} + \hat{\beta} x^*$, as we will now see.

If we desire a confidence interval for $\alpha + \beta x^*$, we need to know

$$\text{Var}\left((\hat{\alpha} + \hat{\beta} x^*) - (\alpha + \beta x^*)\right) = \sigma^2 \left(\frac{1}{n} + \frac{(x^* - \bar{x})^2}{ns_x^2}\right); \qquad (14.3.3)$$

a 95% confidence interval for $\alpha + \beta x^*$ is then (Y_L^*, Y_U^*) where

$$Y_L^* = (\hat{\alpha} + \hat{\beta} x^*) - t_{n-2}^{-1}(.975)\sqrt{\frac{n\hat{\sigma}^2}{n - 2}} \sqrt{\frac{1}{n} + \frac{(x^* - \bar{x})^2}{ns_x^2}} \qquad (14.3.4)$$

and

$$Y_U^* = (\hat{\alpha} + \hat{\beta} x^*) + t_{n-2}^{-1}(.975)\sqrt{\frac{n\hat{\sigma}^2}{n - 2}} \sqrt{\frac{1}{n} + \frac{(x^* - \bar{x})^2}{ns_x^2}} . \qquad (14.3.5)$$

On the other hand, if we desire a confidence interval for Y at x^*, we need to know

$$\text{Var}\left(Y - (\hat{\alpha} + \hat{\beta}x^*)\right)$$

$$= \text{Var}\left((Y - (\alpha + \beta x^*)) - ((\hat{\alpha} + \hat{\beta}x^*) - (\alpha + \beta x^*))\right)$$

$$= \text{Var}\left(Y - (\alpha + \beta x^*)\right) + \text{Var}\left((\hat{\alpha} + \hat{\beta}x^*) - (\alpha + \beta x^*)\right)$$

$$= \sigma^2 + \sigma^2 \left(\frac{1}{n} + \frac{(x^* - \bar{x})^2}{ns_x^2}\right) \qquad (14.3.6)$$

$$= \sigma^2 \left(1 + \frac{1}{n} + \frac{(x^* - \bar{x})^2}{ns_x^2}\right);$$

a 95% confidence interval for Y at x^* is then (Y_L, Y_U) where

$$Y_L = (\hat{\alpha} + \hat{\beta}x^*) - t_{n-2}^{-1}(.975)\sqrt{\frac{n\hat{\sigma}^2}{n-2}}\sqrt{1 + \frac{1}{n} + \frac{(x^* - \bar{x})^2}{ns_x^2}}, \qquad (14.3.7)$$

and

$$Y_U = (\hat{\alpha} + \hat{\beta}x^*) + t_{n-2}^{-1}(.975)\sqrt{\frac{n\hat{\sigma}^2}{n-2}}\sqrt{1 + \frac{1}{n} + \frac{(x^* - \bar{x})^2}{ns_x^2}}. \qquad (14.3.8)$$

[*Note*: Although the length of the interval on $\alpha + \beta x^*$ (i.e., $Y_U^* - Y_L^*$) tends to zero as $n \to \infty$ (the mean of Y at x^* is pinned down very precisely), the length of the interval on Y at x^* (i.e., $Y_U - Y_L$) does not tend to zero as $n \to \infty$ (what does it tend to?) since Y will still vary and cannot be predicted perfectly.]

A plot of (Y_L^*, Y_U^*) for all x^* is called a **confidence band (for the regression line)**, whereas a plot of (Y_L, Y_U) for all x^* is called a **prediction band (for future values)**.

Example 14.3.9. A survey of agricultural yield against the amount of a pest allowed (the latter can be controlled by crop treatment) has produced the data of Table 14.3-1. Find $\hat{\alpha}$ and $\hat{\beta}$. Plot the regression line with confidence bands and prediction bands (each at the 95% confidence level), and with the data points superimposed on the graph. If the pest rate is allowed to go to $x^* = 50$ next year, within what limits can we be 95% sure that our crop yield will fall?

The calculations needed here may be organized as follows:

Step 1. Compute $n = 12$, $\sum x_i = 288$, $\sum Y_i = 540$, $\sum x_i Y_i = 9324$,

$$\sum x_i^2 = 5256, \ \sum Y_i^2 = 25522.$$

Step 2. Compute $SS_{xx} = \sum x_i^2 - \left(\sum x_i\right)^2 \big/ n = 924$

$$SS_{xY} = \sum x_i Y_i - \left(\sum x_i\right)\left(\sum Y_i\right) \big/ n = -936$$

$$SS_{YY} = \sum Y_i^2 - \left(\sum Y_i\right)^2 \big/ n = 1222.$$

Step 3. Then [see (14.2.3)]

$$\bar{x} = \sum x_i / n = 19, \ \bar{Y} = \sum Y_i / n = 45,$$

$$\hat{\beta} = SS_{xY} / SS_{xx} = -1.0130$$

$$\hat{\alpha} = \bar{Y} - \hat{\beta}\bar{x} = 64.247.$$

Hence the regression line is estimated as $y = 64.247 - 1.0130x$.

Step 4. Compute $SSE = SS_{YY} - \hat{\beta}SS_{xY} = 273.832$, $MSE = SSE/(n-2) = 27.3832$,

$$SS(\text{Total}) = SS_{YY} = 1222, \ SS(\text{Reg}) = SS(\text{Total}) - SSE = 948.168.$$

Step 5. Then [see (14.2.4)]

$$\widehat{\text{Var}\left(\hat{\beta}\right)} = MSE/SS_{xx} = .02964$$

$$\widehat{\text{Var}\left(\hat{\alpha}\right)} = \left(\sum x_i^2 \big/ (nSS_{xx})\right) MSE = 12.98035.$$

The plot is given in Figure 14.3-1 and shows that if we let our pest reach level $x^* = 50$, we can be 95% sure that our yield will be between 0 and 31.5 units. (The mean yield at $x^* = 50$ is between 1.4 and 26.3 units with 95% confidence.)

95% confidence intervals for α (from (14.3.1) and (14.3.2)) and β are, respectively,

$$\hat{\alpha} \pm t_{n-2}^{-1}(1 - \gamma/2)\sqrt{\widehat{\text{Var}\left(\hat{\alpha}\right)}} = (56.2199, 72.274)$$

and

$$\hat{\beta} \pm t_{n-2}^{-1}(1 - \gamma/2)\sqrt{\widehat{\text{Var}\left(\hat{\beta}\right)}} = (-1.3966, -0.62942).$$

An interpretation is that we are 95% confident that the true value of the intercept (α) is between the bounds $(56.2199, 72.274)$, and also 95% confident that the true value of the slope (β) is between the bounds $(-1.3966, -0.62942)$.

Today, **most regression analysis is performed using computer software packages**. As we discussed in Example 4.8.2, two of the most widely used (and highest quality) such packages are BMDP and SAS. The following program uses the data of Example 14.3.9, stored in a dataset called REGIE (which is printed as a check), to calculate the regression for that example, using the SAS package:

```
1  OPTIONS LINESIZE = 80;
2  DATA REGIE;
3  INPUT PESTRATE CROPYLD;        SAS program
4  CARDS;                         (REGIE was previously entered)
17 ;
18 PROC PRINT;
```

OBS	PESTRATE	CROPYLD
1	8	59
2	6	58
3	11	56
4	22	53
5	14	50
6	17	45
7	18	43
8	24	42
9	19	39
10	23	38
11	26	30
12	40	27

output produced (print of REGIE)

```
19 PROC REG;                      SAS program to regress Y on x
20 MODEL CROPYLD = PESTRATE;
```

DEP VARIABLE: CROPYLD

SOURCE	DF	SUM OF SQUARES	MEAN SQUARE	F VALUE	PROB>F
MODEL	1	948.156	948.156	34.624	0.0002
ERROR	10	273.844	27.384416		
C TOTAL	11	1222.000			

ROOT MSE	5.233012	R - SQUARE	0.7759
DEP MEAN	45.000000	ADJ R - SQ	0.7535
C.V.	11.62892		

VARIABLE	DF	PARAMETER ESTIMATE	STANDARD ERROR	T FOR H0: PARAMETER = 0	PROB>'T'
INTERCEP	1	64.246753	3.602905	17.832	0.0001
PESTRATE	1	-1.012987	0.172153	-5.884	0.0002

$\hat{\alpha}$
$\hat{\beta}$

SS(Reg)
SSE
SS(Total)

In the above output, we have boxed $\hat{\alpha}$ and $\hat{\beta}$, as well as other quantities shown earlier in the hand calculation. (Other items shown are either clear, or will be discussed in Sections 14.6 and 14.7 on analysis of variance.) For further discussion of other SAS options, see SAS Institute (1982).

TABLE 14.3-1
Pest Rate (x_i) and Crop Yield (Y_i) Data

i	1	2	3	4	5	6	7	8	9	10	11	12
x_i	8	6	11	22	14	17	18	24	19	23	26	40
Y_i	59	58	56	53	50	45	43	42	39	38	30	27

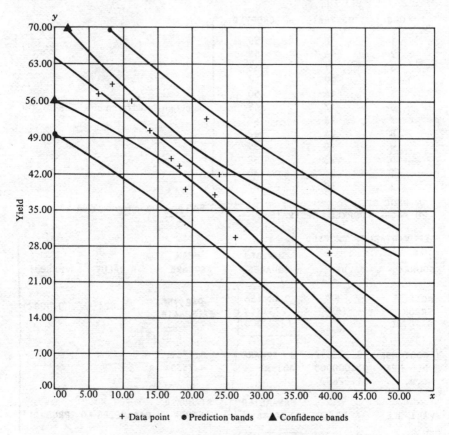

+ Data point   ● Prediction bands   ▲ Confidence bands

Figure 14.3-1. Output for Example 14.3.9.

PROBLEMS FOR SECTION 14.3

14.3.1 For the data set given in Problem 14.2.1
    (a) (i)   Construct a 95% confidence interval for $E(Y|x = 2.5)$.

(ii) Construct a 95% upper confidence bound for $E(Y|x = 2.5)$.

(iii) Construct a 95% lower confidence bound for $E(Y|x = 2.5)$.

(b) (i) Construct a 95% prediction interval for the response Y (i.e., the IQ) when $x = 2.5$.

(ii) Construct a 95% upper prediction bound for Y when $x = 2.5$.

(iii) Construct a 95% lower prediction bound for Y when $x = 2.5$.

(c) Compare the lengths of the respective intervals in parts (a) and (b).

14.3.2 Consider the data set given in Problem 14.1.1, assuming normality of Y given $X = x$. Repeat Problem 14.3.1, with $x = 1.75$ and confidence coefficient .90, for this data set.

14.4. SELECTION OF THE BEST REGRESSION

Examples of problems where selection of the best of several regressions is the experimenter's main concern (rather than the testing of hypotheses or forming of confidence intervals) are not rare. In one class of such problems we assume that r.v.'s drawn from k populations $\pi_1, \ldots, \pi_k$ $(k \geq 2)$ are independent, and that those drawn from π_i are $N(\alpha_i + \beta_i x, \sigma^2)$ r.v.'s if the independent variable is set at level x. If we know that $\alpha_1 = \cdots = \alpha_k$ (the regression lines have the same intercept), it may be our concern to select the regression with the largest slope $\max(\beta_1, \ldots, \beta_k)$; for example, this would be so if $\pi_1, \ldots, \pi_k$ represented k treatments and observations represented yield. If we obtain observations Y_{ij} at level x_{ij} from π_i for $j = 1, \ldots, n_j$ $(1 \leq i \leq k)$, we will naturally (see (14.2.3)) estimate β_i by

$$\hat{\beta}_i = \frac{n_i \sum_{j=1}^{n_i} x_{ij} Y_{ij} - \sum_{j=1}^{n_i} x_{ij} \sum_{j=1}^{n_i} Y_{ij}}{n_i \sum_{j=1}^{n_i} x_{ij}^2 - \left(\sum_{j=1}^{n_i} x_{ij}\right)^2} \tag{14.4.1}$$

and select the population yielding $\max(\hat{\beta}_1, \ldots, \hat{\beta}_k)$ (the largest sample slope). Since $\hat{\beta}_i$ is normally distributed with mean β_i and variance (see (14.2.4))

$$\mathrm{Var}\left(\hat{\beta}_i\right) = \frac{n_i}{n_i \sum_{j=1}^{n_i} x_{ij}^2 - \left(\sum_{j=1}^{n_i} x_{ij}\right)^2} \sigma^2, \tag{14.4.2}$$

the problem is essentially one of ranking and selection of normal means as studied in Chapter 11. If we choose $n_1 = \cdots = n_k = n$ (say) and $x_{1j} = \cdots = x_{kj}$ $(j = 1, \ldots, n)$, all $\hat{\beta}_i$'s have the same variance and the results of Section 11.2 may be used directly if σ^2 is known, while if σ^2 is unknown we proceed as noted in item 1 of Section 11.4.

Similarly for parallel lines $(\beta_1 = \cdots = \beta_k)$, we could derive a procedure for selecting the one with the largest intercept $\max(\alpha_1, \ldots, \alpha_k)$.

If we have regression lines with different slopes *and* different intercepts, the definition of the "best" line may not be clear; for example, we may have to specify an x level of interest (since the line that on the average produces the largest value Y will not be the same for all x).

PROBLEMS FOR SECTION 14.4.

14.4.1 Suppose the yield Y when a crop is planted and amount x of fertilizer i is used on it is a $N(\alpha + \beta_i x, \sigma^2)$ r.v. with $\sigma = 1.2$ bushels per acre $(i = 1, 2, \ldots, 8)$. An experiment will be run with independent observations on each fertilizer at doses $x = 0, 1, 2, 3$. The goal of the experiment is to select (with probability .95 of correct selection) the fertilizer with the highest response coefficient β_i (i.e., the $\max(\beta_1, \beta_2, \ldots, \beta_8)$). The $P(\text{CS})$ will be $\geq .95$, when $\beta_{[8]} - \beta_{[7]} \geq \delta^*$, for what value of δ^*? [Here $\beta_{[1]} \leq \beta_{[2]} \leq \cdots \leq \beta_{[8]}$ are $\beta_1, \ldots, \beta_8$ in numerical order.]

14.5. MULTIPLE REGRESSION*

To this point in this chapter, we have studied the effect of a **single independent variable** x (sometimes called a **predictor variable** or a **regressor variable**) on a dependent variable Y (also known as a **response variable** or a **regressed variable**). Sometimes **several predictor variables** $x_1, \ldots, x_m$ are related to the response variable Y. In an experiment, often the experimenter controls several possible sources of variability, some contribute significantly towards the prediction of the response variable, and others do not. In such situations, it is important to omit the non-significant variables from the model and include only those variables that aid prediction of Y. This process is known as **model building**.

For example, consider prediction of college GPA Y using high-school GPA x_1. Here high-school GPA is not the only variable related to Y. Others include the average number of credit hours x_2 taken by the student each year, the average number of hours spent studying outside of class x_3, the individual's economic status, and so on. A possible model for this situation is

$$E(Y) = \beta_0 + \beta_1 x_1 + \beta_2 x_2 + \cdots + \beta_k x_k \qquad (14.5.1)$$

where

$Y = $ College GPA,

$x_1 = $ High-school GPA,

$x_2 = $ Average number of credit hours taken per year,

$x_3 = $ Average number of hours spent studying,

$\vdots$

---

*This section requires vector and matrix algebra, and may be skipped at a first reading.

Such models are called **multiple** regression models since more than one source of variability is used to "explain" the variation in Y. Thus:

Definition 14.5.2. A model that relates the response variable Y to a set of predictor variables $\{x_1, x_2, \ldots, x_k\}$ by equation (14.5.1) or

$$Y = \beta_0 + \beta_1 x_1 + \beta_2 x_2 + \cdots + \beta_k x_k + \varepsilon, \qquad (14.5.3)$$

is called a **linear statistical model**.

In Definition 14.5.2, Y is a random (response) variable, $\{x_1, x_2, \ldots, x_k\}$ are measured without error, $\beta_0, \beta_1, \ldots, \beta_k$ are unknown parameters, and ε is a random variable. It is **commonly assumed that**

$$E(\varepsilon) = 0, \qquad \text{Var}(\varepsilon) = \sigma^2.$$

In addition, the distribution of ε (and hence of Y) is often assumed to be normal.

Often we have n sets of $(k + 1)$-tuples $\{(Y_i, x_{1i}, x_{2i}, \ldots, x_{ki}): i = 1, 2, \ldots, n\}$. Based on these observations, we estimate and make inferences about equation (14.5.1). **Use of matrices** allows easy and concise specification of the equations and derivations involved. If we hypothesize (14.5.3) as a theoretical relationship between the x's and Y, then we can write (for each $i = 1, 2, \ldots, n$)

$$Y_i = \beta_0 + \beta_1 x_{1i} + \beta_2 x_{2i} + \cdots + \beta_k x_{ki} + \varepsilon_i.$$

Hence the entire set of observations can be written as

$$\begin{cases} Y_1 = \beta_0 + \beta_1 x_{11} + \beta_2 x_{21} + \cdots + \beta_k x_{k1} + \varepsilon_1 \\ Y_2 = \beta_0 + \beta_1 x_{12} + \beta_2 x_{22} + \cdots + \beta_k x_{k2} + \varepsilon_2 \\ \vdots \\ Y_n = \beta_0 + \beta_1 x_{1n} + \beta_2 x_{2n} + \cdots + \beta_k x_{kn} + \varepsilon_n. \end{cases}$$

In matrix notation, this can be written as

$$\mathbf{Y} = \mathbf{X}'\boldsymbol{\beta} + \boldsymbol{\varepsilon}, \qquad (14.5.4)$$

where

$$\mathbf{Y} = \begin{pmatrix} Y_1 \\ Y_2 \\ \vdots \\ Y_n \end{pmatrix}, \; \boldsymbol{\beta} = \begin{pmatrix} \beta_0 \\ \beta_1 \\ \vdots \\ \beta_k \end{pmatrix}, \; \boldsymbol{\varepsilon} = \begin{pmatrix} \varepsilon_1 \\ \varepsilon_2 \\ \vdots \\ \varepsilon_n \end{pmatrix}, \; \mathbf{X} = \begin{pmatrix} 1 & 1 & \cdots & 1 \\ x_{11} & x_{12} & \cdots & x_{1n} \\ x_{21} & x_{22} & \cdots & x_{2n} \\ \vdots \\ x_{k1} & x_{k2} & \cdots & x_{kn} \end{pmatrix}.$$

Here $\mathbf{X}'$ is called the **design matrix**.

From this point, we assume that the ε_i's are independent and identically distributed $N(0, \sigma^2)$ r.v.'s. This assumption is used to allow statistical inference about the parameters and model.

In order to find least-squares estimators of the β's, we consider the sums of squares of errors in predicting Y_i by $\beta_0 + \beta_1 x_{1i} + \cdots + \beta_k x_{ki}$, and find $\hat{\beta}_0, \hat{\beta}_1, \ldots, \hat{\beta}_k$ that minimize

$$Q(\beta) \equiv S(\beta_0, \beta_1, \beta_2, \ldots, \beta_k) = \sum_{i=1}^{n} \left(Y_i - (\beta_0 + \beta_1 x_{1i} + \cdots + \beta_k x_{ki}) \right)^2.$$

Note that

$$\begin{aligned} Q(\beta) &= (\mathbf{Y} - \mathbf{X}'\beta)'(\mathbf{Y} - \mathbf{X}'\beta) \\ &= \mathbf{Y}'\mathbf{Y} - \beta'\mathbf{XY} - \mathbf{Y}'\mathbf{X}'\beta + \beta'\mathbf{XX}'\beta. \end{aligned} \tag{14.5.5}$$

Differentiating $Q(\beta)$ with respect to β, equating to $\mathbf{0}$, and solving for $\hat{\beta}$ yields

$$\hat{\beta} = (\mathbf{XX}')^{-1}\mathbf{XY}. \tag{14.5.6}$$

(The details here are left as exercises, and may be found in books devoted solely to regression analysis and linear models.)

Since $\mathbf{Y}$ has a multivariate normal distribution with mean $\mathbf{X}'\beta$ and variance-covariance matrix $\Sigma_\mathbf{Y} = \sigma^2 \mathbf{I}$, where $\mathbf{I}$ is the $n \times n$ identity matrix, $\hat{\beta}$ is also normally distributed with mean β and variance-covariance matrix

$$\begin{aligned} \Sigma_{\hat{\beta}} &= (\mathbf{XX}')^{-1}\mathbf{X}\sigma^2\mathbf{IX}'\left((\mathbf{XX}')^{-1}\right)' \\ &= \sigma^2(\mathbf{XX}')^{-1}(\mathbf{XX}')(\mathbf{XX}')^{-1}, \qquad \text{by symmetry of } (\mathbf{XX}')^{-1} \quad (14.5.7) \\ &= \sigma^2(\mathbf{XX}')^{-1}. \end{aligned}$$

The maximum likelihood estimator of σ^2 is unbiased when multiplied by $n/(n-k-1)$, yielding the estimator

$$\begin{aligned} \hat{\sigma}^2 &= \left(\mathbf{Y} - \mathbf{X}'\hat{\beta}\right)'\left(\mathbf{Y} - \mathbf{X}'\hat{\beta}\right)/(n-k-1) \\ &= \left(\mathbf{Y}'\mathbf{Y} - \hat{\beta}'\mathbf{XY}\right)/(n-k-1). \end{aligned} \tag{14.5.8}$$

Example 14.5.9. Suppose the following table gives college GPA Y of 7 randomly chosen students, and their high-school GPA x_1, and average weekly number of hours spent studying x_2.

i	Y_i	x_{1i}	x_{2i}
1	3.5	3.1	30
2	3.2	3.4	25
3	3.0	3.0	20
4	2.9	3.2	30
5	4.0	3.9	40
6	2.5	2.8	25
7	2.3	2.2	30

We will use this data set to demonstrate fitting model $Y = \beta_0 + \beta_1 x_1 + \beta_2 x_2 + \varepsilon$. Here

$$
\mathbf{Y} = \begin{pmatrix} 3.5 \\ 3.2 \\ 3.0 \\ 2.9 \\ 4.0 \\ 2.5 \\ 2.3 \end{pmatrix}, \quad \mathbf{X} = \begin{pmatrix} 1 & 1 & 1 & 1 & 1 & 1 & 1 \\ 3.1 & 3.4 & 3.0 & 3.2 & 3.9 & 2.8 & 2.2 \\ 30 & 25 & 20 & 30 & 40 & 25 & 30 \end{pmatrix},
$$

$$
\mathbf{XX'} = \begin{pmatrix} 7 & 21.6 & 200 \\ 21.6 & 68.3 & 626 \\ 200 & 626 & 5950 \end{pmatrix}, \quad \mathbf{XY} = \begin{pmatrix} 21.4 \\ 67.67 \\ 623.5 \end{pmatrix}, \quad \mathbf{Y'Y} = 67.44,
$$

$$
|\mathbf{XX'}| = \det(\mathbf{XX'}) = 7\big((68.3)(5950) - (626)^2\big) - (21.6)\big((21.6)(5950) - (200)(626)\big)
$$
$$
+ (200)\big((21.6)(626) - (68.3)(200)\big)
$$
$$
= 2171.
$$

Thus,

$$
(\mathbf{XX'})^{-1} = \begin{pmatrix} 6.6831 & -1.52925 & -0.06375 \\ -1.52925 & 0.76002 & -0.0285583 \\ -0.06375 & -0.028558 & 0.00531553 \end{pmatrix},
$$

and

$$
\hat{\boldsymbol{\beta}} = (\mathbf{XX'})^{-1}\mathbf{XY} = (\mathbf{XX'})^{-1}\begin{pmatrix} 21.4 \\ 67.67 \\ 623.5 \end{pmatrix} = \begin{pmatrix} -0.2141325 \\ 0.89850335 \\ 0.017442794 \end{pmatrix}.
$$

(Thus, $\hat{\beta}_0 = -0.2141325$, $\hat{\beta}_1 = 0.89850335$, and $\hat{\beta}_2 = 0.017442794$.) Also,

$$
\hat{\sigma}^2 = \frac{(67.44 - \hat{\boldsymbol{\beta}}'\mathbf{XY})}{4} = \frac{(67.44 - 67.09486825)}{4} = 0.0862829375,
$$

$$
\boldsymbol{\Sigma}_{\boldsymbol{\beta}} = (\mathbf{XX'})^{-1}\sigma^2, \quad \hat{\boldsymbol{\Sigma}}_{\boldsymbol{\beta}} = (\mathbf{XX'})^{-1}\hat{\sigma}^2 = (\mathbf{XX'})^{-1}(0.0862829375).
$$

Therefore,

$$
\text{Var}\left(\hat{\beta}_0\right) = 6.6831\sigma^2, \qquad \widehat{\text{Var}\left(\hat{\beta}_0\right)} = 0.5766375,
$$

$$
\text{Var}\left(\hat{\beta}_1\right) = 0.76002\sigma^2, \qquad \widehat{\text{Var}\left(\hat{\beta}_1\right)} = 0.065577,
$$

$$
\text{Var}\left(\hat{\beta}_2\right) = 0.0053155\sigma^2, \qquad \widehat{\text{Var}\left(\hat{\beta}_2\right)} = 0.00045864.
$$

Discussion 14.5.10. Under the normality assumption on the ε_i's in model (14.5.4), it can be shown (compare with Theorem 14.2.5) that $\hat{\beta}_i \sim$

$N(\beta_i, a_{i+1,i+1}\sigma^2)$, where $a_{i+1,i+1}$ is the $i + 1$st diagonal entry of $(\mathbf{XX}')^{-1}$, $i = 0, 1, 2, \ldots, k$. Thus, in Example 14.5.9, $\hat{\beta}_2 \sim N(\beta_2, .0053155\sigma^2)$ and

$$\frac{\hat{\beta}_i - \beta_i}{\sqrt{a_{i+1,i+1}}\,\hat{\sigma}}$$

has a t-distribution with $n - (k + 1)$ degrees of freedom. Hence hypotheses about $\beta_0, \beta_1, \beta_2, \ldots, \beta_k$ can be tested and confidence intervals can be constructed.

Example 14.5.11. Continuing Example 14.5.9, test the following pairs of hypotheses and construct a 95% confidence interval for β_0, a 90% upper confidence limit for β_1, and a 95% lower confidence limit for β_2.

(a) H_0^0: $\beta_0 = 0$ versus H_1^0: $\beta_0 \neq 0$. Here we compute

$$T_0 = \hat{\beta}_0 / \left(\sqrt{a_{11}}\,\hat{\sigma}\right) = -0.2141325 / \sqrt{0.5766375} = -0.282,$$

and since we have $n - (k + 1) = 4$ degrees of freedom, at level 0.05 we reject H_0^0 iff $|T_0| > 2.776$.

(b) H_0^1: $\beta_1 = 0$ versus H_1^1: $\beta_1 > 0$. Here we compute

$$T_1 = \hat{\beta}_1 / \left(\sqrt{a_{22}}\,\hat{\sigma}\right) = 0.89850335 / \sqrt{0.065577} = 3.5087,$$

and since we have 4 degrees of freedom, at level 0.05 we reject H_0^1 iff $T_1 > 2.132$.

(c) H_0^2: $\beta_2 = 0$ versus H_1^2: $\beta_2 > 0$. Here we compute

$$T_2 = \hat{\beta}_2 / \left(\sqrt{a_{33}}\,\hat{\sigma}\right) = 0.017442794 / \sqrt{0.00045864} = 0.8145,$$

and since we have 4 degrees of freedom, at level .05 we reject H_0^2 iff $T_2 > 2.132$.

At level .05, we reject H_0^1, but not H_0^0 and H_0^2. Thus, based on the given data, high-school GPA is the strongest predictor of college GPA. (The other variable may have an effect, but of a lesser magnitude needing more data to show significance.)

The 95% confidence interval for β_0 is

$$\hat{\beta}_0 \pm t_{n-k-1}^{-1}(1 - \alpha/2)\sqrt{a_{11}}\,\hat{\sigma} = -0.2141325 \pm (2.776)(0.75993)$$

$$= -0.2141325 \pm 2.108$$

$$= (-2.322134, 1.89387).$$

The 90% upper confidence limit for β_1 is

$$\left(-\infty, \hat{\beta}_1 + t_{n-k-1}^{-1}(1 - \alpha)\sqrt{a_{22}}\,\hat{\sigma} \right) = (-\infty, 0.89850335 + (1.533)(0.25608))$$

$$= (-\infty, 1.29107).$$

The 95% lower confidence limit for β_2 is

$$\left(\hat{\beta}_2 - t_{n-k-1}^{-1}(1 - \alpha)\sqrt{a_{33}}\,\hat{\sigma}, \infty \right) = (0.017442794 - (2.132)(0.02142), \infty)$$

$$= (-0.028216, \infty).$$

To develop a model, we often desire to test a simultaneous hypothesis about parameters, for example to test H_0: $\beta_{m+1} = \beta_{m+2} = \cdots = \beta_k = 0$. Under H_0 our model would be

$$H_0: Y = \beta_0 + \beta_1 x_1 + \beta_2 x_2 + \cdots + \beta_m x_m + \varepsilon, \qquad (14.5.12)$$

as opposed to

$$H_1: Y = \beta_0 + \beta_1 x_1 + \beta_2 x_2 + \cdots + \beta_m x_m + \beta_{m+1} x_{m+1} + \cdots + \beta_k x_k + \varepsilon.$$

$$(14.5.13)$$

Here H_0 is called a **reduced model,** whereas H_1 is called a **full model.** The procedure described below for testing H_0 versus H_1 is known as the **general linear model (GLM) procedure.**

Let $\mathbf{X}'$ be the design matrix for the full model, and $\mathbf{X}^{*\prime}$ the associated design matrix for the reduced model. Further, let $\hat{\boldsymbol{\beta}}$ be the least squares estimator of $\boldsymbol{\beta}$ for the full model, and $\hat{\boldsymbol{\beta}}^*$ the least squares estimator of $\boldsymbol{\beta}^*$ for the reduced model. Note that, under H_0, the estimator of σ^2 is

$$\hat{\sigma}_0^2 = \left(\mathbf{Y}'\mathbf{Y} - \hat{\boldsymbol{\beta}}^{*\prime}\mathbf{X}^*\mathbf{Y} \right) / (n - m - 1)$$

(if $m = 0$, then $\hat{\boldsymbol{\beta}}' = \mathbf{0}$), whereas under H_1 the estimator of σ^2 is

$$\hat{\sigma}_1^2 = (\mathbf{Y}'\mathbf{Y} - \boldsymbol{\beta}'\mathbf{XY}) / (n - k - 1).$$

Then

$$F = \frac{\left((n - m - 1)\hat{\sigma}_0^2 - (n - k - 1)\hat{\sigma}_1^2 \right) / (k - m)}{(n - k - 1)\hat{\sigma}_1^2 / (n - k - 1)}$$

$$= \frac{\left(\hat{\boldsymbol{\beta}}'\mathbf{XY} - \hat{\boldsymbol{\beta}}^{*\prime}\mathbf{X}^*\mathbf{Y} \right) / (k - m)}{\left(\mathbf{Y}'\mathbf{Y} - \hat{\boldsymbol{\beta}}'\mathbf{XY} \right) / (n - k - 1)}$$

can be shown to have an $F_{k-m,\,n-k-1}$ distribution. Therefore we reject H_0 (at level α) if $F > F_{k-m,\,n-k-1,1-\alpha}^{-1}$.

We conclude this section with a discussion of **confidence intervals, and prediction intervals for a new observation.** Let $\mathbf{x}_0' = (1, x_{1,0}, x_{2,0}, \ldots, x_{k,0})$ be a specific vector of predictor variables. If we desire a confidence interval for $E(Y|\mathbf{x}_0)$ then, as in (14.3.3), it can be shown that

$$
\begin{aligned}
\operatorname{Var}\left(\widehat{E(Y|\mathbf{x}_0)}\right) &= \operatorname{Var}\left(\hat{\beta}_0 + \hat{\beta}_1 x_{1,0} + \hat{\beta}_2 x_{2,0} + \cdots + \hat{\beta}_k x_{k,0}\right) \\
&= \sigma^2 \mathbf{x}_0'(\mathbf{XX}')^{-1}\mathbf{x}_0,
\end{aligned}
\tag{14.5.14}
$$

hence $100(1 - \alpha)\%$ confidence limits for $E(Y|\mathbf{x}_0)$ are

$$
\left(\hat{\beta}_0 + \hat{\beta}_1 x_{1,0} + \hat{\beta}_2 x_{2,0} + \cdots + \hat{\beta}_k x_{k,0}\right) \pm t_{n-k-1}^{-1}(1 - \alpha/2)\sqrt{\hat{\sigma}^2 \mathbf{x}_0'(\mathbf{XX}')^{-1}\mathbf{x}_0}.
\tag{14.5.15}
$$

Similarly, a prediction interval for Y at $\mathbf{x}_0$ is found using an argument similar to (14.3.6). It can be shown that

$$
\operatorname{Var}\left(Y - \left(\hat{\beta}_0 + \hat{\beta}_1 x_{1,0} + \hat{\beta}_2 x_{2,0} + \cdots + \hat{\beta}_k x_{k,0}\right)\right) = \sigma^2\left(1 + \mathbf{x}_0'(\mathbf{XX}')^{-1}\mathbf{x}_0\right).
\tag{14.5.16}
$$

Hence a $100(1 - \alpha)\%$ prediction interval for a new observation Y at $\mathbf{x}_0$ is

$$
\begin{aligned}
&\left(\hat{\beta}_0 + \hat{\beta}_1 x_{1,0} + \hat{\beta}_2 x_{2,0} + \cdots + \hat{\beta}_k x_{k,0}\right) \\
&\pm t_{n-k-1}^{-1}(1 - \alpha/2)\hat{\sigma}\sqrt{1 + \mathbf{x}_0'(\mathbf{XX}')^{-1}\mathbf{x}_0}.
\end{aligned}
\tag{14.5.17}
$$

Example 14.5.18. In Example 14.5.9, at $\mathbf{x}_0' = (1, 2.5, 20)$ find confidence and prediction intervals for $E(Y)$ and for Y, respectively.

Here, $\hat{Y} = \hat{\beta}_0 + \hat{\beta}_1 x_{1,0} + \hat{\beta}_2 x_{2,0} = (-0.2141325)(1) + (0.89850335)(2.5) + (0.017442794)(20) = 2.381$,

$$
\mathbf{x}_0'(\mathbf{XX}')^{-1}\mathbf{x}_0 = (1 \quad 2.5 \quad 20)(\mathbf{XX}')^{-1}\begin{pmatrix} 1 \\ 2.5 \\ 20 \end{pmatrix} = 0.5073574,
$$

$\hat{\sigma}^2(\mathbf{x}_0'(\mathbf{XX}')^{-1}\mathbf{x}_0) = .0437763$, and $\hat{\sigma}^2(1 + \mathbf{x}_0'(\mathbf{XX}')^{-1}\mathbf{x}_0) = 0.13006$. Thus, 95% confidence limits on the mean at $\mathbf{x}_0$ are

$$
2.381 \pm (2.776)\sqrt{0.0437763} = 2.381 \pm 0.58 = (1.801, 2.961),
$$

whereas 95% prediction limits on the future observation at $\mathbf{x}_0$ are

$$
2.381 \pm (2.776)\sqrt{0.13006} = 2.381 \pm 1 = (1.381, 3.381).
$$

PROBLEMS FOR SECTION 14.5

14.5.1 The data below is a classic data set obtained from operation of a plant for the oxidation of ammonia to nitric acid. Here Y is 10 times the percentage of in-going ammonia that is lost as unabsorbed nitric oxides, x_1 is flow of air to the plant, x_2 is temperature of cooling water entering the nitric oxide absorption tower, and x_3 is concentration of nitric acid in the absorbing liquid (with 50 subtracted and then multiplied by 10).

i	Y_i	x_{1i}	x_{2i}	x_{3i}
1	42	80	27	89
2	37	80	27	88
3	37	75	25	90
4	28	62	24	87
5	18	62	22	87
6	18	62	23	87
7	19	62	24	93
8	20	62	24	93
9	15	58	23	87
10	14	58	18	80
11	14	58	18	89
12	13	58	17	88
13	11	58	18	82
14	12	58	19	93
15	8	50	18	89
16	7	50	18	86
17	8	50	19	72
18	8	50	19	79
19	9	50	20	80
20	15	56	20	82
21	15	70	20	91

(a) Find least-squares estimates of $\beta_0, \beta_1, \beta_2, \beta_3$, and the least-squares estimate of Y, say $\hat{Y}$.

(b) Test $H_0: \beta_1 = \beta_2 = \beta_3 = 0$ at level .05.

(c) Test $H_0^1: \beta_1 = 0$ versus $H_1^1: \beta_1 \neq 0$, and $H_1^2: \beta_2 = 0$ versus $H_1^2: \beta_2 \neq 0$.

(d) Construct 95% confidence intervals for β_0 and β_3.

(e) At $(40, 8, 95)$ find 95% confidence and prediction limits for $E(Y)$ and Y, respectively.

14.5.2 Consider the linear statistical model

$$Y = \beta_0 + \beta_1 w + \beta_2 w^2 + \cdots + \beta_k w^k + \varepsilon.$$

Suppose we take n measurements, and model

$$Y_i = \beta_0 + \beta_1 w_i + \beta_2 w_i^2 + \cdots + \beta_k w_i^k + \varepsilon_i \ (i = 1, 2, \ldots, n)$$

(note that $x_1 = w, x_2 = w^2, \ldots, x_k = w^k$). Assuming that the ε_i's are independent $N(0, \sigma^2)$ r.v.'s, use the matrix methods developed in Section 14.5 and

(a) Find least-squares estimators of $\beta_0, \beta_1, \ldots, \beta_k$.

(b) Find the least-squares estimator of σ^2.

(c) Test H_0: $\beta_i = 0$ for $i = 0, 1, \ldots, k$ at level α.

(d) Construct a confidence interval for β_i $(i = 0, 1, 2, \ldots, k)$.

(e) Test H_0: $\beta_1 = \beta_2 = \cdots = \beta_k = 0$ at level α.

(f) If at a future observation $w = w_0$, construct a confidence interval and a prediction interval respectively for $E(Y)$ and for Y. (Use confidence coefficient α.)

14.5.3 Consider the data set

x	1	2	1.5	3	3.5	2.5	4
Y	9	40	28.6	140.0	210	86	300

Fit the model $Y = \beta_0 + \beta_1 x + \beta_2 x^2 + \beta_3 x^3 + \varepsilon$ and work parts (a) through (f) of Problem 14.5.2 for this model (with $x_0 = 4$).

14.6. ONE-WAY ANALYSIS OF VARIANCE

Let $\pi_1, \pi_2, \ldots, \pi_k$ be k normal populations (sources of observations), with observations from π_i being independent and $N(\mu_i, \sigma^2)$. One-way analysis of variance (or **ANOVA**) deals with testing the hypothesis H_0: $\mu_1 = \mu_2 = \cdots = \mu_k$ versus H_1: {At least one of $\mu_1, \mu_2, \ldots, \mu_k$ differs from the others}. (The case $k = 2$, testing H_0: $\mu_1 = \mu_2$, was dealt with earlier, in Section 9.9.)

Such situations arise frequently in practice. For example, if k different drugs are being tested, the response measured being the time to relief of pain after the drug has been administered, a natural question is "Do the drugs under consideration have the same mean time to relief, or does at least one of the drugs have a significantly different mean relief time?" As a **second example,** consider the problem of comparing the vitamin content of a food when it is prepared in k different ways. As a **third example,** consider k different varieties of an agricultural crop (e.g., soybeans), where a problem of concern is to find if all the varieties have the same yield, or if at least one of the varieties has a significantly different yield.

We will first consider the testing problem for the hypothesis H_0: $\mu_1 = \mu_2 = \cdots = \mu_k$, and then consider methods for deciding which of the means are different from which others. Although space does not permit a full consideration of the latter problem, it is a very important one in practice: very rarely does one simply reject H_0 and then leave the problem (since in practice one needs to know *which* means are different, are they larger or smaller, etc.).

To formalize the problem, let X_{ij} $(j = 1, 2, \ldots, n_i; i = 1, 2, \ldots, k)$ be independent r.v.'s with $X_{ij} \sim N(\mu_i, \sigma^2)$. To approach the problem of testing H_0: $\mu_1 = \mu_2 = \cdots = \mu_k$ we will develop a likelihood ratio test (this method of development of a test was discussed in general in Section 9.11). Here the p.d.f. of the X_{ij}'s is

$$f(\mathbf{x}|\mu_1,\ldots,\mu_k,\sigma^2) = \left(\frac{1}{\sqrt{2\pi}\,\sigma}\right)^{n_1+n_2+\,\cdots\,+n_k} e^{-\sum_{i=1}^{k}\sum_{j=1}^{n_i}(x_{ij}-\mu_i)^2/(2\sigma^2)} \quad (14.6.1)$$

with parameter space for $(\mu_1,\mu_2,\ldots,\mu_k,\sigma^2)$ *either*

$$\omega = \left\{(\mathbf{\mu},\sigma^2):\mu_1=\mu_2=\,\cdots\,=\mu_k,\sigma^2>0\right\} \quad (14.6.2)$$

(the above being when H_0 is true), *or*

$$\Omega = \left\{(\mathbf{\mu},\sigma^2):\sigma^2>0\right\} \quad (14.6.3)$$

(the above being in general). **The likelihood ratio test (see (9.11.2)) sets**

$$\phi(\mathbf{x}) = \begin{cases} 1, & \text{if } \lambda(\mathbf{x}) < c \\ 0, & \text{otherwise,} \end{cases} \quad (14.6.4)$$

where c is a constant such that

$$\max_{(\mathbf{\mu},\sigma^2)\in\omega} E(\phi(\mathbf{X})) = \alpha$$

and

$$\lambda(\mathbf{x}) = \sup_{\omega} f(\mathbf{x}|\mathbf{\mu},\sigma^2)\Big/\sup_{\Omega} f(\mathbf{x}|\mathbf{\mu},\sigma^2).$$

When H_0 is true (i.e., under ω), $f(\mathbf{x}|\mathbf{\mu},\sigma^2)$ is maximized over $(\mathbf{\mu},\sigma^2)$ in ω by taking (for $i=1,2,\ldots,k$)

$$\mu_i = \hat{\mu}_i = \overline{\overline{X}} \equiv \sum_{i=1}^{k}\sum_{j=1}^{n_i} X_{ij}/(n_1+n_2+\,\cdots\,+n_k) = \frac{\sum_{i=1}^{k} n_i\overline{X}_i}{\sum_{i=1}^{k} n_i} \quad (14.6.5)$$

where $\overline{X}_i = (X_{i1}+X_{i2}+\,\cdots\,+X_{in_i})/n_i$, and

$$\sigma^2 = \hat{\sigma}_{\omega}^2 = \sum_{i=1}^{k}\sum_{j=1}^{n_i}\left(X_{ij}-\overline{\overline{X}}\right)^2\Big/(n_1+n_2+\,\cdots\,+n_k). \quad (14.6.6)$$

(These are, of course, the maximum likelihood estimators of μ and σ^2 when ω is known to be true.) **In general under** Ω, $f(\mathbf{x}|\mu, \sigma^2)$ is maximized at

$$\mu_i = \hat{\mu}_i = \bar{X}_i = \sum_{j=1}^{n_i} X_{ij}/n_i \ (i = 1, 2, \ldots, k) \tag{14.6.7}$$

and

$$\sigma^2 = \hat{\sigma}_\Omega^2 = \sum_{i=1}^{k} \sum_{j=1}^{n_i} \left(X_{ij} - \bar{X}_i \right)^2 \Big/ (n_1 + n_2 + \cdots + n_k). \tag{14.6.8}$$

It follows that

$$\lambda(\mathbf{X}) = f\big(\mathbf{X}|\bar{\bar{\mathbf{X}}}, \hat{\sigma}_\omega^2\big) \Big/ f\big(\mathbf{X}|\bar{\mathbf{X}}, \hat{\sigma}_\Omega^2\big)$$

where $\bar{\bar{\mathbf{X}}} = (\bar{\bar{X}}, \bar{\bar{X}}, \ldots, \bar{\bar{X}})$ and $\bar{\mathbf{X}} = (\bar{X}_1, \bar{X}_2, \ldots, \bar{X}_k)$; more explicitly, after algebraic simplification,

$$\lambda(\mathbf{X}) = \left(\frac{\hat{\sigma}_\Omega^2}{\hat{\sigma}_\omega^2} \right)^{n_1 + n_2 + \cdots + n_k}, \tag{14.6.9}$$

or $\lambda(\mathbf{X})^{1/(n_1 + n_2 + \cdots + n_k)} = \hat{\sigma}_\Omega^2 / \hat{\sigma}_\omega^2$, or

$$\lambda(\mathbf{X})^{1/(n_1 + n_2 + \cdots + n_k)} = \frac{\displaystyle\sum_{i=1}^{k} \sum_{j=1}^{n_i} \left(X_{ij} - \bar{X}_i \right)^2}{\displaystyle\sum_{i=1}^{k} \sum_{j=1}^{n_i} \left(X_{ij} - \bar{\bar{X}} \right)^2}. \tag{14.6.10}$$

To obtain a further simplification, because

$$\sum_i \sum_j \left(X_{ij} - \bar{X}_i \right)\left(\bar{X}_i - \bar{\bar{X}} \right) = \sum_i \left(\bar{X}_i - \bar{\bar{X}} \right) \sum_j \left(X_{ij} - \bar{X}_i \right) = 0$$

(where i runs from 1 to k, and j from 1 to n_i), we have

$$\sum_i \sum_j \left(X_{ij} - \bar{\bar{X}} \right)^2 = \sum_i \sum_j \left(X_{ij} - \bar{X}_i + \bar{X}_i - \bar{\bar{X}} \right)^2$$

$$= \sum_i \sum_j \left(X_{ij} - \bar{X}_i \right)^2 + \sum_i \sum_j \left(\bar{X}_i - \bar{\bar{X}} \right)^2,$$

hence (using the above in (14.6.10)) we find

$$\lambda(\mathbf{X})^{1/(n_1+n_2+\cdots+n_k)} = \cfrac{1}{1 + \sum\limits_{i=1}^{k}\sum\limits_{j=1}^{n_i}\left(\overline{X}_j - \overline{\overline{X}}\right)^2 \bigg/ \sum\limits_{i=1}^{k}\sum\limits_{j=1}^{n_i}\left(X_{ij} - \overline{X}_i\right)^2}.$$

It follows from (14.6.4) that the likelihood ratio test is thus equivalent to

$$\phi(\mathbf{X}) = \begin{cases} 1, & \text{if } \sum\limits_{i=1}^{k}\sum\limits_{j=1}^{n_i}\left(\overline{X}_i - \overline{\overline{X}}\right)^2 \bigg/ \sum\limits_{i=1}^{k}\sum\limits_{j=1}^{n_i}\left(X_{ij} - \overline{X}_i\right)^2 > c^{-\sum_i n_i} - 1 \equiv c^* \\ 0, & \text{otherwise,} \end{cases}$$

$$(14.6.11)$$

where c^* is yet to be set so the test has level α, that is, $\max\limits_{(\mu,\sigma^2)\in\omega} E(\phi(\mathbf{X})) = \alpha$. **To determine c^*, the distribution of the ratio of sums of squares in (14.6.11) is needed under H_0. This follows from three key results** (similar to those used in Example 9.11.3). Now

$$\sum_j \left(X_{ij} - \overline{X}_i\right)^2\Big/\sigma^2 \sim \chi^2_{n_i-1}(0),$$

and, since the samples from the various populations are independent, by the reproductive property of the chi-square distribution we obtain **the first key result (giving us the distribution of the denominator sum of squares)**

$$\sum_i \sum_j \left(X_{ij} - \overline{X}_i\right)^2\Big/\sigma^2 \sim \chi^2_{n_1+n_2+\cdots+n_k-k}(0).$$

(In fact, note that this result holds whether H_0 is true or not.) Now, under H_0 it is true that

$$(1/\sigma^2)\sum_i \sum_j \left(X_{ij} - \overline{\overline{X}}\right)^2 \sim \chi^2_{n_1+n_2+\cdots+n_k-1}(0)$$

(since then the X_{ij}'s are independent with the same mean and variance). Also, under H_0 the $\overline{X}_i$ are independent r.v.'s and $\sqrt{n_i}(\overline{X}_i - \mu)/\sigma \sim N(0,1)$, hence

$$\sum_i n_i(\overline{X}_i - \mu)^2/\sigma^2 \sim \chi^2_k(0).$$

This quantity is similar to the numerator sum of squares in (14.6.11), though there μ is replaced by $\overline{\overline{X}}$. The two are, however, closely related since

$$\sum_i n_i(\overline{X}_i - \mu)^2 \Big/ \sigma^2 = \sum_i n_i(\overline{X}_i - \overline{\overline{X}} + \overline{\overline{X}} - \mu)^2 \Big/ \sigma^2$$

$$= \sum_i n_i(\overline{X}_i - \overline{\overline{X}})^2 \Big/ \sigma^2 + \sum_i n_i(\overline{\overline{X}} - \mu)^2 \Big/ \sigma^2$$

$$+ 2\sum_i n_i(\overline{X}_i - \overline{\overline{X}})(\overline{\overline{X}} - \mu) \Big/ \sigma^2$$

$$= \sum_i n_i(\overline{X}_i - \overline{\overline{X}})^2 \Big/ \sigma^2 + \sum_i n_i(\overline{\overline{X}} - \mu)^2 \Big/ \sigma^2$$

since the third term equals

$$(2/\sigma^2)(\overline{\overline{X}} - \mu)\sum_i n_i(\overline{X}_i - \overline{\overline{X}}) = (2/\sigma^2)(\overline{\overline{X}} - \mu)\left(\sum_i \sum_j X_{ij} - (n_1 + \cdots + n_k)\overline{\overline{X}}\right) = 0.$$

The second key result, that the numerator sum of squares

$$\sum_i n_i\left(\overline{X}_i - \overline{\overline{X}}\right)^2 \Big/ \sigma^2 \sim \chi^2_{k-1}(0),$$

and **the third key result, that the numerator and denominator sum of squares are independent r.v.'s,** follow from Cochran's theorem, which is basic to both one-way ANOVA and more advanced analyses of variance. We will state the theorem without proof [for a proof, see, e.g., Scheffé (1959), pp. 419–423]:

Theorem 14.6.12. Cochran's Theorem. Let $Y_1, Y_2, \ldots, Y_m$ be independent $N(0, \sigma^2)$ r.v.'s. Let $Q_l = \sum_i \sum_j a_{lij} Y_i Y_j$, where the summations run over $1, 2, \ldots, m$ (such a Q_l is called a **quadratic form** in $Y_1, Y_2, \ldots, Y_m$), and denote the rank of the matrix $B_l = (A_l + A_l')/2$, where $A_l = (a_{lij})$, by r_l for $l = 1, 2, \ldots, s$. Suppose

$$\sum_1^m Y_i^2 = Q_1 + Q_2 + \cdots + Q_s. \tag{14.6.13}$$

Then $Q_1, Q_2, \ldots, Q_s$ are independent r.v.'s, and $Q_l/\sigma^2 \sim \chi^2_{r_l}(0)$, if and only if $r_1 + r_2 + \cdots + r_s = m$.

We will not show in detail that Cochran's theorem yields the desired key results. However (except for the consideration of the ranks of the matrices involved, which involves matrix algebra) the application is straightforward. It

follows that under H_0

$$\frac{\sum_{i=1}^{k} n_i (\bar{X}_i - \bar{\bar{X}})^2 / (k - 1)}{\sum_{i=1}^{k} \sum_{j=1}^{n_i} (X_{ij} - \bar{X}_i)^2 / (n_1 + n_2 + \cdots + n_k - k)} \sim F_{k-1, n_1 + n_2 + \cdots + n_k - k}.$$

Traditionally, the numerator is denoted by **MSB** (mean square between populations), and the denominator is denoted by **MSW** (mean square within populations), so that the **likelihood test (14.6.11)** reduces to

$$\phi(x) = \begin{cases} 1, & \text{if } \dfrac{\text{MSB}}{\text{MSW}} > c^* \dfrac{n_1 + n_2 + \cdots + n_k - k}{k - 1} \\[2em] 0, & \text{otherwise.} \end{cases} \qquad (14.6.14)$$

The level of the test will be α if we set c^* such that

$$c^* \frac{n_1 + n_2 + \cdots + n_k - k}{k - 1} = F_{k-1, n_1 + n_2 + \cdots + n_k - k, 1 - \alpha}^{-1}, \qquad (14.6.15)$$

which completes specification of the likelihood ratio test for the hypothesis H_0: $\mu_1 = \mu_2 = \cdots = \mu_k$.

Intuitive reasoning is often used to obtain the test just found to be the likelihood ratio test. We will now develop that intuitive reasoning, since it yields a great deal of insight into the analysis of variance. Let us talk in terms of the experiment with different pain relievers described earlier in this section. The response time with the ith pain reliever on its jth subject is denoted by X_{ij}, which is assumed to be an $N(\mu_i, \sigma^2)$ r.v. (This normality can be tested as discussed in Section 13.4. If the variance is not the same for the various pain relievers, methods similar to those in Section 9.10 can be used.) The jth observation in the ith pain reliever can be written as

$$X_{ij} = \mu_i + \varepsilon_{ij} \; (j = 1, 2, \ldots, n_i; \, i = 1, 2, \ldots, k), \qquad (14.6.16)$$

a linear model (see Definition 14.5.2) that expresses X_{ij} as its mean value μ_i plus a deviation ε_{ij}. Here the ε_{ij} are independent $N(0, \sigma^2)$ r.v.'s called **errors**. This model is often rewritten (or, **reparametrized**) by expressing μ_i as the average $\mu = (\mu_1 + \mu_2 + \cdots + \mu_k)/k$ of all the means plus a deviation α_i $(i = 1, 2, \ldots, k)$:

$$\mu_i = \mu + \alpha_i \; (i = 1, 2, \ldots, k).$$

If we sum over i, we find $k\mu = k\mu + (\alpha_1 + \alpha_2 + \cdots + \alpha_k)$, or in other words the reparametrized model has a **constraint** on its parameters:

$$\alpha_1 + \alpha_2 + \cdots + \alpha_k = 0.$$

We have then rewritten model (14.6.16) as

$$X_{ij} = \mu + \alpha_i + \varepsilon_{ij} \ (j = 1, 2, \ldots, n_i; \ i = 1, 2, \ldots, k) \qquad (14.6.17)$$

where $\alpha_1 + \alpha_2 + \cdots + \alpha_k = 0$. α_i is called **the ith treatment effect**. Note that the hypotheses $H_0: \mu_1 = \mu_2 = \cdots = \mu_k$ and $H_0^*: \alpha_1 = \alpha_2 = \cdots = \alpha_k = 0$ are equivalent.

Since ε_{ij} is $N(0, \sigma^2)$, the smaller σ^2, the more concentrated the data will be about its mean. The **method of least squares** [developed by Gauss in the nineteenth century and by Markov in the twentieth century, and already introduced at (14.1.21)] seeks to estimate the unknowns $\mu, \alpha_1, \alpha_2, \ldots, \alpha_k$ so as to make X_{ij} as close as possible to its mean, in the sense of minimizing

$$\sum_i \sum_j (X_{ij} - \mu - \alpha_i)^2.$$

Differentiating with respect to μ and α_i, respectively, and setting the derivative to zero yields the $k + 1$ equations

$$\begin{cases} \dfrac{\partial}{\partial \mu} \sum_i \sum_j (X_{ij} - \mu - \alpha_i)^2 = -2 \sum_i \sum_j (X_{ij} - \mu - \alpha_i) = 0 \\[2mm] \dfrac{\partial}{\partial \alpha_i} \sum_i \sum_j (X_{ij} - \mu - \alpha_i)^2 = -2 \sum_{j=1}^{n_i} (X_{ij} - \mu - \alpha_i) = 0 \quad (i = 1, 2, \ldots, k). \end{cases}$$

$$(14.6.18)$$

Solving this system, we find the estimators

$$\begin{cases} \hat{\mu} = \overline{\overline{X}} = \sum_i \sum_j X_{ij} / (n_1 + n_2 + \cdots + n_k) \\[2mm] \hat{\alpha}_i = \sum_j X_{ij} / n_i - \hat{\mu} = \overline{X}_i - \overline{\overline{X}} \quad (i = 1, 2, \ldots, k). \end{cases} \qquad (14.6.19)$$

Denote

$$N \equiv n_1 + n_2 + \cdots + n_k, \quad X_{..} \equiv \sum_i \sum_j X_{ij}, \quad \overline{X}_{..} \equiv \sum_i \sum_j X_{ij} / N,$$

$$X_{i.} \equiv \sum_j X_{ij}, \quad \overline{X}_{i.} \equiv \sum_j X_{ij} / n_i,$$

so that $\hat{\mu} = \overline{X}_{..}$ and $\hat{\alpha}_i = \overline{X}_{i.} - \overline{X}_{..}$ $(i = 1, 2, \ldots, k)$ are the least-squares estimators of μ and α_i.

To reason to an estimate of σ^2, note that $\varepsilon_{ij} \sim N(0, \sigma^2)$, and that while ε_{ij} is not observable it can be estimated by $\hat{\varepsilon}_{ij} = X_{ij} - \hat{\mu} - \hat{\alpha}_i$. Since k independent parameters were estimated, one is led to the estimator

$$\hat{\sigma}^2 = \sum_i \sum_j \hat{\varepsilon}_{ij}^2 / (N - k) = \sum_i \sum_j (X_{ij} - \overline{X}_{i.})^2 \big/ (N - k) = \text{MSW}. \quad (14.6.20)$$

It is easy to see directly that $\hat{\sigma}^2$ in equation (14.6.20) is an unbiased estimator of σ^2. The numerator is a sum of squares of estimated errors, and is called SSE; $SSE/(N - k)$ is called MSE (mean square due to error). Note that MSE is an unbiased estimator of σ^2 whether H_0 is true or not.

If H_0 is true (i.e., $\alpha_1 = \alpha_2 = \cdots = \alpha_k = 0$), the samples from all k populations constitute one sample from a normal distribution with mean μ and variance σ^2. Then, $SST / (N - 1) \equiv \sum_i \sum_j (X_{ij} - \overline{X}..)^2 / (N - 1)$ is an unbiased estimator of σ^2, and we then have two estimators of σ^2: MSE and $SST/(N - 1)$. If H_0 is true, these estimate the same quantity (but are not independent). By summing the equality

$$X_{ij} - \overline{X}.. = \left(X_{ij} - \overline{X}_i. \right) + \left(\overline{X}_i. - \overline{X}.. \right)$$

after squaring both sides, and showing (as seen earlier in this section) that the cross-product is zero, we are able to decompose SST into two parts:

$$SST = \sum_i \sum_j \left(X_{ij} - \overline{X}.. \right)^2 = \sum_i \sum_j \left(X_{ij} - \overline{X}_i. \right)^2 + \sum_i \sum_j \left(\overline{X}_i. - \overline{X}.. \right)^2$$

$$\equiv \quad\quad SSW \quad\quad + \quad\quad SSB, \tag{14.6.21}$$

where we have defined names SSW and SSB for the respective parts. Since SSW was already used in the first estimator [see equation (14.6.20)], it seems reasonable to take SSB by itself; this quantity is (when divided by $k - 1$) an unbiased estimator of σ^2 when H_0 is true, and in general it can be shown that

$$E(SSB/(k - 1)) = \sigma^2 + \sum_{i=1}^{k} n_i \alpha_i^2/(k - 1). \tag{14.6.22}$$

SSW is sometimes also called SSE, and SSB is also sometimes called SS(treatments). Since

$$\frac{1}{k - 1} \frac{E(SS(treatments))}{E(SSE/(N - k))} = \frac{\sigma^2 + \sum_i n_i \alpha_i^2/(k - 1)}{\sigma^2} \tag{14.6.23}$$

$$= 1 + \sum_i \frac{n_i \alpha_i^2}{(k - 1)\sigma^2},$$

the ratio is expected to be close to 1 if H_0 is true, and otherwise larger than 1, so it seems reasonable to test H_0 by computing

$$\frac{SS(treatments) / (k - 1)}{SSE / (N - k)} \tag{14.6.24}$$

and rejecting for large values. This is, of course, exactly what the likelihood ratio test did [see (14.6.14)].

The one-way ANOVA computations can be organized as in Table 14.6-1, after which the results are often summarized in what is called an analysis of variance table (or ANOVA table), as in Table 14.6-2.

TABLE 14.6-1
One-Way ANOVA Computations

	π_1	π_2	$\cdots$	π_k
Population:	π_1	π_2	$\cdots$	π_k
Population mean:	μ_1	μ_2		μ_k
Population variance:	σ^2	σ^2		σ^2
Sample (data):	$X_{11}, X_{12}, \ldots, X_{1n_1}$	$X_{21}, X_{22}, \ldots, X_{2n_2}$	$\cdots$	$X_{k1}, X_{k2}, \ldots, X_{kn_k}$
Sample total:	$T_1 = X_{11} + X_{12} + \cdots + X_{1n_1}$	$T_2 = X_{21} + X_{22} + \cdots + X_{2n_2}$	$\cdots$	$T_k = X_{k1} + X_{k2} + \cdots + X_{kn_k}$
Sample size:	n_1	n_2		n_k

Compute: $T = T_1 + T_2 + \cdots + T_k$, $N = n_1 + n_2 + \cdots + n_k$, $\mathrm{CM} = T^2/N$

$$\mathrm{SS(Total)} = \sum_{i=1}^{k} \sum_{j=1}^{n_i} X_{ij}^2 - \mathrm{CM}$$

$$\mathrm{SSB} = \mathrm{SS(Between)} = \mathrm{SS(Treatments)} = \sum_{i=1}^{k} T_i^2/n_i - \mathrm{CM}$$

$$\mathrm{SSW} = \mathrm{SS(Within)} = \mathrm{SS(Error)} = \mathrm{SSE} = \mathrm{SS(Total)} - \mathrm{SS(Treatments)}$$

TABLE 14.6-2
One-Way ANOVA Table

Source of Variation	Degrees of Freedom (d.f.)	Sum of Squares (SS)	Mean Square (MS)	Expected Mean Square (E(MS))
Treatments	$k - 1$	SSB	$MS(\text{Treat}) = \dfrac{SSB}{k - 1}$	$\sigma^2 + \dfrac{\sum_i n_i \alpha_i^2}{k - 1}$
Error	$N - k$	SSE	$MSE = \dfrac{SSE}{N - k}$	σ^2
Total	$N - 1$	SS(Total)		

$$\text{F-Ratio: } F_c = \frac{MS(\text{Treat})}{MSE}$$

Example 14.6.25. Suppose three pain relievers are tested. Thirty subjects are available who take the pain reliever assigned to them and record the time to relief from pain. Random assignment of pain relievers to subjects is made in such a way that each pain reliever is assigned to 10 subjects. Using a one-way analysis of variance model, test the hypothesis that there is no pain reliever effect, that is, $H_0: \alpha_1 = \alpha_2 = \alpha_3 = 0$ (or $H_0: \mu_1 = \mu_2 = \mu_3$, where the μ_i's are the mean relief times for the pain relievers) versus the alternative that at least one of the μ_i's is different, with the following data (times in seconds).

Pain Reliever 1	Pain Reliever 2	Pain Reliever 3
395	358	348
360	372	356
382	377	365
374	343	363
364	348	377
385	365	380
342	368	364
388	359	370
393	350	353
410	355	340

Here we have $n_1 = n_2 = n_3 = 10$, $T_1 = 3793$, $T_2 = 3595$, $T_3 = 3616$, $T = T_1 + T_2 + T_3 = 11004$, $CM = T^2/N = (11004)^2/30 = 4036267.2$, and

$$SS(\text{total}) = 4044656 - CM = 8388.8,$$

$$SS(\text{treatments}) = 4038633 - CM = 2365.8,$$

$$MS(\text{treat}) = SS(\text{treatments})/(3 - 1) = 1182.9,$$

$$SSE = SS(total) - SS(treatments) = 6023,$$

$$MSE = SSE/(30 - 3) = 223.0741,$$

$$F_c = MS(treat)/MSE = 5.3027,$$

and the ANOVA table is

Source	d.f.	SS	MS	E(MS)	F-ratio
Pain reliever	2	2365.8	1182.9	$\sigma^2 + 5(\alpha_1^2 + \alpha_2^2 + \alpha_3^2)$	5.30
Error	27	6023.0	223.1	σ^2	
Total	29	8388.8			

Now at level .05, since $F_{2,27,.95}^{-1} = 3.35 < 5.30 = F_c$, we reject H_0 and conclude that at least one of the pain relievers has a different mean relief time than the rest.

Note on Experimental Design. By "experimental design" is meant the decisions made, before the experiment is run, as to **what experiments will be run, how the treatments will be allocated to the subjects, and so forth.** Much more information can be extracted from experiments that are designed in advance, than from experiments that are run (without prior design) in the vague hope that statistical analysis will work some sort of magic to extract more information from the data than it contains.

For example, let us consider Example 14.6.25. Experimental design aspects there include choice of the number of subjects and allocation of treatments to subjects. **Choice of the number of subjects** is often made so the power of the test will be at least some minimal amount when the treatment differences are at least some specified threshold (such as, e.g., 15 seconds); details are beyond the scope of this text [see, e.g., the discussion following equation (10) on p. 112 of Dudewicz and Bishop (1981)]. **Allocation of treatments to subjects is often done with randomization** (using tables of random numbers discussed earlier). For example, if it has been decided to have 30 subjects with 10 allocated to each of the 3 treatments, then 30 random numbers will be drawn, 10 for each of the treatments. The random numbers are then put in increasing order; whichever treatment was associated with the smallest random number is given to the first subject to enter the study, and so on until the last subject to enter the study receives the treatment associated with the largest random number. (Subjects often are acquired sequentially, as they come to the hospital clinic or other organization running the study. The randomization assures that, if there is a time order of severity of the ailment being treated, it will be as likely to be assigned to any one treatment as to any other, and so will not be likely to invalidate the results of the experiment. For example, if we gather 10 subjects each day and assign the first 10 to treatment 1, the second 10 to treatment 2, and the third 10 to treatment 3, the experiment will be somewhat easier to conduct. However, suppose the days are Wednesday, Thursday, and Friday, and the headaches on Friday are typically most severe. Then treatment 3 may look inferior just because it was assigned the worst cases. Randomization obviates this possibility.) In addition, **such an experiment is usually run blind**, which means that the subjects do not know which of the three treatments they are receiving. This is so that their expectations (which may differ because of, e.g., the advertising they have seen for a certain pain reliever) will not affect the outcome of the experiment. (To achieve the "blind" aspect, pills are often repackaged or given an outer covering to make them indistinguishable.) Running an experiment blind is also very important when a **control** (such as "**sugar pills**," a **placebo**) is included among the experimental treatments, since patients who know they are receiving a placebo may report no relief when, in fact, their relief is as great as with many of the "over-the-counter" treatments (many of which are useless for the maladies for which they are often taken). In fact, **many experiments are now run double-blind**, which means the physician who sees the patient does not control, or even know, which of the treatments the patient will receive (but instead only certifies that the patient is appropriate for inclusion in the study, and gives him/her instructions on how to proceed). This is important because physicians also have perceptions as to how effective the various treatments may be, and it is important to keep these from affecting the outcome of the study. (For example, if a patient is to take treatment number 2, and the physician thinks it is useless and in any way communicates this to the patient, then the patient may have an inclination to report no relief even if there is (objectively) substantial relief.

The need for experimental design leads to most high-quality studies having a statistician knowledgable in this area associated with them from the outset. (Studies that lack statistical design are subject to great variability, and their results are not to be trusted until a well-designed study is run to check their results—which are not uncommonly invalidated by the elements that would be controlled in a designed study, by randomization, double-blind running, and so on.)

After the null hypothesis has been rejected, an obvious question is "**Which means are actually different?**" Procedures called "**multiple comparison procedures**" have been developed to answer this question. We give one simple traditional such procedure, called **Fisher's least significant difference (LSD) procedure**. (For alternatives, see Dudewicz and Karian (1985), pp. 462–466.) This procedure makes pairwise comparisons of the sample means and is essentially the two-group t-test, except that instead of using the pooled estimate of the variance computed from the two involved groups in each comparison, one in general uses the pooled estimate of variance based on all groups, the MSE. At a given level α, **if H_0 is not rejected, then no multiple comparisons are made**. Otherwise, the experimenter (after rejecting H_0) may compare all $\binom{k}{2}$ possible pairs of means. Although making many inferences (one for each possible pair) at level α may tend to inflate

714 REGRESSION AND LINEAR STATISTICAL INFERENCE; ANOVA

the Type I error rate, Carmer and Swanson (1973) ran a Monte Carlo study comparing many multiple comparison procedures and concluded that Fisher's LSD is a reasonable procedure to use in practice. **At level α, about $100\alpha\%$ of the inferences made will be incorrect with Fisher's LSD.** For example, with $k = 10$, $\binom{10}{2} = 45$ inferences are made, so one expects that $(45)(.05) = 2.25$ incorrect inferences will be made (if level .05 is used). The other multiple comparison procedures referred to [Dudewicz and Karian (1985)] control this number to (e.g.) .05 and should be seriously considered if $k \geq 5$.

Fisher's LSD can be summarized as: If the F-test accepts H_0, make no comparisons. Otherwise calculate $\overline{X}_{i.} = T_i/n_i$, and (for the desired pairs μ_i, μ_j) calculate $|\overline{X}_{i.} - \overline{X}_{j.}|$. For the given level α, the LSD for comparing μ_i and μ_j is

$$t^{-1}_{N-k,1-\alpha/2} \sqrt{\text{MSE}\left(\frac{1}{n_i} + \frac{1}{n_j}\right)}$$

where MSE is obtained from the experiment's ANOVA table. For all pairs of means to be compared, declare μ_i and μ_j to be different at level α if

$$|\overline{X}_{i.} - \overline{X}_{j.}| > t^{-1}_{N-k,1-\alpha/2} \sqrt{\text{MSE}\left(\frac{1}{n_i} + \frac{1}{n_j}\right)}.$$

Example 14.6.26. In Example 14.6.25, H_0: $\mu_1 = \mu_2 = \mu_3$ was rejected. Find which means are significantly different from each other.

Using Fisher's LSD procedure at level .05, we will analyze all $\binom{3}{2} = 3$ pairs of means. Here $\overline{X}_{1.} = 379.3$, $\overline{X}_{2.} = 359.5$, $\overline{X}_{3.} = 361.6$, and for the comparison of:

$$\mu_1 \text{ and } \mu_2 \qquad |\overline{X}_{1.} - \overline{X}_{2.}| = 19.8$$

$$\mu_1 \text{ and } \mu_3 \qquad |\overline{X}_{1.} - \overline{X}_{3.}| = 17.7$$

$$\mu_2 \text{ and } \mu_3 \qquad |\overline{X}_{2.} - \overline{X}_{3.}| = 2.1.$$

Since $n_1 = n_2 = n_3 = 10$, we need compute the LSD yardstick only once for all 3 comparisons:

$$\text{LSD} = t^{-1}_{27,.975}\sqrt{(223.0741)(.10 + .10)} = (2.052)(6.68) = 13.71.$$

We conclude that μ_1 and μ_2 are significantly different since $19.8 > 13.71$, and that μ_1 and μ_3 are significantly different since $17.7 > 13.71$, but that μ_2 and μ_3 are not significantly different (since $2.1 < 13.71$). In other words,

$$\{\mu_2, \mu_3\} < \mu_1.$$

Today, most ANOVA is performed using computer software packages. The following program uses the data of Example 14.6.24, stored in a data set called

DRUG, to calculate the ANOVA, using the SAS package:

```
 1  OPTIONS LINESIZE = 80;
 2  DATA DRUG;
 3  INPUT RELTIME DRUGTYPE;
 4  CARDS;
35  ;
36  PROC PRINT;
```
⎱ SAS program
⎰ (DRUG was previously entered)

OBS	RELTIME	DRUGTYPE
1	395	1
2	358	2
3	348	3
4	360	1
5	372	2
6	356	3
7	382	1
8	377	2
9	365	3
10	374	1
11	343	2
12	363	3
13	364	1
14	348	2
15	377	3
16	385	1
17	365	2
18	380	3
19	342	1
20	368	2
21	364	3
22	388	1
23	359	2
24	370	3
25	393	1
26	350	2
27	353	3
28	410	1
29	355	2
30	340	3

output produced (print of DRUG)

```
37  PROC ANOVA;
38  CLASSES    DRUGTYPE;
39  MODEL RELTIME = DRUGTYPE;
```
⎱ SAS program for ANOVA

```
                  ANALYSIS OF VARIANCE PROCEDURE
                    CLASS LEVEL INFORMATION
              CLASS        LEVELS          VALUES
              DRUGTYPE       3             1 2 3
           NUMBER OF OBSERVATIONS IN DATA SET = 30
                  ANALYSIS OF VARIANCE PROCEDURE
```

DEPENDENT VARIABLE: RELTIME

SOURCE	DF	SUM OF SQUARES	MEAN SQUARE	F VALUE
MODEL	2	2365.80000000	1182.90000000	5.30
ERROR	27	6023.00000000	223.07407407	PR > F
CORRECTED TOTAL	29	8388.80000000		0.0114

On the preceding output, we see the same results previously found in Example 14.6.25. (In addition, note that the probability in the $F_{2,27}$ distribution above the computed value $F_c = 5.30$ has been calculated and is .0114. This is the significance probability of the data, hence at level .05 we reject H_0.)

Example 14.6.27. Calculations for regression are often presented in an analysis of variance table. For Example 14.3.9, such a table is

Source	d.f.	SS	MS	Hypothesis	F-Ratio
Regression	1	948.168	948.168	$H_0: \beta = 0$	$F_{\text{reg}} = \text{MS (Reg)}/\text{MSE}$
Error	$n - 2 = 10$	273.832	27.3832		$= 34.626$
Total	$n - 1 = 11$	1222.			

Since $F_{\text{reg}} > F^{-1}_{1,10,.95} = 4.96$, at level .05 we reject H_0 and conclude that in the proposed model $E(Y|x) = \alpha + \beta x$ the pest-rate x contributes significant information towards the prediction of crop yield Y.

PROBLEMS FOR SECTION 14.6

14.6.1 For the data of Example 9.8.11, perform a one-way ANOVA. Compare your results with those of Example 9.8.11.

14.6.2 For the data of Problem 9.8.5, perform a one-way ANOVA to test $H_0: \mu_1 = \mu_2$, where μ_i is the mean time for company i ($i = 1, 2$).

14.7. TWO-WAY ANALYSIS OF VARIANCE

In Section 14.6, we dealt with **one-way** ANOVA, which is a setting where our observations are classified by one factor (such as pain relief treatment). However, in many settings two or more factors may be used to classify the observations. In this section we deal with the case of two factors, or **two-way** ANOVA.

As an **example**, suppose there are four different methods of teaching reading, and they are to be studied in several schools. "School" as well as "Method" may affect reading score, so we are led to a two-way classification. Suppose there are 5 schools in the study, and we randomly choose four classes from each of the 5 schools, randomly assigning them each to one of the four methods. The children stay in their respective groups for a full academic program, and then take a standard reading test. The average class scores on the test can be laid out as in Table 14.7-1, by method and school. Such a classification is called a **two-way classification** (since it is based on two variables). Situations with two or more classification variables are common; for instance, the example of k_1 different varieties of tomato plants, with k_2 different types of pesticide, k_3 different

TABLE 14.7-1
Reading Scores Two-Way Data

			School			
		1	2	3	4	5
	1	79	92	86	85	84
Method	2	84	96	94	91	81
	3	95	65	98	86	88
	4	94	78	92	95	90

fertilizers, k_4 irrigation procedures, and so on, where crop yield is studied as a function of variety, pesticide, fertilizer, irrigation method, and so on.

The examples just described have in common the characteristic that experimental units are not all exactly alike. **Variation in these units** (schools, different types of pesticide, etc.) **could distort the true picture of treatment yields, were it not controlled for.** This type of heterogeneity is often controlled by a **randomized blocks experiment.** Among the heterogeneous sample units, some units (such as, classes within a school) are often more homogeneous among themselves and are the basis for the **blocks.** Such **blocking (having each treatment in each block)** is a very effective way of controlling extraneous variation in the experiment. One advantage over the one-way layout of Section 14.6 (which is often called a **completely randomized design**) is that **by the simple process of randomizing the treatments within each block we can control the effect of variability due to different sets of homogeneous units (blocks).** The data from such an experiment can be organized as shown in Table 14.7-2. **A linear model** often used in this setting is

$$X_{ij} = \mu + \alpha_i + \beta_j + \varepsilon_{ij} \ (i = 1, 2, \ldots, k; \ j = 1, 2, \ldots, b), \quad (14.7.1)$$

where X_{ij} is the observed value of the r.v. for the ith treatment in the jth block, μ is the **overall mean**, α_i is the ith **treatment effect**, β_j is the jth **block effect**, and ε_{ij} is the **error variable**. It is often assumed that the α_i's and β_j's are fixed unknown numbers, and the ε_{ij} are independent $N(0, \sigma^2)$ r.v.'s ($i = 1, 2, \ldots, k$;

TABLE 14.7-2
Randomized Blocks Data

				Block		
		1	2	3	$\cdots$	b
	1	X_{11}	X_{12}	X_{13}	$\cdots$	X_{1b}
	2	X_{21}	X_{22}	X_{23}	$\cdots$	X_{2b}
Treatment	3	X_{31}	X_{32}	X_{33}	$\cdots$	X_{3b}
	$\vdots$	$\vdots$				
	k	X_{k1}	X_{k2}	X_{k3}	$\cdots$	X_{kb}

$j = 1, 2, \ldots, b)$, with $\sum_i \alpha_i = 0 = \sum_j \beta_j$. Thus $E(X_{ij}) = \mu + \alpha_i + \beta_j$, and $\mathrm{Var}(X_{ij}) = \sigma^2$. **Hypotheses to be tested** are commonly

$$H_{01}: \alpha_i = 0 \qquad (i = 1, 2, \ldots, k)$$

(no treatment effect) and

$$H_{02}: \beta_j = 0 \qquad (j = 1, 2, \ldots, b)$$

(no block effect).

To develop a test here, recall that, if $Y_1, Y_2, \ldots, Y_n$ are independent $N(0, \tau^2)$ r.v.'s, then $\hat{\tau}^2 = s^2 = \sum(Y_i - \overline{Y})^2/(n - 1)$ is an unbiased estimator of σ^2. Now

$$\varepsilon_{ij} = X_{ij} - \mu - \alpha_i - \beta_j = X_{ij} - E(X_{ij})$$

are independent $N(0, \sigma^2)$ r.v.'s, hence the numerator of the estimator of σ^2 should be

$$Q = \sum_j \sum_i \left(X_{ij} - \hat{E}(X_{ij}) \right)^2,$$

where we need an estimate $\hat{E}(X_{ij})$ of $E(X_{ij})$ since $E(X_{ij})$ is unknown. As in Section 14.6, the method of least squares can be used to obtain estimates of μ, α_i, and β_j [hence of $E(X_{ij})$]: We minimize Q with respect to μ, α_i, and β_j, by differentiating with respect to μ, α_i, β_j, equating to zero, and solving the equations. Thus,

$$\frac{\partial}{\partial \mu} Q = -2 \sum_j \sum_i (X_{ij} - \mu - \alpha_i - \beta_j) = 0 \qquad (14.7.2)$$

yields $\hat{\mu} = \overline{X}..$ (since $\sum \alpha_i = 0 = \sum \beta_j$),

$$\frac{\partial}{\partial \alpha_i} Q = -2 \sum_j (X_{ij} - \mu - \alpha_i - \beta_j) = 0 \qquad (14.7.3)$$

yields $X_{i.} - b\hat{\mu} - b\hat{\alpha}_i = 0$ (since $\sum \beta_j = 0$), thus $\hat{\alpha}_i = \overline{X}_{i.} - \overline{X}..$ $(i = 1, 2, \ldots, k)$, and similarly

$$\frac{\partial}{\partial \beta_j} Q = 0$$

yields $\hat{\beta}_j = \overline{X}_{.j} - \overline{X}..$ $(j = 1, 2, \ldots, b)$. **Therefore we estimate σ^2 by**

$$\hat{\sigma}^2 = \sum_{j=1}^{b} \sum_{i=1}^{k} \left(X_{ij} - \hat{\mu} - \hat{\alpha}_i - \hat{\beta}_j \right)^2 \Big/ ((k-1)(b-1))$$

$$= \sum_{j=1}^{b} \sum_{i=1}^{k} \left(X_{ij} - \overline{X}_{i.} - \overline{X}_{.j} + \overline{X}.. \right)^2 \Big/ ((k-1)(b-1)). \qquad (14.7.4)$$

The $(k-1)(b-1)$ in the denominator is reasonable, since we had kb total observations and estimated $k-1$ α-parameters, $b-1$ β-parameters, and μ (because of the constraints $\sum_i \alpha_i = 0 = \sum_j \beta_j$), hence there are $kb - (k-1) - (b-1) - 1 = kb - k - b + 1 = (k-1)(b-1)$ degrees of freedom. It is straightforward to show that $E(\hat{\sigma}^2) = \sigma^2$.

As in Section 14.6, we can write

$$X_{ij} - \overline{X}.. = (\overline{X}_{i\cdot} - \overline{X}..) + (\overline{X}._j - \overline{X}..) + (X_{ij} - \overline{X}_{i\cdot} - \overline{X}._j + \overline{X}..).$$

Squaring both sides and summing over i and j, algebraic computations show that

$$\sum_{j=1}^{b} \sum_{i=1}^{k} (X_{ij} - \overline{X}..)^2 = \sum_{j=1}^{b} \sum_{i=1}^{k} (\overline{X}_{i\cdot} - \overline{X}..)^2 + \sum_{j=1}^{b} \sum_{i=1}^{k} (\overline{X}._j - \overline{X}..)^2$$

$$+ \sum_{j=1}^{b} \sum_{i=1}^{k} (X_{ij} - \overline{X}_{i\cdot} - \overline{X}._j + \overline{X}..)^2$$

$$= b \sum_{i=1}^{k} (\overline{X}_{i\cdot} - \overline{X}..)^2 + k \sum_{j=1}^{b} (\overline{X}._j - \overline{X}..)^2 \quad (14.7.5)$$

$$+ \sum_{j=1}^{b} \sum_{i=1}^{k} (X_{ij} - \overline{X}_{i\cdot} - \overline{X}._j + \overline{X}..)^2.$$

The left side of equation (14.7.5) is called the **total variation** in the data, the first term on the right side is called the **variation due to treatments**, the second term on the right side is called the **variation due to blocks**, and the third term on the right side is called the **error sum of squares**. (Note that the error sum of squares is the numerator of $\hat{\sigma}^2$ in equation (14.7.4).) Note that the so-called "total variation" is the numerator of the estimator of σ^2 one would use if one assumed the data were independent and identically distributed. Denote the total and its components respectively by **SS(Total)**, **SS(Treatments)**, **SS(Blocks)**, and **SSE**. It can be shown that

$$\begin{cases} E(\text{SS(Treatments)}) = (k-1)\sigma^2 + b \sum_{i=1}^{k} \alpha_i^2 \\ \\ E(\text{SS(Blocks)}) = (b-1)\sigma^2 + k \sum_{j=1}^{b} \beta_j^2 \quad (14.7.6) \\ \\ E(\text{SSE}) = (k-1)(b-1)\sigma^2. \end{cases}$$

By use of Cochran's theorem (Theorem 14.6.12), it follows that SS(Treatments), SS(Blocks), and SSE are independent r.v.'s; and, SS(Treatments)$/\sigma^2$,

TABLE 14.7-3
Two-Way Layout ANOVA Table

Source of Variation	Degrees of Freedom	Sum of Squares	Mean Square	Hypothesis	F-Ratio
Treatments	$k-1$	SS(Treatments)	MS(Treatments)	$\alpha_1 = \cdots = \alpha_k = 0$	$F_t = \dfrac{\text{MS(Treatments)}}{\text{MSE}}$
Blocks	$b-1$	SS(Blocks)	MS(Blocks)	$\beta_1 = \cdots = \beta_b = 0$	$F_b = \dfrac{\text{MS(Blocks)}}{\text{MSE}}$
Error	$(k-1)(b-1)$	SSE	MSE		
Total	$kb-1$	SS(Total)			

Reject H_{01} if $F_t > F^{-1}_{k-1,(k-1)(b-1),1-\alpha}$

Reject H_{02} if $F_b > F^{-1}_{b-1,(k-1)(b-1),1-\alpha}$.

SS(blocks)$/\sigma^2$, and SSE$/\sigma^2$ are respectively distributed as χ^2 with $k - 1$, $b - 1$, and $(k - 1)(b - 1)$ degrees of freedom. **Thus a test of H_{01}: $\alpha_i = 0$ ($i = 1, 2, \ldots, k$)** versus H_{11}: {At least one of the α_i's is not zero}, follows since under H_{01} the ratio

$$F_t = \frac{\text{SS(Treatments)}/(\sigma^2(k - 1))}{\text{SSE}/(\sigma^2(k - 1)(b - 1))} = \frac{\text{SS(Treatments)}/(k - 1)}{\text{SSE}/((k - 1)(b - 1))}$$

has an $F_{k-1,(k-1)(b-1)}$ distribution. At level α this test is

$$\phi_t(\mathbf{X}) = \begin{cases} 1, & \text{if } F_t > F^{-1}_{k-1,(k-1)(b-1),1-\alpha} \\ 0, & \text{otherwise.} \end{cases} \tag{14.7.7}$$

Similarly, to test the hypothesis about blocks, H_{02}: $\beta_1 = \beta_2 = \cdots = \beta_b = 0$ versus H_{12}: {At least one of $\beta_1, \beta_2, \ldots, \beta_b$ is not 0}, we use the ratio

$$F_b = \frac{\text{SS(Blocks)}/(b - 1)}{\text{SSE}/((k - 1)(b - 1))},$$

which has an F-distribution with $b - 1$ and $(k - 1)(b - 1)$ degrees of freedom under H_{02}. At level α this test is

$$\phi_b(\mathbf{X}) = \begin{cases} 1, & \text{if } F_b > F^{-1}_{b-1,(k-1)(b-1),1-\alpha} \\ 0, & \text{otherwise.} \end{cases} \tag{14.7.8}$$

Denote SS(Treatments)$/(k - 1)$ by **MS(Treatments)**, SS(Blocks)$/(b - 1)$ by **MS(Blocks)**, and SSE$/((k - 1)(b - 1))$ by **MSE**. Then the ANOVA is summarized in Table 14.7-3. Computations can be organized as in Table 14.7-4.

If H_0 is rejected, one can use Fisher's LSD (discussed in Section 14.6) to do **multiple comparisons**. One uses MSE as the estimate of σ^2, and the degrees of freedom for error as degrees of freedom for the t-distribution in the multiple comparisons. (This discussion applies equally to H_{01} and to H_{02}.)

TABLE 14.7-4
Two-Way ANOVA Computations

Compute: $X_{..} = \sum_j \sum_i X_{ij}$, $N = bk$, SS $= \sum_j \sum_i X_{ij}^2$, $X_{i\cdot} = \sum_j X_{ij}$, $X_{\cdot j} = \sum_i X_{ij}$

$\text{CM} = X_{..}^2/N$

$\text{SS(Total)} = \text{SS} - \text{CM}$

$\text{SS(Treatments)} = \sum_{i=1}^{k} X_{i\cdot}^2/b - \text{CM}$, $\text{MS(Treatments)} = \text{SS(Treatments)}/(k - 1)$

$\text{SS(Blocks)} = \sum_{j=1}^{b} X_{\cdot j}^2/k - \text{CM}$, $\text{MS(Blocks)} = \text{SS(Blocks)}/(b - 1)$

$\text{SSE} = \text{SS(Total)} - \text{SS(Treatments)} - \text{SS(Blocks)}$, $\text{MSE} = \text{SSE}/((k - 1)(b - 1))$

Example 14.7.9. For the data given in Table 14.7-1, rows represent different methods of teaching and columns represent different schools. Proceeding as in Table 14.7-4,

$$k = 4, \ b = 5, \ N = (4)(5) = 20,$$

$$X_1. = 426, \ X_2. = 446, \ X_3. = 432, \ X_4. = 449,$$

$$X._1 = 352, \ X._2 = 331, \ X._3 = 370, \ X._4 = 357, \ X._5 = 343,$$

$$X.. = 1753, \ CM = 153650.45, \ SS = 154835,$$

$$SS(\text{Total}) = 1184.55,$$

$$SS(\text{Methods}) = 153723.40 - 153650.45 = 72.95,$$

$$MS(\text{Methods}) = 24.3167,$$

$$SS(\text{Schools}) = 153865.75 - 153650.45 = 215.30,$$

$$MS(\text{Schools}) = 53.8250,$$

$$SSE = 1184.55 - 72.95 - 215.30 = 896.30,$$

$$MSE = 74.6917.$$

Our ANOVA table (see Table 14.7-3) is then

Source	d.f.	SS	MS	Hypothesis	F-Ratio
Method	3	72.95	24.3167	$\alpha_1 = \alpha_2 = \alpha_3 = \alpha_4 = 0$	$F_t = .3256$
Schools	4	215.30	53.8250	$\beta_1 = \beta_2 = \beta_3 = \beta_4 = \beta_5 = 0$	$F_b = .7206$
Error	12	896.30	74.6917		
Total	19	1184.55			

At level .05, $F_{3,12,.95}^{-1} = 3.49$ and $F_{4,12,.95}^{-1} = 3.26$. Since $F_t = .33 < 3.49$, we do not reject the hypothesis of no difference among methods (i.e., we will act as if $\alpha_1 = \alpha_2 = \alpha_3 = \alpha_4 = 0$). Since $F_b = .72 < 3.26$, we do not reject the hypothesis of no difference among schools (i.e., we will act as if $\beta_1 = \beta_2 = \beta_3 = \beta_4 = \beta_5 = 0$). (*If* we had rejected one or more of the hypotheses, it would be appropriate to make multiple comparisons using Fisher's LSD procedure. Note that it *may* be appropriate to construct confidence intervals even if neither H_{01} nor H_{02} is rejected, since failure to reject does not necessarily mean effects are zero, but can also mean that the sample size is not large enough to have a substantial probability (called **power of the test**) of detecting the effects. The length of the confidence interval on, for example, $\alpha_1 - \alpha_2$ tells us whether indeed the difference is close to zero, or (while the interval includes zero) the difference may still be large. (For details of how to construct such intervals, see, e.g., Dudewicz and Karian (1985).)

Today, **computer packages are commonly used to perform such ANOVA's** as that in Example 14.7.9. The following program shows use of the SAS package to analyze Example 14.7.9.

```
1 OPTIONS LINESIZE = 80;
2 DATA READSKIL;                        SAS program
3 INPUT METHOD SCHOOL SCORE;            (READSKIL was previously entered)
4 CARDS;
```

OBS	METHOD	SCHOOL	SCORE
1	1	1	79
2	1	2	92
3	1	3	86
4	1	4	85
5	1	5	84
6	2	1	84
7	2	2	96
8	2	3	94
9	2	4	91
10	2	5	81
11	3	1	95
12	3	2	65
13	3	3	98
14	3	4	86
15	3	5	88
16	4	1	94
17	4	2	78
18	4	3	92
19	4	4	95
20	4	5	90

output produced (print of READSKIL)

```
27 PROC ANOVA;
28 CLASSES METHOD SCHOOL;               SAS program for ANOVA
29 MODEL SCORE = METHOD SCHOOL;
```

ANALYSIS OF VARIANCE PROCEDURE
CLASS LEVEL INFORMATION

CLASS	LEVELS	VALUES
METHOD	4	1 2 3 4
SCHOOL	5	1 2 3 4 5

NUMBER OF OBSERVATIONS IN DATA SET = 20

DEPENDENT VARIABLE: SCORE

SOURCE	DF	SUM OF SQUARES	MEAN SQUARE	F VALUE
MODEL	7	288.25000000	41.17857143	0.55
ERROR	12	896.30000000	74.69166667	PR > F
CORRECTED TOTAL	19	1184.55000000		0.7809

R - SQUARE	C.V.	ROOT MSE	SCORE MEAN
0.243341	9.8602	8.64243407	87.65000000

SOURCE	DF	ANOVA SS	F VALUE	PR > F
METHOD	3	72.95000000	0.33	0.8069
SCHOOL	4	215.30000000	0.72	0.5942

In the preceding output, we see the same results previously found in Example 14.7.9. (In addition, significance probability values have been given for the F statistics.)

PROBLEMS FOR SECTION 14.7

14.7.1 For the data of Example 14.6.24, suppose a second factor (the first is "pain reliever") is "study site" and that each line of the data table represents another clinical site. Perform a two-way ANOVA. Is there a site effect? Is there a pain reliever effect?

14.7.2 Suppose a 6th school is added to the study of Table 14.7-1, and its data for Methods 1, 2, 3, 4 are respectively 74, 71, 78, 80. Perform a two-way ANOVA. Is there a school effect? Is there a method effect? What method do you suggest the school system adopt?

PROBLEMS FOR CHAPTER 14

14.1 Show that the quantity $E(Y - c)^2$ is minimized when $c = E(Y)$. Thus, the "best" predictor of a r.v.'s value (in the sense of minimizing mean-squared prediction error), in the absence of any auxiliary r.v. X, is the mean of the r.v. [*Hint*: Use Theorem 14.1.3.]

14.2 For the case of Example 5.3.29, find and graph both the regression curve of Y on X, and the regression line of Y on X. Calculate and compare the respective mean square errors of prediction (14.1.2) and (14.1.16).

14.3 Find the regression line of Y on X in the case $\rho(X, Y) = 0$. What is the mean square error of prediction in this case?

14.4 Find the regression line of Y on X in the case $\rho(X, Y) = 1.0$. Similarly, in the case $\rho(X, Y) = -1.0$. What is the mean-square error of prediction in each case?

14.5 Suppose (as we did following Lemma 5.3.22) that $Y = X^2$. Find the regression curve of Y on X and the regression line of Y on X. Compare their mean square errors of prediction.

14.6 Prove that simultaneous solution of the system of equations (14.1.29) for α and β yields $\hat{\alpha}$ and $\hat{\beta}$ as at (14.1.23) and (14.1.24).

14.7 In a certain class $(X_1, Y_1), \ldots, (X_7, Y_7)$ were measured where X_i was the score on homework of student i and Y_i was student i's subsequent score on an examination. The data are

i	1	2	3	4	5	6	7
X_i	0	10	49	52	59	64	64
Y_i	12	20	60	43	37	58	63

Find the estimated regression line of Y on X (see Theorem 14.1.22). Plot the seven data points and the line $y = \hat{\alpha} + \hat{\beta}x$ on the same graph. If a similar student in a similar situation in the future obtained a homework score of 30, what would be the best linear estimate of his subsequent examination score?

14.8 Suppose that the regression line of Y on X is $Y = \alpha + \beta X$, and that $X_1, \ldots, X_n$ are not r.v.'s, but are fixed values. If (as in Theorem 14.1.22) α and β are estimated from the data $(X_1, Y_1), \ldots, (X_n, Y_n)$, show that $E(\hat{\alpha}) = \alpha$ and $E(\hat{\beta}) = \beta$. Find $\mathrm{Var}(\hat{\alpha})$ and $\mathrm{Var}(\hat{\beta})$. [Assume $E(Y_i) = \alpha + \beta X_i$ and $\mathrm{Var}(Y_i) = \sigma^2$ (all i).]

14.9 In the proof of Theorem 14.1.30, verify that $\sum_{i=1}^{n} v_i = 1$ and $\sum_{i=1}^{n} v_i x_i = 0$; that is, verify that

$$\sum_{i=1}^{n} \frac{\sum_{i=1}^{n} x_i^2 - \left(\sum_{i=1}^{n} x_i\right) x_i}{n \sum_{i=1}^{n} x_i^2 - \left(\sum_{i=1}^{n} x_i\right)^2} = 1$$

and

$$\sum_{i=1}^{n} \frac{\sum_{i=1}^{n} x_i^2 - \left(\sum_{i=1}^{n} x_i\right) x_i}{n \sum_{i=1}^{n} x_i^2 - \left(\sum_{i=1}^{n} x_i\right)^2} x_i = 0.$$

14.10 Let $x_1, \ldots, x_n$ be fixed numbers. Using calculus methods, find among all $u_1, \ldots, u_n$ such that $u_1 + \cdots + u_n = 1$ and $u_1 x_1 + \cdots + u_n x_n = 0$, those $(u_1, \ldots, u_n)$ that minimize $u_1^2 + \cdots + u_n^2$. Use this result to prove Theorem 14.1.30.

14.11 In completing the proof of Theorem 14.1.30, show that $\sum_{i=1}^{n} v_i \Delta_i = 0$, that $\sum_{i=1}^{n} v_i^2$ $+ \sum_{i=1}^{n} \Delta_i^2 \geq \sum_{i=1}^{n} v_i^2$, and that (see equation (14.1.36)) hence the theorem follows.

[*Hint*: Use equation (14.1.34) and the facts $\sum_{i=1}^{n} \Delta_i = 0$, $\sum_{i=1}^{n} \Delta_i x_i = 0$. Note that $\Delta_1 = \cdots = \Delta_n = 0$ satisfies the restrictions and minimizes (14.1.36). Note that v_i as in (14.1.34) yields $\hat{\alpha}$.]

14.12 Theorem 14.1.30 claimed results for $\hat{\alpha}$ and $\hat{\beta}$, but these were proved only for $\hat{\alpha}$. State and prove similar results for $\hat{\beta}$.

14.13 Suppose that the joint probability distribution of two discrete random variables (X, Y) assigns probability $1/67$ to each of the 67 pairs of values (x, y) given in the table below (and probability zero to all other pairs of values).
(a) Find $E(X)$, $E(Y)$, $\mathrm{Var}(X)$, $\mathrm{Var}(Y)$, $\mathrm{Cov}(X, Y)$, $\mathrm{Corr}(X, Y)$.
(b) Plot (carefully and neatly) the 67 possible (x, y) pairs on coordinate axes.

(c) Denote $E(X)$ by μ_1, $E(Y)$ by μ_2, Var(X) by σ_1^2, Var(Y) by σ_2^2, and Corr(X, Y) by ρ. Plot the lines

$$x = \mu_1 + \rho \frac{\sigma_1}{\sigma_2}(y - \mu_2)$$

and

$$y = \mu_2 + \rho \frac{\sigma_2}{\sigma_1}(x - \mu_1)$$

on the same graph used in part (b).

(d) Which of the lines in part (c) is the "regression line of y on x"? Show that the other line is the "regression line of x on y."

Data From Two Examinations

1	(64, 41)	(94, 70)	(72, 22)	(73, 61)
2	(48, 15)	(47, 15)	(61, 20)	(100, 87)
3	(89, 39)	(83, 40)	(65, 28)	(95, 54)
4	(97, 64)	(93, 81)	(70, 67)	(97, 100)
5	(74, 72)	(87, 68)	(74, 24)	(70, 28)
6	(86, 38)	(68, 57)	(57, 31)	(84, 34)
7	(74, 50)	(80, 78)	(90, 68)	(94, 54)
8	(85, 63)	(90, 53)	(75, 45)	
9	(78, 62)	(90, 36)	(57, 50)	
10	(73, 30)	(76, 26)	(69, 45)	
11	(81, 39)	(100, 68)	(91, 61)	
12	(72, 57)	(70, 18)	(74, 29)	
13	(80, 32)	(80, 22)	(98, 81)	
14	(26, 0)	(81, 37)	(97, 78)	
15	(42, 23)	(66, 44)	(63, 18)	
16	(80, 35)	(75, 51)	(78, 75)	
17	(73, 25)	(67, 80)	(65, 40)	
18	(61, 31)	(70, 59)	(76, 38)	
19	(100, 71)	(81, 73)	(72, 70)	
20	(72, 38)	(71, 49)	(49, 52)	

14.14 Suppose that the joint probability distribution of two continuous random variables (X, Y) is bivariate normal with $E(X) = \mu_1$, $E(Y) = \mu_2$, Var$(X) = \sigma_1^2$, Var$(Y) = \sigma_2^2$, and Corr$(X, Y) = \rho$ where the values of $\mu_1, \mu_2, \sigma_1^2, \sigma_2^2, \rho$ are the numbers calculated in Problem 14.13. Then the joint probability density function of (X, Y) is

$$f(x, y) = \frac{1}{2\pi\sigma_1\sigma_2\sqrt{1 - \rho^2}} e^{-\frac{1}{2(1-\rho^2)}\left[\left(\frac{x-\mu_1}{\sigma_1}\right)^2 - 2\rho\left(\frac{x-\mu_1}{\sigma_1}\right)\left(\frac{y-\mu_2}{\sigma_2}\right) + \left(\frac{y-\mu_2}{\sigma_2}\right)^2\right]}.$$

For any $c(0 < c < 1/(2\pi\sigma_1\sigma_2\sqrt{1 - \rho^2}))$, the locus of $f(x, y) = c$ consists of those points (x, y) on the ellipse.

$$\left(\frac{x - \mu_1}{\sigma_1}\right)^2 - 2\rho\left(\frac{x - \mu_1}{\sigma_1}\right)\left(\frac{y - \mu_2}{\sigma_2}\right) + \left(\frac{y - \mu_2}{\sigma_2}\right)^2 \quad (*)$$

$$= -2(1 - \rho^2) \ln\left(2\pi\sigma_1\sigma_2\sqrt{1 - \rho^2}\, c\right).$$

It can be shown that

$$\iint_A f(x, y)\, dx\, dy = 1 - 2\pi\sigma_1\sigma_2\sqrt{1 - \rho^2}\, c, \quad (**)$$

where A is the set of all points (x, y) such that

$$\left(\frac{x - \mu_1}{\sigma_1}\right)^2 - 2\rho\left(\frac{x - \mu_1}{\sigma_1}\right)\left(\frac{y - \mu_2}{\sigma_2}\right) + \left(\frac{y - \mu_2}{\sigma_2}\right)^2$$

$$\leq -2(1 - \rho^2) \ln\left(2\pi\sigma_1\sigma_2\sqrt{1 - \rho^2}\, c\right).$$

Below we table $(**)$ as a function of $\sqrt{-2\ln\left(2\pi\sigma_1\sigma_2\sqrt{1 - \rho^2}\, c\right)}$:

$\iint_A f(x, y)\, dx\, dy = 1 - 2\pi\sigma_1\sigma_2\sqrt{1 - \rho^2}\, c$	$\sqrt{-2\ln\left(2\pi\sigma_1\sigma_2\sqrt{1 - \rho^2}\, c\right)}$
.25	.7585
.50	1.177
.75	1.665
.90	2.146
.95	2.448
.99	3.035

(a) Plot (on the same graph as in Problem 14.13, which already contains 67 points and 2 lines) the two ellipses $(*)$ associated with values of $\iint_A f(x, y)\, dx\, dy$ of .50 and .95.

(b) Of the 67 data points, how many are inside the ellipse associated with .50? What percent? How many are inside the ellipse associated with .95? What percent?

14.15 Prove Theorem 14.2.1.

14.16 Show that $\hat{\alpha}$ and $\hat{\beta}$ can be simplified from (14.1.23) and (14.1.24), respectively, to (14.2.3).

14.17 Derive the formulas for $\text{Var}(\hat{\alpha})$ and $\text{Var}(\hat{\beta})$ given in (14.2.4).

14.18 Prove that (14.2.6) yields a level α test of $H_0 = \{\sigma_0^2\}$. [*Hint:* See Theorem 9.6.4ff.]

14.19 Develop a quantity similar to (14.2.7), but involving $\hat{\beta} - \beta_0$ in the numerator, which has the t_{n-2} distribution. Show how to use this quantity to test hypotheses about β.

14.20 For the data of Problem 14.7
(a) Find $\hat{\alpha}$, $\hat{\beta}$, and $\hat{\sigma}^2$.
(b) Find two-sided equal-tail confidence intervals for each of α, β, σ^2 (each with confidence coefficient .95).

14.21 Show that, as $n \to \infty$, $Y_U^* - Y_L^* \not\to 0$ (see (14.3.4) and (14.3.5)).

14.22 Show that, as $n \to \infty$, $Y_U - Y_L \not\to c$ with $c \neq 0$. Find c. (See (14.3.7) and (14.3.8).)

14.23 Show that Var$(\hat{\beta}_i)$ in (14.4.2) is the same for all $i = 1, \ldots, k$ if: $n_1 = \cdots = n_k = n$ (say) and $x_{1j} = \cdots = x_{kj}$ for $j = 1, \ldots, n$.

14.24 Derive in detail a procedure for selecting that one of k parallel regression lines which has the largest intercept max$(\alpha_1, \ldots, \alpha_k)$.

14.25 If $n_1 = \cdots = n_k = n$ with n even and $x_{1j} = \cdots = x_{kj} = x_j$ (say) $(j = 1, \ldots, n)$ in (14.4.2), what choice of $x_1, \ldots, x_n$ will produce the best $P(CS)$ function? How does your answer change if you are only allowed to choose x's between some bounds, say $x_L \leq x \leq x_U$?

HONORS PROBLEMS FOR CHAPTER 14

14.1H Show that the only critical point of (14.1.27) is $(\hat{\alpha}, \hat{\beta})$ as in Theorem 14.1.22. Quote and use appropriate theorems on minimization of bivariate functions to show that $(\hat{\alpha}, \hat{\beta})$ yields a unique minimum of $S(\alpha, \beta)$.

14.2H Find the method of least squares estimators of $\beta_0, \beta_1, \ldots, \beta_m$ for predicting Y by $\beta_0 + \beta_1 X + \beta_2 X^2 + \cdots + \beta_m X^m$. [Hint: Choose $\beta_0, \beta_1, \ldots, \beta_m$ to minimize

$$S(\beta_0, \beta_1, \ldots, \beta_m) = \sum_{i=1}^{n} \left(Y_i - \left(\beta_0 + \beta_1 X_i + \cdots + \beta_m X_i^m \right) \right)^2.$$

Be sure you have a minimum $(\hat{\beta}_0, \hat{\beta}_1, \ldots, \hat{\beta}_m)$; see Problem 14.1H. The case $m = 1$ was covered in Theorem 14.1.22.]

14.3H Find the best quadratic ($m = 2$ in Problem 14.2H) for the data of Problem 14.7. Plot it on the graph used in Problem 14.7. How does the examination estimate for a homework score of 30 change?

14.4H Give a result and proof like those of Theorem 14.1.30 for the general model of Problem 14.2H.

14.5H Derive equation (**) of Problem 14.14.

14.6H Find the correlation coefficient in the bivariate normal distribution of $(\hat{\alpha}, \hat{\beta})$ (see Theorem 14.2.5).

14.7H (a) Prove (using a proof similar to that of Lemma 9.5.15) that $n\hat{\sigma}^2/\sigma^2$ (see Theorem 14.2.1) is a $\chi_{n-2}^2(0)$ r.v.
(b) Prove the result of (a) by using the theory of distributions of functions of r.v.'s.
(c) Prove the result of (a) by using Cochran's theorem.

14.8H (a) Prove directly that $\hat{\sigma}^2$ [see equation (14.2.2)] is stochastically independent of $\hat{\alpha}$ and of $\hat{\beta}$.
(b) Prove part (a) using Cochran's theorem.

14.9H [Refer to the discussion following (14.3.2).] We know that $\hat{\alpha} + \hat{\beta}x^*$ is an unbiased estimator of $\alpha + \beta x^*$, and that $\hat{\alpha}$ has the smallest variance of all unbiased linear estimators of α, while $\hat{\beta}$ has the smallest variance of all unbiased linear estimators of β.

    (a) Does $\hat{\alpha}$ have the smallest variance of all unbiased estimators of α? (We seek to drop the linearity restriction in this example.) Similarly for $\hat{\beta}$ and β.

    (b) Does $\hat{\alpha} + \hat{\beta}x^*$ have the smallest variance of all unbiased linear estimators of $\alpha + \beta x^*$? Of all unbiased estimators?

14.10H Derive the variance in (14.3.3).

14.11H Perform an analysis similar to that of Example 14.3.9 for the data

i	1	2	3	4	5
x_i	35	45	55	65	75
Y_i	114	124	143	158	166

CHAPTER 15

Robust Statistical Procedures

While "nonparametric statistics" deals with developing statistical procedures that make fewer and weaker assumptions (see Chapter 13), "robust statistics" deals with developing statistical procedures which are insensitive to violation of the assumptions under which they were developed. A major activity of statisticians in the last two decades has been the development of robust statistical procedures for a wide variety of problems, where such procedures have now often become feasible in practice because of the availability of the modern digital computer (lack of which prevented such procedures from being of use earlier, as robust procedures often—though not always—require substantial computations that until recently were not feasible). In this chapter we introduce this important area by looking at problems that carry the flavor of the area, especially the interplay between theory, data, and computation. These are the **influence curve** used to find observations that (if incorrect) would greatly influence the analysis (studied in Sections 15.1 through 15.3), **M-estimation** (a robust generalization of maximum likelihood estimation, studied in Section 15.4), the **jackknife estimator** (a technique for reducing bias in estimation, studied in Section 15.5), and **bootstrap methods** (which amount to simulation and Monte Carlo methods, given a new name in their statistical context, studied in Section 15.6), which are a special case of the general **Statistical Simulation Procedure (SSP)** given in Section 15.6.

15.1. THE INFLUENCE CURVE

Suppose that $X_1, X_2, \ldots, X_n$ are independent r.v.'s, each with d.f. $F(x)$, and that of interest to us is some function of $F(\cdot)$, which we will call $\theta(F)$. For example, $\theta(F)$ could be the mean of the d.f.:

$$\theta(F) = \int_{-\infty}^{\infty} x f(x) \, dx \tag{15.1.1}$$

where $f(x)$ is the p.d.f. corresponding to the d.f. $F(x)$. Often $F(x)$ will be **unknown**; then one might use $\theta(F_n)$ to estimate $\theta(F)$, where $F_n(x)$ is the empiric

730

d.f. defined in Definition 4.8.1. For example, one might estimate the mean by

$$\theta(F_n) = \int_{-\infty}^{\infty} x\, dF_n(x) = (X_1 + \cdots + X_n)/n = \overline{X}. \qquad (15.1.2)$$

[When F in equation (15.1.1) assigns probabilities to points, the integral is replaced by a sum over those points, with weightings of the probabilities of the points; technically, this is then called a Stieltjes integral, although that technicality need not concern us here.]

The basic item of concern in robust estimation is the effect of throwing in a small amount of "contamination" at some point x. **The effect of this contamination is often measured by the "influence curve" at x:**

Definition 15.1.3. The **influence curve** at x is given by

$$w(x) = \lim_{\varepsilon \to 0} \frac{\theta((1 - \varepsilon)F + \varepsilon I_x) - \theta(F)}{\varepsilon} \qquad (15.1.4)$$

where I_x is the d.f. that puts all probability at the point x.

Example 15.1.5. If $\theta(F)$ is the mean of the d.f. as in equation (15.1.1), then we find that the influence curve at x is (denoting the mean of F by μ)

$$\begin{aligned}
w(x) &= \lim_{\varepsilon \to 0} \frac{\theta((1 - \varepsilon)F + \varepsilon I_x) - \theta(F)}{\varepsilon} \\
&= \lim_{\varepsilon \to 0} \frac{(1 - \varepsilon)\mu + \varepsilon x - \mu}{\varepsilon} = x - \mu.
\end{aligned}$$

Thus, in this problem contamination at the mean will have influence 0, whereas in general contamination at a point x has an influence that is proportional to how far x is from the mean μ.

PROBLEMS FOR SECTION 15.1

15.1.1 Let $X_1, X_2, \ldots, X_{10}$ be independent exponential r.v.'s with mean λ. Let $\theta(F) = \mathrm{Var}(F)$. *Find* an estimator $\theta(F_n)$ of $\theta(F)$ based on the empiric d.f. F_n. *Derive* $w(x)$, the influence curve at x. *Plot* $w(x)$ as a function of $\mathrm{Var}(F)$.

15.2. THE INFLUENCE CURVE IN TWO DIMENSIONS

If our observations are bivariate, say n independent r.v.'s (X_{11}, X_{12}), $(X_{21}, X_{22}), \ldots, (X_{n1}, X_{n2})$ each with d.f. $F(x_{11}, x_{12})$, then some function of $F(\cdot, \cdot)$ may be of interest to us. For example,

$$\theta(F) = \int_{-\infty}^{\infty} \int_{-\infty}^{\infty} x_{11} x_{12} f(x_{11}, x_{12})\, dx_{11}\, dx_{12} \qquad (15.2.1)$$

where $f(x_{11}, x_{12})$ is the p.d.f. corresponding to the d.f. $F(x_{11}, x_{12})$. When $F(\cdot, \cdot)$ is *unknown*, one may use $\theta(F_n)$ to estimate $\theta(F)$, where $F_n(x_{11}, x_{12})$ is the bivariate empiric d.f.:

Definition 15.2.2. Suppose that r.v.'s $(X_{11}, X_{12}), (X_{21}, X_{22}), \ldots, (X_{n1}, X_{n2})$ are independent with d.f. $F(x_{11}, x_{12})$. The **(bivariate) empiric d.f.** (based on this sample) is defined by

$$F_n(x_{11}, x_{12} | (X_{11}, X_{12}), (X_{21}, X_{22}), \ldots, (X_{n1}, X_{n2}))$$

$$= \frac{(\text{Number of the pairs } (X_{i1}, X_{i2}) \text{ for which } X_{i1} \leqslant x_{11} \text{ and } X_{i2} \leqslant x_{12})}{n}.$$

Example 15.2.3. If $\theta(F)$ is the **correlation coefficient** of the bivariate d.f. F, that is, if

$$\theta(F) = \text{Cov}(X_{11}, X_{12}) / (\text{Var}(X_{11})\,\text{Var}(X_{12}))^{0.5},$$

then it can be shown that **the influence curve turns out to be**

$$w((x_1, x_2)) = \lim_{\varepsilon \to 0} \frac{\theta\big((1 - \varepsilon)F + \varepsilon I_{(x_1, x_2)}\big) - \theta(F)}{\varepsilon}$$

$$= \frac{x_1 - \mu_1}{\sigma_1} \frac{x_2 - \mu_2}{\sigma_2} - \frac{\rho}{2}\left(\left(\frac{x_1 - \mu_1}{\sigma_1}\right)^2 + \left(\frac{x_2 - \mu_2}{\sigma_2}\right)^2\right) \tag{15.2.4}$$

where $\rho, \mu_1, \mu_2, \sigma_1, \sigma_2$ are the respective correlation coefficient, means, and standard deviations of the bivariate d.f. F.

   Contours of constant influence are given by the equation $w(x_1, x_2) = c$; algebraic manipulation shows that these contours can be expressed as

$$(1 - \rho^2)v_1 v_2 = c \tag{15.2.5}$$

where $y_1 = (x_1 - \mu_1)/\sigma_1$, $y_2 = (x_2 - \mu_2)/\sigma_2$,

$$v_1 = 2^{-1}\left(\frac{y_1 + y_2}{(1 + \rho)^{0.5}} + \frac{y_1 - y_2}{(1 - \rho)^{0.5}}\right)$$

and

$$v_2 = 2^{-1}\left(\frac{y_1 + y_2}{(1 + \rho)^{0.5}} - \frac{y_1 - y_2}{(1 - \rho)^{0.5}}\right),$$

that is, **hyperbolas.**

PROBLEMS FOR SECTION 15.2

15.2.1 In Example 15.2.3, suppose $\theta(F) = \rho^2$. Find the influence curve. Derive and plot the contours of constant influence $w(x_1, x_2) = c$.

15.3. THE EMPIRIC INFLUENCE CURVE IN TWO DIMENSIONS

In practical applications of the material of Section 15.2, we have n bivariate data points, and we calculate their sample correlation, sample means, and sample variances r, m_1, m_2, s_1^2, s_2^2. These sample estimates are then used (respectively) to replace ρ, μ_1, μ_2, σ_1^2, σ_2^2 in equation (15.2.5) to yield **contours of equal**

TABLE 15.3-1
Electric utility data as submitted to the Federal Power Commission

Observation Number	Consumption	Generation
1	71	12074
2	4	681
3	3	1072
4	5	1204
5	4	1372
6	3	1090
7	48	22040
8	11	5130
9	11	4656
10	5	1910
11	4	2590
12	16	7380
13	3	143
14	4	2090
15	6	2290
16	15	7100
17	5	2190
18	3	1190
19	4	1910
20	13	6410
21	6	2880
22	5	2030
23	93	330
24	4	1830
25	8	3700
26	4	2200
27	5	1990
28	5	2320
29	4	1920
30	6	2670
31	19	9540
32	4	2117
33	3	960
34	3	1210
35	5	1760
36	4	1830

estimated influence. In a paper that won the 1983 Jacob Wolfowitz Prize, Chernick (1982) proposed to **superimpose estimated influence contours over a scatter plot of bivariate data in order to detect very influential observations**—which **then should be subject to extensive checking** (as they will have affected the correlation estimate markedly, and if they are in error then the correlation estimate will likewise be badly in error).

Example 15.3.1. Table 15.3-1 gives 36 bivariate observations from an electric utility company, as submitted to the Federal Power Commission on FPC Form 4.

```
      PROGRAM INFL(INFDAT,OUTPUT,TAPE5 = INFDAT,TAPE6 = OUTPUT)
C FINF IS THE INFLUENCE FUNCTION
C X AND Y ARE THE BIVARIATE OBSERVATIONS
      DIMENSION FINF(1000),X(1000),Y(1000),XS(1000),YS(1000)
      REWIND 5
C NCASE IS THE NUMBER OF CASES IN THE RUN
      READ(5,10) NCASE
  10 FORMAT(I2)
      DO 20 M = 1,NCASE
C N IS THE SAMPLE SIZE
C IM IS A FLAG,IF IM = 1, THEN THE MEANS OF X AND Y ARE INPUT
C IF IM = 0, THE MEANS ARE COMPUTED
C IS IS A FLAG, IF IS = 1, THEN THE STANDARD DEVIATIONS ARE INPUT
C IF IS = 0, THE STANDARD DEVIATIONS ARE COMPUTED
      WRITE(6,333) M
 333 FORMAT(" THE CASE NUMBER IS ",I2)
      READ(5,100)N,IM,IS
 100 FORMAT(2X,I4,2(2X,I2)
      NM1 = N - 1
      READ(5,200) (X(I), Y(I), I = 1,N)
 200 FORMAT(6(2X,F10.5))
      IF(IM.EQ.1) GO TO 1
C MEANS ARE CALCULATED HERE
      XB = 0
      YB = 0
      DO 11 I = 1,N
      XB = XB + X(I)
      YB = YB + Y(I)
  11 CONTINUE
      RN = N
      XB = XB / RN
      YB = YB / RN
      GO TO 3
   1 READ(5,300)XB,YB
 300 FORMAT(2(2X,F10.5))
   3 IF(IS.EQ.1) GO TO 4
      SX = 0.
      SY = 0.
C STANDARD DEVIATIONS ARE COMPUTED HERE
      DO 21 I = 1,N
      SX = (X(I) - XB)*(X(I) - XB) + SX
      SY = (Y(I) - YB)*(Y(I) - YB) + SY
```

Figure 15.3-1. Computer program for influence curve calculations.

```
   21 CONTINUE
      RN = N
      RN = SQRT(RN)
      SX = SQRT(SX) / RN
      SY = SQRT(SY) / RN
      GO TO 5
    4 READ(5,300)SX, SY
    5 Z = SX*SY
C THE CORRELATION IS CALCULATED HERE
      COV = 0.
      DO 22 I = 1,N
      COV = (X(I) - XB)*(Y(I) - YB) + COV
   22 CONTINUE
      RN = N
      COV = COV / RN
      COR = COV / Z
C COMPUTATION OF THE INFLUENCE FUNCTION
      WRITE(6,999)
  999 FORMAT(2X,"THE NORMALIZED OBSERVATIONS")
      DO 25 I = 1,N
      XS(I) = (X(I) - XB) / SX
      YS(I) = (Y(I) - YB) / SY
      FINF(I) = XS(I)*YS(I) - COR*(XS(I)*XS(I) + YS(I)*YS(I)) / 2.
C THE NORMALIZED OBSERVATIONS ARE PRINTED HERE
      WRITE(6,990)I,XS(I),YS(I)
  990 FORMAT(I5,5X,F10.5,5X,F10.5)
   25 CONTINUE
C THE CORRELATION COEFFICIENT IS PRINTED
      WRITE(6,700) COR
  700 FORMAT(2X,"THE CORRELATION IS",F10.5)
C THE MEANS ARE PRINTED
      WRITE(6,800) XB,YB
  800 FORMAT(2X,"XBAR = ",F15.5,5X,"YBAR = ",F15.5)
C THE STANDARD DEVIATIONS ARE PRINTED
      WRITE(6,900) SX,SY
  900 FORMAT(2X,"SX = ",F15.5,2X,"SY = ",F15.5)
C THE INFLUENCE FUNCTION ESTIMATES ARE PRINTED
      WRITE(6,600)
  600 FORMAT(2X,"THE INFLUENCE FUNCTION ESTIMATES")
      DO 26 I = 1,N
      WRITE(6,500)I,FINF(I)
  500 FORMAT(2X,I3,5X,F10.5)
   26 CONTINUE
   20 CONTINUE
      END
```

Figure 15.3-1. continued

The first component of each observation is fuel consumption; the second component is electricity generation. Perform an influence analysis of this data set, with special attention to the correlation.

In Figure 15.3-1, we have a computer program for performing the calculations for the influence curve estimates, with the output given in Figure 15.3-2. [This program and example were first given by Chernick (1982).] A plot of these results

```
THE CASE NUMBER IS 2
THE NORMALIZED OBSERVATIONS
```

1	3.12807	2.12473
2	-.39759	-.67868
3	-.45021	-.58247
4	-.34496	-.54999
5	-.39759	-.50865
6	-.45021	-.57804
7	1.91777	4.57701
8	-.02923	.41606
9	-.02923	.29943
10	-.34496	-.37627
11	-.39759	-.20894
12	.23387	.96971
13	-.45021	-.81106
14	-.39759	-.33197
15	-.29234	-.28276
16	.18125	.90081
17	-.34496	-.30737
18	-.45021	-.55343
19	-.39759	-.37627
20	.07601	.73102
21	-.29234	-.13758
22	-.34496	-.34674
23	4.28574	-.76505
24	-.39759	-.39595
25	-.18710	.06419
26	-.39759	-.30491
27	-.34496	-.35658
28	-.34496	-.27538
29	-.39759	-.37381
30	-.29234	-.18926
31	.39174	1.50120
32	-.39759	-.32533
33	-.45021	-.61003
34	-.45021	-.54851
35	-.34496	-.41318
36	-.39759	-.39595

```
THE CORRELATION IS .48442
XBAR =  11.55556    YBAR =  3439.13889
SX  =  19.00357     SY   =  4063.97810
```

Figure 15.3-2. Output of influence program (Figure 15.3-1) for data of Table 15.3-1.

is given in Figure 15.3-3, where the contours are those for influence $c = \pm 1$. From the influence figures in Figure 15.3-2, we know that three points will fall outside these contours, and that is, of course, confirmed in Figure 15.3-3.

In interpretation, note that high correlation is expected between consumption and generation, while in this case $r = .48442$ has been found (see Figure 15.3-2). The approximate effect of an observation on the correlation is the influence

```
THIS IS CASE NUMBER 2
THE INFLUENCE FUNCTION ESTIMATES
```

1	3.18290		
2	.11998	19	.07702
3	.13097	20	-.07527
4	.08764	21	.01494
5	.10128	22	.06167
6	.13022	23	-7.86934
7	2.81283	24	.08117
8	-.05430	25	-.02149
9	-.03068	26	.06042
10	.06668	27	.06339
11	.03421	28	.04781
12	-.01421	29	.07649
13	.15672	30	.02595
14	.06701	31	.00507
15	.04260	32	.06542
16	-.04122	33	.13541
17	.05433	34	.12498
18	.12588	35	.07236
		36	.08117

Figure 15.3-2. continued

function divided by the sample size, hence observation number 23 (with influence function estimate of -7.86934) has decreased the r value by $-7.86934/36 = -.219$. Indeed, we find that if we remove observation number 23, then the correlation increase is even more dramatic, as r now changes to .8457.

In conclusion, we note that **robustness is a key topic in modern statistics, and that the methods studied in this chapter will become of increasing use in applications as they allow assessment of influence on the statistic of interest in the**

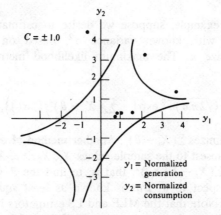

Figure 15.3-3. Scatterplot of normalized observations (data set of Table 15.3-1), with estimated influence function contours.

application (and here we have concentrated on the correlation). Extensions to multiple regression are studied by Chernick (1982).

PROBLEMS FOR SECTION 15.3

15.3.1 For the data (X_{1i}, X_{2i}), $i = 1, 2, \ldots, 7$, of Example 14.5.9, perform an analysis as in Example 15.3.1, seeking to detect very influential observations. Include a plot of estimated influence contours over a scatter plot of the bivariate data. What is r? Do you recommend this estimate be revised? (If so, why, and to what value?)

15.4. M-ESTIMATION

For many parametric families of distributions the maximum likelihood estimator (MLE) (studied in detail in Chapter 7) is a consistent and asymptotically minimum variance estimator of the parameters (see Section 7.4). However, there are cases of interest where the MLE is not consistent, and (in certain cases) the MLE either may not exist, or may not exist in a simple closed form (such as $\hat{\theta} = \bar{X}$). Also, if we do not know the exact distribution of the data (up to within some unknown parameters), then an MLE cannot be obtained. Even if we do know the exact distribution (up to within some unknown parameters), one wonders: "If the true distribution deviates from the assumed underlying distribution, how good is the MLE estimator?"

The idea of **M-estimation, generalizing the MLE**, was introduced by P. J. Huber in 1964. It seeks to have "good" properties of estimation under distributions "closely resembling" the underlying assumed distribution, that is, to be a **distributionally robust estimator**. Huber's original work concerned estimating the "center" of a distribution, and it is this aspect on which we will concentrate in this section.

As a **motivating example**, suppose we desire to estimate the mean θ of a normal population with known variance σ^2, based on a random sample $X_1, X_2, \ldots, X_n$ of size n. The maximum likelihood method seeks a θ that maximizes

$$(\sqrt{2\pi}\,\sigma)^{-n} \exp\left(-\sum(X_i - \theta)^2 / (2\sigma^2)\right),$$

or equivalently minimizes $\sum(X_i - \theta)^2$. **Another method of estimating θ** is to use the θ value that is closest to the sample values $X_1, X_2, \ldots, X_n$ in the sense of the Euclidean distance $\sum(X_i - E(X_i))^2$, that is, to find the θ value that minimizes $\sum(X_i - \theta)^2$ with respect to θ; this is known as **least squares estimation** [see equation (14.1.21)]. (Note that the MLE and LS estimators here both turn out to be $\hat{\theta} = \bar{X}$, but that is not the case in general.) Huber's **M-estimation** generalizes the Euclidean distance between the sample values and the expectation (which involves the parameter value) to a **general distance function** $d(\cdot)$ **with the**

properties:

$$d(x) \geq 0 \text{ for all } x,$$

$$d(x) = d(-x) \text{ for all } x,$$

$$d(0) = 0,$$

$$d(x) \text{ has a derivative } d'(x) \text{ at all } x,$$

and

$$d''(x) \geq 0$$

(i.e., $d(x)$ is a nondecreasing function of x). (Although it is assumed that $d(x)$ is differentiable for all x, later we will examine a case where the derivative fails to exist at a finite number of points x.)

Definition 15.4.1. Let $X_1, X_2, \ldots, X_n$ be a random sample of size n from d.f. $F(x|\theta)$, where θ is a location parameter, that is, $F(x|\theta) = F(x - \theta)$. The **M-estimator** for distance function $d(\cdot)$ is the value $T_n(X_1, X_2, \ldots, X_n)$ of θ that minimizes the **objective function** $\sum_{i=1}^{n} d(X_i - \theta)$, that is, the T_n that solves

$$\sum_{i=1}^{n} d'(X_i - T_n) = 0. \tag{15.4.2}$$

Example 15.4.3. (a) If $d(x) = x^2$, or if $d'(x) = x$, and if the p.d.f. is symmetric about θ, the M-estimator equals the least squares estimator of θ. (b) If $d'(x) = f'(x)/f(x)$, then the M-estimator equals the MLE of θ, since then $d(x) = \ln(f(x))$.

Note that **equation (15.4.2) can be written as**

$$\sum_{i=1}^{n} w_i(X_i - T_n) = 0 \tag{15.4.4}$$

where

$$w_i = \frac{d'(X_i - T_n)}{X_i - T_n}. \tag{15.4.5}$$

Thus,

$$T_n = \frac{\sum w_i X_i}{\sum w_i}, \tag{15.4.6}$$

so that **the M-estimator T_n of θ can be thought of as a weighted average of the sample values, with the weights depending on the data.**

In Example 15.4.3 we noted how different choices of $d(x)$ (or $d'(x)$) lead to different estimators. We next examine some additional choices of $d(x)$ and their resulting estimators.

Example 15.4.7. Consider minimizing $\sum\limits_{i=1}^{n} d(X_i - \theta)$ where

$$d(x) = \begin{cases} x^2 & \text{if } |x| \leq k \\ k^2 & \text{if } |x| > k \end{cases}$$

for some $k > 0$. Here

$$d'(x) = \begin{cases} 2x & \text{if } |x| \leq k \\ 0 & \text{if } |x| > k, \end{cases}$$

hence solving

$$\sum_{i=1}^{n} d'(X_i - T_n) = 0$$

yields

$T_n =$ (Average of those of $X_1, X_2, \ldots, X_n$ for which $|X_i| < k$)

$\quad = \overline{X}_{n,k}$ (say).

Note that this estimator discards all sample values that are less than $-k$ or greater than k, and then averages those that are left. Such an average is called a **trimmed mean.** In practice one might choose k so that the upper $100p\%$ and lower $100p\%$ of the observations would be trimmed from the data. By such trimming one hopes to remove any extreme observations so that the estimator may be less sensitive to outliers.

Note that, **in Example 15.4.7, the function $d(x)$ used was not differentiable at $x = k$,** thus technically violating the properties the function $d(\cdot)$ was assumed to have. However, if we are dealing with a continuous case (so that $P(X_i = k) = 0$), or a discrete case where k is not a possible value of X_i (so that again $P(X_i = k) = 0$), then clearly the value of $d'(\cdot)$ at k will have no effect on the estimator (since the probability is zero that an $X_i = k$ will be encountered). Thus, in this case (and many similar cases) it is reasonable to allow $d'(\cdot)$ to fail to exist at a finite number of points.

Example 15.4.8. Consider minimizing $\sum\limits_{i=1}^{n} d(X_i - \theta)$ where

$$d(x) = \begin{cases} x^2/2, & \text{if } |x| \leq k \\ k|x| - k^2/2, & \text{if } |x| > k \end{cases}$$

where $k > 0$ is a constant. Since $d(x)$ grows linearly as $x \to \pm \infty$, the M-estimator will be less sensitive to outliers. Here we have

$$d'(x) = \begin{cases} -k, & \text{if } x < -k \\ x, & \text{if } |x| \le k \\ k, & \text{if } x > k, \end{cases}$$

and solving

$$\sum_{i=1}^{n} d'(X_i - T_n) = 0$$

yields (see (15.4.6))

$$T_n = \frac{\sum w_i X_i}{\sum w_i} \tag{15.4.9}$$

with

$$w_i = \frac{d'(X_i - T_n)}{X_i - T_n} = \begin{cases} 1, & \text{if } |X_i - T_n| \le k \\ k/|X_i - T_n|, & \text{if } |X_i - T_n| > k \end{cases}$$

which decreases as X_i increases.

In Example 15.4.8 the weights assigned to outliers decrease (but do not abruptly drop to zero as in the case of Example 15.4.7), yielding what is called a **Winsorized mean**. To find a p-Winsorized mean based on a random sample of size n, we let $k = [np]$ with $0 < p < 0.5$, let $Y_1 \le Y_2 \le \cdots \le Y_n$ denote the order statistics, and then (with $[y]$ denoting the largest integer $\le y$) set

$$T_n = \frac{(k+1)Y_{k+1} + Y_{k+2} + \cdots + Y_{n-k-1} + (k+1)Y_{n-k}}{n}. \tag{15.4.10}$$

As a final example, we consider the distance function $d(x) = |x|$.

Example 15.4.11. Consider minimizing $\sum_{i=1}^{n} d(X_i - \theta)$ where

$$d(x) = |x|. \tag{15.4.12}$$

Here we have

$$d'(x) = \text{sgn}(x)$$

where

$$\text{sgn}(x) = \begin{cases} 1, & \text{if } x > 0 \\ 0, & \text{if } x = 0 \\ -1, & \text{if } x < 0. \end{cases}$$

(Actually, $d(x)$ is not differentiable at $x = 0$, but, as in the discussion following Example 15.4.7, this does not matter as long as the probability $X_i = 0$ is zero.) To find the M-estimator we solve

$$\sum d'(X_i - T_n) = \sum \text{sgn}(X_i - T_n) = 0.$$

Since this is a sum of $\text{sgn}(X_i - T_n)$, the sum counts $+1$ for each observation above T_n and -1 for each observation below T_n, hence $T_n = \text{Median}(X_1, X_2, \ldots, X_n)$ yields a sum of zero. If n is even, T_n is any point between the two middle ordered observations; while, if n is odd, T_n is the middle observation. Thus, T_n **is the median**, which we have previously seen is in some senses not as sensitive to extreme observations as is the mean.

Additional sources for further reading on M-estimation include Huber (1981); Hoaglin, Mosteller, and Tukey (1983); and Serfling (1980). Some additional key results are:

Influence Curve for M-estimators. Huber (1981), p. 45, showed that for an M-estimator the influence curve at x (see Definition 15.1.3) is

$$w(x) = \frac{d'(x - \theta)}{Ed'(X_i - \theta)} = \frac{d'(x - \theta)}{-\dfrac{d}{d\theta} Ed'(X_i - \theta)}. \qquad (15.4.13)$$

Thus, the influence curve of an M-estimator is proportional to $d'(\cdot)$ (since the denominator is a constant). Therefore the desired properties of an influence curve may be achieved by choosing a d'-function with those desired properties.

Limiting Distribution of M-estimators. Under conditions, $T_n \to \theta$ w.p. 1, and

$$\sqrt{n}(T_n - \theta) \overset{d}{\to} N(0, \tau^2) \qquad (15.4.14)$$

where

$$\tau^2 = \frac{E(d'(X_i - \theta))^2}{(Ed''(X_i - \theta))^2}.$$

PROBLEMS FOR SECTION 15.4

15.4.1 Show that in equation (15.4.13), $E(w(X_i)) = 0$.

15.4.2 Draw the influence curve of the M-estimator in Example 15.4.7. Find the limiting distribution of T_n if the parent distribution is
(a) Uniform on $[0, \theta]$, so that $f(x|\theta) = (1/\theta) \cdot I_{[0, \theta]}(x)$.
(b) A symmetric triangular distribution with median at θ.

15.4.3 Suppose a random sample of size 10 from a $N(\theta, 1)$ distribution yields (in some order) the data $\{1.2, 2.3, 3.4, 3.6, 3.8, 4.1, 4.8, 4.9, 5.0, 5.8\}$. Compute the estimate of θ discussed in

(a) Example 15.4.7 with $p = .1$.
(b) Example 15.4.8 with $p = .2$.
(c) Example 15.4.11.
(d) Compute the MLE of θ.

15.5. THE JACKKNIFE ESTIMATOR

The **jackknife estimator** was introduced by Quenouille in 1949 and named by Tukey in 1958. This technique's purpose is **to decrease the bias of an estimator and provide an approximate confidence interval** for the parameter of interest.

As discussed in Chapters 7 and 8, for many d.f.'s the MLE and a UMVUE exist. If a parameter has a UMVUE associated with it, then clearly there is no chance of improving such an estimator's bias (since it is already zero). However, MLE's are often biased, and hence improvement may be possible in the sense of an estimator with lower bias. Jackknifing is an important technique for accomplishing such bias reduction. The name "jackknife" was coined due to the fact that, like a Scout's trusty jackknife, it is rough and ready in all situations. (To some this terminology seems tacky, and even to obscure matters; however, the terminology is well-established and will therefore be used here.)

The procedure operates as follows. Let $X_1, X_2, \ldots, X_n$ be a random sample of size n from a population with real-valued parameter θ. Let $\hat{\theta}$ be an estimator of θ. Divide the random sample into N groups of equal size $m = n/N$ observations each (where, of course, N is one of the factors of n). Delete one group at a time, and estimate θ based on the remaining $(N - 1)m$ observations, using the same estimation procedure previously used with a sample of size n. Denote the estimator of θ obtained with the ith group deleted by $\hat{\theta}_i$, called a **jackknife statistic** ($i = 1, 2, \ldots, N$). For $i = 1, 2, \ldots, N$, form **pseudovalues**

$$J_i = N\hat{\theta} - (N - 1)\hat{\theta}_i, \qquad (15.5.1)$$

and consider

$$J(\hat{\theta}) = \frac{1}{N} \sum_{i=1}^{N} \left(N\hat{\theta} - (N - 1)\hat{\theta}_i \right) = N\hat{\theta} - (N - 1)\bar{\hat{\theta}}_i \qquad (15.5.2)$$

where

$$\bar{\hat{\theta}}_i = \frac{1}{N} \sum_{i=1}^{N} \hat{\theta}_i.$$

Definition 15.5.3. $J(\hat{\theta})$ is called the **jackknife estimator of** θ.

Remark 15.5.4. Note that the jackknife estimator can be written as

$$J(\hat{\theta}) = \hat{\theta} + (N - 1)\left(\hat{\theta} - \bar{\hat{\theta}}_i\right),$$

which shows the estimator $J(\hat{\theta})$ as an adjustment to $\hat{\theta}$, with the amount of adjustment depending on the difference between $\hat{\theta}$ and $\hat{\theta}_i$. The special case $m = 1$ is the most commonly used jackknife, in which case

$$J(\hat{\theta}) = n\hat{\theta} - (n - 1)\bar{\hat{\theta}}_i. \tag{15.5.5}$$

Example 15.5.6. Let $X_1, X_2, \ldots, X_n$ be a random sample of size n from a $N(\theta, 1)$ distribution. Then $\hat{\theta} = \bar{X}$. With $m = 1$ as in Remark 15.5.4 and equation (15.5.5),

$$\hat{\theta}_i = \frac{1}{n - 1} \sum_{j \neq i} X_j, \qquad \bar{\hat{\theta}}_i = \frac{1}{n} \sum_{i=1}^{n} \hat{\theta}_i = \bar{X},$$

and hence $J(\hat{\theta}) = n\bar{X} - (n - 1)\bar{X} = \bar{X}$. Thus, the jackknife estimator is still $\bar{X}$ (which is desirable since $\bar{X}$ is a UMVUE of θ).

Example 15.5.7. Let $X_1, X_2, \ldots, X_n$ be a random sample of size n from a $N(\mu, \sigma^2)$ distribution with μ and σ^2 both unknown. Consider estimating σ^2. The MLE of σ^2 is $\hat{\theta} = \hat{\sigma}^2 = \Sigma(X_i - \bar{X})^2/n = \Sigma X_i^2/n - \bar{X}^2$, which is biased. Taking $m = 1$ (see Remark 15.5.4), we find

$$\hat{\sigma}_i^2 = \frac{1}{n - 1} \sum_{j \neq i} X_j^2 - \left(\frac{1}{n - 1} \sum_{j \neq i} X_j\right)^2 = \frac{1}{n - 1} \sum_{j \neq i} X_j^2 - \left(\frac{n\bar{X} - X_i}{n - 1}\right)^2$$

$$= \frac{1}{n - 1} \sum_{j \neq i} X_j^2 - \frac{n^2\bar{X}^2 - 2nX_i\bar{X} + X_i^2}{(n - 1)^2},$$

hence

$$\bar{\hat{\sigma}}_i^2 = \frac{1}{n} \sum_{i=1}^{n} \hat{\sigma}_i^2 = \frac{1}{n(n - 1)} \sum_{i=1}^{n} \sum_{j \neq i} X_j^2 - \frac{n^2\bar{X}^2 - 2n\bar{X}^2 + \sum_{i=1}^{n} X_i^2}{(n - 1)^2}$$

$$= \frac{1}{n} \sum_{i=1}^{n} X_i^2 - \frac{(n^2 - 2n)\bar{X}^2}{(n - 1)^2} - \frac{1}{n(n - 1)^2} \sum_{i=1}^{n} X_i^2$$

$$= \frac{(n - 1)^2 - 1}{n(n - 1)^2} \sum_{i=1}^{n} X_i^2 - \frac{(n^2 - 2n)\bar{X}^2}{(n - 1)^2} = \frac{n(n - 2)}{(n - 1)^2}\left(\frac{1}{n} \sum_{i=1}^{n} X_i^2 - \bar{X}^2\right)$$

$$= \frac{n(n - 2)}{(n - 1)^2}\hat{\sigma}^2$$

and **the jackknife variance estimator is**

$$J(\hat{\sigma}^2) = n\hat{\sigma}^2 - (n-1)\bar{\hat{\sigma}}_i^2 = n\hat{\sigma}^2 - \frac{n(n-2)}{n-1}\hat{\sigma}^2$$

$$= \frac{n}{n-1}\hat{\sigma}^2 = \frac{1}{n-1}\sum_{i=1}^{n}(X_i - \bar{X})^2,$$

which (as seen at (7.1.13)) is unbiased for σ^2. Thus, the bias of $\hat{\sigma}^2$ has not only been reduced, but an unbiased estimator has been found.

In the next example, the range of possible values of the X_i's depends on θ.

Example 15.5.8. Let $X_1, X_2, \ldots, X_n$ be a random sample of size n from the displaced exponential p.d.f. $e^{-(x-\theta)} \cdot I_{[\theta, \infty)}(x)$. Let $Y_1 \le Y_2 \le \cdots \le Y_n$ be the order statistics. Note that

$$E(Y_1) = \theta + \frac{1}{n}, \qquad E(Y_2) = \theta + \frac{2n-1}{n(n-1)}.$$

The MLE of θ is Y_1, which is a biased estimator. With $m = 1$ as in Remark 15.5.4,

$$\hat{\theta}_i = \begin{cases} Y_1 & \text{if } X_i \ne Y_1 \\ Y_2 & \text{if } X_i = Y_1, \end{cases}$$

and

$$\bar{\theta}_i = \frac{1}{n}\sum_{i=1}^{n}\hat{\theta}_i = \frac{1}{n}((n-1)Y_1 + Y_2),$$

hence the jackknife estimator is

$$J(\hat{\theta}) = n\hat{\theta} - (n-1)\bar{\hat{\theta}}_i = nY_1 - (n-1)\left(\frac{n-1}{n}Y_1 + \frac{1}{n}Y_2\right)$$

$$= nY_1 - \frac{(n-1)^2}{n}Y_1 - \frac{n-1}{n}Y_2 = Y_1 - \frac{n-1}{n}(Y_2 - Y_1).$$

(15.5.9)

Since

$$E(J(\hat{\theta})) = E(Y_1) + \frac{n-1}{n}(E(Y_1) - E(Y_2))$$

$$= \theta + \frac{1}{n} + \frac{n-1}{n}\left(\theta + \frac{1}{n} - \theta - \frac{2n-1}{n(n-1)}\right) = \theta,$$

$J(\hat{\theta})$ is unbiased for θ.

Our final example is for a discrete case.

Example 15.5.10. Let $X_1, X_2, \ldots, X_n$ be a random sample of size n with $P(X_1 = 0) = 1 - p$, $P(X_1 = 1) = p$. Let $X = X_1 + X_2 + \cdots + X_n$. Here $\hat{p} = X/n = $ (Number of successes)/(Number of trials) is the MLE of p. Hence (see Theorem 7.2.15), the MLE of $\theta = pq$ is

$$\hat{\theta} = \hat{p}\hat{q} = \frac{X}{n}\left(1 - \frac{X}{n}\right)$$

and

$$E(\hat{\theta}) = pq - \frac{pq}{n} = \frac{n-1}{n}pq,$$

so $\hat{p}\hat{q}$ is biased for pq.

To find the jackknife estimator, let $m = 1$ as in Remark 15.5.4. Then

$$\hat{p}_i = \begin{cases} \dfrac{X-1}{n-1}, & \text{if } X_i = 1 \text{ (i.e. if the } i\text{th trial is a success)} \\[2ex] \dfrac{X}{n-1}, & \text{if } X_i = 0 \text{ (i.e., if the } i\text{th trial is a failure)}, \end{cases}$$

so

$$\hat{\theta}_i = \begin{cases} \left(\dfrac{X-1}{n-1}\right)\left(1 - \dfrac{X-1}{n-1}\right) = \left(\dfrac{X-1}{n-1}\right)\left(\dfrac{n-X}{n-1}\right) & \text{if } X_i = 1 \\[2ex] \dfrac{X}{n-1}\left(1 - \dfrac{X}{n-1}\right) = \dfrac{X}{n-1}\left(\dfrac{n-X-1}{n-1}\right) & \text{if } X_i = 0, \end{cases}$$

and (since there are X successes and $n - X$ failures to be removed)

$$\bar{\hat{\theta}}_i = \frac{1}{n}\sum_{i=1}^{n}\hat{\theta}_i = \frac{1}{n}\left(X\left(\frac{X-1}{n-1}\right)\left(\frac{n-X}{n-1}\right) + (n-X)\left(\frac{X}{n-1}\right)\left(\frac{n-X-1}{n-1}\right)\right)$$

$$= \frac{n(n-2)}{(n-1)^2}\hat{p}\hat{q}.$$

Therefore the jackknife estimator of pq is

$$J(\hat{\theta}) = n\hat{\theta} - (n-1)\bar{\hat{\theta}}_i = n\hat{p}\hat{q} - \frac{n(n-2)}{n-1}\hat{p}\hat{q}$$

$$= \frac{n}{n-1}\hat{p}\hat{q}.$$

(15.5.11)

Note that $E(J(\hat{\theta})) = pq$, and $J(\hat{\theta})$ is unbiased and UMVUE for $\theta = pq$.

The **jackknife estimator of** θ **of Definition 15.5.3 can be generalized as follows.**

Definition 15.5.12. Let $\hat{\theta}_1$ and $\hat{\theta}_2$ be two estimators of θ, and let $R \ne 1$ be a constant. The **generalized jackknife estimator** $G(\hat{\theta}_1, \hat{\theta}_2)$ is defined as

$$G\left(\hat{\theta}_1, \hat{\theta}_2\right) = \frac{\hat{\theta}_1 - R\hat{\theta}_2}{1 - R}. \tag{15.5.13}$$

Remark 15.5.14. If we choose $R = (N - 1)/N$ in equation (15.5.13), and also $\hat{\theta}_1 = \hat{\theta}$, $\hat{\theta}_2 = \hat{\theta}_i$, then we obtain the jackknife estimator of equation (15.5.2). Therefore the name "generalized jackknife estimator" is valid (since the new estimator does generalize the previous jackknife estimation procedure). We will not consider the generalized jackknife further in this chapter, but will touch on *confidence intervals for* θ. Also, note that although all the preceding examples are in parametric settings the jackknife can be extended to bias reduction in nonparametric settings as well.

Use of the jackknife estimator to obtain approximate confidence intervals (and tests) for θ is the final jackknife technique we will consider. Tukey (one of the first to deal with this topic) suggested that the pseudovalues J_i of equation (15.5.1) be treated as independent and identically distributed r.v.'s. Then (with $m = 1$ as in Remark 15.5.4)

$$t = \frac{\sqrt{n}\left(J(\hat{\theta}) - \theta\right)}{\left(\sum_{i=1}^{n} \frac{\left(J_i - J(\hat{\theta})\right)^2}{n - 1}\right)^{0.5}} = \frac{\sqrt{n}\left(J(\hat{\theta}) - \theta\right)}{\sqrt{\sigma_{J(\theta)}^2}} \tag{15.5.15}$$

is approximately a Student's t r.v., which (for large n) converges to a standard normal distribution. [For proofs under various conditions, see Schucany and Gray (1972).] Therefore an approximate $100(1 - \alpha)\%$ confidence interval for θ is

$$\left(J(\hat{\theta}) - \Phi^{-1}(1 - \alpha/2)\sqrt{\sigma_{J(\theta)}^2/n}, \quad J(\hat{\theta}) + \Phi^{-1}(1 - \alpha/2)\sqrt{\sigma_{J(\theta)}^2/n}\right).$$
$$\tag{15.5.16}$$

Example 15.5.17. A survey was conducted in Mobile, Alabama, to estimate the percentage of households that have at least one videocassette recorder (VCR). A sample of 200 households from West Mobile yielded 75 homes with at least one VCR. Construct a 95.44% confidence interval for pq.

Referring to Example 15.5.10 for $J(\widehat{pq})$, we use this in conjunction with (15.5.16), and a large-sample approximation uses $\Phi^{-1}(.9772) = 2.0$. Here $n = 200$,

$X = 75$, and

$$
J_i = \begin{cases}
n\hat{p}\hat{q} - (n-1)\left(\dfrac{X-1}{n-1}\right)\left(\dfrac{n-X}{n-1}\right) \\
\quad = 200\left(\dfrac{75}{200}\right)\left(\dfrac{125}{200}\right) - 74\left(\dfrac{125}{199}\right) = .3925879397 \quad \text{if } X_i = 1 \\[2mm]
n\hat{p}\hat{q} - (n-1)\left(\dfrac{X}{n-1}\right)\left(\dfrac{n-X-1}{n-1}\right) \\
\quad = 200\left(\dfrac{75}{200}\right)\left(\dfrac{125}{200}\right) - 75\left(\dfrac{124}{199}\right) = .1413316583 \quad \text{if } X_i = 0.
\end{cases}
$$

Therefore

$$
J(\hat{\theta}) = \frac{n}{n-1}\hat{p}\hat{q} = \frac{200}{199}\left(\frac{75}{200}\right)\left(\frac{125}{200}\right) = .2355527638,
$$

and

$$
\sigma^2_{J(\theta)} = \sum_{i=1}^{n} \left(J_i - J(\hat{\theta})\right)^2 \big/ (n-1)
$$

$$
= \left(X(.3926 - J(\hat{\theta}))^2 + (n-X)(.1413 - J(\hat{\theta}))^2\right)\big/(n-1)
$$

$$
= \left(75(.3926 - .2356)^2 + 125(.1413 - .2356)^2\right)\big/199 = .014066552.
$$

Hence the approximate 95.44% confidence interval for pq is

$$
\left(.2356 - 2.0\sqrt{.014/200}\,,\quad .2356 + 2.0\sqrt{.014/200}\,\right) = (.218, .253).
$$

PROBLEMS FOR SECTION 15.5

15.5.1 Let $X_1, X_2, \ldots, X_n$ be independent uniform r.v.'s on $(0, \theta)$. Find $J(\hat{\theta})$ for estimation of θ. Compare the biases of the MLE of θ and of $J(\hat{\theta})$.

15.5.2 Let $X_1, X_2, \ldots, X_n$ be independent r.v.'s with $P(X_i = 0) = 1 - p$, $P(X_i = 1) = p$. Find $J(p^2)$ for estimation of $\theta = p^2$. Compare the biases of the MLE of θ and of $J(p^2)$.

15.5.3 Let $X_1, X_2, \ldots, X_n$ be independent r.v.'s with p.d.f. $f(x|\alpha) = x^{\alpha-1}e^{-x}/\Gamma(\alpha)$ if $x > 0$ (and $= 0$ otherwise). Find $J(\hat{\alpha})$ for estimation of $\theta = \alpha$. Compare the biases of the MME of α and of $J(\hat{\alpha})$. [The MLE of α is difficult to find.]

15.5.4 Construct an approximate 95% confidence interval for p^2 based on $n = 200$, $X = 75$, and the estimator developed in the setting of Problem 15.5.2.

15.6. THE GENERAL STATISTICAL SIMULATION PROCEDURE (SSP) AND BOOTSTRAP METHODS

If we know the distribution function $F(\cdot)$ of a random variable X and wish to evaluate some function of it, say $\theta(F)$, we can proceed in two ways: (1) evaluate $\theta(F)$ exactly; and (2) simulate to estimate $\theta(F)$.

Example 15.6.1. Suppose that X is a r.v. which is $N(0, 1)$ so that $F(x) = \Phi(x)$, and that we wish to know the 8th moment of X, so that $\theta(F) = \int_{-\infty}^{\infty} x^8 \phi(x)\, dx$. Then **one way we may proceed is to (1) evaluate the integral exactly.**

If the integral involved in the preceding method is such that no simple way to evaluate it exists, an alternate method may be sought. **A second way we may proceed is (2) simulate to estimate** $\theta(F)$. From Example 4.7.11, we know how to generate (on a computer) r.v.'s $X_1, X_2, \ldots, X_n$ that are $N(0, 1)$ and independent. From those we can estimate $\theta(F)$ using the principles of estimation in Chapters 7 and 8. Thus, we might estimate $\theta(F)$ by $(X_1^8 + X_2^8 + \cdots + X_n^8)/n$, which is a consistent estimator (as shown in Theorem 7.1.12, where it was called m_8').

The preceding discussion assumed that we knew the d.f. $F(\cdot)$, and that is sometimes the case. However, **often we have** not a known d.f. $F(\cdot)$ for which we wish to know $\theta(F)$, but rather a **random sample** $X_1, X_2, \ldots, X_n$ **drawn from d.f.** $F(\cdot)$ **with** $F(\cdot)$ **unknown, and wish to estimate** $\theta(F)$. Since in settings like that of Example 15.6.1 we used the known $F(\cdot)$ only to draw the random sample, and we now have a random sample from $F(\cdot)$ given to use, we can proceed as in that example's part (2)—and with even greater simplicity since we do not need to generate $X_1, X_2, \ldots, X_n$, but they are instead given to us.

Now suppose we are taking approach (2), and wish to specify the variance of our estimator. (For example, making the variance of the estimator suitably small is one rational way to choose the sample size n.) With $F(\cdot)$ known, we can proceed as follows to solve this problem:

Step 1. Generate $X_1, X_2, \ldots, X_n$ and estimate $\theta(F)$; call the estimate $\hat{\theta}_1$.

Step 2. Generate $X_{n+1}, X_{n+2}, \ldots, X_{2n}$ and estimate $\theta(F)$ from these new r.v.'s (which are to be independent of all r.v.'s previously generated); call the estimate $\hat{\theta}_2$.

Step 3. Generate $X_{2n+1}, X_{2n+2}, \ldots, X_{3n}$ and estimate $\theta(F)$ from these new n r.v.'s (which are to be independent of all previously generated r.v.'s); call the estimate $\hat{\theta}_3$.

$\vdots$

Step N. Generate $X_{(N-1)n+1}, X_{(N-1)n+2}, \ldots, X_{Nn}$ and estimate $\theta(F)$ from these new n r.v.'s (which are to be independent of all previously generated r.v.'s); call the estimate $\hat{\theta}_N$.

Then $\hat{\theta}_1, \hat{\theta}_2, \hat{\theta}_3, \ldots, \hat{\theta}_N$ are N independent and identically distributed r.v.'s, each estimating $\theta(F)$. Their variance may be estimated by

$$\hat{\sigma}^2 = \sum_{i=1}^{N} \left(\hat{\theta}_i - \bar{\theta} \right)^2 \Big/ (N-1), \qquad \bar{\theta} = \left(\hat{\theta}_1 + \hat{\theta}_2 + \cdots + \hat{\theta}_N \right) \Big/ N,$$

and the variance of the estimator $\bar{\theta}$ is estimated by $\hat{\sigma}^2/N$. We call this procedure the **Statistical Simulation Procedure SSP(θ, F, n, N)**.

If $F(\cdot)$ is unknown, the SSP(θ, F, n, N) cannot be used. However, then one will have a random sample $X_1, X_2, \ldots, X_n$ taken from the unknown d.f. $F(\cdot)$. Using the random sample, the d.f. may be estimated, say by some estimator $\hat{F}$, and then Step 1, Step 2, ..., Step N followed (with all r.v.'s being generated from the estimated d.f. $\hat{F}$). We call this the General **Statistical Simulation Procedure SSP($\theta, \hat{F}, X_1, \ldots, X_n, N$)**.

There are many ways to choose the estimate $\hat{F}$ of F in the SSP $(\theta, \hat{F}, X_1, \ldots, X_n, N)$. One of the very simplest is to take $\hat{F}$ to be the empiric d.f. based on the sample $X_1, \ldots, X_n$. If that is done, then the procedure is called the **bootstrap procedure**, and any similar methods are called **bootstrap methods**. Bootstrap methods essentially rely on sampling the empiric d.f., which is (unless n is large) a rough step-function estimate of the true $F(x)$, which is often known to be continuous. For this reason, a smoothed version, such as the empiric p.d.f. (see Section 4.8), which is also easy to sample from, should yield more reliable estimates. (State-of-the-art practice in simulation is to sample from a smoothed d.f. or p.d.f. estimate that incorporates all knowledge the experimenter has about the true d.f.)

Example 15.6.2. Estimating the Standard Error of $\bar{X}$. Let $\theta = E(X)$ and $\sigma^2 = \text{Var}(X)$. Then from a random sample $X_1, X_2, \ldots, X_n$ with the same d.f. as X, we find $\bar{X}$ (the sample mean) and it has mean θ and $\text{Var}(\bar{X}) = \sigma^2/n$.

The **bootstrap method of estimating Var($\bar{X}$)** is the SSP($\theta, \hat{F}, X_1, \ldots, X_n, N$) with $\hat{F}$ taken to be the empiric d.f., and **proceeds as follows:**

Step 1. Take a sample of size n (with replacement) from $\{X_1, X_2, \ldots, X_n\}$, say

$$\{X_{11}, X_{12}, X_{13}, \ldots, X_{1n}\}, \text{ and calculate its sample mean } \bar{X}_1.$$

Step 2. Repeat Step 1 independently $N - 1$ additional times, finding $\bar{X}_2, \ldots, \bar{X}_N$. The bootstrap estimate of Var($\bar{X}$) is

$$\hat{\sigma}^2 = \sum_{i=1}^{N} \left(\bar{X}_i - \bar{X}_. \right)^2 \Big/ (N-1), \qquad \bar{X}_. = \left(\bar{X}_1 + \bar{X}_2 + \cdots + \bar{X}_N \right) \Big/ N. \quad (15.6.3)$$

Example 15.6.4. Estimating Bias. Suppose that, based on a random sample $X_1, X_2, \ldots, X_n$, some quantity θ of interest is estimated by $\hat{\theta}$. The estimator $\hat{\theta}$ has some bias $b = E(\hat{\theta} - \theta)$. To estimate the bias, consider use of SSP

$(b, \hat{F}, X_1, \ldots, X_n, N)$ with $\hat{F}$ taken to be the empiric d.f. (so we have a bootstrap estimate). Based on N bootstrap samples of size n each, one finds the estimators $\hat{\theta}_1, \hat{\theta}_2, \ldots, \hat{\theta}_N$, with $\bar{\theta} = (\hat{\theta}_1 + \hat{\theta}_2 + \cdots + \hat{\theta}_N)/N$, and estimates the bias of $\hat{\theta}$ by

$$b = \bar{\theta} - \hat{\theta}. \tag{15.6.5}$$

Example 15.6.6. Let $X_1, X_2, \ldots, X_n$ be a random sample of size n from a Poisson distribution with unknown mean λ. If the parameter of interest is $\theta = P(X \le 1) = e^{-\lambda}(1 + \lambda)$, the MLE is $e^{-\bar{X}}(1 + \bar{X})$, which is biased. To reduce the bias, let us investigate the bootstrap method.

Let X_{ij} $(i = 1, 2, \ldots, N; \; j = 1, 2, \ldots, n)$ be the N bootstrap samples, that is, samples taken at random with replacement from $\{X_1, X_2, \ldots, X_n\}$, and (for $i = 1, 2, \ldots, N$)

$$\hat{\theta}_i = e^{-\bar{X}_i}\left(1 + \bar{X}_i\right) - (\text{Number of } X_{i1}, X_{i2}, \ldots, X_{in} \text{ that are } \le 1)/n.$$

Then the bootstrap estimate of the bias of θ is

$$\bar{\theta} = \left(\hat{\theta}_1 + \hat{\theta}_2 + \cdots + \hat{\theta}_N\right)/N, \tag{15.6.7}$$

i.e. the associated estimate of bias is simply

$$\hat{b} = \bar{\theta}. \tag{15.6.8}$$

Then, one might use $e^{-\bar{X}}(1 + \bar{X}) - \hat{b}$ to estimate θ.

Remark 15.6.9. Note that an approximate $100(1 - \alpha)\%$ confidence interval for θ can be constructed using bootstrap methods, as follows. If $\bar{\theta}$ is the bootstrap estimate of θ and $\hat{\sigma}^2$ its sample variance based on $\hat{\theta}_1, \hat{\theta}_2, \ldots, \hat{\theta}_N$, for N large we take the interval

$$\left(\hat{\theta} - \Phi^{-1}(1 - \alpha/2)\hat{\sigma}, \quad \hat{\theta} + \Phi^{-1}(1 - \alpha/2)\hat{\sigma}\right). \tag{15.6.10}$$

Note that we use the original estimate of θ (not the bootstrap estimate), and the bootstrap procedure has been used to provide us with an estimate of variability for $\hat{\theta}$.

Note that the exact same details apply to the more general Statistical Simulation Procedure $\mathrm{SSP}(\theta, \hat{F}, X_1, \ldots, X_n, N)$, in which the only difference is what estimate of F is being sampled from.

PROBLEMS FOR SECTION 15.6

15.6.1 Let $X_1, X_2, \ldots, X_n$ be a random sample of size n from a $N(\mu, \sigma^2)$ d.f. with μ and σ^2 both unknown. Detail how to proceed in a bootstrap method for obtaining an estimate of $\theta = \Phi((2 - \mu)/\sigma)$.

15.6.2 The MLE for the θ of Problem 15.6.1 is $\hat{\theta} = \Phi((2 - \overline{X})/s_n)$, where $s_n^2 = \sum\limits_{i=1}^{n} (X_i - \overline{X})^2/n$. Find a bootstrap estimator of the variance of $\hat{\theta}$, and use it to construct a $100(1 - \alpha)\%$ confidence interval for θ.

15.6.3 Let the sample in Problem 15.6.1 be $\{3.1, 2.9, 1.6, 3.4, 4.2, 1.08, 2.4, 3.0, 2.9, 2.5\}$. Take $N = 4$ random samples of size 10 each (bootstrap samples) and find the bootstrap estimate of θ described in Problem 15.6.1. Compare this with the MLE of Problem 15.6.2. Estimate the bias of each estimator.

15.6.4 Based on the bootstrap samples obtained in Problem 15.6.3, compute a numerical estimate of the variance of the MLE, and then construct a 95% (approximate) confidence interval for θ using
(a) The bootstrap estimate of θ.
(b) The MLE of θ.
[Note: Use the Student's t-distribution with $N - 1$ degrees of freedom in (15.6.10) since here N is not very large.]

15.6.5 As in Problem 15.6.3, with $N = 7$.

15.6.6 As in Problem 15.6.3, with $N = 10$.

15.6.7 As in Problem 15.6.3, but use the Statistical Simulation Procedure instead of the bootstrap and draw your samples from the empiric p.d.f. for the data set given.

PROBLEMS FOR CHAPTER 15

15.1 As in Problem 15.4.2, but for Example 15.4.8.

15.2 As in Problem 15.4.2, but for Example 15.4.11.

15.3 Let $X_1, X_2, \ldots, X_n$ be independent Poisson r.v.'s, each with mean λ. Find $J(\hat{\theta})$ for estimation of $\theta = \lambda^2$. Compare the biases of the MLE of λ^2 and of $J(\hat{\theta})$.

15.4 Develop approximate $100(1 - \alpha)\%$ confidence limits for λ^2 based on the jackknife estimator developed in Problem 15.3.

15.5 Let $X_1, X_2, \ldots, X_n$ be a random sample of size n with $P(X_i = 0) = 1 - p$, $P(X_i = 1) = p$. A jackknife technique for constructing a confidence interval for pq was given in Section 15.5. Use bootstrap techniques to develop a $100(1 - \alpha)\%$ confidence interval for pq.

15.6 Take a random sample of size 10 from a uniform density on $(0, \theta)$ with $\theta = 8$. Then generate 50 bootstrap samples of size 10 each to estimate the variance of $\hat{\theta}$, the MLE of θ. Construct a 95% confidence interval for θ.

Statistical Tables

TABLE 1
Auxiliary Function $\sqrt{x}$

x	$\sqrt{x}$	$\sqrt{10x}$	x	$\sqrt{x}$	$\sqrt{10x}$	x	$\sqrt{x}$	$\sqrt{10x}$
1	1.0000	3.1623	34	5.8310	18.439	67	8.1854	25.884
2	1.4142	4.4721	35	5.9161	18.708	68	8.2462	26.077
3	1.7321	5.4772	36	6.0000	18.974	69	8.3066	26.268
4	2.0000	6.3246	37	6.0828	19.235	70	8.3666	26.458
5	2.2361	7.0711	38	6.1644	19.494	71	8.4261	26.646
6	2.4495	7.7460	39	6.2450	19.748	72	8.4853	26.833
7	2.6458	8.3666	40	6.3246	20.000	73	8.5440	27.019
8	2.8284	8.9443	41	6.4031	20.248	74	8.6023	27.203
9	3.0000	9.4868	42	6.4807	20.494	75	8.6603	27.386
10	3.1623	10.000	43	6.5574	20.736	76	8.7178	27.568
11	3.3166	10.488	44	6.6332	20.976	77	8.7750	27.749
12	3.4641	10.954	45	6.7082	21.213	78	8.8318	27.928
13	3.6056	11.402	46	6.7823	21.448	79	8.8882	28.107
14	3.7417	11.832	47	6.8557	21.679	80	8.9443	28.284
15	3.8730	12.247	48	6.9282	21.909	81	9.0000	28.460
16	4.0000	12.649	49	7.0000	22.136	82	9.0554	28.636
17	4.1231	13.038	50	7.0711	22.361	83	9.1104	28.810
18	4.2426	13.416	51	7.1414	22.583	84	9.1652	28.983
19	4.3589	13.784	52	7.2111	22.804	85	9.2195	29.155
20	4.4721	14.142	53	7.2801	23.022	86	9.2736	29.326
21	4.5826	14.491	54	7.3485	23.238	87	9.3274	29.496
22	4.6904	14.832	55	7.4162	23.452	88	9.3808	29.665
23	4.7958	15.166	56	7.4833	23.664	89	9.4340	29.833
24	4.8990	15.492	57	7.5498	23.875	90	9.4868	30.000
25	5.0000	15.811	58	7.6158	24.083	91	9.5394	30.166
26	5.0990	16.125	59	7.6811	24.290	92	9.5917	30.332
27	5.1962	16.432	60	7.7460	24.495	93	9.6437	30.496
28	5.2915	16.733	61	7.8102	24.698	94	9.6954	30.659
29	5.3852	17.029	62	7.8740	24.900	95	9.7468	30.822
30	5.4772	17.321	63	7.9373	25.100	96	9.7980	30.984
31	5.5678	17.607	64	8.0000	25.298	97	9.8489	31.145
32	5.6569	17.889	65	8.0623	25.495	98	9.8995	31.305
33	5.7446	18.166	66	8.1240	25.690	99	9.9499	31.464

TABLE 2
Auxiliary Function $n!$

n	$n!$	n	$n!$
1	1	26	4.03291×10^{26}
2	2	27	1.08889×10^{28}
3	6	28	3.04888×10^{29}
4	24	29	8.84176×10^{30}
5	120	30	2.64253×10^{32}
6	720	31	8.22284×10^{33}
7	5040	32	2.63131×10^{35}
8	40320	33	8.68332×10^{36}
9	362880	34	2.95233×10^{38}
10	3.62880×10^{6}	35	1.03331×10^{40}
11	3.99168×10^{7}	36	3.71993×10^{41}
12	4.79002×10^{8}	37	1.37638×10^{43}
13	6.22702×10^{9}	38	5.23023×10^{44}
14	8.71783×10^{10}	39	2.03979×10^{46}
15	1.30767×10^{12}	40	8.15915×10^{47}
16	2.09228×10^{13}	41	3.34525×10^{49}
17	3.55687×10^{14}	42	1.40501×10^{51}
18	6.40237×10^{15}	43	6.04153×10^{52}
19	1.21645×10^{17}	44	2.65827×10^{54}
20	2.43290×10^{18}	45	1.19622×10^{56}
21	5.10909×10^{19}	46	5.50262×10^{57}
22	1.12400×10^{21}	47	2.58623×10^{59}
23	2.58520×10^{22}	48	1.24139×10^{61}
24	6.20448×10^{23}	49	6.08282×10^{62}
25	1.55112×10^{25}	50	3.04141×10^{64}

TABLE 3
Auxiliary Function $\binom{n}{r}$

n \ r	2	3	4	5	6	7	8	9	10	11	12	13
2	1											
3	3	1										
4	6	4	1									
5	10	10	5	1								
6	15	20	15	6	1							
7	21	35	35	21	7	1						
8	28	56	70	56	28	8	1					
9	36	84	126	126	84	36	9	1				
10	45	120	210	252	210	120	45	10	1			
11	55	165	330	462	462	330	165	55	11	1		
12	66	220	495	792	924	792	495	220	66	12	1	
13	78	286	715	1,287	1,716	1,716	1,287	715	286	78	13	1
14	91	364	1,001	2,002	3,003	3,432	3,003	2,002	1,001	364	91	14
15	105	455	1,365	3,003	5,005	6,435	6,435	5,005	3,003	1,365	455	105
16	120	560	1,820	4,368	8,008	11,440	12,870	11,440	8,008	4,368	1,820	560
17	136	680	2,380	6,188	12,376	19,448	24,310	24,310	19,448	12,376	6,188	2,380
18	153	816	3,060	8,568	18,564	31,824	43,758	48,620	43,758	31,824	18,564	8,568
19	171	969	3,876	11,628	27,132	50,388	75,582	92,378	92,378	75,582	50,388	27,132
20	190	1,140	4,845	15,504	38,760	77,520	125,970	167,960	184,756	167,960	125,970	77,520
21	210	1,330	5,985	20,349	54,264	116,280	203,490	292,930	352,716	352,716	293,930	203,490
22	231	1,540	7,315	26,334	76,613	170,544	319,770	497,420	646,646	705,432	646,646	497,420
23	253	1,771	8,855	33,649	100,947	245,157	490,314	817,190	1,144,066	1,352,078	1,352,078	1,144,066
24	276	2,024	10,626	42,504	134,596	346,104	735,471	1,307,504	1,961,256	2,496,144	2,704,156	2,496,144
25	300	2,300	12,650	53,130	177,100	480,700	1,081,575	2,042,975	3,268,760	4,457,400	5,200,300	5,200,300
26	325	2,600	14,950	65,780	230,230	657,800	1,562,275	3,124,550	5,311,735	7,726,160	9,657,700	10,400,600

TABLE 4
Auxiliary Function e^{-x}

x	e^{-x}	x	e^{-x}	x	e^{-x}	x	e^{-x}
.00	1.00000	.50	.60653	1.00	.36788	1.50	.22313
.01	.99005	.51	.60050	1.01	.36422	1.51	.22091
.02	.98020	.52	.59452	1.02	.36059	1.52	.21871
.03	.97045	.53	.58860	1.03	.35701	1.53	.21654
.04	.96079	.54	.58275	1.04	.35345	1.54	.21438
.05	.95123	.55	.57695	1.05	.34994	1.55	.21225
.06	.94176	.56	.57121	1.06	.34646	1.56	.21014
.07	.93239	.57	.56553	1.07	.34301	1.57	.20805
.08	.92312	.58	.55990	1.08	.33960	1.58	.20598
.09	.91393	.59	.55433	1.09	.33622	1.59	.20393
.10	.90484	.60	.54881	1.10	.33287	1.60	.20190
.11	.89583	.61	.54335	1.11	.32956	1.61	.19989
.12	.88692	.62	.53794	1.12	.32628	1.62	.19790
.13	.87810	.63	.53259	1.13	.32303	1.63	.19593
.14	.86936	.64	.52729	1.14	.31982	1.64	.19398
.15	.86071	.65	.52205	1.15	.31664	1.65	.19205
.16	.85214	.66	.51685	1.16	.31349	1.66	.19014
.17	.84366	.67	.51171	1.17	.31037	1.67	.18825
.18	.83527	.68	.50662	1.18	.30728	1.68	.18637
.19	.82696	.69	.50158	1.19	.30422	1.69	.18452
.20	.81873	.70	.49659	1.20	.30119	1.70	.18268
.21	.81058	.71	.49164	1.21	.29820	1.71	.18087
.22	.80252	.72	.48675	1.22	.29523	1.72	.17907
.23	.79453	.73	.48191	1.23	.29229	1.73	.17728
.24	.78663	.74	.47711	1.24	.28938	1.74	.17552
.25	.77880	.75	.47237	1.25	.28650	1.75	.17377
.26	.77105	.76	.46767	1.26	.28365	1.76	.17204
.27	.76338	.77	.46301	1.27	.28083	1.77	.17033
.28	.75578	.78	.45841	1.28	.27804	1.78	.16864
.29	.74826	.79	.45384	1.29	.27527	1.79	.16696
.30	.74082	.80	.44933	1.30	.27253	1.80	.16530
.31	.73345	.81	.44486	1.31	.26982	1.81	.16365
.32	.72615	.82	.44043	1.32	.26714	1.82	.16203
.33	.71892	.83	.43605	1.33	.26448	1.83	.16041
.34	.71177	.84	.43171	1.34	.26185	1.84	.15882
.35	.70469	.85	.42741	1.35	.25924	1.85	.15724
.36	.69768	.86	.42316	1.36	.25666	1.86	.15567
.37	.69073	.87	.41895	1.37	.25411	1.87	.15412
.38	.68368	.88	.41478	1.38	.25158	1.88	.15259
.39	.67706	.89	.41066	1.39	.24908	1.89	.15107
.40	.67032	.90	.40657	1.40	.24660	1.90	.14957
.41	.66365	.91	.40252	1.41	.24414	1.91	.14808
.42	.65705	.92	.39852	1.42	.24171	1.92	.14661
.43	.65051	.93	.39455	1.43	.23931	1.93	.14515
.44	.64404	.94	.39063	1.44	.23693	1.94	.14370
.45	.63763	.95	.38674	1.45	.23457	1.95	.14227
.46	.63128	.96	.38289	1.46	.23224	1.96	.14086
.47	.62500	.97	.37908	1.47	.22993	1.97	.13946
.48	.61878	.98	.37531	1.48	.22764	1.98	.13807
.49	.61263	.99	.37158	1.49	.22537	1.99	.13670

TABLE 4
Auxiliary Function e^{-x} (Continued)

x	e^{-x}	x	e^{-x}	x	e^{-x}	x	e^{-x}
2.00	.13534	2.50	.08208	3.00	.04979	5.50	.00409
2.01	.13399	2.51	.08127	3.05	.04736	5.60	.00370
2.02	.13266	2.52	.08046	3.10	.04505	5.70	.00335
2.03	.13134	2.53	.07966	3.15	.04285	5.80	.00303
2.04	.13003	2.54	.07887	3.20	.04076	5.90	.00274
2.05	.12873	2.55	.07808	3.25	.03877	6.00	.00248
2.06	.12745	2.56	.07730	3.30	.03688	6.10	.00224
2.07	.12619	2.57	.07654	3.35	.03508	6.20	.00203
2.08	.12493	2.58	.07577	3.40	.03337	6.30	.00184
2.09	.12369	2.59	.07502	3.45	.03175	6.40	.00166
2.10	.12246	2.60	.07427	3.50	.03020	6.50	.00150
2.11	.12124	2.61	.07353	3.55	.02872	6.75	.00117
2.12	.12003	2.62	.07280	3.60	.02732	7.00	.00091
2.13	.11884	2.63	.07208	3.65	.02599	7.25	.00071
2.14	.11765	2.64	.07136	3.70	.02472	7.50	.00055
2.15	.11648	2.65	.07065	3.75	.02352	7.75	.00043
2.16	.11533	2.66	.06995	3.80	.02237	8.00	.00034
2.17	.11418	2.67	.06925	3.85	.02128	8.25	.00026
2.18	.11304	2.68	.06856	3.90	.02024	8.50	.00020
2.19	.11192	2.69	.06788	3.95	.01925	8.75	.00016
2.20	.11080	2.70	.06721	4.00	.01832	9.00	.00012
2.21	.10970	2.71	.06654	4.05	.01742	9.25	.00010
2.22	.10861	2.72	.06587	4.10	.01657	9.50	.00007
2.23	.10753	2.73	.06522	4.15	.01576	9.75	.00006
2.24	.10646	2.74	.06457	4.20	.01500	10.00	.00005
2.25	.10540	2.75	.06393	4.25	.01426		
2.26	.10435	2.76	.06329	4.30	.01357		
2.27	.10331	2.77	.06266	4.35	.01291		
2.28	.10228	2.78	.06204	4.40	.01228		
2.29	.10127	2.79	.06142	4.45	.01168		
2.30	.10026	2.80	.06081	4.50	.01111		
2.31	.09926	2.81	.06020	4.55	.01057		
2.32	.09827	2.82	.05961	4.60	.01005		
2.33	.09730	2.83	.05901	4.65	.00956		
2.34	.09633	2.84	.05843	4.70	.00910		
2.35	.09537	2.85	.05784	4.75	.00865		
2.36	.09442	2.86	.05727	4.80	.00823		
2.37	.09348	2.87	.05670	4.85	.00783		
2.38	.09255	2.88	.05613	4.90	.00745		
2.39	.09163	2.89	.05558	4.95	.00708		
2.40	.09072	2.90	.05502	5.00	.00674		
2.41	.08982	2.91	.05448	5.05	.00641		
2.42	.08892	2.92	.05393	5.10	.00610		
2.43	.08804	2.93	.05340	5.15	.00580		
2.44	.08716	2.94	.05287	5.20	.00552		
2.45	.08629	2.95	.05234	5.25	.00525		
2.46	.08544	2.96	.05182	5.30	.00499		
2.47	.08458	2.97	.05130	5.35	.00475		
2.48	.08374	2.98	.05079	5.40	.00452		
2.49	.08291	2.99	.05029	5.45	.00430		

TABLE 5
The Binomial Distribution

A random variable X is said to have the binomial distribution if (for some positive integer n, and some p with $0 \leq p \leq 1$; see Definition 3.2.3)

$$p_X(x) = \begin{cases} \binom{n}{x} p^x (1-p)^{n-x}, & x = 0, 1, \ldots, n \\ 0, & \text{otherwise.} \end{cases}$$

The following table gives values of $p_X(x)$ (for various values of n, p).

n	x	.05	.10	.15	.20	.25	.30	.35	.40	.45	.50
1	0	.9500	.9000	.8500	.8000	.7500	.7000	.6500	.6000	.5500	.5000
1	1	.0500	.1000	.1500	.2000	.2500	.3000	.3500	.4000	.4500	.5000
2	0	.9025	.8100	.7225	.6400	.5625	.4900	.4225	.3600	.3025	.2500
2	1	.0950	.1800	.2550	.3200	.3750	.4200	.4550	.4800	.4950	.5000
2	2	.0025	.0100	.0225	.0400	.0625	.0900	.1225	.1600	.2025	.2500
3	0	.8574	.7290	.6141	.5120	.4219	.3430	.2746	.2160	.1664	.1250
3	1	.1354	.2430	.3251	.3840	.4219	.4410	.4436	.4320	.4084	.3750
3	2	.0071	.0270	.0574	.0960	.1406	.1890	.2389	.2880	.3341	.3750
3	3	.0001	.0010	.0034	.0080	.0156	.0270	.0429	.0640	.0911	.1250
4	0	.8145	.6561	.5220	.4096	.3164	.2401	.1785	.1296	.0915	.0625
4	1	.1715	.2916	.3685	.4096	.4219	.4116	.3845	.3456	.2995	.2500
4	2	.0135	.0486	.0975	.1536	.2109	.2646	.3105	.3456	.3675	.3750
4	3	.0005	.0036	.0115	.0256	.0469	.0756	.1115	.1536	.2005	.2500
4	4	.0000	.0001	.0005	.0016	.0039	.0081	.0150	.0256	.0410	.0625
5	0	.7738	.5905	.4437	.3277	.2373	.1681	.1160	.0778	.0503	.0313
5	1	.2036	.3281	.3915	.4096	.3955	.3602	.3124	.2592	.2059	.1563
5	2	.0214	.0729	.1382	.2048	.2637	.3087	.3364	.3456	.3369	.3125
5	3	.0011	.0081	.0244	.0512	.0879	.1323	.1811	.2304	.2757	.3125
5	4	.0000	.0004	.0022	.0064	.0146	.0284	.0488	.0768	.1128	.1563
5	5	.0000	.0000	.0001	.0003	.0010	.0024	.0053	.0102	.0185	.0313
6	0	.7351	.5314	.3771	.2621	.1780	.1176	.0754	.0467	.0277	.0156
6	1	.2321	.3543	.3993	.3932	.3560	.3025	.2437	.1866	.1359	.0938
6	2	.0305	.0984	.1762	.2458	.2966	.3241	.3280	.3110	.2780	.2344
6	3	.0021	.0146	.0415	.0819	.1318	.1852	.2355	.2765	.3032	.3125
6	4	.0001	.0012	.0055	.0154	.0330	.0595	.0951	.1382	.1861	.2344
6	5	.0000	.0001	.0004	.0015	.0044	.0102	.0205	.0369	.0609	.0938
6	6	.0000	.0000	.0000	.0001	.0002	.0007	.0018	.0041	.0083	.0156
7	0	.6983	.4783	.3206	.2097	.1335	.0824	.0490	.0280	.0152	.0078
7	1	.2573	.3720	.3960	.3670	.3115	.2471	.1848	.1306	.0872	.0547
7	2	.0406	.1240	.2097	.2753	.3115	.3177	.2985	.2613	.2140	.1641
7	3	.0036	.0230	.0617	.1147	.1730	.2269	.2679	.2903	.2918	.2734
7	4	.0002	.0026	.0109	.0287	.0577	.0972	.1442	.1935	.2388	.2734
7	5	.0000	.0002	.0012	.0043	.0115	.0250	.0466	.0774	.1172	.1641
7	6	.0000	.0000	.0001	.0004	.0013	.0036	.0084	.0172	.0320	.0547
7	7	.0000	.0000	.0000	.0000	.0001	.0002	.0006	.0016	.0037	.0078
8	0	.6634	.4305	.2725	.1678	.1001	.0576	.0319	.0168	.0084	.0039
8	1	.2793	.3826	.3847	.3355	.2670	.1977	.1373	.0896	.0548	.0313
8	2	.0515	.1488	.2376	.2936	.3115	.2965	.2587	.2090	.1569	.1094
8	3	.0054	.0331	.0839	.1468	.2076	.2541	.2786	.2787	.2568	.2188
8	4	.0004	.0046	.0185	.0459	.0865	.1361	.1875	.2322	.2627	.2734
8	5	.0000	.0004	.0026	.0092	.0231	.0467	.0808	.1239	.1719	.2188
8	6	.0000	.0000	.0002	.0011	.0038	.0100	.0217	.0413	.0703	.1094
8	7	.0000	.0000	.0000	.0001	.0004	.0012	.0033	.0079	.0164	.0313
8	8	.0000	.0000	.0000	.0000	.0000	.0001	.0002	.0007	.0017	.0039

TABLE 5
The Binomial Distribution (Continued)

$$p_X(x) = \binom{n}{x} p^x (1-p)^{n-x}$$

n	x	.05	.10	.15	.20	.25	.30	.35	.40	.45	.50
9	0	.6302	.3874	.2316	.1342	.0751	.0404	.0207	.0101	.0046	.0020
9	1	.2985	.3874	.3679	.3020	.2253	.1556	.1004	.0605	.0339	.0176
9	2	.0629	.1722	.2597	.3020	.3003	.2668	.2162	.1612	.1110	.0703
9	3	.0077	.0446	.1069	.1762	.2336	.2668	.2716	.2508	.2119	.1641
9	4	.0006	.0074	.0283	.0661	.1168	.1715	.2194	.2508	.2600	.2461
9	5	.0000	.0008	.0050	.0165	.0389	.0735	.1181	.1672	.2128	.2461
9	6	.0000	.0001	.0006	.0028	.0087	.0210	.0424	.0743	.1160	.1641
9	7	.0000	.0000	.0000	.0003	.0012	.0039	.0098	.0212	.0407	.0703
9	8	.0000	.0000	.0000	.0000	.0001	.0004	.0013	.0035	.0083	.0176
9	9	.0000	.0000	.0000	.0000	.0000	.0000	.0001	.0003	.0008	.0020
10	0	.5987	.3487	.1969	.1074	.0563	.0282	.0135	.0060	.0025	.0010
10	1	.3151	.3874	.3474	.2684	.1877	.1211	.0725	.0403	.0207	.0098
10	2	.0746	.1937	.2759	.3020	.2816	.2335	.1757	.1209	.0763	.0439
10	3	.0105	.0574	.1298	.2013	.2503	.2668	.2522	.2150	.1665	.1172
10	4	.0010	.0112	.0401	.0881	.1460	.2001	.2377	.2508	.2384	.2051
10	5	.0001	.0015	.0085	.0264	.0584	.1029	.1536	.2007	.2340	.2461
10	6	.0000	.0001	.0012	.0055	.0162	.0368	.0689	.1115	.1596	.2051
10	7	.0000	.0000	.0001	.0008	.0031	.0090	.0212	.0425	.0746	.1172
10	8	.0000	.0000	.0000	.0001	.0004	.0014	.0043	.0106	.0229	.0439
10	9	.0000	.0000	.0000	.0000	.0000	.0001	.0005	.0016	.0042	.0098
10	10	.0000	.0000	.0000	.0000	.0000	.0000	.0000	.0001	.0003	.0010
11	0	.5688	.3138	.1673	.0859	.0422	.0198	.0088	.0036	.0014	.0005
11	1	.3293	.3835	.3248	.2362	.1549	.0932	.0518	.0266	.0125	.0054
11	2	.0867	.2131	.2866	.2953	.2581	.1998	.1395	.0887	.0513	.0269
11	3	.0137	.0710	.1517	.2215	.2581	.2568	.2254	.1774	.1259	.0806
11	4	.0014	.0158	.0536	.1107	.1721	.2201	.2428	.2365	.2060	.1611
11	5	.0001	.0025	.0132	.0388	.0803	.1321	.1830	.2207	.2360	.2256
11	6	.0000	.0003	.0023	.0097	.0268	.0566	.0985	.1471	.1931	.2256
11	7	.0000	.0000	.0003	.0017	.0064	.0173	.0379	.0701	.1128	.1611
11	8	.0000	.0000	.0000	.0002	.0011	.0037	.0102	.0234	.0462	.0806
11	9	.0000	.0000	.0000	.0000	.0001	.0005	.0018	.0052	.0126	.0269
11	10	.0000	.0000	.0000	.0000	.0000	.0000	.0002	.0007	.0021	.0054
11	11	.0000	.0000	.0000	.0000	.0000	.0000	.0000	.0000	.0002	.0005
12	0	.5404	.2824	.1422	.0687	.0317	.0138	.0057	.0022	.0008	.0002
12	1	.3413	.3766	.3012	.2062	.1267	.0712	.0368	.0174	.0075	.0029
12	2	.0988	.2301	.2924	.2835	.2323	.1678	.1088	.0639	.0339	.0161
12	3	.0173	.0852	.1720	.2362	.2581	.2397	.1954	.1419	.0923	.0537
12	4	.0021	.0213	.0683	.1329	.1936	.2311	.2367	.2128	.1700	.1208
12	5	.0002	.0038	.0193	.0532	.1032	.1585	.2039	.2270	.2225	.1934
12	6	.0000	.0005	.0040	.0155	.0401	.0792	.1281	.1766	.2124	.2256
12	7	.0000	.0000	.0006	.0033	.0115	.0291	.0591	.1009	.1489	.1934
12	8	.0000	.0000	.0001	.0005	.0024	.0078	.0199	.0420	.0762	.1208
12	9	.0000	.0000	.0000	.0001	.0004	.0015	.0048	.0125	.0277	.0537
12	10	.0000	.0000	.0000	.0000	.0000	.0002	.0008	.0025	.0068	.0161
12	11	.0000	.0000	.0000	.0000	.0000	.0000	.0001	.0003	.0010	.0029
12	12	.0000	.0000	.0000	.0000	.0000	.0000	.0000	.0000	.0001	.0002

TABLE 5
The Binomial Distribution (Continued)

$$p_X(x) = \binom{n}{x} p^x (1 - p)^{n-x}$$

n	x	.05	.10	.15	.20	.25	p .30	.35	.40	.45	.50
13	0	.5133	.2542	.1209	.0550	.0238	.0097	.0037	.0013	.0004	.0001
13	1	.3512	.3672	.2774	.1787	.1029	.0540	.0259	.0113	.0045	.0016
13	2	.1109	.2448	.2937	.2680	.2059	.1388	.0836	.0453	.0220	.0095
13	3	.0214	.0997	.1900	.2457	.2517	.2181	.1651	.1107	.0660	.0349
13	4	.0028	.0277	.0838	.1535	.2097	.2337	.2222	.1845	.1350	.0873
13	5	.0003	.0055	.0266	.0691	.1258	.1803	.2154	.2214	.1989	.1571
13	6	.0000	.0008	.0063	.0230	.0559	.1030	.1546	.1968	.2169	.2095
13	7	.0000	.0001	.0011	.0058	.0186	.0442	.0833	.1312	.1775	.2095
13	8	.0000	.0000	.0001	.0011	.0047	.0142	.0336	.0656	.1089	.1571
13	9	.0000	.0000	.0000	.0001	.0009	.0034	.0101	.0243	.0495	.0873
13	10	.0000	.0000	.0000	.0000	.0001	.0006	.0022	.0065	.0162	.0349
13	11	.0000	.0000	.0000	.0000	.0000	.0001	.0003	.0012	.0036	.0095
13	12	.0000	.0000	.0000	.0000	.0000	.0000	.0000	.0001	.0005	.0016
13	13	.0000	.0000	.0000	.0000	.0000	.0000	.0000	.0000	.0000	.0001
14	0	.4877	.2288	.1028	.0440	.0178	.0068	.0024	.0008	.0002	.0001
14	1	.3593	.3559	.2539	.1539	.0832	.0407	.0181	.0073	.0027	.0009
14	2	.1229	.2570	.2912	.2501	.1802	.1134	.0634	.0317	.0141	.0056
14	3	.0259	.1142	.2056	.2501	.2402	.1943	.1366	.0845	.0462	.0222
14	4	.0037	.0349	.0998	.1720	.2202	.2290	.2022	.1549	.1040	.0611
14	5	.0004	.0078	.0352	.0860	.1468	.1963	.2178	.2066	.1701	.1222
14	6	.0000	.0013	.0093	.0322	.0734	.1262	.1759	.2066	.2088	.1833
14	7	.0000	.0002	.0019	.0092	.0280	.0618	.1082	.1574	.1952	.2095
14	8	.0000	.0000	.0003	.0020	.0082	.0232	.0510	.0918	.1398	.1833
14	9	.0000	.0000	.0000	.0003	.0018	.0066	.0183	.0408	.0762	.1222
14	10	.0000	.0000	.0000	.0000	.0003	.0014	.0049	.0136	.0312	.0611
14	11	.0000	.0000	.0000	.0000	.0000	.0002	.0010	.0033	.0093	.0222
14	12	.0000	.0000	.0000	.0000	.0000	.0000	.0001	.0005	.0019	.0056
14	13	.0000	.0000	.0000	.0000	.0000	.0000	.0000	.0001	.0002	.0009
14	14	.0000	.0000	.0000	.0000	.0000	.0000	.0000	.0000	.0000	.0001
15	0	.4633	.2059	.0874	.0352	.0134	.0047	.0016	.0005	.0001	.0000
15	1	.3658	.3432	.2312	.1319	.0668	.0305	.0126	.0047	.0016	.0005
15	2	.1348	.2669	.2856	.2309	.1559	.0916	.0476	.0219	.0090	.0032
15	3	.0307	.1285	.2184	.2501	.2252	.1700	.1110	.0634	.0318	.0139
15	4	.0049	.0428	.1156	.1876	.2252	.2186	.1792	.1268	.0780	.0417
15	5	.0006	.0105	.0449	.1032	.1651	.2061	.2123	.1859	.1404	.0916
15	6	.0000	.0019	.0132	.0430	.0917	.1472	.1906	.2066	.1914	.1527
15	7	.0000	.0003	.0030	.0138	.0393	.0811	.1319	.1771	.2013	.1964
15	8	.0000	.0000	.0005	.0035	.0131	.0348	.0710	.1181	.1647	.1964
15	9	.0000	.0000	.0001	.0007	.0034	.0116	.0298	.0612	.1048	.1527
15	10	.0000	.0000	.0000	.0001	.0007	.0030	.0096	.0245	.0515	.0916
15	11	.0000	.0000	.0000	.0000	.0001	.0006	.0024	.0074	.0191	.0417
15	12	.0000	.0000	.0000	.0000	.0000	.0001	.0004	.0016	.0052	.0139
15	13	.0000	.0000	.0000	.0000	.0000	.0000	.0001	.0003	.0010	.0032
15	14	.0000	.0000	.0000	.0000	.0000	.0000	.0000	.0000	.0001	.0005
15	15	.0000	.0000	.0000	.0000	.0000	.0000	.0000	.0000	.0000	.0000

TABLE 5
The Binomial Distribution (Continued)

$$p_X(x) = \binom{n}{x} p^x (1-p)^{n-x}$$

n	x	.05	.10	.15	.20	.25	p .30	.35	.40	.45	.50
16	0	.4401	.1853	.0743	.0281	.0100	.0033	.0010	.0003	.0001	.0000
16	1	.3706	.3294	.2097	.1126	.0535	.0228	.0087	.0030	.0009	.0002
16	2	.1463	.2745	.2775	.2111	.1336	.0732	.0353	.0150	.0056	.0018
16	3	.0359	.1423	.2285	.2463	.2079	.1465	.0888	.0468	.0215	.0085
16	4	.0061	.0514	.1311	.2001	.2252	.2040	.1553	.1014	.0572	.0278
16	5	.0008	.0137	.0555	.1201	.1802	.2099	.2008	.1623	.1123	.0667
16	6	.0001	.0028	.0180	.0550	.1101	.1649	.1982	.1983	.1684	.1222
16	7	.0000	.0004	.0045	.0197	.0524	.1010	.1524	.1889	.1969	.1746
16	8	.0000	.0001	.0009	.0055	.0197	.0487	.0923	.1417	.1812	.1964
16	9	.0000	.0000	.0001	.0012	.0058	.0185	.0442	.0840	.1318	.1746
16	10	.0000	.0000	.0000	.0002	.0014	.0056	.0167	.0392	.0755	.1222
16	11	.0000	.0000	.0000	.0000	.0002	.0013	.0049	.0142	.0337	.0667
16	12	.0000	.0000	.0000	.0000	.0000	.0002	.0011	.0040	.0115	.0278
16	13	.0000	.0000	.0000	.0000	.0000	.0000	.0002	.0008	.0029	.0085
16	14	.0000	.0000	.0000	.0000	.0000	.0000	.0000	.0001	.0005	.0018
16	15	.0000	.0000	.0000	.0000	.0000	.0000	.0000	.0000	.0001	.0002
16	16	.0000	.0000	.0000	.0000	.0000	.0000	.0000	.0000	.0000	.0000
17	0	.4181	.1668	.0631	.0225	.0075	.0023	.0007	.0002	.0000	.0000
17	1	.3741	.3150	.1893	.0957	.0426	.0169	.0060	.0019	.0005	.0001
17	2	.1575	.2800	.2673	.1914	.1136	.0581	.0260	.0102	.0035	.0010
17	3	.0415	.1556	.2359	.2393	.1893	.1245	.0701	.0341	.0144	.0052
17	4	.0076	.0605	.1457	.2093	.2209	.1868	.1320	.0796	.0411	.0182
17	5	.0010	.0175	.0668	.1361	.1914	.2081	.1849	.1379	.0875	.0472
17	6	.0001	.0039	.0236	.0680	.1276	.1784	.1991	.1839	.1432	.0944
17	7	.0000	.0007	.0065	.0267	.0668	.1201	.1685	.1927	.1841	.1484
17	8	.0000	.0001	.0014	.0084	.0279	.0644	.1134	.1606	.1883	.1855
17	9	.0000	.0000	.0003	.0021	.0093	.0276	.0611	.1070	.1540	.1855
17	10	.0000	.0000	.0000	.0004	.0025	.0095	.0263	.0571	.1008	.1484
17	11	.0000	.0000	.0000	.0001	.0005	.0026	.0090	.0242	.0525	.0944
17	12	.0000	.0000	.0000	.0000	.0001	.0006	.0024	.0081	.0215	.0472
17	13	.0000	.0000	.0000	.0000	.0000	.0001	.0005	.0021	.0068	.0182
17	14	.0000	.0000	.0000	.0000	.0000	.0000	.0001	.0004	.0016	.0052
17	15	.0000	.0000	.0000	.0000	.0000	.0000	.0000	.0001	.0003	.0010
17	16	.0000	.0000	.0000	.0000	.0000	.0000	.0000	.0000	.0000	.0001
17	17	.0000	.0000	.0000	.0000	.0000	.0000	.0000	.0000	.0000	.0000
18	0	.3972	.1501	.0536	.0180	.0056	.0016	.0004	.0001	.0000	.0000
18	1	.3763	.3002	.1704	.0811	.0338	.0126	.0042	.0012	.0003	.0001
18	2	.1683	.2835	.2556	.1723	.0958	.0458	.0190	.0069	.0022	.0006
18	3	.0473	.1680	.2406	.2297	.1704	.1046	.0547	.0246	.0095	.0031
18	4	.0093	.0700	.1592	.2153	.2130	.1681	.1104	.0614	.0291	.0117
18	5	.0014	.0218	.0787	.1507	.1988	.2017	.1664	.1146	.0666	.0327
18	6	.0002	.0052	.0301	.0816	.1436	.1873	.1941	.1655	.1181	.0708
18	7	.0000	.0010	.0091	.0350	.0820	.1376	.1792	.1892	.1657	.1214
18	8	.0000	.0002	.0022	.0120	.0376	.0811	.1327	.1734	.1864	.1669
18	9	.0000	.0000	.0004	.0033	.0139	.0386	.0794	.1284	.1694	.1855
18	10	.0000	.0000	.0001	.0008	.0042	.0149	.0385	.0771	.1248	.1669
18	11	.0000	.0000	.0000	.0001	.0010	.0046	.0151	.0374	.0742	.1214
18	12	.0000	.0000	.0000	.0000	.0002	.0012	.0047	.0145	.0354	.0708
18	13	.0000	.0000	.0000	.0000	.0000	.0002	.0012	.0045	.0134	.0327
18	14	.0000	.0000	.0000	.0000	.0000	.0000	.0002	.0011	.0039	.0117
18	15	.0000	.0000	.0000	.0000	.0000	.0000	.0000	.0002	.0009	.0031
18	16	.0000	.0000	.0000	.0000	.0000	.0000	.0000	.0000	.0001	.0006
18	17	.0000	.0000	.0000	.0000	.0000	.0000	.0000	.0000	.0000	.0001
18	18	.0000	.0000	.0000	.0000	.0000	.0000	.0000	.0000	.0000	.0000

STATISTICAL TABLES

TABLE 5
The Binomial Distribution (Continued)

$$p_X(x) = \binom{n}{x} p^x (1-p)^{n-x}$$

n	x	.05	.10	.15	.20	.25	.30	.35	.40	.45	.50
19	0	.3774	.1351	.0456	.0144	.0042	.0011	.0003	.0001	.0000	.0000
19	1	.3774	.2852	.1529	.0685	.0268	.0093	.0029	.0008	.0002	.0000
19	2	.1787	.2852	.2428	.1540	.0803	.0358	.0138	.0046	.0013	.0003
19	3	.0533	.1796	.2428	.2182	.1517	.0869	.0422	.0175	.0062	.0018
19	4	.0112	.0798	.1714	.2182	.2023	.1491	.0909	.0467	.0203	.0074
19	5	.0018	.0266	.0907	.1636	.2023	.1916	.1468	.0933	.0497	.0222
19	6	.0002	.0069	.0374	.0955	.1574	.1916	.1844	.1451	.0949	.0518
19	7	.0000	.0014	.0122	.0443	.0974	.1525	.1844	.1797	.1443	.0961
19	8	.0000	.0002	.0032	.0166	.0487	.0981	.1489	.1797	.1771	.1442
19	9	.0000	.0000	.0007	.0051	.0198	.0514	.0980	.1464	.1771	.1762
19	10	.0000	.0000	.0001	.0013	.0066	.0220	.0528	.0976	.1449	.1762
19	11	.0000	.0000	.0000	.0003	.0018	.0077	.0233	.0532	.0970	.1442
19	12	.0000	.0000	.0000	.0000	.0004	.0022	.0083	.0237	.0529	.0961
19	13	.0000	.0000	.0000	.0000	.0001	.0005	.0024	.0085	.0233	.0518
19	14	.0000	.0000	.0000	.0000	.0000	.0001	.0006	.0024	.0082	.0222
19	15	.0000	.0000	.0000	.0000	.0000	.0000	.0001	.0005	.0022	.0074
19	16	.0000	.0000	.0000	.0000	.0000	.0000	.0000	.0001	.0005	.0018
19	17	.0000	.0000	.0000	.0000	.0000	.0000	.0000	.0000	.0001	.0003
19	18	.0000	.0000	.0000	.0000	.0000	.0000	.0000	.0000	.0000	.0000
19	19	.0000	.0000	.0000	.0000	.0000	.0000	.0000	.0000	.0000	.0000
20	0	.3585	.1216	.0388	.0115	.0032	.0008	.0002	.0000	.0000	.0000
20	1	.3774	.2702	.1368	.0576	.0211	.0068	.0020	.0005	.0001	.0000
20	2	.1887	.2852	.2293	.1369	.0669	.0278	.0100	.0031	.0008	.0002
20	3	.0596	.1901	.2428	.2054	.1339	.0716	.0323	.0123	.0040	.0011
20	4	.0133	.0898	.1821	.2182	.1897	.1304	.0738	.0350	.0139	.0046
20	5	.0022	.0319	.1028	.1746	.2023	.1789	.1272	.0746	.0365	.0148
20	6	.0003	.0089	.0454	.1091	.1686	.1916	.1712	.1244	.0746	.0370
20	7	.0000	.0020	.0160	.0545	.1124	.1643	.1844	.1659	.1221	.0739
20	8	.0000	.0004	.0046	.0222	.0609	.1144	.1614	.1797	.1623	.1201
20	9	.0000	.0001	.0011	.0074	.0271	.0654	.1158	.1597	.1771	.1602
20	10	.0000	.0000	.0002	.0020	.0099	.0308	.0686	.1171	.1593	.1762
20	11	.0000	.0000	.0000	.0005	.0030	.0120	.0336	.0710	.1185	.1602
20	12	.0000	.0000	.0000	.0001	.0008	.0039	.0136	.0355	.0727	.1201
20	13	.0000	.0000	.0000	.0000	.0002	.0010	.0045	.0146	.0366	.0739
20	14	.0000	.0000	.0000	.0000	.0000	.0002	.0012	.0049	.0150	.0370
20	15	.0000	.0000	.0000	.0000	.0000	.0000	.0003	.0013	.0049	.0148
20	16	.0000	.0000	.0000	.0000	.0000	.0000	.0000	.0003	.0013	.0046
20	17	.0000	.0000	.0000	.0000	.0000	.0000	.0000	.0000	.0002	.0011
20	18	.0000	.0000	.0000	.0000	.0000	.0000	.0000	.0000	.0000	.0002
20	19	.0000	.0000	.0000	.0000	.0000	.0000	.0000	.0000	.0000	.0000
20	20	.0000	.0000	.0000	.0000	.0000	.0000	.0000	.0000	.0000	.0000

TABLE 6
The Hypergeometric Distribution

A random variable X is said to have the hypergeometric distribution if (for some integers n, a, N with $1 \le n \le N$ and $0 \le a \le n$; see Definition 3.2.7)

$$p_X(x) = \begin{cases} \dfrac{\dbinom{a}{x}\dbinom{N-a}{n-x}}{\dbinom{N}{n}}, & x = \max(0, n - (N-a)), \ldots, \min(n, a) \\ 0, & \text{otherwise.} \end{cases}$$

The following table gives values of $p_X(x)$ (for various values of n, a, N).

N	n	a	x	$p_X(x)$	N	n	a	x	$p_X(x)$	N	n	a	x	$p_X(x)$
2	1	1	0	.500000	6	2	1	0	.666667	7	3	3	0	.114286
			1	.500000				1	.333333				1	.514286
3	1	1	0	.666667	6	2	2	0	.400000				2	.342857
			1	.333333				1	.533333				3	.028571
3	2	1	0	.333333				2	.066667	7	4	1	0	.428571
			1	.666667	6	3	1	0	.500000				1	.571429
3	2	2	1	.666667				1	.500000	7	4	2	0	.142857
			2	.333333	6	3	2	0	.200000				1	.571429
4	1	1	0	.750000				1	.600000				2	.285714
			1	.250000				2	.200000	7	4	3	0	.028571
4	2	1	0	.500000	6	3	3	0	.050000				1	.342857
			1	.500000				1	.450000				2	.514286
4	2	2	0	.166667				2	.450000				3	.114286
			1	.666667				3	.050000	7	4	4	1	.114286
			2	.166667	6	4	1	0	.333333				2	.514286
4	3	1	0	.250000				1	.666667				3	.342857
			1	.750000	6	4	2	0	.066667				4	.028571
4	3	2	1	.500000				1	.533333	7	5	1	0	.285714
			2	.500000				2	.400000				1	.714286
4	3	3	2	.750000	6	4	3	1	.200000	7	5	2	0	.047619
			3	.250000				2	.600000				1	.476190
5	1	1	0	.800000				3	.200000				2	.476190
			1	.200000	6	4	4	2	.400000	7	5	3	1	.142857
5	2	1	0	.600000				3	.533333				2	.571429
			1	.400000				4	.066667				3	.285714
5	2	2	0	.300000	6	5	1	0	.166667	7	5	4	2	.285714
			1	.600000				1	.833333				3	.571429
			2	.100000	6	5	2	1	.333333				4	.142857
5	3	1	0	.400000				2	.666667	7	5	5	3	.476190
			1	.600000	6	5	3	2	.500000				4	.476190
5	3	2	0	.100000				3	.500000				5	.047619
			1	.600000	6	5	4	3	.666667	7	6	1	0	.142857
			2	.300000				4	.333333				1	.857143
5	3	3	1	.300000	6	5	5	4	.833333	7	6	2	1	.285714
			2	.600000				5	.166667				2	.714286
			3	.100000	7	1	1	0	.857143	7	6	3	2	.428571
5	4	1	0	.200000				1	.142857				3	.571429
			1	.800000	7	2	1	0	.714286	7	6	4	3	.571429
5	4	2	1	.400000				1	.285714				4	.428571
			2	.600000	7	2	2	0	.476190	7	6	5	4	.714286
5	4	3	2	.600000				1	.476190				5	.285714
			3	.400000				2	.047619	7	6	6	5	.857143
5	4	4	3	.800000	7	3	1	0	.571429				6	.142857
			4	.200000				1	.428571	8	1	1	0	.875000
6	1	1	0	.833333	7	3	2	0	.285714				1	.125000
			1	.166667				1	.571429	8	2	1	0	.750000
								2	.142857				1	.250000

TABLE 6
The Hypergeometric Distribution (Continued)

$$p_X(x) = \frac{\binom{a}{x}\binom{N-a}{n-x}}{\binom{N}{n}}$$

N	n	a	x	$p_X(x)$	N	n	a	x	$p_X(x)$	N	n	a	x	$p_X(x)$
8	2	2	0	.535714	8	6	4	2	.214286	9	5	1	0	.444444
			1	.428571				3	.571429				1	.555556
			2	.035714				4	.214286	9	5	2	0	.166667
8	3	1	0	.625000	8	6	5	3	.357143				1	.55556
			1	.375000				4	.535714				2	.277778
8	3	2	0	.357143				5	.107143	9	5	3	0	.047619
			1	.535714	8	6	6	4	.535714				1	.357143
			2	.107143				5	.428571				2	.476190
8	3	3	0	.178571				6	.035714				3	.119048
			1	.535714	8	7	1	0	.125000	9	5	4	0	.007937
			2	.267857				1	.875000				1	.158730
			3	.017857	8	7	2	1	.250000				2	.476190
8	4	1	0	.500000				2	.750000				3	.317460
			1	.500000	8	7	3	2	.375000				4	.039683
8	4	2	0	.214286				3	.625000	9	5	5	1	.039683
			1	.571429	8	7	4	3	.500000				2	.317460
			2	.214286				4	.500000				3	.476190
8	4	3	0	.071429	8	7	5	4	.625000				4	.158730
			1	.428571				5	.375000				5	.007937
			2	.428571	8	7	6	5	.750000	9	6	1	0	.333333
			3	.071429				6	.250000				1	.666667
8	4	4	0	.014286	8	7	7	6	.875000	9	6	2	0	.083333
			1	.228571				7	.125000				1	.500000
			2	.514286	9	1	1	0	.888889				2	.416667
			3	.228571				1	.111111	9	6	3	0	.011905
			4	.014286	9	2	1	0	.777778				1	.214286
8	5	1	0	.375000				1	.222222				2	.535714
			1	.625000	9	2	2	0	.583333				3	.238095
8	5	2	0	.107143				1	.388889	9	6	4	1	.047619
			1	.535714				2	.027778				2	.357143
			2	.357143	9	3	1	0	.666667				3	.476190
8	5	3	0	.017857				1	.333333				4	.119048
			1	.267857	9	3	2	0	.416667	9	6	5	2	.119048
			2	.535714				1	.500000				3	.476190
			3	.178571				2	.083333				4	.357143
8	5	4	1	.071429	9	3	3	0	.238095				5	.047619
			2	.428571				1	.535714	9	6	6	3	.238095
			3	.428571				2	.214286				4	.535714
			4	.071429				3	.011905				5	.214286
8	5	5	2	.178571	9	4	1	0	.555556				6	.011905
			3	.535714				1	.444444	9	7	1	0	.222222
			4	.267857	9	4	2	0	.277778				1	.777778
			5	.017857				1	.555556	9	7	2	0	.027778
8	6	1	0	.250000				2	.166667				1	.388889
			1	.750000	9	4	3	0	.119048				2	.583333
8	6	2	0	.035714				1	.476190	9	7	3	1	.083333
			1	.428571				2	.357143				2	.500000
			2	.535714				3	.047619				3	.416667
8	6	3	1	.107143	9	4	4	0	.039683	9	7	4	2	.166667
			2	.535714				1	.317460				3	.555556
			3	.357143				2	.476190				4	.277778
								3	.158730	9	7	5	3	.277778
								4	.007937				4	.555556
													5	.166667

TABLE 6
The Hypergeometric Distribution (Continued)

$$p_X(x) = \frac{\binom{a}{x}\binom{N-a}{n-x}}{\binom{N}{n}}$$

N	n	a	x	$p_X(x)$	N	n	a	x	$p_X(x)$	N	n	a	x	$p_X(x)$
9	7	6	4	.416667	10	5	3	0	.083333	10	7	6	3	.166667
			5	.500000				1	.416667				4	.500000
			6	.083333				2	.416667				5	.300000
9	7	7	5	.583333				3	.083333				6	.033333
			6	.388889	10	5	4	0	.023810	10	7	7	4	.291667
			7	.027778				1	.238095				5	.525000
9	8	1	0	.111111				2	.476190				6	.175000
			1	.888889				3	.238095				7	.008333
9	8	2	1	.222222				4	.023810	10	8	1	0	.200000
			2	.777778	10	5	5	0	.003968				1	.800000
9	8	3	2	.333333				1	.099206	10	8	2	0	.022222
			3	.666667				2	.396825				1	.355556
9	8	4	3	.444444				3	.396825				2	.622222
			4	.555556				4	.099206	10	8	3	1	.066667
9	8	5	4	.555556				5	.003968				2	.466667
			5	.444444	10	6	1	0	.400000				3	.466667
9	8	6	5	.666667				1	.600000	10	8	4	2	.133333
			6	.333333	10	6	2	0	.133333				3	.533333
9	8	7	6	.777778				1	.533333				4	.333333
			7	.222222				2	.333333	10	8	5	3	.222222
9	8	8	7	.888889	10	6	3	0	.033333				4	.555556
			8	.111111				1	.300000				5	.222222
10	1	1	0	.900000				2	.500000	10	8	6	4	.333333
			1	.100000				3	.166667				5	.533333
10	2	1	0	.800000	10	6	4	0	.004762				6	.133333
			1	.200000				1	.114286	10	8	7	5	.466667
10	2	2	0	.622222				2	.428571				6	.466667
			1	.355556				3	.380952				7	.066667
			2	.022222				4	.071429	10	8	8	6	.622222
10	3	1	0	.700000	10	6	5	1	.023810				7	.355556
			1	.300000				2	.238095				8	.022222
10	3	2	0	.466667				3	.476190	10	9	1	0	.100000
			1	.466667				4	.238095				1	.900000
			2	.066667				5	.023810	10	9	2	1	.200000
10	3	3	0	.291667	10	6	6	2	.071429				2	.800000
			1	.525000				3	.380952	10	9	3	2	.300000
			2	.175000				4	.428571				3	.700000
			3	.008333				5	.114286	10	9	4	3	.400000
10	4	1	0	.600000				6	.004762				4	.600000
			1	.400000	10	7	1	0	.300000	10	9	5	4	.500000
10	4	2	0	.333333				1	.700000				5	.500000
			1	.533333	10	7	2	0	.066667	10	9	6	5	.600000
			2	.133333				1	.466667				6	.400000
10	4	3	0	.166667				2	.466667	10	9	7	6	.700000
			1	.500000	10	7	3	0	.008333				7	.300000
			2	.300000				1	.175000	10	9	8	7	.800000
			3	.033333				2	.525000				8	.200000
10	4	4	0	.071429				3	.291667	10	9	9	8	.900000
			1	.380952	10	7	4	1	.033333				9	.100000
			2	.428571				2	.300000					
			3	.114286				3	.500000					
			4	.004762				4	.166667					
10	5	1	0	.500000	10	7	5	2	.083333					
			1	.500000				3	.416667					
10	5	2	0	.222222				4	.416667					
			1	.555556				5	.083333					
			2	.222222										

STATISTICAL TABLES

TABLE 7
The Poisson Distribution

A random variable X is said to have the Poisson distribution if (for some $\mu > 0$; see Definition 3.2.11)

$$p_X(x) = \begin{cases} e^{-\mu}\dfrac{\mu^x}{x!}, & x = 0, 1, 2, \ldots \\ 0, & \text{otherwise.} \end{cases}$$

The following table gives values of $p_X(x)$ (for various values of μ).

x	0.1	0.2	0.3	0.4	0.5	0.6	0.7	0.8	0.9	1.0
0	.9048	.8187	.7408	.6703	.6065	.5488	.4966	.4493	.4066	.3679
1	.0905	.1637	.2222	.2681	.3033	.3293	.3476	.3595	.3659	.3679
2	.0045	.0164	.0333	.0536	.0758	.0988	.1217	.1438	.1647	.1839
3	.0002	.0011	.0033	.0072	.0126	.0198	.0284	.0383	.0494	.0613
4	.0000	.0001	.0003	.0007	.0016	.0030	.0050	.0077	.0111	.0153
5	.0000	.0000	.0000	.0001	.0002	.0004	.0007	.0012	.0020	.0031
6	.0000	.0000	.0000	.0000	.0000	.0000	.0001	.0002	.0003	.0005
7	.0000	.0000	.0000	.0000	.0000	.0000	.0000	.0000	.0000	.0001

x	1.1	1.2	1.3	1.4	1.5	1.6	1.7	1.8	1.9	2.0
0	.3329	.3012	.2725	.2466	.2231	.2019	.1827	.1653	.1496	.1353
1	.3662	.3614	.3543	.3452	.3347	.3230	.3106	.2975	.2842	.2707
2	.2014	.2169	.2303	.2417	.2510	.2584	.2640	.2678	.2700	.2707
3	.0738	.0867	.0998	.1128	.1255	.1378	.1496	.1607	.1710	.1804
4	.0203	.0260	.0324	.0395	.0471	.0551	.0636	.0723	.0812	.0902
5	.0045	.0062	.0084	.0111	.0141	.0176	.0216	.0260	.0309	.0361
6	.0008	.0012	.0018	.0026	.0035	.0047	.0061	.0078	.0098	.0120
7	.0001	.0002	.0003	.0005	.0008	.0011	.0015	.0020	.0027	.0034
8	.0000	.0000	.0001	.0001	.0001	.0002	.0003	.0005	.0006	.0009
9	.0000	.0000	.0000	.0000	.0000	.0000	.0001	.0001	.0001	.0002

x	2.1	2.2	2.3	2.4	2.5	2.6	2.7	2.8	2.9	3.0
0	.1225	.1108	.1003	.0907	.0821	.0743	.0672	.0608	.0550	.0498
1	.2572	.2438	.2306	.2177	.2052	.1931	.1815	.1703	.1596	.1494
2	.2700	.2681	.2652	.2613	.2565	.2510	.2450	.2384	.2314	.2240
3	.1890	.1966	.2033	.2090	.2138	.2176	.2205	.2225	.2237	.2240
4	.0992	.1082	.1169	.1254	.1336	.1414	.1488	.1557	.1622	.1680
5	.0417	.0476	.0538	.0602	.0668	.0735	.0804	.0872	.0940	.1008
6	.0146	.0174	.0206	.0241	.0278	.0319	.0362	.0407	.0455	.0504
7	.0044	.0055	.0068	.0083	.0099	.0118	.0139	.0163	.0188	.0216
8	.0011	.0015	.0019	.0025	.0031	.0038	.0047	.0057	.0068	.0081
9	.0003	.0004	.0005	.0007	.0009	.0011	.0014	.0018	.0022	.0027
10	.0001	.0001	.0001	.0002	.0002	.0003	.0004	.0005	.0006	.0008
11	.0000	.0000	.0000	.0000	.0000	.0001	.0001	.0001	.0002	.0002
12	.0000	.0000	.0000	.0000	.0000	.0000	.0000	.0000	.0000	.0001

TABLE 7
The Poisson Distribution (Continued)

$$p_X(x) = e^{-\mu}\frac{\mu^x}{x!}$$

x	3.1	3.2	3.3	3.4	3.5	3.6	3.7	3.8	3.9	4.0
0	.0450	.0408	.0369	.0334	.0302	.0273	.0247	.0224	.0202	.0183
1	.1397	.1304	.1217	.1135	.1057	.0984	.0915	.0850	.0789	.0733
2	.2165	.2087	.2008	.1929	.1850	.1771	.1692	.1615	.1539	.1465
3	.2237	.2226	.2209	.2186	.2158	.2125	.2087	.2046	.2001	.1954
4	.1733	.1781	.1823	.1858	.1888	.1912	.1931	.1944	.1951	.1954
5	.1075	.1140	.1203	.1264	.1322	.1377	.1429	.1477	.1522	.1563
6	.0555	.0608	.0662	.0716	.0771	.0826	.0881	.0936	.0989	.1042
7	.0246	.0278	.0312	.0348	.0385	.0425	.0466	.0508	.0551	.0595
8	.0095	.0111	.0129	.0148	.0169	.0191	.0215	.0241	.0269	.0298
9	.0033	.0040	.0047	.0056	.0066	.0076	.0089	.0102	.0116	.0132
10	.0010	.0013	.0016	.0019	.0023	.0028	.0033	.0039	.0045	.0053
11	.0003	.0004	.0005	.0006	.0007	.0009	.0011	.0013	.0016	.0019
12	.0001	.0001	.0001	.0002	.0002	.0003	.0003	.0004	.0005	.0006
13	.0000	.0000	.0000	.0000	.0001	.0001	.0001	.0001	.0002	.0002
14	.0000	.0000	.0000	.0000	.0000	.0000.	.0000	.0000	.0000	.0001

x	4.1	4.2	4.3	4.4	4.5	4.6	4.7	4.8	4.9	5.0
0	.0166	.0150	.0136	.0123	.0111	.0101	.0091	.0082	.0074	.0067
1	.0679	.0630	.0583	.0540	.0500	.0462	.0427	.0395	.0365	.0337
2	.1393	.1323	.1254	.1188	.1125	.1063	.1005	.0948	.0894	.0842
3	.1904	.1852	.1798	.1743	.1687	.1631	.1574	.1517	.1460	.1404
4	.1951	.1944	.1933	.1917	.1898	.1875	.1849	.1820	.1789	.1755
5	.1600	.1633	.1662	.1687	.1708	.1725	.1738	.1747	.1753	.1755
6	.1093	.1143	.1191	.1237	.1281	.1323	.1362	.1398	.1432	.1462
7	.0640	.0686	.0732	.0778	.0824	.0869	.0914	.0959	.1002	.1044
8	.0328	.0360	.0393	.0428	.0463	.0500	.0537	.0575	.0614	.0653
9	.0150	.0168	.0188	.0209	.0232	.0255	.0281	.0307	.0334	.0363
10	.0061	.0071	.0081	.0092	.0104	.0118	.0132	.0147	.0164	.0181
11	.0023	.0027	.0032	.0037	.0043	.0049	.0056	.0064	.0073	.0082
12	.0008	.0009	.0011	.0013	.0016	.0019	.0022	.0026	.0030	.0034
13	.0002	.0003	.0004	.0005	.0006	.0007	.0008	.0009	.0011	.0013
14	.0001	.0001	.0001	.0001	.0002	.0002	.0003	.0003	.0004	.0005
15	.0000	.0000	.0000	.0000	.0001	.0001	.0001	.0001	.0001	.0002

x	5.1	5.2	5.3	5.4	5.5	5.6	5.7	5.8	5.9	6.0
0	.0061	.0055	.0050	.0045	.0041	.0037	.0033	.0030	.0027	.0025
1	.0311	.0287	.0265	.0244	.0225	.0207	.0191	.0176	.0162	.0149
2	.0793	.0746	.0701	.0659	.0618	.0580	.0544	.0509	.0477	.0446
3	.1348	.1293	.1239	.1185	.1133	.1082	.1033	.0985	.0938	.0892
4	.1719	.1681	.1641	.1600	.1558	.1515	.1472	.1428	.1383	.1339
5	.1753	.1748	.1740	.1728	.1714	.1697	.1678	.1656	.1632	.1606
6	.1490	.1515	.1537	.1555	.1571	.1584	.1594	.1601	.1605	.1606
7	.1086	.1125	.1163	.1200	.1234	.1267	.1298	.1326	.1353	.1377
8	.0692	.0731	.0771	.0810	.0849	.0887	.0925	.0962	.0998	.1033
9	.0392	.0423	.0454	.0486	.0519	.0552	.0586	.0620	.0654	.0688
10	.0200	.0220	.0241	.0262	.0285	.0309	.0334	.0359	.0386	.0413
11	.0093	.0104	.0116	.0129	.0143	.0157	.0173	.0190	.0207	.0225
12	.0039	.0045	.0051	.0058	.0065	.0073	.0082	.0092	.0102	.0113
13	.0015	.0018	.0021	.0024	.0028	.0032	.0036	.0041	.0046	.0052
14	.0006	.0007	.0008	.0009	.0011	.0013	.0015	.0017	.0019	.0022
15	.0002	.0002	.0003	.0003	.0004	.0005	.0006	.0007	.0008	.0009
16	.0001	.0001	.0001	.0001	.0001	.0002	.0002	.0002	.0003	.0003
17	.0000	.0000	.0000	.0000	.0000	.0001	.0001	.0001	.0001	.0001

STATISTICAL TABLES

TABLE 7
The Poisson Distribution (Continued)

$$p_X(x) = e^{-\mu} \frac{\mu^x}{x!}$$

x	6.1	6.2	6.3	6.4	6.5	6.6	6.7	6.8	6.9	7.0
0	.0022	.0020	.0018	.0017	.0015	.0014	.0012	.0011	.0010	.0009
1	.0137	.0126	.0116	.0106	.0098	.0090	.0082	.0076	.0070	.0064
2	.0417	.0390	.0364	.0340	.0318	.0296	.0276	.0258	.0240	.0223
3	.0848	.0806	.0765	.0726	.0688	.0652	.0617	.0584	.0552	.0521
4	.1294	.1249	.1205	.1162	.1118	.1076	.1034	.0992	.0952	.0912
5	.1579	.1549	.1519	.1487	.1454	.1420	.1385	.1349	.1314	.1277
6	.1605	.1601	.1595	.1586	.1575	.1562	.1546	.1529	.1511	.1490
7	.1399	.1418	.1435	.1450	.1462	.1472	.1480	.1486	.1489	.1490
8	.1066	.1099	.1130	.1160	.1188	.1215	.1240	.1263	.1284	.1304
9	.0723	.0757	.0791	.0825	.0858	.0891	.0923	.0954	.0985	.1014
10	.0441	.0469	.0498	.0528	.0558	.0588	.0618	.0649	.0679	.0710
11	.0244	.0265	.0285	.0307	.0330	.0353	.0377	.0401	.0426	.0452
12	.0124	.0137	.0150	.0164	.0179	.0194	.0210	.0227	.0245	.0263
13	.0058	.0065	.0073	.0081	.0089	.0099	.0108	.0119	.0130	.0142
14	.0025	.0029	.0033	.0037	.0041	.0046	.0052	.0058	.0064	.0071
15	.0010	.0012	.0014	.0016	.0018	.0020	.0023	.0026	.0029	.0033
16	.0004	.0005	.0005	.0006	.0007	.0008	.0010	.0011	.0013	.0014
17	.0001	.0002	.0002	.0002	.0003	.0003	.0004	.0004	.0005	.0006
18	.0000	.0001	.0001	.0001	.0001	.0001	.0001	.0002	.0002	.0002
19	.0000	.0000	.0000	.0000	.0000	.0000	.0001	.0001	.0001	.0001

x	7.1	7.2	7.3	7.4	7.5	7.6	7.7	7.8	7.9	8.0
0	.0008	.0007	.0007	.0006	.0006	.0005	.0005	.0004	.0004	.0003
1	.0059	.0054	.0049	.0045	.0041	.0038	.0035	.0032	.0029	.0027
2	.0208	.0194	.0180	.0167	.0156	.0145	.0134	.0125	.0116	.0107
3	.0492	.0464	.0438	.0413	.0389	.0366	.0345	.0324	.0305	.0286
4	.0874	.0836	.0799	.0764	.0729	.0696	.0663	.0632	.0602	.0573
5	.1241	.1204	.1167	.1130	.1094	.1057	.1021	.0986	.0951	.0916
6	.1468	.1445	.1420	.1394	.1367	.1339	.1311	.1282	.1252	.1221
7	.1489	.1486	.1481	.1474	.1465	.1454	.1442	.1428	.1413	.1396
8	.1321	.1337	.1351	.1363	.1373	.1381	.1388	.1392	.1395	.1396
9	.1042	.1070	.1096	.1121	.1144	.1167	.1187	.1207	.1224	.1241
10	.0740	.0770	.0800	.0829	.0858	.0887	.0914	.0941	.0967	.0993
11	.0478	.0504	.0531	.0558	.0585	.0613	.0640	.0667	.0695	.0722
12	.0283	.0303	.0323	.0344	.0366	.0388	.0411	.0434	.0457	.0481
13	.0154	.0168	.0181	.0196	.0211	.0227	.0243	.0260	.0278	.0296
14	.0078	.0086	.0095	.0104	.0113	.0123	.0134	.0145	.0157	.0169
15	.0037	.0041	.0046	.0051	.0057	.0062	.0069	.0075	.0083	.0090
16	.0016	.0019	.0021	.0024	.0026	.0030	.0033	.0037	.0041	.0045
17	.0007	.0008	.0009	.0010	.0012	.0013	.0015	.0017	.0019	.0021
18	.0003	.0003	.0004	.0004	.0005	.0006	.0006	.0007	.0008	.0009
19	.0001	.0001	.0001	.0002	.0002	.0002	.0003	.0003	.0003	.0004
20	.0000	.0000	.0001	.0001	.0001	.0001	.0001	.0001	.0001	.0002
21	.0000	.0000	.0000	.0000	.0000	.0000	.0000	.0001	.0001	.0001

TABLE 7
The Poisson Distribution (Continued)

$$p_X(x) = e^{-\mu}\,\frac{\mu^x}{x!}$$

x	8.1	8.2	8.3	8.4	8.5	8.6	8.7	8.8	8.9	9.0
0	.0003	.0003	.0002	.0002	.0002	.0002	.0002	.0002	.0001	.0001
1	.0025	.0023	.0021	.0019	.0017	.0016	.0014	.0013	.0012	.0011
2	.0100	.0092	.0086	.0079	.0074	.0068	.0063	.0058	.0054	.0050
3	.0269	.0252	.0237	.0222	.0208	.0195	.0183	.0171	.0160	.0150
4	.0544	.0517	.0491	.0466	.0443	.0420	.0398	.0377	.0357	.0337
5	.0882	.0849	.0816	.0784	.0752	.0722	.0692	.0663	.0635	.0607
6	.1191	.1160	.1128	.1097	.1066	.1034	.1003	.0972	.0941	.0911
7	.1378	.1358	.1338	.1317	.1294	.1271	.1247	.1222	.1197	.1171
8	.1395	.1392	.1388	.1382	.1375	.1366	.1356	.1344	.1332	.1318
9	.1256	.1269	.1280	.1290	.1299	.1306	.1311	.1315	.1317	.1318
10	.1017	.1040	.1063	.1084	.1104	.1123	.1140	.1157	.1172	.1186
11	.0749	.0776	.0802	.0828	.0853	.0878	.0902	.0925	.0948	.0970
12	.0505	.0530	.0555	.0579	.0604	.0629	.0654	.0679	.0703	.0728
13	.0315	.0334	.0354	.0374	.0395	.0416	.0438	.0459	.0481	.0504
14	.0182	.0196	.0210	.0225	.0240	.0256	.0272	.0289	.0306	.0324
15	.0098	.0107	.0116	.0126	.0136	.0147	.0158	.0169	.0182	.0194
16	.0050	.0055	.0060	.0066	.0072	.0079	.0086	.0093	.0101	.0109
17	.0024	.0026	.0029	.0033	.0036	.0040	.0044	.0048	.0053	.0058
18	.0011	.0012	.0014	.0015	.0017	.0019	.0021	.0024	.0026	.0029
19	.0005	.0005	.0006	.0007	.0008	.0009	.0010	.0011	.0012	.0014
20	.0002	.0002	.0002	.0003	.0003	.0004	.0004	.0005	.0005	.0006
21	.0001	.0001	.0001	.0001	.0001	.0002	.0002	.0002	.0002	.0003
22	.0000	.0000	.0000	.0000	.0001	.0001	.0001	.0001	.0001	.0001

x	9.1	9.2	9.3	9.4	9.5	9.6	9.7	9.8	9.9	10.0
0	.0001	.0001	.0001	.0001	.0001	.0001	.0001	.0001	.0001	.0000
1	.0010	.0009	.0009	.0008	.0007	.0007	.0006	.0005	.0005	.0005
2	.0046	.0043	.0040	.0037	.0034	.0031	.0029	.0027	.0025	.0023
3	.0140	.0131	.0123	.0115	.0107	.0100	.0093	.0087	.0081	.0076
4	.0319	.0302	.0285	.0269	.0254	.0240	.0226	.0213	.0201	.0189
5	.0581	.0555	.0530	.0506	.0483	.0460	.0439	.0418	.0398	.0378
6	.0881	.0851	.0822	.0793	.0764	.0736	.0709	.0682	.0656	.0631
7	.1145	.1118	.1091	.1064	.1037	.1010	.0982	.0955	.0928	.0901
8	.1302	.1286	.1269	.1251	.1232	.1212	.1191	.1170	.1148	.1126
9	.1317	.1315	.1311	.1306	.1300	.1293	.1284	.1274	.1263	.1251
10	.1198	.1210	.1219	.1228	.1235	.1241	.1245	.1249	.1250	.1251
11	.0991	.1012	.1031	.1049	.1067	.1083	.1098	.1112	.1125	.1137
12	.0752	.0776	.0799	.0822	.0844	.0866	.0888	.0908	.0928	.0948
13	.0526	.0549	.0572	.0594	.0617	.0640	.0662	.0685	.0707	.0729
14	.0342	.0361	.0380	.0399	.0419	.0439	.0459	.0479	.0500	.0521
15	.0208	.0221	.0235	.0250	.0265	.0281	.0297	.0313	.0330	.0347
16	.0118	.0127	.0137	.0147	.0157	.0168	.0180	.0192	.0204	.0217
17	.0063	.0069	.0075	.0081	.0088	.0095	.0103	.0111	.0119	.0128
18	.0032	.0035	.0039	.0042	.0046	.0051	.0055	.0060	.0065	.0071
19	.0015	.0017	.0019	.0021	.0023	.0026	.0028	.0031	.0034	.0037
20	.0007	.0008	.0009	.0010	.0011	.0012	.0014	.0015	.0017	.0019
21	.0003	.0003	.0004	.0004	.0005	.0006	.0006	.0007	.0008	.0009
22	.0001	.0001	.0002	.0002	.0002	.0002	.0003	.0003	.0004	.0004
23	.0000	.0001	.0001	.0001	.0001	.0001	.0001	.0001	.0002	.0002
24	.0000	.0000	.0000	.0000	.0000	.0000	.0000	.0001	.0001	.0001

TABLE 7
The Poisson Distribution (Continued)

$$p_X(x) = e^{-\mu}\frac{\mu^x}{x!}$$

x	11.0	12.0	13.0	14.0	15.0	16.0	17.0	18.0	19.0	20.0
0	.0000	.0000	.0000	.0000	.0000	.0000	.0000	.0000	.0000	.0000
1	.0002	.0001	.0000	.0000	.0000	.0000	.0000	.0000	.0000	.0000
2	.0010	.0004	.0002	.0001	.0000	.0000	.0000	.0000	.0000	.0000
3	.0037	.0018	.0008	.0004	.0002	.0001	.0000	.0000	.0000	.0000
4	.0102	.0053	.0027	.0013	.0006	.0003	.0001	.0001	.0000	.0000
5	.0224	.0127	.0070	.0037	.0019	.0010	.0005	.0002	.0001	.0001
6	.0411	.0255	.0152	.0087	.0048	.0026	.0014	.0007	.0004	.0002
7	.0646	.0437	.0281	.0174	.0104	.0060	.0034	.0019	.0010	.0005
8	.0888	.0655	.0457	.0304	.0194	.0120	.0072	.0042	.0024	.0013
9	.1085	.0874	.0661	.0473	.0324	.0213	.0135	.0083	.0050	.0029
10	.1194	.1048	.0859	.0663	.0486	.0341	.0230	.0150	.0095	.0058
11	.1194	.1144	.1015	.0844	.0663	.0496	.0355	.0245	.0164	.0106
12	.1094	.1144	.1099	.0984	.0829	.0661	.0504	.0368	.0259	.0176
13	.0926	.1056	.1099	.1060	.0956	.0814	.0658	.0509	.0378	.0271
14	.0728	.0905	.1021	.1060	.1024	.0930	.0800	.0655	.0514	.0387
15	.0534	.0724	.0885	.0989	.1024	.0992	.0906	.0786	.0650	.0516
16	.0367	.0543	.0719	.0866	.0960	.0992	.0963	.0884	.0772	.0646
17	.0237	.0383	.0550	.0713	.0847	.0934	.0963	.0936	.0863	.0760
18	.0145	.0255	.0397	.0554	.0706	.0830	.0909	.0936	.0911	.0844
19	.0084	.0161	.0272	.0409	.0557	.0699	.0814	.0887	.0911	.0888
20	.0046	.0097	.0177	.0286	.0418	.0559	.0692	.0798	.0866	.0888
21	.0024	.0055	.0109	.0191	.0299	.0426	.0560	.0684	.0783	.0846
22	.0012	.0030	.0065	.0121	.0204	.0310	.0433	.0560	.0676	.0769
23	.0006	.0016	.0037	.0074	.0133	.0216	.0320	.0438	.0559	.0669
24	.0003	.0008	.0020	.0043	.0083	.0144	.0226	.0328	.0442	.0557
25	.0001	.0004	.0010	.0024	.0050	.0092	.0154	.0237	.0336	.0446
26	.0000	.0002	.0005	.0013	.0029	.0057	.0101	.0164	.0246	.0343
27	.0000	.0001	.0002	.0007	.0016	.0034	.0063	.0109	.0173	.0254
28	.0000	.0000	.0001	.0003	.0009	.0019	.0038	.0070	.0117	.0181
29	.0000	.0000	.0001	.0002	.0004	.0011	.0023	.0044	.0077	.0125
30	.0000	.0000	.0000	.0001	.0002	.0006	.0013	.0026	.0049	.0083
31	.0000	.0000	.0000	.0000	.0001	.0003	.0007	.0015	.0030	.0054
32	.0000	.0000	.0000	.0000	.0001	.0001	.0004	.0009	.0018	.0034
33	.0000	.0000	.0000	.0000	.0000	.0001	.0002	.0005	.0010	.0020
34	.0000	.0000	.0000	.0000	.0000	.0000	.0001	.0002	.0006	.0012
35	.0000	.0000	.0000	.0000	.0000	.0000	.0000	.0001	.0003	.0007
36	.0000	.0000	.0000	.0000	.0000	.0000	.0000	.0001	.0002	.0004
37	.0000	.0000	.0000	.0000	.0000	.0000	.0000	.0000	.0001	.0002
38	.0000	.0000	.0000	.0000	.0000	.0000	.0000	.0000	.0000	.0001
39	.0000	.0000	.0000	.0000	.0000	.0000	.0000	.0000	.0000	.0001

TABLE 8
The Beta Distribution

A random variable X is said to have the beta distribution $B(x|\alpha, \lambda)$ if (for some $\alpha, \lambda > -1$; see Definition 4.2.1)

$$f_X(x) = \begin{cases} \dfrac{1}{\beta(\alpha+1, \lambda+1)} x^\alpha(1-x)^\lambda, & 0 \le x \le 1 \\ 0, & \text{otherwise.} \end{cases}$$

The following graphs show beta distribution densities with various selections of parameters α, λ. (The symbol a, b means $\alpha = a, \lambda = b$.)

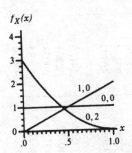 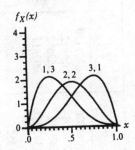 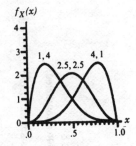

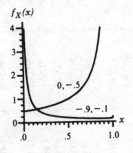 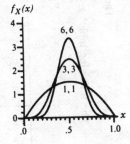

TABLE 8
The Beta Distribution (Continued)

The following table* gives values of y such that (for various values of α, λ)

$$P[X \le y] = \int_0^y f_X(x)\, dx = .05$$

α \ λ	3.5	3.0	2.5	2.0	1.5	1.0	.5	.0	−.5
−.5	0^346170	0^352300	0^360300	0^371179	0^386820	.0011119	.0015429	.0025000	.0061558
.0	.011334	.012741	.014548	.016952	.020308	.025321	.033617	.050000	.097500
.5	.036447	.040671	.046007	.052962	.062413	.076010	.097308	.13572	.22852
1.0	.068979	.076440	.085727	.097611	.11338	.13535	.16825	.22361	.34163
1.5	.10427	.11482	.12778	.14409	.16528	.19403	.23553	.30171	.43074
2.0	.13989	.15316	.16927	.18926	.21477	.24860	.29599	.36840	.50053
2.5	.17461	.19019	.20890	.23182	.26063	.29811	.34929	.42489	.55593
3.0	.20783	.22532	.24613	.27134	.30260	.34259	.39607	.47287	.60071
3.5	.23930	.25835	.28082	.30777	.34080	.38245	.43716	.51390	.63751
4.0	.26894	.28924	.31301	.34126	.37553	.41820	.47338	.54928	.66824
4.5	.29677	.31807	.34283	.37203	.40712	.45033	.50546	.58003	.69425
5.0	.32286	.34494	.37044	.40031	.43590	.47930	.53402	.60696	.71654
5.5	.34732	.37000	.39604	.42635	.46219	.50551	.55958	.63073	.73583
6.0	.37025	.39338	.41980	.45036	.48626	.52932	.58256	.65184	.75268

6.5	.76754	.67070	.60333	.55102	.50836	.47255	.44187	.41521	.39176
7.0	.78072	.68766	.62217	.57086	.52872	.49310	.46242	.43563	.41196
7.5	.79249	.70297	.63933	.58907	.54750	.51217	.48159	.45474	.43094
8.0	.80307	.71687	.65503	.60584	.56490	.52991	.49949	.47267	.44880
8.5	.81263	.72954	.66944	.62131	.58103	.54645	.51624	.48951	.46564
9.0	.82131	.74113	.68271	.63564	.59605	.56189	.53194	.50535	.48152
9.5	.82923	.75178	.69496	.64894	.61004	.57635	.54669	.52027	.49652
10.0	.83647	.76160	.70632	.66132	.62312	.58990	.56056	.53434	.51071
10.5	.84313	.77067	.71687	.67287	.63536	.60263	.57363	.54764	.52415
11.0	.84927	.77908	.72669	.68366	.64684	.61461	.58596	.56022	.53689
11.5	.85494	.78690	.73586	.69377	.65764	.62590	.59761	.57213	.54898
12.0	.86021	.79418	.74444	.70327	.66780	.63656	.60864	.58343	.56048
12.5	.86511	.80099	.75249	.71219	.67738	.64663	.61909	.59416	.57141
13.0	.86967	.80736	.76004	.72060	.68643	.65617	.62900	.60436	.58183
13.5	.87394	.81334	.76715	.72854	.69499	.66522	.63842	.61407	.59177
14.0	.87794	.81896	.77386	.73604	.70311	.67381	.64738	.62332	.60125
19.0	.90734	.86089	.82447	.79327	.76559	.74053	.71758	.69636	.67663
29.0	.93748	.90497	.87881	.85591	.83517	.81606	.79824	.78150	.76569
59.0	.96837	.95130	.93720	.92458	.91290	.90192	.89148	.88150	.87191
∞	1.00000	1.00000	1.00000	1.00000	1.00000	1.00000	1.00000	1.00000	1.00000

*Adapted from Table 16 on pp. 156–157 of *Biometrika Tables for Statisticians*, *Vol. I* (Third edition reprinted with additions), edited by E. S. Pearson and H. O. Hartley, Cambridge University Press, London, 1970. Used with the kind permission of the Biometrika Trustees.

TABLE 8
The Beta Distribution (Continued)

$$y \text{ such that } P[X \leq y] = \int_0^y f_X(x)\,dx = .05$$

α \ λ	59.0	29.0	19.0	14.0	11.0	9.0	6.5	5.0	4.0
$-.5$	$.0^4 32904$	$.0^4 66082$	$.0^4 99535$	$.0^3 13326$	$.0^3 16727$	$.0^3 20156$	$.0^3 27098$	$.0^3 34154$	$.0^3 41325$
$.0$	$.0^3 85452$	.0017083	.0025614	.0034137	.0042653	.0051162	.0068158	.0085124	.010206
$.5$	.0029157	.0057991	.0086511	.011472	.014264	.017026	.022465	.027794	.033020
1.0	.0058568	.011585	.017191	.022679	.028053	.033319	.043541	.053376	.062850
1.5	.0093841	.018458	.027240	.035747	.043994	.051995	.067312	.081790	.095510
2.0	.013317	.026043	.038224	.049898	.061103	.071870	.092207	.11111	.12876
2.5	.017540	.034103	.049781	.064651	.078783	.092238	.11733	.14029	.16142
3.0	.021976	.042481	.061676	.079695	.096658	.11267	.14216	.16875	.19290
3.5	.026572	.051068	.073748	.094827	.11449	.13288	.16638	.19618	.22292
4.0	.031288	.059786	.085885	.10991	.13211	.15272	.18984	.22244	.25137
4.5	.036094	.068575	.098008	.12484	.14943	.17207	.21244	.24746	.27823
5.0	.040967	.077394	.11006	.13955	.16636	.19086	.23413	.27125	.30354
5.5	.045889	.086209	.12199	.15401	.18288	.20908	.25492	.29383	.32737
6.0	.050847	.094994	.13377	.16818	.19895	.22669	.27481	.31524	.34981

774

6.5	.37095	.33554	.29382	.24370	.21457	.18203	.14539	.10373	.055827
7.0	.39086	.35480	.31199	.26011	.22972	.19556	.15682	.11240	.060821
7.5	.40965	.37307	.32936	.27594	.24441	.20877	.16805	.12099	.065820
8.0	.42738	.39041	.34596	.29120	.25865	.22164	.17908	.12950	.070818
8.5	.44414	.40689	.36183	.30591	.27244	.23418	.18989	.13791	.075809
9.0	.45999	.42256	.37701	.32009	.28580	.24639	.20050	.14622	.080789
9.5	.47501	.43746	.39154	.33375	.29874	.25828	.21088	.15442	.085753
10.0	.48925	.45165	.40544	.34693	.31126	.26985	.22106	.16252	.090698
10.5	.50276	.46518	.41877	.35964	.32340	.28112	.23102	.17051	.095622
11.0	.51560	.47808	.43154	.37190	.33515	.29208	.24077	.17838	.10052
11.5	.52782	.49040	.44379	.38373	.34653	.30275	.25032	.18615	.10539
12.0	.53945	.50217	.45554	.39516	.35756	.31314	.25966	.19379	.11024
12.5	.55054	.51343	.46683	.40619	.36826	.32325	.26880	.20133	.11505
13.0	.56112	.52420	.47768	.41685	.37862	.33309	.27775	.20875	.11983
13.5	.57122	.53452	.48812	.42715	.38867	.34267	.28650	.21606	.12458
14.0	.58088	.54442	.49816	.43711	.39842	.35200	.29507	.22326	.12930
19.0	.65819	.62459	.58083	.52099	.48175	.43321	.37136	.28936	.17453
29.0	.75070	.72282	.68535	.63185	.59522	.54807	.48477	.39458	.25416
59.0	.86266	.84504	.82047	.78342	.75661	.72016	.66738	.58326	.42519
8	1.00000	1.00000	1.00000	1.00000	1.00000	1.00000	1.00000	1.00000	1.00000

TABLE 9
The Gamma Distribution

A random variable X is said to have the gamma distribution $G(x|\alpha, \beta, A)$ if (for some $\alpha > -1, \beta > 0, -\infty < A < +\infty$; see Definition 4.2.7)

$$f_X(x) = \begin{cases} \dfrac{1}{\beta^{\alpha+1}\Gamma(\alpha+1)}(x-A)^{\alpha}e^{-(x-A)/\beta}, & A \le x < \infty \\ 0, & \text{otherwise.} \end{cases}$$

The following graphs show gamma distribution densities with $A = 0, \beta = 1$ and various selections of α.

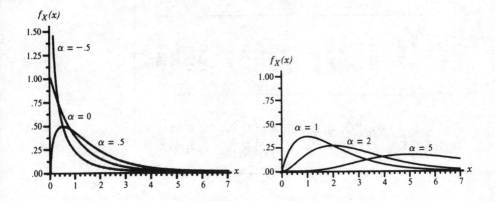

The following graphs show, respectively, gamma distribution densities with $A = 0, \alpha = 1$ and various selections of β, and $A = 0$ and various selections of α, β with $\alpha\beta = 2$.

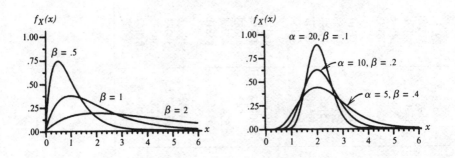

TABLE 9
The Gamma Distribution (Continued)

The following table* gives values of $(y - A)/\beta$ such that (for various α, γ)

$$P[X \leq y] = \int_A^y f_X(x)\, dx = \gamma$$

α \ γ	.01	.05	.10	.25	.50	.75	.90	.95	.99
- .5	.0000785	.00197	.00790	.0508	.227	.662	1.353	1.921	3.317
0	.01005	.0513	.105	.288	.693	1.386	2.303	2.996	4.605
.5	.0574	.176	.292	.606	1.183	2.054	3.126	3.907	5.672
1.0	.149	.355	.532	.961	1.678	2.693	3.890	4.744	6.638
1.5	.277	.573	.805	1.337	2.176	3.313	4.618	5.535	7.543
2.0	.436	.818	1.102	1.727	2.674	3.920	5.322	6.296	8.406
2.5	.620	1.084	1.417	2.127	3.173	4.519	6.008	7.034	9.238
3.0	.823	1.366	1.745	2.535	3.672	5.109	6.681	7.754	10.045
3.5	1.044	1.663	2.084	2.949	4.171	5.694	7.342	8.460	10.833
4.0	1.279	1.970	2.433	3.369	4.671	6.274	7.994	9.154	11.605
4.5	1.527	2.287	2.789	3.792	5.170	6.850	8.638	9.838	12.362
5.0	1.785	2.613	3.152	4.219	5.670	7.423	9.275	10.513	13.108
5.5	2.053	2.946	3.521	4.650	6.170	7.992	9.906	11.181	13.844
6.0	2.330	3.285	3.895	5.083	6.670	8.558	10.532	11.842	14.571
6.5	2.615	3.630	4.273	5.518	7.169	9.123	11.154	12.498	15.289
7.0	2.906	3.981	4.656	5.956	7.669	9.684	11.771	13.148	16.000
7.5	3.204	4.336	5.043	6.396	8.169	10.244	12.384	13.794	16.704
8.0	3.507	4.695	5.432	6.838	8.669	10.802	12.995	14.435	17.403
8.5	3.816	5.058	5.825	7.281	9.169	13.359	13.602	15.072	18.095
9.0	4.130	5.425	6.221	7.726	9.669	11.914	14.206	15.705	18.783
9.5	4.449	5.796	6.620	8.172	10.169	12.467	14.808	16.335	19.466
10.0	4.771	6.169	7.021	8.620	10.668	13.020	15.407	16.962	20.145
11.0	5.428	6.924	7.829	9.519	11.668	14.121	16.598	18.208	21.490
12.0	6.099	7.690	8.646	10.422	12.668	15.217	17.782	19.443	22.821
13.0	6.782	8.464	9.470	11.329	13.668	16.310	18.958	20.669	24.139
14.0	7.477	9.246	10.300	12.239	14.668	17.400	20.128	21.886	25.446
15.0	8.180	10.035	11.135	13.152	15.668	18.487	21.293	23.098	26.744
20.0	11.825	14.072	15.382	17.755	20.668	23.883	27.045	29.062	33.104
25.0	15.623	18.218	19.717	22.404	25.667	29.234	32.711	34.916	39.308
30.0	19.532	22.444	24.113	27.085	30.667	34.552	38.315	40.691	45.401

*Adapted from C. M. Thompson, "Tables of percentage points of the chi-square distribution", *Biometrika*, Vol. 32 (1941), pp. 188–189. Used with the kind permission of the Biometrika Trustees.

TABLE 10
The Chi-Square Distribution

A random variable X is said to have the chi-square distribution with n degrees of freedom $\chi_n^2(0)$ if (for some integer $n > 0$; see Definition 4.2.13)

$$f_X(x) = \begin{cases} \dfrac{1}{2^{n/2}\Gamma(n/2)} x^{(n/2)-1} e^{-x/2}, & 0 \le x < \infty \\ 0, & \text{otherwise.} \end{cases}$$

The following graph shows chi-square distribution densities with various selections of n.

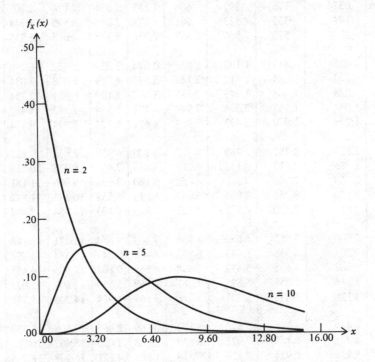

TABLE 10
The Chi-Square Distribution (Continued)

The following table* gives values of y such that (for various values of n, γ)

$$P[X \le y] = \int_0^y f_X(x)\, dx = \gamma$$

n \ γ	.005	.01	.025	.05	.10	.25	.50
1	$392704 \cdot 10^{-10}$	$157088 \cdot 10^{-9}$	$982069 \cdot 10^{-9}$	$393214 \cdot 10^{-8}$	.0157908	.1015308	.454936
2	.0100251	.0201007	.0506356	.102587	.210721	.575364	1.38629
3	.0717218	.114832	.215795	.351846	.584374	1.212534	2.36597
4	.206989	.297109	.484419	.710723	1.063623	1.92256	3.35669
5	.411742	.554298	.831212	1.145476	1.61031	2.67460	4.35146
6	.675727	.872090	1.23734	1.63538	2.20413	3.45460	5.34812
7	.989256	1.239043	1.68987	2.16735	2.83311	4.25485	6.34581
8	1.34441	1.64650	2.17973	2.73264	3.48954	5.07064	7.34412
9	1.73493	2.08790	2.70039	3.32511	4.16816	5.89883	8.34283
10	2.15586	2.55821	3.24697	3.94030	4.86518	6.73720	9.34182
11	2.60322	3.05348	3.81575	4.57481	5.57778	7.58414	10.3410
12	3.07382	3.57057	4.40379	5.22603	6.30380	8.43842	11.3403
13	3.56503	4.10692	5.00875	5.89186	7.04150	9.29907	12.3398
14	4.07467	4.66043	5.62873	6.57063	7.78953	10.1653	13.3393
15	4.60092	5.22935	6.26214	7.26094	8.54676	11.0365	14.3389
16	5.14221	5.81221	6.90766	7.96165	9.31224	11.9122	15.3385
17	5.69722	6.40776	7.56419	8.67176	10.0852	12.7919	16.3382
18	6.26480	7.01491	8.23075	9.39046	10.8649	13.6753	17.3379
19	6.84397	7.63273	8.90652	10.1170	11.6509	14.5620	18.3377
20	7.43384	8.26040	9.59078	10.8508	12.4426	15.4518	19.3374
21	8.03365	8.89720	10.28293	11.5913	13.2396	16.3444	20.3372
22	8.64272	9.54249	10.9823	12.3380	14.0415	17.2396	21.3370
23	9.26043	10.19567	11.6886	13.0905	14.8480	18.1373	22.3369
24	9.88623	10.8564	12.4012	13.8484	15.6587	19.0373	23.3367
25	10.5197	11.5240	13.1197	14.6114	16.4734	19.9393	24.3366
26	11.1602	12.1981	13.8439	15.3792	17.2919	20.8434	25.3365
27	11.8076	12.8785	14.5734	16.1514	18.1139	21.7494	26.3363
28	12.4613	13.5647	15.3079	16.9279	18.9392	22.6572	27.3362
29	13.1211	14.2565	16.0471	17.7084	19.7677	23.5666	28.3361
30	13.7867	14.9535	16.7908	18.4927	20.5992	24.4776	29.3360
40	20.7065	22.1643	24.4330	26.5093	29.0505	33.6603	39.3353
50	27.9907	29.7067	32.3574	34.7643	37.6886	42.9421	49.3349
60	35.5345	37.4849	40.4817	43.1880	46.4589	52.2938	59.3347
70	43.2752	45.4417	48.7576	51.7393	55.3289	61.6983	69.3345
80	51.1719	53.5401	57.1532	60.3915	64.2778	71.1445	79.3343
90	59.1963	61.7541	65.6466	69.1260	73.2911	80.6247	89.3342
100	67.3276	70.0649	74.2219	77.9295	82.3581	90.1332	99.3341

*Adapted from Table 8 on pp. 136–137 of *Biometrika Tables for Statisticians*, Vol. I (Third edition reprinted with additions), edited by E. S. Pearson and H. O Hartley, Cambridge University Press, London, 1970. Used with the kind permission of the Biometrika Trustees.

TABLE 10
The Chi-Square Distribution (Continued)

$$y \text{ such that } P[\, X \le y\,] = \int_0^y f_X(x)\, dx = \gamma$$

n \ γ	.75	.90	.95	.975	.99	.995	.999
1	1.32330	2.70554	3.84146	5.02389	6.63490	7.87944	10.828
2	2.77259	4.60517	5.99146	7.37776	9.21034	10.5966	13.816
3	4.10834	6.25139	7.81473	9.34840	11.3449	12.8382	16.266
4	5.38527	7.77944	9.48773	11.1433	13.2767	14.8603	18.467
5	6.62568	9.23636	11.0705	12.8325	15.0863	16.7496	20.515
6	7.84080	10.6446	12.5916	14.4494	16.8119	18.5476	22.458
7	9.03715	12.0170	14.0671	16.0128	18.4753	20.2777	24.322
8	10.2189	13.3616	15.5073	17.5345	20.0902	21.9550	26.125
9	11.3888	14.6837	16.9190	19.0228	21.6660	23.5894	27.877
10	12.5489	15.9872	18.3070	20.4832	23.2093	25.1882	29.588
11	13.7007	17.2750	19.6751	21.9200	24.7250	26.7568	31.264
12	14.8454	18.5493	21.0261	23.3367	26.2170	28.2995	32.909
13	15.9839	19.8119	22.3620	24.7356	27.6882	29.8195	34.528
14	17.1169	21.0641	23.6848	26.1189	29.1412	31.3194	36.123
15	18.2451	22.3071	24.9958	27.4884	30.5779	32.8013	37.697
16	19.3689	23.5418	26.2962	28.8454	31.9999	34.2672	39.252
17	20.4887	24.7690	27.5871	30.1910	33.4087	35.7185	40.790
18	21.6049	25.9894	28.8693	31.5264	34.8053	37.1565	42.312
19	22.7178	27.2036	30.1435	32.8523	36.1909	38.5823	43.820
20	23.8277	28.4120	31.4104	34.1696	37.5662	39.9968	45.315
21	24.9348	29.6151	32.6706	35.4789	38.9322	41.4011	46.797
22	26.0393	30.8133	33.9244	36.7807	40.2894	42.7957	48.268
23	27.1413	32.0069	35.1725	38.0756	41.6384	44.1813	49.728
24	28.2412	33.1962	36.4150	39.3641	42.9798	45.5585	51.179
25	29.3389	34.3816	37.6525	40.6465	44.3141	46.9279	52.618
26	30.4346	35.5632	38.8851	41.9232	45.6417	48.2899	54.052
27	31.5284	36.7412	40.1133	43.1945	46.9629	49.6449	55.476
28	32.6205	37.9159	41.3371	44.4608	48.2782	50.9934	56.892
29	33.7109	39.0875	42.5570	45.7223	49.5879	52.3356	58.301
30	34.7997	40.2560	43.7730	46.9792	50.8922	53.6720	59.703
40	45.6160	51.8051	55.7585	59.3417	63.6907	66.7660	73.402
50	56.3336	63.1671	67.5048	71.4202	76.1539	79.4900	86.661
60	66.9815	74.3970	79.0819	83.2977	88.3794	91.9517	99.607
70	77.5767	85.5270	90.5312	95.0232	100.425	104.215	112.317
80	88.1303	96.5782	101.879	106.629	112.329	116.321	124.839
90	98.6499	107.565	113.145	118.136	124.116	128.299	137.208
100	109.141	118.498	124.342	129.561	135.807	140.169	149.449

TABLE 11
The Normal Distribution

A random variable X is said to have the normal distribution $N(\mu, \sigma^2)$ if (for some $-\infty < \mu < +\infty$, $\sigma^2 > 0$; see Definition 4.2.18)

$$f_X(x) = \frac{1}{\sqrt{2\pi}\,\sigma} e^{-\frac{1}{2}\left(\frac{x-\mu}{\sigma}\right)^2}, \quad -\infty < x < +\infty.$$

The following graph shows normal distribution densities with $\mu = 0$ and various selections of σ.

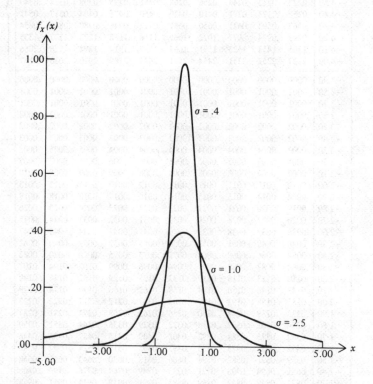

TABLE 11
The Normal Distribution (Continued)

The following table gives*, for various values of y (when $\mu = 0$ and $\sigma^2 = 1$), the probability

$$P[X \le y] = \int_{-\infty}^{y} f_X(x)\, dx$$

x	9	8	7	6	5	4	3	2	1	0	
− 4.90	.0030	.0032	.0033	.0035	.0037	.0039	.0041	.0043	.0046	.0048	
− 4.80	.0050	.0053	.0056	.0059	.0062	.0065	.0068	.0072	.0075	.0079	
− 4.70	.0083	.0088	.0092	.0097	.0102	.0107	.0112	.0118	.0124	.0130	
− 4.60	.0137	.0143	.0151	.0158	.0166	.0174	.0183	.0192	.0201	.0211	
− 4.50	.0222	.0232	.0244	.0256	.0268	.0281	.0295	.0309	.0324	.0340	$\times 10^{-4}$
− 4.40	.0356	.0373	.0391	.0410	.0429	.0450	.0471	.0494	.0517	.0541	
− 4.30	.0567	.0593	.0621	.0650	.0681	.0712	.0746	.0780	.0816	.0854	
− 4.20	.0893	.0934	.0977	.1022	.1069	.1118	.1168	.1222	.1277	.1335	
− 4.10	.1395	.1458	.1523	.1591	.1662	.1737	.1814	.1894	.1978	.2066	
− 4.00	.2157	.2252	.2351	.2454	.2561	.2673	.2789	.2910	.3036	.3167	
− 3.90	.0000	.0000	.0000	.0000	.0000	.0000	.0000	.0000	.0000	.0000	
− 3.80	.0001	.0001	.0001	.0001	.0001	.0001	.0001	.0001	.0001	.0001	
− 3.70	.0001	.0001	.0001	.0001	.0001	.0001	.0001	.0001	.0001	.0001	
− 3.60	.0001	.0001	.0001	.0001	.0001	.0001	.0001	.0001	.0002	.0002	
− 3.50	.0002	.0002	.0002	.0002	.0002	.0002	.0002	.0002	.0002	.0002	
− 3.40	.0002	.0003	.0003	.0003	.0003	.0003	.0003	.0003	.0003	.0003	
− 3.30	.0003	.0004	.0004	.0004	.0004	.0004	.0004	.0005	.0005	.0005	
− 3.20	.0005	.0005	.0005	.0006	.0006	.0006	.0006	.0006	.0007	.0007	
− 3.10	.0007	.0007	.0008	.0008	.0008	.0008	.0009	.0009	.0009	.0010	
− 3.00	.0010	.0010	.0011	.0011	.0011	.0012	.0012	.0013	.0013	.0013	
− 2.90	.0014	.0014	.0015	.0015	.0016	.0016	.0017	.0018	.0018	.0019	
− 2.80	.0019	.0020	.0021	.0021	.0022	.0023	.0023	.0024	.0025	.0026	
− 2.70	.0026	.0027	.0028	.0029	.0030	.0031	.0032	.0033	.0034	.0035	
− 2.60	.0036	.0037	.0038	.0039	.0040	.0041	.0043	.0044	.0045	.0047	
− 2.50	.0048	.0049	.0051	.0052	.0054	.0055	.0057	.0059	.0060	.0062	
− 2.40	.0064	.0066	.0068	.0069	.0071	.0073	.0075	.0078	.0080	.0082	
− 2.30	.0084	.0087	.0089	.0091	.0094	.0096	.0099	.0102	.0104	.0107	
− 2.20	.0110	.0113	.0116	.0119	.0122	.0125	.0129	.0132	.0136	.0139	
− 2.10	.0143	.0146	.0150	.0154	.0158	.0162	.0166	.0170	.0174	.0179	
− 2.00	.0183	.0188	.0192	.0197	.0202	.0207	.0212	.0217	.0222	.0228	
− 1.90	.0233	.0239	.0244	.0250	.0256	.0262	.0268	.0274	.0281	.0287	
− 1.80	.0294	.0301	.0307	.0314	.0322	.0329	.0336	.0344	.0351	.0359	
− 1.70	.0367	.0375	.0384	.0392	.0401	.0409	.0418	.0427	.0436	.0446	
− 1.60	.0455	.0465	.0475	.0485	.0495	.0505	.0516	.0526	.0537	.0548	
− 1.50	.0559	.0571	.0582	.0594	.0606	.0618	.0630	.0643	.0655	.0668	
− 1.40	.0681	.0694	.0708	.0721	.0735	.0749	.0764	.0778	.0793	.0808	
− 1.30	.0823	.0838	.0853	.0869	.0885	.0901	.0918	.0934	.0951	.0968	
− 1.20	.0985	.1003	.1020	.1038	.1056	.1075	.1093	.1112	.1131	.1151	
− 1.10	.1170	.1190	.1210	.1230	.1251	.1271	.1292	.1314	.1335	.1357	
− 1.00	.1379	.1401	.1423	.1446	.1469	.1492	.1515	.1539	.1562	.1587	
− .90	.1611	.1635	.1660	.1685	.1711	.1736	.1762	.1788	.1814	.1841	
− .80	.1867	.1894	.1922	.1949	.1977	.2005	.2033	.2061	.2090	.2119	
− .70	.2148	.2177	.2206	.2236	.2266	.2296	.2327	.2358	.2389	.2420	
− .60	.2451	.2483	.2514	.2546	.2578	.2611	.2643	.2676	.2709	.2743	
− .50	.2776	.2810	.2843	.2877	.2912	.2946	.2981	.3015	.3050	.3085	
− .40	.3121	.3156	.3192	.3228	.3264	.3300	.3336	.3372	.3409	.3446	
− .30	.3483	.3520	.3557	.3594	.3632	.3669	.3707	.3745	.3783	.3821	
− .20	.3859	.3897	.3936	.3974	.4013	.4052	.4090	.4129	.4168	.4207	
− .10	.4247	.4286	.4325	.4364	.4404	.4443	.4483	.4522	.4562	.4602	
− .00	.4641	.4681	.4721	.4761	.4801	.4840	.4880	.4920	.4960	.5000	

*For $x \le -4.00$, $\Phi(x)$ to four decimal places $= .0000$; for example, $\Phi(-4.45) = .0000$. The true value to eight decimals is $\Phi(-4.45) = .00000429$, or $= .0429 \times 10^{-4}$.

TABLE 11
The Normal Distribution (Continued)

$$P[X \le y] = \int_{-\infty}^{y} f_X(x)\, dx \text{ for various* } y$$

x	0	1	2	3	4	5	6	7	8	9
.00	.5000	.5040	.5080	.5120	.5160	.5199	.5239	.5279	.5319	.5359
.10	.5398	.5438	.5478	.5517	.5557	.5596	.5636	.5675	.5714	.5753
.20	.5793	.5832	.5871	.5910	.5948	.5987	.6026	.6064	.6103	.6141
.30	.6179	.6217	.6255	.6293	.6331	.6368	.6406	.6443	.6480	.6517
.40	.6554	.6591	.6628	.6664	.6700	.6736	.6772	.6808	.6844	.6879
.50	.6915	.6950	.6985	.7019	.7054	.7088	.7123	.7157	.7190	.7224
.60	.7257	.7291	.7324	.7357	.7389	.7422	.7454	.7486	.7517	.7549
.70	.7580	.7611	.7642	.7673	.7704	.7734	.7764	.7794	.7823	.7852
.80	.7881	.7910	.7939	.7967	.7995	.8023	.8051	.8078	.8106	.8133
.90	.8159	.8186	.8212	.8238	.8264	.8289	.8315	.8340	.8365	.8389
1.00	.8413	.8438	.8461	.8485	.8508	.8531	.8554	.8577	.8599	.8621
1.10	.8643	.8665	.8686	.8708	.8729	.8749	.8770	.8790	.8810	.8830
1.20	.8849	.8869	.8888	.8907	.8925	.8944	.8962	.8980	.8997	.9015
1.30	.9032	.9049	.9066	.9082	.9099	.9115	.9131	.9147	.9162	.9177
1.40	.9192	.9207	.9222	.9236	.9251	.9265	.9279	.9292	.9306	.9319
1.50	.9332	.9345	.9357	.9370	.9382	.9394	.9406	.9418	.9429	.9441
1.60	.9452	.9463	.9474	.9484	.9495	.9505	.9515	.9525	.9535	.9545
1.70	.9554	.9564	.9573	.9582	.9591	.9599	.9608	.9616	.9625	.9633
1.80	.9641	.9649	.9656	.9664	.9671	.9678	.9686	.9693	.9699	.9706
1.90	.9713	.9719	.9726	.9732	.9738	.9744	.9750	.9756	.9761	.9767
2.00	.9772	.9778	.9783	.9788	.9793	.9798	.9803	.9808	.9812	.9817
2.10	.9821	.9826	.9830	.9834	.9838	.9842	.9846	.9850	.9854	.9857
2.20	.9861	.9864	.9868	.9871	.9875	.9878	.9881	.9884	.9887	.9890
2.30	.9893	.9896	.9898	.9901	.9904	.9906	.9909	.9911	.9913	.9916
2.40	.9918	.9920	.9922	.9925	.9927	.9929	.9931	.9932	.9934	.9936
2.50	.9938	.9940	.9941	.9943	.9945	.9946	.9948	.9949	.9951	.9952
2.60	.9953	.9955	.9956	.9957	.9959	.9960	.9961	.9962	.9963	.9964
2.70	.9965	.9966	.9967	.9968	.9969	.9970	.9971	.9972	.9973	.9974
2.80	.9974	.9975	.9976	.9977	.9977	.9978	.9979	.9979	.9980	.9981
2.90	.9981	.9982	.9982	.9983	.9984	.9984	.9985	.9985	.9986	.9986
3.00	.9987	.9987	.9987	.9988	.9988	.9989	.9989	.9989	.9990	.9990
3.10	.9990	.9991	.9991	.9991	.9992	.9992	.9992	.9992	.9993	.9993
3.20	.9993	.9993	.9994	.9994	.9994	.9994	.9994	.9995	.9995	.9995
3.30	.9995	.9995	.9995	.9996	.9996	.9996	.9996	.9996	.9996	.9997
3.40	.9997	.9997	.9997	.9997	.9997	.9997	.9997	.9997	.9997	.9998
3.50	.9998	.9998	.9998	.9998	.9998	.9998	.9998	.9998	.9998	.9998
3.60	.9998	.9998	.9999	.9999	.9999	.9999	.9999	.9999	.9999	.9999
3.70	.9999	.9999	.9999	.9999	.9999	.9999	.9999	.9999	.9999	.9999
3.80	.9999	.9999	.9999	.9999	.9999	.9999	.9999	.9999	.9999	.9999
3.90	1.0000	1.0000	1.0000	1.0000	1.0000	1.0000	1.0000	1.0000	1.0000	1.0000
4.00	.6833	.6964	.7090	.7211	.7327	.7439	.7546	.7649	.7748	.7843
4.10	.7934	.8022	.8106	.8186	.8263	.8338	.8409	.8477	.8542	.8605
4.20	.8665	.8723	.8778	.8832	.8882	.8931	.8978	.9023	.9066	.9107
4.30	.9146	.9184	.9220	.9254	.9288	.9319	.9350	.9379	.9407	.9433
4.40	.9459	.9483	.9506	.9529	.9550	.9571	.9590	.9609	.9627	.9644
4.50	.9660	.9676	.9691	.9705	.9719	.9732	.9744	.9756	.9768	.9778
4.60	.9789	.9799	.9808	.9817	.9826	.9834	.9842	.9849	.9857	.9863
4.70	.9870	.9876	.9882	.9888	.9893	.9898	.9903	.9908	.9912	.9917
4.80	.9921	.9925	.9928	.9932	.9935	.9938	.9941	.9944	.9947	.9950
4.90	.9952	.9954	.9957	.9959	.9961	.9963	.9965	.9967	.9968	.9970

$\times 10^{-4} + .9999$ (for x ≥ 4.00 block)

*For $x \ge 4.00$, $\Phi(x)$ to four decimal places $= 1.0000$; for example, $\Phi(4.69) = 1.0000$. The true value to eight decimals is $\Phi(4.69) = .99999863$, or $.9863 \times 10^{-4} + .9999$.

TABLE 12
The *F*-Distribution

A random variable X is said to have the F-distribution $F(n_1, n_2)$ if (for some integers $n_1, n_2 \geq 1$; see Definition 4.2.23)

$$f_X(x) = \begin{cases} \dfrac{\Gamma\left(\dfrac{n_1 + n_2}{2}\right)\left(\dfrac{n_1}{n_2}\right)^{.5n_1}}{\Gamma\left(\dfrac{n_1}{2}\right)\Gamma\left(\dfrac{n_2}{2}\right)} \dfrac{x^{.5(n_1 - 2)}}{\left(1 + \dfrac{n_1}{n_2}x\right)^{.5(n_1 + n_2)}}, & 0 < x < \infty \\ 0, & \text{otherwise.} \end{cases}$$

The following graphs show F-distribution densities with various selections of n_1 and n_2.

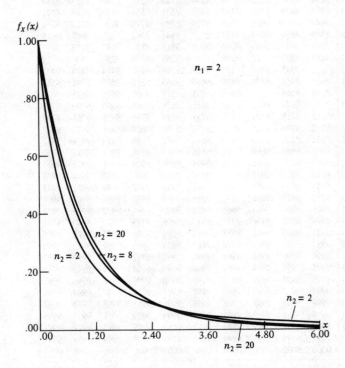

TABLE 12
The *F*-Distribution (Continued)

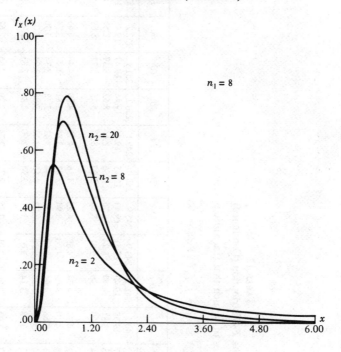

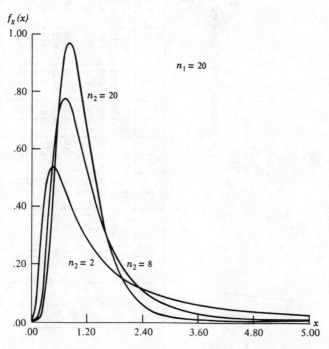

TABLE 12
The F-Distribution (Continued)

The following table* gives values of y such that (for various values of n_1, n_2)

$$P[X \leq y] = \int_0^y f_X(x)\,dx = .95$$

n_1 \ n_2	1	2	3	4	5	6	7	8	9	10	12	15	20	24	30	40	60	120	∞
1	161.4	199.5	215.7	224.6	230.2	234.0	236.8	238.9	240.5	241.9	243.9	245.9	248.0	249.1	250.1	251.1	252.2	253.3	254.3
2	18.51	19.00	19.16	19.25	19.30	19.33	19.35	19.37	19.38	19.40	19.41	19.43	19.45	19.45	19.46	19.47	19.48	19.49	19.50
3	10.13	9.55	9.28	9.12	9.01	8.94	8.89	8.85	8.81	8.79	8.74	8.70	8.66	8.64	8.62	8.59	8.57	8.55	8.53
4	7.71	6.94	6.59	6.39	6.26	6.16	6.09	6.04	6.00	5.96	5.91	5.86	5.80	5.77	5.75	5.72	5.69	5.66	5.63
5	6.61	5.79	5.41	5.19	5.05	4.95	4.88	4.82	4.77	4.74	4.68	4.62	4.56	4.53	4.50	4.46	4.43	4.40	4.36
6	5.99	5.14	4.76	4.53	4.39	4.28	4.21	4.15	4.10	4.06	4.00	3.94	3.87	3.84	3.81	3.77	3.74	3.70	3.67
7	5.59	4.74	4.35	4.12	3.97	3.87	3.79	3.73	3.68	3.64	3.57	3.51	3.44	3.41	3.38	3.34	3.30	3.27	3.23
8	5.32	4.46	4.07	3.84	3.69	3.58	3.50	3.44	3.39	3.35	3.28	3.22	3.15	3.12	3.08	3.04	3.01	2.97	2.93
9	5.12	4.26	3.86	3.63	3.48	3.37	3.29	3.23	3.18	3.14	3.07	3.01	2.94	2.90	2.86	2.83	2.79	2.75	2.71
10	4.96	4.10	3.71	3.48	3.33	3.22	3.14	3.07	3.02	2.98	2.91	2.85	2.77	2.74	2.70	2.66	2.62	2.58	2.54
11	4.84	3.98	3.59	3.36	3.20	3.09	3.01	2.95	2.90	2.85	2.79	2.72	2.65	2.61	2.57	2.53	2.49	2.45	2.40
12	4.75	3.89	3.49	3.26	3.11	3.00	2.91	2.85	2.80	2.75	2.69	2.62	2.54	2.51	2.47	2.43	2.38	2.34	2.30
13	4.67	3.81	3.41	3.18	3.03	2.92	2.83	2.77	2.71	2.67	2.60	2.53	2.46	2.42	2.38	2.34	2.30	2.25	2.21
14	4.60	3.74	3.34	3.11	2.96	2.85	2.76	2.70	2.65	2.60	2.53	2.46	2.39	2.35	2.31	2.27	2.22	2.18	2.13

15	4.54	3.68	3.29	3.06	2.90	2.79	2.71	2.64	2.59	2.54	2.48	2.40	2.33	2.29	2.25	2.20	2.16	2.11	2.07
16	4.49	3.63	3.24	3.01	2.85	2.74	2.66	2.59	2.54	2.49	2.42	2.35	2.28	2.24	2.19	2.15	2.11	2.06	2.01
17	4.45	3.59	3.20	2.96	2.81	2.70	2.61	2.55	2.49	2.45	2.38	2.31	2.23	2.19	2.15	2.10	2.06	2.01	1.96
18	4.41	3.55	3.16	2.93	2.77	2.66	2.58	2.51	2.46	2.41	2.34	2.27	2.19	2.15	2.11	2.06	2.02	1.97	1.92
19	4.38	3.52	3.13	2.90	2.74	2.63	2.54	2.48	2.42	2.38	2.31	2.23	2.16	2.11	2.07	2.03	1.98	1.93	1.88
20	4.35	3.49	3.10	2.87	2.71	2.60	2.51	2.45	2.39	2.35	2.28	2.20	2.12	2.08	2.04	1.99	1.95	1.90	1.84
21	4.32	3.47	3.07	2.84	2.68	2.57	2.49	2.42	2.37	2.32	2.25	2.18	2.10	2.05	2.01	1.96	1.92	1.87	1.81
22	4.30	3.44	3.05	2.82	2.66	2.55	2.46	2.40	2.34	2.30	2.23	2.15	2.07	2.03	1.98	1.94	1.89	1.84	1.78
23	4.28	3.42	3.03	2.80	2.64	2.53	2.44	2.37	2.32	2.27	2.20	2.13	2.05	2.01	1.96	1.91	1.86	1.81	1.76
24	4.26	3.40	3.01	2.78	2.62	2.51	2.42	2.36	2.30	2.25	2.18	2.11	2.03	1.98	1.94	1.89	1.84	1.79	1.73
25	4.24	3.39	2.99	2.76	2.60	2.49	2.40	2.34	2.28	2.24	2.16	2.09	2.01	1.96	1.92	1.87	1.82	1.77	1.71
26	4.23	3.37	2.98	2.74	2.59	2.47	2.39	2.32	2.27	2.22	2.15	2.07	1.99	1.95	1.90	1.85	1.80	1.75	1.69
27	4.21	3.35	2.96	2.73	2.57	2.46	2.37	2.31	2.25	2.20	2.13	2.06	1.97	1.93	1.88	1.84	1.79	1.73	1.67
28	4.20	3.34	2.95	2.71	2.56	2.45	2.36	2.29	2.24	2.19	2.12	2.04	1.96	1.91	1.87	1.82	1.77	1.71	1.65
29	4.18	3.33	2.93	2.70	2.55	2.43	2.35	2.28	2.22	2.18	2.10	2.03	1.94	1.90	1.85	1.81	1.75	1.70	1.64
30	4.17	3.32	2.92	2.69	2.53	2.42	2.33	2.27	2.21	2.16	2.09	2.01	1.93	1.89	1.84	1.79	1.74	1.68	1.62
40	4.08	3.23	2.84	2.61	2.45	2.34	2.25	2.18	2.12	2.08	2.00	1.92	1.84	1.79	1.74	1.69	1.64	1.58	1.51
60	4.00	3.15	2.76	2.53	2.37	2.25	2.17	2.10	2.04	1.99	1.92	1.84	1.75	1.70	1.65	1.59	1.53	1.47	1.39
120	3.92	3.07	2.68	2.45	2.29	2.17	2.09	2.02	1.96	1.91	1.83	1.75	1.66	1.61	1.55	1.50	1.43	1.35	1.25
∞	3.84	3.00	2.60	2.37	2.21	2.10	2.01	1.94	1.88	1.83	1.75	1.67	1.57	1.52	1.46	1.39	1.32	1.22	1.00

*Adapted from Table 18 on p. 171 of *Biometrika Tables for Statisticians*, *Vol. I* (Third edition reprinted with additions), edited by E. S. Pearson and H. O. Hartley, Cambridge University Press, London, 1970. Used with the kind permission of the Biometrika Trustees.

TABLE 13
The *t*-Distribution

A random variable X is said to have the *t*-distribution with n degrees of freedom if (for some integer $n \geq 1$; see Definition 4.2.26)

$$f_X(x) = \frac{\Gamma\left(\dfrac{n+1}{2}\right)}{\sqrt{n\pi}\,\Gamma\left(\dfrac{n}{2}\right)} \frac{1}{\left(1 + \dfrac{x^2}{n}\right)^{(n+1)/2}}, \quad -\infty < x < +\infty.$$

The following graph shows *t*-distribution densities with several selections of n, and the $N(0,1)$ density (labeled $n = \infty$).

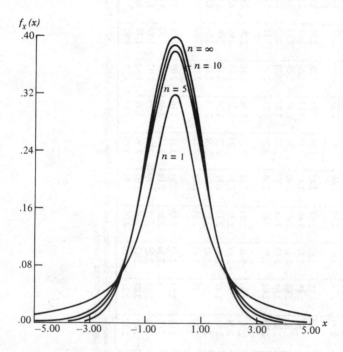

TABLE 13
The t-Distribution (Continued)

The following table* gives values of y such that (for various values of n, γ)

$$P[X \le y] = \int_{-\infty}^{y} f_X(x)\, dx = \gamma$$

n \ γ	.60	.75	.90	.95	.975	.99	.995	.9975	.999	.9995
1	.325	1.000	3.078	6.314	12.706	31.821	63.657	127.32	318.31	636.62
2	.289	.816	1.886	2.920	4.303	6.965	9.925	14.089	22.327	31.598
3	.277	.765	1.638	2.353	3.182	4.541	5.841	7.453	10.214	12.924
4	.271	.741	1.533	2.132	2.776	3.747	4.604	5.598	7.173	8.610
5	.267	.727	1.476	2.015	2.571	3.365	4.032	4.773	5.893	6.869
6	.265	.718	1.440	1.943	2.447	3.143	3.707	4.317	5.208	5.959
7	.263	.711	1.415	1.895	2.365	2.998	3.499	4.029	4.785	5.408
8	.262	.706	1.397	1.860	2.306	2.896	3.355	3.833	4.501	5.041
9	.261	.703	1.383	1.833	2.262	2.821	3.250	3.690	4.297	4.781
10	.260	.700	1.372	1.812	2.228	2.764	3.169	3.581	4.144	4.587
11	.260	.697	1.363	1.796	2.201	2.718	3.106	3.497	4.025	4.437
12	.259	.695	1.356	1.782	2.179	2.681	3.055	3.428	3.930	4.318
13	.259	.694	1.350	1.771	2.160	2.650	3.012	3.372	3.852	4.221
14	.258	.692	1.345	1.761	2.145	2.624	2.977	3.326	3.787	4.140
15	.258	.691	1.341	1.753	2.131	2.602	2.947	3.286	3.733	4.073
16	.258	.690	1.337	1.746	2.120	2.583	2.921	3.252	3.686	4.015
17	.257	.689	1.333	1.740	2.110	2.567	2.898	3.222	3.646	3.965
18	.257	.688	1.330	1.734	2.101	2.552	2.878	3.197	3.610	3.922
19	.257	.688	1.328	1.729	2.093	2.539	2.861	3.174	3.579	3.883
20	.257	.687	1.325	1.725	2.086	2.528	2.845	3.153	3.552	3.850
21	.257	.686	1.323	1.721	2.080	2.518	2.831	3.135	3.527	3.819
22	.256	.686	1.321	1.717	2.074	2.508	2.819	3.119	3.505	3.792
23	.256	.685	1.319	1.714	2.069	2.500	2.807	3.104	3.485	3.767
24	.256	.685	1.318	1.711	2.064	2.492	2.797	3.091	3.467	3.745
25	.256	.684	1.316	1.708	2.060	2.485	2.787	3.078	3.450	3.725
26	.256	.684	1.315	1.706	2.056	2.479	2.779	3.067	3.435	3.707
27	.256	.684	1.314	1.703	2.052	2.473	2.771	3.057	3.421	3.690
28	.256	.683	1.313	1.701	2.048	2.467	2.763	3.047	3.408	3.674
29	.256	.683	1.311	1.699	2.045	2.462	2.756	3.038	3.396	3.659
30	.256	.683	1.310	1.697	2.042	2.457	2.750	3.030	3.385	3.646
40	.255	.681	1.303	1.684	2.021	2.423	2.704	2.971	3.307	3.551
60	.254	.679	1.296	1.671	2.000	2.390	2.660	2.915	3.232	3.460
120	.254	.677	1.289	1.658	1.980	2.358	2.617	2.860	3.160	3.373
∞	.253	.674	1.282	1.645	1.960	2.326	2.576	2.807	3.090	3.291

References

In the text, these items are referred to by citing author(s) and year of publication; for example, Chernick (1982), or Cohen and Whitten (1981).

ARKIN, H., and COLTON, R. R. (1963). *Tables for Statisticians* (2nd ed.). Barnes & Noble, New York.

ARMITAGE, J. V., and KRISHNAIAH, P. R. (1966). Tables for multivariate *t*-distribution. *Sankhyā*, **28B**, 31–56.

ARNOLD, B. C. (1972). Some examples of minimum variance unbiased estimates. *The American Statistician*, **26**(4), 34–36.

BECHHOFER, R. E. (1954). A single-sample multiple decision procedure for ranking means of normal populations with known variances. *Annals of Mathematical Statistics*, **25**, 16–39.

BECHHOFER, R. E., DUNNETT, C. W., and SOBEL, M. (1954). A two-sample multiple decision procedure for ranking means of normal populations with a common unknown variance. *Biometrika*, **41**, 170–176.

BECHHOFER, R. E., ELMAGHRABY, S., and MORSE, N. (1959). A single-sample multiple-decision procedure for selecting the multinomial event which has the highest probability. *Annals of Mathematical Statistics*, **30**, 102–119.

BECHHOFER, R. E., and SOBEL, M. (1954). A single-sample multiple decision procedure for ranking variances of normal populations. *Annals of Mathematical Statistics*, **25**, 273–289.

BECKER, W. A. (1961). Comparing entries in random sample tests. *Poultry Science*, **40**, 1507–1514.

BERK, R. H. (1967). Review #1922. *Mathematical Reviews*, **33**, 342–343.

BLOOM, D. M. (1972). Unions of finite sets of subsets. *American Mathematical Monthly*, **79**, 1039–1040.

BLUMENTHAL, S., and COHEN, A. (1968). Estimation of the larger of two normal means. *Journal of the American Statistical Association*, **63**, 861–876.

BLYTH, C. R. (1972). On Simpson's paradox and the sure-thing principle. *Journal of the American Statistical Association*, **67**, 364–366.

BOOS, D. D. (1985). A converse to Scheffé's theorem. *Annals of Statistics*, **13**, 423–427.

BOYLES, R. A., MARSHALL, A. W., and PROSCHAN, F. (1985). Inconsistency of the maximum likelihood estimator of a distribution having increasing failure rate average. *Annals of Statistics*, **13**, 413–417.

BROWN, A. (1969). An elementary example of a continuous singular function. *American Mathematical Monthly*, **76**, 295–297.

BRYSON, M. C. (1971). A Gibbs-type phenomenon in the failure rates of parallel systems. *Technometrics*, **13**, 692–695.

CARMER, S. G., and SWANSON, M. R. (1973). An evaluation of two pairwise multiple comparison procedures by Monte Carlo methods. *Journal of the American Statistical Association*, **68**, 66–74.

CHERNICK, M. R. (1982). The influence function and its application to data validation. *American Journal of Mathematical and Management Sciences*, 2, 263–288.

CHRISTOPHER, M. (1970). *ESP, Seers & Psychics*. Crowell, New York.

CHUNG, K. L. (1942). On mutually favorable events. *Annals of Mathematical Statistics*, 13, 338–349.

COHEN, A. C., and WHITTEN, B. J. (1981). Estimation of lognormal distributions. *American Journal of Mathematical and Management Sciences*, 1, 139–153.

CRAMÉR, H. (1946). *Mathematical Methods of Statistics*. Princeton University Press, Princeton, N.J.

DAWSON, J. M., HANKEY, B. F., and MYERS, M. H. (1982). Stratification and the adjusted chi-square statistic: Application to analysis of employment discrimination data. *American Journal of Mathematical and Management Sciences*, 2, 289–318.

DEMING, W. E. (1966). *Some Theory of Sampling*. Dover, New York.

DIXON, W. J. (ed.) (1985). *BMPD Statistical Software*. University of California Press, Berkeley.

DUDEWICZ, E. J. (1969a). An approximation to the sample size in selection problems. *Annals of Mathematical Statistics*, 40, 492–497.

DUDEWICZ, E. J. (1969b). Selection procedures: An introduction for practitioners. *Estadística, Journal of the Inter-American Statistical Institute*, 27, 377–382.

DUDEWICZ, E. J. (1971a). Maximum likelihood estimators for non-1-1 functions. *Trabajos de Estadística y de Investigación Operativa*, 22, 65–70.

DUDEWICZ, E. J. (1971b). Nonexistence of a single-sample selection procedure whose P(CS) is independent of the variances. *South African Statistical Journal*, 5, 37–39.

DUDEWICZ, E. J. (1973). Research program evaluation (quality control of research) via estimation of ordered parameters. *Annual Technical Conference Transactions of the American Society for Quality Control*, 27, 361–366.

DUDEWICZ, E. J. (1974). A note on selection procedures with unequal observation numbers. *Zastosowania Matematyki*, 14, 31–35.

DUDEWICZ, E. J. (1976). *Introduction to Statistics and Probability*. Holt, Rinehart & Winston, New York.

DUDEWICZ, E. J. (ed.) (1985). *The Frontiers of Modern Statistical Inference Procedures*. American Sciences Press, Columbus, Ohio.

DUDEWICZ, E. J., and BISHOP, T. A. (1981). Analysis of variance with unequal variances. *Journal of Quality Technology*, 13, 111–114.

DUDEWICZ, E. J., and DALAL, S. R. (1972). On approximations to the *t*-distribution. *Journal of Quality Technology*, 4, 196–198.

DUDEWICZ, E. J., and DALAL, S. R. (1975). Allocation of observations in ranking and selection with unequal variances. *Sankhyā*, 37B, 28–78.

DUDEWICZ, E. J., and KARIAN, Z. A. (1985). *Modern Design and Analysis*. IEEE Computer Society Press, Washington, D.C.

DUDEWICZ, E. J., and KOO, J. O. (1982). *The Complete Categorized Guide to Statistical Selection and Ranking Procedures*. American Sciences Press, Columbus, Ohio.

DUDEWICZ, E. J., and RALLEY, T. G. (1981). *The Handbook of Random Number Generation and Testing with TESTRAND Computer Code*. American Sciences Press, Columbus, Ohio.

DUDEWICZ, E. J., RAMBERG, J. S., and CHEN, H. J. (1975). New tables for multiple comparisons with a control (unknown variances). *Biometrical Journal*, **17**, 13–26.

DUDEWICZ, E. J., and VAN DER MEULEN, E. C. (1981). Entropy-based tests of uniformity. *Journal of the American Statistical Association*, **76**, 967–974.

DUDEWICZ, E., and ZAINO, N A., JR. (1971). Sample size for selection. *In* Gupta, S. S., and Yackel, J. (eds.). *Statistical Decision Theory and Related Topics*. Academic Press, New York, pp. 363–376.

DUNNETT, C. W. (1960). On selecting the largest of k normal population means. *Journal of the Royal Statistical Society*, **22B**, 1–30.

DUNNETT, C. W., and SOBEL, M. (1954). A bivariate generalization of Student's t-distribution with tables for certain special cases. *Biometrika*, **41**, 153–169.

DUNNETT, C. W., and SOBEL, M. (1955). Approximations to the probability integral and certain percentage points of a multivariate analogue of Student's t-distribution. *Biometrika*, **42**, 258–260.

DYNKIN, E. B. (1961). Necessary and sufficient statistics for a family of probability distributions. *Selected Translations in Mathematical Statistics and Probability*, vol. 1. American Mathematical Society, Providence, R.I., pp. 17–40.

DYKSTRA, R. L., and PIERCE, D. A. (1969). Independence and the normal distribution. *The American Statistician*, **23**, 39.

EATON, M. L. (1967). Some optimum properties of ranking procedures. *Annals of Mathematical Statistics*, **38**, 124–137.

EFRON, B. (1982). *The Jackknife, the Bootstrap and Other Resampling Plans*. Society for Industrial and Applied Mathematics, Philadelphia.

ESARY, J. D., PROSCHAN, F., AND WALKUP, D. W. (1967). Association of random variables, with applications. *Annals of Mathematical Statistics*, **38**, 1466–1474.

FEFERMAN, S. (1964). *The Number Systems: Foundations of Algebra and Analysis*. Addison-Wesley, Reading, Mass.

FELLER, W. (1966). *An Introduction to Probability Theory and Its Applications*, vol. II. Wiley, New York.

FELLER, W. (1968). *An Introduction to Probability Theory and Its Applications*, vol. I (3rd ed.). Wiley, New York.

FERGUSON, T. S. (1967). *Mathematical Statistics: A Decision Theoretic Approach*. Academic Press, New York.

FERGUSON, T. S. (1973). A Bayesian analysis of some nonparametric problems. *Annals of Statistics*, **1**, 209–230.

FISZ, M. (1980). *Probability Theory and Mathematical Statistics* (3rd ed.). Krieger, New York.

FRASER, D. A. S. (1958). *Statistics: An Introduction*. Wiley, New York.

FREEMAN, H. (1963). *Introduction to Statistical Inference*. Addison-Wesley, Reading, Mass.

FREEMAN, H., KUZMACK, A., and MAURICE, R. (1967). Multivariate t and the ranking problem. *Biometrika*, **54**, 305–308.

GIBBONS, J. D. (1985). *Nonparametric Methods for Quantitative Analysis* (2nd ed.). American Sciences Press, Columbus, Ohio.

GOVINDARAJULU, Z. (1987). *The Sequential Statistical Analysis* (corrected ed.). American Sciences Press, Columbus, Ohio.

GRAYBILL, F. A. (1961). *An Introduction to Linear Statistical Models, Volume I.* McGraw-Hill, New York.

GUPTA, S. S. (1956). On a decision rule for a problem in ranking means. Ph.D. thesis, Department of Statistics, University of North Carolina, Chapel Hill.

GUPTA, S. S. (1963). Probability integrals of multivariate normal and multivariate *t*. *Annals of Mathematical Statistics*, **34**, 792–828.

HAHN, G. J. (1970). Additional factors for calculating prediction intervals for samples from a normal distribution. *Journal of the American Statistical Association*, **65**, 1668–1676.

HALL, W. J. (1959). The most economical character of some Bechhofer and Sobel decision rules. *Annals of Mathematical Statistics*, **30**, 964–969.

HALMOS, P. R. (1950). *Measure Theory*. Van Nostrand, Princeton, N.J.

HAMMOND, E. C., AUERBACH, O., KIRMAN, D., and GARFINKEL, I. (1970). Effects of cigarette smoking on dogs. *Archives of Environmental Health*, **21**, 740–768.

HANSEL, C. E. M. (1966). *ESP: A Scientific Evaluation*. Scribner's, New York.

HARTER, H. L. (1961). Expected values of normal order statistics. *Biometrika*, **48**, 151–165.

HAYES, R. H. (1971). Efficiency of simple order statistics estimates when losses are piecewise linear. *Journal of the American Statistical Association*, **66**, 127–135.

HEUER, C. V. (1972). Solution of Problem E2318. *American Mathematical Monthly*, **79**, 912.

HOAGLIN, D. C., MOSTELLER, F., and TUKEY, J. W. (1983). *Understanding Robust and Exploratory Data Analysis*. Wiley, New York.

HOLLANDER, M., and WOLFE, D. A. (1973). *Nonparametric Statistical Methods*. Wiley, New York.

HUBER, P. (1981). *Robust Statistics*. Wiley, New York.

JOHN, P. W. M. (1971). *Statistical Design and Analysis of Experiments*. Macmillan, New York.

KAZARINOFF, N. D., MOSER, L., and WILANSKY, A. (1969). Problem B-1 and Solution. *American Mathematical Monthly*, **76**, 912, 914.

KEILSON, J., and GERBER, H. (1971). Some results for discrete unimodality. *Journal of the American Statistical Association*, **66**, 386–389.

KENDALL, M. G., and STUART, A. (1967). *The Advanced Theory of Statistics, Volume 2, Inference and Relationship* (2nd ed.). Hafner, New York.

KENDALL, M. G., and STUART, A. (1969). *The Advanced Theory of Statistics, Volume 1, Distribution Theory* (3rd ed.). Hafner, New York.

KIEFER, J. (1952). On minimum variance estimators. *Annals of Mathematical Statistics*, **23**, 627–629.

KOOPMANS, L. H. (1969). Some simple singular and mixed probability distributions. *American Mathematical Monthly*, **76**, 297–299.

LACHENBRUCH, P. A., and BROGAN, D. R. (1971). Some distributions on the positive real line which have no moments. *The American Statistician*, **25**, 46–47.

LAHA, R. G., and LUKACS, E. (1964). *Applications of Characteristic Functions*. Griffin, London.

LAMPERTI, J., and RUDIN, W. (1967). Annihilators of some function algebras. *American Mathematical Monthly*, **74**, 1204–1208.

LARSON, H. J. (1982). *Introduction to Probability Theory and Statistical Inference* (3rd ed.). Wiley, New York.

LEE, Y. J., and DUDEWICZ, E. J. (1974). Nonparametric ranking and selection procedures. *Technical Report No. 105*, Department of Statistics, The Ohio State University, Columbus.

LEHMANN, E. L. (1986). *Testing Statistical Hypotheses* (2nd ed.). Wiley, New York.

LEHMANN, E. L., and SCHEFFÉ, H. (1950). Completeness, similar regions, and unbiased estimation—Part I. *Sankhyā*, **10**, 305–340.

LEVEY, G. A. (1982). *Light, Milk and Vitamins*. Paperboard Packaging Council, 1101 Vermont Avenue, N.W., Suite 411 N, Washington, D.C. 20005.

LEVY, M. S. (1985). A note on nonunique MLE's and sufficient statistics. *The American Statistician*, **39**, 66.

LILLIEFORS, H. W. (1967). On the Kolmogorov-Smirnov test for normality with mean and variance unknown. *Journal of the American Statistical Association*, **62**, 399–402.

LINDGREN, B. W. (1979). *Statistical Theory* (3rd ed.). Macmillan, New York.

LOÈVE, M. (1977). *Probability Theory* (4th ed.). Springer, New York.

LUKACS, E. (1960). CHARACTERISTIC FUNCTIONS. GRIFFIN, LONDON.

MARSHALL, A. W., and OLKIN, I. (1967). A multivariate exponential distribution. *Journal of the American Statistical Association*, **62**, 30–40.

MARTIN, W. T., and REISSNER, E. (1956). *Elementary Differential Equations*. Addison-Wesley, Reading, Mass.

MILTON, R. C. (1963). Tables of the equally correlated multivariate normal probability integral. *Technical Report No. 27*, Department of Statistics, University of Minnesota, Minneapolis.

MISHRA, S. N., SHAH, A. K., and LEFANTE, J. J. (1986). Overlapping coefficient: The generalized t-approach. *Communications in Statistics*, **15**, 123–128.

MITCHELMORE, M. C., and RAYNOR, B. (eds.) (1969). *Joint Schools Project, Mathematics, Textbook 3*. Longmans, London.

MOORE, D. S. (1969). Limiting distributions for sample quantiles. *American Mathematical Monthly*, **76**, 927–929.

MOORE, D. S. (1971). Maximum likelihood and sufficient statistics. *American Mathematical Monthly*, **78**, 50–52.

MOSTELLER, F., ROURKE, R. E. K., and THOMAS, G. B. JR., (1979). *Probability with Statistical Applications* (2nd ed.). Addison-Wesley, Reading, Mass.

MUNROE, M. E. (1960). *Theory of Probability* (2nd ed.). McGraw–Hill, New York.

NAKANO, H. (1969). Russell's paradox in set spaces (axiomatic set theory is not set theory), Abstract. *Notices of the American Mathematical Society*, **16**, 764.

NAYLOR, T. H., BALINTFY, J. L., BURDICK, D. S., and CHU, K. (1966). *Computer Simulation Techniques*. Wiley, New York.

NORTON, R. M. (1984). The double exponential distribution: Using calculus to find a maximum likelihood estimator. *The American Statistician.* **38**, 135–136.

PARZEN, E. (1960). *Modern Probability Theory and Its Applications.* Wiley, New York.

PARZEN, E. (1962). *Stochastic Processes.* Holden-Day, San Francisco.

PEARSON, E. S., and HARTLEY, H. O. (eds.) (1970). *Biometrika Tables for Statisticians*, vol. 1 (3rd ed. with additions). Cambridge University Press, London.

RAJ, D. (1968). *Sampling Theory.* McGraw-Hill, New York.

RAMBERG, J. S., TADIKAMALLA, P. R., DUDEWICZ, E. J., AND MYKYTKA, E. F. (1979). A probability distribution and its uses in fitting data. *Technometrics*, **21**, 201–214.

RAND CORPORATION (1955). *A Million Random Digits with 100,000 Normal Deviates.* The Free Press, Glencoe, Ill.

RAO, C. R. (1973). *Linear Statistical Inference and Its Applications* (2nd ed.). Wiley, New York.

REINHARDT, H. E. (1966). A maximization problem suggested by *Baker vs. Carr. American Mathematical Monthly*, **73**, 1069–1073.

RIZVI, M. H. (ed.) (1985). Special Issue on Ranking and Selection. *American Journal of Mathematical and Management Sciences*, **5**(3, 4).

ROSENBERG, L. (1965). Nonnormality of linear combinations of normally distributed random variables. *American Mathematical Monthly*, **72**, 888–890.

ROSENBLATT, J. (1966). Confidence interval for standard deviation from a single observation. *Technometrics*, **8**, 367–368.

RUDIN, W. (1964). *Principles of Mathematical Analysis* (2nd ed.). McGraw-Hill, New York.

SAMUELSON, P. A. (1968). How deviant can you be? *Journal of the American Statistical Association*, **63**, 1522–1525.

SARKAR, T. K. (1971). An exact lower confidence bound for the reliability of a series system where each component has an exponential time to failure distribution. *Technometrics*, **13**, 535–546.

SAS INSTITUTE (1982). *SAS User's Guide: Statistics, 1982 Edition.* SAS Institute, Cary, N.C.

SCHEFFÉ, H. (1943). On solutions of the Behrens-Fisher problem, based on the *t*-distribution. *Annals of Mathematical Statistics*, **14**, 33–44.

SCHEFFÉ, H. (1944). A note on the Behrens-Fisher problem. *Annals of Mathematical Statistics*, **15**, 430–432.

SCHEFFÉ, H. (1947). A useful convergence theorem for probability distributions. *Annals of Mathematical Statistics*, **18**, 434–458.

SCHEFFÉ, H. (1959). *The Analysis of Variance.* Wiley, New York.

SCHEFFÉ, H. (1970). Practical solutions of the Behrens-Fisher problem. *Journal of the American Statistical Association*, **65**, 1501–1508.

SCHUCANY, W. R., and GRAY, H. L. (1972). *The Generalized Jackknife Statistics.* Dekker, New York.

SERFLING, R. J. (1980). *Approximation Theorems of Mathematical Statistics.* Wiley, New York.

SHAH, A. K. (1985). A simpler approximation for areas under the standard normal curve. *The American Statistician*, **39**, 80.

SIEVERS, S. (1971). A solution to an open problem of Bech[h]ofer-Kiefer-Sobel, Abstract. *Annals of Mathematical Statistics*, **42**, 1795.

SIMONS, G. (1971). Identifying probability limits. *Annals of Mathematical Statistics*, **42**, 1429–1433.

SIMONS, G., and JOHNSON, N. L. (1971). On the convergence of binomial to Poisson distributions. *Annals of Mathematical Statistics*, **42**, 1735–1736.

SIMPSON, E. H. (1951). The interpretation of interaction in contingency tables. *Journal of the Royal Statistical Society*, **13B**, 238–241.

SIOTANI, M., HAYAKAWA, Y., AND FUJIKOSHI, Y. (1985). *Modern Multivariate Statistical Analysis*. American Sciences Press, Columbus, Ohio.

SITEK, M. (1972). Application of the selection procedure *R* to unequal observation numbers. *Zastosowania Matematyki*, **12**, 355–371.

SOLOMON, D. L. (1975). A note on the non-equivalence of the Neyman-Pearson and generalized likelihood ratio tests for testing a simple null versus a simple alternative hypothesis. *The American Statistician*, **29**, 101–102.

STEIN, C. (1945). A two-sample test for a linear hypothesis whose power is independent of the variance. *Annals of Mathematical Statistics*, **16**, 243–258.

STIGLER, S. M. (1984). Kruskal's proof of the joint distribution of $\bar{X}$ and s^2. *The American Statistician*, **38**, 134–135.

SUZUKI, Y. (1964–1965). On uniform convergence in probability. *Proceedings of the Institute of Statistical Mathematics*, **12**, 221–224.

SVERDRUP, E. (1952). The limit distribution of a continuous function of random variables. *Skandinavisk Aktuarietidskrift*, **35**, 1–10.

TAKEUTI, G., and ZARING, W. M. (1971). *Introduction to Axiomatic Set Theory*. Springer-Verlag, New York.

TEICHROEW, D. (1955). Probabilities associated with order statistics in samples from two normal populations with equal variance. *ENASR No. ES-3*, Chemical Corps Engineering Agency, Engineering Statistics Unit, Army Chemical Center, Maryland, December 7.

THOMAS, G. B., JR. (1960). *Calculus and Analytic Geometry* (3rd ed.). Addison–Wesley, Reading, Mass.

THOMPSON, C. M. (1941). Tables of percentage points of the chi-square distribution. *Biometrika*, **32**, 188–189.

TIPPETT, L. H. C. (1927). *Random Sampling Numbers*. Cambridge University Press, England.

TUCKER, H. G. (1967). *A Graduate Course in Probability*. Academic Press, New York.

VAN DER WAERDEN, B. L. (1969). *Mathematical Statistics*. Springer-Verlag, New York.

VARBERG, D. E. (1971). Changes of variables in multiple integrals. *American Mathematical Monthly*, **78**, 42–45.

WADSWORTH, G. P., and BRYAN, J. G. (1960). *Introduction to Probability and Random Variables*. McGraw-Hill, New York.

WAGNER, C. H. (1982). Simpson's paradox in real life. *The American Statistician*, **36**, 46–48.

WALD, A. (1949). Note on the consistency of the maximum likelihood estimate. *Annals of Mathematical Statistics*, **20**, 595–601.

WALD, A. (1950). *Statistical Decision Functions*. Wiley, New York.

WALLIS, W. A., and ROBERTS, H. V. (1965). *The Nature of Statistics*. The Free Press, New York.

WALSH, J. E. (1946). On the power function of the sign test for slippage of means. *Annals of Mathematical Statistics*, **17**, 358–362.

WEISS, L. (1961). *Statistical Decision Theory*. McGraw-Hill, New York.

WEISS, L. (1970). Asymptotic distributions of quantiles in some nonstandard cases. *Nonparametric Techniques in Statistical Inference*. Cambridge University Press, London, pp. 343–348.

WETHERILL, G. B. (1982). *Elementary Statistical Methods*, (3rd ed.). Methuen, London.

WHITTAKER, E. T., and WATSON, G. N. (1965). *A Course on Modern Analysis*. Cambridge University Press, London.

WIDDER, D. (1961). *Advanced Calculus* (2nd ed.). Prentice–Hall, Englewood Cliffs, N.J.

WILK, M. B., GNANADESIKAN, R., and HUYETT, M. J. (1962). Estimation of parameters of the gamma distribution using order statistics. *Biometrika*, **49**, 525–545.

WILKS, S. S. (1962). *Mathematical Statistics*. Wiley, New York.

WOLFOWITZ, J. (1962). Bayesian inference and axioms of consistent decision. *Econometrica*, **30**, 470–479.

ZEHNA, P. W. (1966). Invariance of maximum likelihood estimators. *Annals of Mathematical Statistics*, **37**, 744.

Answers to
Selected Problems

To aid students working problems not assigned in their classes (as well as persons studying the material on their own) to check the correctness of their work, below we give fairly detailed answers (but not solutions) to those Chapter Problems (but not Honors Problems) whose problem numbers are divisible by five.

CHAPTER 1

1.5 (Poretsky's law) First, to show that if $X = \varnothing$ then $T = (X \cap T^c) \cup (X^c \cap T)$, note that $X \cap T^c = \varnothing \cap T^c = \varnothing$ and $X^c \cap T = \varnothing^c \cap T = \Omega \cap T = T$, hence $(X \cap T^c) \cup (X^c \cap T) = \varnothing \cup T = T$. Next, to show that if $T = (X \cap T^c) \cup (X^c \cap T)$ then $X = \varnothing$, assume that $T = (X \cap T^c) \cup (X^c \cap T)$ and show that (for each $\omega \in \Omega$) $\omega \notin X$ because $\omega \in X \Rightarrow \omega \in T$, which yields a contradiction ($\omega \in T$ and $\omega \notin (X \cap T^c) \cup (X^c \cap T)$).

CHAPTER 2

2.5 If the vehicle from the U.S.A. has probability p_1 of succeeding ($0 \le p_1 \le 1$), the vehicle from the U.S.S.R. has probability p_2 of suceeding ($0 \le p_2 \le 1$), and the success or failure of one vehicle does not affect the other's chances, then the desired probability is $p_1(1 - p_2) + p_2(1 - p_1)$.

2.10 (a) Use mathematical induction on r.
(b) Use mathematical induction on k.

2.15 $P(B|A \cup \bar{B}) = 0.25$.

2.20 $5/6$.

2.25 (a) $\left(\dfrac{k}{N}\right)^n$.

(b) $\dfrac{1}{N+1} \dfrac{1^n + 2^n + \cdots + N^n}{N^n}$.

(c) $\dfrac{1}{N+1} \dfrac{1^{n+1} + 2^{n+1} + \cdots + N^{n+1}}{N^{n+1}}$.

(d) $\dfrac{1}{N} \dfrac{1^{n+1} + 2^{n+1} + \cdots + N^{n+1}}{1^n + 2^n + \cdots + N^n}$.

(e) $\dfrac{n+1}{n+2}$.

2.30 $R(p) = 2p^2 - p^4$.

CHAPTER 3

3.5 If X is the number of questions directed to the first student, then

$$p_X(x) = \begin{cases} \dbinom{10}{x}\left(\dfrac{1}{4}\right)^x\left(\dfrac{3}{4}\right)^{10-x}, & x = 0, 1, \ldots, 10 \\ 0, & \text{otherwise} \end{cases}$$

and

$$F_X(x) = \begin{cases} 1, & x > 10 \\ \displaystyle\sum_{t=0}^{|x|} p_X(t), & 0 \le x \le 10 \\ 0, & x > 0, \end{cases}$$

where $[x]$ denotes the largest integer $\le x$ (so, e.g., $[5.3] = 5$ and $[6] = 6$).

3.10 This involves plotting $P[X = 1]$ as a function of p on coordinate axes, using the following values:

p	0	.1	.2	.3	.4	
$P[X = 1]$	0	.0028	.0333	.1260	.2897	
p	.5	.6	.7	.8	.9	1
$P[X = 1]$	.5	.7103	.8740	.9667	.9972	1

3.15 First find $P[X + Y = z]$ (thus showing that $X + Y$ is Poisson with parameter $\lambda_1 + \lambda_2$) and then calculate $P[X = x \mid X + Y = z]$ (using the definition of conditional probability) and recognize the result as a binomial distribution with z trials and probability $\lambda_1/(\lambda_1 + \lambda_2)$ of success on each trial.

3.20 $F_X\left(\dfrac{z-b}{a}\right)$.

3.25 (a) 2^n.

(b) $n + 1$.

3.30 For the geometric distribution, the function to be plotted is $q(x) = p$ for $x = 1, 2, 3, \ldots$ ($q(x) = 0$ otherwise), whereas for the uniform distribution the function to be plotted is $q(x) = \dfrac{1}{n - i + 1}$ if x is the ith smallest of the possible values $x_1, \ldots, x_n$ ($q(x) = 0$ otherwise).

CHAPTER 4

4.5 (a) $1 - (.01)^{1/5}$ thousand gallons.
(b) 1000 gallons.

4.10 The d.f. of Y is

$$F_Y(y) = \begin{cases} F_X(y), & y > 0 \\ F_X(0), & y = 0 \\ 0, & y < 0. \end{cases}$$

4.15 The density of X is

$$f_X(x) = \begin{cases} \dfrac{1}{\pi} \dfrac{1}{\sqrt{1 - x^2}}, & |x| < 1 \\ 0, & \text{otherwise.} \end{cases}$$

4.20 We find

$$P[Z_n \le x] = \begin{cases} 0, & x > 0 \\ x^n, & 0 \le x \le 1 \\ 1, & x > 1, \end{cases}$$

and $n \ge 44$ is needed in order that $P[Z_n > .9] \ge .99$.

4.25 We find

$$f_V(v) = \begin{cases} \dfrac{\Gamma\left(\dfrac{m + n}{2}\right)}{\Gamma\left(\dfrac{m}{2}\right)\Gamma\left(\dfrac{n}{2}\right)} \dfrac{v^{\frac{m}{2}-1}}{(v + 1)^{(m+n)/2}}, & v > 0 \\ 0, & v \le 0 \end{cases}$$

and

$$f_U(u) = \begin{cases} \dfrac{\Gamma\left(\dfrac{m + n}{2}\right)}{\Gamma\left(\dfrac{m}{2}\right)\Gamma\left(\dfrac{n}{2}\right)} u^{\frac{m}{2}-1}(1 - u)^{\frac{n}{2}-1}, & 0 < u < 1 \\ 0, & \text{otherwise.} \end{cases}$$

CHAPTER 5

5.5 The mode may be found by examination of the derivative of $f_X(x)$. When $n = 1$, the mode is zero and $EX = 1$.

5.10 (a) $\phi_X(t) = Ee^{itX}$ $\quad (-\infty < t < +\infty)$.

    (b) $\phi_{X_1}(t) = pe^{it} + q$.

    (c) $\phi_{S_n}(t) = (pe^{it} + q)^n$.

    (d) From $\phi_{S_n}(t)$ we conclude via the Uniqueness Theorem (Theorem 5.5.50) that S_n is binomial, and then $P[S_n = j]$ follows.

5.15 Use direct calculation.

5.20 $E(Y) = n/4$ and $\text{Var}(Y) = (5n - 2)/16$.

CHAPTER 6

6.5 Using the CLT, $n \geq (128.8)^2$.

6.10 (a) Via Chebyshev's Inequality,

$$P\left[\left|\frac{W_1 + \cdots + W_{100}}{100} + \frac{13}{36}\right| > \frac{1}{2}\sqrt{\frac{1235}{1296}}\right] < \frac{1}{25}.$$

    (b) (1) Show by Chebyshev's Inequality that

$$P\left[\left|\frac{W_1 + \cdots + W_n}{n} + \frac{13}{36}\right| > \delta\right] \to 0 \text{ as } n \to \infty.$$

    (2) Show that

$$\phi_{\frac{W_1 + \cdots + W_n}{n}}(t) \to e^{-\frac{13}{36}it} \text{ as } n \to \infty.$$

    (3) The conditions of the WLLN are satisfied.

    (4) The conditions of Khinchin's Theorem are satisfied.

CHAPTER 7

7.5 (a) "The" MLE is $\hat{\lambda} = (X_1 + \cdots + X_n)/n$ if $X_1 + \cdots + X_n \neq 0$. If $X_1 + \cdots + X_n = 0$, the supremum of $L(\lambda)$ is the value at $\lambda = 0$, but $0 \notin \Theta$. If we redefine Θ as $\Theta = \{x: x \geq 0\}$, the MLE will always exist.

    (b) λ^* is an ε-MLE iff

$$e^{-n\lambda^*}(\lambda^*)^{X_1 + \cdots + X_n} \geq (1 - \varepsilon)e^{-n\hat{\lambda}}(\hat{\lambda})^{X_1 + \cdots + X_n}.$$

If $X_1 + \cdots + X_n = 0$, this means

$$\lambda^* \leq \frac{-\ln(1 - \varepsilon)}{n}.$$

7.10 Here we must show that (for any fixed $\varepsilon > 0$ and $\gamma > 0$) there is an integer $N(\varepsilon, \gamma)$ such that $n > N(\varepsilon, \gamma)$ implies $P_\theta[|t_n - \theta| < \varepsilon] > 1 - \gamma$. Let $N_1(\varepsilon, \delta)$ be such that, for $n \geq N_1$,

$$P_\theta\big[|Y| < n^\delta \varepsilon\big] > 1 - \frac{\gamma}{2}$$

where Y is a $N(0, J^2(\theta))$ r.v. [Note that existence of such an N_1 does not require that the supremum (over θ) of $J^2(\theta)$ be $< \infty$.] Then, for $n \geq N_1(\varepsilon, \delta)$,

$$\lim_{n \to \infty} P_\theta[|t_n - \theta| < \varepsilon]$$

$$= \lim_{n \to \infty} P_\theta\big[|n^\delta(t_n - \theta)| < n^\delta \varepsilon\big]$$

$$\geq \lim_{n \to \infty} P_\theta\big[|n^\delta(t_n - \theta)| < N_1^\delta \varepsilon\big]$$

$$= P_\theta\big[|Y| < N_1^\delta \varepsilon\big] > 1 - \frac{\gamma}{2}.$$

Then, for $n \geq N_2(\varepsilon, \delta)$,

$$\frac{\gamma}{2} > P_\theta[|t_n - \theta| < \varepsilon] - \left(1 - \frac{\gamma}{2}\right) > -\frac{\gamma}{2}$$

(since a sequence must get uniformly close to its limit), that is,

$$P_\theta[|t_n - \theta| < \varepsilon] > 1 - \gamma$$

as was to be shown.

7.15 Since $(\overline{X} - \mu)/(\sigma/\sqrt{n})$ is asymptotically $N(0, 1)$ by the CLT [the precise meaning of this: the d.f. F_n of $(\overline{X} - \mu)/(\sigma/\sqrt{n})$ satisfies $F_n \to \Phi$], it follows that $\sqrt{n}(\overline{X} - \mu)$ is asymptotically $N(0, \sigma^2)$, hence $\overline{X}$ is a CAN estimator of μ. (The footnote can also be used as stated, and should be emphasized: it is often useful when dealing with normal r.v.'s.)

7.20 $\hat{\theta} = 2\overline{X}$.

CHAPTER 8

8.5 First, if (x_1, x_2) is a permutation of (y_1, y_2), then (8.1.22) is the equation $a \overset{\theta}{\equiv} 0$ with $a = Q(x_1, x_2, y_1, y_2) - 1 = 0$, hence $b = c = d = e = 0$.

Next, suppose that $b = c = d = e = 0$. The fact $e = 0$ means that $Q(x_1, x_2, y_1, y_2) = 1$, since the coefficient of θ^4 is $e = Q(x_1, x_2, y_1, y_2) - 1$. Using this fact, $d = 0$ means that $x_1 + x_2 = y_1 + y_2$, while $c = 0$ means that $x_1 x_2 = y_1 y_2$, and (using $x_1 x_2 = y_1 y_2$) $b = 0$ means that $x_1^2 + x_2^2 =$

$y_1^2 + y_2^2$. If at least one of (y_1, y_2) is zero, so is at least one of (x_1, x_2) (since $x_1 x_2 = y_1 y_2$), hence the other x and y are also equal (since $x_1 + x_2 = y_1 + y_2$). If neither of (y_1, y_2) is zero, then (since $x_1 x_2 = y_1 y_2$) neither of (x_1, x_2) is zero and using $x_2 = y_1 y_2 / x_1$ in $x_1 + x_2 = y_1 + y_2$ we find

$$x_1^2 - (y_1 + y_2)x_1 + y_1 y_2 = 0$$

which (using the quadratic formula) has solutions $x_1 = y_1$ and $x_1 = y_2$, hence (since also $x_1 + x_2 = y_1 + y_2$) (x_1, x_2) is a permutation of (y_1, y_2). Thus in all possible cases (x_1, x_2) is a permutation of (y_1, y_2).

8.10 Define $h(x) = f(x|\theta_0)$, $g(a|\theta) = 1$ if $\theta = \theta_0$, and $g(a|\theta) = a$ if $\theta = \theta_1$. Then

$$f(x|\theta) = h(x)g(t(x)|\theta),$$

where $t(x) = f(x|\theta_1)/f(x|\theta_0)$, holds for all $\theta \in \Theta = [\theta_0, \theta_1]$, hence the likelihood ratio statistic $t(X) = f(X|\theta_1)/f(X|\theta_0)$ is a sufficient statistic in this case. [The value of $t(x)$ for x such that $f(x|\theta_0) = 0$ is perhaps best kept as $f(x|\theta_1)/0$, with the zero in the denominator regarded as able to be cancelled by multiplying by zero.]

8.15 Here we find that

$$\frac{f(x|\mu)}{f(y|\mu)} = \frac{e^{-\mu}\mu^x/x!}{e^{-\mu}\mu^y/y!} = \frac{y!}{x!} \mu^{x-y},$$

which is independent of μ iff $x = y$. Hence X is a minimal sufficient statistic for μ (by Theorem 8.1.23), and X is also a trivial sufficient statistic. Since (see Definition 8.1.15) a minimal sufficient statistic is a function of every other sufficient statistic, no nontrivial sufficient statistic exists. [Note that in this problem we only had $n = 1$ observation. Also, values x and y with probability zero can be handled.]

8.20 Let X have the Bernoulli distribution with p unknown. Then by Problem 8.17 (with $n = 1$), $T = X$ is a sufficient statistic for p. We know that T is (see Definition 8.2.3) a complete sufficient statistic. Since $\varphi(T) = T$ has the property that $E_p \varphi(T) \equiv p$, it follows from Theorem 8.3.8 that $\varphi(T) = T = X$ is the unique MVUE of p. Of course (note that $\theta = p$ here)

$$\mathrm{Var}_\theta \varphi(T) = \mathrm{Var}_\theta X = p(1 - p).$$

[This problem extends easily to the case $n > 1$, where X is replaced by $(X_1, \ldots, X_n)$, and is a good extra credit problem.]

CHAPTER 9

9.5 $c = .07\sigma/\sqrt{n}$. This test is worse than "flipping a coin," since this test rejects precisely when we have the strongest evidence for accepting, and thus uses the data to our disadvantage.

9.10 At $\mu_2 = 2\mu_0 - \mu_1 + 2\Phi^{-1}(1-\alpha)\dfrac{\sigma}{\sqrt{n}}$.

9.15 Setting the level to α will specify the C at (9.3.56) at the same value regardless of the θ_1 chosen.

9.20 Several risk points may qualify since (see the geometrical interpretation of Bayes rules given following Definition 9.4.8) the line may hit the convex set along a whole side, hence at more than one risk point.

9.25 The minimax rule rejects when $X_1 + \cdots + X_n > nC$, where C is such that

$$P[Y > nC/\theta_0] = P[Y < nC/\theta_1]$$

where Y has the gamma distribution $G(x|30, 1, 0)$.

9.30 This follows easily from the theorems mentioned in the hint.

9.35 This follows easily upon writing down the level of the test as

$$t_{n-1}\big(t_{n-1}^{-1}(\alpha p)\big) + t_{n-1}\big(t_{n-1}^{-1}(\alpha(1-p))\big) = \alpha p + \alpha(1-p) = \alpha.$$

9.40 Use the hint, noting that if Z is a $N(0,1)$ r.v. then $EZ^2 = \mathrm{Var}(Z) = 1$.

9.45 $(\overline{X}, \overline{Y})$ is a complete minimal sufficient statistic for (μ_1, μ_2). $\overline{X}$ is the unique MVU estimator of μ_1, and $\overline{Y}$ is the unique MVU estimator of μ_2.

9.50 The two-sided equal-tail test rejects if either $\sum_1^{10}(X_i - \mu)^2 < 3.94$ or $\sum_1^{10}(X_i - \mu)^2 > 18.3$. The one-sided test rejects if $\sum_1^{10}(X_i - \mu)^2 > 16.0$.

The respective power curves are as follows:

σ^2	0	.25	.50	.75	1.0
P [One-sided rejects]	0	.00	.00	.02	.10
P [Two-sided rejects]	1	.89	.35	.13	.10
σ^2	1.5	2.0	2.5	3.0	
P [One-sided rejects]	.40	.63	.78	.88	
P [Two-sided rejects]	.30	.51	.70	.82	

CHAPTER 10

10.5 This follows upon noting that $\Phi^{-1}(1) = +\infty$ (so that $L(\overline{X}) = -\infty$ while $U(\overline{X}) = \overline{X} - (\sigma/\sqrt{n})\Phi^{-1}(\alpha) = \overline{X} + (\sigma/\sqrt{n})\Phi^{-1}(1-\alpha)$).

10.10 The length is

$$f(p) = -\frac{s}{\sqrt{n}}\left\{ t_{n-1}^{-1}(\alpha p) - t_{n-1}^{-1}(1-\alpha(1-p)) \right\}$$

which (via differentiation) is easily seen to have a minimum (for each fixed s) at $p = 1/2$, in which case its value is $f(1/2)$ as given at (10.2.14).

10.15 (a) $-.16 \leq \mu_B - \mu_A \leq .56$.
   (b) $-.24 \leq \mu_B - \mu_A \leq .64$.
   (c) $-.59 \leq \mu_B - \mu_A \leq .99$.
   (d) Using the Hsu solution given in Section 9.9, just before equation (9.9.9), $-3.00 \leq \mu_B - \mu_A \leq 3.40$.

10.20 This is clear if one writes down precisely how the confidence interval procedure changes when the points $(0,0)$ and $(1,1)$ are added in the manner noted following Figure 10.4-4.

CHAPTER 11

11.5 Consider the case $\rho = 0.5$. Then

$$h = H/\sqrt{.5} = \sqrt{2}\,H.$$

11.10 Consider choosing a population at random without any observations being taken. Then one finds a P^* of $1/k$ trivially.

11.15 (a) Writing down an expression for the $P(\text{CS})$ in terms of the decision procedure specified and simplifying, we come to the $P(\text{CS})$ formula given in the statement of Problem 11.15. Noting that this is a continuous function with $dP(\text{CS})/d(\sigma_{(k)}) > 0$ at $\mu_{[1]} = \cdots = \mu_{[k]}$, it follows that $dP(\text{CS})/d(\sigma_{(k)})$ is positive in a neighborhood of $\mu_{[1]} = \cdots = \mu_{[k]}$, and the desired deduction follows.
   (b) No.

CHAPTER 12

12.5 Use mathematical induction on the number of vectors.

12.10 If $s_1 \notin A'$, then there is a rule $t \in A'$ that is at least as good as s_1, hence A' is essentially complete. A' is minimal essentially complete because $A' - \{t\}$ (where t is any rule in A') is not essentially complete (since t is admissible) while A' is essentially complete.

12.15 Any rule with risk point of the form $(9, 9p + 8q)$, for some $p, q \geq 0$ with $p + q = 1$, is minimax. Graphically, this is where a certain orthant intersects the set of risk points.

12.20 Let S be the set of risk points of Figure 12.1-3 but with all boundary points removed. Then (by Problem 12.18) S is the set of risk points of some statistical decision problem. However, the set of Bayes rules is empty, and the empty set of rules is not a complete class, let alone a minimal complete class or a minimal essentially complete class.

12.25 We know that, for any other rule t,

$$\sup_\theta r_\theta(t) \geq \sup_\theta r_\theta(s) = r_\theta(s)$$

(otherwise s could not be a Bayes rule: since s has constant risk, t would have a smaller Bayes risk); hence s is minimax.

12.30 A Bayes rule $s_w(X)$ chooses decision d_1 iff

$$\bar{X} \geq \frac{1}{2} - \frac{1}{5} \ln\left(\frac{2(1-w)}{3w}\right).$$

12.35 Use the hint and the geometrical interpretation of Bayes, $+$-Bayes, and minimax rules.

12.40

	θ	\multicolumn{4}{c}{$l(\theta, d)$}			
d		\multicolumn{4}{c}{Player I (Nature)}			
		θ_1	θ_2	θ_3	θ_4
	d_1	0	-2	3	0
Player II	d_2	2	0	0	-3
	d_3	-3	0	0	4
	d_4	0	3	-4	0

12.45 A Bayes rule's estimate is $(X(t) + 1)/(t + 1)$. For this rule s,

$$r_\theta(s) = \frac{1}{(t+1)^2}(\theta^2 + (t-2)\theta + 1).$$

The basis for determining t is the risk function $r_\theta(s)$, which depends on the choice of t. The ideal theoretical t would be $+\infty$, which is unachievable. If we could bound θ by θ_0, we could choose t to make

$$\sup_{\theta \leq \theta_0} r_\theta(s) \leq K$$

where K is the largest risk we are willing to accept.

CHAPTER 13

13.5 Specify in detail the quantities in Theorem 10.1.5 and you have derived the desired test. (The quantities are $X = (X_1, \ldots, X_n)$, $\theta = \xi_p$, $\Theta = \{x: x \in \mathscr{R}\}$, $C_\theta = \{X: Y_i \leq \xi_p \leq Y_j\}$, and $1 - \alpha = Q(i, j; p, n)$.)

CHAPTER 14

14.5 The regression curve is $f(x) = x^2$. The regression line is $y = \alpha + \beta x$ with

$$
\begin{cases}
\alpha = E(X^2) - \dfrac{EX^3 - EXEX^2}{EX^2 - (EX)^2} EX \\[2ex]
\beta = \dfrac{EX^3 - EXEX^2}{EX^2 - (EX)^2}.
\end{cases}
$$

The mean square errors of prediction are, respectively, zero for the regression curve and

$$
\mathrm{Var}(X^2) - \frac{(EX^3 - EXEX^2)^2}{\mathrm{Var}(X)}
$$

for the regression line.

14.10 Using the method of Lagrange multipliers, we must solve the system of equations $\{2u_i + \lambda_1 + \lambda_2 x_i = 0 \ (i = 1, \ldots, n), \ u_1 + \cdots + u_n - 1 = 0, \ u_1 x_1 + \cdots + u_n x_n = 0\}$, which yields (after some manipulations) a solution u_i equal to the v_i of (14.1.34).

14.15 This follows by writing out the likelihood function and (considering it as a function of the three variables α, β, σ^2) maximizing it.

14.20 We find $\hat{\alpha} = 13.3$, $\hat{\beta} = .675$, and $\hat{\sigma}^2 = 74.34$ (hence $y = 13.3 + .675x$). The best linear estimate would be $\hat{y} = 33$ at $x = 30$.

14.25 The best $P(\mathrm{CS})$ function will be obtained by choosing half the x_i's to equal x_U, the other half to equal x_L.

CHAPTER 15

15.5 The jackknife interval for pq was given in Example 15.5.17. To find a bootstrap confidence interval for pq, we proceed as follows. First, estimate the d.f. of $X_1, X_2, \ldots, X_n$ by the empiric d.f., which takes value 1 with probability $(X_1 + X_2 + \cdots + X_n)/n$ (and takes value 0 otherwise). Here $\theta(F) = \mathrm{Var}(X) = pq$, and the MLE is $\bar{X}(1 - \bar{X}) = \hat{\theta}$, which is biased.

Taking random samples of size n from the empiric d.f. N times, we obtain the bootstrap estimates $\hat{\theta}_1, \hat{\theta}_2, \ldots, \hat{\theta}_N$, whose mean $\bar{\theta}$ is the bootstrap estimate of θ. The sample variance of $\hat{\theta}_1, \hat{\theta}_2, \ldots, \hat{\theta}_N$ is used as at (15.6.10) to provide the desired (approximate) confidence interval.

Glossary of Symbols

This glossary is intended to aid the reader in finding the main place(s) in the text where a symbol is introduced. Most symbols which recur frequently are included in this glossary. The Glossary lists functions and operators first (e.g., $A \cup B$ is listed in order to include the operator $\cup$; the "A" and "B" are incidental to the listing), followed by an alphabetical listing[1] (in which the Greek alphabet is alphabetized with its Latin equivalents). For each listing a brief descriptive phrase is given as well as a page number. (If the item occurs in a problem, in many cases the problem number is given in parentheses following the page number.) For example, "$S(A, B)$" can be briefly described as the "symmetric difference" and occurs on page 12 in Problem 1.6.

OPERATORS AND FUNCTIONS

$A \cup B, A + B$	Union of sets	2
$\bigcup_{A \in \mathcal{M} A}$	Extended union	7
$A \cap B, AB, A \cdot B$	Intersection of sets	2
$\bigcap_{A \in \mathcal{M} A}$	Extended intersection	7
$A^c, \bar{A}, A'$	Complement of a set	2
$A - B$	Difference of sets	3
$A = B$	Identity of sets	4
$A \neq B$	Inequality of sets	4
$A \subseteq B, B \supseteq A,$ $A \subset B, B \supset A$	Subset relation	4, 5
$A \subsetneqq B, B \supsetneqq A$	Proper subset relation	4, 5
E	Expectation operator	210
$n(\cdot)$	Number of points operator	16
$(n)_0, (n)_r$	Product of successive integers	24

---

[1] This listing is largely alphabetical (but not strictly alphabetical, since similar terms have been grouped together for the reader's ease of reference).

$n!$	n-factorial	24
$\binom{n}{r}, {}^nC_r$	Binomial coefficients	25
$\#(\cdot)$	Number of points operator	32
Var	Variance operator	214
$\approx$	Approximate equality operator	318
$\sim$	Asymptotic equality operator	35
w.p.1	Convergence with probability 1	300
$\overset{2}{\to}$	Convergence in mean square operator	300
$\overset{p}{\to}$	Convergence in probability operator	300
$\overset{d}{\to}$	Convergence in distribution operator	300
$\succ, \succsim, \sim$	Relations comparing decision rules	611

a, A, α

$(a_{j_1}, b_{j_2}, \ldots, x_{j_r})$	r-tuplets	23
A	Acceptance region	435
α_3	Skewness of a r.v.	215
α_4	Kurtosis of a r.v.	216
$\alpha, \alpha(\phi)$	Level of a test	441
$\alpha_{SP}(x, \phi_\alpha)$	Significance probability of x	539
α	Regression intercept	679
$\hat{\alpha}$	Least squares estimator	681
α_i	i^{th} treatment effect	708

b, B, β

$b_n(\theta)$	Bias	337
$(BC)_1, (BC)_i, (BC)_\infty$	Ball and cell models	30
$B(x\vert\alpha, \lambda)$	Beta distribution	137
$B(\theta)$	Distribution function on Θ	618
$\beta(m, n)$	Beta function	133
$\beta(\theta)$	Probability of error of Type II	441
$1 - \beta(\phi)$	Probability of error of Type II	473
β	Regression slope	679
$\hat{\beta}$	Least squares estimator	681, 696
$\beta_0, \beta_1, \ldots, \beta_m$	Unknown constants in a linear model	684

c, C

$c_{1-\gamma}(n_0)$	Percentage point of $t_1 + t_2$	511
c_m	Stopping limit for SPRT	521
$\text{Corr}(X_1, X_2)$	Correlation of X_1 and X_2	239
$\text{Cov}(X_1, X_2)$	Covariance of X_1 and X_2	233
$\text{C.V.}(X)$	Coefficient of variation σ/μ	328

d, D, δ, Δ

e, E, ε

f, F

g, G, γ, Γ

$$h, H, \eta$$

$$i, I$$

$$j, J$$

$$k, K, \kappa$$

$$l, L, \lambda, \Lambda$$

m, M, μ

n, N, ν

o, O, ω, Ω

$$p, P, \varphi, \phi, \Phi, \Psi, \pi, \Pi$$

$\mathscr{P}(\theta)$	Power of a test	441
$\mathscr{P}_M(n_1, \ldots, n_k)$	Means procedure	606
$p_{[1]}, \ldots, p_{[k]}$	Ranked multinomial probabilities	608
$p(x), p_X(x)$	Probability function	73, 76, 103
$p_{X_1 \mid X_2 = 2, X_3 = 1}(1)$	Conditional probability function	109
$p_m(r, n)$	Probability exactly m cells are empty	290
$P(\cdot)$	Probability function	15
$P(\cdot \mid \cdot)$	Conditional probability	39
$P_n(T)$	Poisson process probability	87
$P(CS)$	Probability of correct selection	580
$\varphi_n(X_1, \ldots, X_n)$	Estimator	370
$\phi_X(t)$	Characteristic function	273
$\phi(x)$	Test function, or	
	$N(0, 1)$ density	436
$\Phi(x)$	Normal d.f.	318
$\Psi_X(t)$	Moment-generating function	255
$\Psi_{X_1, \ldots, X_n}(t_1, \ldots, t_n)$	Joint m.g.f.	260
$\pi_1, \ldots, \pi_k$	Populations	581
$\Pi(\cdot, \ldots, \cdot)$	Polynomial	341
Π	Set $\{\pi_1, \ldots, \pi_k\}$	600
$+$-**Bayes**	Positive-Bayes	624

$$q, Q$$

q	$1 - p$	92
$q(x)$	Failure rate	121(3.30)
$Q(i, j; p, n)$	Nonparametric quantile coverage	657
$Q(x)$	Lower orthant at x	623

$$r, R, \rho$$

$\mathscr{R}$	The real line	69
$\mathscr{R}^n$	Euclidean n-space	70
$\mathscr{R}^+$	$\{x: x > 0\}$	337
$r(\cdot)$	Risk point of a test	471
$\mathrm{reg}(\theta, d)$	Regret function	638
$r_\theta(s)$	Risk function	610
r_{XY}	Sample correlation	681
R	Critical region, or set of risk points	435, 471
$R(A)$	Relative frequency	16
$R(p)$	System reliability	53
$R(A \mid B)$	Conditional relative frequency	39
$R_{B(\theta)}(t)$	Bayes risk of t	618
$\mathrm{Re}\, z$	Real part of z	273
$\rho(X_1, X_2)$	Correlation coefficient	239

$$s, S, \sigma, \sum$$

$s(\cdot)$	Statistical decision rule	610
s^2	Unbiased estimator of σ^2	303, 480
s_p^2	Pooled variance estimator	496
sup	Supremum	305
$s_{[1]}^2, \ldots, s_{[k]}^2$	Ranked $s_1^2, \ldots, s_k^2$	596
S	Subset of $\Pi = \{\pi_1, \ldots, \pi_k\}$	600
$S(A, B)$	Symmetric difference	12(1.6)
$S(\alpha, \beta)$	Sum of squared deviations	681
S_n	$X_1 + \cdots + X_n$	315
S.N. (X)	Signal-to-noise ratio μ/σ	328
$S(X)$	Confidence set	552
$\sigma(X)$	Standard deviation of X	218
$\sigma^2(X)$	Variance of X	214
$\hat{\sigma}^2$	MLE of σ^2	685
$\sigma_{[1]}^2, \ldots, \sigma_{[k]}^2$	Ranked variances	595
$\sum$	Symmetric positive definite matrix	165

$$t, T, \tau, \theta, \Theta, \Theta$$

t_m	Student's t-distribution	483
$t_m^{-1}(\alpha)$	$100\alpha\%$ point of the t_m distribution	483
$t_n(x_1, \ldots, x_n)$	Estimate	336
$t_n(X_1, \ldots, X_n)$	Statistic or estimator	336
$T(X)$	Statistic	461
θ	State of nature	610
$\hat{\theta}, \hat{\theta}_n(X_1, \ldots, X_n)$	Maximum likelihood estimator	347
Θ	Set of parameter values	336
$(\Theta, \mathcal{D}, l), X$	Statistical decision problem	610

$$u, U$$

$U(X)$	Upper confidence limit	550

$$v, V$$

Var (X)	Variance of X	214, 298

$$w, W$$

w_i	Legislators-per-person in district i	467
W_X	Sum of ranks	666

| $w(x)$ | Influence curve at x | 731 |
| $W(\theta; d; x)$ | Loss function | 654 |

x, X, χ, ξ

x^+	Positive part of x	205(4.10)
x^-	Negative part of x	205(4.10)
X	Random variable	69, 98
X^*	Standardized X	218
$\bar{X}, \bar{X}(n), \bar{X}_n$	$(X_1 + \cdots + X_n)/n$	303, 339
$\tilde{\bar{X}}$	Generalized sample mean	505
$\mathscr{X}$	Set of possible values of X	435
X'	Design matrix in regression	695
$\chi_n^2(0)$	Chi-square distribution	140
$\chi_n^2(\lambda)$	Noncentral chi-square distribution	141
$\chi^2(\theta)$	Criterion for MCS estimation	528
$(\chi'(\theta))^2$	Criterion for MMCS estimation	528
ξ, ξ_p	Quantile of order p	373

y, Y

$Y_{[np]+1}$	Sample quantile of order p	374
Y_L^*	Lower confidence limit	688
Y_U^*	Upper confidence limit	688
Y_L	Lower prediction limit	689
Y_U	Upper prediction limit	689

z, Z, ζ

| Z_p | Sample quantile of order p | 374, 656 |
| $\zeta(N)$ | Estimator based on number of trials | 342 |

Author Index

This index lists each author or other person mentioned at least once in the text.

Subject Index

In this index most subentries are in order of first appearance in the text.

Printed and Bound by KIN KEONG PRINTING CO. PTE. LTD. – Republic of Singapore.